# SOUTHERN MAINE'S PREMIER DAILY FEE GOLF CLUBS

Fox Ridge Golf Club
550 Penley Corner Road
Auburn, Maine
207-777-GOLF (4653)
**www.foxridgegolfclub.com**

## NONESUCH RIVER
### GOLF CLUB

Nonesuch River Golf Club
304 Gorham Rd
Scarborough, Maine
207-883-0007
**nonesuchgolf.com**

### BRIDGTON HIGHLANDS
EST. 1926

Bridgton Highlands Golf and Tennis
379 Highland Rd
Bridgton, Maine
207-647-3491
**bridgtonhighlands.com**

# SANFORD
## COUNTRY CLUB

Sanford Country Club
588 Country Club Rd
Sanford, ME
207-324-5462
sanfordcountryclub.com

**Visit our websites for additional information, or to book your tee time today!**

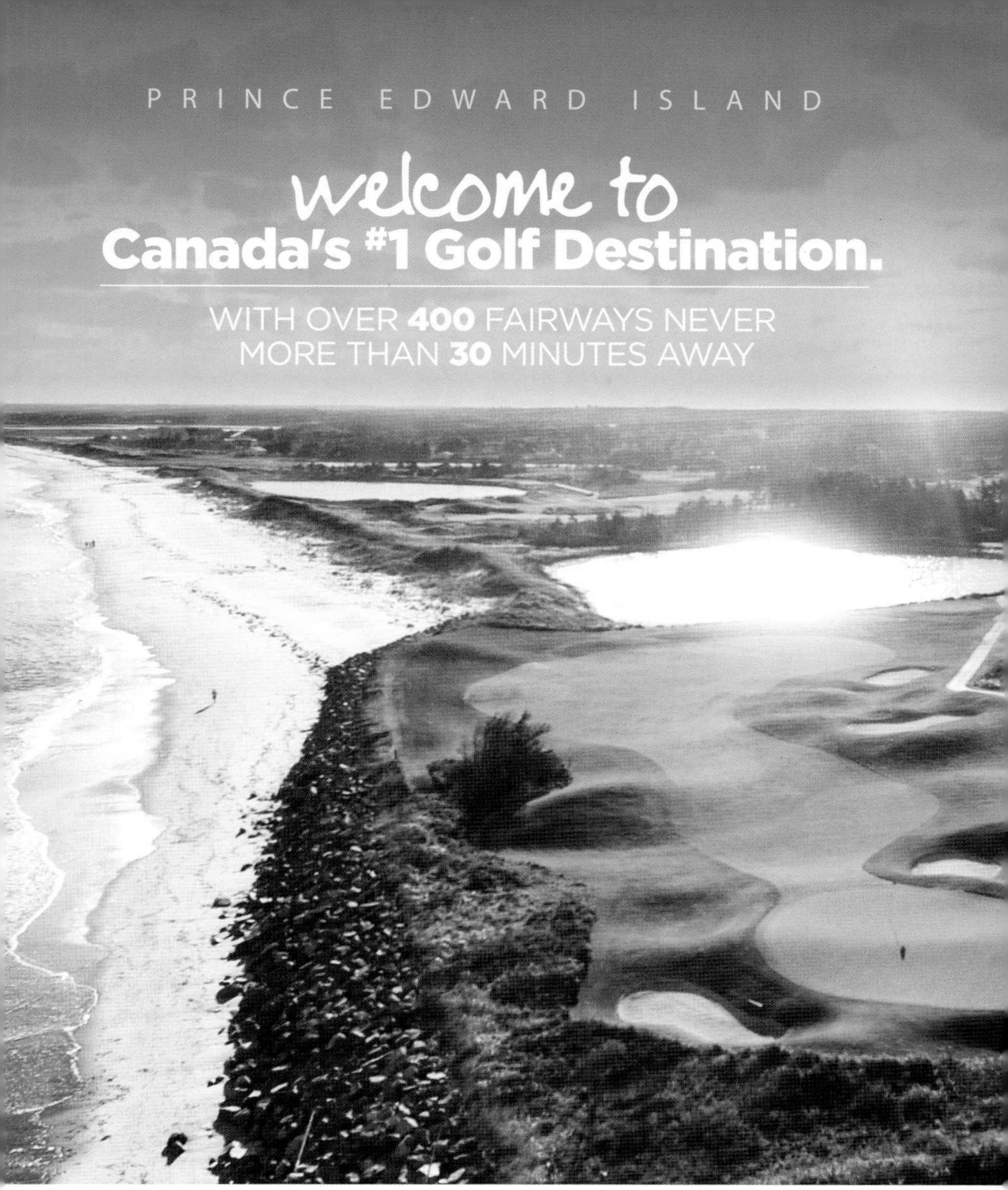
PRINCE EDWARD ISLAND
welcome to
Canada's #1 Golf Destination.
WITH OVER 400 FAIRWAYS NEVER
MORE THAN 30 MINUTES AWAY

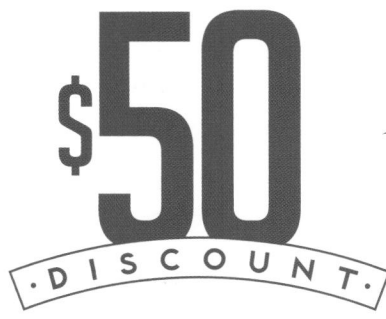

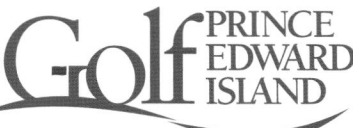

# Southers Marsh Golf Club

## The Best Golf Value in Massachusetts

### 13 Consecutive Years, 2005-2017

Plymouth, Massachusetts

www.southersmarsh.com ◊ 508-830-3535

# Links at Outlook
## "Golf in the Scottish Tradition"

# NEW ENGLAND
# GOLFGUIDE®
## THE DIRECTORY FOR GOLF IN NEW ENGLAND
## 2017

*Mohegan Sun Golf Club, Baltic, CT*

Welcome to our **28th year** of providing New England's most complete listing of information on private and public courses in Connecticut, Maine, Massachusetts, New Hampshire, Rhode Island, and Vermont. Reader comments welcome and encouraged. Visit us online.

Callarose, LLC
464 Common Street Suite 358
Belmont, MA 02478
www.newenglandgolfguide.com
Sales: (508) 330-6007  Administration: (214) 417-7469

Six States. 675 Courses. One Book.™

# NEW ENGLAND
# GOLFGUIDE® 2017

Publisher: The MRS Company
Editor: Mike Suvalle
Owner: Callarose, LLC
Book and Web Designer: Adam Katz, www.atomikdesignstudio.com
Web Tech Development: Mike Regan, Empire Software
Contributors: Christina Ricci, Adam Stanley

Website: www.newenglandgolfguide.com

Course Ratings by Steve Dailey, Gene Goldstein, Mark Hall, PGA, Jim Martone, Glenn McIntyre, Frank Procopio, and Dennis Walch.

Special thanks to Adam Katz, Mike Regan, Atty. Michael MacClary of Burns & Levinson, LLP, Marcia MacClary, Derick Fors, Joe Pisco, Roger Adams, Bo MacClary, John DiCocco, Dennis Walch, Annie Déziel.

# Welcome to 2017

**A**s we enter our 28th year we would like to thank all of our advertisers for their support throughout the years.

According to Editor Mike Suvalle and Owner Callarose, LLC, the 2017 Guide is the biggest and best ever providing even more coupons, information, stories and articles that readers will enjoy.

### Special features in the 2017 Guide:

■ **Private Course Section**

■ **Coupon For Free Warrior Golf Clubs** (*shipping not included*)

■ **Entry into a drawing for a full set of TaylorMade graphite golf clubs and golf bag**

### Continuing Features in the 2017 Guide:

■ **Updated Course Ratings**

■ **Top Rated Courses for 2017**

■ **Top 60 Golfing Values in New England**

■ **Coupons worth over $5,000**

### Charity Golf Events

Our "Hit the Green" and "Hit the Fairway" programs have raised more than $175,000 for charities and golf courses throughout New England in the past 7 years and promise to be even more successful in 2017. Special pricing for sunglasses, golf balls and *New England GolfGuides* are available for your events.

### E-Mail Blasts

Our expanded e-mail blast program enables golf courses and advertising partners to connect directly with a captive and interested audience. The database is regularly refreshed and represents thousands of potential customers that have purchased golf-related items.

For information on any of these programs contact us at (508) 330-6007.

Thanks for your continued support.

Please visit us at www.newenglandgolfguide.com.

*If we have made any mistakes or failed to report thoroughly, please let us know. We pride ourselves on listening to our readers. Contact us at info@newenglandgolfguide.com.*

# Contents

YOUR GUIDE TO THE GOLFGUIDE

## Finding the Courses

## Features

## Featured Courses For 2017

## The Extras: Coupons & Offers

# The Course Listings

# Index to Public Golf Courses

## ALPHABETICALLY BY STATE & COURSE

# Maine

# Massachusetts

| Course | City | Page |
|---|---|---|
| Acushnet River Valley GC | Acushnet | 150 |
| Agawam Municipal GC | Feedng Hills | 180 |
| Allendale Country Club | Dartmouth | 150 |
| Amesbury Golf & CC | Amesbury | 100 |
| Amherst Golf Club | Amherst | 180 |
| Ashfield Community GC | Ashfield | 181 |
| Atlantic Country Club | Plymouth | 100 |
| Back Nine Club, The | Lakeville | 151 |
| Bas Ridge Golf Course | Hinsdale | 181 |
| Bass River Golf Course | South Yarmouth | 151 |
| Bay Path Golf Course | East Brookfield | 182 |
| Bay Pointe Club | Onset | 152 |
| Bayberry Hills GC | South Yarmouth | 152 |
| Beaver Brook Country Club | Haydenville | 182 |
| Bedrock Golf Club | Rutland | 183 |
| Berlin Country Club | Berlin | 183 |
| Beverly Golf & Tennis | Beverly | 101 |
| Blackstone National GC | Sutton | 184 |
| Black Swan GC | Georgetown | 101 |
| Blissful Meadows GC | Uxbridge | 184 |
| Blue Rock Golf Club | South Yarmouth | 153 |
| Bradford Country Club | Bradford | 102 |
| Braintree Muni Golf Course | Braintree | 102 |
| Brookmeadow CC | Canton | 103 |
| Brookside Club | Bourne | 153 |
| Bungay Brook Golf Club | Bellingham | 103 |
| Butter Brook Golf Club | Westford | 104 |
| Butternut Farm GC | Stow | 104 |
| Candlewood Golf Club | Ipswich | 105 |
| Cape Ann Golf Club | Essex | 105 |
| Cape Club, The | North Falmouth | 154 |
| Cape Cod CC | East Falmouth | 154 |
| Captains GC (Port) | Brewster | 155 |
| Captains GC (Starboard) | Brewster | 155 |
| Cedar Glen Golf Club | Saugus | 106 |
| Cedar Hill Golf Club | Stoughton | 106 |
| Chatham Seaside Links | Chatham | 156 |
| Chelmsford Country Club | Chelmsford | 107 |
| Chemawa Golf Course | N. Attleboro | 156 |
| Chequessett Golf Club | Wellfleet | 157 |
| Cherry Hill GC | Amherst | 185 |
| Chicopee Municipal GC | Chicopee | 185 |
| Clearview Golf Course | Millbury | 186 |
| Cold Spring CC | Belchertown | 186 |
| Cotuit-Highground GC | Cotuit | 157 |
| Country Club of Billerica | Billerica | 107 |
| Country Club of Greenfield | Greenfield | 187 |
| Country Club of Wilbraham | Wilbraham | 187 |
| Cranberry Valley GC | Harwich | 158 |
| Cranwell Spa & Golf Resort | Lenox | 188 |
| Crestview Country Club | Agawam | 188 |
| Crosswinds Golf Club | Plymouth | 108 |
| Crumpin-Fox Club | Bernardston | 189 |
| Crystal Lake GC | Haverhill | 108 |
| Cyprian Keyes Golf Club | Boylston | 189 |
| Cyprian Keyes GC/Par 3 | Boylston | 190 |
| D.W. Field Golf Course | Brockton | 109 |
| Dennis Highlands | South Dennis | 158 |
| Dennis Pines GC | South Dennis | 159 |
| Donnybrook CC | Lanesborough | 190 |
| Dudley Hill Golf Club | Dudley | 191 |
| Dunroamin CC | Gilbertville | 191 |
| East Mountain CC | Westfield | 192 |
| Easton Country Club | South Easton | 109 |
| Edge Hill GC | Ashfield | 192 |
| Edgewood Golf Club | Southwick | 193 |
| Egremont Country Club | Great Barrington | 193 |
| Ellinwood CC | Athol | 194 |
| Elmcrest Country Club | East Longmeadow | 194 |
| Evergreen Valley GC | Newburyport | 110 |
| Falmouth Country Club | Falmouth | 159 |
| Far Corner Golf Course | West Boxford | 110 |
| Farm Neck Golf Club | Oak Bluffs | 160 |
| Fire Fly Country Club | Seekonk | 160 |
| Fore Kicks GC & Sports | Norfolk | 111 |
| Forest Park CC | Adams | 195 |
| Four Oaks Country Club | Dracut | 111 |
| Foxborough Country Club | Foxborough | 112 |
| Franconia Municipal GC | Springfield | 195 |
| Fresh Pond Golf Club | Cambridge | 112 |
| Furnace Brook Golf Club | Quincy | 113 |
| Gannon Golf Course | Lynn | 113 |
| Gardner Municipal GC | Gardner | 196 |
| Garrison Golf Center | Haverhill | 114 |
| GEAA Golf Club | Pittsfield | 196 |
| George Wright GC | Hyde Park | 114 |
| Glen Ellen CC | Millis | 115 |
| Grandview Golf Course | Leominster | 197 |
| Granite Links Golf Club | Quincy | 115 |
| Green Harbor Golf Club | Marshfield | 116 |
| Green Hill Municipal GC | Worcester | 197 |
| Greenock Country Club | Lee | 198 |
| Groton Pool & Golf Center | Groton | 198 |
| Harwich Port Golf Club | Harwich Port | 161 |
| Hazleton Golf Club | Rehoboth | 161 |
| Heather Hill CC | Plainville | 162 |
| Hemlock Ridge GC | Fiskdale | 199 |
| Heritage Country Club | Charlton | 199 |
| Hickory Hill GC | Methuen | 116 |
| Hickory Ridge GC | S. Amherst | 200 |
| Hidden Hollow Country Club | Rehoboth | 162 |
| Highfields Golf & CC | Grafton | 200 |
| Highland Links | North Truro | 163 |
| Hillcrest Country Club | Leicester | 201 |
| Hillside Country Club | Rehoboth | 163 |
| Hillview Golf Course | North Reading | 117 |
| Holden Hills CC | Jefferson | 201 |
| Holly Ridge Golf Club | South Sandwich | 164 |
| Holyoke Country Club | Holyoke | 202 |
| Hopedale CC | Hopedale | 202 |
| Hyannis Golf Club | Hyannis | 164 |
| Indian Meadows Golf Club | Westboro | 203 |
| John F. Parker Municipal GC | Taunton | 165 |
| Juniper Hill GC/Lakeside | Northboro | 203 |
| Juniper Hill GC/Riverside | Northboro | 204 |
| Kelley Greens Golf Course | Nahant | 117 |
| Kettle Brook Golf Club | Paxton | 204 |
| Lakeville Country Club | Lakeville | 165 |
| Ledges Golf Club | South Hadley | 205 |
| Leicester Country Club | Leicester | 205 |
| Leo J. Martin GC | Weston | 118 |
| Links at Lancaster Golf | Lancaster | 206 |
| Little Harbor CC | Wareham | 166 |
| Lost Brook Golf Club | Norwood | 118 |
| Maplegate Country Club | Bellingham | 119 |
| Marion Golf Course | Marion | 166 |
| Maynard Golf Course | Maynard | 119 |
| Meadow at Peabody, The | Peabody | 120 |

# Massachusetts cont'd.

# New Hampshire

# Rhode Island

# Vermont

# Driving Range Directory

## Connecticut Driving Ranges by Town

| | | |
|---|---|---|
| Mountain-View Golf Driving Range | 2061 Berlin Turnpike, Berlin 06037 | (860) 828-5358 |
| Woodhaven Country Club | 275 Miller Road, Bethany 06524 | (203) 393-3230 |
| Stony Hill Long Drive | 46 Stony Hill Road, Bethel 06801 | (203) 778-2777 |
| Mar-Lea Miniature Golf Range | 244 Boston Turnpike, Bolton 06043 | (860) 649-7023 |
| Golf Quest Family Sports Center | 1 Sandout Road, Brookfield 06804 | (203) 775-3556 |
| Burlington Golf Center & Practice | Rural Route 4, Burlington 06013 | (860) 675-7320 |
| Chesire Academy Of Golf | 1550 Highland Avenue, Cheshire 06410 | (203) 271-1403 |
| Colchester Driving Range | 160 Old Hebron Road, Colchester 06415 | (860) 537-4653 |
| Rockpile Driving Range | 113 Rock Hall Road, Colebrook 06021 | (860) 379-5161 |
| Torza's Professional Golf Center | 98 Sebethe Drive, Cromwell 06416 | (860) 632-1132 |
| Meadowridge Golf Center | 20 North Road, East Windsor 06088 | (860) 623-9500 |
| Pleasant View Golf Park | 110 North Street, Enfield 06082 | (860) 763-4202 |
| Tunxis Fore | 1024 Farmington Ave., Farmington 06032 | (860) 674-8924 |
| Great Brook Golf Center | 850 Route 84, Groton 06340 | (860) 448-0938 |
| East Hartford Golf Center | 55 Hillside Avenue, Hartford 06106 | (860) 282-7809 |
| Goodwin Golf Course | 1130 Maple Avenue, Hartford 06114 | (860) 956-3601 |
| Toll Gate Golf Range | 590 Torrington Road, Litchfield 06759 | (860) 496-4653 |
| Klein's Golf Range | 391 Durham Road, Madison 06443 | (203) 245-1139 |
| Golf Center Of Manchester | 60 Progress Drive, Manchester 06040 | (860) 646-6479 |
| Club Golf | 109 Adams Street, Manchester 06040 | (860) 645-6363 |
| Highland Ridge Golf Range | 87 Highland Road, Mansfield Center 06250 | (860) 423-9494 |
| Indian Springs Golf Club | 132 Mack Road, Middlefield 06455 | (860) 349-8109 |
| Newfield Golf Driving Range | 500 Newfield Street, Middletown 06457 | (860) 347-1750 |
| Stanley Golf Club | 245 Hartford Road, New Britain, CT 06053 | (860) 827-8570 |
| Connecticut Golf Center | 562 Danbury Road, New Milford 06776 | (860) 354-0012 |
| Only Game In Town | 275 Valley Service Road, New Haven 06473 | (203) 239-4653 |
| Golf Training Center | 145 Main Street, Norwalk 06851 | (203) 847-8008 |
| Malerba's Golf Driving Range | 650 New London Turnpike, Norwich 06360 | (860) 889-5770 |
| CherryStones | 218 Shore Road, Old Lyme 06371 | (860) 434-1721 |
| Prospect Golf Driving Range | 144 Waterbury Road, Prospect 06712 | (203) 758-4121 |
| Belmont's Ridgefield Golf Range | 824 Ethan Allen Highway, Ridgefield 06877 | (203) 431-8989 |
| Golf Center of Connecticut | 784 River Road, Shelton 06484 | (203) 929-6500 |
| Pleasant View Golf Center | 452 South Road, Somers 06071 | (860) 749-5868 |
| Golf Quest Family Sports Center | 125 Jude Lane, Southington 06489 | (860) 621-3663 |
| Raceway Golf Club | 252 E. Thompson Road, Thompson 06277 | (860) 923-9591 |
| Rockledge Golf Shop & Driving | 289 S. Main Street, West Hartford 06107 | (860) 521-3156 |
| Brown's Driving Range | 1847 Poquonock Avenue, Windsor 06095 | (860) 688-1745 |

## Maine Driving Ranges by Town

| | | |
|---|---|---|
| Roy's Golf Center | 2514 Turner Road, Auburn 04210 | (207) 782-2801 |
| XL Indoor/Outdoor Golf | 620 Hammond Street, Bangor 04401 | (207) 848-5850 |
| Long Shot Golf Center | 305 Bath Road, Brunswick 04011 | (207) 725-6377 |
| Vokes' Mini-Strokes | Bar Harbor Road, Ellsworth 04605 | (207) 667-9519 |
| Tee 'Em Up Golf Center | Route 100, Gray 04039 | (207) 657-4653 |
| Sugarloaf Sports & Fitness Center | Sugarloaf Access Road, Kingfield 04947 | (207) 237-2000 |
| College Street Driving Range | 601 College Road, Lewiston 04240 | (207) 786-7818 |

| T's Golf | Range Way & Route 202, Manchester 04351 | (207) 621-8633 |
| Fore Season Golf | 1037 Forest Avenue, Portland 04103 | (207) 797-8835 |
| Riverside Municipal Golf Course | 1158 Riverside St., Portland 04103 | (207) 797-3524 |
| Cascade Golf Range | Rural Route 1, Saco 04072 | (207) 282-3524 |
| Mountain View Golf Range | Route 109, Sanford 04073 | (207) 324-0436 |
| Nonesuch River Golf Club | 304 Gorham Road, Scarborough 04074 | (207) 883-0007 |
| Pine Ridge Golf Center | Route 15, Box 4660, Sedgwick 04676 | (207) 359-6788 |
| Tee Shots | 1126 N. Berwick Road, Wells 04090 | (207) 646-2727 |
| Tee 'N Tee Golf Land | 27 Bridgton Road, Westbrook 04092 | (207) 797-6753 |
| Sonny's Driving Range | 108 Cove Hill Road, Winterport 04496 | (207) 223-5242 |

**Massachussetts Driving Ranges by Town**

| Crestview Country Club | 281 Shoemaker Lane, Agawam 01001 | (413) 786-2593 |
| Mushy's Driving Range | 369 Main Street, Agawam 01001 | (413) 786-6672 |
| Sarkisian Driving Range | 153 Chandler Road, Andover 01810 | (978) 688-5522 |
| Atlantic Golf Center | 754 Newport Ave, Attleboro 02703 | (508) 761-5484 |
| McGolf Driving Range | 541 Southbridge Street, Auburn 01501 | (508) 832-0557 |
| South Meadow Golf Range | 317 South Street, Berlin 01503 | (978) 838-2333 |
| Sun 'n' Air Driving Range | 210 Conant Street, Danvers 01923 | (978) 774-8180 |
| McGolf Limited | 150 Bridge Street, Dedham 02026 | (781) 326-9616 |
| Ridder Golf Course | 300 Oak Street, East Bridgewater 02333 | (781) 447-6613 |
| Falmouth Country Club | 630 Carriage Shop Rd., East Falmouth 02536 | (508) 548-3211 |
| Fenway Golf Range & Pitch | 112 Allen Street, East Longmeadow 01028 | (413) 525-6495 |
| Easthampton Golf | 103 Northampton St., Easthampton 01027 | (413) 529-2300 |
| Groton Country Club | 94 Lovers Lane, Groton 01450 | (978) 448-2564 |
| Groveland Fairways | 156 Main Street, Groveland 01834 | (978) 373-2872 |
| Western Mass Family Golf Center | 294 Russell Street, Hadley 01035 | (413) 586-2311 |
| Garrison Par 3 Golf Center | 660 Hilldale Avenue, Haverhill 01832 | (978) 374-9380 |
| Pine Crest Golf Club | 212 Prentice Street, Holliston 01746 | (508) 429-9871 |
| Hyannis Golf Club | Route 132, Hyannis 02601 | (508) 362-2606 |
| Tee Time Driving Range | New Report Turnpike, Ipswich 01938 | (978) 356-6599 |
| Lancaster Golf Center | 138 Old Union Turnpike, Lancaster 01523 | (978) 537-8922 |
| Bakers Driving Range & Golf | 658 South Main Street, Lanesboro 01237 | (413) 443-6102 |
| Stone Meadow Golf | 675 Waltham Street, Lexington 02173 | (781) 863-0445 |
| Lakeview Driving Range | 449 Whalom Road, Lunenburg 01462 | (978) 345-7070 |
| Sagamore Spring Golf Club | 1282 Main Street, Lynnfield 01940 | (781) 334-3151 |
| Mendon Driving Range | Route 16, Mendon 01756 | (508) 478-6295 |
| Whirlaway Sports Center | 500 Merrimack Street, Methuen 01844 | (978) 688-8356 |
| Lakeville Golf Practice Range | 10 Rock Street, Middleboro 02346 | (508) 947-1865 |
| Golf Country | 160 S. Main Street, Middleton 01949 | (978) 774-4476 |
| Paradise Springs Golf | 25 Lonergan Road, Middleton 01949 | (978) 750-4653 |
| Quaboag Valley Mini-Golf | 15 Hospital Road, Monson 01057 | (413) 283-4388 |
| Natick Golf Learning Center | 218 Speen Street, Natick 01760 | (508) 651-2406 |
| Airport Golf Driving Range | 582 Kelley Boulevard, N. Attleboro 02760 | (508) 643-2229 |
| Pappas Indoor Golf & Baseball | 70 Princeton Street, N. Chelmsford 01863 | (978) 251-3933 |
| Caddy Shack | 900 State Road, N. Dartmouth 02747 | (508) 991-7976 |
| East Coast Golf Academy | 333 SW Cutoff, Northborough 01532 | (508) 842-3311 |
| Golf Learning Center | 19 Leonard Street, Norton 02766 | (508) 285-4500 |
| Sandbaggers Practice Range | 829 Washington St., Pembroke 02339 | (781) 826-1234 |
| Holly Ridge Golf Club | 121 Country Club Road, Sandwich 02563 | (508) 428-5577 |
| Seekonk Driving Range | 1977 Fall River Avenue, Seekonk 02771 | (508) 336-8074 |
| Southborough Golf | 20 Turnpike Road, Southborough 01772 | (508) 480-9992 |

**Massachussetts Driving Ranges by Town (continued)**

| | | |
|---|---|---|
| Easton Country Club | 265 Purchase Street, S. Easton 02375 | (508) 238-2500 |
| Coles River Family Fun Center | 358 G.A.R. Highway, Swansea 02777 | (508) 675-8767 |
| Max's Country Golf | 383 Middlesex Road, Tyngsboro 01879 | (978) 649-2020 |
| Golf Masters | 2250 Providence Highway, Walpole 02081 | (508) 668-8222 |
| Bryant Farm Driving Range | 123 Sandwich Road, Wareham 02571 | (508) 295-8773 |
| Rotary Driving Range | Route 9, Westborough 01581 | (508) 366-5327 |
| East Mountain Country Club | 1458 East Mountain Road, Westfield 01085 | (413) 568-1539 |
| Golf Acres | 319 Union Street, Westfield 01085 | (413) 568-1075 |
| Waubeeka Golf Links | 137 New Ashford Road, Williamstown 01267 | (413) 458-5869 |

**New Hampshire Ranges by Town**

| | | |
|---|---|---|
| Souhegan Woods Golf Club | 65 Thornton Ferry Road, Amherst 03031 | (603) 673-0200 |
| White Mountain Country Club | 3 Country Club Lane, Ashland 03217 | (603) 536-2227 |
| Candia Woods Golf Links | 313 South Road, Candia 03034 | (603) 483-2307 |
| Beaver Meadow Golf Course | 1 Beaver Meadow Street, Concord 03301 | (603) 224-2828 |
| Twin Pines Driving Range | Route 125, Epping 03042 | (603) 679-9911 |
| Driving Range | Route 124, Greenville 03048 | (603) 878-1324 |
| Legends Golf & Family | 18 Legends Drive, Hooksett 03106 | (603) 627-0099 |
| World Golf Cup Center | 4 Friel Golf Road, Hudon 03051 | (603) 598-3838 |
| Funspot | Rural Route 3, Laconia 03246 | (603) 366-4377 |
| Lisbon Village Country Club | Bishop Road, Lisbon 03585 | (603) 838-6004 |
| John Cain Golf Club | Unity Road, Newport 03773 | (603) 863-7787 |
| Sagamore Golf Club | North Road, North Hampton 03862 | (603) 964-8393 |
| Campbell's Scottish Highlands | 72 Brady Avenue, Salem, NH 03079 | (603) 896-5000 |
| Lochmere Golf & Country Club | Rural Route 3, Tilton 03276 | (603) 528-4653 |
| Fore-U Golf Center | 298 Plainfield Road, West Lebanon 03784 | (603) 298-9702 |

**Rhode Island Driving Ranges by Town**

| | | |
|---|---|---|
| Narragansett Driving Range | 1141 Boston Neck Road, Narragansett 02882 | (401) 284-0005 |
| Smithfield Driving Range | 661 Douglas Pike, Smithfield 02917 | (401) 231-3726 |
| Green Meadows Golf | 117 Dunns Corner Road, Westerly 02891 | (401) 322-9888 |

**Vermont Driving Ranges by Town**

| | | |
|---|---|---|
| Mt. Anthony Country Club | 180 Country Club Drive, Bennington 05201 | (802) 447-7079 |
| Essex Country Club | 332 Old Stage Road, Essex Junction 05451 | (802) 879-3232 |
| Practice Tee | Route 7A, Manchester 05254 | (802) 362-3100 |
| Arrowhead Golf Course | 350 Muray Avenue, Milton 05468 | (802) 893-0234 |
| Mount Snow Golf Club | Country Club Road, Mount Snow 05356 | (802) 464-4254 |
| Proctor Pittsford Country Club | Corn Hill Road, Pittsford 05763 | (802) 483-9379 |
| St. Johnsbury Country Club | Route, St. Johnsbury 05819 | (802) 748-9894 |
| Stratton Mountain | Rural Route 1, Stratton Mountain 05155 | (802) 297-4114 |
| Basin Harbor Club | Basin Harbor Road, Vergennes 05491 | (802) 475-2309 |
| Blush Hill Country Club | Blush Hill Road, Waterbury 05676 | (802) 244-8974 |

# The Top New England Golf Courses

**T**he following is the 2017 list of the very best golf courses in New England. To make this cut, a course has to earn a *New England GolfGuide* ✪✪✪½ star rating or greater. Of the 666 public courses covered in this book, approximately 18 percent make it on this list.

We determine ratings using a uniform set of criteria and compiled by our experienced multi-state rating team. We also take reader feedback seriously and incorporate your comments when appropriate. It is our view that providing you with current and accurate course rating information will only add to your golfing pleasure. In the spirit of constant improvement, we continue to enhance our Course Rating Methodology as well as expand the use of our popular Value Rating™.

**Course Rating**–The course ratings are based on a 1 to 5 star scale. For example, we reserve the 5-star (✪✪✪✪✪) rating for only a handful of the clearly outstanding courses followed by ✪✪✪✪ for excellent, ✪✪✪ for very good, ✪✪ for good and ✪ for average and below. As an added enhancement, we also include ½ star ratings to help distinguish the unique characteristics of one course from another.

The *New England GolfGuide* rating uses criteria which include:

1. **Course layout.** Is it interesting and varied? How many of the holes are memorable? Is the course challenging but also fair? Would this course present an interesting and different challenge every time you played it?

2. **Course Condition.** What are the average conditions of the tees, fairways, rough, hazards, and greens? What is the overall level of maintenance and attention to detail? How mature is the course?

3. **Course Staff, Facilities, and Restrictions.** How helpful and courteous is the staff? Are there adequate amenities? Are there any restrictions that would detract from the golfing experience and are walkers allowed?

4. **Golfer Feedback.** We view this as an important means of gaining insight into the courses of New England. As in years past we strongly encourage you to provide us with your assessment of the courses you have played. Your feedback provides additional support for our ratings.

# 2017 NEGG
# Top Rated Courses

(18-hole, non-par 3 courses, based on star ratings and reader feedback).

## 5 Star Courses ✪✪✪✪✪

### Massachusetts
| | |
|---|---|
| Blackstone National GC | Sutton, MA |
| Butter Brook GC | Westford, MA |
| Granite Links GC | Quincy, MA |
| Pinehills GC (Jones) | Plymouth, MA |
| Pinehills GC (Nicklaus) | Plymouth, MA |
| Red Tail Golf Club | Devens, MA |
| Shaker Hills CC | Harvard, MA |

### Connecticut
| | |
|---|---|
| Mohegan Sun Golf Club | Baltic, CT |

### Maine
| | |
|---|---|
| Belgrade Lakes | Belgrade Lakes, ME |

### New Hampshire
| | |
|---|---|
| Atkinson Resort | Atkinson, NH |
| Mt. Washington GC | Bretton Woods, NH |

## 4¹/₂ Star Courses ✪✪✪✪¹/₂

### Massachusetts
| | |
|---|---|
| Cranwell Resort | Lenox, MA |
| Crestview CC | Agawam, MA |
| Crumpin-Fox Club | Bernardston, MA |
| Farm Neck Golf Club | Oak Bluffs, MA |
| Foxborough CC | Foxborough, MA |
| Shining Rock GC | Northbridge, MA |
| Taconic GC | Williamstown, MA |
| Waubeeka Golf Links | S. Williamstown, MA |
| Waverly Oaks GC | Plymouth, MA |

### Connecticut
| | |
|---|---|
| Fox Hopyard CC | East Haddam, CT |
| Lake of Isles GC | N. Stonington, CT |
| Wintonbury Hills GC | Bloomfield, CT |

### Maine
| | |
|---|---|
| Fox Ridge GC | Auburn, ME |

### New Hampshire
| | |
|---|---|
| Owl's Nest GC | Campton, NH |

### Vermont
| | |
|---|---|
| Green Mountain National | Killington, VT |

## 4 Star Courses ✪✪✪✪

### Connecticut
| | |
|---|---|
| Great River GC | Milford, CT |
| Richter Park GC | Danbury, CT |

### Maine
| | |
|---|---|
| Boothbay Harbor CC | Boothbay, ME |
| Dunegrass GC | Old Orchard Beach, ME |
| Kebo Valley GC | Bar Harbor, ME |
| The Ledges GC | York, ME |
| Links at Outlook | South Berwick, ME |
| Old Marsh CC | Wells, ME |
| Penobscot Valley CC | Oreno, ME |
| Samoset Resort | Rockport, ME |
| Sugarloaf | Carrabassett, ME |
| Sunday River | Newry, ME |

### New Hampshire
| | |
|---|---|
| Eastman Golf Links | Grantham, NH |
| Portsmouth CC | Greenland, NH |

### Massachusetts
| | |
|---|---|
| Cranberry Valley GC | Harwich, MA |
| Crosswinds GC | Plymouth, MA |
| George Wright GC | Hyde Park, MA |
| Highfields Golf & CC | Grafton, MA |
| Olde Barnstable | Marsten Mills, MA |
| Pembroke CC | Pembroke, MA |
| The Ranch GC | Southwick, MA |
| Townsend Ridge CC | Townsend, MA |

### Rhode Island
| | |
|---|---|
| Meadow Brook | Richmond, RI |
| Newport National GC | Middletown, RI |

### Vermont
| | |
|---|---|
| Hermitage GC | Wilmington, VT |
| Okemo Valley GC | Ludlow, VT |
| Rutland CC | Rutland, VT |
| Sugarbush GC | Warren, VT |

# 3½ Star Courses ✪✪✪½

## Connecticut

| | |
|---|---|
| Elmridge GC | Pawcatuck, CT |
| Longshore GC | Westport, CT |
| Lyman Orchards CC (Player) | Middlefield, CT |
| Lyman Orchards CC (Jones) | Middlefield, CT |
| Oxford Green GC | Oxford, CT |
| Quarry Ridge GC | Portland, CT |
| Rockledge CC | West Hartford, CT |
| Stanley GC | New Britain, CT |
| Sterling Farms GC | Stamford CT |
| Topstone GC | South Windsor, CT |
| Tower Ridge | Simsbury, CT |
| Tunxis Plantation CC | Farmington, CT |

## Massachusetts

| | |
|---|---|
| Acushnet River Valley GC | Acushnet, MA |
| Atlantic CC | Plymouth, MA |
| Black Swan CC | Georgetown, MA |
| Blue Rock GC | S. Yarmouth, MA |
| Captains GC (Port) | Brewster, MA |
| Captains GC (Starboard) | Brewster, MA |
| Chemawa GC | North Attleboro, MA |
| Cold Spring CC | Belchertown, MA |
| Cyprian Keyes GC | Boylston, MA |
| Dennis Pines GC | East Dennis, MA |
| Far Corner GC | West Boxford, MA |
| Glen Ellen | Millis MA |
| Green Hill Municipal GC | Worcester, MA |
| Hickory Ridge | Amherst, MA |
| Juniper Hill (Lakeside) | Northborough, MA |
| Juniper Hill (Riverside) | Northborough, MA |
| Kettle Brook GC | Paxton, MA |
| Miacomet GC | Nantucket, MA |
| New England CC | Bellingham, MA |
| Poquoy Brook GC | Lakeville, MA |
| Southers Marsh GC | Plymouth, MA |
| Wachusett CC | West Boylston, MA |
| Wentworth Hills CC | Plainville, MA |

## Maine

| | |
|---|---|
| Aroostook Valley CC | Fort Fairfield, ME |
| Brunswick GC | Brunswick, ME |
| Clinton GC | Clinton, ME |
| Diadema GC | North Anson, ME |
| Martindale CC | Auburn, ME |
| Natanis GC (Tomahawk) | Vassalboro, ME |
| Nonesuch River GC | Scarborough, ME |
| Northeast Harbor GC | N.E. Harbor, ME |
| Point Sebago GC | Casco, ME |
| Sable Oaks GC | S. Portland, ME |
| Spring Meadows GC | Gray, ME |
| Toddy Brook GC | N. Yarmouth, ME |
| Waterville CC | Oakland, ME |
| Webhannet GC | Kennebunk, ME |

## New Hampshire

| | |
|---|---|
| Bretwood GC (North) | Keene, NH |
| Campbell's Scot. Highlds | Salem NH |
| Crotched Mountain GC | Francestown, NH |
| Hanover CC | Hanover, NH |
| Lochmere GC | Tilton, NH |
| Overlook GC | Hollis, NH |
| Passaconaway CC | Litchfield, NH |
| Ridgewood CC | Moultonbourough, NH |
| Rochester CC | Rochester, NH |
| Stonebridge CC | Goffstown, NH |
| The Oaks GL | Somersworth, NH |

## Rhode Island

| | |
|---|---|
| Cranston CC | Cranston, RI |
| Montaup CC | Portsmouth, RI |

## Vermont

| | |
|---|---|
| Equinox GC | Manchester, VT |
| Jay Peak Resort GC | Jay, VT |
| Mt. Anthony CC | Bennington, VT |
| Stowe CC | Stowe, VT |
| Stratton Mountain | Stratton Mountain, VT |
| Williston GC | Williston, VT |
| Woodstock Inn & Resort | Woodstock, VT |

---

*The *New England GolfGuide* uses a five star rating system when evaluating golf courses. This rating takes into account course layout, condition, variety, challenge, amenities, and professionalism of the staff. A course that has earned a rating of ✪ is average, ✪✪ represents a good course, ✪✪✪ is considered very good. A ✪✪✪✪ course offers an superior experience and a ✪✪✪✪✪ rating is reserved for only the most exceptional courses.

# Top 60 Golfing Values in New England 2017

The *New England GolfGuide* Value Rating™ is provided to help our reader's identify the courses that deliver the best value for golfing dollar ($$$). This year we have provided you with the Top 23 (❂❂❂) rated courses with an 18 hole weekend rate of $59 or less, the Top 21 (❂❂❂½) rated courses with an 18 hole weekend rate of $62 or less and the Top 11 (❂❂❂❂) rated courses with an 18 hole weekend rate of $78 or less. We have also included the Top (❂❂❂❂½) and (❂❂❂❂❂) courses.

Of the 666 public golf courses listed in this book, there are only a select group of courses, less than 9 percent, which are on this list. Our list not only reflects price but includes reader feedback and the reports from our NEGG Course Rater team.

Of course, only you can judge the value of a day on Course A versus Course B. But we've compiled the data on the most objective basis we can and we'll stand by our list. This is just another opportunity for you to send us feedback. Did we miss any great values? Did we rate some course too high or too low? If enough readers tell us something they can move the needle.

Each year, the biggest task of our editorial staff is to update the listed information for all of the courses. As was the case last year, due to the economy, most course have told us that their rates will remain unchanged. As we reviewed the rates we discovered that the average weekend cost of playing 18 holes of golf, with cart, across New England has gone up slightly to just over $65.

In addition to the Top 60 Golfing Values in New England, golfers who like to play into fall or start in early spring can also find a wide variety of wonderful off-season specials. Many of the courses listed in our book have substantial off-season discounts from the standard green fee which can be accessed by going directly to their websites.

Also, don't forget the Fall golf bonus; many courses in the southern areas of New England including Cape Cod provide fine playing conditions and discounts starting in October (and a few stay open year-round). Try **Farm Neck** on Martha's Vineyard in April or October for what might be the best deal of all.

In addition, here are a few recommended resort courses and golf courses which offer excellent Stay and Play packages:

## Connecticut

**Foxwoods Resort Casino** in Mashantucket
**Lake of Isles Golf Club & Resort** in Stonington
**Mohegan Sun** in Baltic

## Maine

**Point Sebago Golf Club** in Casco
**Poland Spring** in Poland Spring
**Samoset Resort** in Rockport
**Sugarloaf Golf Club** in Carrabassett Valley
**Sunday River Golf Club** in Newry

## Massachusetts

**Blue Rock Golf Course** in South Yarmouth
**Cranwell Resort** in Lenox
**Crumpin- Fox Club** in Bernardston
**Ocean Edge Resort** in Brewster
**The International** in Bolton

## New Hampshire

**Atkinson Resort** in Atkinson
**Crotched Mountain Resort** in Francestown
**Mt. Washington Golf Club** in Bretton Woods
**Owl's Nest** in Campton

## Vermont

**Equinox Golf Club** in Manchester
**Hermitage Golf Club** in Wilmington
**Lake Morey Resort** in Fairlee
**Mount Snow Golf Club** in West Dover
**Okemo Mountain Resort** in Ludlow
**Sugarbush Resort** in Warren
**Woodstock Inn & Resort** in Woodstock

In addition to the top 60 values and recommended resort courses their are many wonderful golf courses throughout New England that can provide you with a fun and enjoyable day.

# Top 60 Value Ratings
## *New England GolfGuide*
## 2017 Season

The *New England GolfGuide* takes the top-rated courses in our listings, and using a formula that balances price, star ratings, reader comments, and rater evaluations. The resulting list below is a ranking of the Top 60 Best Golfing Values in New England for prices as predicted for 2017.

| ✪✪✪ RATING | COURSE | STATE | GOLF | CART | $ TOTAL |
|---|---|---|---|---|---|
| ✪✪✪ | Lake Kezar | ME | 36 | 13 | 49 |
| ✪✪✪ | The Shattuck | NH | 49 | INC | 49 |
| ✪✪✪ | Laurel View | CT | 35 | 15 | 50 |
| ✪✪✪ | Lake St. Catherine | VT | 36 | 15 | 51 |
| ✪✪✪ | Westminster | MA | 35 | 16 | 51 |
| ✪✪✪ | Leicester | MA | 36 | 16 | 52 |
| ✪✪✪ | Bath | ME | 40 | 13 | 53 |
| ✪✪✪ | Bridgton Highlands | ME | 36 | 17 | 53 |
| ✪✪✪ | Ceder Knob | CT | 38 | 15 | 53 |
| ✪✪✪ | Natansis (Arrowhead) | ME | 37 | 16 | 53 |
| ✪✪✪ | Skungamaug River | CT | 38 | 15 | 53 |
| ✪✪✪ | Cedar Knoll | VT | 33 | 21 | 54 |
| ✪✪✪ | Hunter | CT | 39 | 15 | 54 |
| ✪✪✪ | Traditions of Wallingford | CT | 55 | INC | 55 |
| ✪✪✪ | Laurel Lane | RI | 38 | 18 | 56 |
| ✪✪✪ | Southington | CT | 40 | 16 | 56 |
| ✪✪✪ | Poland Spring | ME | 40 | 17 | 57 |
| ✪✪✪ | Richmond | RI | 42 | 15 | 57 |
| ✪✪✪ | Canterbury Woods | NH | 58 | INC | 58 |
| ✪✪✪ | Triggs Memorial | RI | 40 | 18 | 58 |
| ✪✪✪ | Nippo Lake | NH | 42 | 16 | 58 |
| ✪✪✪ | Connecticut National | CT | 43 | 15 | 58 |
| ✪✪✪ | North Kingston Municipal | RI | 41 | 18 | 59 |

| ✪✪✪½ RATING | COURSE | STATE | GOLF | CART | $ TOTAL |
|---|---|---|---|---|---|
| ✪✪✪½ | Crotched Mountain | NH | 35 | 14 | 49 |
| ✪✪✪½ | Southers Marsh | MA | 37 | 14 | 51 |
| ✪✪✪½ | Rockledge | CT | 37 | 14 | 51 |
| ✪✪✪½ | Williston | VT | 35 | 18 | 53 |
| ✪✪✪½ | Green Hill | MA | 40 | 15 | 55 |
| ✪✪✪½ | Bretwood | NH | 42 | 13 | 55 |
| ✪✪✪½ | Nonesuch | ME | 40 | 18 | 58 |

**INC = INCLUDED IN WEEKEND GREENS FEES**

(Prices reflect anticipated 2017 fees but are subject to change without notice. Please call ahead.)

| ○○○½ RATING | COURSE | STATE | GOLF | CART | $ TOTAL |
|---|---|---|---|---|---|
| ○○○½ | Rochester | NH | 42 | 16 | 58 |
| ○○○½ | Stanley | CT | 40 | 18 | 58 |
| ○○○½ | Quarry Ridge | CT | 59 | INC | 59 |
| ○○○½ | Topstone | CT | 46 | 13 | 59 |
| ○○○½ | Tower Ridge | CT | 59 | INC | 59 |
| ○○○½ | Ridgewood | NH | 42 | 17 | 59 |
| ○○○½ | Sable Oaks | ME | 45 | 15 | 60 |
| ○○○½ | Kettle Brook | MA | 60 | INC | 60 |
| ○○○½ | Lochmere | NH | 45 | 16 | 61 |
| ○○○½ | Toddy Brook | ME | 43 | 18 | 61 |
| ○○○½ | Aroostock Valley | ME | 45 | 17 | 62 |
| ○○○½ | Far Corner | MA | 46 | 16 | 62 |
| ○○○½ | Spring Meadows | ME | 44 | 18 | 62 |
| ○○○½ | Wachusett | MA | 45 | 17 | 62 |

| ○○○○ RATING | COURSE | STATE | GOLF | CART | $ TOTAL |
|---|---|---|---|---|---|
| ○○○○ | Penobscott Valley | ME | 39 | 15 | 54 |
| ○○○○ | George Wright | MA | 44 | 20 | 64 |
| ○○○○ | Highfields | MA | 65 | INC | 65 |
| ○○○○ | Townsend Ridge | MA | 45 | 20 | 65 |
| ○○○○ | Old Marsh | ME | 68 | INC | 68 |
| ○○○○ | Eastman | NH | 49 | 20 | 69 |
| ○○○○ | Pembroke | MA | 50 | 19 | 69 |
| ○○○○ | Crosswinds | MA | 70 | INC | 70 |
| ○○○○ | Dunegrass | ME | 57 | 18 | 75 |
| ○○○○ | Meadow Brook | RI | 60 | 15 | 75 |
| ○○○○ | Richter Park | CT | 78 | INC | 78 |

| ○○○○½ RATING | COURSE | STATE | GOLF | CART | $ TOTAL |
|---|---|---|---|---|---|
| ○○○○½ | Fox Ridge | ME | 48 | 17 | 65 |
| ○○○○½ | Crestview | MA | 59 | 18 | 77 |
| ○○○○½ | Shining Rock | MA | 62 | 17 | 79 |
| ○○○○½ | Wintonbury Hills | CT | 79 | INC | 79 |

| ○○○○○ RATING | COURSE | STATE | GOLF | CART | $ TOTAL |
|---|---|---|---|---|---|
| ○○○○○ | Blackstone | MA | 79 | INC | 79 |

**INC = INCLUDED IN WEEKEND GREENS FEES**

(Prices reflect anticipated 2017 fees but are subject to change without notice. Please call ahead.)

In addition, there are numerous great courses that offer reduced rates during off-peak times and off-peak months.

The *New England GolfGuide* uses a five star rating system when evaluating golf courses. This rating takes into account both course layout and condition. A course that has earned a rating of ○ is average, ○○ represents a good course, ○○○ is considered very good where as a course that has earned a ○○○○ is excellent and a ○○○○○ rating is reserved for only the most exceptional courses.

# Snell Golf

## Great Performance – Lower Price.

In 2015, after 25 years of experience working in research and development for companies like Titleist® and Taylormade®, Dean Snell set his eyes on a new goal: to bring industry leading technology and performance at affordable pricing to every golfer. With headquarters in New Bedford, Massachusetts, Snell has quickly seen his golf ball line-up chalk up record sales numbers and earn high praise from independent golfers and media including rave reviews in *Golf Digest's* 2016 Hot List issue.

At the heart of Snell Golf is an e-commerce business model, zero player contracts and low overheads. The company's intent is to create a high-quality golf ball and sell it an attractive price lower than comparable balls in the market. Golfers everywhere – including Canadians – are starting to take notice. Snell's goal is to provide avid and recreational golfers with easy access to purchase and enjoy golf balls with excellent performance at affordable prices.

A premium multi-layered ball with a thin cast urethane cover, Snell Golf's "My Tour Ball" (MTB) is the company's flagship model and its performance is akin to the balls played on today's professional tours. The ball features a low compression high velocity core allowing lower driver spin rates and faster ball speeds for all swing speeds to promote longer and straighter drives. The cast urethane cover is a Tour-proven technology that produces excellent short game spin and control while delivering soft feel and outstanding durability.

Snell Golf's second offering, "Get Sum", is a high-performance, two-piece golf ball geared toward golfers who desire more control and require help getting the ball airborne. A large core keeps the driver spin rates low and creates fast ball speeds for all swing types.

"Testing Packs," which offer six of each ball, provide the consumer a chance to determine which product is best for their game. Snell Golf also offers "Value Packs" and customers are able to purchase six dozen MTBs or Get Sum balls. Like all Snell Golf orders, shipping is free inside the continental U.S.

For more information regarding Snell golf balls, Test Packs and Value Packs visit **www.snellgolf.com**.

# Prince Edward Island

## Small Island, Big Character.

As one of the oldest sayings in the books goes, big things come in small packages. And that's no truer than when it comes to the picturesque landscape of Prince Edward Island.

As Canada's smallest province – measuring just over 5,600 kilometres – it proudly boasts the most golf courses per capita in the entire country, making it an idyllic place to visit when golfers are thinking about travelling this year.

And the uniqueness of PEI golf is made no more evident than when you speak with the Executive Director of Golf PEI, Mark McLane, who says that on the island, you're no more than 15 minutes away from a golf course or the ocean – in any direction.

"We're much more than a golf destination though," he says. "Because the courses are so close, you can play golf in the morning and you're back to your hotel or cottage by noon. You can go sight-seeing, hit the beach, go on a fishing tour, or visit one of our iconic landmarks like the Anne of Green Gables House."

With over 1 million tourists coming to PEI each year, you can be sure the team involved with planning an ideal visit to the island is an experienced one. "With over 400 fairways on PEI, Golf PEI has our own online and direct call reservation centre," he says. "Customers can call us directly or book their entire golf vacation online any time they wish. Our golf travel specialists at Golf PEI have more than 40 years of combined experience in booking golf vacations. As an industry association, our golf travel specialists listen and help you plan and book your next unforgettable golf vacation."

Golf in PEI ranges from award-winning and Canada-renowned tracks like the Links at Crowbush Cove and Dundarave to courses that fit any skill level, but one thing is for sure – the quality and value are unmatched.

"It's our golf, it's countless miles of beaches, welcoming people, our culture, and world famous seafood that makes us Canada's golf destination" says McLane.

So this year when you're thinking of a golf trip with friends, or if you want an escape with family to explore part of this beautiful country that is equal parts fabulous and fun, think about Prince Edward Island. And, you'll easily discover why big, beautiful things often come in smallest of packages.

For more information or to book your unforgettable trip to PEI, visit www.golfpei.ca.

# 2017 U.S. Senior Open

## History Returns to Salem Country Club.

Salem Country Club in Peabody, Massachusetts, site of five prior United States Golf Association (USGA) championships filled with drama and history-making moments, hosts its sixth national tournament June 26-July 2, the 38th United States Senior Open.

Less than a decade after opening in 1926, Salem was approached by the USGA about hosting the 1932 U.S. Women's Amateur. The club obliged and Virginia Van Wie, a 23-year-old from Chicago, routed five-time titlist Glenna Collett Vare, 10 and 8, in the 36-hole final match. It was Van Wie's first of three consecutive U.S. Amateur titles.

The USGA returned twenty-two years later to stage the 1954 U.S. Women's Open in what proved to be one of the most historic U.S. Women's Opens ever. Babe Didrikson Zaharias, already a legend in American athletic circles, including golf, won her third and final Open fifteen months after major cancer surgery that required her living with a colostomy bag. The Babe routed the field by twelve strokes with a three-over 291. It was Zaharias's last great victory. She died two years later at the age of 42.

Dale Morey won the 1977 U.S. Senior Amateur at Salem during a week plagued by rain. Morey was qualifying medalist for match play with a one-under 143 and beat defender Lew Oehmig in the title match, 4 and 3.

The U.S. Women's Open returned for a second time in 1984. More history was made when Hollis Stacy broke a three-way tie coming to the last hole with Amy Alcott and Rosie Jones. She made the only par on the home hole and won her sixth USGA title with a 69 closing round and a 290 total.

Seventeen years later, in 2001, the club hosted its first USGA Senior Open – another doozie down the stretch – with Bruce Fleisher outlasting a group of challengers the last four holes, including Jack Nicklaus, to win the prestigious event with an even par 280 total. Fleisher thus became only the third player to win the U.S. Open and U.S. Amateur, joining Jack Nicklaus and Arnold Palmer in that unique class.

Another extraordinary competition is anticipated when the Senior Open is back on Salem Country Club soil this June. Gene Sauers will defend the title he won last summer at Scioto Country Club in Columbus, Ohio, with a five-foot par putt on the 72nd hole and a three-under-par 277 total, good for a one-stroke margin of victory over Miguel Angel Jimenez and Billy Mayfair.

Tickets for this once in a generation event are on sale now. Children 17 and under are admitted free of charge to the championship grounds when accompanied by a ticketed adult. Get behind the scenes of this national champion as a volunteer.

Visit www.2017ussenioropen.com for more info on tickets and volunteering.

# Is a Short Course For You?

Executive Courses and Par 3 Courses are excellent for beginners and juniors. For the more advanced player these courses can provide an excellent opportunity to practice your short game. Remember, these courses require far less time to play and are usually very reasonably priced.

## Par 3 Courses

| Course | Yards | Course | Yards |
|---|---|---|---|
| **Connecticut** | | **Massachusetts** | |
| Cedar Ridge (18) | 3025 | Back Nine Club (18) | 2588 |
| Gainfield Farms (9) | 1203 | Blue Rock (18) | 2520 |
| Guilford Lakes (9) | 1165 | Cyprian Keyes Par 3 (9) | 1230 |
| Highland Greens (9) | 1398 | Fore Kicks (9) | 1003 |
| Short Beach (9) | 1270 | Garrison Golf Center (9) | 1005 |
| South Pine Creek (9) | 1242 | Holly Ridge (18) | 2715 |
| The Pines (18) | 2666 | Little Harbor (18) | 3038 |
| Villa Hills Par 3 (9) | 1158 | Links at Lancaster (9) | 1125 |
| **Maine** | | Lost Brook (18) | 3002 |
| Country Fairways (9) | 1190 | MGA Links (18) | 2421 |
| Loons Cove (9) | 1214 | Middleton (18) | 3000 |
| Pine Ridge (9) | 1285 | Pine Knoll (9) | 1567 |
| **New Hampshire** | | Rockland (18) | 2764 |
| Kona Mansion (9) | 1170 | Stoneham Oaks (9) | 1125 |
| Twin Lake Villa (9) | 1356 | Stoneybrook (9) | 1342 |
| **Rhode Island** | | Swansea Executive (9) | 1196 |
| Button Hole (9) | 1035 | Twin Brooks (18) | 2621 |
| Lindbrook (18) | 2869 | **Vermont** | |
| Rose Hill (9) | 1206 | Apple Island Resort (9) | 1171 |
| The Preserve (18) | 2590 | Arrowhead (9) | 1330 |
| Windmill Hill (9) | 1191 | Stonehedge (9) | 1107 |
| | | Woodbury (9) | 1264 |

## 18 Hole Executive Courses

| Course | Yards |
|---|---|
| Fire Fly Country Club, Seekonk, MA | 3083 Yards |
| Links at Long Farm, Essex Junction, VT | 3444 Yards |
| Londonberry Country Club, Londonberry, NH | 3258 Yards |
| Paul Harney Golf Club, East Falmouth, MA | 3315 Yards |
| Sitzmark Golf Course, Wilmington, VT | 2650 Yards |
| Southers Marsh Golf Club, Plymouth, MA* | 3694 Yards |
| Squirrel Run Golf Course, Plymouth, MA | 2338 Yards |

*The Best Golf Value in Massachusetts for 13 consecutive years

# Championship Golf in the Northern Catskills

Thunderhart Golf Course at Sunny Hill is a championship 18-hole golf course located in the Northern Catskills and is part of Sunny Hill Resort. The resort boasts 36 holes of golf which includes 18-holes of resort-style golf at Sunny Hill and 18-holes of championship golf at Thunderhart. For avid golfers, dual memberships are available for both courses.

This championship course, par 72, is set in the Catskill Basin, and offers 11 ponds and 19 sand traps. In addition to breathtaking views, this 6482 yard course is a "must play" with its scenic beauty and challenging design.

The back nine was created in the Parkland style, which has each hole cut through the beautiful forest of the Catskills.

Acquired in 2007 by the Nicholsen family, owners of Sunny Hill Resort & Golf Course, Thunderhart has been transformed into one of the region's premier golf complexes, under the supervision of the golf course superintendent, Erik Nicholsen, and his experienced staff.

Thunderhart offers a fully equipped Pro Shop and is an authorized Nike dealer. With the Clubhouse Grille, Fireside Lounge, and outdoor Pavilion situated next to a scenic pond, Thunderhart is the perfect setting for a group outing or just to sit and discuss the day's round with a group of friends.

Thunderhart at Sunny Hill has everything a golfer could want: scenic beauty, challenging design and layout.

*Please see Thunderhart's full color ad at the back of the book.*

# New England GolfGuide
## What's New in 2017

### New Public Golf Courses

**Elmcrest Country Club** – *East Longmeadow, MA*
*This nicely maintained 18 hole private club was recently purchased and is now open to the general public.*

**Furnace Brook Golf Club** – *Quincy, MA*
*This quaint little 9 hole regulation course is Semi-Private but open to the public Monday-Friday.*

**Gillette Ridge Golf Club** – *Bloomington, CT*
*This championship course was closed for the past 2 years but now open for play. Challenging and enjoyable.*

**Mohegan Sun Golf Club** – *Baltic, CT*
*New England GolfGuide's newest 5-star course. This great golf course was previously private but is now open for general play.*

**The Tradition Golf Club at Oak Lane** – *Woodridge, CT*
*This 18-Hole Geoffrey Cornish designed course, formerly the private Oak Lane CC has reopened as a public golf course.*

### Name Changes

**Black Birch Golf Club** *was previously named Banner Country Club in Moodus, CT*

**Bomoseen Golf Club** *was previously named Prospect Bay Country Club in Bomoseen, VT*

**East Hartford Golf Club** *was previously named Long Hill Country Club in East Hartford, CT*

**Hazelton Golf Club** *was previously named Sun Valley Golf Course in Rehoboth, MA*

**North Ridge Golf Club** *was previously named Pine Valley Golf Course in Southington, CT*

**The Cape Cod Club** *was previously named Ballymeade Country Club in North Falmouth, MA*

**The Pines Golf Course** *was previously named Birch Plain Golf Course in Groton, CT*

# Featured Courses 2017

## Put these on your must-play list.

This section gives you a closer look at some of our region's most highly rated and enjoyed courses. Whenever you visit, tell them you saw them in the *New England GolfGuide* and rate the course at newenglandgolfguide.com.

## Private Courses

CC of Halifax, Halifax, MA
CC of New Bedford, N. Dartmouth, MA
Crestwood, Rehoboth, MA
Hop Meadow, Simsbury, CT
Indian Pond, Kingston, MA
Indian Ridge, Andover, MA
The International, Bolton, MA
Marlborough, Marlborough, MA
Ocean Edge, Brewster, MA
Pleasant Valley, Sutton, MA
The Preserve, Wyoming, RI

## Public Courses

### CONNECTICUT
Mohegan Sun, Baltic
Stanley, New Britain

### MAINE
Bridgton Highlands, Bridgton
Dunegrass, Old Orchard Beach
Fox Ridge, Auburn
Lake Kezar, Lovell
Links at Outlook, South Berwick
Nonesuch River, Scarborough
Sanford Country Club, Sanford
Spring Meadows, Gray
Toddy Brook, North Yarmouth

### MASSACHUSETTS
Acushnet River Valley, Acushnet
Allendale, Dartmouth
Back Nine Club, Lakeville
Blackstone National, Sutton
Butter Brook, Westford
Cranberry Valley, Harwich
Cranwell, Lenox

Crestview, Agawam
Elmcrest, East Longmeadow
Foxborough, Foxborough
Glen Ellen, Millis
Granite Links, Quincy
Heather Hill, Plainville
Highfields, Grafton
Hyannis, Hyannis
Maplegate, Bellingham
Olde Barnstable, Marstons Mills
Pembroke, Pembroke
Pinehills, Plymouth
Red Tail, Devens
Shaker Hills, Harvard
Shining Rock, Northridge
Southers Marsh, Plymouth
Stow Acres, Stow
Townsend Ridge, Townsend
Unicorn, Stoneham
Waubeeka, South Williamstown
Wentworth Hills, Plainville
Winchendon, Winchendon

### NEW HAMPSHIRE
Atkinson, Atkinson
Nippo Lake, Barrington
Rochester, Rochester

### RHODE ISLAND
Cranston Country Club, Cranston
Laurel Lane, West Kingston
Newport National, Middletown

### VERMONT
Green Mountain, Killington
Hermitage, Wilmington
Lake Morey, Fairlee

# Country Club of Halifax

## Halifax, MA

### A Secluded Masterpiece with Casual Elegance.

Designed by noted golf architect Phil Wogan in 1966, the Country Club of Halifax offers 18 holes of challenging golf playing at 6,738 yards from the tips. This par 72 course is designed for players of all abilities. Whether you are a beginner, a junior player or a low handicap golfer, you are in for a treat on one of the best championship layouts in Massachusetts.

Membership at Halifax offers all of the luxury that you would expect from a private club. Whether you have just finished 18 holes of golf, are keeping in shape in the fitness room or entertaining friends at our fantastic restaurant, you will feel right at home while being attended to by our dedicated staff.

This family friendly club has membership options that can match each individual's needs. All membership categories allow access to the golf practice facilities, fitness room and restaurant.

For both members and non-members the Country Club of Halifax is the perfect venue for your next golf outing, holiday party or private function. Just give us a call and we will make it happen.

Country Club of Halifax · Halifax, MA
www.ccofhalifax.org 781-293-9061

# Country Club of New Bedford | North Dartmouth, MA

## Tradition at its Best.

Founded in 1902, the Country Club of New Bedford is a club built on tradition and boasts one of the premier golf courses in New England. Designed by Donald Ross, this beautiful and challenging 18 hole, par 70 course plays to slightly over 6400 yards. The traditional clubhouse features a main dining room, a grill room and a main bar and lounge.

The Country Club of New Bedford is an ensemble of many treasures evolving from more than 100 years of tradition, vision and celebration which has led to its current prestigious reputation in the New England area. Located in North Dartmouth, it sets itself apart from other private clubs in the Boston-Providence corridor by offering unpretentious service, championship golf, and warmth and intimacy that is generated and honored in a contemporary setting.

Membership categories include Golf, Social, Junior and Corporate. To learn more about membership opportunities or to schedule a golf tournament, banquet, wedding or other special events, just give us a call at 508-993-3453 or visit us on the web at www.ccnbgolfclub.com.

# Hop Meadow Country Club | Simsbury, CT

## Simply Elegant.

From the moment you step into Hop Meadow Country Club you will be embraced by the beauty of the Northeast and the views of the pristinely manicured grounds. Established in 1961 by local residents and nestled in picturesque Simsbury, Hop Meadow is one of central Connecticut's finest full service private clubs.

Whether your interest is golf, tennis or social, Hop Meadow will meet your needs and most certainly exceed your expectations. New memberships are available.

The long and challenging championship 18 hole golf course was designed by Geoffrey Cornish and plays to 6,915 yards from the tips. The golf shop is open to the general public and there is a full service practice facility. There are eight outdoor Har-tru tennis courts and platform paddle courts, many illuminated for night play. Or if you prefer, enjoy the spectacular Olympic size swimming pool.

For your next golf outing or special event why not plan to call The Hop Meadow Country Club with our classic style banquet rooms, creative gourmet cuisine and the service and attention that only a private club can provide.

Hop Meadow Country Club, Simsbury, CT 860-658-7623
www.hopmeadowcc.net

# Crestwood Country Club

## Rehoboth, MA

## Casual – Comfortable – Complete

Crestwood Country Club is a private country club situated on 180 rolling acres in scenic Rehoboth, MA. Located only 10 minutes from providence and 45 minutes from Boston, this 18-hole, 6,600 yard par 71 course is a pleasure and challenge for golfers of all skill levels. Members and guests enjoy outstanding cuisine and service in Crestwood's 39,000 square foot clubhouse. Their new state-of-the-art pool complex provides a wonderful place to spend warm summer days and the full sized practice facility is the finest in the area.

Crestwood Country Club was designed by Geoffrey Cornish and opened in 1959. The course is well laid out with wide and generous, well-defined fairways that feature a variety of doglegs and some water hazards; each hole being quite unique. With generous landing areas come well-guarded greens, placing a premium on approach shots. Crestwood is one of the finest groomed layouts in the area, immaculately conditioned and known for its landscape of maples, pines and oaks that provide a picturesque backdrop for every round of golf. Crestwood features an 8-acre driving range where you can hit all of your clubs, two practice greens with a chipping area and bunker area for your short game.

Crestwood Country Club is the ideal place for your golf outing, wedding, graduation party or any other special event. Take advantage of their beautiful space overlooking water and the lush green golf course, as well as a large outdoor deck. They have a variety of function spaces for you to choose from that can accommodate between 25-200 people. They specialize in small, intimate gatherings and their on-site event planner will help you and your family plan a most memorable occasion.

So whether you want to spend a day at the golf course or in the pool, treat yourself to a delightful meal, schedule a golf outing or special event, Crestwood Country Club is the place for you. For information on memberships or to schedule an event please contact (508) 336-8582.

# Indian Pond Country Club | Kingston, MA

## Stylish Tradition and Elegance.

Indian Pond Country Club is a championship golf club surrounded by wooded conservation lands and a community of homes known as Indian Pond Estates. Dramatically cut into the wooded hills of Kingston, the 18-hole championship course measures almost 6,800 yards and offers five sets of tees. Designed by Damian Pascuzzo, Ocean Pond has been ranked among the Top 20 Best in State by *Golf Digest*.

The magnificent 52,000 square foot clubhouse includes the pro-shop, golfer's lounge, The Grand Ballroom and The Blackstones Room. A convenient distance from Boston and Cape Cod, Indian Pond presents the perfect setting for your special event including holiday parties, reunions, proms, sweet sixteen parties, bah/bat mitzvah, bereavement gatherings, engagement parties, showers and rehearsal dinners. Our array of settings, including poolside and terrace events, can accommodate a small intimate affair of 20 guests to an extravagant celebration of up to 500 guests.

The Member's Grille includes a classic 135-seat dining room with a circular bar and an attached private card room. Membership also includes access to one of the finest pro shops featuring New England's premier men's and ladies' boutique. At Indian Pond, all the amenities are provided for, including comfortable and convenient men's, ladies, and guest locker rooms. Nestled in the wooded hills of Kingston, Massachusetts, Indian Pond is simply elegant.

# Indian Ridge Country Club | Andover, MA

## A Private Club with the Warmth of Home.

Conveniently located minutes from the intersection of Routes 495 and 93, Indian Ridge Country Club is the premiere destination for golfers in the Merrimack Valley. Golfers of every skill level are impressed with the challenge and playability of our beautifully groomed 18 hole Geoffrey Cornish design. The championship tees stretch to over 6,500 yards and provide a challenging Par 72 course. 4 sets of tees, however, make it playable for all skill levels. Indian Ridge has 2 putting greens for chipping and putting, practice bunkers and a full turf driving range with a designated pitching area.

A visit to Indian Ridge Country Club allows you to experience a family friendly environment that provides a memorable setting for golf, tennis, swimming, dining and special events. A true home away from home. Indian Ridge facilities accommodate all types of special occasions, such as Weddings, Anniversary Parties, Bat/Bar Mitzvahs, Holiday Parties, Corporate Golf Outings, Business Meetings, Bereavement Gatherings and much more. Membership is not required to host your event. For more information, please call 978-475-9484 or visit our website at www.indianridgecountryclub.us.

# The International

## Bolton, MA

### A World Class Golf & Special Event Destination.

- Less than an hour from Boston, MA and Providence, RI.
- Our Tom Fazio designed golf course, The Oaks and our Geoffrey Cornish designed golf course, The Pines offer 36 holes of the finest golf in New England.
- Our Fireplace Room restaurant welcomes everyone six days a week, featuring casual and upscale cuisine.
- We throw the best parties and special events on the planet!
- Our facilities are perfect for your wedding, corporate event, or golf tournament.
- 53 rooms at our on site boutique lodge.
- A variety of options for business meetings and conferences of any size.
- 100 years of golf history on 500 acres of natural beauty.
- Book hotel rooms or make dinner reservations all online at: www.theinternational.com or call us at (978) 779-6911.

*Please see The International's full color ad at the back of the book.*

EAT, SLEEP, PLAY, repeat.

# Marlborough Country Club | Marlborough, MA

## What's Your Pleasure?

Welcome to Marlborough Country Club, a charming semi-private golf course that is open for public play on Mondays and Tuesdays. Beautifully manicured and challenging for players of all levels, this 18 hole, par 71 layout plays to 6,464 yards from the back tees. Marlborough Country Club provides an excellent, competitive layout for club play, tournaments and outings.

The Marlborough Country Club has enjoyed a rich history having opened in 1922 with an inaugural exhibition match featuring U.S. Open Champion Francis Ouiment and later becoming one of the very first hosts of the PGA Senior Tour. The original course was designed by well known architect Wayne Styles and later expanded in 1970 by New England architect Geoffrey Cornish.

### Functions and Outings

Public bookings welcome. Book your next function or outing now. Our dining room, players lounge and new function room offer perfect venues for your business meeting, corporate outing, charity event, civic function or special occasion. The softly lit Marlborough Room is our largest reception facility and can host daytime and evening events. Replete with a large dance floor and a full service bar, this room accommodates 180 people.

### The Eastside Grille

The restaurant, open to the public, embraces patrons with upscale, casual dining that is rich with history and complete with a contemporary menu. It is the oldest established restaurant in Marlborough and was voted #1 banquet facility for 3 consecutive years.

### Membership

Marlborough Country Club is currently accepting new applications for membership and has several different membership classifications to accommodate people's needs. Our Full Membership, which includes individuals and corporations, provides unlimited golfing and clubhouse privileges. Our Limited membership provides unlimited golfing on weekdays and unlimited golfing on weekends and holidays after 1:00 PM. We also offer Young Executive Memberships for people up to 35 years old and Junior Memberships for those 12-22.

Please come visit our facility. Dine with the views of the golf course or play a round of golf on one of the most popular and best conditioned golf courses in Central Massachusetts. It will be a day to remember.

*Please see Marlborough's full color ad inside the front of the book.*

# Ocean Edge | Brewster, Cape Cod, MA

## Freedom to Play a Round.

Play Ocean Edge Resort and Golf Club featuring Cape Cod's only Nicklaus Design golf course. The $8.5 million private golf course was completely redesigned in 2008 and is designed for all levels of play. You'll be captivated by the Ocean Edge natural landscape, rolling topography and dramatic elevation changes. Ocean Edge offers memberships for the serious golfer, as well as lessons, women-only clinics and twilight tee times. To encourage the next Tiger Woods, golfers under 10 golf free with an accompanying adult.

Golf aficionados will enjoy spacious accommodations in our 1, 2 and 3-bedroom villas, or in the Guest Wings adjacent to the historic Mansion. Special packages include unlimited golf throughout the year. Relax in one of the resort's 5 restaurants, including the Linx Tavern & Bar in the Golf Clubhouse with indoor or alfresco dining overlooking the 18th hole. You will also find a fully stocked Golf Pro Shop.

Non-golfers can enjoy 2 tennis complexes, a 26-mile bike trail and bike rentals, a Cardio Room and Fitness Center plus 4 outdoor and 2 indoor pools. Resort to freedom at Ocean Edge with golf and so much more.

OCEAN EDGE
RESORT & GOLF CLUB

*resort to freedom*

BREWSTER, CAPE COD, MA   508.896.9000   OCEANEDGE.COM

# Pleasant Valley Country Club | Sutton, MA

## A Club Like No Other.

In 1959, Pleasant Valley Country Club was carved out of an expansive three hundred fifty acre apple orchard and in 1961, under the watchful eye of Cosmo "Cuz" Mingolla, the club opened its doors. Today Pleasant Valley Country Club is owned by the Magill Family who once were members, opened the Highfields Golf & Country Club in Grafton and returned to purchase the course they love.

Rich in history and tradition, Pleasant Valley Country Club has built a nationally acclaimed reputation since its debut in 1961. Known as New England's Home of Professional Golf, Pleasant Valley is also considered one of central New England's finest banquet & golf-outing facilities.

Professional golf came to Sutton, Massachusetts beginning with the 1962 LPGA Lady Carling Open. The PGA Tour began its annual retreat to Sutton in 1965 with the Carling World Open, which welcomed international golfers from eleven countries and offered a record purse of $200,000. Since then, Pleasant Valley has hosted forty-seven National Championships on both the LPGA and PGA Tours.

Come experience the history, the comfort and the excitement of Pleasant Valley Country Club, celebrating over 50 years of service to its members and guests.

*Here is your opportunity to join a legendary country club at legendary pricing.*
For more information contact Bob Recore, membership chair,
at membership@pleasantvalleycc.com or 508-865-4441 ext. 307.

# The Preserve | Wyoming, RI

## Adventure-Exclusivity-Serenity.

The Preserve at Boulder Hills is New England's only private four season sporting retreat where luxury and pristine wilderness find common ground. Nestled in the heart of Wyoming, Rhode Island, The Preserve is spread over several hundred acres of natural beauty and is close to the Ocean State's storied beaches and waterfront. Whether comfortably ensconced in an exquisite private lodge or gathered among friends in the 25,000 square foot clubhouse, members can leisurely enjoy gourmet dining with only the finest wines and spirits.

The Preserve sports a world-class 18-hole executive golf course, six large fishing ponds, bird hunting fields, tennis courts and miles of hiking and mountain biking paths that will present you with a variety of activities only limited by your imagination. Should you want to stay for more than a day, exquisite private cabins are available on site.

The Preserve is home to legendary golf architect Robert McNeil's ingeniously conceived masterpiece playable as 9-hole regulation Par 34 or an 18-hole par three course. In either case, you will take advantage of the beautiful scenery around you on a finely manicured course. In 2016, The Preserve hosted The Preserve 18. The event was an overwhelming success, boosting over $18 million in cash and prizes, and it will played again in the summer of 2017. More information can be found at www.thepreserve18.com.

The Preserve is the ideal host facility for private and public events, including weddings, corporate retreats, seminars and golf outings. A full-time event planner works with the clients. From the very beginning of the planning your event to the selection of food and decorations the goal is to make sure that you have an event to remember and talk about forever. For information regarding private events, golf outings or ownership please contact us at 401-539-GOLF (4653) or visit www.thepreserveri.com.

*Please see The Preserve's full color ad at the back of the book.*

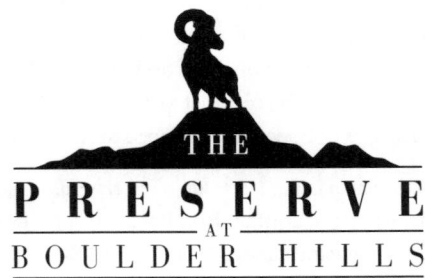

THE
## PRESERVE
AT
### BOULDER HILLS

# Mohegan Sun Golf Club

## Baltic, CT

**Great News!** Mohegan Sun Golf Club, located in Baltic, CT is now open to the public. That's right, one of *Golfweek* magazine's best Connecticut course you can play is now available for public play. Conveniently located less than an hour from Providence, RI and Hartford, CT this spectacular course, originally designed by Geoffrey Cornish, stretches to almost 6,800 yards from the back tees.  Known for it's beauty and charm, and with four sets of tees it is playable and enjoyable for all levels of golfers. After a round of golf, stop in at the  upscale Pautipaug Pub with its full menu and great daily specials.

At the Golf Shop at Mohegan Sun you can expect a pleasant, consistent and knowledgeable staff. The Golf Shop features the latest equipment, apparel, footwear and electronics. Certified PGA Professional instruction is available to help you improve your golfing experience. The newly redesigned practice facility includes a 30,000 square foot natural turf tee and a 5,000 square foot chipping and pitching area with two full size sand traps.

Mohegan Sun's Momentum Program lets you earn rewards and benefits in conjunction with the Mohegan Sun Casino. Benefits include complimentary rounds of golf, preferred guest rates, lessons and discounts at the Golf Shop. For information regarding the Momentum Program or to inquire about golf outings, corporate events, weddings and parties, just give us at call at 860-862-9660 or visit our web site at www.mohegansungolfclub.com.

*Please see Mohegan Sun's full color ad inside the front of the book.*

# Stanley Golf Course

## New Britain, CT

## Hartford Area Golf at its Finest.

Stanley Golf Course is one of the more pristine golf courses in the Greater Hartford area located just minutes from Hartford, CT and conveniently close to all major highways. Since the 1930's, Stanley Golf Course has offered the golfing public a great combination of holes that often seem easy until you play them. With a tremendous array of holes, some elevated tees and tree-lined fairways; Stanley is quite enjoyable and exciting to play.

Come try the recently redesigned Red Nine with more distinct and challenging holes including the 424-yard, par-4, 15th and the deceiving 16th, a par-5 that features one of the two new ponds added during the construction.

Stanley Golf Course also offers one of the best practice range facilities in the area, featuring a 19 station driving range, 10 of which are covered, lighted and heated for inclement weather and winter practice. Upgraded golf carts feature GPS systems including projected yardages, course info and live tournament scoring for outing events.

The remodeled Whinstone Tavern in the historic fieldstone clubhouse will serve lunch and dinner, seven days a week, and is available for special events. Stanley Golf Course is a favorite of central Connecticut golfers, offering something for every caliber golfer. A must add to your list of courses to play and enjoy!

Stanley Golf Course, New Britain, CT www.stanleygolf.com 860-827-8570

# Bridgton Highlands Country Club | Bridgton, ME

## A Western Maine Original.

In 1925-1926, noted golf course designer A.W. Tillinghast was contracted to design a course on Highland Ridge. Tillinghast, noted for many famous courses including Baltusrol, Winged Foot and Bethpage, designed a par 37 nine hole course which measured 3212 yards with the assistance of Ralph Martin Barton, who also worked with Tillinghast on the Mid-Ocean and Yale University Courses. In the 1980's, Geoffrey Cornish and Brian Silva were hired to redesign several holes and finally, in 1992 the course was expanded to the 18-hole venue that exists today. The 18-hole layout, was opened for play in 1992.

Today, Bridgton Highlands is a fun and friendly, open-to-the-public golf and tennis facility located in the heart of Maine's Lakes Region with a range of activities for men, women, couples and youth.

The 18-hole layout provides a challenging and enjoyable golf experience in a scenic setting — the best in western Maine with views of Pleasant Mountain — Shawnee Peak, New Hampshire's White Mountains and Mount Washington — where you can leave distractions behind and focus on your game. Located one hour from Portland, ME and 20 miles from the New Hampshire Border, the course has four sets of tees and a maximum length of 6,224 yards.

With four courts and a tennis program led by noted tennis professional, Bob Kimnach, the tennis program features, lessons, round robins, couples doubles, tournaments, junior programs and more.

Bridgton Highlands welcomes individual play, group outings and tournaments. Come and enjoy a quality golf or tennis experience in a fun, friendly and welcoming environment.

*Please see Bridgton Highlands' full color ad inside the front of the book.*

# Dunegrass Golf Club

## Old Orchard Beach, ME

Designed by internationally renowned golf architect Dan Maples, Dunegrass Golf Club has gained the reputation as one of Portland's premier public golf courses. The signature first hole is recognized as one of the prettiest in New England and sets the pace for a challenging round of golf. Natural features including streams, hillsides, undulations and rock croppings have been preserved to produce a visual feast.

Fairways guarded by strategically placed bunkers, ample water throughout and large greens make Dunegrass a "target style" course. However, the landing areas are large and few forced carries exist, to ensure an enjoyable golf experience for players of all levels.

While at Dunegrass don't forget lunch or dinner at Dunes Bar & Grill. Enjoy a full meal or just cocktails and appetizers. The gracious dining room is complemented by the Dunes patio overlooking the 18th hole.

Allow Dunegrass to assist your group or company with a golf outing or event. Your guests or clients will appreciate the opportunity to experience the challenge and pure enjoyment of the course. We can accommodate groups of all sizes to create a memorable day of golf. Choosing Dunegrass for your next golfing experience is an easy decision.

# Fox Ridge | Auburn, ME

## Is This Your New Must-Play Course?

With so many courses in New England, it's easy to overlook a number of great ones. This one deserves more notice. Readers, please put Fox Ridge on your must-play list.

This delightful track, in the words of a *New England GolfGuide* course rater, is "a blend of St. Andrews and the Maine seacoast: stone walls, stone bridges, and island greens." The course features a gentle blend of rolling hills, lined with native fescue, babbling brooks, and century-old stone walls, the traditional property lines of New England farmers.

The mostly links-style course is situated on over 200 acres of rolling countryside in south Auburn, Maine and is designed to take advantage of the natural lay of the land. This is truly a design that will demand every shot in your bag.

Superbly maintained and stretching a bold 6814 yards, the par 72 Fox Ridge is a 132 slope from the back, and a bit tamer 126 from the 6297 middle tees.

Part of the higher slope comes from the subtle greens. Putt well—or putt often. Give yourself a treat; come to Fox Ridge for a change of pace soon.

*Please see Fox Ridge's full color ad inside the front of the book.*

# Lake Kezar Country Club | Lovell, ME

## The Best Kept Secret in Western Maine.

Nestled in the foothills of the White Mountains, Lake Kezar Country Club is a par 72 gem that combines a 1924 Donald Ross design, with a spectacular and breathtaking back nine opened in 1998. The challenge and beauty of the brooks, ponds, stonewalls, and majestic Eastern white pines are never ending. Lake Kezar Country Club offers four sets of tees on every hole to accommodate any level of golfer.

With superior public accessibility and discounted group rates, Lake Kezar Country Club has become the destination for many corporate, group and family outings. We don't have houses, condos, tennis courts, or swimming pools, we just have Cadillac conditions at Volkswagen prices. If you plan to golf in Northern New England, Lake Kezar Country Club is a must visit.

*Lake Kezar Country Club has been rated the Number One Golfing Value in New England for 2017 by the New England GolfGuide.*

Lake Kezar Country Club, Lovell, Maine   www.lakekezargolf.com   (207) 925-2462

# Links at Outlook

## South Berwick, ME

## 18 Holes, Two Experiences.

If you're seeking a different golf experience, consider the Links at Outlook. You can play two styles of courses, but all in one scenic setting. It's just 45 minutes from Portland or 75 minutes from Boston.

The Links at Outlook start you off with a links-style nine, but without the ocean. The front nine (a former farm) is mostly treeless, with high grasses and gentle mounding defining the fairways. Here you'll find challenging, undulating greens, where you can run a ball up along the ground (a seemingly forgotten art). Open land usually means breezes, and often there are plenty enough to keep you alert on this lovely track.

The back nine has a distinctly different character. Fir trees line the fairways as the course climbs over and around a hill that eventually places you nearly 200 feet over the flatter front nine. From several spots up here, you can see the front nine holes, as well as some of the mountains many miles distant.

It's the front-to-back difference that makes for the appeal of the Links at Outlook. On the front nine, you can hit lots of drivers and play the big game. On the back, you have to play more strategically through the narrower fairways.

To really have a different look at the course, play different tees on successive visits. There's a difference of about 1000 yards between the blacks and the whites, and the former makes for a very tough course. Says head pro Dave Paskowski, PGA, "We hosted the Seacoast Amateur last year, the area's most prestigious event, and they found it all they could handle from the back. Many had played a scramble here from the blues earlier in the year, and thought they knew the course. Well, only about 20 players even broke 80. It was definitely a surprise for them." Most players will have a fine time from the whites or blues, he says.

Paskowski says the staff is happy to host outings, tournaments, weddings, and personal and business meetings of all kinds. The restaurant stays open and even offers Sunday brunch through the winter. Make the trip.

*Please see Links at Outlook's full color ad inside the front of the book.*

# Nonesuch River Golf Club
## Scarborough, ME

Just a bit south of Portland, Maine, sits Scarborough, a charming town with a four season appeal and home of Nonesuch River Golf Club and its full practice facility. This 18-hole par 70 course attracts players of all levels from across New England and points beyond. Known for its outstanding customer service and course conditions, Nonesuch River Golf Club provides an affordable and memorable golfing experience to all.

As a rule, the greens putt true, and medium fast. Rolling hills and visual interest help guide well-hit shots further down the fairway. Nonesuch River Golf Club provides you with a quality golf experience with bent grass fairways and greens with loads of variety. The practice facility is perhaps the most extensive in Greater Portland, and includes grass tees on the range, a practice bunker and two putting greens, and a full golf academy for individual and group lessons for all levels.

With great golf, wonderful scenery, an inviting clubhouse and courteous staff, picking Nonesuch River Golf Club for your next golfing experience is an easy decision.

www.nonesuchgolf.com | 207-883-0007

*Please see Nonesuch's full color ad inside the front of the book.*

# Sanford Country Club

## Sanford, ME

### Your Perfect Home For Golfing Fun.

Voted as one of "Maine's Best Semi-Private Courses," Sanford Country Club is conveniently located near Kennebunkport, Wells and Portsmouth. This historic 18-hole golf course, which played host to the 2012 U.S. Amateur Qualifying Round, sports four sets of tees ranging from 4,900 yards to 6,700 yards offering an enjoyable round to both beginners and avid golfers. With fast bent grass greens, manicured fairways and bunkers, beautiful scenery and a fun, friendly atmosphere, Sanford offers a great value.

At Sanford Country Club golf instruction is about making the game more enjoyable. Whether you are new to the game or an experienced golfer Sanford has a program to fit your needs. Both individual lessons and group clinics are available. Sanford is an authorized Callaway Fitting location with Callaway Certified Club Fitters and provides discount lesson packages and video analysis, all driven by their desire to make the game more enjoyable for you.

For weddings, special events or golf outings you should certainly consider Sanford Country Club. The Barn at Sanford is a newly renovated elegant event venue near the NH and Maine coastline. The rustic charm of The Barn is the perfect setting for your wedding, anniversary party, celebration, family reunion or business meeting. The staff at Sanford is dedicated to exceeding your expectations and producing a sensational event for you and your guests to cherish and remember. Start planning your event today by contacting us at 207-324-5462. Check us out at www.sanfordcountryclub.com.

*Please see Sanford's full color ad inside the front of the book.*

# Spring Meadows | Gray, ME

## Green Fees? Affordable. Fun? Priceless.

Spring Meadows Golf Club can be played from a range of tees that can challenge golfer's from all skill levels. The course yardage ranges from the Ladies' tee at 4706 to the Black tee at 6656.

As you prepare to hit your first tee shot, you are blown away by the different colors showcased by the trees lining the left side of the fairway. As you approach your ball in the fairway, you notice that the fairway is like a living room carpet and your ball is sitting up like nothing you have ever experienced before in golf. A crisp 7 iron and 2 putt for par later, you begin thinking to yourself that this is going to be the dream round. This is golf at Spring Meadows Golf Club.

It doesn't end with the first hole, the elevated 7th tee gives the golfer a view over much of the front 9 and a challenge as well. Although only measuring 320 yards, the seventh hole challenges the golfers with a pond that has a history of collecting miscalculated wedge shots.

You will enjoy the entire experience at Spring Meadows. The course condition, the scenery, the staff, and of course the Player's Lounge, serving all your favorite beverages. Call us and reserve your tee time today to enjoy Maine golf at its best.

'Must-Play' Golf
Spring Meadows Golf Club at Cole Farms
"100 Must-Play Courses of New England"
GolfStyles Boston

Spring Meadows
GOLF CLUB AT COLE FARMS
Gray, Maine
**(207) 657-2586**

- Naturally beautiful, challenging layout
- 30 minutes to the new Oxford Casino
- Plush fairways, superb greens, four sets of tees
- A great experience for golfers of all abilities

20 minutes from Portland. 1 mile from Turnpike Exit 63. Route 100 North.

VISIT www.springmeadowsgolf.com AND THEN COME PLAY THE COURSE

# Toddy Brook | North Yarmouth, ME

## Best Kept Secret in Southern Maine.

Entering its 15th season, the Toddy Brook Golf Course has quickly become a favorite of golfers who visit or live in Southern Maine. The dream-come-true of owner and designer Robert Anderson, Jr., the course began as just a putting green in his front yard in North Yarmouth. The first 9 holes, built on his family's farmland, opened to the public in 2002. The beautiful back nine was finished in 2005 and offers amazing views from the wooded hills across Route 9 overlooking Bradbury Mountain State Park.

The two nines have their own identity for sure, as the front is situated on wide open farmland while the back boasts dramatic elevation changes and tree-lined fairways. Both sides offer their own challenges and birdie opportunities. Water comes into play on both nines, as do well-placed bunkers and undulating greens. The five par-3's on the course are sure to test your shot-making ability as well as your nerves. The finishing par-3 18th plays 125 yards from the men's tee with an island green set in front of the popular clubhouse deck. Imagine combining the 17th hole at TPC Sawgrass with the 16th hole at TPC Scottsdale and you've got the 18th at Toddy Brook. Pressure golf at its finest.

The par-71 Toddy Brook Golf Course offers four sets of tees, with the championship black tees playing 6,214 yards and a slope of 126. The forward red tees are a great blend of challenge and playability for ladies, measuring 4,409 yards with a slope of 110. Toddy Brook is also a great place to come practice, with a full driving range that offers a grass tees.

The Toddy Brook Café is newly renovated and can hold 150-person functions including tournaments and weddings. The café stays open year round and offers breakfast, lunch and dinner with daily specials at a great price.

Just minutes from I-295, a short drive from Portland and Freeport, and only 20 minutes from the new Oxford Casino. Toddy Brook is just a little off the beaten path, but definitely worth a try. Call to book your tee time today, or visit us online at www.toddybrookgolf.com.

# Acushnet River | Acushnet, MA

## Acushnet, Where Silva Created Gold.

Acushnet River Valley Golf Course, in Acushnet, MA, designed by nationally renowned golf course architect Brian Silva, opened for play in 1998. He created a premiere golfing experience with four sets of tees measuring 5,099 yards to 6,807 yards allowing golfers of all skill levels to enjoy their rounds of golf. While the course plays to a par of 72, the tees can be set up to offer a superb championship course with a par of 70.

Acushnet River Valley offers two diverse layouts in one 18 hole beautiful and challenging layout. On the front nine, you stroll through tall pines, each hole its own cathedral. The back nine are sculpted over a Scottish links layout, with mounding and grasses reminiscent of the original traditions of course design and layout. The two sides complement one another in perfect balance.

You'll need to play Acushnet only once to realize the reason why people thoroughly enjoy their experience. But the more you return, perhaps the more you'll unravel the secrets of scoring well against this proud layout. It's the kind of place that definitely grows on you.

Acushnet River Valley is an excellent setting for your next golf outing, whether it's a small group or full shotgun. Their experienced and friendly staff are prepared to service all of your needs from initial setup to finish including the preparation of a special menu for those interested in dining in their outdoor facility.

Acushnet River Valley is an upscale public golf facility with bent grass greens that provide smooth and fast putting surfaces. Their full service practice facility includes a 12 station driving range and 12,000 square foot putting green. They are dedicated to the growth of the game and provide lessons, golf clinics, golf schools and a variety of junior programs throughout the summer to assist you in improving all aspects of your game. Whether it's a quick tune up that's needed or a series of lessons, they have the right program for you.

*Travel & Leisure - Golf Boston* ranks Acushnet River Valley "in the Top 10 Best Values in the State of Massachusetts" and according to the *Fall River Herald,* "a course well worth checking out. It's worth the money and certainly worth the drive to get a taste of Carolina golf right up the road."

Acushnet River Valley has developed the most unique season pass program in the golf market. It offers golf in quantities of 20, 40 or 60 rounds, walking or riding. The season passes are available at the Pro Shop every month and they are good for one year from the date of purchase! Season Passes are transferable and offer the best value to golf at Acushnet River Valley. Forty rounds of golf for $1540.00 equates to $38.50 per round of golf with a cart! Limited quantities are available. Call today to make your purchase (508-998-7777).

# Allendale Country Club

## North Dartmouth, MA

### Best Kept Secret in Southeastern MA.

Designed by famed golf course architect Geoffrey Cornish, Allendale Country Club, previously a private club, is now open to the public and offers golfers of all ages and abilities the opportunity to enjoy a fair but challenging layout on a relatively quick course. Stretching to 6,764 yards from the back tees, this beautifully maintained par 72 course is known for its challenging greens and beauty. Allendale Country Club has excellent practice facilities including a driving range, chipping area and putting green.

Allendale Country Club is a perfect spot for golf outings and small groups. The professional staff will ensure you have a great golfing experience. Golf instruction is also available to the general public.

Whether your interests are golf, swimming in an Olympic size pool or social, Allendale Country Club is the place to be. New memberships are currently available. For information on memberships, to schedule a golf outing or a golf lesson please contact Stephen Brown, Director of Golf at (508) 992-8682.

# The Back Nine Club

## Lakeville, MA

In 2008 three golf fanatics decided to bring Par 3 Golf back to Lakeville, MA. The famous Geoffrey Cornish layout was kept intact but many practical and aesthetic changes were made and on May 23rd, 2008 the new Back Nine Club opened its doors. The new course was made better than ever, including paved cart paths and additional tees to accommodate all levels of golfers. The Back Nine Club offers a unique golfing experience. With three sets of tees, The Back Nine Club offers something for every skill level. With idyllic ponds often coming into play and big inviting greens surrounded by sandtraps, picking the right set of tees is the first challenge.

This executive style course certified as "Beginner Friendly" has pristine bent grass greens and lush fairways and tees. The average round takes 3 to 3½ hours, which leaves time for life's other commitments. A new, larger full service clubhouse has been built and inside, the kitchen, dining area and function facility have been fully upgraded and rebuilt to better serve the customers' needs. This transformation has resulted in an even more family-friendly environment and has allowed the club to expand its services for outings, parties and functions.

The Back Nine Club is committed to giving every single person who walks on the property a memorable golfing and/or dining experience. In 2016, Bob Guisti, former Head Pro at The Country Club of Halifax has taken over the reins. Bob was the 2015 Cape Cod Professional of the year and the recipient of the 2015 New England Patriot Award. Give him a call for information on memberships, outings or functions.

# Blackstone National Golf Club | Sutton, MA

## Great Value, Great Destination, Great Venue.

Set amongst the feeder streams, hardwood swamps and mixed forests of the Blackstone Valley National Heritage Corridor in Sutton, Massachusetts, Blackstone meanders through the Corridor's rolling hills just 12 miles south of downtown Worcester. Upon a canvas unmatched in Southern New England, Rees Jones devised a memorable routing replete with mystery and intrigue.

Navigating Blackstone is a visually stunning experience, and with a slope of 139 and a rating approaching 75, the course is not for the faint of heart. But while Blackstone boasts length (the black tee measures over 6,900 yards), it is the visual deception incorporated into virtually every hole that serves as Blackstone's primary defense.

Blackstone's challenges are not limited to the mental gymnastics encountered on the tee. In fact, Blackstone's approach shots are typically where the fun really begins. Considering that most greens incorporate well defined swales, ridges, bowls and slopes, attacking any of the multiple pin placement options availed by each green from the proper position is essential.

Competing with the golf course as the crown jewel of Blackstone is the club's restaurant, the National Grill. Depending on your taste, one (or more) of the Grill's twenty plus beer selections surely will complement perfectly any post-round meal choice from the compact, but quality-laden, menu. But what truly distinguishes the National Grill is its breakfast and brunch buffet.

Even if your day is not capped off by eagle on the uphill par five 18th, your experience will surely cause you to contemplate where Blackstone National Golf Club places among New England's elite golf clubs. Order that omelet with your coffee on your next visit (we recommend mushrooms, tomatoes, bacon and cheddar), and Blackstone's rank might then be cemented.

BLACKSTONE NATIONAL *Golf Club*

Blackstone National Golf Club
227 Putnam Hill Rd
Sutton, MA 01590-1118
(508) 865-2111

www.bngc.net

# Butter Brook Golf Club

## Westford, MA

## Massachusetts' Hidden Gem.

Butter Brook Golf Club, located in the Boston suburb of Westford, is the masterful creation of world renowned golf course architect Mark Mungeam. He has beautifully transformed a farm into a hidden gem of a layout set upon 210 acres of sandy soil, rolling hills, mature trees, and expansive wetlands. The course's name is derived from the Butter Brook, which gently meanders through the property.

Having opened for play in 2007, the championship course satisfies all skill levels by having four sets of tees which range from 4,900 to just over 6,700 yards. Featuring bent grass greens and fairways, the A4 and L93 varieties provide for an exceptionally smooth and true putting experience. The club is also equipped with a practice facility (mats and grass tee capabilities), putting and chipping areas, and a grille room to host your next corporate golf outing.

Seeking the best golfing value in a serene setting conveniently located less than 25 miles from downtown Boston? Look no further than the unforgettable Butter Brook Golf Club. Please visit www.butterbrookgc.com online or call us at (978) 692-6560 to book your next tee time!

BUTTER BROOK GOLF CLUB | 157 CARLISLE ROAD, WESTFORD, MA | WWW.BUTTERBROOKGC.COM | (978) 692-6560

# Cranberry Valley
# Golf Course | Harwich, MA

## One of Cape Cod's Favorites.

If you ask serious golfers what their favorite course on Cape Cod is the name that often pops up is Cranberry Valley Golf Course which opened in 1974 in the beautiful Cape Cod town of Harwich. The course was designed by Geoffrey Cornish and Bill Robinson and quickly became a very popular golf destination for players from all over. Cranberry Valley is well maintained and features a superb routing that flows easily over beautiful terrain, which includes marshes, and of course a few cranberry bogs. Every hole has its own personality and no two are the same.

Management enhanced the course a few years ago through an extensive bunker redesign and restoration, overseen by noted architect Mark Mungeam. Several fairway bunkers were relocated so as to come into play and protect par against today's modern equipment, although the best players can still accept the challenge of attempting to fly the traps off the tee.

Mungeam also redesigned the driving range and practice facilities. Cranberry Valley now has one of the finest practice facilities on Cape Cod, which includes a short game area with bunkers and a chipping area, providing players with the opportunity to work on all aspects of their game.

Cranberry Valley isn't overly long by today's standards at 6,745 yards, but this par 72 layout has a number of dogleg holes that add invisible yardage which demand proper club selection and placement off the tee. With challenging Par 3s and an exciting double dogleg finale on Hole #18, Cranberry Valley offers a full golf experience whether you are a beginner or long-time player.

---

2015 PGA JR NORTHEAST REGIONAL CHAMPIONSHIP
2014 MASSACHUSETTS PUBLIC LINKS CHAMPIONSHIP
2006 MASSACHUSETTS WOMEN'S STATE OPEN
2006 MASSACHUSETTS OPEN QUALIFIER

FULLY STOCKED PRO SHOP
Breakfast ~ Lunch ~ Golf Lessons ~ Golf Carts ~ Club Rentals
18 Holes ~ Full Practice Facility ~ New Driving & Short Game Area

183 Oak Street Harwich, MA
www.cranberrygolfcourse.com

For tee times, call **774-408-8100**
2 days in advance; or to prepay 10 days
in advance call **508-430-5234**

---

# Cranwell Golf Club

## Lenox, MA

### *Golf Digest's* "Best Places to Play"

Golf is a beloved tradition at the historic course at Cranwell Spa & Golf Resort. Magnificent views, tree-lined fairways and naturally contoured greens have been carefully preserved in the more than 80 years since the beautiful Berkshire course was built.

Renowned for its outstanding natural beauty, Cranwell's 18-hole golf course combines spectacular views with challenging golf. This magnificent course was built by Wayne Stiles and John Van Kleek in 1926 on the site of the original Berkshire Hunt Club. In "The Life and Work of Wayne Stiles," Bob Labbance and Kevin Mendik write "One key aspect of the golf course remains unchanged; the terrain and green complexes are classic Stiles and Van Kleek. Many holes have their own environment unseen from any others. The hidden bunkers and narrow necks are constant, and many fairways sloped in the direction of the greens provide classic Stiles challengers."

When it comes to golf, Cranwell has it all. Historic golf course, private lessons with PGA pros, 105 guest rooms, fine dining, tennis, and a world-class spa. Cranwell is a golf lover's paradise. **Just 2½ hours from NYC and Boston, in the heart of the Berkshires.**

Lenox, MA    800-272-6935    cranwell.com

# Crestview Country Club

## Agawam, MA

### The Gem of Western Massachussetts.

Crestview Country Club, while continuing to offer an exclusive membership, has been open to the public for the first time since its opening in 1958 after being purchased in 2012 by a family operated partnership headed by Managing Partner and International Golf Course Architect David Fleury.

Crestview has also become part of a new multi-course brand "Crest Golf" during a new purchase in April of 2016. After operating Crestview for the past 5 seasons as one of the best semi-private facilities in the region Fleury said, "We are excited to announce the recent purchase of Elmcrest Country Club in East Longmeadow, MA and make it available to the entire golf community as a semi-private club while continuing to grow our portfolio of family operated golf and entertainment facilities. Being able to have these great clubs in the same family of golf will allow us to offer reciprocal benefits to our members and preferred guests. One of the special attributes of Crestview and Elmcrest is they capture the player's attention every time you play!"

With 400 acres of gentle rolling New England farmland, Geoffrey Cornish created an American classic with Crestview. Immersed in nature, Crestview is a true "walk in the park" experience. The conditioning at Crestview has always been known as "tournament ready", and the strength of the course has made it a perennial favorite to host numerous events, including U.S. amateur qualifiers and the LPGA tour event, The Friendly's Classic.

In keeping with the new owner's vision, Crestview has something for everyone and can be enjoyed by all at a great value. While the heart of the property is the championship golf course, that's just the beginning at Crestview, the expansive facilities include Har-Tru tennis courts, an Olympic size salt water pool and separate kiddy pool, playground, fitness facility, and one of the largest practice in the region.

The clubhouse at Crestview enjoys panoramic vistas with commanding views, a perfect setting for weddings, corporate outings, and charity functions, with rooms for up to 280 guests and additional capacity for up to 500 guests. The dining experience at "The View" restaurant is now open to the public year-round. Crestview is home to some of the premier charity golf outings in the region, and is a natural selection for anyone planning a golf event, or corporate function.

For more information about Crestview's public play rates, membership options, event planning, restaurant reservations, or upcoming events series, please visit the club's website at www.crestviewcc.com or our Facebook page at crestview country club, or call at (413) 786-2593.

*Please see Crestview's full color ad inside the front of the book.*

# Elmcrest Country Club

## East Longmeadow, MA

## New Ownership Makes Course Available to Public.

Established in 1964, Elmcrest was a labor of love by its late founder Joe Pagos. The golf course has a long history as one of the most enjoyable and fun courses to play in Western Mass, but was a well kept secret operating as a private club up until its recent sale in the spring of 2016. Now it is available for all to play operating as a semi-private club.

In April of 2016 Elmcrest was purchased by the ownership of Crestview Country Club, which is regarded as one of the best golf courses in the region, hosting the LPGA Friendly's Classic for 4 years. This purchase has created the new golf brand "Crest Golf".

After operating Crestview as one of the best semi-private facilities in the region for the past 6 years, Managing Partner and International Golf Course Architect David Fleury said, "We are excited to make Elmcrest available to the entire golf community as a semi-private club while continuing to grow our portfolio of family operated golf and entertainment facilities. This golf course has always had a tremendous appeal to players of all abilities because of its location and playability. The golf course is not overly long, but the routing requires the player to hit all types of shots and judge each shot carefully, this makes for an exciting round. Considering the fact that Elmcrest has some of the most interesting green complexes in the area, this golf course is a pleasure to play without being overbearing. One of our goals has always been to ensure our golf courses are very well maintained while being a good test of golf, but we focus on making sure the course is fun to play and Elmcrest is right in line with this philosophy. Like Crestview, Elmcrest is a great golf course because it captures a player's attention every time they play it. With so many great attributes we consider this an excellent addition to our golf portfolio!"

Elmcrest and Crestview are perfectly situated on the MA/CT line just 10 minutes off the I-91 corridor, to the East and West respectively. Call us at (413) 525-4653, or visit our website at www.elmcrestcc.com, or our Facebook page at: elmcrest country club, east longmeadow mass.

Come let the "Crest Golf" team of Event Planners, Culinary Experts and PGA Golf Professionals show you why Elmcrest is the best "new" golf course and entertainment facility in the region!

# Foxborough Country Club | Foxborough, MA

Foxborough Country Club (FCC) is the premier semi-private country club in Southeastern Massachusetts. Its pristine 18 hole course was designed in 1955 by legendary golf course architect Geoffrey Cornish. The 6,849 yard classic Cornish design is a tree lined layout with 4 sets of tees, 37 bunkers, and a few water hazards for every skill level. A player must move the ball in both directions and read the tricky fast greens to score well.

Public play is normally Tuesday & Thursdays: 10am to 4pm; Wednesday: 7am to 12pm; Friday: 7am to 11:30am; Saturday, Sundays & Holidays after 1:30pm (before May 1 and after October 1). No tee times are given. First come — first on the tee. Call the Golf Shop (508-543-4661 ext. 4) for current availabilities.

Second to its great golf course is FCC's membership. "Super friendly", "easy to get a game" are just some of the many attributes of FCC.

Lunches and Friday night dining are engineered specifically for member and guest satisfaction. To include affordability! A special "On The Turn" menu is available in the clubhouse in order to expedite the turn. Recent renovations to the Clubhouse allow for function and Monday golf outings up to 140 people.

FCC's location is within a mile of I-95, I-495 and Route 1 and within minutes of Gillette Stadium and Patriot Place.

Foxborough Country Club

- 2015 Memberships Available (Full, Limited, Intermediate & Trial)
- Superb Practice Facilities
- Individual + Group Instructions Given By Lou Rivers, PGA
- Full Service Restaurant + Bar

www.foxboroughcc.com • (508) 543-4661

# Glen Ellen Country Club

## Millis, MA

### The Total Experience.

Glen Ellen Country Club, also known as The Glen, is located on 250 rolling acres conveniently located between Routes 495 and 128 an easy ride from Boston or Worcester. The 18-hole championship golf course with a grass tee driving range is always in ideal condition and is playable for golfers at all levels. The PGA Professional staff offers golf lessons and golf camps for juniors throughout the summer.

Glen Ellen is the perfect course for your golf outing. Having hosted thousands of golf tournaments, they have developed a successful formula for these events that provide an excellent experience at a reasonable cost. They are also the ideal spot for weddings, reunions, company outings and any special event you might have. Glen Ellen doesn't just offer activities, they offer experiences. The grounds are meticulously maintained and provide scenic background for your event.

Glen Ellen also has an Olympic size pool, kiddie pool, tennis courts, horseshoe pits, miniature golf and a playground that offers the opportunity to participate in basketball, sandpit volleyball, softball, soccer and bocce. Glen Ellen is a club that has something for everyone in the family. As a result, there are a variety of memberships for golf, the pool and juniors that do not require an initiation fee or monthly minimums. For more information call 508-376-2775 or go to their website at www.theglencc.com.

# Granite Links Golf Club | Quincy, MA

## A Superior Experience in a Spectacular Setting.

When first opened, Granite Links was voted "Top Ten Best New Upscale Golf Course in the Country" by *Golf Digest* and more recently was named to this publication's prestigious list of "100 Greatest Golf Courses in America!" where the public can play. Granite Links is a private membership club that also provides a limited level of non-member access. The course is conveniently located just 7 miles south of Boston.

27 challenging holes of links style golf offer the most scenic vistas anywhere, including breathtaking views of Boston's skyline to the North, the Harbor Islands to the South and East, and the densely forested backdrop of the Blue Hills Reservation to the West.

As the name indicates, this is a links style course, situated atop what were once actively mined quarries. Remnants of the quarries will be revealed on the course in the form of granite outcroppings and some rather impressive water hazards — some of which run 40 to 400 feet deep!

Granite Links offers one of the few lighted driving ranges in the region for nighttime practice and enjoyment. Adjacent to the Driving Range is the newly expanded Crossing Nines Turn Shack. It's the perfect spot to refresh when at the range or making the turn. Starting at 7AM, golfers can enjoy muffins, bagels, freshly made hot breakfast sandwiches, fruit cups and hot brewed coffee. Later in the day there's hot off the grill burgers and dogs, flat bread pizzas and made-to-order sandwiches, plus full bar service.

Our shingled Nantucket Style clubhouse sits 300 feet above sea level with outdoor balconies perched above a water-filled quarry overlooking the 18th green. The Members Only Grille and locker rooms are located here along with the very popular Tavern Restaurant, which is open to non-members.

The elegant clubhouse Ballroom and tented Pavilion each provide spectacular and much sought after settings for weddings, corporate events and social events.

# Heather Hill Country Club
# Wentworth Hills
# Country Club | Plainville, MA

Heather Hill Country Club and Wentworth Hills Country Club, both in Plainville, MA have strived to improve their operations and focus on customer service with the end game being to put Plainville golf on the map. From the time you arrive at these courses until you leave you will appreciate the friendly and accommodating atmosphere. The plan over the next 10 years is to convert Heather Hill into a golfing community with an excellent golf course surrounded by superior housing. In the meantime, it's business as usual.

**Heather Hill Country Club** is Southern New England's only 27 hole golf course. The 18 hole, Par 70 Middle/South course measures 6005 yards and the 9 Hole, Par 36 North Course measures 3,368 yards. Comfortable yardages but both challenging and enjoyable with all new tees. Heather Hill has a newly renovated function room and their newly renovated clubhouse is a great place to relax after a round of golf. The redecorated bar and grill offers a new menu that that has never been better. Their affordable rates make Heather Hill a great place to visit and play.

**Wentworth Hills Country Club** is an 18 hole masterpiece that is affordable, challenging and delightful for golfers of all abilities. The 18 hole, Par 71 course measures 6202 yards and is a particularly pleasant walking course offering beautiful views and premium course conditions. The rolling landscape includes tree-lined fairways, dramatic elevation changes, open meadows, well placed bunkers and demanding water features. Once played, you will certainly agree that Wentworth Hills may be a public course but certainly has a private club feel.

For golf leagues, outings, weddings or other functions call:
Heather Hill Country Club | (508) 695-0309
Wentworth Hills Country Club | (508) 316-0240

# Highfields | Grafton, MA

The first thought after a round at Highfields is "Now that was a challenge!" This strategic Mark Mungeam design demands your full attention the entire round. Pars are meant to be earned, and the rewards for a well-played hole are well worth the effort.

From the back tees of 7021, the slope is 140. For those with stronger feelings of self-preservation, the middle tees at 6024 still offer a 131 slope and plenty of course to maneuver around.

Every occasion shines at Highfield's Golf & Country Club. The club provides a beautiful backdrop for Wedding receptions, rehearsal dinners, corporate socials, business meetings, golf outings, luncheons and a host of other special occasions. Customized event planning and impeccable service make any event at Highfields truly a special occasion. Our dedication and attention to detail will allow everyone to relax and enjoy the event.

Our beautifully decorated Clubhouse surrounds you with warmth and casual elegance. Our spacious Claddagh Room can seat up to 225 guests and boasts magnificent views of our perfectly manicured golf course and the Worcester Hills, with a private patio overlooking the 18th green.

For occasions where the guest list is smaller and the moments more intimate, Highfield's Golf & Country Club offer smaller private dining rooms.

Make an impression without saying a word...

**Highfields**
HF
Golf & Country Club

www.highfieldsgolfcc.com • 508-839-1945

Grafton, Massachusetts

# Hyannis Golf Course

## Hyannis, MA

Situated at the center of Cape Cod, just minutes from a wide variety of local attractions, Hyannis Golf Club offers convenience and a friendly atmosphere that is conducive to families, beginners, juniors and seniors.

The course is a short drive from Barnstable Airport and the Mid-Cape Highway, while the ferries departing to Martha's Vineyard and Nantucket are also within easy reach. The area's popular beaches and the bustling Hyannis Main Street, where shopping, dining and live music are summertime staples, beckon once your round of golf is over.

But it might be difficult to leave quickly. The club's grille room and outdoor deck provide a relaxing spot to add up your score. With a large banquet room, Hyannis is a popular choice for golf outings. It also annually plays host to the Cape Cod Open, the area's premier professional tournament.

Since being purchased by the town of Barnstable in 2007, the club has worked to attract golfers of all abilities by moving up tees, widening fairways and setting up a course that promotes speedy play and low scoring. Scratch golfers who choose to play the championship tees will still find it plenty challenging, but those in search of a more casual experience will enjoy the numerous improvements. Playing from the white tees (or red ladies tees), they will hit to generous fairways from elevated tees, with expansive, receptive greens that are considered among the finest on the Cape.

At approximately 6,000 yards from the white tees and 6600 from the Blues, the par-71 course is not long, and golfers won't be required to hit driver off every tee. Unlike many newer, tricked-up designs, good shots are rewarded.

The course includes a large practice area and two putting greens, offering ample opportunity to sharpen your game. With a wooded, hilly natural setting, Hyannis Golf is a pleasant course where beginners, juniors, seniors and families are welcomed and where they will find a layout that is intriguing and fair.

# Olde Barnstable Fairgrounds Golf Course

## Marston Mills, MA

The Olde Barnstable Fairgrounds Golf Course, which borders the Cape Cod's largest sand plain conservation area, opened in 1992. The Mark Mungeon design has 18 holes of golf that are as challenging as they are scenic. This par 71 course is owned and operated by the Town of Barnstable.

Olde Barnstable Fairgrounds is located in Marstons Mills, less than 1 mile from Exit 5 (Route 6). This area of Cape Cod is a combination of wooded conservation area and a quiet residential area. Next door there is a grass air field that has gliders and sky divers that can be seen from the course.

The Course has four sets of tees for players of all abilities with yardages ranging from 6479 yards from the tips and 5072 yards from the forward tees. It is one of the best walkable courses on Cape Cod and has large undulating greens and an attractive layout, which is nicely maintained with professional and courteous staff.

The Golf Shop is fully stocked with name brand products and the restaurant has a fully menu of pub food. The practice area has 23 hitting stations with a chipping area, sand bunker and putting green.

Olde Barnstable Fairgrounds Golf Course has played host to several USGA qualifiers, WGAM, NEPGA events as well as the home of the Cape Cod Open. This is a municipal course with the private course feel, it should be on your "Must Play" list on Cape Cod.

# Maplegate Country Club

## Bellingham, MA

### Spectacular Golf in Peaceful Surroundings.

Maplegate Country Club is located just off Interstate 495 in Bellingham and Franklin. Established in 1990, Maplegate is a beautiful golf course set on 150 acres of rolling hills nestled amongst large pine, maple, oak and beech trees with many holes bordered by picturesque old stone walls. Exceptional detail went into all aspects of building the course and its facilities, resulting in a championship golf course that provides interesting, challenging and relaxing rounds of golf for everyone. Known for its great landing areas, you can take out your driver on every Par 4 and Par 5 on the course. From the championship tees Maplegate's par 72 course stretches to over 6,800 yards.

The Golf School at Maplegate is the perfect place to learn how to play or to improve your golf game. The teaching staff, led by PGA professional Greg Dowdell, are dedicated to the advancement of your game in an atmosphere that is both professional and enjoyable. The key to their success, and yours, is the ability to customize a program to each person's need.

# Pembroke Country Club

## Pembroke, MA

### More Ways to Play.

Pembroke Country Club is a championship par 71 course measuring 6,677 from the blue tees with a slope of 132 and a 73.3 rating. The course layout designed by Philip A. Wogan has long been recognized as one of the best layouts on the South Shore requiring use of almost all the clubs in your bag. Facilities include an all grass full size driving range, full service restaurant, pro-shop and banquet facilities. Pembroke Country Club is a public golf course with limited memberships available.

Opened in 1973, Pembroke Country Club is located a short 25 minute drive from Boston nestled among the tall pines of the South Shore. Five par fours are over 420 yards providing a challenge for golfers of all abilities. In 2009 the course was purchased by former NHL all-star Jeremy Roenick who grew up playing at PCC and loving the course. Over the past several years, under the direction of Golf Course Architect and Superintendent Patrick Sullivan, much work has been done to clear out and open the course to enhance playability. Also course conditions, tee boxes, fairways and greens have been upgraded to provide an excellent golfing experience.

In addition to course improvements, the pro shop, grille room, and function halls have been upgraded. The view from the grille room patio overlooking the course is spectacular. PCC's two function halls can accommodate functions from 50 to 500 occupants for weddings, fundraisers, parties, meetings and special events.

At Pembroke Country Club we are continually striving to enhance our customers golfing experience by focusing our efforts on course playing conditions, customer service and providing a value to the golfing public.

*Please see Pembroke Country Club's full color ad inside the front of the book.*

### Pembroke Country Club
94 West Elm Street, Pembroke MA
781-829-2273  WWW.PEMBROKEGOLF.COM

# Pinehills Jones & Nicklaus | Plymouth, MA

### Five Star Choices. Times Two.

At Pinehills, it's all about the golf. From the attended bag drop to the extensive practice facilities, Pinehills leaves no doubt about its purpose.

Two 18-hole designs await your pleasure: Jones and Nicklaus. The Rees Jones, as the website says, "is characterized by his signature style, challenging to play, enjoyable for both experts and novices alike, and respectful of the land, with built-in subtleties that offer a new playing experience every time."

Of the two, the Jones course requires more precise tee shots and approaches, and rewards you with easier putts. From the first tee, you're off to work, negotiating an uphill dogleg left to a well-guarded green. The ninth is an eye-opening par 5 that requires a carry over a hillside, a medium-length second shot, and an approach to a thin but wide green, fronted by a pond. The par 5 15th hole requires a carry over an abyss of brush to a rising fairway and a distant elevated green.

The Nicklaus 18, designed by Jack Nicklaus II, has a different character, with much of the same appeal. Also cut around and through the kettles (carved by glaciers), the Nicklaus design offers somewhat broader landing areas, but more challenging putts once you reach the green. Favorites include the daunting third hole, a long par 3 that requires a carry over a fronting trap, and the wonderful eighteenth, which requires a semi-blind tee shot that must find the fairway rather than the long-stretching pond which guards the green.

There is great variety, beauty, and challenge all around. The marvelous practice facilities and cart are included in your fee. Arrive early enough to take advantage. After your round, enjoy the inviting grill and lounge.

Pinehills is one of only ten five-star rated courses in the *New England GolfGuide* 2017 Edition. Come play once and you'll return again and again.

# Red Tail Golf Club

## Devens, MA

### One of the Best.

Nestled within a natural environment interspersed through the former U.S. Army base that was Fort Devens, the 18-hole march at Red Tail Golf Club can be tantamount to a war of attrition over one of Massachusetts' top public golf courses. And whether it is the guard tower seemingly randomly situated overlooking the 18th tee box, or the hidden old munitions bunker laying aside the 17th green, reminders abound at Red Tail of the property's military history.

Commissioned for play in 2002, Brian Silva of New England's top design firm of Cornish, Silva and Mungeam, devised a 7,000 yard masterpiece composed upon a varied and visually stunning landscape. Although brute force and power are certainly assets in engaging Red Tail, pinpoint target acquisition is equally rewarded in the golfer's battle to strategically evade the variety of minefields and other hidden ambush opportunities lying in wait at Red Tail.

Red Tail is a study in variety. While some holes such as the par three 11th and the par four 17th are defined by sandy waste bunkers reminiscent of the Sandhills of North Carolina, other holes like the par four 4th and 14th, as well as the classic risk-reward par five finishing 18th, incorporate dramatic elevation drops evoking comparisons to the spectacular mountain golf of northern New England. And with the blind approach or tee shots required on the par four 14th and 16th, respectively, you can even detect subtleties perhaps inspired by the great links courses of Scotland and Ireland.

Perhaps Red Tail's most unique and memorable design feature is the manner in which many of its greens are camouflaged naturally into the surrounding terrain. Whether it be the plateau greens of the 2nd and 9th, the semi-punchbowl surfaces of the 4th and 14th or the greens emanating out of the hillsides on the 7th and 8th, the somewhat refreshing absence of wetlands, bunkers and other beachhead obstacles fronting many of Red Tail's green complexes encourage frontal assaults characterized by run-up approach shots played low.

Located 35 miles northwest of Boston in Devens, Massachusetts, Red Tail boasts New England's first Audubon International Signature Sanctuary designation. In melding varied and strategic shot values into this natural splendor, Red Tail served as the host to the 2009 U.S. Women's Amateur Public Links Championship and the 2016 MGA Amateur Public Links Championship. In 2017 Red Tail will host the MGA Senior Four Ball State Championship. Clearly, Red Tail Golf Club rates among the best golf courses in New England.

*Please see Red Tail's full color ad at the back of the book.*

# Shaker Hills
# Country Club | Harvard, MA

## A Distinctively Unique Experience.

Beautiful golf courses are usually akin to beautiful properties — and Shaker Hills in Harvard, MA is no exception. The dynamics of the extraordinary 2012 renovations accomplished by new owner Fred Curtis, Jr. truly set this golf course apart. A classic New England layout is only the starting point of adjectives to describe Shaker Hills. It is in the details of the creative renovations that one truly finds its splendor.

Among one of the major renovations to the golf course was the redesign of the 18th hole — now a sweeping 562 yard dogleg Par 5 finishing at the club house creating a serene and wholesome "natural theatre" of golf. An impressive new top deck, adorned with a center fireplace, allows dramatic seated views of this "amphitheatre" of golf including views of the 1st, 9th, 10th and 18th holes.

Shaker Hills Country Club — A Par 72, playing close to 7000 yards from the tips, has become an attractive destination for daily fee golf, golf outings and tournaments. Our membership offerings are the perfect opportunity to experience membership amenities at a price to suit your budget. Check out the "Shaker Pass", which is $500 down and $60 per round (including cart), and offers many other full membership options. The Shaker Hills experience not only offers spectacular golfing conditions, but also offers great hospitality, great food and blends the finest of natural tranquility and crafted beauty to create a genuinely peaceful setting and a distinctively unique experience. Tee Times can be booked up to 7 days in advance by calling 978-772-3330 or online at www.shakerhills.com.

*Please see Shaker Hills full color ad on the inside front cover.*

# Shining Rock Golf Club | Northbridge, MA

## One of America's Best New Courses.

Carved through over 165 acres, and with an elevation change of over 400 feet, the golf course at Shining Rock provides members and daily guests with a true test of golf in an idyllic setting. First opened in 2010, Shining Rock is already a multiple award recipient, Shining Rock is one of Boston area's finest 18 hole championship golf course. Elevated tees, large multi-tiered greens and dramatic views of the Blackstone Valley are among the highlights that golfers will speak of in the coming years.

Going into only its 7th year, Shining Rock was named the 5th best public course in the state by *Golf Magazine*. The course also entered great company when it was named to *Golfweek's* list of 40 best new courses in America, joining only one other club in New England to achieve this prestigious honor.

With a multi-club membership available to its members, members get to call Shining Rock home. It is a par 72 course, which measures out at over 6875 yards from the tips. It features a great blend of holes that force you to use every club in your bag. Shining Rock has an excellent restaurant and bar and in 2014 added a new set of tees to accommodate an even greater range of players.

# Southers Marsh | Plymouth, MA

## What's Red and Green and Fun All Over?

*New England GolfGuide* calls Southers Marsh in Plymouth "The best golf value in Massachusetts. It has 18 wonderful holes, and the nicest, most sincere group of owner managers you'll find anywhere, the Stearns family. They care about their golfers, and they care about their course."

Maybe they're always in such a good mood because of their surroundings. The course was designed around and through a working cranberry bog. That means from the clubhouse, or anywhere around the course itself, there is a visual feast of pink and lime, or red and green, for much of the year.

Southers Marsh is a par 31-30-61 with seven par 4s and eleven par 3s. Total yardage from the back tees is 4111, perfect for a quicker-than-usual 18, but stop right there if you're thinking "pitch-and-putt." No way. There are carries a-plenty over the bogs, strategically placed bunkers, and long grasses designed to force certain shots. And contoured greens to keep par a challenge. The shortest hole on the course, the 12th, a mere 97 yards, is actually one of the toughest because it's an island green which looks like a sliver from the tee. There's no bailout either— it's hit-the-green or surrender to the bog.

That's followed by the 13th, a dogleg right par 4 of 304 yards that plays like 395 because it's all uphill, with a well-defended green. The finishing holes of 4-3-3-4 can crunch many a good scorecard.

Even the most accomplished golfers will be challenged, but four sets of tees ensure that golfers of all abilities will be able to enjoy themselves. The club has a 300-yard driving range and a full service restaurant with a beautiful mahogany deck overlooking the course. The restaurant is well known locally for the good food and good cheer well after the last golfer has come in and the Stearns are happy to host a party or wedding in a most inviting setting.

*Please see Southers Marsh's full color ad inside the front of the book.*

### The Best Golf Value in Massachusetts
### 13 Consecutive Years, 2005-2017

**Plymouth, Massachusetts**
**www.southersmarsh.com • 508-830-3535**

# Stow Acres Country Club | Stow, MA

## 36 of the Best.

Stow Acres Country Club has a new owner and Black Swan Management is committed to bringing fantastic conditions to this wonderful facility.

Stow Acres is conveniently located just 25 miles west of Boston. Situated on 350 acres in the heart of the Massachusetts apple country. The beautiful grounds are comprised of two award winning championship 18-Hole golf courses centered around a Victorian clubhouse. The two courses, designed by noted architect Geoffrey Cornish, have been heavily invested in under this new ownership.

The Par 72 North Course stretches to 7,000 yards from the tips winding through pine forests, ponds and streams. The North, the longer and flatter of the two courses hosted the 70th U.S. Amateur Public Links Championship and has also hosted the PGA Open Qualifier for the Deutsche Bank Championship. The North was recognized by *Golf Digest* as one of America's 50 best public courses.

Many believe that the Par 72 South Course rivals the nationally recognized North Course. The South Course is a little shorter in yardage thus making it a more player friendly option.

Stow Acres is also known for it's outstanding golf outing accommodations, golf school and practice facility. Opportunities are available for you, your business associates, and your friends and family to enjoy these picturesque country surroundings. Stow Acres is definitely an extraordinary venue for any golf related activities.

# Townsend Ridge

## Townsend, MA

### Central Massachusetts' Most Enjoyable Golfing Experience!

Built in 1996, Townsend Ridge Country Club is one of New England's most enjoyable golf courses. Townsend Ridge Country Club is a daily fee course with a private club atmosphere. This 18 hole par 70 championship course is just minutes from Routes 2, 3, and 495. Townsend Ridge's magnificent 18 holes are spread over 140 acres that wind through the countryside offering breathtaking views. With three sets of tees ranging from 4709 yards to 6215 yards, the course will challenge all golfers of any age and skill level.

The front nine typically plays a little easier than the back nine, though the front side boasts one of the most formidable holes in New England with the fourth hole. This narrow uphill par four requires a strong accurate drive followed by an uphill second shot to a deep green bunkered on the left and the back. Both nines offer a wonderful mix of holes that will be sure to test all ability levels. Set back off the hustle and bustle, and nestled amongst the vast array of hemlock, pine and birch trees you will feel like you are on a little mini vacation in the New England country side during your round.

The recently renovated golf shop includes two, new state-of-the-art, Full Swing golf simulators. These simulators boast world championship golf courses such as Pebble Beach, St. Andrews, Pinehurst #2 & Bay Hill, just to name a few. Interactive practice situations allow golfers to stay sharp even when the outside elements don't allow it. Other amazing features include real time ball flight, multiple hitting surfaces, high definition projection and infrared tracking systems. Whether you like practicing, playing a round with friends, or joining our nightly leagues, Townsend Ridge is open all winter long.

Rounding out Townsend Ridge's club amenities is our newest addition, Bistro on the Green. This upscale pub and restaurant boasts a sophisticated menu and an extensive cocktail selection, as well as two flat screen high definition televisions, a gas fire place and Keno. It is the perfect place to spend some time following your round of golf or to visit for your next dining experience.

With a picturesque ballroom overlooking the 9th and 18th greens, it is the perfect spot to host your next function. Townsend Ridge specializes in corporate & charity outings as well so be sure to inquire about hosting your event here. Affordable memberships are also available and with seven membership types you will be sure to find the perfect one for your golfing needs.

*Please see Townsend Ridge's full color ad on the back cover of the book.*

# Unicorn Golf Course
## Stoneham, MA
# Winchendon Golf Club
## Winchendon, MA

Sterling Golf Management strives to provide private club conditions and service at public golf prices. The company began operating the Unicorn Golf Course and the Winchendon Golf Club in early 2016 and has already started the process of improving the conditions at both courses, as well as implementing their customer-friendly, service-oriented staff. All their facilities provide the perfect backdrop for golf outings and golf leagues and some offer function halls for banquets, weddings, reunions and other events.

**Unicorn Golf Course** was originally designed by Stiles and Van Kleek and is a classic municipal 9-hole course with fairly straight fairways and multiple out of bounds in adjoining fairways. The course is actually quite long from the back tees and both beginners and experienced golfers will love the way it pushes you to work on your accuracy and short game. Practice facilities include a very nice putting green and two chipping greens.

**Winchendon Golf Club** is a short, but challenging 18-hole course with small undulating greens and hilly fairways, redesigned by Donald Ross in 1926. Like many Ross courses, it looks far easier than it is. Known for its magnificent views of the surrounding mountains and extensive woodlands, the course requires an accurate short game and local knowledge will help the golfer overcome the often tricky lies.

Unicorn Golf Course | (781)-438-9732 | www.sterlinggolf.com
Winchendon Golf Club | (978) 297-9897 | www.sterlinggolf.com

# Waubeeka Golf Links

## Williamstown, MA

### A Spectacular Hidden Gem.

Set in the beautiful Berkshire mountains, Waubeeka Golf Links is an 18-hole championship golf course located in Williamstown, MA. The course, driving range, practice green and The W Bar and Grill restaurant are open to the public. Their practice facility is the best in Berkshire County.

The course was purchased in March, 2014 by Michael Deep, a North Adams native, who has taken a hands-on approach while creating a family oriented golf club with a large emphasis on Junior golf. Many course updates are already underway and it's showing as the course is in pristine condition. Waubeeka hosted the 2015 MGA Amateur Public Links qualifier and the 2016 MGA Amateur Public Links Championship. In 2017 they will host an AJGA Preview event in May and the MGA Amateur Championship qualifier in June.

The course provides breathtaking views of the surrounding mountains, including Mount Greylock, the highest peak in Massachusetts. With large, undulated, true rolling greens, mixed with many elevation changes, Waubeeka provides a fun golf experience while challenging players of all ability levels.

Waubeeka is an excellent choice for golf outings, banquets or any special occasion. They specialize in small intimate events including bridal showers, bachelor outings or rehersal dinners. The beautiful mountain views coupled with excellent personalized meals will make your event an extreme pleasure and very memorable. For more information call 413-458-5869 or check out their web site at www.waubeeka.com.

# Atkinson Resort & Country Club | Atkinson, NH

Atkinson Resort & Country Club is a public country club with a distinguished reputation for golf and the amenities that draw players on and off the course. Conveniently located in scenic Atkinson, New Hampshire, just over the Massachusetts line near Plaistow and Salem, the resort is dedicated to the education and advancement of golfers of all skill levels and abilities and to welcoming all guests with warm, inviting hospitality. In 2015, Atkinson was named the NGCOA National Golf Course of the year.

The resort's 18-hole championship golf course, rated five stars by *New England GolfGuide*, rolls across 420 acres of New Hampshire field and forest. The 9-hole Par 3 course, which has earned "PGA Family Course" designation, is a favorite for casual games, family events and beginners.

Skill growth is a commitment at the course, especially at the Willowcreek Golf Academy where state-of-the-art analysis tools give the resort's PGA professionals a customized approach to the lessons, clinics and outfitting they provide to golfers seeking to improve their games. This facility is unequalled anywhere else in New England, with 12 heated hitting bays for year-round live flight practice and three coaching studios that feature the Trackman radar-based, club-fitting system and V1 Pro Golf video swing analysis.

A highly-coveted wedding spot, the Atkinson Resort & Country Club maintains a sterling reputation for guest service and attention to detail, core to delivering an exceptional experience. With over 15,000 square feet of meeting space, superior culinary creativity, and expert planning services, Atkinson Resort & Country Club will exceed your expectations. The resort boasts two restaurants, the Stagecoach Grille and Merrill's Tavern, each with chef-inspired selections to suit all tastes. Overnight guests can take full advantage of the services and amenities in the resort's well-appointed, oversized Fieldstone Suites. From top-notch golf to elegant weddings, superb dining and overnight accommodations, come and experience everything Atkinson Resort & Country Club has to offer.

# Nippo Lake Golf Course

### Barrington, NH

### "It's Where Your Friends Are."

Nestled in the woods of Barrington lies Nippo Lake Golf Club, one of the finest 18-hole public golf courses in the state. With breathtaking views and abundant wildlife, the challenging Nippo Lake course provides an enjoyable day for golfers of all levels. The practice facility at Nippo Lake is a great spot to keep your golf swing finely-tuned as you hit golf balls with a view of the Blue Hills mountain range. The serene setting and friendly staff will make you want to return day after day.

Nippo Lake's restaurant is a great place to gather whether you have just finished a round of golf or you're just stopping by for a bite to eat for lunch or dinner. Open all year long, the restaurant offers Blue Grass music every Sunday night from November to April and hosts a winter Cribbage League.

There are a variety of membership options at Nippo Lake including their Alliance Membership with Rochester Country Club in Rochester, making Nippo Lake the best membership value in New Hampshire.

Whether you are looking to hold a wedding, business meeting, charity event, family affair or golf outing, Nippo Lake is the place to go. Nippo Lake prides itself on providing their golfers with a place where they can gather and experience the warmth of friendship, the friendly spirit of competition and a cozy atmosphere in which to relax and dine.

**Nippo Lake Golf Club** • 88 Stagecoach Road • Barrington, NH 03825
603-664-7616 (Pro Shop) 603-664-2030 (Restaurant) • www.nippolake.com

# Rochester Country Club

## Rochester, NH

Rochester Country Club is a public, 18-hole, par 72 golf course located on 150-acres along the Cocheco River. Beautiful views of the sprawling pastoral countryside and their Alliance Membership with Nippo Lake Golf Club in Barrington makes RCC "The Best Membership Value in NH".

In addition to its impeccable 18 holes, Rochester Country Club is home to "The SIMs @ RCC" – 3 state of the art indoor golf simulators – allowing you to keep your game going year round. Play a round at St. Andrews, Pebble Beach or The Carolinas, or simply practice your swing on a variety of virtual driving ranges. Indoor leagues, scrambles and other simulator events are the perfect way to enjoy the company of friends on the "links" when New England weather hits hard.

Rochester CC is a great venue for any business, charity group and family to host a golf tournament. Their expert staff is available every step of the way to help you plan your event. Known as one of the most beautiful wedding venues in the area, their attention to detail will make your day most memorable.

SK's Greenside Grille is a public, pub-style restaurant offering delicious food ranging from a quick snack to a leisurely lunch or dinner. Open year round, the Grille is host to many wintertime activities such as darts, ping-pong, and cribbage leagues.

Come and experience the NEW Rochester Country Club. Call for a tee time and let them "make your day".

Rochester Country Club • 94 Church Street, Rochester, NH
603-332-9892 (Pro Shop) 603-332-1395 (Restaurant) • www.rochestercc.com

# Cranston Country Club

## Cranston, RI

## One of Rhode Island's Most Outstanding Values.

Cranston Country Club is your home for championship golf, modern and luxurious banquet facilities and first rate service. Centrally located just minutes from Interstate 95 & 295 in scenic western Cranston is a Geoffrey Cornish Design par 71 championship length golf course laid out over 170 acres of rolling terrain.

Playing from 6900 yards from the tips Cranston Country Clubs wide landing areas and large greens offer a fair test of golf for golfers of all abilities. Seniors love our 5256 yard Silver tees and the opportunity to "Play it forward". The signature hole #8 is a true island green with yardages playing from 100 yards to 160 yards. It is a conversation piece for all after your round. The golf course is meticulously maintained and has a reputation for its conditions from tee to green.

Cranston Country Club has a great practice facility offering golfers the opportunity to practice on a natural grass tee and a large practice putting green. The range is perfect for golfers looking to warm up before a round or a player looking to improve their game without hitting off mats.

**Cranston Country Club**

Cranston Country Club
69 Burlingame Road
Cranston, RI 02921
Phone: 401-826-1683
www.cranstoncc.com

# Laurel Lane Country Club | West Kingston, RI

Welcome to Laurel Lane Country Club, the favorite place to play golf in the South County for over 55 years. Open to the public since 1960, this 18 hole, par 71 course is beautifully maintained and conveniently located just off Route 138, four miles west of the University of Rhode Island. Laurel Lane is fun to play yet challenging, affordable priced and is an excellent course for all skill levels.

Laurel Lane is operated by a courteous and friendly staff dedicated to making your day as enjoyable as possible. There are two very different "nines" at Laurel Lane. The front nine is moderately open with level terrain. The back nine is tree lined with a rolling terrain. The course is easy to walk measuring a comfortable 6,177 yards. Carts with roofs are always available along with rental clubs.

Laurel Lane has one of the best short game practice areas in Rhode Island. A huge 4-tiered putting green with two practice bunkers and pitching areas are open to the public at "no charge." There is also a driving range with both natural and synthetic grass tees.

A specialty at Laurel Lane is their Golf Outing Program. If you have been looking for a professional full service staff to help you organize a special event of any size, than look no further. The beautiful clubhouse provides a picturesque setting for wedding receptions, anniversary parties, reunions, and of course, golf outings. The clubhouse is tastefully appointed creating an inviting and comfortable atmosphere. An elegant ballroom with doors opening to a deck overlooks the golf course. The restaurant, "Rudy's", is open daily during the season and has an outstanding reputation for its food, service and reasonable prices. In short, Laurel Lane will take care of the details while you and your guests enjoy the day.

To learn more about Laurel Lane Country Club, visit their website, www.laurellanecountryclub.com, or simply give them a call at 401-783-3844. You will definitely enjoy your day at Laurel Lane!

309 Laurel Lane (off Route 138) • West Kingston, RI 02892 • (401) 783-3844

# Newport National
# Golf Club | Middletown, RI

Opened in 2002, architects Arthur Hills and Drew Rogers used this former orchard and nursery farm as an exquisite canvas upon which they have crafted their masterpiece. Newport National is a par 72 championship semi-private course as well as an open-space tribute to environmental sensitivity. There's a lot to like at Newport National, but the real star of the show here is the diverse and high quality course layout. Newport National is a links style course that manages to cater to golfers of all ages and skill levels. The furthest tees play at a 7,244 challenging yards. Seasoned players will feel challenged as they work to conquer the course. While newcomers will be able to relax as they enjoy learning this class game. Newport National is a must-play course with everything you need to create an ideal day.

Newport National has been voted the
#1 Course You Can Play in Rhode Island Year after Year!

"#1 Golf Course You Can Play in New England"
*New England Golf Monthly*

"#1 Golf Course You Can Play in Rhode Island"
*Golf Digest, Golfweek, Golfing Magazine, Golf Magazine*

www.newportnational.com • (401) 848-9690

# Hermitage | Wilmington, VT

At the southern end of Vermont lies a wonderful Desmond Muirhead design: Hermitage Golf Club in Wilmington. Though the course has undergone many changes since Muirhead's original work in 1972, most are in the area of conditioning, new grasses, and refinement.

Today a first-time player is struck by the beauty of the course, as it wraps around the hillsides and ridges of this ski-region landscape. Such placement means elevated tees and greens, and occasional sidehill lies if one isn't driving right down the middle. Several greens have sizeable breaks, influenced by the surrounding hillsides, one of the quirks of mountain golf, and one of the delights of a little local knowledge. Though hilly, many find it eminently walkable.

For those who love drivers, come on down. Several generous fairways await the "big dog," including the spectacular par 5 eleventh hole, which features a 250-foot drop-off from the tee. Whale away and you might have just a short iron to the green. From there, you face long and short, up and down holes that will delight just about any player. Hermitage stretches to 6549 yards from the blues and plays at 6164 yards from the whites presenting an opportunity to score well or card a few double bogeys — that part is up to you.

The clubhouse sports a fine grill and bar overlooking the course, the 19th Hole Lounge, complete with a billiards table if you still have that urge to sink a few.

Hermitage has new and exciting ownership news, as it is now owned by The Hermitage. Adjacent to Haystack Mountain, The Hermitage is an elegant four-star country inn, complete with its own covered bridge, fine dining restaurant, upscale pub, art collection and nationally renowned wine cellar. For onsite offerings, this unique property also provides a 9-mile hiking and cross-country ski trail, mountain biking, and fly-fishing. With the spectacular views outside and breathtaking décor inside, guests find themselves completely surrounded by the utmost in Vermont beauty and serenity. The Hermitage's establishment as a charming, all-encompassing property combined with its commitment for service and luxury make it a perfect base lodge for the Hermitage community.

- Hermitage is now offering affordable club memberships for unlimited golf, skiing and countless other activities and amenities.
- Only 4-Star golf course in Southern Vermont, and continues to receive accolades from the golf media.
- What was once considered a diamond in the rough is getting closer to being that "perfect stone".
- The Hermitage is a highly recognized wedding destination in New England.
- Special stay & play packages are available. Stay for two nights or two months, but all packages include golf daily with cart.

# Green Mountain National

## Killington, VT

### Green Mountain: Accessible & Exceptional.

While Vermont has some of the finest golf courses in Northeast, the beauty and design of Green Mountain National Golf Course ranks among the entire region's finest. *New England GolfGuide* has given Green Mountain a four-star rating, and considers it one of the best courses in Vermont.

With an exceptionally varied, and some might say robust, layout, the course exudes a championship feel, from the pro shop to the lounge, from the mountain setting to the last putt on 18.

It's a great experience for golfers of all ability levels. Multiple tees allow you to take on the course at the appropriate level for your game. In fact, it's not a bad idea at all to play your first round from the middle tees before hiking to the back tees. A little local knowledge might save a few balls and a few surprises, and give you more confidence for the second round.

Located in the heart of Central Vermont, just off Route 100, the Vermont Golf Trail, just minutes away from the Killington Resort, there are many exceptional lodging choices available within minutes of the course and multiple activities for you and your family to enjoy during your visit.

Green Mountain National is also perfect for outings or tournaments. The course specializes in golf instruction as well as activities designed specifically for women golfers.

What separates this course from others is its unique and challenging design features. Generously carved out of the Green Mountains, the course offers solitude and a private golf experience that delights players and changes from hole to hole.

Although you'll know you're in the mountains, you needn't be a Sherpa to play. Gently sloping fairways that feature generous landing areas, distinctive changes in elevation, and undulating greens provide natural beauty. View the centuries-old rock formations carved by the glaciers, and be sure to stop a moment on the #16 Tee, as you enjoy the panoramic views in a spectacular setting.

Take a moment to explore the website www.gmngc.com and see what Green Mountain National Golf Course has to offer.

**PICTURED:** *One of the many picturesque greens at Green Mountain National.*

# Lake Morey Resort

## Fairlee, VT

Nestled in the green Vermont hills above the Connecticut River, Lake Morey Resort provides the perfect getaway any time of the year. Fresh air, crystal clear Lake Morey and unspoiled Green Mountain beauty will draw you to this full service resort.

Home of the Vermont Open for over 50 years, you'll appreciate the same challenges the professionals face. The course is impeccably maintained and any golfer will admire the sweeping fairways and plush greens. The par 70, 6024 yard course features sand traps, water hazards and well-guarded greens. Don't let the yardage fool you as the fairways are lined with spruce trees from tee to green, demanding accuracy and precision. The fairly open front nine is complimented by the rolling back nine that provides breathtaking views.

There are certified teaching professionals that can fine tune your game or simply teach the basics. Private lessons are available by appointment. Lake Morey also offers group golf clinics and multi-day packages.

Whether you are looking for a convenient four-season resort brimming with activities, a stunning setting for your wedding or a conference center ready to cater to your every need, it's all at your doorstep at the Lake Morey Resort.

Fairlee, Vermont   (800) 423-1211   www.lakemoreyresort.com

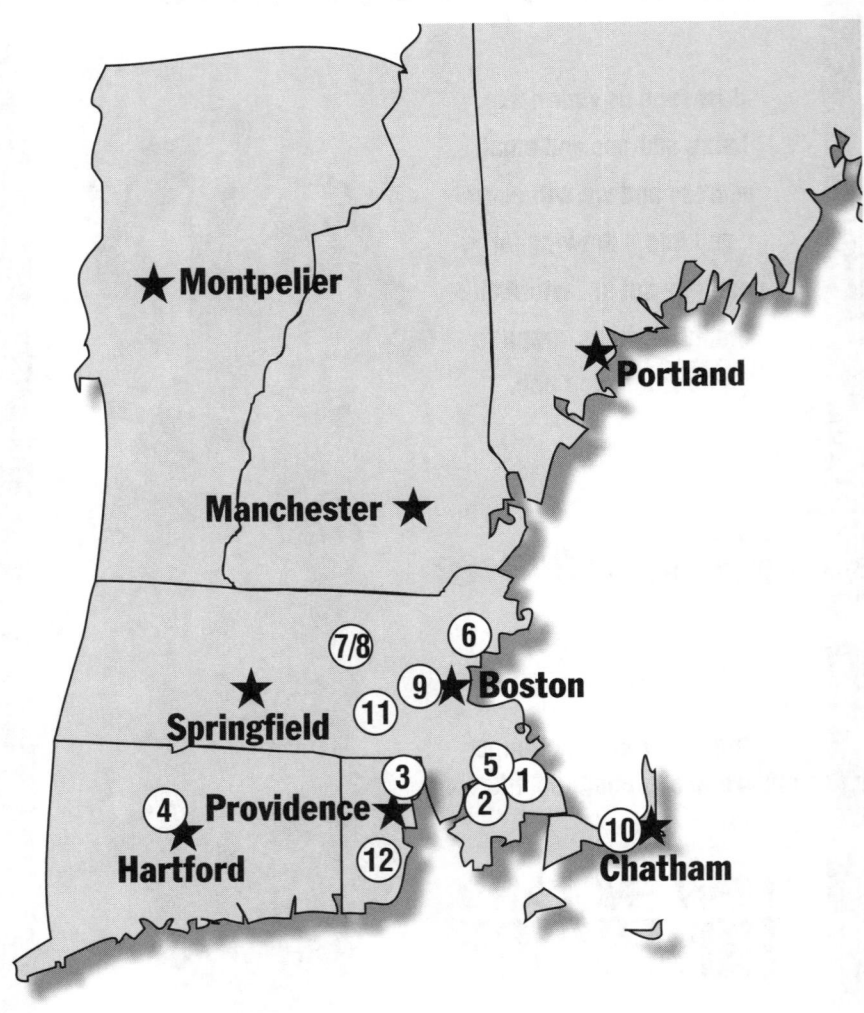

| | | | |
|---|---|---|---|
| Country Club of Halifax, Halifax, MA | 1 | The International (The Oaks), Bolton, MA | 7 |
| CC of New Bedford, N. Dartmouth, MA | 2 | The International (The Pines), Bolton, MA | 8 |
| Crestwood CC, Rehoboth, MA | 3 | Marlborough CC, Marlborough, MA | 9 |
| Hop Meadow CC, Simsbury, CT | 4 | Ocean Edge, Brewster, MA | 10 |
| Indian Pond Country Club | 5 | Pleasant Valley CC, Sutton, MA | 11 |
| Indian Ridge Country Club | 6 | The Preserve, Wyoming, RI | 12 |

# Country Club of Halifax

## 1

100 Country Club Drive
Halifax, MA  (781) 293-9063
www.halifaxcc.com

**Club Pro:** Joe Peck, GM
**Payment:** All Types
**Tee Times:** Private Club

| Tees | Holes | Yards | Par | USGA | Slope |
|------|-------|-------|-----|------|-------|
| BACK | 18 | 6708 | 72 | 73.1 | 130 |
| MIDDLE | 18 | 6482 | 72 | 72.0 | 127 |
| FRONT | 18 | 5465 | 73 | 73.2 | 128 |

**Fee  9 Holes: Weekday:**     **Weekend:**
**Fee 18 Holes: Weekday:**     **Weekend:**
**Twilight Rates:**     **Discounts:**
**Cart Rental:**     **Driving Range:** Yes
**Lessons:** Yes (open to public) **Schools:** Yes   **Junior Golf:** Yes
**Membership:** Yes     **Architect/Yr Open:** Phil Wogan/1966
**Other:** Restaurant / Clubhouse / Lockers / Showers / Bar-Lounge / Lodging Partner

Gently rolling terrain, easy walking course. From the middle tees playing 6482 yards, you might think "oh pretty easy course." Not so fast—this course will give you all you can handle. You will use almost every club in your bag, and the greens—the best you'll ever play on.

| | 1 | 2 | 3 | 4 | 5 | 6 | 7 | 8 | 9 |
|------|-----|-----|-----|-----|-----|-----|-----|-----|-----|
| PAR | 4 | 5 | 3 | 4 | 4 | 4 | 4 | 3 | 5 |
| YARDS | 347 | 486 | 151 | 377 | 406 | 379 | 392 | 180 | 463 |
| | 10 | 11 | 12 | 13 | 14 | 15 | 16 | 17 | 18 |
| PAR | 4 | 5 | 3 | 4 | 4 | 5 | 3 | 4 | 4 |
| YARDS | 323 | 473 | 197 | 422 | 392 | 503 | 165 | 404 | 422 |

**Directions:** I-95 (Route 128) to Route 24 South to Exit 16. Follow Route 106 East 15 minutes through Bridgewater and through the center of Halifax. Course is on the right. From the south take Route 3 to Route 106 West.

# Country Club of New Bedford

585 Slocum Road
N. Dartmouth, MA (508) 992-9339
www.ccnbgolfclub.com

**Club Pro:** Larry Demers, PGA
**Payment:** Visa, MC, Amex, Cash
**Tee Times:** Private Club

| Tees | Holes | Yards | Par | USGA | Slope |
|------|-------|-------|-----|------|-------|
| BACK | 18 | 6417 | 70 | 71.4 | 127 |
| MIDDLE | 18 | 6116 | 70 | 69.9 | 124 |
| FRONT | 18 | 5634 | 72 | 73.4 | 129 |

**Fee  9 Holes: Weekday:**     **Weekend:**
**Fee 18 Holes: Weekday:**     **Weekend:**
**Twilight Rates:**     **Discounts:**
**Cart Rental:**     **Driving Range:** No
**Lessons:** Yes (open to public) **Schools:** Yes   **Junior Golf:** Yes
**Membership:** Yes     **Architect/Yr:** Donald Ross/1902
**Other:** Restaurant / Clubhouse / Lockers / Showers / Bar-Lounge

A traditional country club that boasts one of the premier golf courses in New England. Home of the region's Women's Invitational Fourball Tournament.

| | 1 | 2 | 3 | 4 | 5 | 6 | 7 | 8 | 9 |
|------|-----|-----|-----|-----|-----|-----|-----|-----|-----|
| PAR | 4 | 4 | 4 | 5 | 4 | 4 | 3 | 4 | 4 |
| YARDS | 324 | 359 | 362 | 498 | 450 | 345 | 154 | 371 | 410 |
| | 10 | 11 | 12 | 13 | 14 | 15 | 16 | 17 | 18 |
| PAR | 4 | 4 | 4 | 4 | 4 | 3 | 4 | 3 | 4 |
| YARDS | 387 | 394 | 367 | 318 | 387 | 122 | 310 | 154 | 404 |

**Directions:** Route 24 South to Exit 12 (Route 140). Take Route 140 South to Route 6 and turn right on Route 6. Follow 6/10 mile to Slocum Road. Turn right and the course is 1/10 mile on left.

# Crestwood Country Club

3 ▶

90 Wheeler Street
Rehoboth, MA (508) 336-8582
www.crestwoodcc.com

| Tees | Holes | Yards | Par | USGA | Slope |
|------|-------|-------|-----|------|-------|
| BACK | 18 | 6599 | 71 | 72.2 | 130 |
| MIDDLE | 18 | 6342 | 71 | 71.4 | 127 |
| FRONT | 18 | 5656 | 74 | 72.9 | 126 |

**Club Pro:** Greg Rounds
**Payment:** All Types
**Tee Times:** Private Club
**Fee 9 Holes: Weekday:**    **Weekend:**
**Fee 18 Holes: Weekday:**    **Weekend:**
**Twilight Rates:**    **Discounts:**
**Cart Rental:**    **Driving Range:** Yes
**Lessons:** Yes (open to public) **Schools:** Yes   **Junior Golf:** Yes
**Membership:** Yes    **Architect/Yr Open:** Geoffrey Cornish/1959
**Other:** Restaurant / Clubhouse / Lockers / Showers / Bar-Lounge

Challenging 18-hole championship course situated on 180 rolling acres in scenic Rehoboth, Massachusetts. Located only 10 minutes from Providence and 45 minutes from Boston. Great course for players of any skill level; known for its superb, fast and slippery greens.

| | 1 | 2 | 3 | 4 | 5 | 6 | 7 | 8 | 9 |
|---|---|---|---|---|---|---|---|---|---|
| PAR | 4 | 4 | 3 | 4 | 3 | 4 | 4 | 5 | 4 |
| YARDS | 346 | 435 | 158 | 325 | 170 | 375 | 351 | 517 | 423 |
| | 10 | 11 | 12 | 13 | 14 | 15 | 16 | 17 | 18 |
| PAR | 4 | 4 | 5 | 4 | 4 | 3 | 4 | 3 | 5 |
| YARDS | 407 | 354 | 491 | 410 | 372 | 174 | 381 | 139 | 514 |

**Directions:** Take I-95 South to 195 to exit 1 in MA. Follow Route 114A North. Take a right at the first light which is County Street. Follow County Street for 2.7 miles, take a left onto Reed Street. Follow Reed Street to Wheeler Street, take a right on Wheeler the club will be on the left hand side.

# Hop Meadow Country Club

4 ▶

85 Firetown Road
Simsbury, CT (860) 658-7623
www.hopmeadowcc.net

| Tees | Holes | Yards | Par | USGA | Slope |
|------|-------|-------|-----|------|-------|
| BACK | 18 | 6915 | 72 | 73.9 | 136 |
| MIDDLE | 18 | 6531 | 72 | 72.3 | 132 |
| FRONT | 18 | 5395 | 72 | 71.1 | 124 |

**Club Pro:** Joe Cordani, Jr., PGA
**Payment:** Visa, MC, Amex, Check, Cash
**Tee Times:** Private Club
**Fee 9 Holes: Weekday:**    **Weekend:**
**Fee 18 Holes: Weekday:**    **Weekend:**
**Twilight Rates:**    **Discounts:**
**Cart Rental:**    **Driving Range:** Yes
**Lessons:** Yes (open to public) **Schools:** Yes   **Junior Golf:** Yes
**Membership:** Yes    **Architect/Yr Open:** Geoffrey Cornish/1961
**Other:** Restaurant / Clubhouse / Lockers / Showers / Bar-Lounge

COUPON

Beautiful and Challenging course. Golf shop and lessons open to the public. For information on membership contact Danielle Hermanowski, Membership Director. Excellent facility for golf outings, banquets, weddings and private parties.

| | 1 | 2 | 3 | 4 | 5 | 6 | 7 | 8 | 9 |
|---|---|---|---|---|---|---|---|---|---|
| PAR | 4 | 5 | 3 | 4 | 4 | 5 | 4 | 4 | 3 |
| YARDS | 376 | 524 | 142 | 385 | 301 | 475 | 422 | 436 | 212 |
| | 10 | 11 | 12 | 13 | 14 | 15 | 16 | 17 | 18 |
| PAR | 4 | 4 | 3 | 4 | 4 | 4 | 3 | 5 | 5 |
| YARDS | 322 | 432 | 175 | 346 | 405 | 427 | 187 | 484 | 480 |

**Directions:** I-84 Exit 39 to Route 4 then Route 10 North. Go 5 miles, cross over Route 44 to Nod Road. Left on Route 185, right on Route 10, left on Route 167, right on Firetown Road. Course is ½ mile on left.

# Indian Pond Country Club 5 ▶

60 Country Club Way
Kingston, MA (781) 585-0555
www.indianpondcountryclub.com

| Tees | Holes | Yards | Par | USGA | Slope |
|------|-------|-------|-----|------|-------|
| BACK | 18 | 6614 | 72 | 73.0 | 138 |
| MIDDLE | 18 | 6012 | 72 | 70.4 | 131 |
| FRONT | 18 | 5425 | 72 | 71.9 | 133 |

**Club Pro:** Brian Langevin, PGA
**Payment:** Visa, MC, Amex, Check, Cash
**Tee Times:** Private Club
**Fee 9 Holes: Weekday:**           **Weekend:**
**Fee 18 Holes: Weekday:**          **Weekend:**
**Twilight Rates:**                 **Discounts:**
**Cart Rental:**                    **Driving Range:** Yes
**Lessons:** Yes (open to public) **Schools:** No   **Junior Golf:** Yes
**Membership:** Yes                 **Architect/Yr Open:** Damian Pascuzzo/2001
**Other:** Restaurant / Clubhouse / Lockers / Showers / Bar-Lounge

Ranked in the Top 20 Best in State by *Golf Digest*. The premier 18-hole golf club of the South Shore.
5 sets of tees provide playability for all levels of golfers.

|  | 1 | 2 | 3 | 4 | 5 | 6 | 7 | 8 | 9 |
|------|---|---|---|---|---|---|---|---|---|
| PAR | 4 | 5 | 4 | 4 | 3 | 4 | 3 | 5 | 4 |
| YARDS | 348 | 521 | 313 | 346 | 169 | 243 | 143 | 531 | 372 |
|  | 10 | 11 | 12 | 13 | 14 | 15 | 16 | 17 | 18 |
| PAR | 5 | 4 | 4 | 3 | 4 | 4 | 4 | 3 | 5 |
| YARDS | 530 | 381 | 317 | 122 | 285 | 380 | 352 | 155 | 504 |

**Directions:** Route 3 South to Exit 9 (Kingston/N. Plymouth). Merge onto Main Street/3A. Turn left
on Brook St (MA-80). Turn left on Country Club Way.

# Indian Ridge Country Club 6 ▶

75 Lovejoy Road
Andover, MA (978) 475-5233
www.indianridgecountryclub.us

| Tees | Holes | Yards | Par | USGA | Slope |
|------|-------|-------|-----|------|-------|
| BACK | 18 | 6501 | 72 | 72.1 | 133 |
| MIDDLE | 18 | 6151 | 72 | 70.2 | 130 |
| FRONT | 18 | 5441 | 74 | 72.8 | 127 |

**Club Pro:** Mike Miller, PGA
**Payment:** Visa, MC, Amex, Check, Cash
**Tee Times:** Private Club
**Fee 9 Holes: Weekday:**           **Weekend:**
**Fee 18 Holes: Weekday:**          **Weekend:**
**Twilight Rates:**                 **Discounts:**
**Cart Rental:**                    **Driving Range:** Yes
**Lessons:** Yes (open to public) **Schools:** Yes   **Junior Golf:** Yes
**Membership:** Yes                 **Architect/Yr Open:** Geoffrey Cornish/1962
**Other:** Restaurant / Clubhouse / Lockers / Showers / Bar-Lounge

The premier destination for golfers in the Merrimack Valley. Beautifully groomed and challenging
(but playable) for all level of golfers. Excellent practice facilities.

|  | 1 | 2 | 3 | 4 | 5 | 6 | 7 | 8 | 9 |
|------|---|---|---|---|---|---|---|---|---|
| PAR | 4 | 3 | 4 | 5 | 4 | 4 | 3 | 4 | 5 |
| YARDS | 390 | 174 | 406 | 437 | 322 | 307 | 156 | 341 | 463 |
|  | 10 | 11 | 12 | 13 | 14 | 15 | 16 | 17 | 18 |
| PAR | 4 | 4 | 5 | 3 | 4 | 4 | 3 | 4 | 5 |
| YARDS | 348 | 421 | 485 | 163 | 433 | 345 | 122 | 373 | 465 |

**Directions:** I-93 to Exit 42 (Dascomb Road). Bear right towards Andover. Travel ½ mile and take
a left on Lovejoy Road. Travel ½ mile to the course.

# The International (The Oaks) ✪✪✪✪✪

159 Ballville Road
Bolton, MA (978) 779-6910
www.theinternational.com

**Club Pro:** Chris Kasheta, Dir. of Golf
**Payment:** Visa, MC, Amex, Disc
**Tee Times:** Private Club w/access for resort guests

| Tees | Holes | Yards | Par | USGA | Slope |
|------|-------|-------|-----|------|-------|
| BACK | 18 | 6944 | 72 | 73.5 | 132 |
| MIDDLE | 18 | 6565 | 72 | 72.5 | 129 |
| FRONT | 18 | 5243 | 71 | 70.8 | 126 |

**Fee 9 Holes: Weekday:**        **Weekend:**
**Fee 18 Holes: Weekday:**       **Weekend:**
**Twilight Rates:**              **Discounts:** No
**Cart Rental:** Included        **Driving Range:** Yes
**Lessons:** Yes **Schools:** Yes   **Junior Golf:** Yes
**Membership:** Yes              **Architect/Yr Open:** Tom Fazio/2001
**Other:** Clubhouse / Restaurant / Hotel / Lockers / Showers / Bar-Lounge

The first and only Tom Fazio designed golf course in New England. A natural wonder that provides a unique experience that celebrates the ebb and flow of the geography. Visage GPS on all carts.

| | 1 | 2 | 3 | 4 | 5 | 6 | 7 | 8 | 9 |
|---|---|---|---|---|---|---|---|---|---|
| PAR | 5 | 3 | 4 | 3 | 4 | 4 | 4 | 5 | 4 |
| YARDS | 494 | 163 | 330 | 161 | 325 | 375 | 405 | 515 | 436 |
| | 10 | 11 | 12 | 13 | 14 | 15 | 16 | 17 | 18 |
| PAR | 4 | 3 | 5 | 3 | 5 | 4 | 4 | 3 | 5 |
| YARDS | 428 | 200 | 537 | 144 | 515 | 401 | 402 | 194 | 540 |

**Directions:** Route 495 to Exit 27 (Route 117). West on 117 for 1.5 miles. Left onto Wilder Road. Left onto Ballville Road. Club is ½ mile on right.

# The International (The Pines) ✪✪✪✪✪

159 Ballville Road
Bolton, MA (978) 779-6910
www.theinternational.com

**Club Pro:** Chris Kasheta
**Payment:** Visa, MC, Amex, Disc
**Tee Times:** Private Club w/access for resort guests

| Tees | Holes | Yards | Par | USGA | Slope |
|------|-------|-------|-----|------|-------|
| BACK | 18 | 8325 | 73 | 80.0 | 164 |
| MIDDLE | 18 | 6547 | 72 | 71.7 | 132 |
| FRONT | 18 | 5191 | 72 | 79.2 | 120 |

**Fee 9 Holes: Weekday:**        **Weekend:**
**Fee 18 Holes: Weekday:**       **Weekend:**
**Twilight Rates:** No           **Discounts:** No
**Cart Rental:** $25pp/18        **Driving Range:** No
**Lessons:** Yes **Schools:** Yes   **Junior Golf:** Yes
**Membership:** Yes              **Architect/Yr Open:** Robert Trent Jones/1957
**Other:** Clubhouse / Restaurant / Hotel / Lockers / Showers / Bar-Lounge

Known as the world's longest golf course with five different sets of tees to allow for all abilities to enjoy the course. Consistently rated one of the toughest courses in the continental U.S.

| | 1 | 2 | 3 | 4 | 5 | 6 | 7 | 8 | 9 |
|---|---|---|---|---|---|---|---|---|---|
| PAR | 4 | 4 | 5 | 3 | 5 | 4 | 3 | 4 | 4 |
| YARDS | 327 | 371 | 525 | 141 | 575 | 360 | 186 | 369 | 378 |
| | 10 | 11 | 12 | 13 | 14 | 15 | 16 | 17 | 18 |
| PAR | 4 | 5 | 4 | 3 | 4 | 4 | 3 | 4 | 5 |
| YARDS | 363 | 528 | 416 | 168 | 368 | 351 | 199 | 399 | 523 |

**Directions:** Route 495 to Exit 27 (Route 117). West on 117 for 1.5 miles. Left onto Wilder Road. Left onto Ballville Road. Club is ½ mile on right.

# Marlborough Country Club

9

200 Concord Road
Marlborough, MA  (508) 481-5340
www.marlboroughcc.com

**Club Pro:** Greg Farland, PGA
**Payment:** All Types
**Tee Times:** Private Club

| Tees | Holes | Yards | Par | USGA | Slope |
|------|-------|-------|-----|------|-------|
| BACK | 18 | 6476 | 71 | 72.0 | 131 |
| MIDDLE | 18 | 6155 | 71 | 70.2 | 129 |
| FRONT | 18 | 5624 | 72 | 73.7 | 130 |

**Fee  9 Holes: Weekday:**         **Weekend:**
**Fee 18 Holes: Weekday:** $75 inc. cart (M-T subject to availabilty)
**Discounts:** Seniors $64 inc. cart (M-T subject to availabilty)
**Cart Rental:**                  **Driving Range:** Yes
**Lessons:** Yes (open to public)  **Schools:** Yes   **Junior Golf:** Yes
**Membership:** Yes               **Architect/Yr Open:** Wayne Stiles/1922
**Other:**

COUPON

Beautiful and challenging with many elevated tees and greens. Open to the public on Mondays and Tuesdays. Subject to availability.

|       | 1 | 2 | 3 | 4 | 5 | 6 | 7 | 8 | 9 |
|-------|-----|-----|-----|-----|-----|-----|-----|-----|-----|
| PAR | 4 | 4 | 4 | 4 | 3 | 4 | 3 | 5 | 4 |
| YARDS | 330 | 410 | 358 | 316 | 218 | 357 | 155 | 485 | 466 |
|       | 10 | 11 | 12 | 13 | 14 | 15 | 16 | 17 | 18 |
| PAR | 4 | 5 | 3 | 5 | 4 | 3 | 4 | 4 | 3 |
| YARDS | 312 | 539 | 162 | 435 | 398 | 365 | 405 | 368 | 176 |

**Directions:** I-95 to Exit 26, Route 20 towards Weston. Travel 14.1 miles, right on Concord Road, course in .4 miles on the left.

# Ocean Edge Resort & Golf Club

10

2907 Main Street
Brewster, MA  (774) 323-6200
www.oceanedge.com

**Club Pro:** Brandon Roseth, PGA
          Ross Singmaster
**Payment:** All Types
**Tee Times:** Private Club w/access for resort guests

| Tees | Holes | Yards | Par | USGA | Slope |
|------|-------|-------|-----|------|-------|
| BACK | 18 | 7011 | 72 | 73.1 | 133 |
| MIDDLE | 18 | 6404 | 72 | 70.7 | 130 |
| FRONT | 18 | 4886 | 72 | 78.5 | 130 |

**Fee  9 Holes: Weekday:**         **Weekend:**
**Fee 18 Holes: Weekday:**         **Weekend:**
**Twilight Rates:**               **Discounts:**
**Cart Rental:**                  **Driving Range:** Yes
**Lessons:** Yes (open to public)
**Schools:** Yes                  **Junior Golf:** Yes
**Membership:** Yes               **Architect/Yr Open:** Nicklaus Design/2008
**Other:** Restaurant / Clubhouse / Lockers / Showers / Bar-Lounge

Challenging but strategically appropriate for all levels of play. Golf and sport memberships available. Sport members have access to the golf course in fringe season only. New electric carts with GPS units.

|       | 1 | 2 | 3 | 4 | 5 | 6 | 7 | 8 | 9 |
|-------|-----|-----|-----|-----|-----|-----|-----|-----|-----|
| PAR | 4 | 4 | 3 | 5 | 4 | 4 | 4 | 3 | 5 |
| YARDS | 332 | 376 | 163 | 496 | 357 | 300 | 409 | 171 | 544 |
|       | 10 | 11 | 12 | 13 | 14 | 15 | 16 | 17 | 18 |
| PAR | 4 | 4 | 4 | 4 | 4 | 4 | 3 | 5 | 4 |
| YARDS | 386 | 418 | 327 | 381 | 316 | 340 | 185 | 559 | 347 |

**Directions:** Tak Exit 10 on Route 6 (Mid-Cape Highway). Follow Route 124 North to Route 6A. Turn right. Entrance is 1.5 miles on the right.

# Pleasant Valley Country Club

**11** ▶

95 Armsby Road
Sutton, MA (508) 865-5244
www.pleasantvalleycc.com
**Club Pro:** Paul Parajeckas, PGA
**Payment:** Visa, MC, Amex, Disc, Cash
**Tee Times:** Private Club

| Tees | Holes | Yards | Par | USGA | Slope |
|------|-------|-------|-----|------|-------|
| BACK | 18 | 6864 | 72 | 73.3 | 135 |
| MIDDLE | 18 | 6313 | 72 | 71.0 | 133 |
| FRONT | 18 | 5385 | 73 | 70.9 | 125 |

**Fee 9 Holes: Weekday:**     **Weekend:**
**Fee 18 Holes: Weekday:**     **Weekend:**
**Twilight Rates:**     **Discounts:**
**Cart Rental:**     **Driving Range:** Yes
**Lessons:** Yes (members only)   **Schools:** Yes   **Junior Golf:** Yes
**Membership:** Yes     **Architect/Yr Open:** Don Hoening/1962
**Other:** Restaurant / Clubhouse / Lockers / Showers / Bar-Lounge

Known as New England's Home of Professional Golf. Considered one of central New England's finest banquet and golf outing facilities.

| | 1 | 2 | 3 | 4 | 5 | 6 | 7 | 8 | 9 |
|---|---|---|---|---|---|---|---|---|---|
| PAR | 4 | 5 | 3 | 4 | 4 | 5 | 5 | 4 | 3 |
| YARDS | 438 | 455 | 162 | 375 | 330 | 495 | 548 | 384 | 137 |
| | 10 | 11 | 12 | 13 | 14 | 15 | 16 | 17 | 18 |
| PAR | 4 | 4 | 4 | 4 | 3 | 4 | 3 | 4 | 5 |
| YARDS | 394 | 354 | 322 | 346 | 190 | 317 | 187 | 368 | 511 |

**Directions:** I-90 (Mass Pike) to Exit 10A. Exit onto Route 146 South (Providence). Travel 4 miles to Exit 7. Turn right onto Armsby Road at the Pleasant Valley sign.

# The Preserve at Boulder Hills

**12** ▶

87 Kingstown Rd
Wyoming, RI (401) 539-4653
www.thepreserveri.com
**Club Pro:** Matt Hall, PGA
**Payment:** Visa, MC, Amex, Cash
**Tee Times:** Private Club

| Tees | Holes | Yards | Par | USGA | Slope |
|------|-------|-------|-----|------|-------|
| BACK | 18 | 3021 | 36 | 56.8 | 98 |
| MIDDLE | 18 | 2590 | 36 | 55.4 | 95 |
| FRONT | 18 | 2223 | 36 | 53.2 | 91 |

**Fee 9 Holes: Weekday:**     **Weekend:**
**Fee 18 Holes: Weekday:**     **Weekend:**
**Twilight Rates:**     **Discounts:**
**Cart Rental:**     **Driving Range:** Yes
**Lessons:** Yes (members only)   **Schools:** No   **Junior Golf:** No
**Membership:** Yes     **Architect/Yr Open:** Robert McNeil/2015
**Other:** Restaurant / Clubhouse / Lockers / Showers / Bar-Lounge

New England's finest four season sporting retreat. Beautifully maintained 18-hole Par 3 golf course that can be played as a challenging 9-hole regulation course as well. American Society of Golf Course Architects 2015 Design Excellence Award. One of *New England Golf Monthly's* Top 25 Best Private Courses in NE. One of *Golf Digest's* exceptional hybrid courses in the U.S. (designed to be fast & fun).

| | 1 | 2 | 3 | 4 | 5 | 6 | 7 | 8 | 9 |
|---|---|---|---|---|---|---|---|---|---|
| PAR | 3 | 3 | 3 | 3 | 3 | 3 | 3 | 3 | 3 |
| YARDS | 128 | 170 | 147 | 150 | 122 | 132 | 153 | 135 | 152 |
| | 10 | 11 | 12 | 13 | 14 | 15 | 16 | 17 | 18 |
| PAR | 3 | 3 | 3 | 3 | 3 | 3 | 3 | 3 | 3 |
| YARDS | 108 | 187 | 135 | 169 | 117 | 137 | 165 | 140 | 143 |

**Directions:** I-95 to Exit 3A in RI. Continue on Route 138 East. Travel 3 miles to entrance of course on right.

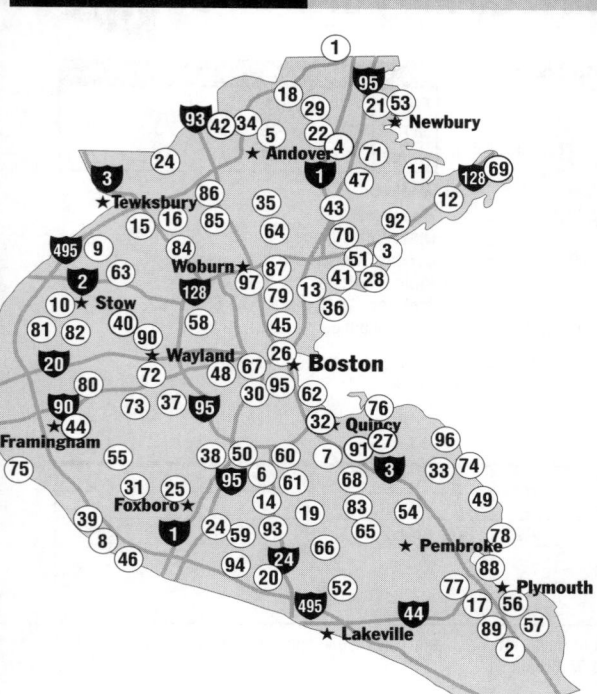

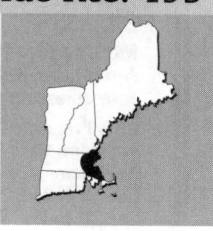

| | |
|---|---|
| Ponkapoag GC (#1) | 60 |
| Ponkapoag GC (#2) | 61 |
| Presidents Golf Course | 62 |
| Quail Ridge Country Club | 63 |
| Reedy Meadow GC | 64 |
| Ridder Golf Club | 65 |
| River Bend CC | 66 |
| Robert T. Lynch GC | 67 |
| Rockland Country Club | 68 |
| Rockport GC | 69 |
| Rowley CC | 70 |
| Sagamore Spring GC | 71 |
| Sandy Burr CC | 72 |
| Sassamon Trace Golf Course | 73 |
| Scituate Country Club | 74 |
| Shining Rock Golf Club | 75 |
| South Shore CC | 76 |
| Southers Marsh Golf Club | 77 |
| Squirrel Run GC | 78 |
| Stoneham Oaks | 79 |
| Stonybrook Golf Course | 80 |
| Stow Acres CC (North) | 81 |
| Stow Acres CC (South) | 82 |
| Strawberry Valley GC | 83 |
| Swanson Meadows | 84 |
| Tewksbury CC | 85 |

| | | | | |
|---|---|---|---|---|
| Amesbury Golf & CC | 1 | George Wright GC | 30 | |
| Atlantic Country Club | 2 | Glen Ellen CC | 31 | |
| Beverly Golf & Tennis | 3 | Granite Links Golf Club | 32 | |
| Black Swan CC | 4 | Green Harbor Golf Club | 33 | |
| Bradford Country Club | 5 | Hickory Hill GC | 34 | |
| Braintree Municipal GC | 6 | Hillview Golf Course | 35 | |
| Brookmeadow CC | 7 | Kelley Greens GC | 36 | |
| Bungay Brook Golf Club | 8 | Leo J. Martin GC | 37 | |
| Butter Brook Golf Club | 9 | Lost Brook Golf Club | 38 | |
| Butternut Farm GC | 10 | Maplegate Country Club | 39 | |
| Candlewood Golf Club | 11 | Maynard Golf Club | 40 | |
| Cape Ann Golf Club | 12 | Meadow at Peabody, The | 41 | |
| Cedar Glen Golf Club | 13 | Merrimack Valley GC | 42 | |
| Cedar Hill Golf Club | 14 | Middleton Golf Course | 43 | |
| Chelmsford Country Club | 15 | Millwood Golf Course | 44 | |
| Country Club of Billerica | 16 | Mt. Hood Golf Course | 45 | |
| Crosswinds Golf Club | 17 | New England CC | 46 | |
| Crystal Lake GC | 18 | New Meadows GC | 47 | |
| D.W. Fields Golf Course | 19 | Newton Commonwealth GC | 48 | |
| Easton Country Club | 20 | North Hill CC | 49 | |
| Evergreen Valley GC | 21 | Norwood Country Club | 50 | |
| Far Corner Golf Course | 22 | Olde Salem Greens | 51 | |
| Fore Kicks GC & | | Olde Scotland Links | 52 | |
| Sports Complex | 23 | Ould Newbury GC | 53 | |
| Foxborough Country Club | 24 | Pembroke Country Club | 54 | |
| Four Oaks Country Club | 25 | Pinecrest Golf Club | 55 | |
| Fresh Pond Golf Club | 26 | Pinehills Golf Club (Jones) | 56 | |
| Furnace Brook Golf Club | 27 | Pinehills Golf Club (Nicklaus) | 57 | |
| Gannon Golf Course | 28 | Pine Meadows GC | 58 | |
| Garrison Golf Center | 29 | Pine Oaks GC | 59 | |

| | |
|---|---|
| Trull Brook Golf Course | 86 |
| Unicorn Golf Course | 87 |
| Village Links | 88 |
| Waverly Oaks Golf Club | 89 |
| Wayland Country Club | 90 |
| Weathervane GC | 91 |
| Wenham Country Club | 92 |
| White Pines Golf Course | 93 |
| Widow's Walk Golf Course | 94 |
| William J. Devine GC | 95 |
| Willowdale Golf Course | 96 |
| Woburn Country Club | 97 |

**KEY TO THE STAR RATINGS:**
5✪ = Outstanding  4✪ = Excellent  3✪ = Very Good  2✪ = Good  1✪ = Average  **NR** = Not Rated

# Amesbury Golf & Country Club ✪✪

Monroe Street
Amesbury, MA (978) 388-5153
www.amesburygolf.com
**Club Pro:** Butch Mellon
**Payment:** Cash, Personal Checks, Visa, MC
**Tee Times:** 5 days adv.
**Fee 9 Holes: Weekday:** $20
**Fee 18 Holes: Weekday:** $30
**Twilight Rates:** No
**Cart Rental:** $16pp/18, $8pp/9
**Lessons:** No  **Schools:** No
**Membership:** Yes

| Tees | Holes | Yards | Par | USGA | Slope |
|---|---|---|---|---|---|
| BACK | | | | | |
| MIDDLE | 9 | 3048 | 35 | 70.5 | 125 |
| FRONT | 9 | 2691 | 35 | 71.9 | 126 |

**Weekend:** $21
**Weekend:** $32
**Discounts:** None
**Driving Range:** No
**Junior Golf:** Yes
**Architect/Yr Open:** Wayne Stiles/1923
**Other:** Clubhouse / Lockers / Showers / Snack Bar / Bar-Lounge

Great 1st tee panorama. Featured in *Yankee Magazine*. Beaches nearby. Fairways are better!
"Scenic views, friendly players and staff, good mix of holes." –GM

| | 1 | 2 | 3 | 4 | 5 | 6 | 7 | 8 | 9 |
|---|---|---|---|---|---|---|---|---|---|
| PAR | 4 | 3 | 4 | 4 | 5 | 4 | 4 | 3 | 4 |
| YARDS | 381 | 170 | 349 | 309 | 524 | 299 | 365 | 162 | 380 |

| | | | | | | | | | |
|---|---|---|---|---|---|---|---|---|---|
| PAR | | | | | | | | | |
| YARDS | | | | | | | | | |

**Directions:** Take I-95 North to Route 110 West; then take right at lights near Burger King; take right onto Monroe Street. Course is ⅓ mile on left.

# Atlantic Country Club ✪✪✪½

450 Little Sandy Pond Road
Plymouth, MA (508) 759-6644
www.atlanticcountryclub.com
**Club Pro:** Don Daley, PGA
**Payment:** Cash, Visa, MC
**Tee Times:** 7 days adv.
**Fee 9 Holes: Weekday:** $28 M-Th
**Fee 18 Holes: Weekday:** $48 M-Th
**Twilight Rates:** After 3pm
**Cart Rental:** $18pp/18, $9pp/9
**Lessons:** $30/half hour  **Schools:** No
**Membership:** Yes

| Tees | Holes | Yards | Par | USGA | Slope |
|---|---|---|---|---|---|
| BACK | 18 | 6262 | 72 | 70.8 | 127 |
| MIDDLE | 18 | 5840 | 72 | 69.0 | 119 |
| FRONT | 18 | 4918 | 72 | 68.3 | 116 |

**Weekend:** $33 F/S/S/H
**Weekend:** $58 F/S/S/H
**Discounts:** None
**Driving Range:** Yes
**Junior Golf:** No
**Architect/Yr:** Cornish, Silva, & Mungeam/1994
**Other:** Soft Drinks / Snack Bar / Banquet Facilities

COUPON

Mon-Thurs 12:30-2:30pm special. Player Comments: "Great track at a reasonable price. Many fine holes with challenging tee box selection. Compares with the best in state." "Great putting greens." –FP

| | 1 | 2 | 3 | 4 | 5 | 6 | 7 | 8 | 9 |
|---|---|---|---|---|---|---|---|---|---|
| PAR | 4 | 3 | 4 | 5 | 4 | 5 | 3 | 4 | 4 |
| YARDS | 302 | 144 | 410 | 475 | 343 | 467 | 134 | 387 | 345 |
| | 10 | 11 | 12 | 13 | 14 | 15 | 16 | 17 | 18 |
| PAR | 4 | 3 | 4 | 4 | 5 | 4 | 5 | 3 | 4 |
| YARDS | 336 | 156 | 310 | 281 | 460 | 330 | 491 | 105 | 364 |

**Directions:** Route 3 to Exit 2. Take left at bottom of exit ramp. Take first right onto Herring Pond Road. Right onto Long Pond Road. Left onto Carter's Bridge Road. Right onto Upland Road to Little Sandy Pond Road. Course is 1 mile on left.

# Beverly Golf & Tennis  ✪✪✪   3

**134 McKay Street**
**Beverly, MA (978) 922-9072**
www.beverlygolfandtennis.com

**Club Pro:** David Dionne, PGA
**Payment:** All Major
**Tee Times:** 5 days adv.

| Tees | Holes | Yards | Par | USGA | Slope |
|------|-------|-------|-----|------|-------|
| BACK | 18 | 6276 | 70 | 70.8 | 126 |
| MIDDLE | 18 | 5862 | 70 | 68.8 | 122 |
| FRONT | 18 | 5241 | 70 | 70.8 | 116 |

**Fee 9 Hole: Weekday:** $25
**Fee 18 Holes: Weekday:** $42
**Twilight Rates:** None
**Cart Rental:** $16pp/18, $8pp/9
**Lessons:** Yes **Schools:** Yes
**Membership:** Yes
**Other:** Clubhouse / Lockers / Showers / Snack Bar / Restaurant / Bar-Lounge

**Weekend:** $28
**Weekend:** $47
**Discounts:** Senior & Junior
**Driving Range:** Yes
**Junior Golf:** Yes
**Architect/Yr Open:** 1910

Signature hole is #15, the wedding cake. Classic short, downhill par three!

| | 1 | 2 | 3 | 4 | 5 | 6 | 7 | 8 | 9 |
|---|---|---|---|---|---|---|---|---|---|
| PAR | 4 | 4 | 3 | 4 | 4 | 3 | 4 | 5 | 4 |
| YARDS | 445 | 420 | 160 | 395 | 295 | 194 | 397 | 580 | 320 |
| | 10 | 11 | 12 | 13 | 14 | 15 | 16 | 17 | 18 |
| PAR | 4 | 3 | 3 | 5 | 4 | 3 | 4 | 5 | 4 |
| YARDS | 300 | 245 | 195 | 476 | 357 | 163 | 392 | 570 | 393 |

**Directions:** I-95/Route 128 to Exit 20B, right off ramp. Straight through lights to McKay Street. Course is ¼ mile on the right.

# Black Swan Country Club  ✪✪✪½   4

**258 Andover Street**
**Georgetown, MA (978) 352-7926**
www.blackswancountryclub.com

**Club Pro:** Matt Cunningham, PGA
**Payment:** All
**Tee Times:** 6 days adv.

| Tees | Holes | Yards | Par | USGA | Slope |
|------|-------|-------|-----|------|-------|
| BACK | 18 | 6803 | 72 | 72.9 | 129 |
| MIDDLE | 18 | 6425 | 72 | 71.3 | 124 |
| FRONT | 18 | 5379 | 72 | 71.7 | 124 |

**Fee 9 Holes: Weekday:** $22
**Fee 18 Holes: Weekday:** $41
**Twilight Rates:** After 3pm
**Cart Rental:** $19pp/18, $10pp/9
**Lessons:** Yes **Schools:** No
**Membership:** Yes
**Other:** Restaurant / Clubhouse / Lockers / Showers / Bar-Lounge / Function Room / Pro Shop
**GPS:** Yes

**Weekend:** $28
**Weekend:** $52
**Discounts:** Senior & Junior
**Driving Range:** Yes
**Junior Golf:** Yes
**Architect/Yr Open:** Phillp Wogan/1990

Beautiful setting. Numerous water hazards and white sand. Bunkers challenge the best of players, while gentle slopes and wide fairways accommodate the casual golfer.

| | 1 | 2 | 3 | 4 | 5 | 6 | 7 | 8 | 9 |
|---|---|---|---|---|---|---|---|---|---|
| PAR | 4 | 5 | 3 | 5 | 4 | 3 | 4 | 4 | 4 |
| YARDS | 375 | 456 | 190 | 515 | 374 | 164 | 385 | 435 | 416 |
| | 10 | 11 | 12 | 13 | 14 | 15 | 16 | 17 | 18 |
| PAR | 4 | 4 | 3 | 5 | 4 | 4 | 4 | 3 | 5 |
| YARDS | 385 | 300 | 153 | 520 | 355 | 392 | 368 | 138 | 504 |

**Directions:** I-95 North to Exit 54B to Route 97 Georgetown. Follow to Route 133 West. Andover Street is 1.2 miles on the left.

# Bradford Country Club ✪✪✪  5

201 Chadwick Road
Bradford, MA (978) 372-8587
www.bradfordcc.com

| Tees | Holes | Yards | Par | USGA | Slope |
|------|-------|-------|-----|------|-------|
| BACK | 18 | 6077 | 70 | 70.8 | 130 |
| MIDDLE | 18 | 5495 | 70 | 68.2 | 127 |
| FRONT | 18 | 4367 | 70 | 66.5 | 120 |

**Club Pro:** Kevin Murphy
**Payment:** Visa, MC
**Tee Times:** 5 days adv.
**Fee 9 Holes: Weekday:** $19          **Weekend:** $22
**Fee 18 Holes: Weekday:** $37          **Weekend:** $42
**Twilight Rates:** After 4pm          **Discounts:** Senior/Junior
**Cart Rental:** $18pp/18, $10pp/9          **Driving Range:** No
**Lessons:** Yes **Schools:** No          **Junior Golf:** Yes
**Membership:** Yes          **Architect/Yr Open:** Cornish & Silva/1989
**Other:** Clubhouse / Bar-Lounge / Restaurant / Lockers / Outings / Leagues
**GPS:** No

New ownership and management. Open March - November.

| | 1 | 2 | 3 | 4 | 5 | 6 | 7 | 8 | 9 |
|------|---|---|---|---|---|---|---|---|---|
| PAR | 4 | 4 | 3 | 4 | 4 | 3 | 4 | 5 | 4 |
| YARDS | 370 | 326 | 158 | 359 | 364 | 180 | 326 | 488 | 456 |
| | 10 | 11 | 12 | 13 | 14 | 15 | 16 | 17 | 18 |
| PAR | 4 | 3 | 5 | 5 | 3 | 4 | 4 | 4 | 3 |
| YARDS | 327 | 197 | 489 | 440 | 169 | 420 | 393 | 410 | 205 |

**Directions:** I-495 to Exit 48. North on Route 125 to Salem Street. Turn right onto Boxford Road (1st street after Bradford House Restaurant). Take first right on Chadwick Road to Clubhouse.

# Braintree Municipal Golf Course ✪✪✪  6

101 Jefferson Street
Braintree, MA (781) 843-6513
www.braintreegolf.com

| Tees | Holes | Yards | Par | USGA | Slope |
|------|-------|-------|-----|------|-------|
| BACK | 18 | 6554 | 72 | 71.6 | 129 |
| MIDDLE | 18 | 6212 | 72 | 70.5 | 127 |
| FRONT | 18 | 5386 | 72 | 71.0 | 117 |

**Club Pro:** Bob Beach, PGA
**Payment:** Cash, Visa, MC
**Tee Times:** 5 days adv.
**Fee 9 Holes: Weekday:**          **Weekend:**
**Fee 18 Holes: Weekday:** $39          **Weekend:** $49
**Twilight Rates:** After 4pm          **Discounts:** Residents, Seniors, Juniors
**Cart Rental:** $18pp          **Driving Range:** No
**Lessons:** $50/half hour **Schools:** Yes          **Junior Golf:** Yes
**Membership:** $2050/year          **Architect/Yr Open:** Styles & Van Kleek
**Other:** Restaurant / Clubhouse / Snack Bar          **GPS:**

Braintree Municipal now has their own mobile app (free). "An overlooked gem. Generous fairways combine with great sloping greens and excellent conditions. Best value in Greater Boston." –JD

| | 1 | 2 | 3 | 4 | 5 | 6 | 7 | 8 | 9 |
|------|---|---|---|---|---|---|---|---|---|
| PAR | 4 | 4 | 3 | 4 | 3 | 5 | 4 | 5 | 4 |
| YARDS | 335 | 335 | 171 | 302 | 165 | 494 | 383 | 500 | 364 |
| | 10 | 11 | 12 | 13 | 14 | 15 | 16 | 17 | 18 |
| PAR | 5 | 4 | 3 | 5 | 4 | 4 | 3 | 4 | 4 |
| YARDS | 481 | 408 | 172 | 465 | 411 | 391 | 174 | 347 | 314 |

**Directions:** I-93 to Route 3 South to Exit 6. Take Route 37 South for 2 miles. Right on Jefferson Street. Club is on the right.

# Brookmeadow Country Club ✪✪✪ 7

100 Everendon Road
Canton, MA (781) 828-4444
www.brookmeadowgolf.com
**Club Pro:** Ryan MacDonald
**Payment:** Cash, Visa, MC, Amex, Disc
**Tee Times:** 14 days adv.

| Tees | Holes | Yards | Par | USGA | Slope |
|------|-------|-------|-----|------|-------|
| BACK | 18 | 6585 | 36 | 71.7 | 123 |
| MIDDLE | 18 | 6239 | 36 | 70.1 | 118 |
| FRONT | 18 | 5156 | 36 | 71.2 | 114 |

**Fee 9 Holes: Weekday:** $25      **Weekend:** $25
**Fee 18 Holes: Weekday:** $40      **Weekend:** $56
**Twilight Rates:** After 6pm      **Discounts:** Senior & Junior
**Cart Rental:** $16pp/18, $9pp/9      **Driving Range:** Yes
**Lessons:** Call for rates  **Schools:** No      **Junior Golf:** Yes
**Membership:** Yes      **Architect/Yr Open:** Frank Simoni/1966
**Other:** Clubhouse / Lockers / Showers / Snack Bar / Bar-Lounge / Function Room

Brookmeadow is easy to walk and offers an interesting and challenging golf experience to all skill levels. You won't find a better value on the South Shore.

| | 1 | 2 | 3 | 4 | 5 | 6 | 7 | 8 | 9 |
|------|---|---|---|---|---|---|---|---|---|
| PAR | 4 | 4 | 4 | 3 | 4 | 3 | 4 | 5 | 5 |
| YARDS | 376 | 387 | 308 | 163 | 346 | 151 | 385 | 484 | 522 |
| | 10 | 11 | 12 | 13 | 14 | 15 | 16 | 17 | 18 |
| PAR | 4 | 3 | 5 | 4 | 4 | 3 | 5 | 4 | 4 |
| YARDS | 348 | 179 | 464 | 351 | 358 | 192 | 530 | 351 | 404 |

**Directions:** I-95 to Exit 11A (Neponset Street in Canton). Go 1 mile and take a right before the viaduct (stone bridge) onto Walpole Street. Club is 1 mile on right.

# Bungay Brook Golf Club ✪✪½ 8

30 Locust Street
Bellingham, MA (508) 883-1600
www.bungaybrook.com
**Club Pro:** Jim Cook, PGA, Teaching Pro
**Payment:** Visa, MC, Amex
**Tee Times:** 2 weeks adv.

| Tees | Holes | Yards | Par | USGA | Slope |
|------|-------|-------|-----|------|-------|
| BACK | 9 | 3136 | 36 | 70.2 | 120 |
| MIDDLE | 9 | 2885 | 36 | 69.2 | 113 |
| FRONT | 9 | 2314 | 36 | 66.8 | 110 |

**Fee 9 Holes: Weekday:** $21 before noon/$27 after noon
           **Weekend:** $28 F/S/S
**Fee 18 Holes: Weekday:** $42 before noon/$46 after noon
           **Weekend:** $52 F/S/S
**Twilight Rates:** No      **Discounts:** Senior & Junior
**Cart Rental:** $6pp/9      **Driving Range:** Yes
**Lessons:** Yes  **Schools:**      **Junior Golf:**
**Membership:** No      **Architect/Yr Open:** Howard Maurer/2002
**Other:** Restaurant / Bar-Lounge      **GPS:**

COUPON

Fine conditions, fast greens, fast pace. All-grass driving range. Worth a visit.

| | 1 | 2 | 3 | 4 | 5 | 6 | 7 | 8 | 9 |
|------|---|---|---|---|---|---|---|---|---|
| PAR | 4 | 3 | 4 | 5 | 3 | 4 | 5 | 4 | 4 |
| YARDS | 278 | 153 | 313 | 450 | 107 | 421 | 434 | 393 | 336 |
| PAR | | | | | | | | | |
| YARDS | | | | | | | | | |

**Directions:** I-495 to Exit 16. 4 miles to Bellingham town line. Take first left on Locust Street; ½ mile to course.

# Butter Brook Golf Club ✪✪✪✪✪  ▶9

**157 Carlisle Road**
**Westford, MA (978) 692-6560**
**www.butterbrookgc.com**

| Tees | Holes | Yards | Par | USGA | Slope |
|------|-------|-------|-----|------|-------|
| BACK | 18 | 6766 | 72 | 72.6 | 133 |
| MIDDLE | 18 | 6174 | 72 | 70.4 | 128 |
| FRONT | 18 | 4849 | 72 | 69.4 | 120 |

**Club Pro:** Peter Maki, PGA
**Payment:** Visa, MC, Amex, Disc, Cash
**Tee Times:** 7 days adv.
**Fee 9 Holes: Weekday:** $35    **Weekend:** After 3pm
**Fee 18 Holes: Weekday:** $50    **Weekend:** $85 w/cart
**Twilight Rates:** $75 w/cart wknds after 2pm    **Discounts:** Senior - $50 with cart M-Th
**Cart Rental:** $20pp/18, $10pp/9    **Driving Range:** Yes
**Lessons:** Yes **Schools:** Yes    **Junior Golf:** Yes
**Membership:** Yes    **Architect/Yr Open:** Mark Mungeam/2002
**Other:** Bar-Lounge    **GPS:**

"Family-owned and operated with great pride. Challenging track with wonderful variety." –JD
180 acres of serene rolling hills, tall pine trees, beautiful ponds, and a babbling brook. 18 holes.
Voted one of the 100 Must Play Courses in New England. Phenomenal conditions.

| | 1 | 2 | 3 | 4 | 5 | 6 | 7 | 8 | 9 |
|------|---|---|---|---|---|---|---|---|---|
| PAR | 5 | 4 | 3 | 4 | 3 | 4 | 5 | 3 | 5 |
| YARDS | 507 | 293 | 123 | 396 | 132 | 401 | 492 | 157 | 551 |
| | 10 | 11 | 12 | 13 | 14 | 15 | 16 | 17 | 18 |
| PAR | 4 | 3 | 5 | 4 | 3 | 4 | 5 | 4 | 4 |
| YARDS | 374 | 195 | 501 | 370 | 175 | 377 | 475 | 394 | 322 |

**Directions:** I-495 Exit 32 Boston Road toward Route 225/Westford. Proceed toward Route 110
(.3 miles). Cross over Route 110. Follow for 1.2 miles to end of road. Left onto Route 225 East for
1.2 miles. Entrance on right.

# Butternut Farm Golf Club ✪✪✪  ▶10

**115 Wheeler Road**
**Stow, MA (978) 897-3400**
**www.butternutfarm.com**

| Tees | Holes | Yards | Par | USGA | Slope |
|------|-------|-------|-----|------|-------|
| BACK | 18 | 6302 | 70 | 71.2 | 130 |
| MIDDLE | 18 | 5755 | 70 | 69.3 | 126 |
| FRONT | 18 | 4778 | 70 | 67.6 | 117 |

**Club Pro:** Cole Page
**Payment:** Mastercard, Visa, Cash
**Tee Times:** 7 days adv.
**Fee 9 Holes: Weekday:** $30    **Weekend:**
**Fee 18 Holes: Weekday:** $42    **Weekend:** $54
**Twilight Rates:** $42 after 1pm, $32 after 2pm    **Discounts:** Senior
**Cart Rental:** $20pp/18, $12pp/9    **Driving Range:** No
**Lessons:** No **Schools:** No    **Junior Golf:** No
**Membership:** Yes    **Architect/Yr Open:** Robert Page III/1993
**Other:** Clubhouse / Restaurant / Bar-Lounge / Snack Bar / Lockers / Function Rooms

Player comments: "Great shape. Greens are lush. Challenging, fair—but choose the right tees—or else."
Brand new clubhouse. Carolina-type fairways, real tight, bent grass on fairways and tees, tall trees. Four
function rooms.

| | 1 | 2 | 3 | 4 | 5 | 6 | 7 | 8 | 9 |
|------|---|---|---|---|---|---|---|---|---|
| PAR | 4 | 3 | 4 | 3 | 4 | 4 | 5 | 4 | 5 |
| YARDS | 314 | 155 | 375 | 150 | 403 | 383 | 434 | 268 | 452 |
| | 10 | 11 | 12 | 13 | 14 | 15 | 16 | 17 | 18 |
| PAR | 5 | 3 | 4 | 3 | 4 | 4 | 3 | 4 | 4 |
| YARDS | 600 | 128 | 351 | 190 | 364 | 325 | 173 | 340 | 350 |

**Directions:** I-495 to Exit 27. Take Route 117 East for approximately 4 miles. Take right onto Wheeler
Road. Or, Route 2 West to Route 62 West. Follow through Stow center to 1st set of lights. Take left.
2nd right is Wheeler Road.

# Candlewood Golf Course ✪ ▶ 11

**75 Essex Road (Route 133)**
**Ipswich, MA  (978) 356-5377**
www.candlewoodgolf.net

| Tees | Holes | Yards | Par | USGA | Slope |
|------|-------|-------|-----|------|-------|
| BACK | | | | | |
| MIDDLE | 9 | 2108 | 32 | | |
| FRONT | | | | | |

**Club Pro:**
**Payment:** Cash Only
**Tee Times:** No
**Fee  9 Holes: Weekday:** $16        **Weekend:** $17
**Fee 18 Holes: Weekday:** $21        **Weekend:** $23
**Twilight Rates:** $11 after 5pm      **Discounts:** Senior
**Cart Rental:** $20pp/18, $12pp/9    **Driving Range:** No
**Lessons:   Schools:** No             **Junior Golf:** No
**Membership:** Yes                    **Architect/Yr Open:**
**Other:** Snack Bar                   **GPS:**

Course is easy to walk and good for senior citizens and beginners. Monday-Friday Senior Citizens play for $10. "Short but fun" –FP

| | 1 | 2 | 3 | 4 | 5 | 6 | 7 | 8 | 9 |
|------|------|------|------|------|------|------|------|------|------|
| PAR | 4 | 4 | 3 | 3 | 3 | 4 | 4 | 4 | 3 |
| YARDS | 350 | 350 | 120 | 140 | 135 | 253 | 290 | 280 | 190 |
| PAR | | | | | | | | | |
| YARDS | | | | | | | | | |

**Directions:** I-95/Route 128 to Route 1A to Route 133 in Ipswich. Turn right at hospital on Route 133.

# Cape Ann Golf Club ✪✪ ▶ 12

**99 John Wilse Avenue (Route 133)**
**Essex, MA  (978) 768-7544**
www.capeanngolf.com

| Tees | Holes | Yards | Par | USGA | Slope |
|------|-------|-------|-----|------|-------|
| BACK | 9 | 3036 | 35 | 68.3 | 119 |
| MIDDLE | 9 | 2826 | 34 | 68.3 | 119 |
| FRONT | 9 | 2212 | 34 | 65.2 | 113 |

**Club Pro:** Jim Stavros, Club Manager
**Payment:** Cash or Credit
**Tee Times:** Yes
**Fee  9 Holes: Weekday:** $25        **Weekend:** $25
**Fee 18 Holes: Weekday:** $38        **Weekend:** $38
**Twilight Rates:** yes                **Discounts:**
**Cart Rental:** $17pp/18, $11pp/9    **Driving Range:** No
**Lessons:** No **Schools:** No        **Junior Golf:** No
**Membership:**                        **Architect/Yr Open:** Donald Ross/1931
**Other:** Bar-Lounge / Snack Bar      **GPS:**

Recent improvements include irrigation, putting green and new tee boxes. "Great views of the Crane's Beach area." –FP

| | 1 | 2 | 3 | 4 | 5 | 6 | 7 | 8 | 9 |
|------|------|------|------|------|------|------|------|------|------|
| PAR | 4 | 4 | 3 | 4 | 4 | 4 | 3 | 4 | 4 |
| YARDS | 342 | 364 | 169 | 414 | 336 | 278 | 197 | 385 | 341 |
| PAR | | | | | | | | | |
| YARDS | | | | | | | | | |

**Directions:** I-95/Route 128 to Exit 15 (School Street); follow signs toward Essex. Go north on Route 133. Course is 2 miles up on the right.

# Cedar Glen Golf Club   ✪½  ▶ 13

60 Water Street
Saugus, MA (781) 233-3609
www.cedarglengolf.com

**Club Pro:**
**Payment:** Cash Only (ATM on premises)
**Tee Times:** No
**Fee 9 Holes: Weekday:** $21
**Fee 18 Holes: Weekday:** $35
**Twilight Rates:** No
**Cart Rental:** $9pp/9
**Lessons:** No **Schools:** Yes
**Membership:** No
**Other:** Clubhouse / Snack Bar

| Tees | Holes | Yards | Par | USGA | Slope |
|------|-------|-------|-----|------|-------|
| BACK | 9 | 2874 | 35 | 71.7 | 114 |
| MIDDLE | 9 | 2731 | 35 | 67.0 | 107 |
| FRONT | 9 | 2185 | 35 | 67.0 | 107 |

**Weekend:** $23
**Weekend:** $38
**Discounts:** Sr. & Jr - $17 wkdays
**Driving Range:** No
**Junior Golf:** No
**Architect/Yr Open:**
**GPS:**

New watering system. New tees. Friendly fun course; lots of regulars.

|        | 1 | 2 | 3 | 4 | 5 | 6 | 7 | 8 | 9 |
|--------|-----|-----|-----|-----|-----|-----|-----|-----|-----|
| PAR | 4 | 5 | 3 | 4 | 4 | 3 | 4 | 4 | 4 |
| YARDS | 340 | 484 | 233 | 320 | 366 | 136 | 299 | 340 | 356 |

|        | | | | | | | | | |
|--------|-----|-----|-----|-----|-----|-----|-----|-----|-----|
| PAR | | | | | | | | | |
| YARDS | | | | | | | | | |

**Directions:** Take I-95 to Walnut Street. Follow Walnut Street east to Water Street. Take right, course is on left.

# Cedar Hill Golf Course   NR  ▶ 14

1137 Park Street
Stoughton, MA (781) 344-8913
www.cedarhill-stoughton.com

**Club Pro:** Victor Barruzza, Manager
**Payment:** Cash, Visa, MC, Disc
**Tee Times:** No
**Fee 9 Holes: Weekday:** $18
**Fee 18 Holes: Weekday:** $23
**Twilight Rates:** No
**Cart Rental:** $12pp/18, $8pp/9
**Lessons:** Yes **Schools:** No
**Membership:** Yes
**Other:** Snack Bar / Bar-Lounge / Clubhouse

| Tees | Holes | Yards | Par | USGA | Slope |
|------|-------|-------|-----|------|-------|
| BACK | | | | | |
| MIDDLE | 9 | 2208 | 33 | 61.2 | 105 |
| FRONT | 9 | 2155 | 33 | 61.2 | 105 |

**Weekend:** $21
**Weekend:** $26
**Discounts:** Senior & Junior
**Driving Range:** No
**Junior Golf:** Yes
**Architect/Yr Open:**
**GPS:**

A place to come play a quick enjoyable round especially for ladies and seniors. Get a frequent player card, play 9 rounds and get the 10th free.

|        | 1 | 2 | 3 | 4 | 5 | 6 | 7 | 8 | 9 |
|--------|-----|-----|-----|-----|-----|-----|-----|-----|-----|
| PAR | 4 | 4 | 4 | 4 | 3 | 4 | 3 | 3 | 4 |
| YARDS | 258 | 302 | 286 | 268 | 120 | 324 | 140 | 176 | 281 |

|        | | | | | | | | | |
|--------|-----|-----|-----|-----|-----|-----|-----|-----|-----|
| PAR | | | | | | | | | |
| YARDS | | | | | | | | | |

**Directions:** Route 24, Exit 18B, turn onto Route 27. Course is on left.

# Chelmsford Country Club

★½  15 ►

66 Park Road
Chelmsford, MA  (978) 256-1818
www.sterlinggolf.com

| Tees | Holes | Yards | Par | USGA | Slope |
|------|-------|-------|-----|------|-------|
| BACK | 9 | 2467 | 33 | 64.2 | 103 |
| MIDDLE | 9 | 2368 | 33 | 64.2 | 108 |
| FRONT | 9 | 2202 | 34 | 66.1 | 107 |

**Club Pro:** Gary Burke
**Payment:** Visa, MC, Amex, Disc, Cash
**Tee Times:** 4 days adv.
**Fee  9 Holes: Weekday:** $19
**Fee 18 Holes: Weekday:** $26
**Twilight Rates:** Weekends only
**Cart Rental:** $16pp/18, $10pp/9
**Lessons:** Yes  **Schools:** Yes
**Membership:** Yes
**Other:** Snack Bar / Bar-Lounge / Function Hall

**Weekend:** $22
**Weekend:** $30
**Discounts:** Senior & Junior
**Driving Range:** Yes
**Junior Golf:** Yes
**Architect/Yr Open:** 1954; C. Fitzgerald/1962
**GPS:**

COUPON

First tee redesigned. A fun golf course for all playing levels. Overall enhanced conditions. Managed by Sterling Golf Management, Inc. Beginner-friendly course. Bar and lounge. "Helpful hints on the stone markers." –FP

|  | 1 | 2 | 3 | 4 | 5 | 6 | 7 | 8 | 9 |
|---|---|---|---|---|---|---|---|---|---|
| PAR | 4 | 3 | 3 | 5 | 4 | 3 | 4 | 4 | 3 |
| YARDS | 237 | 196 | 140 | 453 | 352 | 120 | 318 | 415 | 196 |
| PAR | | | | | | | | | |
| YARDS | | | | | | | | | |

**Directions:** I-495 to Route 110 to Chelmsford Center. Then take Route 27 South. Take left onto Park Road. Course is 200 yards on left.

# Country Club of Billerica

●●  16 ►

51 Baldwin Road
Billerica, MA
(978) 667-9121 ext. 22
www.countryclubofbillerica.com

| Tees | Holes | Yards | Par | USGA | Slope |
|------|-------|-------|-----|------|-------|
| BACK | 18 | 5798 | 69 | 67.9 | 123 |
| MIDDLE | 18 | 5501 | 69 | 66.4 | 119 |
| FRONT | 18 | 4515 | 69 | 66.5 | 115 |

**Club Pro:** Steve Miller
**Payment:** Cash, Visa, MC, Disc
**Tee Times:** 5 days adv.
**Fee  9 Holes: Weekday:** $22
**Fee 18 Holes: Weekday:** $34
**Twilight Rates:** After 6pm
**Cart Rental:** $17pp/18, $11pp/9
**Lessons:** $45/half hour  **Schools:** Yes
**Membership:** Yes
**Other:** Restaurant / Bar-Lounge / Clubhouse

**Weekend:** $24
**Weekend:** $39
**Discounts:** None
**Driving Range:** $9 large, $7 small
**Junior Golf:** Yes
**Architect/Yr Open:** Phil Wogan/1971
**GPS:**

COUPON

Challenging and affordable for all. Picturesque layout between tall trees. Easy walk. Great 19th hole.

|  | 1 | 2 | 3 | 4 | 5 | 6 | 7 | 8 | 9 |
|---|---|---|---|---|---|---|---|---|---|
| PAR | 5 | 3 | 4 | 5 | 3 | 4 | 3 | 3 | 4 |
| YARDS | 465 | 160 | 371 | 490 | 115 | 376 | 147 | 138 | 392 |
|  | 10 | 11 | 12 | 13 | 14 | 15 | 16 | 17 | 18 |
| PAR | 4 | 4 | 4 | 3 | 4 | 4 | 3 | 5 | 4 |
| YARDS | 296 | 360 | 234 | 153 | 349 | 294 | 190 | 552 | 382 |

**Directions:** I-95/Route 128 to Route 3A North. Take Route 3A North into Billerica Center. Take right before Friendly's restaurant and at the end of the road, take a right and then the third left onto Baldwin Street. Course is on right.

# Crosswinds Golf Club ✪✪✪✪  17

424 Long Pond Road
Plymouth, MA (508) 830-1199
www.golfcrosswinds.com

| Tees | Holes | Yards | Par | USGA | Slope |
|---|---|---|---|---|---|
| BACK | 27/18 | 6528 | 72 | 72.1 | 133 |
| MIDDLE | 27/18 | 6036 | 72 | 70.2 | 129 |
| FRONT | 27/18 | 5371 | 72 | 71.7 | 126 |

**Club Pro:** Dan Neary, PGA
**Payment:** Visa, MC, Amex
**Tee Times:** 7 days adv.
**Fee 9 Holes: Weekday:** $30 M-Th    **Weekend:** $35 F/S/S/H
**Fee 18 Holes: Weekday:** $50 M-Th    **Weekend:** $70 F/S/S/H
**Twilight Rates:** No    **Discounts:**
**Cart Rental:** Included    **Driving Range:** $9 large, $5 small
**Lessons:** Yes **Schools:** Yes    **Junior Golf:** Yes
**Membership:** Yes    **Architect/Yr Open:** Hurdzan/Fry/2002
**Other:** Full Service Clubhouse / All Turf Range / Short Game Practice Area / Bar-Lounge

COUPON

New clubhouse on site with full banquet facilities. Excellent for corporate outings.
Player comments: "Maturing nicely. New superintendent has brought quality way up. "Definitely an upgrade from its first seasons." –JD

**Jones/Ouimet**

|  | 1 | 2 | 3 | 4 | 5 | 6 | 7 | 8 | 9 |
|---|---|---|---|---|---|---|---|---|---|
| PAR | 5 | 4 | 4 | 4 | 5 | 3 | 4 | 3 | 4 |
| YARDS | 490 | 355 | 317 | 326 | 491 | 141 | 340 | 162 | 360 |
|  | 10 | 11 | 12 | 13 | 14 | 15 | 16 | 17 | 18 |
| PAR | 4 | 3 | 4 | 5 | 5 | 4 | 4 | 3 | 4 |
| YARDS | 370 | 138 | 376 | 475 | 471 | 398 | 296 | 164 | 366 |

**Directions:** Route 3 to Exit 5. Right off exit onto Long Pond Road. Follow Long Pond Road 4 miles. Crosswinds Golf Club entrance on left.

# Crystal Lake Golf Club ✪✪½ 18

940 North Broadway
Haverhill, MA (978) 374-9621
www.golfcrystallake.com

| Tees | Holes | Yards | Par | USGA | Slope |
|---|---|---|---|---|---|
| BACK | 18 | 6504 | 72 | 72.4 | 129 |
| MIDDLE | 18 | 6280 | 72 | 71.0 | 126 |
| FRONT | 18 | 5399 | 73 | 70.9 | 120 |

**Club Pro:** Peter Vlahos, PGA
**Payment:** Visa, MC, Disc, Cash
**Tee Times:** Weekends 7 days adv.
**Fee 9 Holes: Weekday:** $19    **Weekend:** $20
**Fee 18 Holes: Weekday:** $28    **Weekend:** $37
**Twilight Rates:** No    **Discounts:** Junior/Senior
**Cart Rental:** $18pp/18, $10pp/9    **Driving Range:** No
**Lessons:** Yes **Schools:** No    **Junior Golf:** Yes
**Membership:** Yes    **Architect/Yr Open:** Geoffrey Cornish/1961
**Other:** Snack Bar / Restaurant / Bar-Lounge    **GPS:**

Under new ownership in 2010.

|  | 1 | 2 | 3 | 4 | 5 | 6 | 7 | 8 | 9 |
|---|---|---|---|---|---|---|---|---|---|
| PAR | 4 | 3 | 4 | 4 | 5 | 3 | 4 | 5 | 4 |
| YARDS | 377 | 228 | 385 | 380 | 498 | 224 | 361 | 495 | 429 |
|  | 10 | 11 | 12 | 13 | 14 | 15 | 16 | 17 | 18 |
| PAR | 4 | 5 | 4 | 3 | 4 | 4 | 3 | 4 | 5 |
| YARDS | 410 | 500 | 372 | 182 | 350 | 321 | 135 | 442 | 455 |

**Directions:** I-495 to Exit 50 (Route 97). At end of ramp, go across Route 97 to monument, and turn left at the blinking red light. Course is 2.5 miles on left. From the north: take Exit 50 (Route 97), left at end of ramp, left at lights.

# D.W. Field Golf Course ★★½ 19 ▶

331 Oak Street
Brockton, MA (508) 580-7855
www.dwfieldgolfcourse.com

**Club Pro:** Brian Mattos, PGA
**Payment:** Visa, MC
**Tee Times:** 7 days adv.

| Tees | Holes | Yards | Par | USGA | Slope |
|------|-------|-------|-----|------|-------|
| BACK | 18 | 5972 | 70 | 68.4 | 120 |
| MIDDLE | 18 | 5630 | 70 | 66.9 | 116 |
| FRONT | 18 | 5370 | 70 | 70.1 | 111 |

**Fee 9 Holes: Weekday:** None
**Fee 18 Holes: Weekday:** $27 (M-Th)
**Twilight Rates:** After 4pm
**Cart Rental:** $16pp
**Lessons:** $30/30 min. **Schools:** No
**Membership:** Yes
**Other:** Snack Bar / Clubhouse

**Weekend:** None
**Weekend:** $32
**Discounts:** Senior
**Driving Range:** No
**Junior Golf:** Yes
**Architect/Yr Open:** Stiles & Van Kleek/1927

Considered an easy walker. Open year round. Rates could change. New dress code.

| | 1 | 2 | 3 | 4 | 5 | 6 | 7 | 8 | 9 |
|------|---|---|---|---|---|---|---|---|---|
| PAR | 4 | 5 | 5 | 4 | 3 | 4 | 4 | 3 | 4 |
| YARDS | 305 | 485 | 485 | 300 | 165 | 340 | 335 | 135 | 355 |
| | 10 | 11 | 12 | 13 | 14 | 15 | 16 | 17 | 18 |
| PAR | 4 | 4 | 4 | 4 | 3 | 4 | 4 | 3 | 4 |
| YARDS | 315 | 340 | 360 | 405 | 125 | 300 | 345 | 175 | 360 |

**Directions:** Route 24 to Exit 18B, 3 sets of lights and take a right onto Oak Street. Course is 1.5 miles on the left.

# Easton Country Club ★★½ 20 ▶

265 Purchase Street
South Easton, MA (508) 238-2500
www.eastoncountryclub.com

**Club Pro:** Rob Citrano
**Payment:** Visa, MC, Amex, Disc
**Tee Times:** 6 days adv. online

| Tees | Holes | Yards | Par | USGA | Slope |
|------|-------|-------|-----|------|-------|
| BACK | 18 | 6497 | 71 | 71.6 | 124 |
| MIDDLE | 18 | 6216 | 71 | 69.8 | 121 |
| FRONT | 18 | 5042 | 71 | 65.5 | 115 |

**Fee 9 Holes: Weekday:** $28 after 12pm
**Fee 18 Holes: Weekday:** $39 (M-Th)
**Twilight Rates:** After 3:30pm
**Cart Rental:** $17pp/18, $13pp/9
**Lessons:** $45/45 min. **Schools:** Yes
**Membership:** Full, Weekday, Junior
**Other:** Restaurant / Clubhouse / Lockers / Showers / Snack Bar / Bar-Lounge / Function Room

**Weekend:** No
**Weekend:** $45
**Discounts:** Senior & Junior M-Th
**Driving Range:** Yes - $5/bucket
**Junior Golf:** Yes
**Architect/Yr Open:** Sam Mitchell/1961

COUPON

New champion tees challenges the better golfers. New Senior/Junior tees offers playability for all levels. "Friendly staff and pro, well run inner club." –FP

| | 1 | 2 | 3 | 4 | 5 | 6 | 7 | 8 | 9 |
|------|---|---|---|---|---|---|---|---|---|
| PAR | 4 | 5 | 4 | 3 | 4 | 3 | 4 | 4 | 5 |
| YARDS | 436 | 483 | 281 | 155 | 387 | 164 | 418 | 315 | 491 |
| | 10 | 11 | 12 | 13 | 14 | 15 | 16 | 17 | 18 |
| PAR | 4 | 4 | 4 | 5 | 4 | 3 | 4 | 4 | 4 |
| YARDS | 338 | 358 | 345 | 525 | 164 | 365 | 165 | 422 | 423 |

**Directions:** Take Route 24 South to Exit 17B. Take Route 123 West to Route 138 South to Purchase Street on right (approx. 2 miles). Take a right onto Purchase Street; course is 7/10 mile on left.

# Evergreen Valley Golf Course  ✪  21 ▶

**18 Boyd Drive**
**Newburyport, MA  (978) 463-8600**
www.evergreenvalleygolf.com

| Tees | Holes | Yards | Par | USGA | Slope |
|------|-------|-------|-----|------|-------|
| BACK | 9 | 2997 | 35 | 67.4 | 108 |
| MIDDLE | 9 | 2902 | 35 | 67.4 | 108 |
| FRONT | 9 | 2631 | 35 | 67.4 | 108 |

**Club Pro:** Donna Koen
**Payment:** Cash, Check
**Tee Times:** No
**Fee  9 Holes: Weekday:** $12  **Weekend:** $10-$14
**Fee 18 Holes: Weekday:** $24  **Weekend:** $20-$25
**Twilight Rates:** No  **Discounts:** Call ahead for info
**Cart Rental:** $25/18, $14/9 per cart, $3/pull  **Driving Range:** No
**Lessons:** Yes  **Schools:** No  **Junior Golf:** No
**Membership:** Yes  **Architect/Yr Open:** Francis Vitale Sr.
**Other:** Snack Bar and Deck  **GPS:**

Located in historic Newburyport, MA. 9 holes, 2 sets of tees. Open April - November. Drainage improvements. "Nice layout and affordable." —GM

| | 1 | 2 | 3 | 4 | 5 | 6 | 7 | 8 | 9 |
|-----|-----|-----|-----|-----|-----|-----|-----|-----|-----|
| PAR | 4 | 4 | 4 | 5 | 3 | 4 | 4 | 3 | 4 |
| YARDS | 370 | 300 | 420 | 460 | 155 | 390 | 305 | 165 | 215 |
| PAR | | | | | | | | | |
| YARDS | | | | | | | | | |

**Directions:** I-95 to Exit 57. Go east. Take left on Noble Road (across from Papa Gino's), then left at stop sign. Entrance to club is 300 feet on left.

# Far Corner Golf Course  ✪✪✪½  22 ▶

**5 Barker Road**
**West Boxford, MA  (978) 352-8300**
www.farcornergolf.com

| Tees | Holes | Yards | Par | USGA | Slope |
|------|-------|-------|-----|------|-------|
| BACK | 27/18 | 6719 | 72 | 72.9 | 130 |
| MIDDLE | 27/18 | 6189 | 72 | 70.9 | 126 |
| FRONT | 27/18 | 5655 | 73 | 71.4 | 115 |

**Club Pro:** John O'Connor, PGA
   Bob Flynn, PGA, Dir. of Golf
**Payment:** Cash, MC, Visa
**Tee Times:** 7 days adv.
**Fee  9 Holes: Weekday:** $21.50  **Weekend:** $24
**Fee 18 Holes: Weekday:** $41  **Weekend:** $46
**Twilight Rates:** After 4pm weekends  **Discounts:** Senior & Junior
**Cart Rental:** $16pp/18, $8pp/9  **Driving Range:** All grass
**Lessons:** $50/half hour, $270/6 lessons  **Junior Golf:** Yes
**Membership:** No  **Schools:** Yes  **Architect/Yr Open:** Geoffrey Cornish/1967
**Other:** Snack Bar / Restaurant / Bar-Lounge / Clubhouse / Showers

A classic on the North Shore. Terrific, friendly staff. 27 holes - 3rd nine: Yardage: 3092, Championship Par: 36, Slope: 131. Enlarged driving range. Open year round.

**Fox/Heron**

| | 1 | 2 | 3 | 4 | 5 | 6 | 7 | 8 | 9 |
|-----|-----|-----|-----|-----|-----|-----|-----|-----|-----|
| PAR | 5 | 4 | 4 | 3 | 4 | 4 | 3 | 4 | 5 |
| YARDS | 510 | 350 | 310 | 190 | 460 | 330 | 170 | 390 | 450 |
| | 10 | 11 | 12 | 13 | 14 | 15 | 16 | 17 | 18 |
| PAR | 4 | 5 | 4 | 5 | 4 | 3 | 4 | 3 | 4 |
| YARDS | 270 | 470 | 360 | 530 | 380 | 170 | 320 | 135 | 390 |

**Directions:** I-95 North, to Exit 53B to Route 97 Georgetown. Follow to Route 133 West, to West Boxford Village. Go right onto Main Street. Course is 2 miles on left.

# Fore Kicks GC & Sports Complex    NR  23 ▶

10 Pine Street
Norfolk, MA (508) 384-4433
www.forekicks.com
**Club Pro:** C. Estes, J. Marston
**Payment:** Cash, Credit
**Tee Times:** Yes

| Tees | Holes | Yards | Par | USGA | Slope |
|------|-------|-------|-----|------|-------|
| BACK | | | | | |
| MIDDLE | 9 | 1003 | 27 | | |
| FRONT | | | | | |

**Fee 9 Holes: Weekday:** $12/day, $15/night  **Weekend:** $15 S/S
**Fee 18 Holes: Weekday:** $17/day, $20/night  **Weekend:** $20 S/S
**Twilight Rates:** No                **Discounts:** Senior & Junior
**Cart Rental:** $3pp/pull             **Driving Range:** Indoors
**Lessons:** Yes  **Schools:** Yes      **Junior Golf:** Yes
**Membership:** Yes                   **Architect/Yr Open:** Brian Silva/2002
**Other:** Lounge / Indoor Soccer / Basketball Courts / Pro Shop / Putting Course /
Fully Lighted Golf Course to 10pm

COUPON

Links-style. Lighted for night play. Features an indoor air-conditioned driving range. "Impressive multi-sport complex." –AP

| | 1 | 2 | 3 | 4 | 5 | 6 | 7 | 8 | 9 |
|------|-----|-----|-----|-----|-----|-----|-----|-----|-----|
| PAR | 3 | 3 | 3 | 3 | 3 | 3 | 3 | 3 | 3 |
| YARDS | 115 | 112 | 81 | 78 | 118 | 93 | 122 | 127 | 157 |
| PAR | | | | | | | | | |
| YARDS | | | | | | | | | |

**Directions:** I-495 to Route 1 North to Pine Street Exit in Foxboro. Right-hand turn after exiting Route 1 onto Pine Street. Course is 2 miles down on left.

# Four Oaks Country Club    ✪✪✪  24 ▶

1 Clubhouse Lane
Dracut, MA (978) 455-0054
www.fouroakscountryclub.com
**Club Pro:** Anthony Martinho, PGA
**Payment:** Cash, Visa, MC, Amex, Disc
**Tee Times:** 6 days adv.

| Tees | Holes | Yards | Par | USGA | Slope |
|------|-------|-------|-----|------|-------|
| BACK | 18 | 6268 | 70 | 71.4 | 136 |
| MIDDLE | 18 | 5789 | 70 | 68.8 | 129 |
| FRONT | 18 | 4348 | 70 | 65.5 | 118 |

**Fee 9 Holes: Weekday:** $22           **Weekend:** $26
**Fee 18 Holes: Weekday:** $40          **Weekend:** $50
**Twilight Rates:** After 2pm          **Discounts:** Senior & Junior
**Cart Rental:** $19pp/18, $10pp/9      **Driving Range:** No
**Lessons:** $60/40 min.  **Schools:** No   **Junior Golf:** Yes
**Membership:** Yes                    **Architect/Yr Open:** Jeffrey Brem/2006
**Other:** Restaurant / Showers / Snack Bar / Bar-Lounge / Function Room
**GPS:** Yes

"Consistently challenging hole-by-hole. Several huge greens with lots of undulation make approach shots critical. Front 9 is wide open, back 9 gets tighter. A great day of golf for any level of player." –JD

| | 1 | 2 | 3 | 4 | 5 | 6 | 7 | 8 | 9 |
|------|-----|-----|-----|-----|-----|-----|-----|-----|-----|
| PAR | 4 | 5 | 4 | 3 | 5 | 4 | 4 | 4 | 3 |
| YARDS | 327 | 478 | 335 | 132 | 468 | 357 | 360 | 364 | 160 |
| | 10 | 11 | 12 | 13 | 14 | 15 | 16 | 17 | 18 |
| PAR | 4 | 4 | 3 | 4 | 4 | 3 | 4 | 4 | 4 |
| YARDS | 400 | 356 | 182 | 305 | 374 | 139 | 320 | 342 | 390 |

**Directions:** I-93 to Route 113 West. Go 5 miles to Meadow Creek Drive.

# Foxborough Country Club ✪✪✪½  25

33 Walnut Street
Foxborough, MA
(508) 543-4661 ext. 3
www.foxboroughcc.com

| Tees | Holes | Yards | Par | USGA | Slope |
|------|-------|-------|-----|------|-------|
| BACK | 18 | 6849 | 72 | 73.9 | 134 |
| MIDDLE | 18 | 6607 | 72 | 72.7 | 130 |
| FRONT | 18 | 5627 | 73 | 73.6 | 127 |

**Club Pro:** Louis Rivers, PGA
**Payment:** Visa, MC, Amex, Disc
**Tee Times:** Call ahead for availability
**Fee 9 Holes: Weekday:** **Weekend:**
**Fee 18 Holes: Weekday:** $60 **Weekend:** $60
**Twilight Rates:** After 4pm **Discounts:** Jr. (up to 18yrs) $15pp/18
**Cart Rental:** $20pp/18, $10pp/9 **Driving Range:** Yes
**Lessons:** $50/half hour **Schools:** No **Junior Golf:** Yes
**Membership:** Full, Limited, Intermediate, Jr. **Architect/Yr Open:** Geoffrey Cornish/1955
**Other:** Restaurant / Bar- Lounge / Clubhouse / Showers

c o U P O N

Be sure to call for tee times. Improved drainage systems. Dress code. Semi-private. No public play
May 1-October 15 on weekends and holidays. Player Comments: "Excellent golf course, tough but fair.
Challenging from whichever tees you select. Great greens." –GG

| | 1 | 2 | 3 | 4 | 5 | 6 | 7 | 8 | 9 |
|---|---|---|---|---|---|---|---|---|---|
| PAR | 4 | 4 | 3 | 5 | 4 | 3 | 4 | 4 | 5 |
| YARDS | 396 | 397 | 199 | 507 | 330 | 186 | 334 | 437 | 529 |
| | 10 | 11 | 12 | 13 | 14 | 15 | 16 | 17 | 18 |
| PAR | 4 | 5 | 3 | 4 | 4 | 4 | 4 | 3 | 5 |
| YARDS | 405 | 555 | 169 | 326 | 330 | 409 | 429 | 157 | 502 |

**Directions:** I-95 to Exit 7B (140 North) towards Foxborough. Take first left onto Walnut Street.
Club will be on left after stop sign.

# Fresh Pond Golf Club ✪✪½ 26

691 Huron Avenue
Cambridge, MA (617) 349-6282
www.freshpondgolf.com

| Tees | Holes | Yards | Par | USGA | Slope |
|------|-------|-------|-----|------|-------|
| BACK | 9 | 2931 | 35 | 70.0 | 120 |
| MIDDLE | 9 | 2732 | 35 | 66.9 | 111 |
| FRONT | 9 | 2306 | 35 | 66.5 | 114 |

**Club Pro:** Bob Carey, Dir. of Golf
**Payment:** Cash, Check, Visa, MC
**Tee Times:** Weekends only
**Fee 9 Holes: Weekday:** $22 **Weekend:** $26
**Fee 18 Holes: Weekday:** $32 **Weekend:** $38
**Twilight Rates:** No **Discounts:** Sr, Jr $14 (residents only)
**Cart Rental:** $14pp/18, $9pp/9 **Driving Range:** No
**Lessons:** $50/half hour **Schools:** No **Junior Golf:** Yes
**Membership:** Yes **Architect/Yr Open:** Donald Ross
**Other:** Snack Bar / Vending Machines **GPS:**

c o U P O N

Great course for all levels. Season tickets available. Off-season rates. Conditions better than ever. Great
pro shop. Open Apr. - Dec.

| | 1 | 2 | 3 | 4 | 5 | 6 | 7 | 8 | 9 |
|---|---|---|---|---|---|---|---|---|---|
| PAR | 4 | 4 | 3 | 4 | 5 | 3 | 4 | 3 | 5 |
| YARDS | 417 | 312 | 169 | 401 | 476 | 221 | 370 | 147 | 465 |
| PAR | | | | | | | | | |
| YARDS | | | | | | | | | |

**Directions:** I-95 to Route 2 East to Cambridge. Go west on Huron Avenue to course.

# Furnace Brook Golf Course

NEW 27 ▶

20 Reservoir Road
Wollaston, MA (617) 479-8529
www.furnacebrookgolfclub.com

**Club Pro:** Michael McBroom
**Payment:** All Major Credit Cards
**Tee Times:** No
**Fee 9 Holes: Weekday:** $30
**Fee 18 Holes: Weekday:** $35
**Twilight Rates:** No
**Cart Rental:** $20pp/18, $10pp/9
**Lessons:** Yes **Schools:** No
**Membership:** Yes

**Weekend:** $35
**Weekend:** $40
**Discounts:**
**Driving Range:** No
**Junior Golf:** Yes
**Architect/Yr Open:** Wayne Stiles/1920

| Tees | Holes | Yards | Par | USGA | Slope |
|------|-------|-------|-----|------|-------|
| BACK | | | | | |
| MIDDLE | 9 | 2926 | 35 | 69.1 | 125 |
| FRONT | 9 | 2567 | 35 | 71.5 | 120 |

**Other:** Snack Bar / Clubhouse / Lockers / Restaraunt / Showers / Bar Lounge / Putting Course
**GPS:**

The original course was laid out in early 1920. Many of the holes still exist. Well known for its excellent course conditions, especially the greens. Open to the general public Monday though Friday.

| | 1 | 2 | 3 | 4 | 5 | 6 | 7 | 8 | 9 |
|------|-----|-----|-----|-----|-----|-----|-----|-----|-----|
| PAR | 4 | 4 | 4 | 4 | 4 | 3 | 4 | 4 | 4 |
| YARDS | 361 | 378 | 347 | 323 | 324 | 189 | 324 | 284 | 341 |
| PAR | | | | | | | | | |
| YARDS | | | | | | | | | |

**Directions:** Exit 8 off Intersate 93, south of Boston. Take the 3rd light from Furnace Brook Parkway, left onto Adams Street, and then right onto Reservoir Road. The golf course is at the top of the hill.

# Gannon Golf Course

✪✪½ 28 ▶

60 Great Woods Road
Lynn, MA (781) 595-5674
www.gannongolfclub.com

**Club Pro:** Mike Foster, PGA
**Payment:** Visa, MC, Disc
**Tee Times:** 2 days adv.
**Fee 9 Holes: Weekday:** $19
**Fee 18 Holes: Weekday:** $34
**Twilight Rates:** After 3:30pm
**Cart Rental:** $15pp/18, $7.50pp/9
**Lessons:** No **Schools:** No
**Membership:** Yes

**Weekend:** $21 after 3:30pm
**Weekend:** $42 Spring/Fall only
**Discounts:** Junior
**Driving Range:** No
**Junior Golf:** Yes
**Architect/Yr Open:** Wayne Stiles/1931

| Tees | Holes | Yards | Par | USGA | Slope |
|------|-------|-------|-----|------|-------|
| BACK | 18 | 6106 | 70 | 69.9 | 118 |
| MIDDLE | 18 | 6036 | 70 | 67.9 | 113 |
| FRONT | 18 | 5215 | 71 | 68.8 | 115 |

**Other:** Snack Bar / Clubhouse / Lockers / Restaraunt / Showers / Bar Lounge
**GPS:**

Golf Course features the rolling terrain which Stiles was famous for. Wonderful views of Boston as well as Lynn Woods Reservation. Challenging 18 holes in magnificent condition.

| | 1 | 2 | 3 | 4 | 5 | 6 | 7 | 8 | 9 |
|------|-----|-----|-----|-----|-----|-----|-----|-----|-----|
| PAR | 4 | 4 | 4 | 4 | 4 | 3 | 4 | 4 | 3 |
| YARDS | 346 | 309 | 357 | 404 | 333 | 187 | 318 | 414 | 216 |
| | 10 | 11 | 12 | 13 | 14 | 15 | 16 | 17 | 18 |
| PAR | 4 | 4 | 4 | 4 | 3 | 5 | 3 | 4 | 5 |
| YARDS | 309 | 335 | 401 | 383 | 158 | 486 | 228 | 319 | 588 |

**Directions:** I-95 North to Exit 44B. Rotary to 129 East - Lynn/Swampscott. 1.9 miles on right (Lynn Woods). I-95 South to Route 1 South. Left onto 129 East, to rotary. Follow 129 East - Lynn/Swampscott. 1.9 miles on right (Lynn Woods).

# Garrison Golf Center

✪½ **29**

654 Hilldale Avenue
Haverhill, MA (978) 374-9380
www.garrisongolf.com

**Club Pro:** Ted Murphy
**Payment:** Cash, Visa, MC
**Tee Times:** No
**Fee 9 Holes: Weekday:** $11
**Fee 18 Holes: Weekday:** $21
**Twilight Rates:** After 6pm
**Cart Rental:**
**Lessons:** Yes **Schools:** Yes
**Membership:** No
**Other:**

| Tees | Holes | Yards | Par | USGA | Slope |
|------|-------|-------|-----|------|-------|
| BACK | | | | | |
| MIDDLE | 9 | 1005 | 27 | | |
| FRONT | | | | | |

**Weekend:** $12
**Weekend:** $23
**Discounts:** $11 Senior & Junior
**Driving Range:** Yes
**Junior Golf:** Yes
**Architect/Yr Open:** Manuel Francis/1969
**GPS:**

COUPON

A short testing 9-hole par 3 with beautiful Vesper Velvet greens. Designed in 1966 by legendary Manuel Francis. Great course for women and juniors. 12 play tickets $90 (seniors $80). Monday AM Ladies clinics.

| | 1 | 2 | 3 | 4 | 5 | 6 | 7 | 8 | 9 |
|------|-----|-----|-----|-----|-----|-----|-----|-----|-----|
| PAR | 3 | 3 | 3 | 3 | 3 | 3 | 3 | 3 | 3 |
| YARDS | 105 | 100 | 130 | 75 | 100 | 130 | 130 | 135 | 100 |
| PAR | | | | | | | | | |
| YARDS | | | | | | | | | |

**Directions:** I-495N to Exit 50 straight for one mile, left at 2nd stop sign for ¼ mile.


# George Wright Golf Club

✪✪✪✪ **30**

420 West Street
Hyde Park, MA (617) 364-2300
www.georgewrightgolfcourse.com

**Club Pro:** Scott Allen, PGA
**Payment:** Visa, MC
**Tee Times:** 2 days adv. S/S
**Fee 9 Holes: Weekday:** $22.50 M-F
**Fee 18 Holes: Weekday:** $37 M-F
**Twilight Rates:** No
**Cart Rental:** $20pp/18, $11pp/9
**Lessons:** $40/half hour **Schools:** No
**Membership:** Yes
**Other:** Snack Bar / Bar-Lounge

| Tees | Holes | Yards | Par | USGA | Slope |
|------|-------|-------|-----|------|-------|
| BACK | 18 | 6367 | 70 | 69.5 | 126 |
| MIDDLE | 18 | 6166 | 70 | 68.6 | 123 |
| FRONT | 18 | 5054 | 70 | 70.3 | 115 |

**Weekend:** $26 S/S/H
**Weekend:** $44 S/S/H
**Discounts:** Senior & Junior
**Driving Range:** No
**Junior Golf:** Yes
**Architect/Yr Open:** Donald Ross/1938
**GPS:**

Rated #14 in *Golfweek's* 2009 rating of the top municipal golf courses in the United States. Boston resident rates available. After 2 easy holes to get you warmed up, it kicks into gear and keeps you working hard the rest of the way. "A must-play if you have not visited this hidden gem recently." –SD

| | 1 | 2 | 3 | 4 | 5 | 6 | 7 | 8 | 9 |
|-------|-----|-----|-----|-----|-----|-----|-----|-----|-----|
| PAR | 4 | 4 | 5 | 3 | 4 | 4 | 4 | 3 | 4 |
| YARDS | 367 | 313 | 480 | 150 | 400 | 380 | 387 | 162 | 440 |
| | 10 | 11 | 12 | 13 | 14 | 15 | 16 | 17 | 18 |
| PAR | 4 | 4 | 4 | 4 | 3 | 5 | 4 | 3 | 4 |
| YARDS | 449 | 347 | 399 | 369 | 182 | 493 | 318 | 158 | 372 |

**Directions:** I-95/Route 128 to Route 1 North to Washington Street (left) in Hyde Park. Take a right onto Beach Street. Follow signs to course.

# Glen Ellen Country Club ✪✪✪½

31 ▶

**GB RTE 495**

84 Orchard Street, Route 115
Millis, MA (508) 376-2775
www.theglencc.com

| Tees | Holes | Yards | Par | USGA | Slope |
|---|---|---|---|---|---|
| BACK | 18 | 6634 | 72 | 72.0 | 125 |
| MIDDLE | 18 | 6237 | 72 | 70.1 | 123 |
| FRONT | 18 | 5148 | 72 | 69.4 | 122 |

**Club Pro:** Devin Bibeau, PGA
**Payment:** Visa, MC, Amex, Disc, Cash, Check
**Tee Times:** 7 days adv.
**Fee 9 Holes: Weekday:** $28
**Fee 18 Holes: Weekday:** $39
**Twilight Rates:** After 3pm weekdays
After 5pm weekends
**Cart Rental:** $20pp/18, $10pp/9
**Lessons:** Yes **Schools:** Yes
**Membership:** Yes
**Other:** Snack Bar / Showers / Bar-Lounge

**Weekend:** $30 after 3pm
**Weekend:** $50 (cart req. until 12pm)
**Discounts:** Senior & Junior
**Driving Range:** Yes
**Junior Golf:** Yes
**Architect/Yr Open:** Ron Pritchard/1963
**GPS:**

COUPON

A well manicured course that is challenging enough for the skilled player yet playable for the average player. Welcoming to women and juniors. Host facility for 2013 Amateur Public Links Championship.
Player Comments: "Great greens, fun to play" –FP

| | 1 | 2 | 3 | 4 | 5 | 6 | 7 | 8 | 9 |
|---|---|---|---|---|---|---|---|---|---|
| PAR | 4 | 3 | 4 | 4 | 4 | 5 | 4 | 3 | 5 |
| YARDS | 431 | 153 | 376 | 316 | 381 | 508 | 325 | 130 | 475 |
| | 10 | 11 | 12 | 13 | 14 | 15 | 16 | 17 | 18 |
| PAR | 5 | 4 | 3 | 4 | 4 | 4 | 4 | 5 | 3 |
| YARDS | 503 | 410 | 168 | 475 | 353 | 333 | 375 | 385 | 145 |

**Directions:** I-495 to Exit 18, take right at end. Straight for 4 miles. Take left onto Holliston Street. Follow 2 miles and take right onto Goulding Street. Course is on left.

# Granite Links Golf Club ✪✪✪✪✪

32 ▶

100 Quarry Hills Drive
Quincy, MA (617) 689-1900
www.granitelinksgolfclub.com

| Tees | Holes | Yards | Par | USGA | Slope |
|---|---|---|---|---|---|
| BACK | 27/18 | 6818 | 72 | 73.4 | 141 |
| MIDDLE | 27/18 | 6300 | 72 | 71.6 | 134 |
| FRONT | 27/18 | 5001 | 72 | 70.6 | 124 |

**Club Pro:** Stephen Clancy, PGA
**Payment:** Visa, MC, Amex, Disc
**Tee Times:** 4 days adv.
**Fee 9 Holes: Mon-Wed:** $70 w/cart
**Fee 18 Holes: Thu-Fri:** $150 w/cart
**Twilight Rates:** After 4pm
**Discounts:** Seniors Tues. & Wed., Milton/Quincy residents
**Cart Rental:** Included
**Lessons:** $50/half hour, $95/hour, 5 lessons/$225
**Membership:** Yes
**Other:** Restaurant / Clubhouse / Lockers (Members Only) / Showers / Bar-Lounge
**GPS:** Yes

**Sat/Sun:** $70 w/cart after 2pm
**Sat-Wed:** $125 w/cart
**Driving Range:** $12/bucket
**Junior Golf:** Yes
**Architect/Yr Open:** John Sanford/2003

*Golf Digest* Top 100 golf courses. 27-hole course with exceptional views and conditions.

**Granite/Milton**

| | 1 | 2 | 3 | 4 | 5 | 6 | 7 | 8 | 9 |
|---|---|---|---|---|---|---|---|---|---|
| PAR | 5 | 4 | 4 | 3 | 4 | 4 | 3 | 5 | 4 |
| YARDS | 488 | 375 | 399 | 154 | 353 | 331 | 187 | 499 | 298 |
| | 10 | 11 | 12 | 13 | 14 | 15 | 16 | 17 | 18 |
| PAR | 4 | 3 | 4 | 5 | 4 | 3 | 4 | 4 | 5 |
| YARDS | 454 | 171 | 411 | 486 | 364 | 188 | 323 | 335 | 484 |

**Directions:** I-93 to Exit 8 and follow signs to Quarry Hills. Turn right onto Riccuti Drive and follow for 1 mile to club entrance.

# Green Harbor Golf Club  ✪✪½  33

624 Webster Street
Marshfield, MA  (781) 834-7303
www.greenharborgolfclub.com

| Tees | Holes | Yards | Par | USGA | Slope |
|------|-------|-------|-----|------|-------|
| BACK | 18 | 6245 | 71 | 69.6 | 122 |
| MIDDLE | 18 | 5757 | 71 | 67.8 | 115 |
| FRONT | 18 | 4967 | 71 | 68.5 | 114 |

**Club Pro:**
**Payment:** Cash, Visa, MC
**Tee Times:** 7 days adv.
**Fee  9 Holes: Weekday:** $23          **Weekend:** $26
**Fee 18 Holes: Weekday:** $39          **Weekend:** $48
**Twilight Rates:** After 5pm            **Discounts:** Seniors Tues 6am-12pm
**Cart Rental:** No                      **Driving Range:** No
**Lessons:** Yes  **Schools:** Yes       **Junior Golf:** Yes
**Membership:** Yes                      **Architect/Yr Open:** Manuel Francis/1971
**Other:** Clubhouse / Snack Bar / Lounge  **GPS:**

Flat, open course, easy to walk. Water on 5 holes. Features velvet bent grass.
Open March 15 - December 15.

|  | 1 | 2 | 3 | 4 | 5 | 6 | 7 | 8 | 9 |
|---|---|---|---|---|---|---|---|---|---|
| PAR | 4 | 4 | 4 | 4 | 3 | 4 | 5 | 3 | 4 |
| YARDS | 406 | 353 | 347 | 300 | 155 | 310 | 507 | 155 | 318 |
|  | 10 | 11 | 12 | 13 | 14 | 15 | 16 | 17 | 18 |
| PAR | 4 | 5 | 5 | 4 | 4 | 3 | 4 | 3 | 4 |
| YARDS | 349 | 505 | 462 | 345 | 280 | 185 | 364 | 158 | 316 |

**Directions:** I-93 to Route 3 South to Exit 12 (Route 139). 139 East 4.5 miles. Right on Webster Street, 1 mile on left.

# Hickory Hill Golf Course  ✪✪½  34

200 North Lowell Street
Methuen, MA (978) 686-0822
www.golfhickoryhill.com

| Tees | Holes | Yards | Par | USGA | Slope |
|------|-------|-------|-----|------|-------|
| BACK | 18 | 6287 | 71 | 70.8 | 123 |
| MIDDLE | 18 | 6017 | 71 | 69.6 | 119 |
| FRONT | 18 | 5367 | 71 | 70.7 | 121 |

**Club Pro:**
**Payment:** Visa, MC, Cash
**Tee Times:** 7 days adv.
**Fee  9 Holes: Weekday:** $23 M-F       **Weekend:** $28
**Fee 18 Holes: Weekday:** $40 M-Th, $45 F  **Weekend:** $50
**Twilight Rates:** After 3pm wknd; 6pm wkdy  **Discounts:** Senior & Junior (Senior T-Th am)
**Cart Rental:** $17pp/18, $12pp/9        **Driving Range:** Yes
**Lessons:**   **Schools:** No            **Junior Golf:** No
**Membership:** No                        **Architect/Yr Open:** Manuel Francis/1968
**Other:** Clubhouse / Showers / Bar-Lounge  **GPS:**

Course offers a senior discount Tuesday, Wednesday and Thursday 7am-12pm, $35/walk, $45/ride.
Good variety of holes, tougher back nine. Great conditions, very friendly staff.

|  | 1 | 2 | 3 | 4 | 5 | 6 | 7 | 8 | 9 |
|---|---|---|---|---|---|---|---|---|---|
| PAR | 4 | 3 | 5 | 4 | 4 | 5 | 4 | 3 | 4 |
| YARDS | 349 | 173 | 511 | 382 | 379 | 513 | 367 | 155 | 348 |
|  | 10 | 11 | 12 | 13 | 14 | 15 | 16 | 17 | 18 |
| PAR | 5 | 4 | 4 | 3 | 4 | 4 | 4 | 3 | 4 |
| YARDS | 489 | 390 | 340 | 141 | 326 | 357 | 304 | 114 | 379 |

**Directions:** I-93 to Exit 46. Take Route 113 West, follow 1.5 miles, course is on left.

# Hillview Golf Course ✪✪ 35 ▶

149 North Street
North Reading, MA (978) 664-4435
www.hillviewgc.com

**Club Pro:** Chris Carter, PGA
**Payment:** Visa, MC, Amex, Disc
**Tee Times:** Yes

| Tees | Holes | Yards | Par | USGA | Slope |
|------|-------|-------|-----|------|-------|
| BACK | 18 | 5802 | 69 | 67.4 | 120 |
| MIDDLE | 18 | 5251 | 69 | 65.2 | 118 |
| FRONT | 18 | 4500 | 69 | 66.0 | 110 |

**Fee 9 Holes: Weekday:** $21
**Fee 18 Holes: Weekday:** $39
**Twilight Rates:** No
**Cart Rental:** $16pp/18, $8pp/9
**Lessons:** Yes **Schools:** No
**Membership:** No
**Other:** Snack Bar / Restaurant / Bar-Lounge / Clubhouse

**Weekend:** $24
**Weekend:** $42
**Discounts:** Sr. & Jr. (M-Th) $16 before 1pm
**Driving Range:** Yes
**Junior Golf:** Yes
**Architect/Yr Open:** 1950s

A popular course in a good location. Interesting layout. New green and fairway improvements. A player-friendly course.

| | 1 | 2 | 3 | 4 | 5 | 6 | 7 | 8 | 9 |
|-----|-----|-----|-----|-----|-----|-----|-----|-----|-----|
| PAR | 5 | 3 | 4 | 4 | 4 | 4 | 4 | 5 | 3 |
| YARDS | 484 | 170 | 410 | 325 | 357 | 323 | 394 | 539 | 191 |
| | 10 | 11 | 12 | 13 | 14 | 15 | 16 | 17 | 18 |
| PAR | 4 | 4 | 4 | 4 | 3 | 4 | 3 | 4 | 3 |
| YARDS | 372 | 310 | 346 | 355 | 180 | 324 | 236 | 239 | 173 |

**Directions:** I-93 to Exit 40 and follow Route 62 East 1½ miles. Turn left on North Street. Course is ½ mile up on left.

# Kelley Greens Golf Course ✪✪ 36 ▶

1 Willow Road
Nahant, MA
(781) 581-0840 ext. 101
www.kelleygreens.com

**Club Pro:**
**Payment:** Visa, MC, Amex, Disc
**Tee Times:** Call (781) 581-0840

| Tees | Holes | Yards | Par | USGA | Slope |
|------|-------|-------|-----|------|-------|
| BACK | 9 | 1940 | 30 | 30.0 | 103 |
| MIDDLE | 9 | 1865 | 30 | 28.5 | 87 |
| FRONT | 9 | 1671 | 30 | 30.0 | 103 |

**Fee 9 Holes: Weekday:** $17
**Fee 18 Holes: Weekday:** $28
**Twilight Rates:** No
**Cart Rental:** $20/18, $12/9 per cart
**Lessons:** No **Schools:** Yes
**Membership:** Yes
**Other:** Ask about our Golf & Lunch special

**Weekend:** $20
**Weekend:** $31
**Discounts:** Senior/Junior memberships
**Driving Range:** No
**Junior Golf:** Yes
**Architect/Yr Open:**
**GPS:**

Full service bar and lottery. Serving lunch and dinner. Functions and outings for up to 200 guests. Open year round. Summer instructional golf programs for boys and girls ages 7-15 offered by David Nyman, PGA.

| | 1 | 2 | 3 | 4 | 5 | 6 | 7 | 8 | 9 |
|-----|-----|-----|-----|-----|-----|-----|-----|-----|-----|
| PAR | 3 | 3 | 3 | 3 | 3 | 4 | 4 | 4 | 3 |
| YARDS | 139 | 177 | 174 | 140 | 187 | 319 | 282 | 251 | 172 |
| PAR | | | | | | | | | |
| YARDS | | | | | | | | | |

**Directions:** Take 1A to rotary, follow Nahant Causeway 2.6 miles. Right after the end of Ocean Avenue. Follow Willow Road to the end. Kelley Greens is on the right. Follow signs to course.

# Leo J. Martin Golf Club  ✪½  ▶ 37

85 Park Road
Weston, MA  (781) 891-1119
www.leojgolf.com

| Tees | Holes | Yards | Par | USGA | Slope |
|---|---|---|---|---|---|
| BACK | 18 | 6320 | 72 | 70.7 | 126 |
| MIDDLE | 18 | 6140 | 72 | 67.6 | 118 |
| FRONT | 18 | 6140 | 75 | 70.9 | 116 |

**Club Pro:** Artie Carlson, PGA
**Payment:** Visa, MC
**Tee Times:** Weekends
**Fee  9 Holes: Weekday:** $19 M-Th
**Fee 18 Holes: Weekday:** $27 M-Th
**Twilight Rates:** After 5pm
**Cart Rental:** $30/18, $16/9 per cart
**Lessons:** $45/half hour  **Schools:** Junior
**Membership:** No
**Other:** Snack Bar

**Weekend:** $19 F/S/S/H
**Weekend:** $30 F/S/S/H
**Discounts:** Sr. & Jr. weekdays M-Th
**Driving Range:** $12/lg, $7/sm
**Junior Golf:** Yes
**Architect/Yr Open:** Donald Ross
**GPS:**

Considered an easy walker. Seniors seem to enjoy it. Tee times first come, first serve M-F. Friendly beginners course.

| | 1 | 2 | 3 | 4 | 5 | 6 | 7 | 8 | 9 |
|---|---|---|---|---|---|---|---|---|---|
| PAR | 4 | 5 | 3 | 5 | 3 | 4 | 4 | 4 | 4 |
| YARDS | 315 | 500 | 155 | 525 | 140 | 360 | 325 | 355 | 265 |
| | 10 | 11 | 12 | 13 | 14 | 15 | 16 | 17 | 18 |
| PAR | 3 | 4 | 3 | 4 | 4 | 4 | 5 | 4 | 5 |
| YARDS | 140 | 290 | 240 | 400 | 420 | 360 | 530 | 260 | 560 |

**Directions:** Where I-95/Route 128 meets I-90 (Mass Pike). From Mass Pike Weston exit (Route 30), take first left onto Park Road to course on left.

# Lost Brook Golf Club  ✪✪✪  ▶ 38

750 University Avenue
Norwood, MA  (781) 769-2550
www.lostbrookgolfclub.com

| Tees | Holes | Yards | Par | USGA | Slope |
|---|---|---|---|---|---|
| BACK | | | | | |
| MIDDLE | 18 | 3002 | 54 | | |
| FRONT | 18 | 2468 | 58 | | |

**Club Pro:** Chris Hawley
**Payment:** Cash, Credit Cards
**Tee Times:** Weekends
**Fee  9 Holes: Weekday:** $16
**Fee 18 Holes: Weekday:** $25
**Twilight Rates:** Yes
**Cart Rental:** $3/pull
**Lessons:** Yes  **Schools:** No
**Membership:** No
**Other:** Clubhouse / Snack Bar

**Weekend:** $18
**Weekend:** $27
**Discounts:** Senior & Junior
**Driving Range:** No
**Junior Golf:** No
**Architect/Yr Open:** Sam Mitchell/1967
**GPS:**

Expertly maintained par 3 golf course. Tree-lined fairways surround the elevated greens. "Excellent conditions, challenging and enjoyable for all levels." —GM

| | 1 | 2 | 3 | 4 | 5 | 6 | 7 | 8 | 9 |
|---|---|---|---|---|---|---|---|---|---|
| PAR | 3 | 3 | 3 | 3 | 3 | 3 | 3 | 3 | 3 |
| YARDS | 93 | 198 | 212 | 202 | 141 | 158 | 176 | 190 | 111 |
| | 10 | 11 | 12 | 13 | 14 | 15 | 16 | 17 | 18 |
| PAR | 3 | 3 | 3 | 3 | 3 | 3 | 3 | 3 | 3 |
| YARDS | 170 | 171 | 168 | 162 | 126 | 148 | 202 | 190 | 185 |

**Directions:** I-95/Route 128 to Exit 13. Follow University Avenue approximately 1.5 miles to course located at Meditech. Course is on the left.

# Maplegate Country Club ✪✪✪ ▶ 39

160 Maple Street
Bellingham, MA (508) 966-4040
www.maplegate.com

| Tees | Holes | Yards | Par | USGA | Slope |
|------|-------|-------|-----|------|-------|
| BACK | 18 | 6815 | 72 | 74.2 | 133 |
| MIDDLE | 18 | 5837 | 72 | 69.5 | 122 |
| FRONT | 18 | 4852 | 72 | 70.2 | 124 |

**Club Pro:** Greg Dowdell
**Payment:** Visa, MC, Amex, Disc
**Tee Times:** 7 days adv.
**Fee 9 Holes: Weekday:** $27 walk, $35 w/cart **Weekend:** $35 w/cart
**Fee 18 Holes: Weekday:** $59 ride **Weekend:** $69 w/cart before noon
**Twilight Rates:** After 1pm **Discounts:** Senior
**Cart Rental:** $20pp/18 **Driving Range:** Yes
**Lessons:** Yes **Schools:** Jr. & Sr. **Junior Golf:** Yes
**Membership:** Yes **Architect/Yr:** Leonard French & Phil Wogan/1990
**Other:** Snack Bar **GPS:**

*COUPON*

Must be straight shooter, but interesting layout for all abilities. Carts required weekends and holidays before noon. "Nice greens. Friendly staff." –FP

| | 1 | 2 | 3 | 4 | 5 | 6 | 7 | 8 | 9 |
|---|---|---|---|---|---|---|---|---|---|
| PAR | 5 | 4 | 3 | 5 | 4 | 4 | 4 | 3 | 4 |
| YARDS | 515 | 335 | 173 | 522 | 431 | 435 | 417 | 145 | 434 |
| | 10 | 11 | 12 | 13 | 14 | 15 | 16 | 17 | 18 |
| PAR | 4 | 4 | 3 | 4 | 5 | 3 | 5 | 4 | 4 |
| YARDS | 376 | 382 | 191 | 388 | 510 | 227 | 530 | 357 | 447 |

**Directions:** I-495 to Exit 18 bear right. Take 126 North. Right at first light to Maple Street. Course is 1 mile on left.

# Maynard Golf Course ✪✪✪ ▶ 40

50 Brown Street
Maynard, MA (978) 637-2268
www.sterlinggolf.com

| Tees | Holes | Yards | Par | USGA | Slope |
|------|-------|-------|-----|------|-------|
| BACK | 9 | 3013 | 35 | 68.2 | 123 |
| MIDDLE | 9 | 2853 | 35 | 68.2 | 123 |
| FRONT | 9 | 2601 | 35 | 71.5 | 124 |

**Club Pro:** Jim Callahan, PGA
Brad Durrin, PGA
**Payment:** Visa, MC, Amex, Disc
**Tee Times:** 7 days adv.
**Fee 9 Holes: Weekday:** $21 **Weekend:** $23
**Fee 18 Holes: Weekday:** $32 **Weekend:** $34
**Twilight Rates:** After 4pm **Discounts:** Senior, Junior, Family
**Cart Rental:** $16pp/18; $10pp/9 **Driving Range:** Hitting Net, Pitching Area
**Lessons:** Yes **Schools:** Yes **Junior Golf:** Yes
**Membership:** Yes **Architect/Yr:** Wayne Stiles/1921
**Other:** Restaurant / Showers / Snack Bar / Bar-Lounge / Function Room

*COUPON*

Formerly Maynard Country Club, a member-owned, semi-private club. Professionally maintained to provide an outstanding golf experience. Sunset rate (1 hour before sunset): $10/adults; $5/kids

| | 1 | 2 | 3 | 4 | 5 | 6 | 7 | 8 | 9 |
|---|---|---|---|---|---|---|---|---|---|
| PAR | 4 | 5 | 3 | 4 | 4 | 3 | 4 | 4 | 4 |
| YARDS | 375 | 487 | 148 | 345 | 355 | 165 | 342 | 338 | 298 |
| PAR | | | | | | | | | |
| YARDS | | | | | | | | | |

**Directions:** I-95 to Route 20 West to Route 27 North. Travel 4 miles and take a left on Waltham Street. Bear right onto Acton Street. Brown Street is ¼ mile on right.

# Meadow at Peabody, The  ✪✪✪  ▶41

80 Granite Street
Peabody, MA  (978) 532-9390
www.peabodymeadowgolf.com

| Tees | Holes | Yards | Par | USGA | Slope |
|------|-------|-------|-----|------|-------|
| BACK | 18 | 6708 | 71 | 72.4 | 128 |
| MIDDLE | 18 | 5869 | 71 | 69.4 | 121 |
| FRONT | 18 | 5136 | 71 | 70.8 | 123 |

**Club Pro:** Peter Cronan
**Payment:** Visa, MC, Amex
**Tee Times:** 3 days adv.
**Fee  9 Holes: Weekday:** $21 ($19/resident)  **Weekend:** $24 ($21/resident)
**Fee 18 Holes: Weekday:** $40 ($35/resident)  **Weekend:** $44 ($38/resident)
**Twilight Rates:** No  **Discounts:** Sr. & Jr. before noon M-F
**Cart Rental:** $16pp/18, $9pp/9  **Driving Range:** No
**Lessons:** $40/45 min.  **Schools:** No  **Junior Golf:** Yes
**Membership:** No  **Architect/Yr Open:** Silva & Cornish/2001
**Other:** Restaurant / Showers  **GPS:**

Player Comments: "A real workout for the first visit, a ton of fun your next few times around."
"Fun layout, hilly, but fair course." "Careful—several blind shots." "Great greens." –FP
Dress code. Lodging available at nearby Marriott.

| | 1 | 2 | 3 | 4 | 5 | 6 | 7 | 8 | 9 |
|------|---|---|---|---|---|---|---|---|---|
| PAR | 5 | 4 | 4 | 4 | 4 | 3 | 5 | 3 | 4 |
| YARDS | 526 | 343 | 312 | 324 | 388 | 110 | 437 | 146 | 372 |
| | 10 | 11 | 12 | 13 | 14 | 15 | 16 | 17 | 18 |
| PAR | 4 | 5 | 3 | 4 | 4 | 4 | 3 | 4 | 4 |
| YARDS | 360 | 457 | 153 | 389 | 319 | 329 | 143 | 341 | 420 |

**Directions:** I-95/Route 128 to Exit 28 (Forest Street/Centennial Drive). Bear right at end of ramp.
Go through lights at bottom of hill to Summit. Left onto Lynnfield Street, Left onto Washington Street.
Immediate right onto Granite Street. Street dead-ends to course.

# Merrimack Valley Golf Course  ✪✪✪  ▶42

210 Howe Street
Methuen, MA (978) 683-7771
www.merrimackvalleygolfclub.com

| Tees | Holes | Yards | Par | USGA | Slope |
|------|-------|-------|-----|------|-------|
| BACK | 18 | 6012 | 70 | 70.4 | 130 |
| MIDDLE | 18 | 5730 | 70 | 69.2 | 126 |
| FRONT | 18 | 5226 | 70 | 67.6 | 117 |

**Club Pro:** Bill Pappas
**Payment:** Cash, Visa, MC
**Tee Times:** 7 days adv.
**Fee  9 Holes: Weekday:** $20  **Weekend:** $25
**Fee 18 Holes: Weekday:** $35  **Weekend:** $45
**Twilight Rates:** $25 after 3pm wknds/holidays  **Discounts:** None
**Cart Rental:** $18pp/18, $9pp/9  **Driving Range:** No
**Lessons:** No  **Schools:** No  **Junior Golf:** Yes
**Membership:** Yes  **Architect/Yr Open:** Donald Ross/1906
**Other:** Restaurant / Bar-Lounge  **GPS:**

Improvements include bent grass from tee to green. Noted for plush greens. One of the best values
in New England. Voted best semi-private course in the region. Redesigned by George Sargent in 2009.

| | 1 | 2 | 3 | 4 | 5 | 6 | 7 | 8 | 9 |
|------|---|---|---|---|---|---|---|---|---|
| PAR | 5 | 4 | 5 | 4 | 3 | 3 | 4 | 5 | 3 |
| YARDS | 485 | 371 | 487 | 305 | 133 | 194 | 383 | 507 | 141 |
| | 10 | 11 | 12 | 13 | 14 | 15 | 16 | 17 | 18 |
| PAR | 4 | 3 | 5 | 4 | 4 | 3 | 4 | 3 | 5 |
| YARDS | 378 | 174 | 461 | 149 | 327 | 178 | 366 | 152 | 539 |

**Directions:** I-495 to Exit 47, Route 213. Take Exit 3 off Route 213. At lights at end of exit ramp,
go left. Club is ¾ mile on left.

# Middleton Golf Course ✪✪✪

43 ▶

**105 South Main Street**
**Middleton, MA (978) 774-4075**
www.middletongolf.com

**Club Pro:** Chris Costa, PGA
**Payment:** Major Credit Cards, Checks, Cash
**Tee Times:** See website
**Fee 9 Holes: Weekday:** $23
**Fee 18 Holes: Weekday:** $36
**Twilight Rates:** After 3:30pm, F/S/S only
**Cart Rental:** $12pp/18, $8pp/9
**Lessons:** Yes **Schools:** Yes
**Membership:** No
**Other:** Clubhouse / Bar (Beer & Wine Only) / Greenside Cafe / Club Fitting Center

| Tees | Holes | Yards | Par | USGA | Slope |
|------|-------|-------|-----|------|-------|
| BACK | 18 | 3215 | 54 | 57.0 | 83 |
| MIDDLE | 18 | 3000 | 54 | 53.9 | 75 |
| FRONT | 18 | 2280 | 54 | 52.1 | 71 |

**Weekend:** $23
**Weekend:** $36
**Discounts:** Senior & Junior
**Driving Range:** Lessons only
**Junior Golf:** Yes
**Architect/Yr Open:** Geoffrey Cornish/1966

COUPON

Beautifully maintained, one of the nation's top par 3 courses. Open year round.

| | 1 | 2 | 3 | 4 | 5 | 6 | 7 | 8 | 9 |
|------|---|---|---|---|---|---|---|---|---|
| PAR | 3 | 3 | 3 | 3 | 3 | 3 | 3 | 3 | 3 |
| YARDS | 170 | 160 | 185 | 170 | 150 | 170 | 145 | 215 | 190 |
| | 10 | 11 | 12 | 13 | 14 | 15 | 16 | 17 | 18 |
| PAR | 3 | 3 | 3 | 3 | 3 | 3 | 3 | 3 | 3 |
| YARDS | 135 | 110 | 195 | 160 | 155 | 240 | 215 | 225 | 225 |

**Directions:** I-95 to Route 114 West about 2.5 miles. Parking lot entrance on the left.

# Millwood Golf Course ✪✪

44 ▶

**175 Millwood Street**
**Framingham, MA (508) 877-1221**
www.millwoodgolfcourse.net

**Club Pro:**
**Payment:** Visa, MC
**Tee Times:** 7 days adv.
**Fee 9 Holes: Weekday:** $27
**Fee 18 Holes: Weekday:**
**Twilight Rates:** After 5pm
**Cart Rental:** $10pp
**Lessons:** Yes **Schools:** No
**Membership:** No
**Other:** Snack Bar

| Tees | Holes | Yards | Par | USGA | Slope |
|------|-------|-------|-----|------|-------|
| BACK | 14 | 4057 | 53 | 64.5 | 108 |
| MIDDLE | 14 | 3816 | 53 | 63.3 | 106 |
| FRONT | 14 | 3361 | 53 | 64.7 | 102 |

**Weekend:** $30
**Weekend:**
**Discounts:** Senior ($21 M-F)
**Driving Range:** No
**Junior Golf:** No
**Architect/Yr Open:** William Drake/1967
**GPS:**

A friendly family-owned course, with 14 holes. Added traps on 7th hole. New tee on 9th. Golf lesson available from Kevin Sullivan. Open April - November.

| | 1 | 2 | 3 | 4 | 5 | 6 | 7 | 8 | 9 |
|------|---|---|---|---|---|---|---|---|---|
| PAR | 4 | 3 | 4 | 4 | 4 | 3 | 4 | 4 | 5 |
| YARDS | 338 | 112 | 306 | 230 | 363 | 156 | 281 | 312 | 438 |
| | 10 | 11 | 12 | 13 | 14 | 15 | 16 | 17 | 18 |
| PAR | 4 | 3 | 4 | 3 | 4 | | | | |
| YARDS | 362 | 160 | 295 | 138 | 307 | | | | |

**Directions:** Route 9 to Edgell Road. At light, make right onto Edgell Road for 1 mile. Turn left onto Belknap Road, then third right onto Millwood Street.

# Mt. Hood Golf Course  ✪✪½  45 ▶

**100 Slayton Road**
**Melrose, MA (781) 665-6656**
www.playgolfne.com

| Tees | Holes | Yards | Par | USGA | Slope |
|------|-------|-------|-----|------|-------|
| BACK | 18 | 5633 | 69 | 67.1 | 117 |
| MIDDLE | 18 | 5312 | 69 | 65.4 | 115 |
| FRONT | 18 | 4462 | 74 | 66.5 | 112 |

**Club Pro:** Mike Farrell, PGA
**Payment:** Visa, MC, Amex, Disc
**Tee Times:** Weekends, 6 days adv. (members 5 days adv.)
**Fee 9 Holes: Weekday:** $24      **Weekend:** $28
**Fee 18 Holes: Weekday:** $41      **Weekend:** $47
**Twilight Rates:** Yes      **Discounts:** Senior & Junior
**Cart Rental:** $17pp/18, $9pp/9      **Driving Range:** No
**Lessons:** $30/half hour  **Schools:**      **Junior Golf:** Yes
**Membership:** Yes      **Architect/Yr Open:**
**Other:** Clubhouse / Showers / Snack Bar / Restaurant / Bar-Lounge

Hole #12 redone, overlooks Boston skyline. Now under Friel Management. "Come visit an old town course with a nice, friendly staff." –FP

| | 1 | 2 | 3 | 4 | 5 | 6 | 7 | 8 | 9 |
|------|---|---|---|---|---|---|---|---|---|
| PAR | 5 | 4 | 3 | 5 | 4 | 4 | 3 | 4 | 3 |
| YARDS | 477 | 340 | 202 | 532 | 303 | 338 | 215 | 362 | 180 |
| | 10 | 11 | 12 | 13 | 14 | 15 | 16 | 17 | 18 |
| PAR | 3 | 4 | 4 | 4 | 5 | 3 | 4 | 4 | 3 |
| YARDS | 140 | 282 | 386 | 332 | 450 | 210 | 321 | 304 | 166 |

**Directions:** From Route 1 – take left onto Essex Street then left onto Waverly Avenue. Take left onto Slayton Road.

# New England Country Club  ✪✪✪½  46 ▶

**180 Paine Street**
**Bellingham, MA (508) 883-2300**
www.newenglandcountryclub.com

| Tees | Holes | Yards | Par | USGA | Slope |
|------|-------|-------|-----|------|-------|
| BACK | 18 | 6483 | 71 | 70.9 | 135 |
| MIDDLE | 18 | 5867 | 71 | 68.2 | 125 |
| FRONT | 18 | 4927 | 71 | 68.9 | 122 |

**Club Pro:** Mark Copithorne
**Payment:** Visa, MC
**Tee Times:** 5 days adv.
**Fee 9 Holes: Weekday:** $39 w/cart M-Th      **Weekend:** $44 w/cart F/S/S
**Fee 18 Holes: Weekday:** $59 w/cart M-Th      **Weekend:** $69 w/cart F/S/S
**Twilight Rates:** After 1pm      **Discounts:** Early Bird, Senior
**Cart Rental:** Included      **Driving Range:** All grass
**Lessons:** $45/45 min.  **Schools:** Clinics      **Junior Golf:** No
**Membership:** Yes, full and partial      **Architect/Yr Open:** Hale Irwin/1990
**Other:** Clubhouse / Restaurant / Pub / Outdoor Deck / Tent / GPS Carts
**GPS:** Yes

*COUPON*

It only looks short on the card; great course from the whites—absolute killer from the blues. Great variety of holes. GPS in carts and multiple sets of tees. Spectacular, well-groomed Hale Irwin championship golf course.

| | 1 | 2 | 3 | 4 | 5 | 6 | 7 | 8 | 9 |
|------|---|---|---|---|---|---|---|---|---|
| PAR | 5 | 4 | 4 | 3 | 5 | 3 | 4 | 4 | 4 |
| YARDS | 497 | 357 | 314 | 145 | 490 | 122 | 386 | 320 | 352 |
| | 10 | 11 | 12 | 13 | 14 | 15 | 16 | 17 | 18 |
| PAR | 4 | 5 | 3 | 4 | 4 | 4 | 3 | 4 | 4 |
| YARDS | 355 | 501 | 145 | 382 | 327 | 297 | 140 | 340 | 397 |

**Directions:** I-495 North to Exit 16 (King Street). Continue west on King Street for 6 miles. At light make a left onto Wrentham Street. Bear right at the fire station onto Paine Street. Course is .25 miles up hill on left.

# New Meadows Golf Club ✪½ 47 ▶

32 Wildes Road
Topsfield, MA (978) 887-9307
www.newmeadowsgolf.com

**Club Pro:** Jerry Peckerman, Manager
**Payment:** Cash, Check
**Tee Times:** Call ahead
**Fee 9 Holes: Weekday:** $19
**Fee 18 Holes: Weekday:** $32
**Twilight Rates:** No
**Cart Rental:** $18pp/18, $9pp/9
**Lessons:** No  **Schools:** No
**Membership:** No
**Other:** Clubhouse / Snack Bar

| Tees | Holes | Yards | Par | USGA | Slope |
|------|-------|-------|-----|------|-------|
| BACK | 9 | 2906 | 35 | 68.6 | 126 |
| MIDDLE | 9 | 2692 | 35 | 66.6 | 121 |
| FRONT | 9 | 2500 | 35 | 69.2 | 117 |

**Weekend:** $22
**Weekend:** $34
**Discounts:** Juniors (under 17) - 50% off
**Driving Range:** No
**Junior Golf:** No
**Architect/Yr Open:** Phil Wogan/1964
**GPS:**

New Meadows offers a relaxed atmosphere for golfers of all ages and handicap ranges. It is especially enjoyable for seniors, women, juniors, and mid- to high- handicap golfers. Please call for tee times. New irrigation and cart paths.

| | 1 | 2 | 3 | 4 | 5 | 6 | 7 | 8 | 9 |
|-----|-----|-----|-----|-----|-----|-----|-----|-----|-----|
| PAR | 4 | 4 | 3 | 4 | 4 | 4 | 5 | 3 | 4 |
| YARDS | 352 | 365 | 160 | 348 | 345 | 368 | 459 | 128 | 358 |
| PAR | | | | | | | | | |
| YARDS | | | | | | | | | |

**Directions:** New Meadows is 1.9 miles north of the US Route 1 and Route 97 intersection, and 3.2 miles south of the US Route 1 and Route 133 intersection.

# Newton Commonwealth GC ✪✪½ 48 ▶

212 Kenrick Street
Newton, MA (617) 630-1971
www.sterlinggolf.com

**Club Pro:** Mike Albrecht, PGA
**Payment:** Cash, Most Credit Cards
**Tee Times:** 2 days adv.
**Fee 9 Holes: Weekday:** $25 M-Th
**Fee 18 Holes: Weekday:** $32 M-Th
**Twilight Rates:** After 5pm
**Cart Rental:** $16pp/18, $10pp/9
**Lessons:** $55/half hour  **Schools:** No
**Membership:** Yes
**Other:** Snack Bar

| Tees | Holes | Yards | Par | USGA | Slope |
|------|-------|-------|-----|------|-------|
| BACK | 18 | 5354 | 70 | 65.8 | 122 |
| MIDDLE | 18 | 4992 | 70 | 64.5 | 117 |
| FRONT | 18 | 4329 | 70 | 65.8 | 118 |

**Weekend:** $31 Fri
**Weekend:** $39 Fri-Sun
**Discounts:** Junior, Senior, College
**Driving Range:** No
**Junior Golf:** No
**Architect/Yr Open:** Donald Ross/1897

*COUPON*

New routing makes this a "new course" for anyone who hasn't been here recently. Resident discounts. Well-stocked pro shop. Friendly staff. Open year round. Donald Ross greens make par a challenge. New irrigation relieves formerly wet holes. New tee boxes on holes #3 and #4.

| | 1 | 2 | 3 | 4 | 5 | 6 | 7 | 8 | 9 |
|-----|-----|-----|-----|-----|-----|-----|-----|-----|-----|
| PAR | 4 | 5 | 3 | 3 | 5 | 4 | 3 | 5 | 3 |
| YARDS | 252 | 476 | 179 | 110 | 435 | 255 | 162 | 473 | 180 |
| | 10 | 11 | 12 | 13 | 14 | 15 | 16 | 17 | 18 |
| PAR | 4 | 4 | 3 | 4 | 4 | 5 | 3 | 4 | 4 |
| YARDS | 259 | 295 | 148 | 263 | 231 | 422 | 130 | 376 | 355 |

**Directions:** I-95/Route 128 to Route 30 East exit. Follow 4.8 miles to Grant Avenue. Go left and follow the golfer logo signs.

# North Hill Country Club ✪✪ 49

29 Merry Avenue
Duxbury, MA (781) 934-3249
www.northhillgolf.com

Club Pro: Paul Coutoumas, PGA
Payment: Most Major Credit Cards
Tee Times: 7 days adv.
Fee 9 Holes: Weekday: $25
Fee 18 Holes: Weekday: $36
Twilight Rates: No
Cart Rental: $22pp/18, $11pp/9
Lessons: Private and Group  Schools: No
Membership: Yes
Other: Snack Bar / Bar-Lounge / Clubhouse

Weekend: $26
Weekend: $38
Discounts: Junior
Driving Range: Limited
Junior Golf: Yes
Architect/Yr Open: William Mitchell/1962
GPS:

| Tees | Holes | Yards | Par | USGA | Slope |
|------|-------|-------|-----|------|-------|
| BACK | 9 | 3456 | 36 | 74.6 | 131 |
| MIDDLE | 9 | 3324 | 36 | 71.2 | 121 |
| FRONT | 9 | 2887 | 736 | 68.2 | 117 |

"Nice layout. Fun track." From the tips, a real challenging course.

| | 1 | 2 | 3 | 4 | 5 | 6 | 7 | 8 | 9 |
|------|-----|-----|-----|-----|-----|-----|-----|-----|-----|
| PAR | 5 | 4 | 4 | 3 | 4 | 5 | 4 | 3 | 4 |
| YARDS | 555 | 438 | 426 | 205 | 350 | 488 | 374 | 190 | 430 |
| PAR | | | | | | | | | |
| YARDS | | | | | | | | | |

Directions: Route 3 to Exit 11, get on Route 14 East, course is approximately 2 miles on right (Merry Avenue).

# Norwood Country Club ✪½ 50

400 Providence Highway
Norwood, MA (781) 769-5880
www.norwoodcc.com

Club Pro: John Resnick
Payment: Most Major Credit Cards
Tee Times: 1 week adv.
Fee 9 Holes: Weekday: $20
Fee 18 Holes: Weekday: $30
Twilight Rates: Yes
Cart Rental: $16pp/18, $10pp/9
Lessons: $60/hour  Schools: No
Membership: Season Passes Available
Other: Clubhouse / LockerShowers / Bar-Lounge / Lighted Driving Range

Weekend: $23 after 12pm
Weekend: $35 ($30 after 1pm)
Discounts: Sr, Jr, military, college
Driving Range: Yes
Junior Golf: Yes
Architect/Yr Open: Sam Mitchell/1975

COUPON

| Tees | Holes | Yards | Par | USGA | Slope |
|------|-------|-------|-----|------|-------|
| BACK | 18 | 5630 | 71 | 67.1 | 112 |
| MIDDLE | 18 | 5344 | 71 | 65.9 | 108 |
| FRONT | 18 | 4676 | 71 | 68.7 | 108 |

A straightaway track. Excellent course for seniors and beginners. Easy to walk. New cart paths in 2012. Rates subject to change. "Good practice facilities." –FP

| | 1 | 2 | 3 | 4 | 5 | 6 | 7 | 8 | 9 |
|------|-----|-----|-----|-----|-----|-----|-----|-----|-----|
| PAR | 4 | 4 | 4 | 4 | 5 | 4 | 3 | 3 | 5 |
| YARDS | 344 | 209 | 332 | 365 | 397 | 287 | 144 | 125 | 420 |
| | 10 | 11 | 12 | 13 | 14 | 15 | 16 | 17 | 18 |
| PAR | 4 | 4 | 5 | 3 | 4 | 3 | 4 | 4 | 4 |
| YARDS | 298 | 298 | 477 | 131 | 332 | 115 | 402 | 326 | 342 |

Directions: I-95/Route 128 to Route 1 South to Norwood. Note: course is on the northbound side of Route 1. To change direction, go to Norwood exit and then go around rotary and head north.

# Olde Salem Greens

**✪½** **51** ▶

75 Wilson Street
Salem, MA (978) 744-2149
www.oldesalemgreens.com

| Tees | Holes | Yards | Par | USGA | Slope |
|------|-------|-------|-----|------|-------|
| BACK | 9 | 3646 | 35 | 68.4 | 116 |
| MIDDLE | 9 | 3028 | 35 | 68.5 | 116 |
| FRONT | 9 | 2483 | 35 | 68.4 | 112 |

**Club Pro:** Scott MacDonald, Pro Shop Mgr.
**Payment:** Cash, Visa, MC, Amex
**Tee Times:** 6 days adv.
**Fee 9 Holes: Weekday:** $20 ($17 resident) **Weekend:** $21 ($18 resident)
**Fee 18 Holes: Weekday:** $35 ($30 resident) **Weekend:** $36 ($32 resident)
**Twilight Rates:** After 5pm **Discounts:** Sr. & Jr. (with restrictions)
**Cart Rental:** $15/18, $7.50/9 per person **Driving Range:** No
**Lessons:** Yes **Schools:** No **Junior Golf:** Yes
**Membership:** Passes available (please call) **Architect/Yr Open:** Stiles and Van Kleek/1933
**Other:** Snack Bar / Bar-Lounge **GPS:**

*COUPON*

Residents' rates. Putting green. Practice hole. New cart paths. Extended collars.

| | 1 | 2 | 3 | 4 | 5 | 6 | 7 | 8 | 9 |
|------|---|---|---|---|---|---|---|---|---|
| PAR | 4 | 3 | 4 | 5 | 4 | 4 | 4 | 3 | 4 |
| YARDS | 374 | 253 | 367 | 545 | 345 | 398 | 291 | 153 | 304 |
| PAR | | | | | | | | | |
| YARDS | | | | | | | | | |

**Directions:** I-95/Route 128 to Route 114 toward Salem. Take Essex Street to Highland Avenue. Take a left on Wilson Street to course.

# Olde Scotland Links

**✪✪✪** **52** ▶

695 Pine Street
Bridgewater, MA (508) 279-3344
www.oldescotlandlinks.com

| Tees | Holes | Yards | Par | USGA | Slope |
|------|-------|-------|-----|------|-------|
| BACK | 18 | 6790 | 72 | 72.6 | 126 |
| MIDDLE | 18 | 6306 | 72 | 70.3 | 124 |
| FRONT | 18 | 5396 | 72 | 70.9 | 117 |

**Club Pro:** Chris Anthony
**Payment:** Visa, MC, Amex, Disc
**Tee Times:** 7 days adv., 10 days adv. online
**Fee 9 Holes: Weekday:** $24 **Weekend:** $27
**Fee 18 Holes: Weekday:** $44 **Weekend:** $53
**Twilight Rates:** Yes **Discounts:** Senior & Junior
**Cart Rental:** $16pp/18, $9pp/9 **Driving Range:** Yes
**Lessons:** Yes **Schools:** Yes **Junior Golf:** Yes
**Membership:** Weekday Season Pass **Architect/Yr:** Cornish, Silva, Mungeam/1997
**Other:** Clubhouse **GPS:**

*COUPON*

Player Comments: "Nice layout." "Beautiful design, affordable." Walkable and enjoyable for all abilities. Open year-round. New clubhouse and function area.

| | 1 | 2 | 3 | 4 | 5 | 6 | 7 | 8 | 9 |
|------|---|---|---|---|---|---|---|---|---|
| PAR | 4 | 4 | 3 | 4 | 4 | 5 | 4 | 3 | 5 |
| YARDS | 400 | 372 | 154 | 302 | 372 | 519 | 359 | 189 | 456 |
| | 10 | 11 | 12 | 13 | 14 | 15 | 16 | 17 | 18 |
| PAR | 4 | 4 | 5 | 3 | 4 | 4 | 3 | 4 | 5 |
| YARDS | 435 | 359 | 520 | 205 | 357 | 362 | 130 | 321 | 494 |

**Directions:** I-95 to Route 24 South to Exit 15. Follow Route 104 East for about ½ mile to first set of lights. Take right onto Old Pleasant Street and follow for 2 miles. Course is on the right.

# Ould Newbury Golf Course  ✪✪   53

319 Newburyport Turnpike (Route 1)
Newbury, MA (978) 465-9888
www.ouldnewbury.com

**Club Pro:** James Hilton
**Payment:** Cash, Disc, MC, Visa
**Tee Times:** No
**Fee 9 Holes: Weekday:** $25
**Fee 18 Holes: Weekday:** $38
**Twilight Rates:** No
**Cart Rental:** $24/18, $15/9 per cart
**Lessons:** $60/45 min.  **Schools:** No
**Membership:** Yes
**Other:** Clubhouse / Lockers / Showers / Snack Bar

**Weekend:**
**Weekend:**
**Discounts:** None
**Driving Range:** No
**Junior Golf:** No
**Architect/Yr Open:** 1916

| Tees | Holes | Yards | Par | USGA | Slope |
|------|-------|-------|-----|------|-------|
| BACK | 9 | 3115 | 35 | 71.8 | 129 |
| MIDDLE | 9 | 2943 | 35 | 69.4 | 120 |
| FRONT | 9 | 2723 | 38 | 71.3 | 126 |

Sig. Hole: #9 is a 207-yard uphill par 3 that requires a shot over a 50-foot hickory tree. Closed to public on weekends.

| | 1 | 2 | 3 | 4 | 5 | 6 | 7 | 8 | 9 |
|------|-----|-----|-----|-----|-----|-----|-----|-----|-----|
| PAR | 4 | 5 | 4 | 4 | 4 | 3 | 4 | 4 | 3 |
| YARDS | 394 | 453 | 359 | 401 | 298 | 143 | 373 | 318 | 204 |
| PAR | | | | | | | | | |
| YARDS | | | | | | | | | |

**Directions:** I-95 to Exit 55 (Central Street/Byfield-Newbury). Turn East and follow signs to Governor Dummer Academy. At the intersection of Route 1, turn left. Club entrance is 600 yards on the right.

# Pembroke Country Club  ✪✪✪✪  54

94 West Elm Street
Pembroke, MA (781) 829-2273
www.pembrokegolf.com

**Club Pro:** Nick Emerson
**Payment:** Visa, MC, Amex, Disc, Cash, Check
**Tee Times:** 7 days adv.
**Fee 9 Holes: Weekday:** $29
**Fee 18 Holes: Weekday:** $40
**Twilight Rates:** Weekends after 2pm
**Cart Rental:** $19pp/18, $10pp/9
**Lessons:** Yes  **Schools:** Yes
**Membership:** Yes
**Other:** Clubhouse / Restaurant / Bar-Lounge

**Weekend:** $29 after 2pm
**Weekend:** $50
**Discounts:** Sr. 60+, Jr. -18
**Driving Range:** Yes
**Junior Golf:** Yes
**Architect/Yr Open:** Phil Wogan/1972

| Tees | Holes | Yards | Par | USGA | Slope |
|------|-------|-------|-----|------|-------|
| BACK | 18 | 6677 | 71 | 73.3 | 132 |
| MIDDLE | 18 | 6329 | 71 | 71.8 | 125 |
| FRONT | 18 | 5343 | 72 | 72.2 | 124 |

Pembroke Country Club is a championship 18 hole golf course. The secluded par 71 is nestled amongst the tall pines of the South Shore. With narrow fairways and five par fours over 420 yards, it provides challenge for all golfers. "Recent ownership change, greatly improved conditions, outing friendly venue." –SD

| | 1 | 2 | 3 | 4 | 5 | 6 | 7 | 8 | 9 |
|------|-----|-----|-----|-----|-----|-----|-----|-----|-----|
| PAR | 5 | 4 | 3 | 4 | 4 | 4 | 3 | 4 | 4 |
| YARDS | 504 | 323 | 181 | 434 | 402 | 346 | 143 | 420 | 341 |
| | 10 | 11 | 12 | 13 | 14 | 15 | 16 | 17 | 18 |
| PAR | 4 | 3 | 4 | 5 | 4 | 4 | 4 | 3 | 5 |
| YARDS | 385 | 159 | 428 | 547 | 343 | 371 | 347 | 182 | 473 |

**Directions:** Route 3 South. Exit 13 turn right (3.2 miles) on Broadway. Stay left at both forks; course is located 2 miles on right-hand side.

# Pinecrest Golf Club

✪✪½ ▶ 55

212 Prentice Street
Holliston, MA (774) 233-0579
www.pinecrestgolfclub.org

**Club Pro:** Bill Allen, PGA
**Payment:** Cash or Credit
**Tee Times:** Sat, Sun

| Tees | Holes | Yards | Par | USGA | Slope |
|------|-------|-------|-----|------|-------|
| BACK | | | | | |
| MIDDLE | 18 | 4906 | 66 | 63.2 | 103 |
| FRONT | 18 | 4260 | 66 | 63.2 | 103 |

**Fee 9 Holes: Weekday:** $17    **Weekend:** $21
**Fee 18 Holes: Weekday:** $28    **Weekend:** $32
**Twilight Rates:** After 5pm wkdys, 4pm wknds   **Discounts:** Senior & Junior
**Cart Rental:** $14pp/18, $8pp/9   **Driving Range:** Yes, grass
**Lessons:** Yes **Schools:** Yes   **Junior Golf:** Yes
**Membership:** Yes   **Architect/Yr Open:** 1955
**Other:** Clubhouse / Snack Bar / Bar-Lounge / Restaurant

COUPON

The course is relatively level and easy to walk. Very tight greens that are a true test of one's iron shot accuracy. The par 3s are fairly long. Most golfers are able to play 18 holes in under 4 hours.

| | 1 | 2 | 3 | 4 | 5 | 6 | 7 | 8 | 9 |
|------|-----|-----|-----|-----|-----|-----|-----|-----|-----|
| PAR | 4 | 3 | 4 | 3 | 4 | 3 | 4 | 4 | 4 |
| YARDS | 398 | 165 | 275 | 153 | 325 | 190 | 317 | 305 | 295 |
| | **10** | **11** | **12** | **13** | **14** | **15** | **16** | **17** | **18** |
| PAR | 3 | 4 | 3 | 5 | 4 | 4 | 4 | 3 | 3 |
| YARDS | 165 | 264 | 205 | 472 | 245 | 405 | 305 | 200 | 222 |

**Directions:** I-495 to Route 85 Exit 20 toward Holliston. Follow 3 miles to first flashing yellow light. Take right onto Chestnut Street, look for signs.

# Pinehills Golf Club (Jones)

✪✪✪✪✪ ▶ 56

54 Clubhouse Drive
Plymouth, MA (508) 209-3000
www.pinehillsgolf.com

**Club Pro:** John Tuffin, PGA
**Payment:** Visa, MC, Amex, Checks
**Tee Times:** 7 days adv.

| Tees | Holes | Yards | Par | USGA | Slope |
|------|-------|-------|-----|------|-------|
| BACK | 18 | 7175 | 72 | 73.8 | 135 |
| MIDDLE | 18 | 6762 | 72 | 72.4 | 131 |
| FRONT | 18 | 6201 | 72 | 69.6 | 125 |

**Fee 18 Holes: Weekday:** $100 cart/range balls M-Th
          **Weekend:** $110 cart/range balls F/S/S/H
**Twilight Rates:** $60 after 3pm M-Th, $70 after 2pm F/S/S
**Discounts:** None
**Cart Rental:** Included
**Lessons:** Yes **Schools:** Yes   **Driving Range:** Natural Grass
**Membership:** Yes   **Junior Golf:** Yes
**Other:** Clubhouse / Grill / Bar / Banquet Facilities / Lockers / Showers / Restaurant   **Architect/Yr Open:** Rees Jones/2001

COUPON

"Excellent layout. Challenging but fair for men or women. Friendliest staff, best service ever encountered." –AP
"Greens slightly easier than Nicklaus, but tougher to get to them. Many dramatic holes." –JD

| | 1 | 2 | 3 | 4 | 5 | 6 | 7 | 8 | 9 |
|------|-----|-----|-----|-----|-----|-----|-----|-----|-----|
| PAR | 4 | 4 | 5 | 3 | 4 | 4 | 3 | 4 | 5 |
| YARDS | 348 | 404 | 501 | 177 | 403 | 431 | 165 | 397 | 552 |
| | **10** | **11** | **12** | **13** | **14** | **15** | **16** | **17** | **18** |
| PAR | 4 | 5 | 4 | 4 | 3 | 5 | 4 | 3 | 4 |
| YARDS | 360 | 548 | 420 | 370 | 219 | 495 | 401 | 169 | 402 |

**Directions:** Route 3 South, Exit 3. Turn left and follow signs.

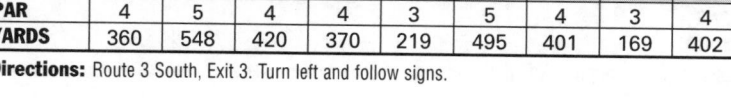

# Pinehills GC (Nicklaus)  ✪✪✪✪✪  57 ▶

54 Clubhouse Drive
Plymouth, MA (508) 209-3000
www.pinehillsgolf.com

**Club Pro:** John Tuffin, PGA
**Payment:** Visa, MC, Amex, Checks
**Tee Times:** 7 days adv. (866) 855-4653

| Tees | Holes | Yards | Par | USGA | Slope |
|------|-------|-------|-----|------|-------|
| BACK | 18 | 6640 | 72 | 71.7 | 131 |
| MIDDLE | 18 | 6129 | 72 | 69.3 | 125 |
| FRONT | 18 | 5185 | 72 | 69.4 | 123 |

**Fee 9 Holes: Weekday:**                    **Weekend:**
**Fee 18 Holes: Weekday:** $100 cart/range balls M-Th
          **Weekend:** $110 cart/range balls F/S/S/H
**Twilight Rates:** After 3:30pm          **Discounts:** None
**Cart Rental:** Included          **Driving Range:** Natural grass/mats
**Lessons:** Yes  **Schools:** Yes          **Junior Golf:** Yes
**Membership:** No          **Architect/Yr Open:** Jack Nicklaus II/2002
**Other:** Clubhouse / Grill / Bar / Banquet Facilites / Lockers / Showers / Restaurant / Caddy Program

Player Comments: "Broader fairways than Jones, trickier greens." Great and beautiful design, fine clubhouse, top-flight service. *New England GolfGuide's* first-ever 5-star course.

|  | 1 | 2 | 3 | 4 | 5 | 6 | 7 | 8 | 9 |
|------|---|---|---|---|---|---|---|---|---|
| PAR | 4 | 5 | 3 | 4 | 4 | 5 | 3 | 4 | 4 |
| YARDS | 357 | 500 | 199 | 365 | 357 | 491 | 145 | 343 | 326 |
|  | 10 | 11 | 12 | 13 | 14 | 15 | 16 | 17 | 18 |
| PAR | 4 | 5 | 4 | 3 | 4 | 3 | 5 | 4 | 4 |
| YARDS | 365 | 486 | 403 | 165 | 280 | 144 | 486 | 344 | 373 |

**Directions:** Route 3 South, Exit 3. Turn left and follow signs.

# Pine Meadows Golf Club  ✪✪  58 ▶

255 Cedar Street
Lexington, MA (781) 862-5516
www.pinemeadowsgolfclub.com

**Club Pro:** Joe McKinney
**Payment:** Cash, Visa, MC
**Tee Times:** 7 days adv.

| Tees | Holes | Yards | Par | USGA | Slope |
|------|-------|-------|-----|------|-------|
| BACK | | | | | |
| MIDDLE | 9 | 2759 | 35 | 64.5 | 105 |
| FRONT | 9 | 2405 | 35 | 69.2 | 117 |

**Fee 9 Holes: Weekday:** $21          **Weekend:** $23
**Fee 18 Holes: Weekday:** $31          **Weekend:** $33
**Twilight Rates:** No          **Discounts:** Srs, Jrs., Residents
**Cart Rental:** $8pp/9          **Driving Range:**
**Lessons:** Yes  **Schools:** No          **Junior Golf:** No
**Membership:** No          **Architect/Yr Open:**
**Other:** Snack Bar          **GPS:**

The course has open fairways and is excellent for beginners and intermediate players.

|  | 1 | 2 | 3 | 4 | 5 | 6 | 7 | 8 | 9 |
|------|---|---|---|---|---|---|---|---|---|
| PAR | 5 | 5 | 4 | 3 | 4 | 3 | 4 | 4 | 3 |
| YARDS | 484 | 481 | 241 | 225 | 336 | 201 | 324 | 301 | 166 |
| PAR | | | | | | | | | |
| YARDS | | | | | | | | | |

**Directions:** I-95/Route 128 to Exit 31A. Go through 2 lights, take right onto Hill Street, take right onto Cedar Street.

# Pine Oaks Golf Course ✪✪½ ▶59

68 Prospect Street
S. Easton, MA (508) 238-2320
www.pineoaks.com

**Club Pro:** Leigh Bader, PGA
**Payment:** Visa, MC, Amex, Disc
**Tee Times:** No

| Tees | Holes | Yards | Par | USGA | Slope |
|------|-------|-------|-----|------|-------|
| BACK | 9 | 2973 | 34 | 67.0 | 115 |
| MIDDLE | 9 | 2912 | 34 | 67.0 | 111 |
| FRONT | 9 | 2500 | 34 | 67.0 | 111 |

**Fee 9 Holes: Weekday:** $23
**Fee 18 Holes: Weekday:** $30
**Twilight Rates:** After 4pm
**Cart Rental:** $13pp/18, $7.50pp/9
**Lessons:** Yes **Schools:** Yes
**Membership:** Yes

**Weekend:** $25
**Weekend:** $36
**Discounts:** Senior & Junior M-F
**Driving Range:** No
**Junior Golf:** Yes
**Architect/Yr Open:** Geoffrey Cornish/1964

COUPON

**Other:** Clubhouse / Lockers / Snack Bar / Bar-Lounge / Discount Golf Shop

New short game practice area. Plenty of water for a 9-hole course. New bunkers with 5 new tee areas. *Golf Shop Operations* "Top 100 Pro Shop" for the last 10 years. A number of Pros on staff for equipment sales or lessons.

| | 1 | 2 | 3 | 4 | 5 | 6 | 7 | 8 | 9 |
|------|---|---|---|---|---|---|---|---|---|
| PAR | 4 | 5 | 4 | 3 | 4 | 3 | 3 | 4 | 4 |
| YARDS | 326 | 558 | 407 | 175 | 378 | 245 | 149 | 302 | 372 |
| PAR | | | | | | | | | |
| YARDS | | | | | | | | | |

**Directions:** Route 24 to Exit 16B, straight for 3.5 miles, right on Prospect Street.

# Ponkapoag Golf Club (#1) ✪½ ▶60

2167 Washington Street
Canton, MA (781) 828-4242
www.ponkapoaggolf.com

**Club Pro:** Michael Fleming, PGA
**Payment:** Visa, MC, Cash
**Tee Times:**

| Tees | Holes | Yards | Par | USGA | Slope |
|------|-------|-------|-----|------|-------|
| BACK | 18 | 6545 | 72 | 72.0 | 126 |
| MIDDLE | 18 | 6010 | 72 | 69.8 | 120 |
| FRONT | 18 | 5316 | 74 | 70.8 | 115 |

**Fee 9 Holes: Weekday:** $19 M-Th
**Fee 18 Holes: Weekday:** $27 M-Th
**Twilight Rates:** No
**Cart Rental:** $17pp/18, $8pp/9
**Lessons:** Yes **Schools:** Junior
**Membership:** Limited, Juniors

**Weekend:** $19 F/S/S
**Weekend:** $30 F/S/S
**Discounts:** Sr. & Jr. weekdays
**Driving Range:** $7/bucket
**Junior Golf:** Yes
**Architect/Yr Open:** Donald Ross

**Other:** Restaurant / Clubhouse / Beer & Wine / Showers

A great design by Donald Ross with a rustic feeling. April -December.

| | 1 | 2 | 3 | 4 | 5 | 6 | 7 | 8 | 9 |
|------|---|---|---|---|---|---|---|---|---|
| PAR | 4 | 3 | 5 | 4 | 4 | 4 | 4 | 3 | 5 |
| YARDS | 370 | 135 | 490 | 304 | 375 | 412 | 380 | 170 | 425 |
| | 10 | 11 | 12 | 13 | 14 | 15 | 16 | 17 | 18 |
| PAR | 4 | 5 | 3 | 5 | 4 | 4 | 3 | 4 | 4 |
| YARDS | 335 | 440 | 162 | 440 | 344 | 382 | 206 | 345 | 295 |

**Directions:** I-93 to Exit 2A. Go south on Route 138 (Washington Street) into Canton. Clubhouse is on left at first light.

# Ponkapoag Golf Club (#2)           ✪½  61 ▶

2167 Washington Street
Canton, MA  (781) 828-4242
www.ponkapoaggolf.com

| Tees | Holes | Yards | Par | USGA | Slope |
|------|-------|-------|-----|------|-------|
| BACK | 18 | 6195 | 71 | 70.3 | 116 |
| MIDDLE | 18 | 5712 | 71 | 67.5 | 112 |
| FRONT | 18 | 5028 | 72 | 68.5 | 113 |

**Club Pro:** Michael Fleming, PGA
**Payment:** Visa, MC, Cash
**Tee Times:**
**Fee 9 Holes: Weekday:** $19 M-Th        **Weekend:** $19 F/S/S
**Fee 18 Holes: Weekday:** $27 M-Th       **Weekend:** $30 F/S/S
**Twilight Rates:** No                     **Discounts:** Senior & Junior
**Cart Rental:** $17pp/18, $8pp/9          **Driving Range:** $7/bucket
**Lessons:** Yes  **Schools:** Junior      **Junior Golf:** Yes
**Membership:** Limited, Juniors           **Architect/Yr Open:** Donald Ross
**Other:** Restaurant / Clubhouse / Beer & Wine / Showers

A great design by Donald Ross with a rustic feeling.

|  | 1 | 2 | 3 | 4 | 5 | 6 | 7 | 8 | 9 |
|------|-----|-----|-----|-----|-----|-----|-----|-----|-----|
| PAR | 4 | 4 | 3 | 5 | 4 | 4 | 4 | 3 | 4 |
| YARDS | 364 | 407 | 188 | 456 | 249 | 389 | 312 | 150 | 377 |
|  | **10** | **11** | **12** | **13** | **14** | **15** | **16** | **17** | **18** |
| PAR | 5 | 3 | 4 | 5 | 4 | 3 | 4 | 4 | 4 |
| YARDS | 450 | 125 | 315 | 448 | 320 | 160 | 340 | 300 | 362 |

**Directions:** I-93 South to Exit 2A. Go south on Route 138 (Washington Street) into Canton.
Clubhouse is on left at first light.

# Presidents Golf Course           ✪✪½  62 ▶

357 West Squantum Street
Quincy, MA  (617) 328-3444
www.presidentsgc.com

| Tees | Holes | Yards | Par | USGA | Slope |
|------|-------|-------|-----|------|-------|
| BACK | 18 | 5750 | 70 | 68.1 | 125 |
| MIDDLE | 18 | 5260 | 70 | 66.2 | 118 |
| FRONT | 18 | 4425 | 71 | 66.8 | 113 |

**Club Pro:** Dana Smith, PGA
**Payment:** Visa, MC
**Tee Times:** 2 days adv. Fri/Sat/Sun
**Fee 9 Holes: Weekday:**                  **Weekend:**
**Fee 18 Holes: Weekday:** $38 M-Th        **Weekend:** $47
**Twilight Rates:** After 4pm              **Discounts:** Senior & Junior (M-Th)
**Cart Rental:** $16pp/18, $16 per cart/9  **Driving Range:** No
**Lessons:** $40/half hour  **Schools:** No  **Junior Golf:** Yes
**Membership:** Yes                        **Architect/Yr Open:** Tom & George Fazio/1977
**Other:** Clubhouse / Lockers / Showers / Snack Bar / Restaurant / Putting Green / Bar-Lounge

Player Comments: "Home of Norfolk County Classic. Championship tees are true test of your short game.
Greens are sloping and fast. You have to have the short stick working well." Incredible views of the
Boston skyline, Neponset River and Blue Hill Reservation.

|  | 1 | 2 | 3 | 4 | 5 | 6 | 7 | 8 | 9 |
|------|-----|-----|-----|-----|-----|-----|-----|-----|-----|
| PAR | 4 | 3 | 4 | 3 | 5 | 4 | 3 | 4 | 4 |
| YARDS | 345 | 90 | 270 | 150 | 440 | 415 | 120 | 350 | 330 |
|  | **10** | **11** | **12** | **13** | **14** | **15** | **16** | **17** | **18** |
| PAR | 3 | 4 | 5 | 3 | 4 | 5 | 5 | 4 | 3 |
| YARDS | 150 | 260 | 465 | 165 | 365 | 460 | 480 | 300 | 105 |

**Directions:** I-93 to Exit 11A (Granite Avenue). Take left at first light (approx. 1 mile). Take left at next
light. From I-93 North, take Exit 9 (Adams Street). Go straight approx. 1 mile. Right 1 mile at lights.
Left at next light.

# Quail Ridge Country Club  ✪✪✪  63 ▶

354 Great Road
Acton, MA  (978) 264-0399
www.quailridgegolfclub.com

**Club Pro:** Mark Laviano, PGA
**Payment:** Visa, MC
**Tee Times:** 7 days adv.

| Tees | Holes | Yards | Par | USGA | Slope |
|------|-------|-------|-----|------|-------|
| BACK | 9 | 3068 | 35 | 70.5 | 134 |
| MIDDLE | 9 | 2882 | 35 | 68.6 | 128 |
| FRONT | 9 | 2740 | 35 | 67.8 | 120 |

**Fee  9 Holes: Weekday:** $22      **Weekend:** $25
**Fee 18 Holes: Weekday:** $33      **Weekend:** $34
**Twilight Rates:** After 4pm       **Discounts:** Sr & Jr (M-Th anytime)
**Cart Rental:** $15pp/18, $10pp/9  **Driving Range:** Yes
**Lessons:** Yes **Schools:** Yes  **Junior Golf:** Yes
**Membership:** Yes, starting at $975 per year  **Architect/Yr Open:** Mark Mungeam/2003
**Other:** Restaurant / Clubhouse / Showers / Bar-Lounge

*COUPON*

Members play golf on a modern, yet classically designed course. Situated in a forested valley in the town of Acton, Massachusetts, just 30 miles from Boston's hub. The course is bound by conservation land and tree lined fairways. Footgolf added it 2014. "Excellent challenge—give it a try." –FP

| | 1 | 2 | 3 | 4 | 5 | 6 | 7 | 8 | 9 |
|------|-----|-----|-----|-----|-----|-----|-----|-----|-----|
| PAR | 5 | 4 | 4 | 3 | 4 | 4 | 4 | 4 | 3 |
| YARDS | 541 | 316 | 415 | 154 | 324 | 316 | 308 | 337 | 168 |
| PAR | | | | | | | | | |
| YARDS | | | | | | | | | |

**Directions:** 495 North or South to Route 2 East, Exit 29A. Then take Exit 42, go left onto Route 27, follow to intersection of 2A and 119. Left at light. Quail Ridge is 100 yards on left.

# Reedy Meadow GC at Lynnfield  ✪  64 ▶

195 Summer Street
Lynnfield, MA  (781) 334-9877
www.town.lynnfield.ma.us/golf

**Club Pro:** Donnie Lyons, PGA
**Payment:** Cash or Credit
**Tee Times:** No

| Tees | Holes | Yards | Par | USGA | Slope |
|------|-------|-------|-----|------|-------|
| BACK | 9 | 2560 | 34 | 63.8 | |
| MIDDLE | 9 | 2485 | 34 | 63.0 | 102 |
| FRONT | 9 | 2240 | 68 | 64.8 | 94 |

**Fee  9 Holes: Weekday:** $21      **Weekend:** $22
**Fee 18 Holes: Weekday:** $31      **Weekend:** $32
**Twilight Rates:** After 6pm       **Discounts:** Senior (M-F) & Junior
**Cart Rental:** $13pp/18, $8pp/9   **Driving Range:** No
**Lessons:** Yes **Schools:** Yes  **Junior Golf:** Yes
**Membership:** $850/5-day; $950/7-day  **Architect/Yr Open:**
**Other:** Clubhouse / Bar-Lounge / Snack Bar  **GPS:**

*COUPON*

Many cosmetic changes to this course. Great greens. Family and junior friendly.

| | 1 | 2 | 3 | 4 | 5 | 6 | 7 | 8 | 9 |
|------|-----|-----|-----|-----|-----|-----|-----|-----|-----|
| PAR | 4 | 4 | 3 | 4 | 5 | 3 | 4 | 4 | 3 |
| YARDS | 350 | 355 | 225 | 260 | 476 | 139 | 270 | 340 | 145 |
| PAR | | | | | | | | | |
| YARDS | | | | | | | | | |

**Directions:** I-95/Route 128 to Exit 41; follow to Main Street in Lynnfield Center.

# Ridder Golf Club

★★  65

Route 14, Oak Street
Whitman, MA (781) 447-9003
www.ridderfarm.com

| Tees | Holes | Yards | Par | USGA | Slope |
|---|---|---|---|---|---|
| BACK | 18 | 5909 | 70 | 68.1 | 113 |
| MIDDLE | 18 | 5857 | 70 | 66.3 | 110 |
| FRONT | 18 | 4981 | 70 | 67.1 | 107 |

**Club Pro:** Tim Kilcoyne
**Payment:** Visa, MC
**Tee Times:** 7 days adv.
**Fee  9 Holes: Weekday:** $20
**Fee 18 Holes: Weekday:** $37.50
**Twilight Rates:** No
**Cart Rental:** $12.50pp/18, $6.25pp/9
**Lessons:** $45/half hour  **Schools:** Jr.
**Membership:** Yes, annual fee
**Other:** Restaurant / Snack Bar / Bar-Lounge

**Weekend:** $25
**Weekend:** $47.50
**Discounts:** Junior
**Driving Range:** Yes
**Junior Golf:** Yes
**Architect/Yr Open:** Hohman & Cornish/1961
**GPS:**

Junior summer program. New 6th tee. Open March - December. Great walking course. Roomy fairways on front, tighter back 9.

| | 1 | 2 | 3 | 4 | 5 | 6 | 7 | 8 | 9 |
|---|---|---|---|---|---|---|---|---|---|
| PAR | 4 | 4 | 3 | 4 | 4 | 4 | 4 | 3 | 4 |
| YARDS | 334 | 368 | 154 | 289 | 384 | 299 | 257 | 197 | 387 |
| | 10 | 11 | 12 | 13 | 14 | 15 | 16 | 17 | 18 |
| PAR | 4 | 5 | 4 | 3 | 4 | 3 | 4 | 5 | 4 |
| YARDS | 312 | 468 | 370 | 166 | 427 | 225 | 385 | 476 | 359 |

**Directions:** Route 3 to Route 18 South for 9-10 miles. Then Route 14 East for 2.2 miles.

# River Bend Country Club

★★★ 66

250 East Center Street
West Bridgewater, MA
(508) 580-3673
www.riverbendcc.com

| Tees | Holes | Yards | Par | USGA | Slope |
|---|---|---|---|---|---|
| BACK | 18 | 6312 | 71 | 69.9 | 125 |
| MIDDLE | 18 | 5773 | 71 | 67.6 | 124 |
| FRONT | 18 | 4915 | 71 | 67.7 | 120 |

**Club Pro:** Lyman J. Doane II, PGA
**Payment:** Most Major Cards, No Checks
**Tee Times:** 7 days adv.
**Fee  9 Holes: Weekday:** $20
**Fee 18 Holes: Weekday:** $37
**Twilight Rates:** After 5pm
**Cart Rental:** $15pp/18, $10pp/9
**Lessons:** No  **Schools:**
**Membership:** Yes, Inner Club
**Other:** Bar-Lounge / Snack Bar

**Weekend:** $24 after 2pm F/S/S
**Weekend:** $44 F, $48 S/S
**Discounts:** Sr. & Jr., M-F
**Driving Range:** No
**Junior Golf:** No
**Architect/Yr Open:** Phil Wogan/1997
**GPS:**

Sig. Hole: #17, 162-yard par 3. "...manicured magnificently, very fair greens." –RW "Great conditions. The greens hold and putt wonderfully." –KR "Key to scoring here is smart course management. Use the driver less." –AG

| | 1 | 2 | 3 | 4 | 5 | 6 | 7 | 8 | 9 |
|---|---|---|---|---|---|---|---|---|---|
| PAR | 4 | 5 | 4 | 3 | 4 | 4 | 4 | 3 | 4 |
| YARDS | 330 | 436 | 286 | 113 | 333 | 345 | 337 | 166 | 361 |
| | 10 | 11 | 12 | 13 | 14 | 15 | 16 | 17 | 18 |
| PAR | 4 | 4 | 4 | 4 | 3 | 4 | 5 | 3 | 5 |
| YARDS | 358 | 326 | 363 | 317 | 171 | 340 | 501 | 162 | 516 |

**Directions:** I-95/Route 128 to Route 24 South. Take Exit 16A onto Route 106 East for 2.5 miles. Course is on the right.

# Robert T. Lynch Municipal GC ✪✪½  67 ▶

1281 West Roxbury Parkway
Brookline, MA (617) 730-2078
www.brooklinegolf.com

| Tees | Holes | Yards | Par | USGA | Slope |
|------|-------|-------|-----|------|-------|
| BACK | 18 | 6317 | 71 | 70.4 | 124 |
| MIDDLE | 18 | 5958 | 71 | 68.4 | 117 |
| FRONT | 18 | 5615 | 72 | 72.5 | 119 |

**Club Pro:** Tom Ellis, PGA
**Payment:** Visa, MC, Amex, Cash
**Tee Times:** 6 days adv. online
**Fee  9 Holes: Weekday:** $26
**Fee 18 Holes: Weekday:** $39
**Twilight Rates:** After 4pm
**Cart Rental:** $19pp/18, $14pp/9
**Lessons:** $45/half hour  **Schools:** Junior
**Membership:** No
**Other:** Restaurant / Clubhouse / Bar-Lounge

**Weekend:** $28
**Weekend:** $41
**Discounts:** Juniors (25/50 play punch cards)
**Driving Range:** Yes
**Junior Golf:** Yes
**Architect/Yr Open:** Stiles & Van Kleek/1931
**GPS:**

Improvements: Tight fairways, elevated greens, low terrain, small hills, and lots of brooks.
Dress code: collared shirts.

| | 1 | 2 | 3 | 4 | 5 | 6 | 7 | 8 | 9 |
|------|---|---|---|---|---|---|---|---|---|
| **PAR** | 5 | 4 | 3 | 4 | 3 | 5 | 4 | 4 | 4 |
| **YARDS** | 460 | 335 | 148 | 317 | 177 | 506 | 340 | 390 | 365 |
| | **10** | **11** | **12** | **13** | **14** | **15** | **16** | **17** | **18** |
| **PAR** | 4 | 4 | 3 | 4 | 4 | 5 | 4 | 3 | 4 |
| **YARDS** | 330 | 290 | 119 | 380 | 400 | 520 | 330 | 160 | 391 |

**Directions:** I-95 to Route 9 East, 4 miles to Chestnut Hill Mall on left. Exit onto Hammond Street. Go to rotary; 4th right to Newton Street. 100 yards on left. From Boston: Route 9 to Hammond Street. Turn left. 1 mile to rotary — 4th right to Newton Street. 100 yards on left.

# Rockland Golf Course ✪✪½  68 ▶

276 Plain Street
Rockland, MA (781) 871-0480
www.rocklandgolfcourse.com

| Tees | Holes | Yards | Par | USGA | Slope |
|------|-------|-------|-----|------|-------|
| BACK | 18 | 3190 | 54 | 56.0 | 78 |
| MIDDLE | 18 | 2764 | 54 | 58.0 | 87 |
| FRONT | 18 | 3062 | 60 | | |

**Club Pro:** John Dalrymple, PGA
**Payment:** Visa, MC, Disc, Amex
**Tee Times:** 3 days adv.
**Fee  9 Holes: Weekday:** $18
**Fee 18 Holes: Weekday:** $28
**Twilight Rates:** After 2pm weekends
**Cart Rental:** $15pp/18, $9pp/9
**Lessons:** Yes  **Schools:** Yes
**Membership:** Yes
**Other:** Clubhouse / Snack Bar / Restaurant / Bar-Lounge

**Weekend:** $22, $18 after 2pm
**Weekend:** $32
**Discounts:** Sr/Jr/Military/College
**Driving Range:** No
**Junior Golf:** Yes
**Architect/Yr Open:** Skip & Phil Wogan/1964

COUPON

Longest par 3 course in the nation. Tees and greens are in excellent shap. Now managed by Sterling Golf Management. Check for early bird rates. You can play every club in your bag at this great 18-hole, par 3 course. "Nice course, easy to play, easy to walk."

| | 1 | 2 | 3 | 4 | 5 | 6 | 7 | 8 | 9 |
|------|---|---|---|---|---|---|---|---|---|
| **PAR** | 3 | 3 | 3 | 3 | 3 | 3 | 3 | 3 | 3 |
| **YARDS** | 220 | 140 | 221 | 140 | 158 | 160 | 170 | 110 | 195 |
| | **10** | **11** | **12** | **13** | **14** | **15** | **16** | **17** | **18** |
| **PAR** | 3 | 3 | 3 | 3 | 3 | 3 | 3 | 3 | 3 |
| **YARDS** | 224 | 215 | 139 | 210 | 164 | 235 | 170 | 142 | 177 |

**Directions:** Route 3 to Exit 16B. Left onto Route 139 for 3 to 4 miles. Course is on right.

# Rockport Golf Club

**✪✪✪**

## 69

36 Country Club Road
Rockport, MA (978) 546-3340
www.rockportgolfclub.net

**Club Pro:** Stephen Clayton, PGA
**Payment:** Visa, MC, Personal Checks
**Tee Times:** 1 day adv.
**Fee 9 Holes: Weekday:** $25
**Fee 18 Holes: Weekday:** $37
**Twilight Rates:** No
**Cart Rental:** $22pp/18, $13pp/9
**Lessons:** $50/half hour  **Schools:** No
**Membership:** Yes
**Other:** Pro Shop

| Tees | Holes | Yards | Par | USGA | Slope |
|------|-------|-------|-----|------|-------|
| BACK | | | | | |
| MIDDLE | 9 | 3077 | 35 | 69.8 | 125 |
| FRONT | 9 | 2795 | 37 | 72.5 | 125 |

**Weekend:** $25
**Weekend:** $37
**Discounts:** No
**Driving Range:** No
**Junior Golf:** No
**Architect/Yr Open:** 1914

Excellent 9-hole course using different tees for 1st and 2nd nines. Easy walking course that provides a good test of golf. Open to the public on weekends after 3:30pm. "Worth the ride to Rockport." –FP

| | 1 | 2 | 3 | 4 | 5 | 6 | 7 | 8 | 9 |
|------|-----|-----|-----|-----|-----|-----|-----|-----|-----|
| **PAR** | 3 | 4 | 4 | 5 | 4 | 4 | 3 | 4 | 4 |
| **YARDS** | 165 | 349 | 353 | 528 | 348 | 430 | 136 | 402 | 368 |
| **PAR** | | | | | | | | | |
| **YARDS** | | | | | | | | | |

**Directions:** 128 North to Gloucester, MA. At intersection of Route 127 – turn left towards Rockport. At the 5 corner interesection proceed onto Broadway and turn right at end. Travel ¾ mile to Country Club Road on right.

# Rowley Country Club

**✪✪**

## 70

235 Dodge Road
Rowley, MA (978) 948-2731
www.rowleycountryclub.com

**Club Pro:** Darin Chin-Aleung, PGA
**Payment:** Visa, MC, Amex, Disc
**Tee Times:** 1 week adv.
**Fee 9 Holes: Weekday:** $20
**Fee 18 Holes: Weekday:** $33
**Twilight Rates:** After 5:30pm
**Cart Rental:** $19pp/18, $9.50 pp/9
**Lessons:** Yes  **Schools:** No
**Membership:** Yes
**Other:** Clubhouse / Bar-Lounge / Short Game School / Parent-Child Lessons

| Tees | Holes | Yards | Par | USGA | Slope |
|------|-------|-------|-----|------|-------|
| BACK | 9 | 3098 | 35 | 71.3 | 125 |
| MIDDLE | 9 | 2838 | 35 | 71.3 | 125 |
| FRONT | 9 | 2380 | 35 | 68.5 | 122 |

**Weekend:** $22
**Weekend:** $35
**Discounts:** Senior & Junior
**Driving Range:** No
**Junior Golf:** Yes
**Architect/Yr Open:**

COUPON

Formerly Carriage Pines Golf Club. "Voted best 9-hole course on the North Shore." –JF (PGA) Nike golf camps. Yardage below from back tees. Opened new kitchen with pub-style menu in August 2015.

| | 1 | 2 | 3 | 4 | 5 | 6 | 7 | 8 | 9 |
|------|-----|-----|-----|-----|-----|-----|-----|-----|-----|
| **PAR** | 4 | 3 | 4 | 5 | 4 | 4 | 3 | 4 | 4 |
| **YARDS** | 346 | 184 | 366 | 460 | 345 | 326 | 151 | 330 | 330 |
| **PAR** | | | | | | | | | |
| **YARDS** | | | | | | | | | |

**Directions:** I-95 to Exit 54A (Rowley/Georgetown) Route 133. Go 2 miles to Rowley Country Club sign and make left. Follow for 1 mile, club is on right.

# Sagamore Spring Golf Club  ✪✪  71 ▶

1287 Main Street
Lynnfield, MA (781) 334-3151
www.sagamoregolf.com

**Club Pro:** Steven Vaughn, PGA
**Payment:** Cash, Credit Cards
**Tee Times:** 7 days adv.

| Tees | Holes | Yards | Par | USGA | Slope |
|------|-------|-------|-----|------|-------|
| BACK | 18 | 5936 | 70 | 68.9 | 124 |
| MIDDLE | 18 | 5505 | 70 | 66.8 | 118 |
| FRONT | 18 | 4784 | 70 | 67.7 | 115 |

**Fee 9 Holes: Weekday:** $26, $37w/cart
**Fee 18 Holes: Weekday:** $44, $62w/cart
**Twilight Rates:** After 3pm weekends
**Cart Rental:** $18pp/18, $11pp/9
**Lessons:** $50/half hour  **Schools:** No
**Membership:** No
**Other:** Clubhouse / Showers / Bar-Lounge

**Weekend:** $28, $39 w/cart
**Weekend:** $50, $68 w/cart
**Discounts:** Senior and Junior
**Driving Range:** $8/xl, $5/lg bucket
**Junior Golf:** Yes
**Architect/Yr Open:** Richard Luff/1929

COUPON

150 acre picturesque 18-hole facility 20 minutes from Boston with the feel of Maine or New Hampshire. Signature hole #9, 210 yard, par 3 over water. Building a new 9th green.

| | 1 | 2 | 3 | 4 | 5 | 6 | 7 | 8 | 9 |
|------|-----|-----|-----|-----|-----|-----|-----|-----|-----|
| PAR | 5 | 4 | 5 | 4 | 4 | 3 | 4 | 3 | 3 |
| YARDS | 465 | 344 | 473 | 364 | 276 | 146 | 336 | 179 | 198 |
| | 10 | 11 | 12 | 13 | 14 | 15 | 16 | 17 | 18 |
| PAR | 4 | 5 | 5 | 4 | 3 | 4 | 4 | 3 | 3 |
| YARDS | 247 | 499 | 431 | 398 | 137 | 330 | 317 | 185 | 180 |

**Directions:** Exit 41 off I-95/Route 128. Bear right off exit, 3 miles on Main Street. Clubhouse on right.

# Sandy Burr Country Club  ✪✪✪  72 ▶

103 Cochituate Road
Wayland, MA (508) 358-7211
www.sandyburr.com

**Club Pro:** Brian Golden
**Payment:** Most Major Credit Cards
**Tee Times:** 5 days adv. (members 7 days adv.)

| Tees | Holes | Yards | Par | USGA | Slope |
|------|-------|-------|-----|------|-------|
| BACK | 18 | 6427 | 72 | 71.9 | 126 |
| MIDDLE | 18 | 6042 | 72 | 68.9 | 122 |
| FRONT | 18 | 4578 | 69 | 66.9 | 110 |

**Fee 9 Holes: Weekday:** $30
**Fee 18 Holes: Weekday:** $50
**Twilight Rates:** After 2pm
**Cart Rental:** $20pp/18, $11pp/9
**Lessons:** $50/half hour  **Schools:** No
**Membership:** Yes
**Other:** Clubhouse / Restaurant / Bar-Lounge

**Weekend:** $35
**Weekend:** $60
**Discounts:** Sr. & Jr. (+60, -16) $30, $45 w/cart
**Driving Range:** No
**Junior Golf:** No
**Architect/Yr Open:** Donald Ross/1922

Player Comments: "A great Donald Ross course with a good mix of holes. Good to very good shape—depending on the month." Early bird and midday 9-hole rate. Twilight rates.

| | 1 | 2 | 3 | 4 | 5 | 6 | 7 | 8 | 9 |
|------|-----|-----|-----|-----|-----|-----|-----|-----|-----|
| PAR | 5 | 5 | 3 | 4 | 3 | 4 | 4 | 4 | 4 |
| YARDS | 462 | 497 | 125 | 423 | 193 | 399 | 323 | 354 | 272 |
| | 10 | 11 | 12 | 13 | 14 | 15 | 16 | 17 | 18 |
| PAR | 3 | 5 | 4 | 3 | 4 | 4 | 4 | 5 | 4 |
| YARDS | 131 | 437 | 319 | 161 | 340 | 345 | 335 | 513 | 363 |

**Directions:** I-95/Route 128 to Route 20 West exit, at Wayland Center take left onto Route 27 South. Course is ¼ mile on right.

# Sassamon Trace Golf Course ✪✪½ ▸ 73

233 South Main Street
Natick, MA (508) 655-1330
www.sassamontrace.com

| Tees | Holes | Yards | Par | USGA | Slope |
|------|-------|-------|-----|------|-------|
| BACK | 9 | 2383 | 32 | 31.7 | 111 |
| MIDDLE | 9 | 2167 | 32 | 30.9 | 107 |
| FRONT | 9 | 1744 | 32 | 29.8 | 96 |

**Club Pro:** Kurt McDowell, PGA
**Payment:** Visa, MC, Amex, Cash
**Tee Times:** 7 days adv.
**Fee 9 Holes: Weekday:** $20
**Fee 18 Holes: Weekday:** $32
**Twilight Rates:** Yes
**Cart Rental:** $16pp/18, $8pp/9
**Lessons:** No **Schools:** No
**Membership:** Yes
**Other:** Restaurant / Clubhouse

**Weekend:** $22
**Weekend:** $36
**Discounts:** Sr. & Jr. (weekdays)
**Driving Range:** No
**Junior Golf:** Yes
**Architect/Yr:** Cornish, Silva, and Mungeam/2001
**GPS:**

*COUPON*

MetroWest's most unique 9-hole layout. Expansive greens place a premium on putting. A blend of links and traditonal styles.

| | 1 | 2 | 3 | 4 | 5 | 6 | 7 | 8 | 9 |
|------|-----|-----|-----|-----|-----|-----|-----|-----|-----|
| PAR | 3 | 4 | 3 | 5 | 3 | 4 | 3 | 3 | 4 |
| YARDS | 158 | 326 | 180 | 529 | 162 | 341 | 177 | 143 | 367 |
| PAR | | | | | | | | | |
| YARDS | | | | | | | | | |

**Directions:** I-95/Route 128, to Exit 20 (Route 9 West) and follow for 6.5 miles to Route 27 South. Course is 3 miles south on Route 27 on right.

# Scituate Country Club ✪✪✪ ▸ 74

91 Driftway
Scituate, MA (781) 545-9768
www.scituatecc.com

| Tees | Holes | Yards | Par | USGA | Slope |
|------|-------|-------|-----|------|-------|
| BACK | 9 | 3077 | 35 | | |
| MIDDLE | 9 | 2974 | 35 | 70.0 | 128 |
| FRONT | 9 | 2564 | 36 | 71.2 | 125 |

**Club Pro:** Jim Dee, PGA
**Payment:** Cash, Credit Cards
**Tee Times:** 1 week adv.
**Fee 9 Holes: Weekday:** $28 after 11am Mon
**Fee 18 Holes: Weekday:** $38 after 11am Mon
**Twilight Rates:** No
**Cart Rental:** $16pp/18, $10pp/9
**Lessons:** $30/half hour **Schools:** No
**Membership:** Yes
**Other:** Restaurant / Clubhouse / Bar-Lounge / Showers / Lockers / Snack Bar

**Weekend:** No public play
**Weekend:** No public play
**Discounts:** None
**Driving Range:** No
**Junior Golf:** Yes (members only)
**Architect/Yr Open:** Wayne Stiles/1919

Open to the public on Mondays only after 11am. Beautifully maintained seaside golf links with rolling terrain. Great shape. Open April - November.

| | 1 | 2 | 3 | 4 | 5 | 6 | 7 | 8 | 9 |
|------|-----|-----|-----|-----|-----|-----|-----|-----|-----|
| PAR | 4 | 3 | 5 | 4 | 4 | 4 | 4 | 3 | 4 |
| YARDS | 407 | 156 | 504 | 373 | 308 | 359 | 357 | 124 | 386 |
| PAR | | | | | | | | | |
| YARDS | | | | | | | | | |

**Directions:** Route 3 South to Exit 13. Go left off exit. Go to first set of lights, take right onto Route 123. 4 miles to roundabout, go towards Scituate Harbor. Go 1 mile, turn right on Driftway. Club on right.

# Shining Rock Golf Club ✪✪✪✪½ 75 ▶

94 Clubhouse Lane
Northbridge, MA (508) 234-0400
www.shiningrock.com

**Club Pro:** Lee Danielian
**Payment:** Visa, MC, Amex
**Tee Times:** 7 days adv.

| Tees | Holes | Yards | Par | USGA | Slope |
|------|-------|-------|-----|------|-------|
| BACK | 18 | 6728 | 72 | 72.9 | 135 |
| MIDDLE | 18 | 6471 | 72 | 71.7 | 133 |
| FRONT | 18 | 5154 | 72 | 70.2 | 128 |

**Fee 9 Holes: Weekday:** $24
**Fee 18 Holes: Weekday:** $45
**Twilight Rates:** After 5pm
**Cart Rental:** $17pp/18, $11pp/9
**Lessons:** Yes **Schools:** No
**Membership:** Yes
**Other:** Restaurant

**Weekend:** $31 (after 1:30pm)
**Weekend:** $62
**Discounts:** Senior & Junior
**Driving Range:** Practice net
**Junior Golf:** No
**Architect/Yr Open:** Patrick Sullivan/2010

A challenging picturesque course with views of Blackstone Valley. Hole #4 will challenge golfers—referred to as "The Rock"—it has a 200 yard carry over a ravine. "Great new course. Fun, fat, and challenging greens." –FP

| | 1 | 2 | 3 | 4 | 5 | 6 | 7 | 8 | 9 |
|------|---|---|---|---|---|---|---|---|---|
| PAR | 4 | 4 | 5 | 4 | 3 | 4 | 4 | 3 | 4 |
| YARDS | 394 | 423 | 513 | 318 | 219 | 288 | 302 | 175 | 423 |
| | 10 | 11 | 12 | 13 | 14 | 15 | 16 | 17 | 18 |
| PAR | 4 | 4 | 3 | 5 | 4 | 3 | 5 | 4 | 5 |
| YARDS | 359 | 370 | 203 | 485 | 346 | 180 | 608 | 301 | 494 |

**Directions:** Take Exit 21B off of Route 495. Follow for 4 miles to set of lights in Upton Center. Take a right onto Route 140 and an immediate left onto Hartford Street. Golf course is 1 mile up on the right.

# South Shore Country Club ✪✪✪ 76 ▶

274 South Street
Hingham, MA (781) 749-8479
www.southshorecc.com

**Club Pro:** Chris Riley, PGA
**Payment:** Visa, MC, Cash, Check
**Tee Times:** 7 days adv.

| Tees | Holes | Yards | Par | USGA | Slope |
|------|-------|-------|-----|------|-------|
| BACK | 18 | 6444 | 72 | 71.0 | 128 |
| MIDDLE | 18 | 6197 | 72 | 69.9 | 124 |
| FRONT | 18 | 5064 | 72 | 69.3 | 116 |

**Fee 9 Holes: Weekday:** $30 M-Th $36 F
**Fee 18 Holes: Weekday:** $42 M-Th $47 F
**Twilight Rates:** After 5pm
**Cart Rental:** $16pp/18, $9pp/9
**Lessons:** Call for details **Schools:** Yes, Jr.
**Membership:** Currently a waiting list
**Other:** Snack Bar / Restaurant / Bar-Lounge / Clubhouse / Lockers / Showers

**Weekend:**
**Weekend:** $47 after 11am
**Discounts:** Sr. & Jr. weekdays
**Driving Range:** Yes
**Junior Golf:** Yes
**Architect/Yr Open:** Stiles & Van Kleek/1922

Gets more enjoyable with every replay. Classic design. Course in excellent condition.

| | 1 | 2 | 3 | 4 | 5 | 6 | 7 | 8 | 9 |
|------|---|---|---|---|---|---|---|---|---|
| PAR | 4 | 3 | 5 | 4 | 4 | 4 | 4 | 3 | 5 |
| YARDS | 277 | 156 | 521 | 319 | 371 | 410 | 360 | 197 | 502 |
| | 10 | 11 | 12 | 13 | 14 | 15 | 16 | 17 | 18 |
| PAR | 4 | 3 | 4 | 4 | 4 | 5 | 4 | 3 | 5 |
| YARDS | 295 | 179 | 372 | 401 | 327 | 530 | 380 | 148 | 452 |

**Directions:** Route 3 to Exit 14 onto Route 228 North. At 4-mile mark, exit Route 228 and continue straight onto Central Street. At 2nd 4-way stop, turn left onto South Street. Go ½ mile, club is on left.

# Southers Marsh Golf Club ✪✪✪½

 **77**

30 Southers Marsh Lane
Plymouth, MA (508) 830-3535
www.southersmarsh.com

**Club Pro:** Jocko Tavares
**Payment:** Visa, MC, Amex, Disc, No Checks
**Tee Times:** 7 days adv.

| Tees | Holes | Yards | Par | USGA | Slope |
|------|-------|-------|-----|------|-------|
| BACK | 18 | 4111 | 61 | 61.8 | 112 |
| MIDDLE | 18 | 3694 | 61 | 60.4 | 109 |
| FRONT | 18 | 2907 | 61 | 58.2 | 93 |

**Fee  9 Holes: Weekday:**
**Fee 18 Holes: Weekday:** $30 M-Th
**Twilight Rates:** After 3pm
**Cart Rental:** $14pp/18
**Lessons:** $30/half hour  **Schools:** No
**Membership:** Yes
**Other:** Clubhouse / Bar-Lounge

**Weekend:**
**Weekend:** $37 F/S/S
**Discounts:** Sr. (M-Th) & Jr. (7 days)
**Driving Range:** Yes
**Junior Golf:**
**Architect/Yr Open:** Dahn Tibbett/2001
**GPS:**

The golf, course conditions, and service of a resort course without the corporate feel, time commitment or expense.

|  | 1 | 2 | 3 | 4 | 5 | 6 | 7 | 8 | 9 |
|--|---|---|---|---|---|---|---|---|---|
| PAR | 4 | 3 | 3 | 4 | 3 | 4 | 3 | 4 | 3 |
| YARDS | 300 | 139 | 175 | 353 | 138 | 285 | 129 | 263 | 158 |
|  | 10 | 11 | 12 | 13 | 14 | 15 | 16 | 17 | 18 |
| PAR | 3 | 3 | 3 | 4 | 3 | 4 | 3 | 3 | 4 |
| YARDS | 123 | 121 | 97 | 304 | 121 | 314 | 157 | 165 | 352 |

**Directions:** Route 3 to Exit 6B (or 6 and turn left at bottom of ramp from the South) toward Carver. At second light, turn left onto Pilgrim Hill Road. Turn right at light onto Federal Furnace Road. After 4 miles, SMGC on left. Also minutes from Exit 2 off Route 495.

# Squirrel Run Golf Course ✪✪

 **78**

32 Elderberry Drive
Plymouth, MA (508) 746-5001
www.golfatsquirrelrun.com

**Club Pro:** David Moore, PGA
**Payment:** Visa, MC
**Tee Times:** 7 days adv.

| Tees | Holes | Yards | Par | USGA | Slope |
|------|-------|-------|-----|------|-------|
| BACK | 18 | 2859 | 57 | 55.4 | 85 |
| MIDDLE | 18 | 2338 | 57 | 53.7 | 82 |
| FRONT | 18 | 1990 | 57 | 56.0 | 83 |

**Fee  9 Holes: Weekday:** $19
**Fee 18 Holes: Weekday:** $27
**Twilight Rates:** After 4pm
**Cart Rental:** $12/18
**Lessons:** Yes  **Schools:** No
**Membership:** Yes
**Other:** Restaurant / Clubhouse / Bar-Lounge / Snack Bar

**Weekend:** $24
**Weekend:** $30
**Discounts:** Senior & Junior
**Driving Range:** No
**Junior Golf:** Yes
**Architect/Yr Open:** Ray Richard/1991

Player Comments: "A challenge to anyone's short game." "Immaculate greens and tees." Sister course: Village Links. Winner of the 2006 Plymouth Golden Sprinkler Award for Service & Condition.

|  | 1 | 2 | 3 | 4 | 5 | 6 | 7 | 8 | 9 |
|--|---|---|---|---|---|---|---|---|---|
| PAR | 4 | 3 | 3 | 3 | 4 | 3 | 3 | 3 | 4 |
| YARDS | 286 | 105 | 125 | 90 | 263 | 98 | 131 | 123 | 206 |
|  | 10 | 11 | 12 | 13 | 14 | 15 | 16 | 17 | 18 |
| PAR | 3 | 3 | 3 | 3 | 3 | 3 | 3 | 3 | 3 |
| YARDS | 99 | 78 | 102 | 102 | 140 | 100 | 116 | 74 | 100 |

**Directions:** Route 3 to Exit 6. Go approximately 2 miles to course on left. Look for Squirrel Run sign.

# Stoneham Oaks Golf Course

NR **79** ▶

101 R Montvale Avenue
Stoneham, MA (781) 438-7888
www.stonehamoaks.com

**Club Pro:** Mike Gaffney
**Payment:** Cash and Credit Cards
**Tee Times:** No

| Tees | Holes | Yards | Par | USGA | Slope |
|------|-------|-------|-----|------|-------|
| BACK | | | | | |
| MIDDLE | 9 | 1125 | 27 | N/A | N/A |
| FRONT | 9 | 811 | 27 | N/A | N/A |

**Fee 9 Holes: Weekday:** $16 ($14 residents) **Weekend:** $18 ($16 residents)
**Fee 18 Holes: Weekday:** **Weekend:**
**Twilight Rates:** After 2pm **Discounts:** Senior, Junior, College, Veteran
**Cart Rental:** $9pp/9, $4/pull **Driving Range:** No
**Lessons:** Yes **Schools:** No **Junior Golf:** No
**Membership:** No **Architect/Yr Open:** 1994
**Other:** **GPS:**

Very hilly, many trees. Very scenic. Various reduced weekday rates between 7am and 2pm. Operated by Sterling Golf Management.

| | 1 | 2 | 3 | 4 | 5 | 6 | 7 | 8 | 9 |
|-------|----|-----|-----|-----|----|-----|-----|-----|----|
| PAR | 3 | 3 | 3 | 3 | 3 | 3 | 3 | 3 | 3 |
| YARDS | 89 | 147 | 179 | 128 | 95 | 113 | 153 | 139 | 82 |
| PAR | | | | | | | | | |
| YARDS | | | | | | | | | |

**Directions:** I-93 to Exit 36, Stoneham, Montvale Avenue, 1 block. Course is at rear of the Stoneham Ice Rink.

# Stonybrook Golf Course

NR **80** ▶

70 Valley Road
Southboro, MA (508) 485-3151
www.stonybrookgolfcourse.com

**Club Pro:**
**Payment:** Visa, MC
**Tee Times:** Yes

| Tees | Holes | Yards | Par | USGA | Slope |
|------|-------|-------|-----|------|-------|
| BACK | | | | | |
| MIDDLE | 9 | 1342 | 27 | | |
| FRONT | | | | | |

**Fee 9 Holes: Weekday:** $14 **Weekend:** $14
**Fee 18 Holes: Weekday:** $18 **Weekend:**
**Twilight Rates:** After 5pm **Discounts:** $12 Senior & Junior
**Cart Rental:** $3/pull **Driving Range:** No
**Lessons:** No **Schools:** No **Junior Golf:** No
**Membership:** Yes **Architect/Yr Open:** Ernest Kallender/1970
**Other:** Snack Bar / Accessories / Kids' Camps **GPS:**

*COUPON*

Player Comments: "No-frills course, but always improving. Plays fair. Greens are beautiful, honest but must be read right. Need accurate iron play." Good for beginners and experienced golfers.

| | 1 | 2 | 3 | 4 | 5 | 6 | 7 | 8 | 9 |
|-------|-----|-----|-----|-----|-----|-----|-----|-----|-----|
| PAR | 3 | 3 | 3 | 3 | 3 | 3 | 3 | 3 | 3 |
| YARDS | 145 | 138 | 210 | 125 | 132 | 165 | 169 | 107 | 151 |
| PAR | | | | | | | | | |
| YARDS | | | | | | | | | |

**Directions:** Accessible from Routes I-90, I-495, and Route 9. Located in Southboro off Route 30 on Valley Road.

# Stow Acres CC (North) ✪✪✪  ▶ 81

**58 Randall Road**
**Stow, MA (978) 568-1100**
www.stowacres.com

| Tees | Holes | Yards | Par | USGA | Slope |
|------|-------|-------|-----|------|-------|
| BACK | 18 | 6939 | 72 | 72.8 | 130 |
| MIDDLE | 18 | 6310 | 72 | 70.5 | 127 |
| FRONT | 18 | 6011 | 72 | 72.5 | 130 |

**Club Pro:** Dave Carlson, PGA
**Payment:** Visa, MC, Amex, Disc, Cash
**Tee Times:** 10 days adv.
**Fee  9 Holes: Weekday:** $30 M-Th
**Fee 18 Holes: Weekday:** $48 M-Th
**Twilight Rates:** After 6pm
**Cart Rental:** $20pp/18, $10pp/9
**Lessons:** Yes **Schools:** Yes
**Membership:** Yes
**Other:** Clubhouse / Showers-Men Only / Snack Bar / Bar-Lounge / Gold Card Membership

**Weekend:** After 12pm
**Weekend:** $65 F/S/S
**Discounts:** Sr & Jr weekdays
**Driving Range:** $12/lg, $6/sm
**Junior Golf:** Yes
**Architect/Yr Open:** Geoffrey Cornish/1972

COUPON

Player Comments: "Sensational greens." PGA Tour Qualifier site. Championship layout. Black tees added. Open mid-March to mid-December. Season passes and family passes.

| | 1 | 2 | 3 | 4 | 5 | 6 | 7 | 8 | 9 |
|------|----|----|----|----|----|----|----|----|----|
| PAR | 5 | 4 | 4 | 4 | 5 | 3 | 4 | 3 | 4 |
| YARDS | 503 | 374 | 354 | 387 | 472 | 180 | 318 | 165 | 426 |
| | 10 | 11 | 12 | 13 | 14 | 15 | 16 | 17 | 18 |
| PAR | 4 | 4 | 5 | 3 | 4 | 4 | 3 | 4 | 5 |
| YARDS | 359 | 392 | 424 | 169 | 340 | 369 | 166 | 376 | 536 |

**Directions:** I-95/Route 128 to Route 20/117 Exit. Go west on Route 117 approximately 15 miles; left in Stow Center onto Route 62 West, follow signs from Route 62 to course.

# Stow Acres CC (South) ✪✪✪  ▶ 82

**58 Randall Road**
**Stow, MA (978) 568-1100**
www.stowacres.com

| Tees | Holes | Yards | Par | USGA | Slope |
|------|-------|-------|-----|------|-------|
| BACK | 18 | 6520 | 72 | 71.8 | 120 |
| MIDDLE | 18 | 6105 | 72 | 70.5 | 118 |
| FRONT | 18 | 5642 | 72 | 72.5 | 120 |

**Club Pro:** Dave Carlson, PGA
**Payment:** Visa, MC, Amex, Disc, Cash
**Tee Times:** 10 days adv.
**Fee  9 Holes: Weekday:** $28 M-Th
**Fee 18 Holes: Weekday:** $40
**Twilight Rates:** After 6pm
**Cart Rental:** $22pp/18, $10pp/9
**Lessons:** Yes **Schools:** Yes
**Membership:** Yes
**Other:** Clubhouse / Snack Bar / Bar-Lounge

**Weekend:** After 12pm
**Weekend:** $52
**Discounts:** Sr & Jr weekdays
**Driving Range:** $12/lg, $6/sm
**Junior Golf:** Yes
**Architect/Yr Open:** Geoffrey Cornish/1965
**GPS:**

COUPON

Player Comments: "Sensational greens." Variety of instructional packages. Variety of inner clubs. New cart paths. Course conditions improved. Prices subject to change. Season passes and family passes.

| | 1 | 2 | 3 | 4 | 5 | 6 | 7 | 8 | 9 |
|------|----|----|----|----|----|----|----|----|----|
| PAR | 4 | 4 | 3 | 4 | 5 | 5 | 3 | 4 | 4 |
| YARDS | 375 | 416 | 123 | 301 | 476 | 487 | 212 | 346 | 368 |
| | 10 | 11 | 12 | 13 | 14 | 15 | 16 | 17 | 18 |
| PAR | 5 | 3 | 4 | 4 | 5 | 3 | 4 | 3 | 5 |
| YARDS | 543 | 127 | 366 | 292 | 441 | 151 | 407 | 167 | 507 |

**Directions:** Route I-95/128 to Route 20/117 Exit. Go west on Route 117 approximately 15 miles; left in Stow Center onto Route 62 West, follow signs from Route 62 to course.

# Strawberry Valley Golf Course  ✪✪  83 ▶

164 Washington Street
Abington, MA (781) 347-4877
www.calmgolf.com

| Tees | Holes | Yards | Par | USGA | Slope |
|------|-------|-------|-----|------|-------|
| BACK | 9 | 2578 | 35 | | |
| MIDDLE | 9 | 2280 | 34 | 66.9 | 99 |
| FRONT | 9 | 2217 | 34 | | |

**Club Pro:** Tony Morosco
**Payment:** Visa, MC, Amex, Disc
**Tee Times:** 7 days adv.
**Fee 9 Holes: Weekday:** $17
**Fee 18 Holes: Weekday:** $28
**Twilight Rates:** $14 after 6pm weekdays
$14 after 4pm weekends
**Cart Rental:** $12.50pp/18, $8.50pp/9
**Lessons:** Yes **Schools:** Yes
**Membership:** Yes
**Other:** Snack Bar

**Weekend:** $19
**Weekend:** $30
**Discounts:** Senior $15, Junior $14

**Driving Range:** No
**Junior Golf:** Yes
**Architect/Yr Open:**
**GPS:**

Player-friendly. Features senior, junior and beginner play. Open year round. New irrigation systems. "Friendly, helpful staff." –FP

| | 1 | 2 | 3 | 4 | 5 | 6 | 7 | 8 | 9 |
|------|---|---|---|---|---|---|---|---|---|
| PAR | 4 | 4 | 4/5 | 4 | 4 | 3 | 3 | 4 | 4 |
| YARDS | 228 | 357 | 475 | 234 | 240 | 119 | 148 | 295 | 306 |
| PAR | | | | | | | | | |
| YARDS | | | | | | | | | |

**Directions:** Route 3 to Route 18 South. Course is approximately 7 miles on right.

# Swanson Meadows  ✪✪  84 ▶

216 Rangeway Road
North Billerica, MA (978) 670-7777
www.swansonmeadows.com

| Tees | Holes | Yards | Par | USGA | Slope |
|------|-------|-------|-----|------|-------|
| BACK | | | | | |
| MIDDLE | 9 | 2180 | 32 | | |
| FRONT | 9 | 1829 | 32 | | |

**Club Pro:** Angelo Scippa, Manager
**Payment:** All Major Credit Cards
**Tee Times:** 7 days adv.
**Fee 9 Holes: Weekday:** $20
**Fee 18 Holes: Weekday:** $40
**Twilight Rates:** After 6pm
**Cart Rental:** $10pp/9
**Lessons:** No **Schools:** No
**Membership:** Yes, Season Passes
**Other:** Restaurant / Lounge

**Weekend:** $23
**Weekend:** $46
**Discounts:** Senior
**Driving Range:** No
**Junior Golf:**
**Architect/Yr:** Cornish, Silva, Mungeam/2001
**GPS:**

Player Comments: "Quick hike after work." "Layout squeezed onto a moderate space." –RW
New clubhouse, restaurant, and lounge.

| | 1 | 2 | 3 | 4 | 5 | 6 | 7 | 8 | 9 |
|------|---|---|---|---|---|---|---|---|---|
| PAR | 4 | 4 | 4 | 3 | 3 | 4 | 3 | 3 | 4 |
| YARDS | 360 | 286 | 345 | 163 | 119 | 296 | 121 | 146 | 344 |
| PAR | | | | | | | | | |
| YARDS | | | | | | | | | |

**Directions:** Route 3 to Exit 29. Take Route 129 East. Off ramp, go 1 mile, take right on to Rangeway Road. Course is 1 mile on left.

# Tewksbury Country Club ✪✪½ ▶ 85

**1880 Main Street**
**Tewksbury, MA** (978) 640-0033
www.tewksburycc.com

| Tees | Holes | Yards | Par | USGA | Slope |
|------|-------|-------|-----|------|-------|
| BACK | 9 | 2632 | 33 | 32.8 | 116 |
| MIDDLE | 9 | 2393 | 33 | 31.8 | 110 |
| FRONT | 9 | 1937 | 33 | 31.0 | 110 |

**Club Pro:** Mike Rogers, PGA
**Payment:** Visa, MC, Amex, Disc, Checks
**Tee Times:** F/S/S (978-640-0033 x21)
**Fee 9 Holes: Weekday:** $22    **Weekend:** $25
**Fee 18 Holes: Weekday:** $36    **Weekend:** $40
**Twilight Rates:** After 3pm S/S    **Discounts:** Senior & Junior
**Cart Rental:** $17pp/18, $11pp/9    **Driving Range:** No
**Lessons:** Yes   **Schools:** Junior    **Junior Golf:** Yes
**Membership:** Yes    **Architect/Yr Open:** Frank Stasio/1998
**Other:** Clubhouse / Restaurant    **GPS:**

Impeccably manicured golf course. A challenge for all ability levels. Beautiful stone walls and fountains. Post and beam clubhouse.

| | 1 | 2 | 3 | 4 | 5 | 6 | 7 | 8 | 9 |
|---|---|---|---|---|---|---|---|---|---|
| **PAR** | 4 | 3 | 3 | 4 | 4 | 5 | 4 | 3 | 3 |
| **YARDS** | 369 | 182 | 165 | 402 | 377 | 477 | 334 | 178 | 150 |

| | | | | | | | | | |
|---|---|---|---|---|---|---|---|---|---|
| **PAR** | | | | | | | | | |
| **YARDS** | | | | | | | | | |

**Directions:** I-93 to Exit 42 (Dascomb Road) toward Tewksbury. Turn left onto Shawsheen Street. Follow Shawsheen to Route 38. Turn right onto Livingston Street. From Route 128, take Route 38 North to Livingston Street.

# Trull Brook Golf Course ✪✪✪ ▶ 86

**170 River Road**
**Tewksbury, MA** (978) 851-6731
www.trullbrook.com

| Tees | Holes | Yards | Par | USGA | Slope |
|------|-------|-------|-----|------|-------|
| BACK | 18 | 6345 | 72 | 69.8 | 123 |
| MIDDLE | 18 | 6006 | 72 | 68.8 | 122 |
| FRONT | 18 | 5193 | 72 | 69.6 | 118 |

**Club Pro:** Sheldon Alman, Manager
**Payment:** Visa, MC, Amex, Disc
**Tee Times:** 1 week adv.
**Fee 9 Holes: Weekday:** $22.50 M-F pm    **Weekend:** $25
**Fee 18 Holes: Weekday:** $42 M-Th    **Weekend:** $50
**Twilight Rates:** After 5pm
**Discounts:** Sr. & Jr. (M-Th); Clergy: $16.50; Junior under 17 accompanied with adult: $31.50/18
**Cart Rental:** $15/18, $7.75/9 per cart    **Driving Range:** No
**Lessons:** Yes   **Schools:** No    **Junior Golf:** Yes
**Membership:** No    **Architect/Yr Open:** Geoffrey Cornish/1962
**Other:** Clubhouse / Lockers / Showers / Snack Bar / Bar-Lounge / Winter Tennis Center

Player Comments: "Very well kept. Nice greens." "Challenging course. Scenic." Geoffrey Cornish design. Dress code. Open dawn to dusk.

| | 1 | 2 | 3 | 4 | 5 | 6 | 7 | 8 | 9 |
|---|---|---|---|---|---|---|---|---|---|
| **PAR** | 4 | 5 | 4 | 3 | 4 | 3 | 5 | 4 | 4 |
| **YARDS** | 338 | 498 | 383 | 123 | 368 | 138 | 470 | 353 | 384 |
| | **10** | **11** | **12** | **13** | **14** | **15** | **16** | **17** | **18** |
| **PAR** | 4 | 3 | 5 | 4 | 4 | 3 | 4 | 5 | 4 |
| **YARDS** | 323 | 168 | 463 | 323 | 343 | 178 | 373 | 458 | 323 |

**Directions:** From I-495 or I-93, take Route 133 exit, follow West toward Lowell. At Mobil station, sharp right onto River Road. Course is ⅓ mile on left.

# Unicorn Golf Course

NR 87

460 William Street
Stoneham, MA (781) 438-9732
www.unicorngc.com

**Club Pro:** Jeffrey Barnes, PGA
**Payment:** Cash and Credit Cards
**Tee Times:** No

| Tees | Holes | Yards | Par | USGA | Slope |
|------|-------|-------|-----|------|-------|
| BACK | 9 | 3234 | 35 | 70.8 | 126 |
| MIDDLE | 9 | 3185 | 35 | 69.6 | 121 |
| FRONT | 9 | 2902 | 37 | 73.0 | 124 |

**Fee 9 Holes: Weekday:** $22 ($20 residents) **Weekend:** $24 ($22 residents)
**Fee 18 Holes: Weekday:** **Weekend:**
**Twilight Rates:** No **Discounts:** Senior, Junior, College
**Cart Rental:** $9pp/9, $3/pull **Driving Range:** No
**Lessons:** Yes **Schools:** No **Junior Golf:** No
**Membership:** No **Architect/Yr Open:** 1972
**Other:** Snack Bar **GPS:**

Stoneham resident rates. The course is relatively level; easy walk. Nice par 3s, and #7 and #9 are great holes. Operated by Sterling Golf Management.

| | 1 | 2 | 3 | 4 | 5 | 6 | 7 | 8 | 9 |
|------|---|---|---|---|---|---|---|---|---|
| PAR | 4 | 4 | 4 | 3 | 4 | 5 | 4 | 3 | 4 |
| YARDS | 389 | 326 | 335 | 168 | 395 | 499 | 448 | 178 | 447 |
| PAR | | | | | | | | | |
| YARDS | | | | | | | | | |

**Directions:** I-93 to Montvale Avenue. Follow to end. Take left onto Route 28, then left at next set of lights (Williams Street). Course is ¼ mile on left.

# Village Links

◑◑ 88

265 South Meadow Road
Plymouth, MA (508) 830-4653
www.golfatvillagelinks.com

**Club Pro:** David L. Moore, PGA
**Payment:** Visa, MC
**Tee Times:** 7 days adv.

| Tees | Holes | Yards | Par | USGA | Slope |
|------|-------|-------|-----|------|-------|
| BACK | | | | | |
| MIDDLE | 18 | 2407 | 54 | | |
| FRONT | 18 | 1986 | 54 | 52.8 | 78 |

**Fee 9 Holes: Weekday:** **Weekend:**
**Fee 18 Holes: Weekday:** $25 **Weekend:** $27
**Twilight Rates:** Yes **Discounts:** Senior & Junior
**Cart Rental:** $16pp/18 **Driving Range:**
**Lessons:** $40/half hour **Schools:** Yes **Junior Golf:** Yes
**Membership:** **Architect/Yr Open:** Ray Richard/2000
**Other:** Restaurant / Clubhouse / Bar-Lounge **GPS:**

COUPON

18-hole par 3, executive-style. Associated with Pinehurst Village. Sister course to Squirrel Run. "Excellent holes include #4, 5, 8, 11, 15, 17." –AP

| | 1 | 2 | 3 | 4 | 5 | 6 | 7 | 8 | 9 |
|------|---|---|---|---|---|---|---|---|---|
| PAR | 3 | 3 | 3 | 3 | 3 | 3 | 3 | 3 | 3 |
| YARDS | 134 | 141 | 159 | 57 | 114 | 124 | 113 | 60 | 76 |
| | 10 | 11 | 12 | 13 | 14 | 15 | 16 | 17 | 18 |
| PAR | 3 | 3 | 3 | 3 | 3 | 3 | 3 | 3 | 3 |
| YARDS | 133 | 112 | 130 | 84 | 79 | 96 | 136 | 74 | 164 |

**Directions:** Route 3 to Exit 6 West (Route 44). Turn left at the 3rd set of lights onto Seven Hills Road. Turn right at the 1st set of lights onto South Meadow Road. Village Links is 2.5 miles on the right.

# Waverly Oaks Golf Club ✪✪✪½ ▶ 89

**444 Long Pond Road**
**Plymouth, MA (508) 224-6700**
www.waverlyoaksgc.com

| Tees | Holes | Yards | Par | USGA | Slope |
|------|-------|-------|-----|------|-------|
| BACK | 18 | 7114 | 72 | 68.5 | 118 |
| MIDDLE | 18 | 6682 | 72 | 65.9 | 113 |
| FRONT | 18 | 5587 | 72 | 63.6 | 108 |

**Club Pro:** John Sheehan
**Payment:** Visa, MC, Amex, Disc
**Tee Times:** 7 days adv.
**Fee 9 Holes: Weekday:** $40 w/cart      **Weekend:** $50 w/cart (F/S/S)
**Fee 18 Holes: Weekday:** $75 w/cart      **Weekend:** $95 w/cart (F/S/S)
**Twilight Rates:** Weekend $60 after 2pm      **Discounts:** Jr/Sr weekday only
**Cart Rental:** Included      **Driving Range:** $5/bucket
**Lessons:** $35/half hour  **Schools:** No      **Junior Golf:** Yes
**Membership:** Season Pass      **Architect/Yr Open:** Brian Silva/1998
**Other:** Full Restaurant / Clubhouse / Bar-Lounge / Showers / Corporate Outings / Small Group Outings / All Rates Include Range Balls

COUPON

Player Comments: "Best course all round I've played. Not a blemish. Money well worth it." "A gem." –RW Improvements at 17th hole. Tee times can be made online at www.waverlyoaksgc.com.

| | 1 | 2 | 3 | 4 | 5 | 6 | 7 | 8 | 9 |
|---|---|---|---|---|---|---|---|---|---|
| PAR | 4 | 4 | 3 | 5 | 5 | 4 | 4 | 3 | 4 |
| YARDS | 325 | 394 | 191 | 502 | 515 | 432 | 410 | 184 | 353 |
| | 10 | 11 | 12 | 13 | 14 | 15 | 16 | 17 | 18 |
| PAR | 4 | 4 | 4 | 5 | 3 | 4 | 5 | 3 | 4 |
| YARDS | 386 | 372 | 311 | 512 | 163 | 449 | 606 | 221 | 356 |

**Directions:** Route 3 to Exit 3. Right off ramp. Right at first stop sign. Entrance is 2 miles on right.

# Wayland Country Club ✪✪ ▶ 90

**121 Old Sudbury Road**
**Wayland, MA (508) 358-4775**
www.waylandcc.com

| Tees | Holes | Yards | Par | USGA | Slope |
|------|-------|-------|-----|------|-------|
| BACK | 18 | 5947 | 70 | 68.5 | 118 |
| MIDDLE | 18 | 5334 | 70 | 65.9 | 113 |
| FRONT | 18 | 4875 | 71 | 68.8 | 117 |

**Club Pro:** John Gordon, PGA
**Payment:** Credit Cards, Cash
**Tee Times:** Call Monday for weekends
**Fee 9 Holes: Weekday:** $25      **Weekend:** $28
**Fee 18 Holes: Weekday:** $37      **Weekend:** $47 ($28 after 2pm)
**Twilight Rates:** After 6pm      **Discounts:** Senior & Junior
**Cart Rental:** $16pp/18, $10pp/9      **Driving Range:** No
**Lessons:** $40-$80/hour  **Schools:** Yes      **Junior Golf:** Yes
**Membership:** Yes      **Architect/Yr Open:** Mitchell/1920s
**Other:** Restaurant / Clubhouse / Snack Bar / Bar-Lounge
**GPS:** No

Course is fairly flat with small greens and alternating wide and narrow fairways. Easy to walk. Great staff.

| | 1 | 2 | 3 | 4 | 5 | 6 | 7 | 8 | 9 |
|---|---|---|---|---|---|---|---|---|---|
| PAR | 5 | 4 | 4 | 3 | 4 | 3 | 4 | 3 | 4 |
| YARDS | 396 | 324 | 364 | 123 | 360 | 170 | 250 | 127 | 390 |
| | 10 | 11 | 12 | 13 | 14 | 15 | 16 | 17 | 18 |
| PAR | 4 | 4 | 5 | 4 | 3 | 4 | 4 | 3 | 5 |
| YARDS | 305 | 250 | 479 | 340 | 152 | 357 | 378 | 180 | 389 |

**Directions:** I-95/Route 128 to Route 20 West; right onto Route 27 North; approximately 1 mile on right.

# Weathervane Golf Club

**○○½** **91** ▶

**14 Sandtrap Circle**
**Weymouth, MA (781) 335-1500**
www.weathervanegolf.com

**Club Pro:** Bill Murphy
**Payment:** Visa, MC, Disc, Personal Checks
**Tee Times:** 7 days adv.

| Tees | Holes | Yards | Par | USGA | Slope |
|------|-------|-------|-----|------|-------|
| BACK | 9 | 3065 | 36 | 69.4 | 125 |
| MIDDLE | 9 | 2790 | 36 | 65.8 | 121 |
| FRONT | 9 | 2465 | 36 | 63.4 | 117 |

**Fee 9 Holes: Weekday:** $25
**Fee 18 Holes: Weekday:** $40
**Twilight Rates:** No
**Cart Rental:** $15pp/18, $10pp/9
**Lessons:** Yes **Schools:** Yes
**Membership:** Yes
**Other:**

**Weekend:** $30
**Weekend:** $50
**Discounts:** Junior
**Driving Range:** Yes
**Junior Golf:** Yes
**Architect/Yr Open:** Cornish, Silva, Mungeam/2010

Weathervane provides an enjoyable experience for golfers at all levels. The natural terrain provides many unique challenges. The sand traps are filled with pristine white sand and the island green on the finishing hole can make or break your round.

| | 1 | 2 | 3 | 4 | 5 | 6 | 7 | 8 | 9 |
|------|-----|-----|-----|-----|-----|-----|-----|-----|-----|
| PAR | 4 | 3 | 4 | 3 | 5 | 4 | 4 | 5 | 4 |
| YARDS | 280 | 130 | 320 | 170 | 480 | 300 | 390 | 480 | 240 |
| PAR | | | | | | | | | |
| YARDS | | | | | | | | | |

**Directions:** South on Route 93 to Route 3 South to Exit 16 B (Route 18). Travel 1 mile to South Shore Hospital and take a left at the lights to Columbian Square. Go straight through the intersection to Union Street. Weathvane Drive is 1 mile on left. Take a right on Sandtrap Circle.

# Wenham Country Club

**○○½** **92** ▶

**94 Main Street**
**Wenham, MA (978) 468-4714**
www.wenhamcountryclub.com

**Club Pro:** Darin Chin-Aleong, PGA
**Payment:** Cash, Visa, MC
**Tee Times:** Take out 1 day advance (wknds)

| Tees | Holes | Yards | Par | USGA | Slope |
|------|-------|-------|-----|------|-------|
| BACK | | | | | |
| MIDDLE | 18 | 4554 | 65 | 63.3 | 118 |
| FRONT | 18 | 4321 | 67 | 65.3 | 111 |

**Fee 9 Holes: Weekday:** $23
**Fee 18 Holes: Weekday:** $36
**Twilight Rates:** 3 hours before sundown
**Cart Rental:** $15pp/18, $9pp/9
**Lessons:** Yes **Schools:** No
**Membership:** Yes
**Other:** Clubhouse

**Weekend:** $27 (after 12pm)
**Weekend:** $40 (after 12pm)
**Discounts:** None
**Driving Range:** No
**Junior Golf:** Yes
**Architect/Yr Open:** 1899
**GPS:**

COUPON

Tee boxes are renovated. This par 65 course offers a challenge for golfers of all abilities; as you play this lovely layout, you'll find opportunities to test each club in your bag.

| | 1 | 2 | 3 | 4 | 5 | 6 | 7 | 8 | 9 |
|------|-----|-----|-----|-----|-----|-----|-----|-----|-----|
| PAR | 4 | 3 | 3 | 4 | 3 | 4 | 3 | 4 | 3 |
| YARDS | 347 | 115 | 187 | 279 | 208 | 309 | 153 | 278 | 170 |
| | **10** | **11** | **12** | **13** | **14** | **15** | **16** | **17** | **18** |
| PAR | 3 | 5 | 3 | 3 | 4 | 4 | 4 | 4 | 4 |
| YARDS | 216 | 413 | 186 | 136 | 357 | 246 | 382 | 300 | 272 |

**Directions:** Take Route 128 North to Exit 20A. Go right at the end of the ramp. Follow Route 1A for 3 miles and the course is on the right.

# White Pines Golf Course    ✪½   93 ▶

**549 Copeland Street**
**Brockton, MA (508) 586-3260**
www.whitepinesbrockton.com

**Club Pro:**
**Payment:** Cash Only
**Tee Times:**
**Fee  9 Holes: Weekday:** $17
**Fee 18 Holes: Weekday:** $24
**Twilight Rates:** No
**Cart Rental:** $12pp/18, $8pp/9
**Lessons:**   **Schools:** No
**Membership:** No
**Other:**

| Tees | Holes | Yards | Par | USGA | Slope |
|------|-------|-------|-----|------|-------|
| BACK | | | | | |
| MIDDLE | 9 | 2687 | 36 | | |
| FRONT | | | | | |

**Weekend:** $18
**Weekend:** $25
**Discounts:** Senior & Junior
**Driving Range:** None
**Junior Golf:**
**Architect/Yr Open:** 1926
**GPS:**

Rolling terrain, friendly staff. "Fun little 9-hole course." —FP

| | 1 | 2 | 3 | 4 | 5 | 6 | 7 | 8 | 9 |
|------|---|---|---|---|---|---|---|---|---|
| PAR | 4 | 4 | 5 | 4 | 4 | 4 | 3 | 4 | 4 |
| YARDS | 235 | 389 | 467 | 267 | 246 | 334 | 127 | 282 | 340 |
| PAR | | | | | | | | | |
| YARDS | | | | | | | | | |

**Directions:** Route 24 to Exit 16A (Route 106). Take left onto Crescent Street. After 1.5 miles, go left onto North Elm. Club is 1.5 miles on left.

# Widow's Walk Golf Course    ✪✪✪   94 ▶

**250 The Driftway**
**Scituate, MA (781) 544-0032**
www.widowswalkgolf.com

**Club Pro:** Bob Sanderson, PGA
**Payment:** Visa, MC, Amex, Disc
**Tee Times:** 4 days adv.
**Fee  9 Holes: Weekday:** $23 M-Th
**Fee 18 Holes: Weekday:** $39 M-Th
**Twilight Rates:** Yes
**Cart Rental:** $16pp/18, $9pp/9
**Lessons:** $60/45 min.   **Schools:** No
**Membership:** Yes
**Other:** Restaurant / Bar

| Tees | Holes | Yards | Par | USGA | Slope |
|------|-------|-------|-----|------|-------|
| BACK | 18 | 6403 | 72 | 71.2 | 129 |
| MIDDLE | 18 | 6062 | 72 | 69.6 | 127 |
| FRONT | 18 | 4562 | 72 | 66.2 | 113 |

**Weekend:** $26 F/S/S
**Weekend:** $47 F/S/S
**Discounts:** Senior & Junior M-Th
**Driving Range:** $4/bucket
**Junior Golf:** Yes
**Architect/Yr Open:** Michael Hurdzan/1997
**GPS:**

*COUPON*

Challenging course, very well groomed, great ocean views. Some of the best public greens anywhere.

| | 1 | 2 | 3 | 4 | 5 | 6 | 7 | 8 | 9 |
|------|---|---|---|---|---|---|---|---|---|
| PAR | 5 | 3 | 4 | 4 | 4 | 5 | 3 | 4 | 5 |
| YARDS | 504 | 126 | 350 | 351 | 302 | 486 | 167 | 313 | 481 |
| | 10 | 11 | 12 | 13 | 14 | 15 | 16 | 17 | 18 |
| PAR | 4 | 3 | 4 | 4 | 3 | 5 | 4 | 3 | 5 |
| YARDS | 425 | 140 | 313 | 412 | 183 | 486 | 312 | 191 | 520 |

**Directions:** Route 3 to Exit 13, Route 53 North to Route 123 East. 6 miles on Route 123 East to rotary. Second right on rotary. Course is 7/10 mile on left.

# William J. Devine Golf Course ✪✪½ | 95 ▶

GB RTE 495

1 Circuit Drive
Dorchester, MA (617) 265-4084
www.cityofbostongolf.com

| Tees | Holes | Yards | Par | USGA | Slope |
|--------|-------|-------|------|------|-------|
| BACK | 18 | 5966 | 70 | 69.8 | 127 |
| MIDDLE | 18 | 5622 | 70 | 68.1 | 121 |
| FRONT | 18 | 5031 | 7270 | 64.7 | 115 |

**Club Pro:** Kevin Frawley
**Payment:** Visa, MC, Cash
**Tee Times:** Weekends & Holidays
**Fee 9 Holes: Weekday:** $18 **Weekend:** $20
**Fee 18 Holes: Weekday:** $31 **Weekend:** $35
**Twilight Rates:** No **Discounts:** Senior & Junior
**Cart Rental:** $20pp/18, $11pp/9 **Driving Range:** No
**Lessons:** $50/half hour **Schools:** No **Junior Golf:** Yes
**Membership:** Yes, waiting list **Architect/Yr Open:** Donald Ross/1896
**Other:** Clubhouse / Snack Bar / Lockers / Function Facility

Second oldest public course in the U.S., a Donald Ross design. Across from Franklin Park Zoo. Great summer programs for juniors. "Some terrific holes with a great Boston skyline." –FP

| | 1 | 2 | 3 | 4 | 5 | 6 | 7 | 8 | 9 |
|-------|-----|-----|-----|-----|-----|-----|-----|-----|-----|
| PAR | 4 | 4 | 4 | 3 | 4 | 4 | 4 | 3 | 4 |
| YARDS | 378 | 302 | 404 | 163 | 344 | 334 | 370 | 149 | 331 |
| | 10 | 11 | 12 | 13 | 14 | 15 | 16 | 17 | 18 |
| PAR | 4 | 5 | 4 | 3 | 4 | 3 | 4 | 4 | 5 |
| YARDS | 299 | 502 | 382 | 118 | 338 | 152 | 327 | 267 | 462 |

**Directions:** Follow signs to Franklin Park Zoo. Take 93 North/South. Take Columbia Road exit. Follow Columbia Road to Franklin Park.

# Willowdale Golf Course ✪½ | 96 ▶

54 Willow Street
Mansfield, MA (508) 339-3197

| Tees | Holes | Yards | Par | USGA | Slope |
|--------|-------|-------|------|------|-------|
| BACK | | | | | |
| MIDDLE | 9 | 1935 | 30 | | |
| FRONT | | | | | |

**Club Pro:** Michael Simonelli, GM
**Payment:** Cash Only
**Tee Times:** No
**Fee 9 Holes: Weekday:** $15 **Weekend:** $17
**Fee 18 Holes: Weekday:** $18 **Weekend:** $20
**Twilight Rates:** No **Discounts:** Senior M-F $1 off
**Cart Rental:** $2/pull **Driving Range:** No
**Lessons:** No **Schools:** No **Junior Golf:** Yes
**Membership:** No **Architect/Yr Open:** 1960
**Other:** Snack Bar / Bar-Lounge / Clubhouse **GPS:**

Executive-style course, considered an easy walker. Open April 1 - December 1. "Fun for all levels of golfers." –FP

| | 1 | 2 | 3 | 4 | 5 | 6 | 7 | 8 | 9 |
|-------|-----|-----|-----|-----|-----|-----|-----|-----|-----|
| PAR | 4 | 3 | 3 | 4 | 4 | 3 | 3 | 3 | 3 |
| YARDS | 265 | 180 | 190 | 320 | 285 | 180 | 100 | 210 | 205 |
| PAR | | | | | | | | | |
| YARDS | | | | | | | | | |

**Directions:** I-95 to Mansfield exit. Route 140 to Mansfield Center, School Street exit. First right on Willow Street.

# Woburn Country Club

5 Country Club Road
Woburn, MA (781) 933-9880
www.thewoburncountryclub.com

| Tees | Holes | Yards | Par | USGA | Slope |
|---|---|---|---|---|---|
| BACK | | | | | |
| MIDDLE | 9 | 2996 | 34 | 68.9 | 121 |
| FRONT | 9 | 2565 | 35 | 68.0 | 104 |

**Club Pro:** Paul Barkhouse, PGA
**Payment:** Visa, MC
**Tee Times:** 2 days adv. (weekends only)
**Fee 9 Holes: Weekday:** $20      **Weekend:** $21
**Fee 18 Holes: Weekday:** $29      **Weekend:** $34
**Twilight Rates:** No      **Discounts:** Senior & Junior (weekdays only)
**Cart Rental:** $28/18, $16/9 per cart      **Driving Range:** No
**Lessons:** $40/half hour  **Schools:** No      **Junior Golf:** Yes
**Membership:** Residents only      **Architect/Yr Open:**
**Other:** Restaurant / Snack Bar / Function Hall      **GPS:**

Small greens. You will need a good short game to score well as this course will provide you with every lie in the book. Dress code required. Resident rates available.

| | 1 | 2 | 3 | 4 | 5 | 6 | 7 | 8 | 9 |
|---|---|---|---|---|---|---|---|---|---|
| PAR | 4 | 4 | 4 | 4 | 4 | 4 | 3 | 4 | 3 |
| YARDS | 373 | 363 | 359 | 371 | 410 | 326 | 190 | 389 | 215 |
| | | | | | | | | | |
| PAR | | | | | | | | | |
| YARDS | | | | | | | | | |

**Directions:** I-93 to I-95/Route 128 South, Exit 33A (Winchester), straight through Woburn Four Corners, take left at first set of lights onto Country Club Road.

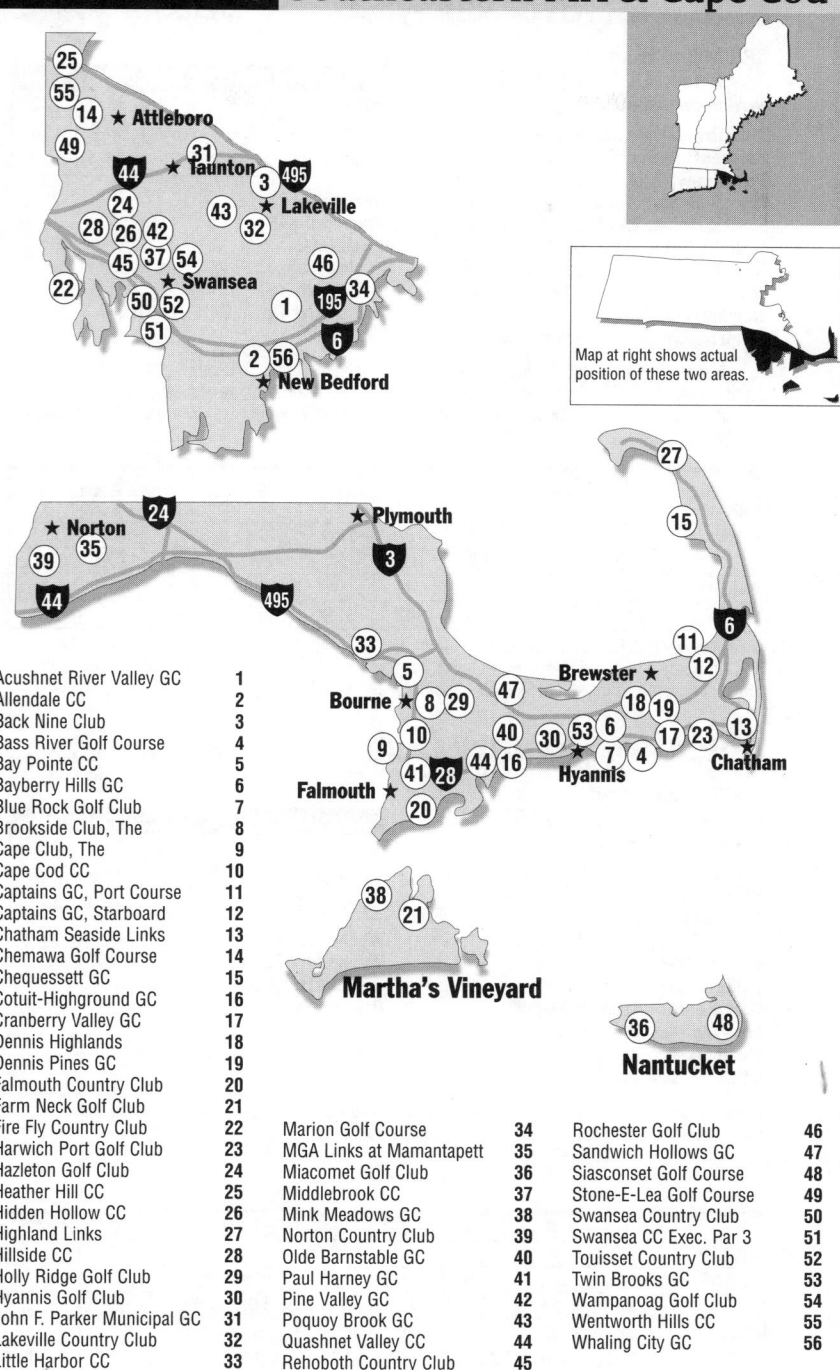

Map at right shows actual position of these two areas.

**Martha's Vineyard**

**Nantucket**

| | | | |
|---|---|---|---|
| Acushnet River Valley GC | 1 | | |
| Allendale CC | 2 | | |
| Back Nine Club | 3 | | |
| Bass River Golf Course | 4 | | |
| Bay Pointe CC | 5 | | |
| Bayberry Hills GC | 6 | | |
| Blue Rock Golf Club | 7 | | |
| Brookside Club, The | 8 | | |
| Cape Club, The | 9 | | |
| Cape Cod CC | 10 | | |
| Captains GC, Port Course | 11 | | |
| Captains GC, Starboard | 12 | | |
| Chatham Seaside Links | 13 | | |
| Chemawa Golf Course | 14 | | |
| Chequessett GC | 15 | | |
| Cotuit-Highground GC | 16 | | |
| Cranberry Valley GC | 17 | | |
| Dennis Highlands | 18 | | |
| Dennis Pines GC | 19 | | |
| Falmouth Country Club | 20 | | |
| Farm Neck Golf Club | 21 | Marion Golf Course | 34 | Rochester Golf Club | 46 |
| Fire Fly Country Club | 22 | MGA Links at Mamantapett | 35 | Sandwich Hollows GC | 47 |
| Harwich Port Golf Club | 23 | Miacomet Golf Club | 36 | Siasconset Golf Course | 48 |
| Hazleton Golf Club | 24 | Middlebrook CC | 37 | Stone-E-Lea Golf Course | 49 |
| Heather Hill CC | 25 | Mink Meadows GC | 38 | Swansea Country Club | 50 |
| Hidden Hollow CC | 26 | Norton Country Club | 39 | Swansea CC Exec. Par 3 | 51 |
| Highland Links | 27 | Olde Barnstable GC | 40 | Touisset Country Club | 52 |
| Hillside CC | 28 | Paul Harney GC | 41 | Twin Brooks GC | 53 |
| Holly Ridge Golf Club | 29 | Pine Valley GC | 42 | Wampanoag Golf Club | 54 |
| Hyannis Golf Club | 30 | Poquoy Brook GC | 43 | Wentworth Hills CC | 55 |
| John F. Parker Municipal GC | 31 | Quashnet Valley CC | 44 | Whaling City GC | 56 |
| Lakeville Country Club | 32 | Rehoboth Country Club | 45 | | |
| Little Harbor CC | 33 | | | | |

**KEY TO THE STAR RATINGS:**
5✪ = Outstanding  4✪ = Excellent  3✪ = Very Good  2✪ = Good  1✪ = Average  NR = Not Rated

# Acushnet River Valley GC  ✪✪✪½  ▶ 1

685 Main Street
Acushnet, MA  (508) 998-7777
www.golfacushnet.com

| Tees | Holes | Yards | Par | USGA | Slope |
|------|-------|-------|-----|------|-------|
| BACK | 18 | 6302 | 72 | 70.0 | 122 |
| MIDDLE | 18 | 5735 | 72 | 66.9 | 116 |
| FRONT | 18 | 5099 | 72 | 68.4 | 115 |

Club Pro: Gary Cardoza, Jr., PGA
Payment: All Types
Tee Times: 7 days adv.
Fee 9 Holes: Weekday: $29 w/cart      Weekend: $27
Fee 18 Holes: Weekday: $47 w/cart     Weekend: $46
Twilight Rates: After 12pm            Discounts: Junior
Cart Rental: $17pp/18, $8pp/9         Driving Range: $6/lg, $4/sm bucket
Lessons: $40/half hour  Schools: Yes  Junior Golf: Yes
Membership: Season Passes             Architect/Yr Open: Brian Silva/1998
Other: Snack Bar / Clubhouse / Bar-Lounge   GPS: Yes

*COUPON*

Gary Cardoza School of Golf. Region's best kept secret. Pine Alley front 9, Scottish Links back 9 —
2 golf courses in 1. *Golf Digest* ranked four stars. Quiet, friendly atmosphere. Outstanding conditions
for fairways and greens. Challenging golf course with excellent weekday rates. "Our group comes down
every year from NH. We love it." –RM

|  | 1 | 2 | 3 | 4 | 5 | 6 | 7 | 8 | 9 |
|------|------|------|------|------|------|------|------|------|------|
| PAR | 4 | 4 | 4 | 5 | 4 | 3 | 4 | 3 | 5 |
| YARDS | 375 | 289 | 275 | 436 | 336 | 119 | 382 | 141 | 501 |
|  | 10 | 11 | 12 | 13 | 14 | 15 | 16 | 17 | 18 |
| PAR | 4 | 3 | 5 | 4 | 5 | 4 | 4 | 3 | 4 |
| YARDS | 315 | 113 | 470 | 388 | 529 | 257 | 328 | 145 | 336 |

Directions: I-95/Route 128 to Route 24 South to Route 140 South. Take Exit 6 to Route 18 South.
Stay on Route 18 South for 2 miles. At lights, turn left onto Tarkiln Hill Road, which becomes Main
Street in Acushnet. Course will be on left about 2 miles after Acushnet Town Hall.

# Allendale Country Club  ✪✪✪½  ▶ 2

1047 Allen Street
Dartmouth, MA  (508) 992-8682
www.allendalecc.net

| Tees | Holes | Yards | Par | USGA | Slope |
|------|-------|-------|-----|------|-------|
| BACK | 18 | 6764 | 72 | 73.4 | 133 |
| MIDDLE | 18 | 6410 | 72 | 71.8 | 128 |
| FRONT | 18 | 5540 | 73 | 72.4 | 127 |

Club Pro: Stephen Brown, PGA
Payment: All Types
Tee Times: 5 days adv. wkdys; Thu. for wknds
Fee 9 Holes: Weekday: $30      Weekend: $30
Fee 18 Holes: Weekday: $50     Weekend: $55
Twilight Rates: After 3pm       Discounts: Junior
Cart Rental: $15pp/18, $10pp/9  Driving Range: Yes
Lessons: Yes  Schools: No       Junior Golf: Yes
Membership: Yes                 Architect/Yr Open: Geoffrey Cornish/1956
Other: Restaurant / Clubhouse / Lockers / Showers / Bar-Lounge

*COUPON*

A fair but challenging course for the beginner as well as the advanced player. Membership includes
the full use of the practice facilities, lockers and swimming pool.

|  | 1 | 2 | 3 | 4 | 5 | 6 | 7 | 8 | 9 |
|------|------|------|------|------|------|------|------|------|------|
| PAR | 4 | 4 | 3 | 4 | 3 | 5 | 4 | 4 | 5 |
| YARDS | 387 | 406 | 170 | 386 | 153 | 466 | 394 | 429 | 485 |
|  | 10 | 11 | 12 | 13 | 14 | 15 | 16 | 17 | 18 |
| PAR | 4 | 5 | 3 | 4 | 3 | 5 | 4 | 4 | 4 |
| YARDS | 356 | 486 | 162 | 352 | 156 | 524 | 353 | 344 | 401 |

Directions: Route 24 South to Exit 12 (Route 140). Take 140 South to Route 6 and take an
immediate right onto Tucker Road. Go 1.5 miles and turn left on Allen Street. Course is on the left.

# Back Nine Club, The ✪✪✪ ▶ 3

17 Heritage Hill Drive
Lakeville, MA (508) 947-9991
www.thebacknineclub.com
**Club Pro:** Bob Giusti, PGA
**Payment:** Visa, MC, Amex, Disc, Cash
**Tee Times:** 7 days adv.

| Tees | Holes | Yards | Par | USGA | Slope |
|------|-------|-------|-----|------|-------|
| BACK | 18 | 2967 | 54 | 57.0 | 97 |
| MIDDLE | 18 | 2588 | 54 | 57.0 | 97 |
| FRONT | 18 | 2080 | 54 | 57.0 | 97 |

**Fee 9 Holes: Weekday:** $15    **Weekend:** $15
**Fee 18 Holes: Weekday:** $25    **Weekend:** $25
**Twilight Rates:** $20 after 5pm    **Discounts:** Junior
**Cart Rental:** $10p/18, $7pp/9    **Driving Range:** No
**Lessons:** Yes **Schools:** Yes    **Junior Golf:** Yes
**Membership:** Yes    **Architect/Yr Open:** Geoffrey Cornish/1974
**Other:** Restaurant / Bar-Lounge / Leagues / Outings / Function Hall

Completely renovated clubhouse now with full restaurant and bar. Renovated pro shop and new outside deck. Course renovations are ongoing. Sig. Hole: #16, 145-yard par 3. Beginner-friendly certified by NGCOA. Open all year round. Challenging and beautiful, excellent Par-3 Course.

SE MA/ CAPE

| | 1 | 2 | 3 | 4 | 5 | 6 | 7 | 8 | 9 |
|---|---|---|---|---|---|---|---|---|---|
| PAR | 3 | 3 | 3 | 3 | 3 | 3 | 3 | 3 | 3 |
| YARDS | 155 | 190 | 160 | 140 | 145 | 155 | 115 | 170 | 145 |
| | 10 | 11 | 12 | 13 | 14 | 15 | 16 | 17 | 18 |
| PAR | 3 | 3 | 3 | 3 | 3 | 3 | 3 | 3 | 3 |
| YARDS | 140 | 130 | 125 | 110 | 145 | 120 | 145 | 160 | 125 |

**Directions:** Take I-495 to Exit 5. Go south on Route 18. Go through intersection of Route 18 and Route 105 and take first right after mini-mart onto Highland Road. Take first right onto Heritage Hill Drive and course is ¼ mile down road.

# Bass River Golf Course ✪✪½ ▶ 4

62 Highbank Road
South Yarmouth, MA
(508) 398-9079
www.golfyarmouthcapecod.com
**Club Pro:** Ron Hewins
**Payment:** Visa, MC, Disc, Amex
**Tee Times:** 7 days adv. (508) 398-4112

| Tees | Holes | Yards | Par | USGA | Slope |
|------|-------|-------|-----|------|-------|
| BACK | 18 | 6138 | 72 | 69.7 | 127 |
| MIDDLE | 18 | 5716 | 72 | 67.3 | 121 |
| FRONT | 18 | 4974 | 69.9 | 70.5 | 122 |

**Fee 9 Holes: Weekday:** $40    **Weekend:** $40
**Fee 18 Holes: Weekday:** $66    **Weekend:** $66
**Twilight Rates:** After 4pm    **Discounts:** Junior
**Cart Rental:** $20pp/18, $12pp/9    **Driving Range:** No
**Lessons:** Yes **Schools:** No    **Junior Golf:** Yes
**Membership:** Yes    **Architect/Yr Open:** Donald Ross/1900
**Other:** Clubhouse / Restaurant / Bar-Lounge    **GPS:**

Regulation seaside layout with wide fairways and smaller greens. Signature Hole #19 borders Bass River. Hosted the Mass Senior 4-Ball Championship in 2014.

| | 1 | 2 | 3 | 4 | 5 | 6 | 7 | 8 | 9 |
|---|---|---|---|---|---|---|---|---|---|
| PAR | 3 | 4 | 4 | 4 | 4 | 4 | 3 | 5 | 3 |
| YARDS | 165 | 282 | 391 | 329 | 348 | 282 | 105 | 464 | 155 |
| | 10 | 11 | 12 | 13 | 14 | 15 | 16 | 17 | 18 |
| PAR | 4 | 4 | 5 | 5 | 3 | 4 | 5 | 4 | 4 |
| YARDS | 247 | 386 | 450 | 500 | 140 | 333 | 474 | 319 | 339 |

**Directions:** Route 6 to Exit 8. Take right off ramp; then take 1st left after high school and go through one intersection to course.

# Bay Pointe Club, The　　　✪✪½　▶5

**19 Bay Pointe Drive**
**Onset, MA (508) 759-8802**
www.baypointeclub.com

| Tees | Holes | Yards | Par | USGA | Slope |
|------|-------|-------|-----|------|-------|
| BACK | 18 | 6201 | 70 | 71.6 | 125 |
| MIDDLE | 18 | 5720 | 70 | 69.6 | 125 |
| FRONT | 18 | 5380 | 72 | 71.3 | 125 |

**Club Pro:** Scott MacArthur, PGA
**Payment:** Cash, Visa, MC, Amex
**Tee Times:** 3 weeks adv.
**Fee　9 Holes: Weekday:** $20　　**Weekend:** $25
**Fee 18 Holes: Weekday:** $30　　**Weekend:** $42
**Twilight Rates:** After 1:30pm　　**Discounts:** Yes
**Cart Rental:** $18pp/18, $9pp/9　　**Driving Range:** Irons only
**Lessons:** $50/45 min.　**Schools:** No　　**Junior Golf:** No
**Membership:** Yes　　**Architect/Yr Open:** Geoffrey Cornish/1963
**Other:** Clubhouse / Lockers / Showers / Snack Bar / Restaurant / Bar-Lounge / Pool / Tennis

Lots of improvements made, under new ownership. Great staff. Located at western mouth of Cape, 5 minutes from Bourne Bridge. Typical Cape course, superbly manicured, excellent greens and fairways. Juniors and senior discounts. Open year round.

| | 1 | 2 | 3 | 4 | 5 | 6 | 7 | 8 | 9 |
|------|----|----|----|----|----|----|----|----|----|
| PAR | 5 | 4 | 4 | 3 | 4 | 4 | 3 | 3 | 5 |
| YARDS | 481 | 465 | 384 | 189 | 452 | 283 | 101 | 227 | 517 |
| | 10 | 11 | 12 | 13 | 14 | 15 | 16 | 17 | 18 |
| PAR | 3 | 4 | 3 | 4 | 3 | 5 | 4 | 5 | 4 |
| YARDS | 195 | 391 | 203 | 360 | 208 | 526 | 337 | 492 | 390 |

**Directions:** I-495 turns into Route 25. Take Exit 2 from Route 25. At 7th light go right, course is ⅔ mile on right. From Route 3 South take Route 6 at Sagamore Rotary toward Buzzard's Bay. Cross bridge into Wareham and go left at first light (Onset Avenue). Course ⅔ mile on right.

# Bayberry Hills Golf Course　　✪✪✪　▶6

**631 West Yarmouth Road**
**South Yarmouth, MA**
**(508) 394-5597**
www.golfyarmouthcapecod.com

| Tees | Holes | Yards | Par | USGA | Slope |
|------|-------|-------|-----|------|-------|
| BACK | 27/18 | 6523 | 72 | 72.0 | 128 |
| MIDDLE | 27/18 | 6087 | 72 | 69.6 | 124 |
| FRONT | 27/18 | 5323 | 72 | 70.5 | 122 |

**Club Pro:** Jim Armentrout, Dir. of Golf
**Payment:** Visa, MC, Disc
**Tee Times:** 7 days adv. (508) 398-4112
**Fee　9 Holes: Weekday:** $33 cart included　　**Weekend:** $33 cart included
**Fee 18 Holes: Weekday:** $85 cart included　　**Weekend:** $85 cart included
**Twilight Rates:** After 4pm　　**Discounts:** Junior
**Cart Rental:** $20pp/18, $12pp/9　　**Driving Range:** $10/lg, $7/md, $4/sm
**Lessons:** Yes; $8/res.; $12/non-res.　**Schools:** No　**Junior Golf:** Yes
**Membership:** Yes, non-resident/resident rates　**Architect/Yr Open:** Cornish/Silva/1988
**Other:** Clubhouse / Bar-Lounge / Restaurant　**GPS:**

*COUPON*

Immaculate condition. 27 holes, with a 9-hole links style course.

**Red/White**

| | 1 | 2 | 3 | 4 | 5 | 6 | 7 | 8 | 9 |
|------|----|----|----|----|----|----|----|----|----|
| PAR | 4 | 5 | 3 | 4 | 4 | 4 | 5 | 3 | 4 |
| YARDS | 395 | 485 | 140 | 336 | 335 | 350 | 505 | 146 | 350 |
| | 10 | 11 | 12 | 13 | 14 | 15 | 16 | 17 | 18 |
| PAR | 4 | 4 | 3 | 4 | 4 | 5 | 4 | 3 | 5 |
| YARDS | 372 | 384 | 130 | 320 | 352 | 503 | 349 | 160 | 475 |

**Directions:** Take Exit 8 off Route 6 East. Turn South onto Station Avenue. Take right at second traffic light onto Old Townhouse Road. Entrance to course at end of street.

# Blue Rock Golf Course  ✪✪✪½

48 Todd Road
South Yarmouth, MA (508) 398-9295
www.bluerockgolfcourse.com

**Club Pro:** Patrick Fannon, PGA
**Payment:** Visa, MC, Cash, Check
**Tee Times:** 7 days adv.

| Tees | Holes | Yards | Par | USGA | Slope |
|------|-------|-------|-----|------|-------|
| BACK | 18 | 2860 | 54 | 56.4 | 83 |
| MIDDLE | 18 | 2520 | 54 | 56.4 | 83 |
| FRONT | 18 | 2154 | 54 | 55.8 | 80 |

**Fee 9 Holes: Weekday:** Call     **Weekend:** Call
**Fee 18 Holes: Weekday:** Call     **Weekend:** Call
**Twilight Rates:** Call for rates     **Discounts:** Call for discounts
**Cart Rental:** $15/single, $28/double     **Driving Range:** Members only
**Lessons:** Yes  **Schools:** Yes     **Junior Golf:** Yes
**Membership:** Yes     **Architect/Yr Open:** Geoffrey Cornish/1962
**Other:** Clubhouse / Snack Bar / Restaurant / Bar-Lounge / Hotel / Tennis / Pool / Golf School / Golf Clinic

COUPON

2011 *Golf* magazine Top 10 par 3 golf course. "Friendly staff, fun to play, easy to walk." –SD "A great test for your short game; lots of wonderful carries and challenges. A better challenge than some regulation courses." –JD

| | 1 | 2 | 3 | 4 | 5 | 6 | 7 | 8 | 9 |
|-----|-----|-----|-----|-----|-----|-----|-----|-----|-----|
| PAR | 3 | 3 | 3 | 3 | 3 | 3 | 3 | 3 | 3 |
| YARDS | 103 | 127 | 118 | 125 | 247 | 145 | 170 | 165 | 165 |
| | 10 | 11 | 12 | 13 | 14 | 15 | 16 | 17 | 18 |
| PAR | 3 | 3 | 3 | 3 | 3 | 3 | 3 | 3 | 3 |
| YARDS | 150 | 117 | 190 | 147 | 185 | 185 | 144 | 129 | 173 |

**Directions:** Take Mid-Cape Highway East to Exit 8. Turn right off the ramp. Take first left on White's Path, right to intersection, turn left on Great Western Road. Course is ¼ mile on right.

# Brookside Club, The  ✪✪✪  8

11 Brigadoon Road (Route 28)
Bourne, MA (508) 743-4653
www.golfbrookside.com

**Club Pro:** Chris Gagnon, PGA
**Payment:** Visa, MC, Amex, Disc, Checks, Cash
**Tee Times:** 7 days adv.

| Tees | Holes | Yards | Par | USGA | Slope |
|------|-------|-------|-----|------|-------|
| BACK | 18 | 6317 | 70 | 71.1 | 126 |
| MIDDLE | 18 | 5826 | 70 | 68.1 | 124 |
| FRONT | 18 | 5169 | 70 | 69.6 | 118 |

**Fee 9 Holes: Weekday:** $35 w/cart     **Weekend:** $45 w/cart
**Fee 18 Holes: Weekday:** $64 w/cart     **Weekend:** $75 w/cart
**Twilight Rates:** After 2pm M-T; After 4pm F/S/S

COUPON

**Discounts:** Senior & Junior M-Th
**Cart Rental:** $20pp/18, $11pp/9     **Driving Range:** $9/lg., $7/sm.
**Lessons:** $45/half hour  **Schools:** No     **Junior Golf:** Yes
**Membership:** Yes     **Architect/Yr Open:** Michael Hurdzan, 1986
**Other:** Bar / Restaurant / Clubhouse     **GPS:**

Hole #1 offers you a breathtaking view of Onset Beach and Cape Cod Canal. The course also features lush fairways, rolling hills and fast greens.

| | 1 | 2 | 3 | 4 | 5 | 6 | 7 | 8 | 9 |
|-----|-----|-----|-----|-----|-----|-----|-----|-----|-----|
| PAR | 4 | 3 | 4 | 4 | 5 | 3 | 4 | 4 | 4 |
| YARDS | 379 | 156 | 359 | 365 | 503 | 96 | 361 | 421 | 332 |
| | 10 | 11 | 12 | 13 | 14 | 15 | 16 | 17 | 18 |
| PAR | 5 | 4 | 4 | 3 | 4 | 4 | 4 | 3 | 4 |
| YARDS | 576 | 336 | 330 | 128 | 354 | 351 | 313 | 130 | 342 |

**Directions:** Routes I-495/25 over Bourne Bridge to Route 28 South. Course is 2 miles on right.

# Cape Club, The

NR ⑨

125 Falmouth Woods Road
North Falmouth, MA (508) 540-4005
www.ballymeade.com

| Tees | Holes | Yards | Par | USGA | Slope |
|------|-------|-------|-----|------|-------|
| BACK | 18 | 6928 | 72 | 74.3 | 139 |
| MIDDLE | 18 | 6358 | 72 | 71.7 | 134 |
| FRONT | 18 | 5001 | 72 | 69.9 | 119 |

**Club Pro:** Ryan Payne, Dir. of Golf
**Payment:** Cash, Credit Cards
**Tee Times:** 1 week adv.
**Fee 9 Holes: Weekday:** **Weekend:**
**Fee 18 Holes: Weekday:** $71/am, $56/12pm, $37/3pm (includes cart)
    **Weekend:** $81/am, $66/12pm, $40/3pm (includes cart)
**Twilight Rates:** After 3pm    **Discounts:** None
**Cart Rental:** Included    **Driving Range:** $8/lg bucket
**Lessons:** $50/half hour; $75/hr **Schools:** No    **Junior Golf:** Yes
**Membership:** Yes    **Architect/Yr Open:** Jim Fazio/1988
**Other:** Restaurant / Clubhouse / Bar-Lounge / Lockers / Snack Bar / Showers
**GPS:** Yes

Player Comments: "Challenging. Scenic." Hole 11: Highest point on Cape; can see the Bay, New Bedford, over Marion to Fairhaven, all the boats in between. Off-season rates. Open year-round.

| | 1 | 2 | 3 | 4 | 5 | 6 | 7 | 8 | 9 |
|---|---|---|---|---|---|---|---|---|---|
| PAR | 4 | 3 | 5 | 4 | 3 | 4 | 4 | 5 | 4 |
| YARDS | 355 | 183 | 464 | 333 | 164 | 419 | 367 | 464 | 390 |
| | 10 | 11 | 12 | 13 | 14 | 15 | 16 | 17 | 18 |
| PAR | 5 | 3 | 4 | 4 | 3 | 4 | 4 | 4 | 5 |
| YARDS | 500 | 164 | 403 | 415 | 380 | 331 | 156 | 367 | 503 |

**Directions:** Over Bourne Bridge to Route 28 South. Exit at North Falmouth Route 151, 9 miles from the bridge. Turn right off the exit ramp. Course is less than 1 mile on the right.

# Cape Cod Country Club

✪✪✪ ⑩

48 Theater Drive
East Falmouth, MA (508) 563-9842
www.capecodcountryclub.com

| Tees | Holes | Yards | Par | USGA | Slope |
|------|-------|-------|-----|------|-------|
| BACK | 18 | 6404 | 71 | 71.7 | 129 |
| MIDDLE | 18 | 6018 | 71 | 69.6 | 125 |
| FRONT | 18 | 5348 | 72 | 71.0 | 120 |

**Club Pro:** C. Holmes, Golf Dir., J. Munroe, PGA
**Payment:** Cash, MC, Visa
**Tee Times:** 7 days adv.
**Fee 9 Holes: Weekday:** $26 M-Th    **Weekend:** $32 F/S/S
**Fee 18 Holes: Weekday:** $43 M-Th    **Weekend:** $57 F/S/S
**Twilight Rates:** After 2pm    **Discounts:** Tues/Ladies, Wed./Sr.
**Cart Rental:** $17pp/18, $9pp/9    **Driving Range:** No
**Lessons:** Call for details **Schools:** No    **Junior Golf:** No
**Membership:** No    **Architect/Yr Open:** Emmet & Tull/1928
**Other:** Clubhouse / Snack Bar / Bar-Lounge    **GPS:**

Signature hole #14: The Volcano is the most talked-about hole. Course plays longer than the scorecard statistics. The impeccable fairways are lined with pine trees.

| | 1 | 2 | 3 | 4 | 5 | 6 | 7 | 8 | 9 |
|---|---|---|---|---|---|---|---|---|---|
| PAR | 4 | 3 | 5 | 4 | 4 | 5 | 4 | 4 | 3 |
| YARDS | 307 | 175 | 460 | 419 | 360 | 509 | 300 | 407 | 156 |
| | 10 | 11 | 12 | 13 | 14 | 15 | 16 | 17 | 18 |
| PAR | 4 | 5 | 3 | 5 | 4 | 3 | 3 | 4 | 4 |
| YARDS | 405 | 515 | 220 | 461 | 351 | 180 | 183 | 300 | 310 |

**Directions:** Take Route 28 South of Bourne Bridge, take right onto Route 151. Course is approximately 3 miles on right.

# Captains Golf Course (Port) ✪✪✪½

11 ▶

1000 Freeman's Way
Brewster, MA (508) 896-1716
www.captainsgolfcourse.com

| Tees | Holes | Yards | Par | USGA | Slope |
|------|-------|-------|-----|------|-------|
| BACK | 18 | 6724 | 72 | 73.5 | 130 |
| MIDDLE | 18 | 6164 | 72 | 70.7 | 128 |
| FRONT | 18 | 5345 | 72 | 71.1. | 119 |

**Club Pro:** Mark O'Brien, Director of Ops.
**Payment:** Visa, MC, Amex, Disc
**Tee Times:** Up to 1 year adv.
**Fee 9 Holes: Weekday:** $35 after 12pm
**Fee 18 Holes: Weekday:** $76 summer
**Twilight Rates:** After 4pm
**Cart Rental:** $20pp/18, $12pp/9
**Lessons:** Yes **Schools:** Yes
**Membership:** Yes
**Other:** Bar / Restaurant / Banquet Facility

**Weekend:** $35 after 12pm
**Weekend:** $76 summer
**Discounts:** Junior, $5 after 5pm
**Driving Range:** $8/lg, $5/sm bucket
**Junior Golf:** Yes
**Architect/Yr Open:** Brian Silva/1985
**GPS:**

Player Comments: "Holes 12 through 16 are a spectacular sequence." Outings are our specialty. Reservations available online. New irrigation system. Lower Cape's best 2 layouts.

| | 1 | 2 | 3 | 4 | 5 | 6 | 7 | 8 | 9 |
|------|----|----|----|----|----|----|----|----|----|
| PAR | 4 | 4 | 3 | 4 | 3 | 5 | 4 | 5 | 4 |
| YARDS | 321 | 374 | 160 | 361 | 141 | 508 | 427 | 529 | 337 |
| | 10 | 11 | 12 | 13 | 14 | 15 | 16 | 17 | 18 |
| PAR | 4 | 3 | 5 | 5 | 4 | 3 | 4 | 3 | 5 |
| YARDS | 357 | 177 | 515 | 408 | 353 | 153 | 336 | 197 | 510 |

**Directions:** Route 6 to Exit 11. Right off exit ramp and travel 1.5 miles to Freeman's Way on right. Turn onto Freeman's and course is 1.5 miles on right.

# Captains GC (Starboard) ✪✪✪½

12 ▶

1000 Freeman's Way
Brewster, MA (508) 896-1716
www.captainsgolfcourse.com

| Tees | Holes | Yards | Par | USGA | Slope |
|------|-------|-------|-----|------|-------|
| BACK | 18 | 6776 | 72 | 72.6 | 130 |
| MIDDLE | 18 | 6198 | 72 | 69.4 | 123 |
| FRONT | 18 | 5359 | 72 | 71.2 | 116 |

**Club Pro:** Mark T. O'Brien, Director of Ops.
**Payment:** Visa, MC, Amex, Disc
**Tee Times:** Up to 1 year in adv.
**Fee 9 Holes: Weekday:** $35 after 12pm
**Fee 18 Holes: Weekday:** $76 summer
**Twilight Rates:** After 4pm
**Cart Rental:** $20pp/18, $12pp/9
**Lessons:** Yes **Schools:** Yes
**Membership:** Yes
**Other:** Bar / Restaurant / Banquet Facility

**Weekend:** $35 after 12pm
**Weekend:** $76 summer
**Discounts:** Junior, $5 after 5pm
**Driving Range:** $8/lg, $5/sm bucket
**Junior Golf:** Yes
**Architect/Yr Open:** Brian Silva/1985
**GPS:**

Outings are our specialty. Player Comments: "Excellent layout. Best-conditioned course I've played." Reservations avaiable online. Come play both sides.

| | 1 | 2 | 3 | 4 | 5 | 6 | 7 | 8 | 9 |
|------|----|----|----|----|----|----|----|----|----|
| PAR | 4 | 3 | 5 | 4 | 3 | 4 | 5 | 4 | 4 |
| YARDS | 352 | 131 | 491 | 401 | 178 | 287 | 507 | 370 | 322 |
| | 10 | 11 | 12 | 13 | 14 | 15 | 16 | 17 | 18 |
| PAR | 4 | 3 | 4 | 5 | 4 | 4 | 4 | 3 | 5 |
| YARDS | 344 | 182 | 326 | 481 | 378 | 361 | 427 | 156 | 504 |

**Directions:** Route 6 to Exit 11. Right off exit ramp and travel 1.5 miles to Freeman's Way on right. Turn onto Freeman's and course is 1.5 miles on right.

# Chatham Seaside Links ✪✪ 13 ▶

**209 Seaview Street**
**Chatham, MA (508) 945-4774**
www.chathamseasidelinks.com

| Tees | Holes | Yards | Par | USGA | Slope |
|------|-------|-------|-----|------|-------|
| BACK | | | | | |
| MIDDLE | 9 | 2465 | 34 | 65.6 | 107 |
| FRONT | 9 | 2400 | 34 | 65.6 | 109 |

**Club Pro:** Dennis Donohoe
**Payment:** Cash, MC, Visa
**Tee Times:** No
**Fee 9 Holes: Weekday:** $19 **Weekend:** $19
**Fee 18 Holes: Weekday:** $30 **Weekend:** $30
**Twilight Rates:** No **Discounts:** Senior & Junior
**Cart Rental:** $12pp/18, $7.50pp/9 **Driving Range:** No
**Lessons: Schools:** No **Junior Golf:** No
**Membership:** Yes **Architect/Yr Open:** 1895
**Other:** Snacks **GPS:**

Links-style golf course with ocean views. Course irrigated. Open April 1 to October 31.

| | 1 | 2 | 3 | 4 | 5 | 6 | 7 | 8 | 9 |
|------|-----|-----|-----|-----|-----|-----|-----|-----|-----|
| PAR | 4 | 4 | 3 | 3 | 4 | 4 | 4 | 4 | 4 |
| YARDS | 295 | 285 | 150 | 140 | 350 | 305 | 325 | 295 | 320 |
| PAR | | | | | | | | | |
| YARDS | | | | | | | | | |

**Directions:** Route 6 to Exit 11 (Route 137). Go left to Route 28 and left again to Main Street Chatham. Take Seaview off Main Street to course.

# Chemawa Golf Course ✪✪✪½ 14 ▶

**350 Cushman Road**
**North Attleboro, MA (508) 399-7330**
www.chemawagolf.com

| Tees | Holes | Yards | Par | USGA | Slope |
|------|-------|-------|-----|------|-------|
| BACK | 18 | 5267 | 68 | 65.1 | 113 |
| MIDDLE | 18 | 4884 | 68 | 63.5 | 110 |
| FRONT | 18 | 4351 | 69 | 64.6 | 109 |

**Club Pro:**
**Payment:** Most Major Credit Cards
**Tee Times:** Weekend and holiday
**Fee 9 Holes: Weekday:** $21 **Weekend:** $23
**Fee 18 Holes: Weekday:** $30 **Weekend:** $36
**Twilight Rates:** No **Discounts:** Sr., $27pp/18, $20pp/9
**Cart Rental:** $14pp/18, $7pp/9 **Driving Range:** No
**Lessons:** No **Schools:** No **Junior Golf:** No
**Membership:** No **Architect/Yr Open:** Steve Espisito/1956
**Other:** Snack Bar / Bar-Lounge / Enlarged Putting Green

Player Comments: "Parkland layout presents water and wetlands in play on 11 holes with generous driving zones. Early version of the island green on 16th." "Challenging, difficult."

| | 1 | 2 | 3 | 4 | 5 | 6 | 7 | 8 | 9 |
|------|-----|-----|-----|-----|-----|-----|-----|-----|-----|
| PAR | 4 | 4 | 4 | 4 | 4 | 4 | 5 | 4 | 3 |
| YARDS | 334 | 286 | 324 | 321 | 312 | 236 | 427 | 265 | 136 |
| | 10 | 11 | 12 | 13 | 14 | 15 | 16 | 17 | 18 |
| PAR | 4 | 3 | 4 | 3 | 3 | 4 | 3 | 4 | 4 |
| YARDS | 348 | 126 | 309 | 146 | 198 | 332 | 109 | 265 | 410 |

**Directions:** I-95 South to I-295 toward Woonsocket, Route 1 South. Take right onto May Street, then take a right onto Cushman Road.

# Chequessett Golf, Tennis & Sailing ✪✪½

680 Chequesset Neck Road
Wellfleet, MA (508) 349-3704
www.cycc.net

**Club Pro:** Chris Hicks, PGA
**Payment:** Visa, MC
**Tee Times:** Unlimited w/CC

| Tees | Holes | Yards | Par | USGA | Slope |
|------|-------|-------|-----|------|-------|
| BACK | | | | | |
| MIDDLE | 9 | 2621 | 35 | 66.1 | 107 |
| FRONT | 9 | 2314 | 37 | 67.9 | 110 |

**Fee 9 Holes: Weekday:** $35
**Fee 18 Holes: Weekday:** $50
**Twilight Rates:** After 4pm
**Cart Rental:** $20pp/18, $13pp/9
**Lessons:** Yes **Schools:** No
**Membership:** Yes
**Other:** Snack Bar (Seasonal) / Tennis / Sailing

**Weekend:** $35
**Weekend:** $50
**Discounts:** Juniors
**Driving Range:** No
**Junior Golf:** Yes
**Architect/Yr Open:** 1929
**GPS:**

COUPON

Nice scenic holes with two sets of tees for 18 holes of play. Small, tough greens. Good for family play. New irrigation system has improved the condition and experience at this semi-private club. "Worth a visit." –SD

| | 1 | 2 | 3 | 4 | 5 | 6 | 7 | 8 | 9 |
|------|---|---|---|---|---|---|---|---|---|
| PAR | 4 | 3 | 4 | 5 | 3 | 4 | 4 | 4 | 4 |
| YARDS | 234 | 127 | 368 | 435 | 109 | 314 | 373 | 380 | 281 |
| PAR | | | | | | | | | |
| YARDS | | | | | | | | | |

**Directions:** From Orleans rotary take Route 6 to Wellfleet. At Wellfleet Center light, go left at light onto Main Street. Take left on Commercial Street toward harbor. Go 1.5 miles past the harbor to the course on the right.

# Cotuit-Highground Golf Course

31 Crockers Neck Road
Cotuit, MA (508) 428-9863
www.cotuithighground.com

**Club Pro:** Steve Heher, PGA
**Payment:** Cash Only
**Tee Times:** No

| Tees | Holes | Yards | Par | USGA | Slope |
|------|-------|-------|-----|------|-------|
| BACK | | | | | |
| MIDDLE | 9 | 1290 | 28 | | |
| FRONT | 9 | 1059 | 28 | | |

**Fee 9 Holes: Weekday:** $15
**Fee 18 Holes: Weekday:** $20
**Twilight Rates:** After 4pm
**Cart Rental:** Some available
**Lessons:** Yes **Schools:** No
**Membership:** Yes
**Other:** Bar-Lounge / Snack Bar

**Weekend:** $15
**Weekend:** $20
**Discounts:** Senior & Junior
**Driving Range:** No
**Junior Golf:** Yes
**Architect/Yr Open:** 1927
**GPS:**

Player comments: "Good value." Family fun. Links-style course, very tight greens. Accuracy is very important. Open year-round.

| | 1 | 2 | 3 | 4 | 5 | 6 | 7 | 8 | 9 |
|------|---|---|---|---|---|---|---|---|---|
| PAR | 3 | 3 | 4 | 3 | 3 | 3 | 3 | 3 | 3 |
| YARDS | 115 | 180 | 290 | 130 | 140 | 110 | 100 | 180 | 115 |
| PAR | | | | | | | | | |
| YARDS | | | | | | | | | |

**Directions:** Take Route 6 to Exit 2 (Route 130 South), left onto Route 28, right onto Main Street in Cotuit Center. Take right onto School Street then second left onto Crocker Neck Road.

# Cranberry Valley Golf Course ✪✪✪✪  17 ▶

**183 Oak Street**
**Harwich, MA** (508) 430-5234
www.cranberrygolfcourse.com
**Club Pro:** Roman Greer, PGA
**Payment:** Cash, Visa, MC
**Tee Times:** Up to 10 days adv.

| Tees | Holes | Yards | Par | USGA | Slope |
|------|-------|-------|-----|------|-------|
| BACK | 18 | 6745 | 72 | 71.9 | 129 |
| MIDDLE | 18 | 6296 | 72 | 70.4 | 125 |
| FRONT | 18 | 5518 | 72 | 71.5 | 115 |

**Fee 9 Holes: Weekday:**
**Fee 18 Holes: Weekday:** $67
**Twilight Rates:** After 4pm
**Cart Rental:** $20pp/18, $10pp/9
**Lessons:** $55/half hour  **Schools:** No
**Membership:** Yes, resident & non-resident
**Other:** Restaurant/Bar

**Weekend:**
**Weekend:** $70
**Discounts:** None
**Driving Range:** Yes
**Junior Golf:** Yes
**Architect/Yr Open:** Cornish & Robinson/1974
**GPS:**

Player Comments: "Very fine play, great condition." Large teeing areas and 53 sand bunkers. Hosted 2014 Mass Public Links Championship. Open March - December. Seasonal rates.

| | 1 | 2 | 3 | 4 | 5 | 6 | 7 | 8 | 9 |
|------|-----|-----|-----|-----|-----|-----|-----|-----|-----|
| PAR | 4 | 5 | 4 | 3 | 4 | 4 | 3 | 5 | 4 |
| YARDS | 365 | 505 | 390 | 197 | 435 | 340 | 176 | 510 | 383 |
| | 10 | 11 | 12 | 13 | 14 | 15 | 16 | 17 | 18 |
| PAR | 4 | 4 | 4 | 3 | 5 | 4 | 4 | 3 | 5 |
| YARDS | 361 | 352 | 372 | 174 | 445 | 308 | 443 | 205 | 521 |

**Directions:** Take Exit 10 off Route 6 East. Take a right off the ramp and take first left at 4-way stop onto Queen Anne Road. Take third right (Oak Street). Course is ½ mile on left.

# Dennis Highlands Golf Course ✪✪✪  18 ▶

**825 Old Bass River Road**
**Dennis, MA** (508) 385-8347
www.dennisgolf.com
**Club Pro:** Mike Cummings
**Payment:** MC, Visa, Disc, Cash
**Tee Times:** 4 days adv.; up to 7 for non-members

| Tees | Holes | Yards | Par | USGA | Slope |
|------|-------|-------|-----|------|-------|
| BACK | 18 | 6464 | 71 | 70.9 | 120 |
| MIDDLE | 18 | 6076 | 71 | 68.5 | 117 |
| FRONT | 18 | 4927 | 71 | 67.8 | 112 |

**Fee 9 Holes: Weekday:** $41, 5:30am-7am and after 1pm
**Fee 18 Holes: Weekday:** $66
**Twilight Rates:** $41 after 1pm; $29 after 4pm
**Cart Rental:** $19pp/18, $13pp/9
**Lessons:** Yes  **Schools:** Yes
**Membership:** Available
**Architect/Yr Open:** Jack Kidwell/Michael Hurdzan/1983
**Other:** Clubhouse / Restaurant / Bar-Lounge

**Weekend:** $66
**Discounts:** Senior/Junior
**Driving Range:** $8/lg., $5/sm.
**Junior Golf:** Yes

ᶜᴼᵁᴾᴼₙ COUPON

Golf instruction - John Boniface, PGA. Putting is key to good round. Added green tee markers. Seasonal rates. Enlarged some tees and rebuilt 7th green. Open year round. Family-friendly venue. Home of the Dennis Fourball.

| | 1 | 2 | 3 | 4 | 5 | 6 | 7 | 8 | 9 |
|------|-----|-----|-----|-----|-----|-----|-----|-----|-----|
| PAR | 4 | 5 | 3 | 4 | 4 | 4 | 3 | 5 | 3 |
| YARDS | 309 | 494 | 151 | 331 | 347 | 409 | 160 | 472 | 141 |
| | 10 | 11 | 12 | 13 | 14 | 15 | 16 | 17 | 18 |
| PAR | 4 | 3 | 4 | 4 | 4 | 5 | 3 | 4 | 5 |
| YARDS | 371 | 151 | 365 | 392 | 383 | 529 | 170 | 377 | 519 |

**Directions:** Take Route 6 to Exit 9B, follow ½ mile. Take left onto Bob Crowell Road. At end take right onto Old Bass River Road, course is 2.4 miles up on left.

# Dennis Pines Golf Course  ✪✪✪½

## 19

50 Golf Course Road
East Dennis, MA  (508) 385-8347
www.dennisgolf.com

| Tees | Holes | Yards | Par | USGA | Slope |
|------|-------|-------|-----|------|-------|
| BACK | 18 | 7029 | 72 | 74.2 | 133 |
| MIDDLE | 18 | 6525 | 72 | 72.1 | 131 |
| FRONT | 18 | 5845 | 72 | 73.6 | 126 |

**Club Pro:** Mike Cummings
**Payment:** Visa, MC, Disc, Cash
**Tee Times:** Up to 7 days adv.
**Fee  9 Holes: Weekday:** $41, 5:30am-7am and after 1pm
**Fee 18 Holes: Weekday:** $66       **Weekend:** $66
**Twilight Rates:** $41 after 1pm, $29 after 4pm    **Discounts:** None
**Cart Rental:** $19pp/18, $13 pp/9      **Driving Range:** $8/lg., $5/sm.
**Lessons:** Yes  **Schools:** Yes     **Junior Golf:** Yes
**Membership:** Available       **Architect/Yr Open:** Henry Mitchell/1964
**Other:** Snack Bar / Restaurant / Bar-Lounge     **GPS:**

Golf instruction - John Boniface, PGA. One of Cape's busiest courses. Wonderful layout with dramatic holes set among tall pines. Call for early morning and twilight rates.

|       | 1 | 2 | 3 | 4 | 5 | 6 | 7 | 8 | 9 |
|-------|---|---|---|---|---|---|---|---|---|
| PAR | 4 | 4 | 5 | 3 | 5 | 4 | 3 | 4 | 4 |
| YARDS | 373 | 369 | 471 | 188 | 476 | 423 | 187 | 442 | 389 |
|       | 10 | 11 | 12 | 13 | 14 | 15 | 16 | 17 | 18 |
| PAR | 4 | 4 | 5 | 3 | 4 | 5 | 4 | 3 | 4 |
| YARDS | 351 | 357 | 518 | 172 | 405 | 472 | 344 | 183 | 405 |

**Directions:** Take Exit 9B off of Route 6, proceed north on Route 134, take a right approximately 2.5 miles to Golf Course Road, Dennis Pines Golf Course is located at the end of Golf Course Road.

# Falmouth Country Club  ✪✪✪

## 20

630 Carriage Shop Road
Falmouth, MA  (508) 548-3211
www.falmouthcountryclub.com

| Tees | Holes | Yards | Par | USGA | Slope |
|------|-------|-------|-----|------|-------|
| BACK | 18 | 6665 | 72 | 72.2 | 133 |
| MIDDLE | 18 | 6234 | 72 | 71.2 | 128 |
| FRONT | 18 | 5551 | 72 | 72.6 | 132 |

**Club Pro:** Matthew Burgess, PGA
**Payment:** Visa, MC
**Tee Times:** 14 days adv.
**Fee  9 Holes: Weekday:** $27/walk; $35/ride   **Weekend:** $27/walk, $35/ride
**Fee 18 Holes: Weekday:** $49/non-res, $35/res  **Weekend:** $64/non-res, $52/res
**Twilight Rates:** After 2pm      **Discounts:** None
**Cart Rental:** $15pp/18, $8pp/9     **Driving Range:** Yes - $6/bucket
**Lessons:** Yes  **Schools:** Yes     **Junior Golf:** Yes
**Membership:** Yes      **Architect/Yr Open:** Vinnie Bartlett/1969
**Other:** Clubhouse / Snack Bar / Bar-Lounge    **GPS:**

27 holes—an 18-hole course and a 9-hole, now managed by Billy Casper Golf Management. "Nice wide open layout. Easy to walk. Great for bird watchers." –FP

|       | 1 | 2 | 3 | 4 | 5 | 6 | 7 | 8 | 9 |
|-------|---|---|---|---|---|---|---|---|---|
| PAR | 4 | 3 | 4 | 4 | 4 | 3 | 4 | 5 | 4 |
| YARDS | 400 | 175 | 370 | 384 | 403 | 174 | 318 | 531 | 426 |
|       | 10 | 11 | 12 | 13 | 14 | 15 | 16 | 17 | 18 |
| PAR | 5 | 4 | 3 | 4 | 5 | 5 | 4 | 3 | 4 |
| YARDS | 516 | 385 | 151 | 427 | 545 | 500 | 380 | 190 | 390 |

**Directions:** Take Route 28 South into Falmouth. Take right onto Route 151 East, follow 3.5 miles to Sandwich Road on right. Look for signs, left onto Carriage Shop Road.

# Farm Neck Golf Club ✪✪✪✪½ 21

1 Farm Neck Way
Oak Bluffs, MA (508) 693-3057
www.farmneck.net

| Tees | Holes | Yards | Par | USGA | Slope |
|------|-------|-------|-----|------|-------|
| BACK | 18 | 6815 | 72 | 72.8 | 135 |
| MIDDLE | 18 | 6301 | 72 | 70.5 | 133 |
| FRONT | 18 | 4987 | 72 | 64.3 | 118 |

**Club Pro:** Don Costello
**Payment:** Visa, MC, Amex, Cash
**Tee Times:** 3-5 days adv.
**Fee 9 Holes: Weekday:** $45-$80 **Weekend:** $45-$80
**Fee 18 Holes: Weekday:** $70-$170 **Weekend:** $70-$170
**Twilight Rates:** After 4pm **Discounts:** None
**Cart Rental:** $20pp/18, $10pp/9 **Driving Range:** Yes
**Lessons:** Yes **Schools:** No **Junior Golf:** Yes
**Membership:** Waiting list **Architect/Yr Open:** Cornish & Robinson/1979
**Other:** Restaurant / Bar-Lounge / Snack Bar / Lockers / Showers

Scenic, splendid, and challenging with ocean breezes and views, meadows and interior woodlands. Off-season rates a great value: call ahead. "A treasure." "Pure golf experience." –JD

| | 1 | 2 | 3 | 4 | 5 | 6 | 7 | 8 | 9 |
|------|---|---|---|---|---|---|---|---|---|
| PAR | 4 | 5 | 4 | 3 | 4 | 3 | 4 | 5 | 3 |
| YARDS | 378 | 490 | 340 | 157 | 325 | 189 | 371 | 486 | 175 |
| | 10 | 11 | 12 | 13 | 14 | 15 | 16 | 17 | 18 |
| PAR | 4 | 5 | 4 | 4 | 4 | 3 | 4 | 4 | 5 |
| YARDS | 376 | 519 | 379 | 343 | 331 | 163 | 388 | 368 | 523 |

**Directions:** Follow Country Road in Oak Bluffs, Martha's Vineyard. Farm Neck Way is off of Country Road.

# Fire Fly Country Club NR 22

320 Fall River Avenue
Seekonk, MA (508) 336-6622

| Tees | Holes | Yards | Par | USGA | Slope |
|------|-------|-------|-----|------|-------|
| BACK | 18 | 3644 | 59 | 58.0 | 87 |
| MIDDLE | 18 | 3083 | 59 | 55.4 | 81 |
| FRONT | 18 | 2786 | 59 | 58.0 | 86 |

**Club Pro:** Keith Allcock, PGA
**Payment:** Visa, MC
**Tee Times:** Weekends only
**Fee 9 Holes: Weekday:** $16 **Weekend:** $17
**Fee 18 Holes: Weekday:** $20 **Weekend:** $23
**Twilight Rates:** After 7pm **Discounts:** Sr & Jr (M-F) $17/18
**Cart Rental:** $13pp/18, $7.50pp/9, $10/Senior **Driving Range:** $6/bucket
**Lessons:** $40/half hour; $25/Jr. **Schools:** No **Junior Golf:** Yes
**Membership:** Yes **Architect/Yr:** Joanne Carner & Don Hoenig/1962
**Other:** Snack Bar / Restaurant / Bar-Lounge

COUPON

Executive course, great for beginners and seasoned golfers who like to practice their short game. Junior clinics available at the Golf Learning Center.

| | 1 | 2 | 3 | 4 | 5 | 6 | 7 | 8 | 9 |
|------|---|---|---|---|---|---|---|---|---|
| PAR | 3 | 3 | 3 | 3 | 4 | 3 | 4 | 4 | 3 |
| YARDS | 145 | 150 | 148 | 147 | 441 | 122 | 286 | 251 | 123 |
| | 10 | 11 | 12 | 13 | 14 | 15 | 16 | 17 | 18 |
| PAR | 4 | 3 | 3 | 3 | 3 | 3 | 3 | 4 | 3 |
| YARDS | 240 | 146 | 126 | 87 | 139 | 155 | 182 | 240 | 134 |

**Directions:** From Providence I-95 to I-195 East to Exit 1 MA (Seekonk/Barrington). (From Fall River take 195 West to Exit 1 MA.) Go north on Route 114. At fork, bear left. Take right at Fire Fly.

# Harwich Port Golf Club ✪✪ 23

51 South Street
Harwich Port, MA (508) 432-0250

| Tees | Holes | Yards | Par | USGA | Slope |
|------|-------|-------|-----|------|-------|
| BACK | | | | | |
| MIDDLE | 9 | 2538 | 34 | | |
| FRONT | | | | | |

**Club Pro:** Rick Blakely, Manager
**Payment:** Cash Only
**Tee Times:** No
**Fee 9 Holes: Weekday:** $24 **Weekend:** $24
**Fee 18 Holes: Weekday:** $34 **Weekend:** $34
**Twilight Rates:** No **Discounts:** None
**Cart Rental:** $4/pull cart **Driving Range:** Members only
**Lessons:** No **Schools:** No **Junior Golf:** Jr. memberships available
**Membership:** Yes **Architect/Yr Open:** Don Blakely/1920
**Other:** **GPS:**

The course is considered an easy walker. Recommended for beginners and senior citizens. Members only after 5:30pm. New state-of-the-art irrigation system. "Friendly staff, family friendly, fun and challenging layout." –SD

| | 1 | 2 | 3 | 4 | 5 | 6 | 7 | 8 | 9 |
|------|---|---|---|---|---|---|---|---|---|
| PAR | 4 | 3 | 4 | 4 | 4 | 4 | 3 | 4 | 4 |
| YARDS | 358 | 170 | 340 | 330 | 325 | 255 | 155 | 295 | 310 |
| PAR | | | | | | | | | |
| YARDS | | | | | | | | | |

**Directions:** Take Route 6 to Exit 9 or 10. Take Route 28 to South Street. Course is 200 yards on right.

# Hazleton Golf Club NR 24

329 Summer Street
Rehoboth, MA

| Tees | Holes | Yards | Par | USGA | Slope |
|------|-------|-------|-----|------|-------|
| BACK | | | | | |
| MIDDLE | | | | | |
| FRONT | | | | | |

**Club Pro:**
**Payment:**
**Tee Times:**
**Fee 9 Holes: Weekday:** **Weekend:**
**Fee 18 Holes: Weekday:** **Weekend:**
**Twilight Rates:** **Discounts:**
**Cart Rental:** **Driving Range:**
**Lessons: Schools:** **Junior Golf:**
**Membership:** **Architect/Yr Open:**
**Other:**

COUPON

Scheduled to open in the summer of 2017.

| | 1 | 2 | 3 | 4 | 5 | 6 | 7 | 8 | 9 |
|------|---|---|---|---|---|---|---|---|---|
| PAR | | | | | | | | | |
| YARDS | | | | | | | | | |
| PAR | | | | | | | | | |
| YARDS | | | | | | | | | |

**Directions:** Route I-195 West to Route 114A to Route 44 East for 3 miles. Take right on Lake Street. Go 1 mile to course.

# Heather Hill Country Club   ✪✪½   ▶ 25

149 West Bacon Street
Plainville, MA (508) 695-0309
www.heatherhillcountryclub.com

| Tees | Holes | Yards | Par | USGA | Slope |
|------|-------|-------|-----|------|-------|
| BACK | 27/18 | 6335 | 72 | 67.8 | 117 |
| MIDDLE | 27/18 | 6034 | 72 | 66.5 | 115 |
| FRONT | 27/18 | 4986 | 70 | 67.1 | 111 |

**Club Pro:** Mike Cosentino, Golf Instruction
**Payment:** Cash, Check, Credit Cards
**Tee Times:** 1 week adv.
**Fee  9 Holes: Weekday:** $21     **Weekend:** $25
**Fee 18 Holes: Weekday:** $30     **Weekend:** $39
**Twilight Rates:** After 4pm (seasonal)   **Discounts:** None
**Cart Rental:** $16pp/18, $8pp/9     **Driving Range:** No
**Lessons:** Yes  **Schools:** No     **Junior Golf:** No
**Membership:** No                    **Architect/Yr Open:** 1955
**Other:** Clubhouse / Snack Bar / Bar-Lounge   **GPS:**

COUPON

27-hole course: Middle and South courses play for 18. North course is 9 holes, 3368 yards. Open year round. 10% discount on greens fees with the Plainridge Players Card. 20% discount for Wentworth Hills University alumni.

**Middle/South**

|       | 1 | 2 | 3 | 4 | 5 | 6 | 7 | 8 | 9 |
|-------|---|---|---|---|---|---|---|---|---|
| PAR   | 4 | 4 | 5 | 4 | 4 | 4 | 3 | 3 | 4 |
| YARDS | 340 | 397 | 489 | 373 | 274 | 419 | 197 | 173 | 339 |
|       | 10 | 11 | 12 | 13 | 14 | 15 | 16 | 17 | 18 |
| PAR   | 4 | 3 | 5 | 4 | 4 | 4 | 3 | 4 | 4 |
| YARDS | 388 | 169 | 518 | 334 | 317 | 367 | 183 | 413 | 315 |

**Directions:** Take I-495 to Exit 15, follow Route 1A South to Route 106; take right on West Bacon Street in Plainville Center. Course is on right.

# Hidden Hollow Country Club   NR   ▶ 26

30 Pierce Lane
Rehoboth, MA (508) 252-9392

| Tees | Holes | Yards | Par | USGA | Slope |
|------|-------|-------|-----|------|-------|
| BACK |  |  |  |  |  |
| MIDDLE | 9 | 2905 | 35 |  |  |
| FRONT |  |  |  |  |  |

**Club Pro:** Priscilla Clark, Owner
**Payment:** Cash Only
**Tee Times:** No
**Fee  9 Holes: Weekday:**          **Weekend:**
**Fee 18 Holes: Weekday:** $19      **Weekend:** $23
**Twilight Rates:** No              **Discounts:** None
**Cart Rental:** $20pp/18, $12pp/9  **Driving Range:** No
**Lessons:** No  **Schools:** No    **Junior Golf:** No
**Membership:** No                  **Architect/Yr Open:** William B. Clark/1962
**Other:** Snack Bar / Bar-Lounge / Clubhouse   **GPS:**

Small, Old-style, picturesque short course. Popular preference of female golfers.

|       | 1 | 2 | 3 | 4 | 5 | 6 | 7 | 8 | 9 |
|-------|---|---|---|---|---|---|---|---|---|
| PAR   | 4 | 4 | 3 | 4 | 4 | 5 | 4 | 3 | 4 |
| YARDS | 341 | 307 | 187 | 382 | 400 | 481 | 313 | 233 | 261 |
| PAR   |  |  |  |  |  |  |  |  |  |
| YARDS |  |  |  |  |  |  |  |  |  |

**Directions:** I-195 to MA Exit 2. North off exit to Davis Street. Left on Pleasant. Course is 1 mile on left.

# Highland Links

⭐⭐  **27**

**Highland Road**
**North Truro, MA (508) 487-9201**
www.trurolinks.com

| Tees | Holes | Yards | Par | USGA | Slope |
|------|-------|-------|-----|------|-------|
| BACK | | | | | |
| MIDDLE | 9 | 2720 | 35 | 67.0 | 114 |
| FRONT | 9 | 2294 | 36 | 67.8 | 117 |

**Club Pro:** Jim Knowles, PGA
**Payment:** Visa, MC
**Tee Times:** Yes
**Fee 9 Holes: Weekday:** $35        **Weekend:** $35
**Fee 18 Holes: Weekday:** $60      **Weekend:** $60
**Twilight Rates:** No                        **Discounts:** None
**Cart Rental:** $18pp/18, $9pp/9     **Driving Range:** No
**Lessons:** $45/half hour  **Schools:** No    **Junior Golf:** Yes
**Membership:** Yes, $575     **Architect/Yr Open:** Isiah M. Small/1892
**Other:** Clubhouse / Snack Bar    **GPS:**

Off-season rates available. The oldest links in New England. Wind, water, and a layout tucked into a natural site. See golf the way it was played in the old days. Improved irrigation and rebuilt #9 tee. "Every golfer should make a journey here. Don't expect anything fancy, but it is a treat to play." –JD

| | 1 | 2 | 3 | 4 | 5 | 6 | 7 | 8 | 9 |
|------|-----|-----|-----|-----|-----|-----|-----|-----|-----|
| PAR | 4 | 5 | 3 | 4 | 4 | 5 | 3 | 4 | 3 |
| YARDS | 250 | 460 | 160 | 346 | 380 | 464 | 171 | 353 | 136 |
| PAR | | | | | | | | | |
| YARDS | | | | | | | | | |

**Directions:** Take Route 6 to Truro. Course is just past the Truro elementary school. (Look for signs on Route 6.)

# Hillside Country Club

⭐⭐½ **28**

**82 Hillside Avenue**
**Rehoboth, MA (508) 252-9761**
www.hillsidecountryclub.com

| Tees | Holes | Yards | Par | USGA | Slope |
|------|-------|-------|-----|------|-------|
| BACK | | | | | |
| MIDDLE | 9 | 5912 | 72 | 68.4 | 126 |
| FRONT | 9 | 5686 | 70 | 67.5 | 119 |

**Club Pro:** John Simmons, PGA
**Payment:** Visa, MC, Disc, Cash
**Tee Times:**
**Fee 9 Holes: Weekday:** $18        **Weekend:** $22
**Fee 18 Holes: Weekday:** $25      **Weekend:** $28
**Twilight Rates:** No                        **Discounts:** None
**Cart Rental:** $18pp/18, $12pp/9    **Driving Range:** No
**Lessons:** No  **Schools:** No      **Junior Golf:** Yes
**Membership:** Yes                         **Architect/Yr Open:** George Cardono/1975
**Other:** Restaurant / Tiki Bar / Day Spa / Salt Water Pool / Fire Pits / Bocce / Tennis Courts / Volleyball Courts / Functions

COUPON

New ownership, new management, major renovations and improvements. Play Blue tees on the front, White on the back. Two sets of tees mean change of par on the second 9. "Friendly staff. Good value." –FP

| | 1 | 2 | 3 | 4 | 5 | 6 | 7 | 8 | 9 |
|------|-----|-----|-----|-----|-----|-----|-----|-----|-----|
| PAR | 4 | 3 | 5 | 3 | 4 | 4 | 5 | 4 | 4 |
| YARDS | 426 | 171 | 463 | 182 | 292 | 315 | 433 | 316 | 358 |
| | 10 | 11 | 12 | 13 | 14 | 15 | 16 | 17 | 18 |
| PAR | 4 | 3 | 5 | 3 | 4 | 4 | 4 | 4 | 4 |
| YARDS | 415 | 164 | 488 | 183 | 316 | 336 | 420 | 355 | 360 |

**Directions:** Take Route 24 South to Route 44 West – Taunton. Right onto River Street, first right onto Hillside Avenue.

# Holly Ridge Golf Club

✪✪½   ▶ 29

121 Country Club Road
Sandwich, MA (508) 428-5577
www.hollyridgegolf.com

| Tees | Holes | Yards | Par | USGA | Slope |
|------|-------|-------|-----|------|-------|
| BACK | 18 | 2952 | 54 | 55.4 | 74 |
| MIDDLE | 18 | 2715 | 54 | 54.1 | N/A |
| FRONT | 18 | 2194 | 54 | 54.8 | N/A |

**Club Pro:** Jean Enright
**Payment:** Visa, MC, Amex, Disc, Checks
**Tee Times:** 7 days adv.
**Fee  9 Holes: Weekday:** $22          **Weekend:** $22
**Fee 18 Holes: Weekday:** $36          **Weekend:** $36
**Twilight Rates:** After 3pm          **Discounts:** Senior & Junior
**Cart Rental:** $131pp/18, $9pp/9
**Driving Range:** $10/lg, $7/med, $4/sm
**Lessons:** $60/half hour  **Schools:** Yes
**Membership:** No          **Junior Golf:** Yes
**Other:** Restaurant / Bar-Lounge / Clubhouse   **Architect/Yr Open:** Geoffrey Cornish/1967
**GPS:**

ᶜᵒᵁᴾᴼ*N* COUPON

With a variety of par 3 holes nestled among the hollies and pines, the course appeals to golfers of all levels and is friendly to couples and families. Fun, friendly and affordable.

| | 1 | 2 | 3 | 4 | 5 | 6 | 7 | 8 | 9 |
|------|---|---|---|---|---|---|---|---|---|
| PAR | 3 | 3 | 3 | 3 | 3 | 3 | 3 | 3 | 3 |
| YARDS | 163 | 183 | 142 | 158 | 120 | 184 | 187 | 130 | 202 |
| | 10 | 11 | 12 | 13 | 14 | 15 | 16 | 17 | 18 |
| PAR | 3 | 3 | 3 | 3 | 3 | 3 | 3 | 3 | 3 |
| YARDS | 124 | 167 | 183 | 128 | 189 | 188 | 211 | 138 | 155 |

**Directions:** Take Route 3 South over Sagamore Bridge onto Route 6/Mid-Cape Highway. Take Exit 2 south on Route 130 for 1.6 miles, then left onto Cotuit Road for 1.4 miles and left onto Farmersville Road for 1.6 miles. Follow signs for Holly Ridge.

# Hyannis Golf Club

✪✪✪   ▶ 30

1840 Route 132
Hyannis, MA (508) 362-2606
www.barnstablegolf.com

| Tees | Holes | Yards | Par | USGA | Slope |
|------|-------|-------|-----|------|-------|
| BACK | 18 | 6621 | 71 | 71.1 | 133 |
| MIDDLE | 18 | 6002 | 71 | 70.6 | 129 |
| FRONT | 18 | 5149 | 72 | 71.9 | 127 |

**Club Pro:** Jesse Schechtman, PGA
**Payment:** Cash, Check, Visa, MC, Amex
**Tee Times:** Anytime
**Fee  9 Holes: Weekday:** $35          **Weekend:** $35
**Fee 18 Holes: Weekday:** $50          **Weekend:** $64
**Twilight Rates:** After 4pm          **Discounts:** Junior after 12pm
**Cart Rental:** $20pp/18, $11pp/9          **Driving Range:** Yes
**Lessons:** $40/half hour; $90/hour          **Schools:** Jr., Sr., First Tee Facility
**Junior Golf:** Yes
**Membership:** Yes          **Architect/Yr Open:** Cornish & Robinson/1975
**Other:** Restaurant / Bar-Lounge / Lodging Partner / Golf Outings

ᶜᵒᵁᴾᴼ*N* COUPON

Home of Cape Cod's Open and Senior Open. Some of the Cape's most memorable holes. Lots of elevation changes from tees to fairways and back up to greens. Four sets of tees now available.

| | 1 | 2 | 3 | 4 | 5 | 6 | 7 | 8 | 9 |
|------|---|---|---|---|---|---|---|---|---|
| PAR | 4 | 4 | 4 | 4 | 5 | 4 | 3 | 3 | 4 |
| YARDS | 342 | 388 | 326 | 392 | 528 | 332 | 144 | 195 | 406 |
| | 10 | 11 | 12 | 13 | 14 | 15 | 16 | 17 | 18 |
| PAR | 5 | 3 | 4 | 4 | 5 | 3 | 4 | 4 | 4 |
| YARDS | 455 | 125 | 367 | 315 | 515 | 138 | 308 | 338 | 388 |

**Directions:** Take Route 6 (Mid-Cape Highway) to Exit 6 (Route 132). Go south on Route 132 for ¼ mile and golf course is on left.

# John F. Parker Municipal GC ✪✪  ▶31

17 Fisher Street
Taunton, MA (508) 822-1797
www.johnfparkergc.com

| Tees | Holes | Yards | Par | USGA | Slope |
|------|-------|-------|-----|------|-------|
| BACK |       |       |     |      |       |
| MIDDLE | 9 | 3068 | 35 | 69.8 | 117 |
| FRONT |     |       |     |      |       |

**Club Pro:** Hank Wojtkunski, PGA
**Payment:** Cash Only
**Tee Times:** No
**Fee  9 Holes: Weekday:** $18
**Fee 18 Holes: Weekday:** $21
**Twilight Rates:** No
**Cart Rental:** $8pp/9
**Lessons:** Yes  **Schools:** Yes
**Membership:** Not Available
**Other:** Snack Bar / Bar-Lounge

**Weekend:** $21
**Weekend:** $24
**Discounts:** Senior
**Driving Range:** No
**Junior Golf:** Yes
**Architect/Yr Open:** 1937
**GPS:**

Fun course to play and great, friendly staff. "Small, true greens with good fairways mowed with false fronts. Good for all levels of play." –GG

|        | 1 | 2 | 3 | 4 | 5 | 6 | 7 | 8 | 9 |
|--------|---|---|---|---|---|---|---|---|---|
| PAR    | 4 | 4 | 4 | 5 | 4 | 3 | 4 | 4 | 3 |
| YARDS  | 360 | 412 | 350 | 478 | 345 | 168 | 330 | 390 | 235 |
| PAR    |   |   |   |   |   |   |   |   |   |
| YARDS  |   |   |   |   |   |   |   |   |   |

**Directions:** Route 24 to Route 140. Go west on Route 140 to center of Taunton. Pick up Route 44 West out of city. Go to 2nd set of traffic lights at Highland Street. Go right on Highland Street. Turn left onto Fisher Street.

# Lakeville Country Club ✪✪½  ▶32

Clear Pond Road
Lakeville, MA (508) 947-6630
www.lakevillecountryclub.com

| Tees | Holes | Yards | Par | USGA | Slope |
|------|-------|-------|-----|------|-------|
| BACK | 18 | 6335 | 72 | 70.6 | 125 |
| MIDDLE | 18 | 5890 | 72 | 68.6 | 123 |
| FRONT | 18 | 4863 | 72 | 67.4 | 111 |

**Club Pro:**
**Payment:** Visa, MC
**Tee Times:** 1 week adv.
**Fee  9 Holes: Weekday:** $26 M-Th $41/cart
**Fee 18 Holes: Weekday:** $40 M-Th $55/cart
**Twilight Rates:** After 1pm
**Cart Rental:** $15pp/18, $10pp/9
**Lessons:** No  **Schools:** No
**Membership:** No
**Other:** Restaurant / Clubhouse / Snack Bar / Bar-Lounge

**Weekend:** $27 F/S/S $42/cart
**Weekend:** $45 F/S/S $60/cart
**Discounts:** Senior
**Driving Range:** No
**Junior Golf:** No
**Architect/Yr Open:** Roger Beach/1970

Early-bird special before 8:30am. Enthusiastic, friendly staff. Course is in good shape. Public course with private conditions. New golf carts.

|        | 1 | 2 | 3 | 4 | 5 | 6 | 7 | 8 | 9 |
|--------|---|---|---|---|---|---|---|---|---|
| PAR    | 4 | 3 | 4 | 4 | 5 | 5 | 3 | 5 | 3 |
| YARDS  | 334 | 216 | 351 | 432 | 533 | 538 | 216 | 521 | 166 |
|        | 10 | 11 | 12 | 13 | 14 | 15 | 16 | 17 | 18 |
| PAR    | 4 | 4 | 5 | 4 | 5 | 4 | 3 | 3 | 4 |
| YARDS  | 339 | 380 | 500 | 324 | 463 | 335 | 139 | 178 | 370 |

**Directions:** I-495 to Exit 5. Go south on Route 18. Take left at first light to Route 79, then first right onto Clear Pond Road. Entrance is ½ mile on right.

# Little Harbor Country Club

NR  33 ▶

1 Little Harbor Road
Wareham, MA (508) 295-2617
www.littleharborcountryclub.com

| Tees | Holes | Yards | Par | USGA | Slope |
|---|---|---|---|---|---|
| BACK | | | | | |
| MIDDLE | 18 | 3038 | 56 | 54.4 | 79 |
| FRONT | 18 | 2692 | 56 | 51.9 | 72 |

**Club Pro:** Shawn Lapworth
**Payment:** Visa, MC, Amex, Cash
**Tee Times:** 3 days adv.
**Fee  9 Holes: Weekday:** $18    **Weekend:** $20
**Fee 18 Holes: Weekday:** $29    **Weekend:** $32
**Twilight Rates:** After 3pm    **Discounts:** Senior & Junior
**Cart Rental:** $11pp/18, $6pp/9    **Driving Range:** No
**Lessons:** $80   **Schools:** No    **Junior Golf:** Yes
**Membership:** Full and Associate    **Architect/Yr Open:** Richard Bowler/1963
**Other:** Clubhouse / Snack Bar    **GPS:**

COUPON

Holes range from 110 yards to 315 yards. Course and greens are in great condition. Open year round. Friendly staff.  You will always feel welcome at Little Harbor.

| | 1 | 2 | 3 | 4 | 5 | 6 | 7 | 8 | 9 |
|---|---|---|---|---|---|---|---|---|---|
| PAR | 3 | 3 | 3 | 3 | 3 | 4 | 4 | 3 | 3 |
| YARDS | 100 | 135 | 142 | 138 | 225 | 291 | 275 | 162 | 189 |
| | 10 | 11 | 12 | 13 | 14 | 15 | 16 | 17 | 18 |
| PAR | 3 | 3 | 3 | 3 | 3 | 3 | 3 | 3 | 3 |
| YARDS | 205 | 125 | 140 | 132 | 183 | 100 | 156 | 132 | 208 |

**Directions:** Take Route 6 to Depot Street. Follow Great Neck Road 2.5 miles. Go right on Stockton Shortcut Street. Take the 2nd right onto Little Harbor Road.

# Marion Golf Course

✪½  34 ▶

10 South Drive
Marion, MA (508) 748-0199
www.mariongolfclub.com

| Tees | Holes | Yards | Par | USGA | Slope |
|---|---|---|---|---|---|
| BACK | 9 | 2695 | 34 | 67.1 | 121 |
| MIDDLE | 9 | 2695 | 34 | 67.1 | 121 |
| FRONT | 9 | 2089 | 35 | 66.0 | 117 |

**Club Pro:**
**Payment:** Cash Only
**Tee Times:** No
**Fee  9 Holes: Weekday:** $15    **Weekend:** $17
**Fee 18 Holes: Weekday:** $22    **Weekend:** $24
**Twilight Rates:** After 5pm    **Discounts:** Sr./Jr. $2 off for 18 holes
**Cart Rental:** $20pp/18, $10pp/9    **Driving Range:** No
**Lessons:** No   **Schools:** No    **Junior Golf:** Yes
**Membership:** Yes    **Architect/Yr Open:** George Thomas/1904
**Other:** Club Rentals    **GPS:**

COUPON

European-style links. Open year round. "Several greens are defended by stone walls and cross bunkers. A wonderful 9 for the golf purist." –AP

| | 1 | 2 | 3 | 4 | 5 | 6 | 7 | 8 | 9 |
|---|---|---|---|---|---|---|---|---|---|
| PAR | 4 | 4 | 3 | 5 | 4 | 4 | 4 | 3 | 3 |
| YARDS | 315 | 290 | 175 | 460 | 365 | 430 | 365 | 180 | 115 |
| PAR | | | | | | | | | |
| YARDS | | | | | | | | | |

**Directions:** I-495 to I-195 East. Route 195 to Exit 20, head towards marina. Left at light onto Route 6. Go 1 mile to Cheek Road. Turn right; golf course is 1 mile on the right.

# MGA Links at Mamantapett ✪✪ 35

300 West Main Street (Route 123)
Norton, MA (508) 222-0555
www.mgalinks.org

**Club Pro:** Pete Walsh, PGA
**Payment:** Cash, Credit Cards, Checks
**Tee Times:** No
**Fee 9 Holes: Weekday:** $17
**Fee 18 Holes: Weekday:** $23
**Twilight Rates:** No
**Cart Rental:** $5/18, $3/9 pull carts only
**Lessons:** Yes  **Schools:** No
**Membership:** Yes
**Other:** Lounge

| Tees | Holes | Yards | Par | USGA | Slope |
|------|-------|-------|-----|------|-------|
| BACK | | | | | |
| MIDDLE | 18 | 2421 | 54 | | |
| FRONT | 18 | 2321 | 56 | | |

**Weekend:** $17
**Weekend:** $23
**Discounts:** Junior & Senior
**Driving Range:** No
**Junior Golf:** Yes
**Architect/Yr Open:** 1972
**GPS:**

Good course for women, seniors, short game and irons practice. First Tee and MGA ForeKids Program Monday through Thursday. Available for adult public play daily. Open year round.

| | 1 | 2 | 3 | 4 | 5 | 6 | 7 | 8 | 9 |
|------|-----|-----|-----|-----|-----|-----|-----|-----|-----|
| PAR | 3 | 3 | 3 | 3 | 3 | 3 | 3 | 3 | 3 |
| YARDS | 117 | 135 | 82 | 140 | 93 | 91 | 115 | 136 | 108 |
| | 10 | 11 | 12 | 13 | 14 | 15 | 16 | 17 | 18 |
| PAR | 3 | 3 | 3 | 3 | 3 | 3 | 3 | 3 | 3 |
| YARDS | 131 | 138 | 125 | 203 | 141 | 113 | 147 | 233 | 173 |

**Directions:** Take I-495 to Exit 10 (Route 123 West). Go approximately 4 miles. Course is on left.

# Miacomet Golf Club ✪✪✪½ 36

12 West Miacomet Road
Nantucket, MA (508) 325-0333
www.miacometgolf.com

**Club Pro:** Phillip Truono, PGA
**Payment:** Visa, MC, Amex, Disc
**Tee Times:** 4 days adv.
**Fee 9 Holes: Weekday:** $80
**Fee 18 Holes: Weekday:** $125
**Twilight Rates:** $50 after 4pm
**Cart Rental:** $25pp/18, $15pp/9
**Lessons:** $125/hour  **Schools:** Yes
**Membership:** Waitlist
**Other:** Restaurant / Clubhouse / Snack Bar / Bar-Lounge / Lodging Partner
**GPS:** Visage on every cart

| Tees | Holes | Yards | Par | USGA | Slope |
|------|-------|-------|-----|------|-------|
| BACK | 18 | 6890 | 72 | 73.6 | 128 |
| MIDDLE | 18 | 6393 | 72 | 71.5 | 125 |
| FRONT | 18 | 5145 | 72 | 70.6 | 121 |

**Weekend:** $80
**Weekend:** $125
**Discounts:** None
**Driving Range:** $10/lg, $5/sm bucket
**Junior Golf:** Yes
**Architect/Yr Open:** H. Maurer/1970

One of the best conditioned courses in New England. A course for all golfers. Difficult par 3's from the Tips. 2014 New England NGCOA Course of the Year.

| | 1 | 2 | 3 | 4 | 5 | 6 | 7 | 8 | 9 |
|------|-----|-----|-----|-----|-----|-----|-----|-----|-----|
| PAR | 4 | 4 | 3 | 5 | 5 | 4 | 4 | 3 | 4 |
| YARDS | 380 | 328 | 191 | 464 | 473 | 350 | 389 | 210 | 357 |
| | 10 | 11 | 12 | 13 | 14 | 15 | 16 | 17 | 18 |
| PAR | 4 | 4 | 3 | 4 | 5 | 3 | 4 | 4 | 5 |
| YARDS | 398 | 331 | 167 | 377 | 450 | 122 | 374 | 393 | 439 |

**Directions:** Nantucket is an island 25 miles off the coast of Cape Cod. Airport and ferry boat dock are in Hyannis.

# Middlebrook Country Club  ✪✪  ▶ 37

**149 Pleasant Street**
**Rehoboth, MA (508) 252-9395**

| Tees | Holes | Yards | Par | USGA | Slope |
|------|-------|-------|-----|------|-------|
| BACK | | | | | |
| MIDDLE | 9 | 2784 | 35 | 67.0 | 122 |
| FRONT | 9 | 2509 | 35 | N/A | 108 |

**Club Pro:** Pete & Lucretia Cupples, Owners
**Payment:** Visa, MC
**Tee Times:** Weekends
**Fee 9 Holes: Weekday:** $17   **Weekend:** $20
**Fee 18 Holes: Weekday:** $22   **Weekend:** $25
**Twilight Rates:** After 2pm   **Discounts:** Senior
**Cart Rental:** $24/18, $14/9 per cart   **Driving Range:** No
**Lessons:** No  **Schools:** No   **Junior Golf:** No
**Membership:** $800/single; $1150/couple   **Architect/Yr Open:** 1950
**Other:** Snack Bar / Bar-Lounge / Clubhouse   **GPS:**

Open April 1 - November 30. Beautiful gardens. 9 hole footgolf course open for play Sat. and Sun, 2–6pm, $10 per round. Member of AFGL.
"Fun layout with hands-on husband and wife owners. Well-kept. Give it a try." –FP

| | 1 | 2 | 3 | 4 | 5 | 6 | 7 | 8 | 9 |
|------|---|---|---|---|---|---|---|---|---|
| PAR | 4 | 4 | 4 | 4 | 5 | 3 | 3 | 4 | 4 |
| YARDS | 340 | 360 | 301 | 350 | 500 | 213 | 130 | 300 | 290 |
| PAR | | | | | | | | | |
| YARDS | | | | | | | | | |

**Directions:** Take I-195 to MA Exit 2. North off exit to Davis Street. Right on Davis to Pleasant Street. Left on Pleasant. Course is one mile on right.


# Mink Meadows Golf Club  ✪✪✪  ▶ 38

**320 Golf Club Road**
**Vineyard Haven, MA (508) 693-0600**
**www.minkmeadowsgc.com**

| Tees | Holes | Yards | Par | USGA | Slope |
|------|-------|-------|-----|------|-------|
| BACK | 9 | 3115 | 36 | 70.4 | 127 |
| MIDDLE | 9 | 2699 | 36 | 67.7 | 122 |
| FRONT | 9 | 2394 | 36 | 70.8 | 122 |

**Club Pro:** Chet Nowak
**Payment:** Visa, MC, Amex, Disc, Check
**Tee Times:** 2 days adv.
**Fee 9 Holes: Weekday:** $60   **Weekend:** $60
**Fee 18 Holes: Weekday:** $88   **Weekend:** $88
**Twilight Rates:** After 4:30pm   **Discounts:** Jr. membership
**Cart Rental:** $18pp/18, $11pp/9   **Driving Range:** $8/lg, $4/sm bucket
**Lessons:** Yes  **Schools:** No   **Junior Golf:** Yes
**Membership:** Yes   **Architect/Yr Open:** Wayne Stiles/1936
**Other:** Snack Bar   **GPS:**

Easy to walk, beautiful, challenging course. Off-season rates.

| | 1 | 2 | 3 | 4 | 5 | 6 | 7 | 8 | 9 |
|------|---|---|---|---|---|---|---|---|---|
| PAR | 4 | 4 | 4 | 4 | 3 | 4 | 3 | 5 | 4 |
| YARDS | 306 | 300 | 288 | 414 | 162 | 300 | 140 | 443 | 346 |
| PAR | | | | | | | | | |
| YARDS | | | | | | | | | |

**Directions:** From ferry, proceed to Main Street in Vineyard Haven. Take 2nd left and proceed to 2nd right (Franklin Street). Go 1.25 miles down Franklin Street to club entrance on left.

# Norton Country Club ✪✪✪

## 39

188 Oak Street
Norton, MA (508) 285-2400
www.nortoncountryclub.com

**Club Pro:** Jeff Martin
**Payment:** Most Major Credit Cards
**Tee Times:** 7 days adv.

| Tees | Holes | Yards | Par | USGA | Slope |
|------|-------|-------|-----|------|-------|
| BACK | 18 | 6545 | 71 | 72.2 | 137 |
| MIDDLE | 18 | 6201 | 71 | 69.9 | 132 |
| FRONT | 18 | 5040 | 71 | 71.0 | 124 |

**Fee 9 Holes: Weekday:** $25 M-Th
**Fee 18 Holes: Weekday:** $40 M-Th
**Twilight Rates:** $30 after 4pm
**Cart Rental:** $16pp/18, $10pp/9
**Lessons:** Yes **Schools:** No
**Membership:** Yes
**Other:** Clubhouse / Lockers / Showers / Snack Bar / Bar-Lounge

**Weekend:** $30 F/S/S
**Weekend:** $66 including cart F/S/S
**Discounts:** Lunch specials M-Th
**Driving Range:** No
**Junior Golf:** No
**Architect/Yr Open:** Cornish & Silva/1989

COUPON

Course is for serious golfers. "Beautiful course, great condition." "Not too long but tough. Course management a must, especially for first 6 holes."

|  | 1 | 2 | 3 | 4 | 5 | 6 | 7 | 8 | 9 |
|------|-----|-----|-----|-----|-----|-----|-----|-----|-----|
| PAR | 4 | 4 | 3 | 5 | 5 | 4 | 3 | 4 | 4 |
| YARDS | 346 | 426 | 143 | 500 | 492 | 419 | 105 | 383 | 313 |
|  | 10 | 11 | 12 | 13 | 14 | 15 | 16 | 17 | 18 |
| PAR | 4 | 4 | 3 | 4 | 5 | 4 | 3 | 4 | 4 |
| YARDS | 328 | 344 | 138 | 298 | 489 | 414 | 120 | 358 | 389 |

**Directions:** Take Route 123 (Exit 10) off I-495. Take 123 West toward Norton Center to Oak Street. Club is 1 mile on the left.

# Olde Barnstable Fairgrounds GC ✪✪✪✪

## 40

1460 Route 149
Marstons Mills, MA (508) 420-1141
www.obfgolf.com

**Club Pro:** Merry Holway, PGA
**Payment:** Cash, MC, Visa, Checks
**Tee Times:** Anytime

| Tees | Holes | Yards | Par | USGA | Slope |
|------|-------|-------|-----|------|-------|
| BACK | 18 | 6479 | 71 | 71.4 | 128 |
| MIDDLE | 18 | 6113 | 71 | 69.7 | 124 |
| FRONT | 18 | 5072 | 71 | 69.1 | 119 |

**Fee 9 Holes: Weekday:** $35
**Fee 18 Holes: Weekday:** $69
**Twilight Rates:** After 4pm
**Cart Rental:** $20pp/18, $11pp/9
**Lessons:** $40/half hour; $90/hour **Schools:** No
**Membership:** Yes
**Other:** Restaurant / Lodging Partner / Bar-Lounge

**Weekend:** $35
**Weekend:** $69
**Discounts:** Junior after 12pm
**Driving Range:** Yes
**Junior Golf:** Yes
**Architect/Yr:** Mark Mungeam/1992

COUPON

Player Comments: "From 1st tee to 18th green, a great test of golf. Great Cape Cod conditions." Rates subject to change. Home to the 2007 Cape Cod Open. Four sets of tees now available.

|  | 1 | 2 | 3 | 4 | 5 | 6 | 7 | 8 | 9 |
|------|-----|-----|-----|-----|-----|-----|-----|-----|-----|
| PAR | 5 | 3 | 5 | 3 | 4 | 4 | 4 | 4 | 4 |
| YARDS | 485 | 140 | 503 | 158 | 365 | 351 | 430 | 317 | 385 |
|  | 10 | 11 | 12 | 13 | 14 | 15 | 16 | 17 | 18 |
| PAR | 5 | 4 | 3 | 4 | 4 | 3 | 4 | 3 | 5 |
| YARDS | 510 | 335 | 157 | 340 | 380 | 172 | 395 | 155 | 535 |

**Directions:** Sagamore Bridge to Route 6, Exit 5, take right off ramp. Bear right on Route 149. Course is ½ mile on left.

# Paul Harney Golf Club   ✪✪½    41

74 Club Valley Drive
East Falmouth, MA (508) 563-3454
www.paulharneygolfcourse.com

| Tees | Holes | Yards | Par | USGA | Slope |
|------|-------|-------|-----|------|-------|
| BACK | 18 | 3570 | 59 | 58.9 | 91 |
| MIDDLE | 18 | 3315 | 59 | 56.7 | 89 |
| FRONT | 18 | 3200 | 61 | 61.0 | 89 |

**Club Pro:** N/A
**Payment:** Disc, Visa, MC, Amex
**Tee Times:** No
**Fee 9 Holes: Weekday:** $30 M-Th    **Weekend:** $30 F/S/S
**Fee 18 Holes: Weekday:** $30 M-Th    **Weekend:** $30 F/S/S
**Twilight Rates:** $25 after 2pm    **Discounts:** None
**Cart Rental:** $15pp/18, $7.50pp/9    **Driving Range:** No
**Lessons:** $40/half hour, $75/hour   **Schools:** Yes   **Junior Golf:** Yes
**Membership:** No    **Architect/Yr Open:** Paul Harney/1968
**Other:** Bar-Lounge / Snack Bar    **GPS:**

A true test for all golfers. Executive-style course. Paul Harney inducted into PGA Hall of Fame in 2005. Family-friendly and fun for all levels and abilities.

| | 1 | 2 | 3 | 4 | 5 | 6 | 7 | 8 | 9 |
|---|---|---|---|---|---|---|---|---|---|
| PAR | 4 | 3 | 3 | 4 | 3 | 3 | 4 | 3 | 3 |
| YARDS | 332 | 152 | 155 | 225 | 160 | 174 | 249 | 152 | 175 |
| | 10 | 11 | 12 | 13 | 14 | 15 | 16 | 17 | 18 |
| PAR | 3 | 3 | 3 | 3 | 4 | 4 | 3 | 3 | 4 |
| YARDS | 190 | 229 | 127 | 105 | 254 | 258 | 160 | 177 | 257 |

**Directions:** From Bourne Bridge take Route 28 East. Then take Route 151 toward Mashpee. Go 3-4 miles and take a left onto Fordham Road. Take left onto Club Valley Road to clubhouse.

# Pine Valley Golf Club   ✪✪½   42

136 Providence Street
Rehoboth, MA (508) 336-5064

| Tees | Holes | Yards | Par | USGA | Slope |
|------|-------|-------|-----|------|-------|
| BACK | | | | | |
| MIDDLE | 9 | 3015 | 35 | | 118 |
| FRONT | 9 | 2375 | 35 | | 113 |

**Club Pro:** Norman Cutter, Manager
**Payment:** Visa, MC
**Tee Times:** No
**Fee 9 Holes: Weekday:**    **Weekend:**
**Fee 18 Holes: Weekday:** $16/sr., $20/reg.    **Weekend:** $22
**Twilight Rates:** Yes    **Discounts:**
**Cart Rental:** $10pp/18, $5pp/9    **Driving Range:** No
**Lessons:** No   **Schools:** No    **Junior Golf:** No
**Membership:** No    **Architect/Yr Open:** 1945
**Other:** Snack Bar / Bar-Lounge    **GPS:**

Rates are for all day play. Carts are $5 per 9 holes. Player Comments: "Interesting layout, friendly staff, affordable prices."

| | 1 | 2 | 3 | 4 | 5 | 6 | 7 | 8 | 9 |
|---|---|---|---|---|---|---|---|---|---|
| PAR | 4 | 3 | 4 | 5 | 4 | 3 | 4 | 4 | 44 |
| YARDS | 387 | 172 | 397 | 568 | 306 | 218 | 383 | 301 | 283 |
| PAR | | | | | | | | | |
| YARDS | | | | | | | | | |

**Directions:** I-95 to I-195 East; take Exit 2 Route 136 North. Left onto Davis; turn right at end of road.

# Poquoy Brook Golf Course ✪✪✪½ ▶ 43

**20 Leonard Street**
**Lakeville, MA (508) 947-5261**
www.poquoybrook.com

**Club Pro:** Nora Berard, Dir. of Golf
**Payment:** Cash, All Major Credit Cards
**Tee Times:** M-F, 7 days adv.; S/S, 5 days adv.

| Tees | Holes | Yards | Par | USGA | Slope |
|------|-------|-------|-----|------|-------|
| BACK | 18 | 6817 | 72 | 72.4 | 128 |
| MIDDLE | 18 | 6291 | 72 | 69.9 | 125 |
| FRONT | 18 | 5415 | 73 | 71.0 | 114 |

**Fee 9 Holes: Weekday:** $24    **Weekend:** $27
**Fee 18 Holes: Weekday:** $40    **Weekend:** $49
**Twilight Rates:** After 5pm    **Discounts:** Junior under 18
**Cart Rental:** $16pp/18, $11pp/9    **Driving Range:** $5/lg, $3/sm
**Lessons:** Yes **Schools:** Yes    **Junior Golf:** Yes
**Membership:** Yes    **Architect/Yr Open:** Geoffrey Cornish/1962
**Other:** Clubhouse / Lockers / Showers / Snack Bar / Restaurant / Bar-Lounge

*COUPON*

Player Comments: "Good conditions, good staff, nice clubhouse." "Interesting layout with great holes." Open year round. Grows on you with each replay. 2 new tees completed and a great new website.

| | 1 | 2 | 3 | 4 | 5 | 6 | 7 | 8 | 9 |
|---|---|---|---|---|---|---|---|---|---|
| PAR | 4 | 4 | 3 | 4 | 5 | 4 | 4 | 3 | 5 |
| YARDS | 351 | 390 | 176 | 307 | 518 | 326 | 381 | 180 | 485 |
| | 10 | 11 | 12 | 13 | 14 | 15 | 16 | 17 | 18 |
| PAR | 4 | 4 | 3 | 4 | 5 | 3 | 4 | 4 | 5 |
| YARDS | 372 | 336 | 185 | 366 | 436 | 173 | 426 | 428 | 455 |

**Directions:** I-495 South: take Exit 5, Route 18 South. Bear right off exit. Take first right (Taunton Street) and then first left onto Leonard Street. Course is on right.

# Quashnet Valley Country Club ✪✪½ ▶ 44

**309 Old Barnstable Road**
**Mashpee, MA (508) 477-4412**
www.quashnetvalley.com

**Club Pro:** Bob Chase, PGA
**Payment:** Visa, MC, Disc
**Tee Times:** 1 week, prepay 6 months

| Tees | Holes | Yards | Par | USGA | Slope |
|------|-------|-------|-----|------|-------|
| BACK | 18 | 6601 | 72 | 71.7 | 132 |
| MIDDLE | 18 | 6093 | 72 | 69.1 | 121 |
| FRONT | 18 | 5094 | 72 | 70.3 | 119 |

**Fee 9 Holes: Weekday:** $24    **Weekend:** $29
**Fee 18 Holes: Weekday:** $47    **Weekend:** $57
**Twilight Rates:** After 2pm    **Discounts:** None
**Cart Rental:** $18pp/18, $9pp/9    **Driving Range:** Yes
**Lessons:** $60 **Schools:** Yes    **Junior Golf:** Yes
**Membership:** Yes    **Architect/Yr Open:** Cornish & Robinson/1973
**Other:** Clubhouse / Showers / Snack Bar / Bar-Lounge / Banquet Facilities

*COUPON*

*Golf Digest's* 4 Star Rating. Host of 2010 MGA Public Links. The experience begins and ends with challenging par 5s. Very natural setting with only one set parallel fairways on the course. No visible homes until the 10th hole. Ponds and streams abound. Player Comments: "Excellent layout. Great shape. Must play when on Cape. Friendly staff. Beautiful setting through old cranberry bogs."

| | 1 | 2 | 3 | 4 | 5 | 6 | 7 | 8 | 9 |
|---|---|---|---|---|---|---|---|---|---|
| PAR | 5 | 3 | 4 | 4 | 3 | 4 | 5 | 3 | 4 |
| YARDS | 505 | 135 | 328 | 310 | 153 | 420 | 488 | 173 | 349 |
| | 10 | 11 | 12 | 13 | 14 | 15 | 16 | 17 | 18 |
| PAR | 4 | 4 | 4 | 5 | 4 | 4 | 4 | 3 | 5 |
| YARDS | 302 | 390 | 322 | 530 | 354 | 360 | 339 | 155 | 480 |

**Directions:** Take Route 6 East to Exit 2. Take right onto Route 130 South, follow 7.2 miles then take a right onto Great Neck Road. Follow 1.6 miles, take right onto Old Barnstable Road. Course is on left at the end.

# Rehoboth Country Club ⭐½ 45

155 Perryville Road
Rehoboth, MA (508) 252-6259
www.rehobothcountryclub.com

| Tees | Holes | Yards | Par | USGA | Slope |
|------|-------|-------|-----|------|-------|
| BACK | 18 | 6760 | 72 | 71.4 | 124 |
| MIDDLE | 18 | 6340 | 72 | 69.3 | 121 |
| FRONT | 18 | 5490 | 72 | 70.6 | 114 |

**Club Pro:**
**Payment:** Visa, MC,
**Tee Times:** 7 days adv.
**Fee 9 Holes: Weekday:** $20    **Weekend:** $26
**Fee 18 Holes: Weekday:** $30    **Weekend:** $36
**Twilight Rates:** After 12pm    **Discounts:** Senior & Junior
**Cart Rental:** $16pp/18, $8pp/9    **Driving Range:** No
**Lessons:** No **Schools:** No    **Junior Golf:** No
**Membership:** Yes    **Architect/Yr Open:** Geoffrey Cornish/1966
**Other:** Snack Bar / Clubhouse / Restaurant / Bar-Lounge
**GPS:** Yes

Greens in best shape ever. Great new menu at our Sandwedges Restaurant. Noted for large true greens and use of every club in bag. 20 minutes outside Providence, RI. Check website for specials.

| | 1 | 2 | 3 | 4 | 5 | 6 | 7 | 8 | 9 |
|---|---|---|---|---|---|---|---|---|---|
| PAR | 4 | 5 | 3 | 5 | 4 | 4 | 4 | 3 | 4 |
| YARDS | 380 | 500 | 155 | 550 | 400 | 310 | 300 | 155 | 410 |
| | 10 | 11 | 12 | 13 | 14 | 15 | 16 | 17 | 18 |
| PAR | 5 | 4 | 3 | 4 | 4 | 4 | 3 | 5 | 4 |
| YARDS | 500 | 345 | 205 | 380 | 330 | 270 | 170 | 540 | 440 |

**Directions:** From Providence: East on Route 44 to Route 118; turn left and 1st left to course. From Taunton: West on Route 44 to Route 118. Turn right, 1st left to course. From Attleboro: East on Route 118, right on Fairview to Homestead. Right, then 1st left onto Perryville.

# Rochester Golf Club ⭐⭐ 46

323 Rounseville Road
Rochester, MA (508) 763-5155
www.rochestergolf.net

| Tees | Holes | Yards | Par | USGA | Slope |
|------|-------|-------|-----|------|-------|
| BACK | 18 | 5280 | 69 | 66 | 119 |
| MIDDLE | 18 | 4830 | 69 | 64 | 114 |
| FRONT | 18 | 4032 | 69 | 64 | 107 |

**Club Pro:** Rusty Gunnerson, PGA
**Payment:** Cash Only
**Tee Times:** 2 days adv. (Sat, Sun, & holidays)
**Fee 9 Holes: Weekday:** $16    **Weekend:** $16
**Fee 18 Holes: Weekday:** $27    **Weekend:** $27
**Twilight Rates:** No    **Discounts:** None
**Cart Rental:** $20/18, $10/9 per cart    **Driving Range:** No
**Lessons:** Private; $60/45 min. **Schools:** No    **Junior Golf:** No
**Membership:** No    **Architect/Yr Open:** 1969
**Other:** Snack Bar    **GPS:**

Course is challenging with beautiful scenery. New sandtraps. Accuracy at premium, not long but tight. "Heavy forest and water on 14 holes define the challenge. Think twice about pulling out the big dawg." –AP

| | 1 | 2 | 3 | 4 | 5 | 6 | 7 | 8 | 9 |
|---|---|---|---|---|---|---|---|---|---|
| PAR | 3 | 4 | 4 | 4 | 3 | 5 | 4 | 4 | 3 |
| YARDS | 156 | 386 | 258 | 252 | 128 | 435 | 250 | 312 | 116 |
| | 10 | 11 | 12 | 13 | 14 | 15 | 16 | 17 | 18 |
| PAR | 4 | 3 | 4 | 4 | 3 | 4 | 4 | 4 | 5 |
| YARDS | 280 | 110 | 272 | 290 | 180 | 260 | 280 | 373 | 492 |

**Directions:** I-195 to Rochester exit, follow Route 105 approximately 4 miles north on right.

# Sandwich Hollows Golf Club ✪✪

1 Round Hill Road
East Sandwich, MA
(508) 888-3384 x0
www.sandwichhollows.com

| Tees | Holes | Yards | Par | USGA | Slope |
|---|---|---|---|---|---|
| BACK | 18 | 6220 | 71 | 70.4 | 124 |
| MIDDLE | 18 | 5891 | 71 | 68.6 | 120 |
| FRONT | 18 | 4894 | 71 | 68.1 | 115 |

**Club Pro:** Jesse Schechtman, PGA
**Payment:** MC, Visa, Check
**Tee Times:** 3 week adv.
**Fee 9 Holes: Weekday:** $20, $29 ride **Weekend:** $22, $31 ride
**Fee 18 Holes: Weekday:** $37.95 M/T/Th w/cart **Weekend:** $62 w/cart
**Twilight Rates:** $30 after 2pm w/cart; $24 after 4pm w/cart
**Discounts:** None
**Cart Rental:** Included **Driving Range:** $5 bucket, all grass tees
**Lessons:** $40/half hour **Schools:** Adult Intro. **Junior Golf:** Yes
**Membership:** Full and Seasonal (wkdays only) **Architect/Yr Open:** Richard Cross/1972
**Other:** Clubhouse / Restaurant / Lounge / Function Facilities

COUPON

The course is hilly. Accurate shots are essential. Open year round. All-day special on Wednesday includes greens fee and cart. Pleasant views of Cape Cod Bay.

|  | 1 | 2 | 3 | 4 | 5 | 6 | 7 | 8 | 9 |
|---|---|---|---|---|---|---|---|---|---|
| PAR | 5 | 4 | 3 | 4 | 4 | 5 | 3 | 4 | 4 |
| YARDS | 485 | 325 | 120 | 305 | 347 | 570 | 177 | 340 | 401 |
|  | 10 | 11 | 12 | 13 | 14 | 15 | 16 | 17 | 18 |
| PAR | 4 | 4 | 3 | 4 | 5 | 3 | 4 | 4 | 4 |
| YARDS | 300 | 380 | 175 | 285 | 520 | 160 | 340 | 355 | 330 |

**Directions:** Located between Exits 3 and 4 on Route 6 (Mid-Cape Highway) on service road.

# Siasconset Golf Course NR

260 Milestone Road
Nantucket, MA (508) 257-6596
www.siasconsetgolf.com

| Tees | Holes | Yards | Par | USGA | Slope |
|---|---|---|---|---|---|
| BACK | 9 | 2603 | 33 | 33.0 | 111 |
| MIDDLE | 9 | 2439 | 33 | 32.4 | 109 |
| FRONT | 9 | 1859 | 33 | 30.3 | 104 |

**Club Pro:** Phillip Truono
**Payment:** Visa, MC, Amex, Disc, Checks
**Tee Times:** No
**Fee 9 Holes: Weekday:** $35 **Weekend:** $35
**Fee 18 Holes: Weekday:** $60 **Weekend:** $60
**Twilight Rates:** No **Discounts:** Junior
**Cart Rental:** Walking carts $5 **Driving Range:** No
**Lessons:** No **Schools:** No **Junior Golf:** No
**Membership:** Yes **Architect/Yr Open:** John Grout/1894
**Other:** **GPS:** Yes

A historic golf course with small greens. Improved greens with permanent irrigation. Renovated clubhouse. A must-play when on Nantucket.

|  | 1 | 2 | 3 | 4 | 5 | 6 | 7 | 8 | 9 |
|---|---|---|---|---|---|---|---|---|---|
| PAR | 3 | 5 | 3 | 4 | 3 | 4 | 3 | 4 | 4 |
| YARDS | 200 | 460 | 205 | 390 | 146 | 232 | 214 | 326 | 266 |
| PAR |  |  |  |  |  |  |  |  |  |
| YARDS |  |  |  |  |  |  |  |  |  |

**Directions:** From Nantucket Town Center - drive 7 miles on Milestone Road.

# Stone-E-Lea Golf Course

✪½ **49** ▶

**1411 County Street**
**Attleboro, MA** (508) 222-9735
www.selgc.com

**Club Pro:**
**Payment:** Cash or Credit
**Tee Times:** No
**Fee 9 Holes: Weekday:** $16
**Fee 18 Holes: Weekday:** $24
**Twilight Rates:** Yes
**Cart Rental:** $24/18, $12/9 per cart
**Lessons:** No  **Schools:** No
**Membership:** No
**Other:** Value Packages

**Weekend:** $20
**Weekend:** $32
**Discounts:** Seniors and Juniors
**Driving Range:** No
**Junior Golf:** Yes
**Architect/Yr Open:**
**GPS:**

| Tees | Holes | Yards | Par | USGA | Slope |
|------|-------|-------|-----|------|-------|
| BACK | | | | | |
| MIDDLE | 18 | 6251 | 69 | 69.5 | 116 |
| FRONT | 18 | 6030 | 69 | 67.8 | 112 |

Discounts for seniors over 62 after 2pm Monday through Friday. Open year round. Clubhouse is newly renovated. "Easy course to walk." –FP

| | 1 | 2 | 3 | 4 | 5 | 6 | 7 | 8 | 9 |
|------|----|----|----|----|----|----|----|----|----|
| PAR | 4 | 4 | 4 | 3 | 4 | 4 | 3 | 4 | 4 |
| YARDS | 360 | 350 | 310 | 185 | 330 | 420 | 175 | 380 | 430 |
| | 10 | 11 | 12 | 13 | 14 | 15 | 16 | 17 | 18 |
| PAR | 5 | 4 | 4 | 4 | 4 | 3 | 4 | 4 | 3 |
| YARDS | 490 | 390 | 410 | 390 | 265 | 190 | 390 | 325 | 240 |

**Directions:** I-95 to Exit 3 to 123 West. At first light take left onto Tiffany Street. Next light take right onto County Street. Course is at top of hill on right.

# Swansea Country Club

✪✪ **50** ▶

**299 Market Street**
**Swansea, MA** (508) 379-9886 x1
www.swanseacountryclub.com

**Club Pro:** Shane Drury, PGA
**Payment:** Visa, MC, Disc, Amex, Cash
**Tee Times:** 6 days adv. (508) 379-9886 x1
**Fee 9 Holes: Weekday:** $24
**Fee 18 Holes: Weekday:** $32
**Twilight Rates:** After 5:45pm
**Cart Rental:** $15pp/18, $8pp/9
**Lessons:** Yes  **Schools:** Yes
**Membership:** See website for details
**Other:** Clubhouse / Snack Bar / Restaurant / Bar-Lounge / Outdoor Patio & Tent Seating for 200

**Weekend:** $28
**Weekend:** $42
**Discounts:** Senior & Junior, wkdys
**Driving Range:** Yes, grass tees
**Junior Golf:** Yes
**Architect/Yr Open:** Geoffrey Cornish/1963

| Tees | Holes | Yards | Par | USGA | Slope |
|------|-------|-------|-----|------|-------|
| BACK | 18 | 6840 | 72 | 72.8 | 126 |
| MIDDLE | 18 | 6429 | 72 | 70.9 | 125 |
| FRONT | 18 | 5598 | 72 | 69.4 | 113 |

COUPON

2nd hole redesigned. Improved irrigation and new sets of tees in 2012. Great value, excellent course conditions. Just 10 minutes outside Providence. Great for large groups and outings. Look for the lunch specials.

| | 1 | 2 | 3 | 4 | 5 | 6 | 7 | 8 | 9 |
|------|----|----|----|----|----|----|----|----|----|
| PAR | 4 | 5 | 4 | 3 | 4 | 3 | 4 | 5 | 4 |
| YARDS | 331 | 496 | 415 | 206 | 353 | 118 | 366 | 475 | 419 |
| | 10 | 11 | 12 | 13 | 14 | 15 | 16 | 17 | 18 |
| PAR | 4 | 3 | 4 | 5 | 4 | 3 | 4 | 5 | 4 |
| YARDS | 323 | 170 | 366 | 615 | 291 | 203 | 368 | 478 | 436 |

**Directions:** I-195 East or West to Exit #2 (Massachusetts). South on Route 136 for 1 mile. Golf course is on right.

# Swansea Executive Par 3 ✪✪ 51

**299 Market Street**
**Swansea, MA (508) 379-9886**
**www.swanseacountryclub.com**

**Club Pro:** Shane Drury, PGA
**Payment:** Most Major Cards, No Checks
**Tee Times:**
**Fee 9 Holes: Weekday:** $12
**Fee 18 Holes: Weekday:** $18
**Twilight Rates:** No
**Cart Rental:** $12pp/18, $7pp/9
**Lessons:** Yes **Schools:** Yes
**Membership:** Yes
**Other:**

| Tees | Holes | Yards | Par | USGA | Slope |
|---|---|---|---|---|---|
| BACK | 9 | 1378 | 27 | 54.8 | 84 |
| MIDDLE | 9 | 1196 | 27 | 54..8 | 84 |
| FRONT | 9 | 957 | 27 | 57.0 | 89 |

**Weekend:** $12
**Weekend:** $18
**Discounts:** None
**Driving Range:** Yes
**Junior Golf:** Yes
**Architect/Yr Open:** M. Weremay/1997
**GPS:**

SE MA/ CAPE

A fine track in the beautiful setting of Narragansett Bay. Inquire about member rates: Family, Adult, Junior. Single-rider cart rates. 10 min. to downtown Providence.

|  | 1 | 2 | 3 | 4 | 5 | 6 | 7 | 8 | 9 |
|---|---|---|---|---|---|---|---|---|---|
| **PAR** | 3 | 3 | 3 | 3 | 3 | 3 | 3 | 3 | 3 |
| **YARDS** | 153 | 115 | 160 | 128 | 134 | 141 | 101 | 122 | 142 |
| **PAR** | | | | | | | | | |
| **YARDS** | | | | | | | | | |

**Directions:** MA Exit 2 off I-195. Course is 1 mile south of freeway.

# Touisset Country Club ✪✪½ 52

**221 Pearse Road**
**Swansea, MA (508) 679-9577**
**www.touissetcc.com**

**Club Pro:** Lef Brigham, GM
**Payment:** Cash, Visa, MC, Disc
**Tee Times:** No
**Fee 9 Holes: Weekday:** $18.50
**Fee 18 Holes: Weekday:** $23
**Twilight Rates:** After 4pm
**Cart Rental:** $18pp/18, $13pp/9
**Lessons:** $19/half hour **Schools:** Yes
**Membership:** Yes
**Other:** Snack Bar / Restaurant / Bar-Lounge / Clubhouse / Lockers / Practice Area and Putting Greens

| Tees | Holes | Yards | Par | USGA | Slope |
|---|---|---|---|---|---|
| BACK | 9 | 3182 | 36 | 69.1 | 111 |
| MIDDLE | 9 | 3024 | 35 | 69.1 | 111 |
| FRONT | 9 | 2776 | 36 | 71.1 | 114 |

**Weekend:** $20.50
**Weekend:** $28
**Discounts:** Senior/Junior/Military
**Driving Range:** No
**Junior Golf:** Yes
**Architect/Yr Open:** Raymond H. Brigham/1961

9 hole course with 4 sets of tees. Fairly flat but challenging. Open year round, weather permitting. Newly renovated pro shop with competitive pricing.

|  | 1 | 2 | 3 | 4 | 5 | 6 | 7 | 8 | 9 |
|---|---|---|---|---|---|---|---|---|---|
| **PAR** | 4 | 4 | 4 | 4 | 3 | 4 | 3 | 5 | 4 |
| **YARDS** | 324 | 291 | 373 | 388 | 118 | 448 | 160 | 534 | 388 |
| **PAR** | | | | | | | | | |
| **YARDS** | | | | | | | | | |

**Directions:** Exit 3 off I-195, Route 6 West. Left at first traffic light onto Maple Street. Straight ¾ mile to 221 Pearse Road.

# Twin Brooks Golf Course　　✪✪✪　　53 ▶

35 Scudder Avenue
Hyannis, MA (508) 862-6980
www.twinbrooksgolf.net

**Club Pro:**
**Payment:** Visa, MC, Amex, Diner's, Cash
**Tee Times:** Call
**Fee 9 Holes: Weekday:** $25
**Fee 18 Holes: Weekday:** $35
**Twilight Rates:** After 4pm
**Cart Rental:** $17pp
**Lessons:** Yes **Schools:** Yes
**Membership:** Yes
**Other:** Restaurant / Hotel / Bar-Lounge / Showers

| Tees | Holes | Yards | Par | USGA | Slope |
|------|-------|-------|-----|------|-------|
| BACK |       |       |     |      |       |
| MIDDLE | 18 | 2621 | 54 |    |       |
| FRONT | 18 | 2239 | 54 |     |       |

**Weekend:** $30
**Weekend:** $40
**Discounts:** Senior/Junior $25
**Driving Range:** No
**Junior Golf:** Yes
**Architect/Yr Open:** Geoffrey Cornish/1965
**GPS:** Yes

*COUPON*

New home of Cape Cod Golf School facility. Perfect for all ages. Very challenging. Open year round.
Rates subject to change. Guest rates available. Pull carts, drive carts, and rentals available. New tee boxes,
golf carts, golf paths and signs. Improved paths. *Golf Digest* - Most challenging course on the Cape.

|       | 1 | 2 | 3 | 4 | 5 | 6 | 7 | 8 | 9 |
|-------|---|---|---|---|---|---|---|---|---|
| PAR   | 3 | 3 | 3 | 3 | 3 | 3 | 3 | 3 | 3 |
| YARDS | 135 | 90 | 165 | 144 | 110 | 102 | 175 | 140 | 135 |
|       | 10 | 11 | 12 | 13 | 14 | 15 | 16 | 17 | 18 |
| PAR   | 3 | 3 | 3 | 3 | 3 | 3 | 3 | 3 | 3 |
| YARDS | 190 | 140 | 150 | 115 | 170 | 215 | 150 | 160 | 135 |

**Directions:** Take Route 6 to Exit 6 (Hyannis), follow Route 132 to Hyannis, follow signs to West End
- Hyannis. At rotary, you will see the resort and confence center.

# Wampanoag Golf Club　　NR　　54 ▶

168 Old Providence Road
North Swansea, MA (508) 379-9832

**Club Pro:** Richard Pistacchio, Manager
**Payment:** Cash Only
**Tee Times:** No
**Fee 9 Holes: Weekday:** $15
**Fee 18 Holes: Weekday:** $20
**Twilight Rates:** No
**Cart Rental:** $14pp/18, $7pp/9
**Lessons:** No **Schools:** No
**Membership:** Yes
**Other:** Snack Bar / Bar-Lounge

| Tees | Holes | Yards | Par | USGA | Slope |
|------|-------|-------|-----|------|-------|
| BACK |       |       |     |      |       |
| MIDDLE | 9 | 2775 | 35 | 69.5 | 112 |
| FRONT | 9 | 2439 | 37 | 69.5 | 112 |

**Weekend:** $20
**Weekend:** $25
**Discounts:** Senior & Junior
**Driving Range:** No
**Junior Golf:** No
**Architect/Yr Open:** Aljenon Barney/1931
**GPS:**

*COUPON*

Good mix of long par 3s and short par 5s. Long ball hitters have a definite advantage. Play front and back
tees for an enjoyable 18 holes. Open year round. Yardage markers, superb greens & improved drainage.

|       | 1 | 2 | 3 | 4 | 5 | 6 | 7 | 8 | 9 |
|-------|---|---|---|---|---|---|---|---|---|
| PAR   | 4 | 3 | 4 | 4 | 4 | 3 | 5 | 4 | 4 |
| YARDS | 305 | 115 | 343 | 400 | 397 | 150 | 417 | 301 | 343 |
| PAR   |   |   |   |   |   |   |   |   |   |
| YARDS |   |   |   |   |   |   |   |   |   |

**Directions:** Take I-95 to Exit 2 (Warren/Newport), turn right onto Route 6. Turn left at Mason Street.
At stop sign turn right on Old Providence Road.

# Wentworth Hills Country Club ✪✪✪¹⁄₂  55 ▶

27 Bow Street
Plainville, MA  (508) 316-0240
www.wentworthhillscountryclub.com

| Tees | Holes | Yards | Par | USGA | Slope |
|------|-------|-------|-----|------|-------|
| BACK | 18 | 6202 | 71 | 71.0 | 128 |
| MIDDLE | 18 | 5817 | 71 | 68.0 | 125 |
| FRONT | 18 | 5325 | 71 | 65.3 | 120 |

**Club Pro:** Barrie Bruce, PGA
**Payment:** Visa, MC, Amex
**Tee Times:** 7 days adv.
**Fee 9 Holes: Weekday:** $26
**Fee 18 Holes: Weekday:** $36
**Twilight Rates:** After 4pm (seasonal)
**Cart Rental:** $18pp/18, $9pp/9
**Lessons:** Yes **Schools:** Yes
**Membership:** No
**Other:** Restaurant / Clubhouse / Bar-Lounge

**Weekend:** $31
**Weekend:** $46
**Discounts:** Senior
**Driving Range:** Yes
**Junior Golf:** Yes
**Architect/Yr Open:** Howard Maurer/2001
**GPS:**

COUPON

Featuring the Barrie Bruce Golf School. Open year-round. 10% discount on greens fees with the Plainridge Players Card. 20% discount for Wentworth Hills University alumni.
"Tight oak and pine tree lined fairways with solid, fast running greens that hold your approach shots. Numerous interesting holes. A real gem." –GG

|       | 1 | 2 | 3 | 4 | 5 | 6 | 7 | 8 | 9 |
|-------|---|---|---|---|---|---|---|---|---|
| PAR | 4 | 3 | 4 | 4 | 5 | 4 | 4 | 3 | 4 |
| YARDS | 334 | 88 | 368 | 350 | 440 | 366 | 282 | 125 | 328 |
|       | 10 | 11 | 12 | 13 | 14 | 15 | 16 | 17 | 18 |
| PAR | 4 | 4 | 5 | 4 | 4 | 5 | 3 | 3 | 4 |
| YARDS | 396 | 320 | 448 | 244 | 268 | 460 | 130 | 122 | 256 |

**Directions:** From Route 495, take Route 1A. Follow 1A South for 1 mile, right on Cross Street. Follow 1 mile to "T" intersection stop sign. Left at "T" intersection (High Street.) Proceed 1 mile, then right on Hancock Street. Follow .4 miles, then left on Bow Street to golf course entrance on right.

# Whaling City Golf Course        ✪¹⁄₂  56 ▶

581 Hathaway Road
New Bedford, MA  (508) 996-9393
www.johnsongolfmanagement.com

| Tees | Holes | Yards | Par | USGA | Slope |
|------|-------|-------|-----|------|-------|
| BACK | 18 | 6780 | 72 | 73 | 131 |
| MIDDLE | 18 | 6527 | 72 | 70.2 | 126 |
| FRONT | 18 | 6457 | 74 | 70.1 | 118 |

**Club Pro:** Bill Allan, PGA
**Payment:** Cash, Credit Cards
**Tee Times:** 7 days adv.
**Fee 9 Holes: Weekday:** $17
**Fee 18 Holes: Weekday:** $29
**Twilight Rates:** No
**Cart Rental:** $15pp/18, $8pp/9
**Lessons:** Yes **Schools:** No
**Membership:** Yes
**Other:** Snack Bar / Restaurant / Bar-Lounge

**Weekend:** $19
**Weekend:** $33
**Discounts:** Junior and Resident
**Driving Range:** Yes
**Junior Golf:** No
**Architect/Yr Open:** Donald Ross/1946
**GPS:**

New tees. Municipal course. Managed by Johnson Management. Reasonable value. "Nice layout." –FP

|       | 1 | 2 | 3 | 4 | 5 | 6 | 7 | 8 | 9 |
|-------|---|---|---|---|---|---|---|---|---|
| PAR | 4 | 4 | 4 | 4 | 3 | 4 | 5 | 3 | 5 |
| YARDS | 448 | 382 | 409 | 343 | 190 | 381 | 530 | 140 | 453 |
|       | 10 | 11 | 12 | 13 | 14 | 15 | 16 | 17 | 18 |
| PAR | 5 | 4 | 4 | 3 | 5 | 4 | 4 | 3 | 4 |
| YARDS | 535 | 379 | 436 | 163 | 499 | 333 | 356 | 179 | 331 |

**Directions:** Take Route 140 in New Bedford to Exit 3. Bear right.

# Feature Your Course
## in New England GolfGuide
## and reach 125,000 readers in 2018

Advertise your Featured Story and Ad in *New England GolfGuide*
(includes 5 email blasts of 5000 names totalling 25,000 names!)

- We Will Put Your **Feature Story** On Our Web Site
- We Will Build A **Link Back To Your Web Site**
- You Will Get **5 Email Blasts** Of 5,000 Names Each

# NEW ENGLAND
# GOLFGUIDE

*Contact us today for details:*
info@newenglandgolfguide.com
**(508) 330-6007**
www.newenglandgolfguide.com

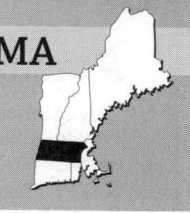

**7**
**87** **77** ★ North Adams
**26**
**19** **15** **59**
**54** **57**
**91**
**33**
**81** **3** **83**
**2**
**79**
**72** **31** **3**
★ Greenfield
**91** **5** **80**
**29**
★ Gardner
**89** **92**
**53** **69** **68** **71**
**38**
**56** **35** Leominster
**82**
**64** **34** **86** **9**
**4**
**17** ★ Pittsfield
**93**
**6**
**61** **41** **2**
**11**
**202**
**24**
**7**
**66**
**190** **85** **21** **495**
**20** **47**
**44** **50**
**36** **88**
**37**
Northampton ★
**28**
**90** **20** **73**
**55** **14**
**45** **51** **90**
**12**
**9**
**43** **5** **60** ★ Worcester
**52** **146** **8** **48** **46** **76**
**49**
**70** **78**
**7**
Southwick ★ **74** **25**
**67** **27**
★ Springfield
**1** **75** **32** **84** **16**
**58** **18** **30** **62**
**90**
**20** **65**
**39** **40** **63**
**23**
**13** **42** **9**
**395**
**10**

| | | | | | |
|---|---|---|---|---|---|
| Agawam Municipal GC | 1 | Franconia Muni. GC | 32 | Pine Ridge Country Club | 63 |
| Amherst Golf Club | 2 | Gardner Municipal GC | 33 | Pontoosuc Lake CC | 64 |
| Ashfield Community Golf Club | 3 | GEAA Golf Club | 34 | Quaboag Country Club | 65 |
| Bas Ridge Golf Course | 4 | Grandview GC | 35 | Quail Hollow Golf & CC | 66 |
| Bay Path Golf Course | 5 | Green Hill Municipal GC | 36 | Ranch Golf Club, The | 67 |
| Beaver Brook Country Club | 6 | Greenock Country Club | 37 | Red Tail Golf Club | 68 |
| Bedrock Golf Club | 7 | Groton Pool & GC | 38 | Settlers Crossing Golf Course | 69 |
| Berlin Country Club | 8 | Hemlock Ridge GC | 39 | Shaker Farms CC | 70 |
| Blackstone National Golf Club | 9 | Heritage Country Club | 40 | Shaker Hills Golf Club | 71 |
| Blissful Meadows GC | 10 | Hickory Ridge GC | 41 | Skyline Country Club | 72 |
| Cherry Hill GC | 11 | Highfields Golf & CC | 42 | Southampton CC | 73 |
| Chicopee Municipal GC | 12 | Hillcrest Country Club | 43 | Southwick CC | 74 |
| Clearview Golf Course | 13 | Holden Hills CC | 44 | St. Anne Country Club | 75 |
| Cold Spring Country Club | 14 | Holyoke Country Club | 45 | St. Mark's Golf Club | 76 |
| Country Club of Greenfield | 15 | Hopedale CC | 46 | Taconic Golf Club | 77 |
| Country Club of Wilbraham | 16 | Indian Meadows Golf Club | 47 | Tekoa Country Club | 78 |
| Cranwell Resort, Spa & GC | 17 | Juniper Hill GC (Lakeside) | 48 | Templewood Golf Course | 79 |
| Crestview CC | 18 | Juniper Hill GC (Riverside) | 49 | Thomas Memorial Golf & CC | 80 |
| Crumpin-Fox Club | 19 | Kettle Brook Golf Club | 50 | Townsend Ridge CC | 81 |
| Cyprian Keyes Golf Club | 20 | Ledges Golf Club | 51 | Twin Springs Golf Club | 82 |
| Cyprian Keyes GC, Par 3 | 21 | Leicester Country Club | 52 | Tyngsboro CC | 83 |
| Donnybrook CC | 22 | Links at Lancaster Golf, The | 53 | Veteran's Golf Club | 84 |
| Dudley Hill Golf Club | 23 | Meadows Golf Club, The | 54 | Wachusett CC | 85 |
| Dunroamin CC | 24 | Mill Valley Links | 55 | Wahconah CC | 86 |
| East Mountain CC | 25 | Monoosnock CC | 56 | Waubeeka Golf Links | 87 |
| Edge Hill GC | 26 | Northfield GC | 57 | Westborough CC | 88 |
| Edgewood Golf Club | 27 | Oak Ridge Golf Club | 58 | Westminster CC | 89 |
| Egremont Country Club | 28 | Oak Ridge GC-Gill | 59 | Westover Golf Course | 90 |
| Ellinwood CC | 29 | Pakachoag Golf Course | 60 | Winchendon GC | 91 |
| Elmcrest CC | 30 | Pine Grove Golf Club | 61 | Woods of Westminster CC | 92 |
| Forest Park CC | 31 | Pine Knoll Par 3 | 62 | Worthington GC | 93 |

**KEY TO THE STAR RATINGS:**
5✪ = Outstanding  4✪ = Excellent  3✪ = Very Good  2✪ = Good  1✪ = Average  **NR** = Not Rated

# Agawam Municipal Golf Course ✪✪

128 Southwick Street (Route 57)
Feeding Hills, MA  (413) 786-2194
www.agawamgc.com

Club Pro: Tony Roberto, PGA
Payment: Cash, Visa, MC, Disc, Amex
Tee Times: 7 days adv.

| Tees | Holes | Yards | Par | USGA | Slope |
|------|-------|-------|-----|------|-------|
| BACK | 18 | 5679 | 71 | 66.9 | 119 |
| MIDDLE | 18 | 5458 | 71 | 65.8 | 116 |
| FRONT | 18 | 4767 | 72 | 62.6 | 110 |

Fee  9 Holes: Weekday: $19
Fee 18 Holes: Weekday: $22
Twilight Rates: After 12pm
Cart Rental: $14pp/18, $8pp/9
Lessons: Yes Schools: Yes
Membership: Yes
Other: Restaurant / 2 Bars / Banquet Facility

Weekend: $20
Weekend: $26
Discounts: Senior & Junior
Driving Range: No
Junior Golf: Yes
Architect/Yr Open: Richard Leao/1929
GPS:

A friendly course. No water holes but 1 creek and 8 sand traps. Total irrigation. The 9th hole is referred to as "Cardiac Hill," and for good reason. New golf carts. New parking lot. Weekend specials before 8am and after 12pm. "Great bang for the buck." –FP

| | 1 | 2 | 3 | 4 | 5 | 6 | 7 | 8 | 9 |
|------|----|----|----|----|----|----|----|----|----|
| PAR | 5 | 4 | 3 | 4 | 3 | 4 | 4 | 5 | 3 |
| YARDS | 457 | 332 | 150 | 430 | 126 | 321 | 319 | 518 | 140 |
| | 10 | 11 | 12 | 13 | 14 | 15 | 16 | 17 | 18 |
| PAR | 5 | 4 | 4 | 3 | 4 | 3 | 5 | 5 | 3 |
| YARDS | 427 | 353 | 329 | 169 | 322 | 143 | 521 | 438 | 184 |

Directions: I-90 (Mass Pike) to I-91 to Route 57 (Agawam). Go west on Route 57. Club is in the town of Feeding Hills.

# Amherst Golf Club ✪✪

365 South Pleasant Street
Amherst, MA (413) 256-6894
www.amherstgolfclub.org

Club Pro: Dave Twohig, PGA
Payment: Visa, MC
Tee Times: No

| Tees | Holes | Yards | Par | USGA | Slope |
|------|-------|-------|-----|------|-------|
| BACK | | | | | |
| MIDDLE | 9 | 3055 | 35 | 68.9 | 117 |
| FRONT | 9 | 2774 | 36 | 68.9 | 122 |

Fee  9 Holes: Weekday: $25
Fee 18 Holes: Weekday: $25
Twilight Rates: No
Cart Rental: $25/18 per cart
Lessons: $45/half hour  Schools: No
Membership: Wait list
Other: Clubhouse / Lockers / Showers / Snack Bar

Weekend: $25
Weekend: $25
Discounts: None
Driving Range: No
Junior Golf: No
Architect/Yr Open: Walter Hatch/1900

Sig. Hole #9 is a long, uphill par 3 with a sloping green. Collared shirts. Course is short in length with small greens, but in good shape. Old New England course.

| | 1 | 2 | 3 | 4 | 5 | 6 | 7 | 8 | 9 |
|------|----|----|----|----|----|----|----|----|----|
| PAR | 4 | 4 | 4 | 3 | 4 | 4 | 5 | 4 | 3 |
| YARDS | 390 | 375 | 405 | 160 | 350 | 340 | 525 | 310 | 200 |
| PAR | | | | | | | | | |
| YARDS | | | | | | | | | |

Directions: Take Mass Pike to Route 181 to Route 9 into Amherst. Course is located by Amherst College.

# Ashfield Community Golf Club     NR  3

134 Norton Hill Road
Ashfield, MA (413) 628-4413

**Club Pro:**
**Payment:** Cash or Check
**Tee Times:** No
**Fee 9 Holes: Weekday:** $12
**Fee 18 Holes: Weekday:** $16
**Twilight Rates:** No
**Cart Rental:** $10pp/18, $7pp/9
**Lessons:** No **Schools:** No
**Membership:** Yes
**Other:** Clubhouse / Snack Bar

| Tees | Holes | Yards | Par | USGA | Slope |
|------|-------|-------|-----|------|-------|
| BACK |       |       |     |      |       |
| MIDDLE | 9 | 2077 | 33 |    |       |
| FRONT | 9 | 1729 | 33 |     |       |

**Weekend:** $12
**Weekend:** $16
**Discounts:** None
**Driving Range:** No
**Junior Golf:** Yes
**Architect/Yr Open:** 1927
**GPS:**

Improved tee boxes. Honor system for play during the week, instructions for payment on clubhouse door. Attendant on weekends and holidays.

|       | 1 | 2 | 3 | 4 | 5 | 6 | 7 | 8 | 9 |
|-------|---|---|---|---|---|---|---|---|---|
| PAR   | 4 | 4 | 3 | 4 | 3 | 4 | 4 | 4 | 3 |
| YARDS | 286 | 289 | 201 | 317 | 102 | 200 | 185 | 341 | 156 |
| PAR   |   |   |   |   |   |   |   |   |   |
| YARDS |   |   |   |   |   |   |   |   |   |

**Directions:** I-91 North to Exit 24. Off ramp, go north on Route 5 and 10. Pass Yankee Candle to Route 116 West to center of Ashfield, MA. Turn left at Norton Hill Road, golf course up the hill on the right.

# Bas Ridge Golf Course     ✪  4

151 Plunkett Street
Hinsdale, MA (413) 655-2605
www.basridge.com

**Club Pro:** Gary Norton, PGA
**Payment:** Cash Only
**Tee Times:** Recommended
**Fee 9 Holes: Weekday:** $12
**Fee 18 Holes: Weekday:** $15
**Twilight Rates:** After 4pm
**Cart Rental:** $10pp/18, $5pp/9
**Lessons:** Yes **Schools:**
**Membership:** Limited
**Other:** Clubhouse / Bar-Lounge

| Tees | Holes | Yards | Par | USGA | Slope |
|------|-------|-------|-----|------|-------|
| BACK |       |       |     |      |       |
| MIDDLE | 18 | 5051 | 70 | 63.7 | 111 |
| FRONT | 18 | 4369 | 70 | 65.9 | 110 |

**Weekend:** $15
**Weekend:** $20
**Discounts:** Senior weekdays
**Driving Range:** No
**Junior Golf:** Yes
**Architect/Yr Open:** Rowland Armacost/1998
**GPS:**

COUPON

"A shorter course, but fun." "Each hole is more beautiful and the greens are incredible." –BB
Open April 1 - November 1. New solar panels for club house plus computerized sprinkler system.

|       | 1 | 2 | 3 | 4 | 5 | 6 | 7 | 8 | 9 |
|-------|---|---|---|---|---|---|---|---|---|
| PAR   | 4 | 4 | 3 | 4 | 3 | 4 | 4 | 4 | 4 |
| YARDS | 335 | 269 | 193 | 280 | 170 | 224 | 233 | 331 | 276 |
|       | 10 | 11 | 12 | 13 | 14 | 15 | 16 | 17 | 18 |
| PAR   | 4 | 4 | 3 | 4 | 5 | 3 | 5 | 4 | 4 |
| YARDS | 270 | 336 | 187 | 313 | 451 | 112 | 466 | 278 | 327 |

**Directions:** Take Mass Pike to Lee exit, go east on Route 20 about 8 miles. Left onto Route 8 North about 10 miles to Plunkett Street. Course is on the left.

# Bay Path Golf Course $\bigstar^{1/2}$ 5 ▶

193 North Brookfield Road
East Brookfield, MA (508) 867-8161
www.baypathgolf.com

**Club Pro:** Justine Smith, GM
**Payment:** Visa, MC
**Tee Times:** No
**Fee 9 Holes: Weekday:** $15
**Fee 18 Holes: Weekday:** $21
**Twilight Rates:** No
**Cart Rental:** $15pp/18, $10pp/9
**Lessons:** No  **Schools:** No
**Membership:** Yes, limited
**Other:** Clubhouse / Snack Bar / Bar-Lounge

| Tees | Holes | Yards | Par | USGA | Slope |
|------|-------|-------|-----|------|-------|
| BACK | 9 | 2952 | 36 | 67.4 | 109 |
| MIDDLE | 9 | 2640 | 36 | 66.0 | 107 |
| FRONT | 9 | 2298 | 36 | 67.6 | 107 |

**Weekend:** $17
**Weekend:** $26
**Discounts:** Junior & Senior
**Driving Range:** No
**Junior Golf:** No
**Architect/Yr Open:** Don Hoenig/1962
**GPS:** No

Player Comments: "Great deal for the money. Nice friendly staff and lounge." Very flat and easy to walk. Open April - November 15. Proper attire required.

| | 1 | 2 | 3 | 4 | 5 | 6 | 7 | 8 | 9 |
|------|---|---|---|---|---|---|---|---|---|
| **PAR** | 4 | 4 | 5 | 4 | 3 | 5 | 4 | 3 | 4 |
| **YARDS** | 297 | 273 | 456 | 305 | 131 | 426 | 270 | 151 | 331 |
| **PAR** | | | | | | | | | |
| **YARDS** | | | | | | | | | |

**Directions:** Mass. Pike to Route 20 East (Sturbridge exit). Then take Route 20 East to Route 49 North to Route 9 West to Route 67 North (North Brookfield Road). Course is approximately ¼ mile on left.

# Beaver Brook Country Club NR 6 ▶

183 Main Street
Haydenville, MA (413) 268-7229
www.beaverbrookma.com

**Club Pro:** Hiroshi Akimoto
**Payment:** Visa, MC
**Tee Times:** Yes
**Fee 9 Holes: Weekday:** $16
**Fee 18 Holes: Weekday:** $24
**Twilight Rates:** After 4pm
**Cart Rental:** Available
**Lessons:** No  **Schools:** No
**Membership:** Yes
**Other:** Clubhouse / Snack Bar / Bar-Lounge

| Tees | Holes | Yards | Par | USGA | Slope |
|------|-------|-------|-----|------|-------|
| BACK | | | | | |
| MIDDLE | 9 | 3046 | 36 | 68.1 | 110 |
| FRONT | 9 | 2480 | 36 | 67.7 | 107 |

**Weekend:** $17
**Weekend:** $25
**Discounts:** Junior & Senior
**Driving Range:** No
**Junior Golf:** Yes
**Architect/Yr Open:** 1964
**GPS:**

Beautifully laid out and maintained 9-hole course. The course sports 2 brooks and 4 ponds. Special Mon-Sat: 2 players w/cart 9 holes $37, 18 holes $58 until 2pm.

| | 1 | 2 | 3 | 4 | 5 | 6 | 7 | 8 | 9 |
|------|---|---|---|---|---|---|---|---|---|
| **PAR** | 4 | 4 | 5 | 3 | 4 | 4 | 4 | 3 | 5 |
| **YARDS** | 343 | 315 | 496 | 146 | 367 | 370 | 287 | 167 | 490 |
| **PAR** | | | | | | | | | |
| **YARDS** | | | | | | | | | |

**Directions:** I-91 to Exit 19 North. Continue to end; make right. Course is 2 miles on State Road (Route 9 West).

# Bedrock Golf Club

87 Barre Paxton Road
Rutland, MA (508) 886-0202
www.bedrockgolfclub.com

**Club Pro:** Joe Carr, PGA
**Payment:** Visa, MC, Cash, Amex
**Tee Times:** Weekends
**Fee 9 Holes: Weekday:** $15
**Fee 18 Holes: Weekday:** $25
**Twilight Rates:** $15 after 12pm/$25 wknds
**Cart Rental:** $20pp/18, $10pp/9
**Lessons:** No **Schools:** No
**Membership:** Yes
**Other:** Clubhouse / Bar-Lounge / Snack Bar

| Tees | Holes | Yards | Par | USGA | Slope |
|------|-------|-------|-----|------|-------|
| BACK | | | | | |
| MIDDLE | 9 | 3131 | 36 | 69.8 | 127 |
| FRONT | | | | | |

**Weekend:** $25
**Weekend:** $40
**Discounts:** Junior, wkdys $12pp/18
**Driving Range:** No
**Junior Golf:** No
**Architect/Yr Open:** Green & Whitehead/1992
**GPS:**

Player Comments: "Absolutely loved it." New tees. Gently rolling, narrow landing areas. Small, undulating greens, challenging. Collared shirts required. Open April - November.

| | 1 | 2 | 3 | 4 | 5 | 6 | 7 | 8 | 9 |
|------|-----|-----|-----|-----|-----|-----|-----|-----|-----|
| PAR | 4 | 5 | 4 | 3 | 4 | 5 | 3 | 4 | 4 |
| YARDS | 340 | 460 | 380 | 184 | 355 | 487 | 166 | 348 | 411 |
| PAR | | | | | | | | | |
| YARDS | | | | | | | | | |

**Directions:** I-90 (Mass Pike) to Auburn Exit (10). Then take Route 20 West to Route 56 North to Route 122 In Paxton. Course is 4 miles on left.

# Berlin Country Club

25 Carr Road
Berlin, MA (978) 838-2733
www.berlincountryclub.com

**Club Pro:**
**Payment:** Cash, Credit, Debit
**Tee Times:** No
**Fee 9 Holes: Weekday:** $16
**Fee 18 Holes: Weekday:** $21
**Twilight Rates:** After 5:30pm
**Cart Rental:** $14pp/18, $9pp/9
**Lessons:** No **Schools:** No
**Membership:** Yes - Annual/Seasonal
**Other:**

| Tees | Holes | Yards | Par | USGA | Slope |
|------|-------|-------|-----|------|-------|
| BACK | | | | | |
| MIDDLE | 9 | 2433 | 33 | 32 | 108 |
| FRONT | 9 | 2072 | 33 | 31.4 | 104 |

**Weekend:** $16
**Weekend:** $26
**Discounts:** Sr./Jr./Early Bird/Month
**Driving Range:** No
**Junior Golf:** Yes - Weekdays
**Architect/Yr Open:** 1954
**GPS:**

Mildly sloping fairways with challenging greens. Golf shirts and golf shoes required. Open March - November. "Nice, friendly staff." –FP

| | 1 | 2 | 3 | 4 | 5 | 6 | 7 | 8 | 9 |
|------|-----|-----|-----|-----|-----|-----|-----|-----|-----|
| PAR | 4 | 4 | 4 | 3 | 4 | 4 | 3 | 4 | 3 |
| YARDS | 312 | 326 | 332 | 127 | 264 | 349 | 108 | 282 | 133 |
| PAR | | | | | | | | | |
| YARDS | | | | | | | | | |

**Directions:** From I-495 take Exit 26 to Route 62 West to Berlin Center. Take a right at Center Street and continue onto Highland Street. Turn left at Randall Road, then right at Carr Road, and follow to course.

# Blackstone National GC ✪✪✪✪✪

**227 Putnam Hill Road**
**Sutton, MA (508) 865-2111**
www.bngc.net

| Tees | Holes | Yards | Par | USGA | Slope |
|------|-------|-------|-----|------|-------|
| BACK | 18 | 6909 | 72 | 73.5 | 132 |
| MIDDLE | 18 | 6396 | 72 | 71.2 | 127 |
| FRONT | 18 | 5203 | 72 | 70.0 | 122 |

**Club Pro:** Matt Stephens, PGA
**Payment:** Visa, MC, Amex, Disc
**Tee Times:** 5 days adv.
**Fee 9 Holes: Weekday:** $27 **Weekend:** $32 F/S/S
**Fee 18 Holes: Weekday:** $43 **Weekend:** $79 (inc. cart + range)
**Twilight Rates:** After 2:30pm **Discounts:** Junior
**Cart Rental:** $21pp/18, $13pp/9 **Driving Range:** Yes
**Lessons:** Yes **Schools:** Yes **Junior Golf:** Yes
**Membership:** Yes **GPS:** Yes **Architect/Yr Open:** Rees Jones/2000
**Other:** Full Restaurant / Clubhouse / Lockers / Showers / Bar-Lounge /
   Henry-Griffitts Precision Golf Club Fitting

COUPON

Player Comments: "Elevated tees and greens call for lots of club decisions—pick the right tees or you'll wish you did. Great scenery." –JD

| | 1 | 2 | 3 | 4 | 5 | 6 | 7 | 8 | 9 |
|------|-----|-----|-----|-----|-----|-----|-----|-----|-----|
| PAR | 4 | 5 | 3 | 4 | 4 | 4 | 3 | 5 | 4 |
| YARDS | 331 | 575 | 154 | 393 | 346 | 425 | 196 | 480 | 363 |
| | 10 | 11 | 12 | 13 | 14 | 15 | 16 | 17 | 18 |
| PAR | 4 | 3 | 4 | 3 | 4 | 4 | 5 | 4 | 5 |
| YARDS | 396 | 160 | 358 | 190 | 387 | 481 | 568 | 372 | 480 |

**Directions:** Mass Pike to Exit 10A to Route 146 South. Go 6 miles and take Central Turnpike toward Oxford 3 miles, to 4-way stop. Take left. Course is on top of hill.

# Blissful Meadows Golf Club ✪✪✪

**801 Chockalog Road**
**Uxbridge, MA (508) 278-6113**
www.blissfulmeadows.com

| Tees | Holes | Yards | Par | USGA | Slope |
|------|-------|-------|-----|------|-------|
| BACK | 18 | 6700 | 72 | 73.4 | 136 |
| MIDDLE | 18 | 6210 | 72 | 71.3 | 131 |
| FRONT | 18 | 5065 | 72 | 70.0 | 126 |

**Club Pro:** Joe Griffith, PGA
**Payment:** Visa, MC, Amex, Disc
**Tee Times:** 7 days adv.
**Fee 9 Holes: Weekday:** $20 M-Th **Weekend:** Fri $24, $30 S/S
**Fee 18 Holes: Weekday:** $31 M-Th **Weekend:** Fri $39, $51 S/S
**Twilight Rates:** After 3:30pm **Discounts:** Sr. & Jr. lunch specials
**Cart Rental:** $17pp/18, $10pp/9 **Driving Range:** $7/lg., $4.50/sm.
**Lessons:** Yes **Schools:** No **Junior Golf:** Yes
**Membership:** Yes
**Other:** Meadowview Tavern / Clubhouse / Bar-Lounge / Available for Outings

COUPON

Bent grass greens and tees. Many holes quite isolated. Front 9 gently rolling with lots of character, Back 9 wild and very hilly. The 3 finishing holes are great. Each replay you'll enjoy it more. Scenic and challenging.

| | 1 | 2 | 3 | 4 | 5 | 6 | 7 | 8 | 9 |
|------|-----|-----|-----|-----|-----|-----|-----|-----|-----|
| PAR | 4 | 3 | 5 | 4 | 3 | 4 | 4 | 5 | 4 |
| YARDS | 325 | 148 | 520 | 343 | 132 | 368 | 312 | 572 | 350 |
| | 10 | 11 | 12 | 13 | 14 | 15 | 16 | 17 | 18 |
| PAR | 5 | 4 | 4 | 3 | 4 | 3 | 5 | 4 | 4 |
| YARDS | 499 | 343 | 375 | 155 | 306 | 176 | 525 | 375 | 398 |

**Directions:** Take Route 146 to Route 16 West. Take first left onto West Street. Follow signs for 3 miles. Take right at dead end.

# Cherry Hill Golf Course

**NR** 11 ▶

323 Montague Road
Amherst, MA (413) 256-4071
www.cherryhillgolf.org

**Club Pro:**
**Payment:** Visa, MC
**Tee Times:** No
**Fee 9 Holes: Weekday:** $15
**Fee 18 Holes: Weekday:** $21
**Twilight Rates:** After 5pm
**Cart Rental:** $24/18, $14/9 per cart
**Lessons:** No **Schools:** No
**Membership:** Yes
**Other:** Snack Bar

| Tees | Holes | Yards | Par | USGA | Slope |
|------|-------|-------|-----|------|-------|
| BACK | 9 | 2944 | 36 | 65.7 | 101 |
| MIDDLE | 9 | 2604 | 35 | 65.3 | 111 |
| FRONT | 9 | 2292 | 36 | 66.6 | 111 |

**Weekend:** $17
**Weekend:** $23
**Discounts:** Senior & Junior
**Driving Range:** No
**Junior Golf:** No
**Architect/Yr Open:** Dave Maxson/1963
**GPS:**

COUPON

CTRL/
WEST
MA

Improvements to bunkers, greens, approaches. A great course for everyone. Incredibly beautiful views of the Berkshires.

| | 1 | 2 | 3 | 4 | 5 | 6 | 7 | 8 | 9 |
|-------|-----|-----|-----|-----|-----|-----|-----|-----|-----|
| PAR | 5 | 4 | 3 | 4 | 4 | 4 | 5 | 3 | 3 |
| YARDS | 452 | 265 | 155 | 382 | 290 | 247 | 525 | 130 | 158 |
| PAR | | | | | | | | | |
| YARDS | | | | | | | | | |

**Directions:** Take I-91 to Hadley exit, right on Route 9 into Amherst. Go north on Route 16 for 3 miles, turn right at light onto Pine Street and onto Route 63. Course is ½ mile on right.

# Chicopee Municipal Golf Course ✪✪½

12 ▶

1290 Burnett Road
Chicopee, MA (413) 594-9295
www.chicopeecc.org

**Club Pro:** Michael O'Neill, PGA
**Payment:** Cash, Credit Cards
**Tee Times:** Yes
**Fee 9 Holes: Weekday:** $17
**Fee 18 Holes: Weekday:** $29 (non-resident)
**Twilight Rates:** After 2pm
**Cart Rental:** $14pp/18, $9pp/9
**Lessons:** Yes **Schools:** Yes
**Membership:** Yes
**Other:** Clubhouse / Bar & Grille

| Tees | Holes | Yards | Par | USGA | Slope |
|------|-------|-------|-----|------|-------|
| BACK | 18 | 6742 | 71 | 73.0 | 126 |
| MIDDLE | 18 | 6109 | 71 | 70.4 | 120 |
| FRONT | 18 | 5123 | 71 | 72.4 | 115 |

**Weekend:** $17
**Weekend:** $29 (non-resident)
**Discounts:** Senior/Residents
**Driving Range:** Yes
**Junior Golf:** Yes
**Architect/Yr Open:** Geoffrey Cornish/1965
**GPS:**

Player Comments: "Course provides the opportunity to hit every club." "A solid test of your skills from tee to green. Between the design and condition, this is one of the region's very best values." –JD Voted by *Golf Digest* and *USA Today* Best Value In Massachusetts.

| | 1 | 2 | 3 | 4 | 5 | 6 | 7 | 8 | 9 |
|-------|-----|-----|-----|-----|-----|-----|-----|-----|-----|
| PAR | 4 | 5 | 3 | 4 | 4 | 4 | 5 | 3 | 4 |
| YARDS | 382 | 481 | 173 | 316 | 433 | 354 | 535 | 193 | 285 |
| | 10 | 11 | 12 | 13 | 14 | 15 | 16 | 17 | 18 |
| PAR | 4 | 3 | 3 | 4 | 4 | 5 | 3 | 5 | 4 |
| YARDS | 362 | 157 | 160 | 340 | 391 | 473 | 173 | 534 | 367 |

**Directions:** I-90 (Mass Pike) to Exit 6, turn right at light; course is 2.5 miles on left.

# Clearview Golf Course

NR ▶ 13

**66 Park Hill Avenue**
**Millbury, MA** (508) 754-5654
www.clearviewcountryclub.com

| Tees | Holes | Yards | Par | USGA | Slope |
|---|---|---|---|---|---|
| BACK | 9 | 2999 | 36 | 67.7 | 112 |
| MIDDLE | 9 | 2724 | 35 | 66.3 | 107 |
| FRONT | 9 | 2724 | 35 | 66.3 | 107 |

**Club Pro:** Neil Loomis
**Payment:** Visa, MC, Amex, Disc, Cash
**Tee Times:** 1 week adv.
**Fee 9 Holes: Weekday:** $10 9am-1pm    **Weekend:** $18 9am-2pm
**Fee 18 Holes: Weekday:** $20 9am-1pm    **Weekend:** $26 9am-2pm
**Twilight Rates:** After 5pm    **Discounts:** Pre-game
**Cart Rental:** $18pp/18, $9pp/9    **Driving Range:** No
**Lessons:** No   **Schools:** No    **Junior Golf:** Yes
**Membership:** Yes    **Architect/Yr Open:** 1962
**Other:** Snack Bar / Bar-Lounge / Ice Cold Beer    **GPS:**

COUPON

Discounts available. Friendly service, great greens, cold beer. "Play the view."

| | 1 | 2 | 3 | 4 | 5 | 6 | 7 | 8 | 9 |
|---|---|---|---|---|---|---|---|---|---|
| **PAR** | 3 | 5 | 5 | 3 | 5 | 3 | 4 | 4 | 3 |
| **YARDS** | 147 | 472 | 484 | 192 | 477 | 135 | 348 | 290 | 179 |
| **PAR** | | | | | | | | | |
| **YARDS** | | | | | | | | | |

**Directions:** I-90 (Mass Pike) to Exit 10A (Route 146). Look for Route 20 East. At first traffic light, go right onto Park Hill Avenue. Course is ½ mile on left.

# Cold Spring Country Club

★★★½ ▶ 14

**336 Chauncey Walker Street**
**Belchertown, MA** (413) 323-4888
www.coldspringcountryclub.com

| Tees | Holes | Yards | Par | USGA | Slope |
|---|---|---|---|---|---|
| BACK | 18 | 6521 | 71 | 71.7 | 130 |
| MIDDLE | 18 | 6001 | 71 | 69.6 | 125 |
| FRONT | 18 | 4676 | 71 | 68.2 | 114 |

**Club Pro:** Chris Tallman
**Payment:** Visa, MC, Amex, Cash
**Tee Times:** 7 days adv.
**Fee 9 Holes: Weekday:** Call    **Weekend:** Call
**Fee 18 Holes: Weekday:** Call    **Weekend:** Call
**Twilight Rates:** After 3pm    **Discounts:** Sr/Jr/College/Military
**Cart Rental:** $19pp/18, $11pp/9    **Driving Range:** Yes
**Lessons:** Yes   **Schools:** Yes    **Junior Golf:** Yes
**Membership:** Yes    **Architect/Yr Open:** 2012
**Other:** Full Restaurant / Clubhouse / Bar-Lounge / Snack Bar / Lockers / Showers

COUPON

A world-class semi-private course in a spectacular New England setting. Open to the public on weekdays and weekends after 1pm. Playable for all levels of golfers. "Take the ride and give it a try." –FP

| | 1 | 2 | 3 | 4 | 5 | 6 | 7 | 8 | 9 |
|---|---|---|---|---|---|---|---|---|---|
| **PAR** | 3 | 5 | 3 | 5 | 4 | 3 | 5 | 4 | 4 |
| **YARDS** | 197 | 490 | 106 | 479 | 384 | 230 | 460 | 325 | 248 |
| | **10** | **11** | **12** | **13** | **14** | **15** | **16** | **17** | **18** |
| **PAR** | 4 | 5 | 4 | 3 | 4 | 3 | 5 | 4 | 4 |
| **YARDS** | 421 | 540 | 387 | 206 | 409 | 145 | 456 | 162 | 356 |

**Directions:** I-90 (Mass Pike) to Exit 7. Take a right and follow Route 21 for 7.5 miles. The entrance to the club is on the left.

# Country Club of Greenfield  ✪✪½  15

Country Club Road
Greenfield, MA  (413) 773-7530
www.countryclubofgreenfield.net

**Club Pro:** Kevin Piecuch, PGA
**Payment:** Cash, Visa
**Tee Times:** No
**Fee  9 Holes: Weekday:** $25
**Fee 18 Holes: Weekday:** $35
**Twilight Rates:** No
**Cart Rental:** $27pp/18, $13.50pp/9
**Lessons:** Yes **Schools:** No
**Membership:** Yes
**Other:** Full Restaurant / Clubhouse / Bar-Lounge / Snack Bar / Showers

Built in 1896. Easy drive from all over New England.

| Tees | Holes | Yards | Par | USGA | Slope |
|------|-------|-------|-----|------|-------|
| BACK | 18 | 6450 | 72 | 70.1 | 117 |
| MIDDLE | 18 | 6210 | 72 | 68.6 | 114 |
| FRONT | 18 | 5444 | 73 | 70.6 | 119 |

**Weekend:** $30
**Weekend:** $45
**Discounts:** Senior & Junior
**Driving Range:** Yes
**Junior Golf:** Yes
**Architect/Yr Open:** R. Alex Findlay/1896

COUPON

**CTRL/ WEST MA**

| | 1 | 2 | 3 | 4 | 5 | 6 | 7 | 8 | 9 |
|------|----|----|----|----|----|----|----|----|----|
| PAR | 4 | 3 | 4 | 4 | 3 | 5 | 4 | 5 | 4 |
| YARDS | 380 | 144 | 421 | 380 | 130 | 565 | 283 | 455 | 362 |
| | 10 | 11 | 12 | 13 | 14 | 15 | 16 | 17 | 18 |
| PAR | 4 | 3 | 5 | 4 | 5 | 3 | 4 | 4 | 4 |
| YARDS | 357 | 185 | 470 | 280 | 570 | 145 | 315 | 387 | 320 |

**Directions:** I-91, take Exit 27. Turn right at Route 5 and 10. Take right at first set of lights onto Silver Street. Country Club Road is fourth street on right.

# Country Club of Wilbraham  ✪✪✪  16

859 Stony Hill Road
Wilbraham, MA  (413) 596-8887
www.countryclubofwilbraham.com

**Club Pro:** Milton Torres, Jr., PGA
**Payment:** Cash, Credit Card
**Tee Times:** No
**Fee  9 Holes: Weekday:** $40/res, $50/non-res, $18/guest
   **Weekend:** $45/res, $55/non-res
**Fee 18 Holes: Weekday:** $40/res, $30/guest  **Weekend:** $45/res
**Twilight Rates:** After 6pm weekdays; after 5pm weekends $25
**Discounts:** Senior discount Mondays $23
**Cart Rental:** $15pp/18, $7.50pp/9
**Lessons:** $60/half hour  **Schools:** No
**Membership:** Yes
**Other:** Clubhouse / Practice Green

**Driving Range:** Yes
**Junior Golf:** For residents
**Architect/Yr Open:** Willie Org/1927
**GPS:**

| Tees | Holes | Yards | Par | USGA | Slope |
|------|-------|-------|-----|------|-------|
| BACK | 18 | 6380 | 72 | 71.2 | 130 |
| MIDDLE | 18 | 5967 | 72 | 68.9 | 125 |
| FRONT | 18 | 5168 | 72 | 65.4 | 115 |

Semi-private. Residents of Wilbraham after 3pm, or as a guest with a member. Challenging even from the middle tees.

| | 1 | 2 | 3 | 4 | 5 | 6 | 7 | 8 | 9 |
|------|----|----|----|----|----|----|----|----|----|
| PAR | 4 | 3 | 4 | 4 | 3 | 5 | 4 | 5 | 4 |
| YARDS | 375 | 162 | 364 | 416 | 142 | 481 | 258 | 528 | 359 |
| | 10 | 11 | 12 | 13 | 14 | 15 | 16 | 17 | 18 |
| PAR | 3 | 5 | 4 | 4 | 3 | 4 | 4 | 4 | 5 |
| YARDS | 136 | 445 | 383 | 304 | 167 | 327 | 295 | 350 | 475 |

**Directions:** Take I-90 (Mass Pike) West to Exit 7, Belchertown/Ludlow. Turn left at end of ramp. Take Route 21 South. Follow signs to Wilbraham. Go left on Route 20 to Stony Hill Road.

# Cranwell Resort, Spa, and GC ✪✪✪✪½  17 ▶

**55 Lee Road**
**Lenox, MA (413) 637-2563**
www.cranwell.com

| Tees | Holes | Yards | Par | USGA | Slope |
|------|-------|-------|-----|------|-------|
| BACK | 18 | 6346 | 70 | 70 | 123 |
| MIDDLE | 18 | 6169 | 70 | 69.4 | 120 |
| FRONT | 18 | 5602 | 72 | 70.2 | 121 |

**Club Pro:** Luke Salvatore, Dir. of Golf
**Payment:** Visa, MC, Amex, Disc, Cash
**Tee Times:** Yes
**Fee  9 Holes: Wkday:** $31 Spring/Fall    **Weekend:** $45 Spring/Fall
**Fee 18 Holes: Wkday:** $39, $59 Summer    **Weekend:** $59, $79 Summer
**Twilight Rates:** After 2pm, after 3pm Summer    **Discounts:** Jr 16 under, 50% off
**Cart Rental:** $20pp/18, $14pp/9    **Driving Range:** $5/bucket
**Lessons:** $50/half hour, $100/hour **Schools:** Yes **Junior Golf:** No
**Membership:** Yes    **Architect/Yr Open:** Stiles & Van Kleek/1926
**Other:** Hotel / Lockers / Showers / Snack Bar / Restaurant / Bar-Lounge/ Major Golf School

Beautiful par 70 with Berkshire Mountain views, tree lined fairways and challenging contoured greens. Spring and Fall play all day specials; $39 to $48 includes carts. Your group will love the experience.

|  | 1 | 2 | 3 | 4 | 5 | 6 | 7 | 8 | 9 |
|------|---|---|---|---|---|---|---|---|---|
| PAR | 4 | 5 | 3 | 4 | 3 | 4 | 4 | 4 | 4 |
| YARDS | 384 | 463 | 144 | 373 | 218 | 370 | 360 | 340 | 405 |
|  | 10 | 11 | 12 | 13 | 14 | 15 | 16 | 17 | 18 |
| PAR | 4 | 4 | 3 | 4 | 4 | 5 | 3 | 4 | 4 |
| YARDS | 263 | 390 | 195 | 426 | 315 | 495 | 148 | 315 | 375 |

**Directions:** I-90 (Mass Pike) to Exit 2, take Route 20 West. Course is 10 minutes up the road.

# Crestview Country Club  ✪✪✪✪½  18 ▶

**281 Shoemaker Lane**
**Agawam, MA (413) 786-0917**
www.crestviewcc.com

| Tees | Holes | Yards | Par | USGA | Slope |
|------|-------|-------|-----|------|-------|
| BACK | 18 | 6902 | 72 | 74.2 | 133 |
| MIDDLE | 18 | 6297 | 72 | 71.0 | 128 |
| FRONT | 18 | 5571 | 72 | 73.4 | 130 |

**Club Pro:** Michael Zaranek, PGA
**Payment:** Visa, MC, Amex, Cash
**Tee Times:** Yes
**Fee  9 Holes: Weekday:**    **Weekend:**
**Fee 18 Holes: Weekday:** $40    **Weekend:** $50 F/S/S
**Twilight Rates:** Available    **Discounts:** Sr, Mil, Police, Fire, Youth
**Cart Rental:** $19pp/18    **Driving Range:** Yes
**Lessons:** Yes **Schools:** Yes    **Junior Golf:** Yes
**Membership:** Yes    **Architect/Yr Open:** Geoffrey Cornish/1958
**Other:** Restaurant / Bar-Lounge / Clubhouse / Lockers / Showers / Al Fresca Dining & Music

Challenging and enjoyable premier championship course. Full service pro shop. Private club conditions. 10 minutes to Bradley Airport. Host site for the PGA Tour's Travelers Championship Qualifier. Call for details on Crestview's Value Rates. "Great greens, great layout." –FP

|  | 1 | 2 | 3 | 4 | 5 | 6 | 7 | 8 | 9 |
|------|---|---|---|---|---|---|---|---|---|
| PAR | 4 | 5 | 3 | 4 | 4 | 3 | 5 | 4 | 4 |
| YARDS | 401 | 526 | 144 | 356 | 373 | 174 | 467 | 359 | 398 |
|  | 10 | 11 | 12 | 13 | 14 | 15 | 16 | 17 | 18 |
| PAR | 4 | 3 | 5 | 4 | 3 | 4 | 4 | 5 | 4 |
| YARDS | 338 | 145 | 447 | 366 | 143 | 383 | 414 | 490 | 373 |

**Directions:** I-90 (Mass Pike) to Exit 6 (I-91 South) to Exit 3 (Agawam). Go halfway around rotary to Route 57 to Route 75 South. At third light turn right onto Shoemaker Lane. Course is ¾ mile on left.

# Crumpin-Fox Club

✪✪✪½ **19** ▶

Parmenter Road
Bernardston, MA (413) 648-9101
www.golfthefox.com

**Club Pro:** John Jackson, Dir. of Golf
**Payment:** Visa, MC, Amex, Disc
**Tee Times:** golfthefox.com
**Fee 9 Holes: Weekday:** $49 w/cart
**Fee 18 Holes: Weekday:** $91 w/cart
**Twilight Rates:** After 2pm
**Cart Rental:** Included
**Lessons:** $45/half hour **Schools:** Jr. & Sr.
**Membership:** Yes
**Other:** Restaurant / Clubhouse / Hotel / Bar-Lounge / Lockers / Snack Bar / Showers / Tennis Courts / Pond

| Tees | Holes | Yards | Par | USGA | Slope |
|------|-------|-------|-----|------|-------|
| BACK | 18 | 7007 | 72 | 73.8 | 141 |
| MIDDLE | 18 | 6508 | 72 | 71.3 | 136 |
| FRONT | 18 | 5432 | 72 | 71.5 | 131 |

**Weekend:** $52 w/cart
**Weekend:** $97 w/cart
**Discounts:** Senior & Junior
**Driving Range:** $6/bag
**Junior Golf:** Yes
**Architect/Yr Open:** Roger Rulewich/1978

COUPON

Player Comments: "Must play." –JD "Variety of holes. You really need to think before you hit. Beautiful landscape. Great staff and atmosphere. Immaculate. The rustic clubhouse and pro shop, the tall trees surrounding the entrance—it just doesn't get any better." –LB

| | 1 | 2 | 3 | 4 | 5 | 6 | 7 | 8 | 9 |
|------|---|---|---|---|---|---|---|---|---|
| PAR | 4 | 4 | 3 | 4 | 5 | 4 | 4 | 5 | 3 |
| YARDS | 386 | 338 | 165 | 345 | 501 | 402 | 353 | 568 | 177 |
| | **10** | **11** | **12** | **13** | **14** | **15** | **16** | **17** | **18** |
| PAR | 4 | 3 | 4 | 4 | 5 | 3 | 4 | 5 | 4 |
| YARDS | 394 | 150 | 374 | 370 | 506 | 172 | 410 | 508 | 389 |

**Directions:** I-91 to Exit 28A (between Brattleboro, VT and Greenfield, MA). Follow Route 10 North for 1 mile; take left on Parmenter Road and follow signs to club.

# Cyprian Keyes Golf Club

✪✪✪½ **20** ▶

284 East Temple Street
Boylston, MA (508) 869-9900
www.cypriankeyes.com

**Club Pro:** Scott Hickey, PGA
**Payment:** Visa, MC, Amex, Disc, Cash
**Tee Times:** 5 days adv.
**Fee 9 Holes: Weekday:**
**Fee 18 Holes: Weekday:** $54 M-F
**Fee 18 Holes: Weekend:** $59 before 11am, $54 after 11am S/S/H
**Twilight Rates:** After 3pm
**Cart Rental:** $18pp/18
**Lessons:** Yes **Schools:** Yes
**Membership:** Yes
**Other:** Restaurant / Clubhouse / Showers / Lockers / Bar-Lounge / Custom Club Fitting

| Tees | Holes | Yards | Par | USGA | Slope |
|------|-------|-------|-----|------|-------|
| BACK | 18 | 6871 | 72 | 74.4 | 136 |
| MIDDLE | 18 | 6134 | 72 | 72.4 | 132 |
| FRONT | 18 | 5029 | 72 | 71.2 | 126 |

**Weekend:**

**Discounts:** Senior & Junior
**Driving Range:** $8/bucket
**Junior Golf:** Yes
**Architect/Yr Open:** Mark Mungeam/1997

Among many great holes, the short, risky 13th and the challenging 11th. Custom fitting center featuring trackman fiting system. Exceptional dining room and outdoor patio. Great pro shop and learning center.

| | 1 | 2 | 3 | 4 | 5 | 6 | 7 | 8 | 9 |
|------|---|---|---|---|---|---|---|---|---|
| PAR | 4 | 4 | 5 | 5 | 4 | 3 | 4 | 4 | 3 |
| YARDS | 332 | 367 | 510 | 476 | 376 | 180 | 357 | 369 | 155 |
| | **10** | **11** | **12** | **13** | **14** | **15** | **16** | **17** | **18** |
| PAR | 5 | 3 | 4 | 4 | 4 | 4 | 3 | 4 | 5 |
| YARDS | 486 | 175 | 350 | 318 | 406 | 348 | 162 | 297 | 470 |

**Directions:** Route 290 to Exit 23B (Route 140 North). Go 1 mile and take third right onto East Temple Street.

# Cyprian Keyes Golf Club, Par 3  ✪✪✪   21

**284 East Temple Street**
**Boylston, MA  (508) 869-9900**
www.cypriankeyes.com
**Club Pro:** Scott Hickey, PGA
**Payment:** Visa, MC, Amex, Disc
**Tee Times:** 5 days adv.

| Tees | Holes | Yards | Par | USGA | Slope |
|------|-------|-------|-----|------|-------|
| BACK | | | | | |
| MIDDLE | 9 | 1230 | 27 | | |
| FRONT | | | | | |

**Fee  9 Holes: Weekday:** $15 M-F      **Weekend:** $18/S/S/H
**Fee 18 Holes: Weekday:** $18      **Weekend:**
**Twilight Rates:** No      **Discounts:** Jr. and Sr.
**Cart Rental:** $9pp      **Driving Range:** $8 bucket
**Lessons:** Yes  **Schools:** Yes      **Junior Golf:** Yes
**Membership:** Juniors      **Architect/Yr Open:** Mark Mungeam/1997
**Other:** Clubhouse / Restaurant/ Function Facilities / Golf School / Custom Club Fitting

Sig. Hole: #9 is a picturesque 165-yard hole framed by trees with water to the left. It provides the golfer with many options. Custim fitting center featuring trackman fitting system. Player comments: "There are some great holes here. They could be part of any full-sized course." –JD Home

| | 1 | 2 | 3 | 4 | 5 | 6 | 7 | 8 | 9 |
|---|---|---|---|---|---|---|---|---|---|
| PAR | 3 | 3 | 3 | 3 | 3 | 3 | 3 | 3 | 3 |
| YARDS | 155 | 85 | 165 | 105 | 135 | 120 | 155 | 145 | 165 |
| PAR | | | | | | | | | |
| YARDS | | | | | | | | | |

**Directions:** Route 290 to Exit 23B (Route 140 North). Go 1 mile and take third right onto East Temple Street.

# Donnybrook Country Club  NR  22

**775 Williamstown Road**
**Lanesborough, MA  (413) 499-7888**
www.donnybrookgolf.com
**Club Pro:** Matt Kelly, GM
**Payment:** All Types
**Tee Times:** Yes

| Tees | Holes | Yards | Par | USGA | Slope |
|------|-------|-------|-----|------|-------|
| BACK | 9 | 3338 | 36 | 74.2 | 139 |
| MIDDLE | 9 | 3038 | 36 | 70.8 | 135 |
| FRONT | 9 | 2426 | 36 | 69.2 | 124 |

**Fee  9 Holes: Weekday:** $35/with cart      **Weekend:** $40
**Fee 18 Holes: Weekday:** $45/with cart      **Weekend:** $50
**Twilight Rates:** Yes, time varies      **Discounts:** Senior and Junior
**Cart Rental:** $10-$15      **Driving Range:** No
**Lessons:** No  **Schools:** No      **Junior Golf:** Yes
**Membership:** Yes      **Architect/Yr Open:** Vinnie Bartlett/2008
**Other:** Restaurant / Club-House / Showers / Bar-Lounge / Pro Shop / Putting Course

A great 9 hole course with multiple tee boxes providing a very different experience for a round of 18 holes. Beautiful, scenic, well maintained. Check our new aerial videos at www.donnybrookgolf.com.

| | 1 | 2 | 3 | 4 | 5 | 6 | 7 | 8 | 9 |
|---|---|---|---|---|---|---|---|---|---|
| PAR | 4 | 4 | 5 | 3 | 5 | 4 | 4 | 3 | 4 |
| YARDS | 333 | 357 | 553 | 135 | 416 | 348 | 393 | 174 | 329 |
| PAR | | | | | | | | | |
| YARDS | | | | | | | | | |

**Directions:** I-90 (Mass Pike) to Exit 2 (Lee) to Route 20 North to Route 7 North. Travel 9.2 miles and the course is on the left.

# Dudley Hill Golf Club

✪✪¹⁄₂　**23** ▶

80 Airport Road
Dudley, MA (508) 943-4538
www.dudleyhillgolf.net

**Club Pro:** Jim Siekierski, GM
**Payment:** Visa, MC
**Tee Times:** Daily
**Fee 9 Holes: Weekday:** $20
**Fee 18 Holes: Weekday:** $30 M-Th
**Twilight Rates:** After 6pm
**Cart Rental:** $12pp/18, $6pp/9
**Lessons:** No **Schools:** No
**Membership:** Yes
**Other:** Snack Bar / Bar-Lounge

| Tees | Holes | Yards | Par | USGA | Slope |
|------|-------|-------|-----|------|-------|
| BACK | | | | | |
| MIDDLE | 9 | 3279 | 36 | 71.4 | 123 |
| FRONT | 9 | 2848 | 36 | 71.3 | 115 |

**Weekend:** $20
**Weekend:** $35 F/S/S
**Discounts:** Junior
**Driving Range:** No
**Junior Golf:** Yes
**Architect/Yr Open:** Devereux Emmett/1926
**GPS:**

Hidden secret, semi-private. Open to public weekdays and after 1pm on weekends. Weekdays before 12pm, $20 for 9 holes with cart and lunch, $35 for 18 holes with cart and lunch. Distances below from back tees.

| | 1 | 2 | 3 | 4 | 5 | 6 | 7 | 8 | 9 |
|------|-----|-----|-----|-----|-----|-----|-----|-----|-----|
| **PAR** | 4 | 4 | 3 | 4 | 4 | 3 | 4 | 5 | 5 |
| **YARDS** | 373 | 380 | 164 | 398 | 321 | 186 | 428 | 509 | 474 |
| **PAR** | | | | | | | | | |
| **YARDS** | | | | | | | | | |

**Directions:** I-395 to Exit 2 (West) in Webster, MA. Head east approximately 4.5 miles (Dudley) to Airport Road. Course is on right at Cumberland Farms.

# Dunroamin Country Club

**NR**　**24** ▶

262 Lower Road
Gilbertville, MA (413) 477-0004
www.dunroamincc.com

**Club Pro:** Bob Lemoine
**Payment:** Cash or Credit Card
**Tee Times:** Weekends/Holidays
**Fee 9 Holes: Weekday:** $18
**Fee 18 Holes: Weekday:** $32
**Twilight Rates:** No
**Cart Rental:** $18pp/18, $9pp/9
**Lessons:** Yes **Schools:** No
**Membership:** Yes
**Other:** Clubhouse / Lockers / Showers / Snack Bar / Bar-Lounge

| Tees | Holes | Yards | Par | USGA | Slope |
|------|-------|-------|-----|------|-------|
| BACK | | | | | |
| MIDDLE | 9 | 2863 | 35 | 68.6 | 117 |
| FRONT | 9 | 2401 | 35 | 66.8 | 106 |

**Weekend:** $18
**Weekend:** $32
**Discounts:** Junior
**Driving Range:** $3/bucket
**Junior Golf:** Yes
**Architect/Yr Open:** Manuel Francis/1966

Come try us. $10 nine hole green fees on Tuesdays until 3pm. $12 green fees for 9 holes on Thursdays.

| | 1 | 2 | 3 | 4 | 5 | 6 | 7 | 8 | 9 |
|------|-----|-----|-----|-----|-----|-----|-----|-----|-----|
| **PAR** | 3 | 4 | 4 | 5 | 4 | 4 | 4 | 3 | 4 |
| **YARDS** | 204 | 331 | 393 | 493 | 322 | 310 | 367 | 166 | 277 |
| **PAR** | | | | | | | | | |
| **YARDS** | | | | | | | | | |

**Directions:** Mass Pike to Exit 8. Take Route 32 North for 15 miles.

# East Mountain Country Club ✪✪ 25

**1458 East Mountain Road**
**Westfield, MA (413) 568-1539**
www.eastmountaincc.com

| Tees | Holes | Yards | Par | USGA | Slope |
|------|-------|-------|-----|------|-------|
| BACK | 18 | 6118 | 71 | 69.4 | 120 |
| MIDDLE | 18 | 5819 | 71 | 68.3 | 113 |
| FRONT | 18 | 4564 | 71 | 65.4 | 104 |

**Club Pro:** Ted Perez Jr., PGA
**Payment:** Visa, MC, Amex, Cash
**Tee Times:** 1 week adv.
**Fee  9 Holes: Weekday:** $15      **Weekend:** $16
**Fee 18 Holes: Weekday:** $23      **Weekend:** $26
**Twilight Rates:** After 5pm      **Discounts:** Sr. & Jr: $16 wkdys $9.50/9 holes
**Cart Rental:** $13.50pp/18, $7.50pp/9      **Driving Range:** Yes
**Lessons:** Yes  **Schools:** Yes      **Junior Golf:** Yes
**Membership:** Full or Associate      **Architect/Yr Open:** Ted Perez Sr./1963
**Other:** Clubhouse / Snack Bar / Lounge      **GPS:**

SR 7200 Velvet Bent Greens seeded in 2003 – fantastic putting surface. Fees subject to change.

| | 1 | 2 | 3 | 4 | 5 | 6 | 7 | 8 | 9 |
|---|---|---|---|---|---|---|---|---|---|
| PAR | 4 | 4 | 3 | 5 | 4 | 4 | 4 | 4 | 3 |
| YARDS | 305 | 361 | 149 | 495 | 372 | 426 | 319 | 352 | 175 |
| | 10 | 11 | 12 | 13 | 14 | 15 | 16 | 17 | 18 |
| PAR | 3 | 5 | 5 | 3 | 4 | 5 | 4 | 3 | 4 |
| YARDS | 159 | 492 | 481 | 168 | 394 | 536 | 429 | 174 | 331 |

**Directions:** I-90 (Mass Pike) to Exit 3, follow Route 202 North to East Mountain Road. Course is 1.5 miles on right.

# Edge Hill Golf Club ✪½ 26

**298 Barnes Road**
**Ashfield, MA (413) 625-6018**
www.edgehillgolfcourse.com

| Tees | Holes | Yards | Par | USGA | Slope |
|------|-------|-------|-----|------|-------|
| BACK | 18 | 5708 | 71 | 68.6 | 124 |
| MIDDLE | 18 | 5293 | 71 | 67.0 | 116 |
| FRONT | 18 | 4188 | 71 | 63.0 | 109 |

**Club Pro:** Mark Graves, Manager
**Payment:** Cash, Visa, MC, Disc
**Tee Times:** Yes
**Fee  9 Holes: Weekday:** $16      **Weekend:** $19
**Fee 18 Holes: Weekday:** $20      **Weekend:** $24
**Twilight Rates:** No      **Discounts:** Junior
**Cart Rental:** $30pp/18, $15pp/9      **Driving Range:** Yes
**Lessons:** No  **Schools:** No      **Junior Golf:** No
**Membership:** Yes      **Architect/Yr Open:** Mark Graves/1994
**Other:** Full Restaurant / Clubhouse / Bar-Lounge

COUPON

Very challenging course demands playing positional golf. Open May - November.

| | 1 | 2 | 3 | 4 | 5 | 6 | 7 | 8 | 9 |
|---|---|---|---|---|---|---|---|---|---|
| PAR | 5 | 4 | 3 | 5 | 4 | 4 | 4 | 3 | 4 |
| YARDS | 490 | 290 | 150 | 420 | 410 | 290 | 240 | 151 | 370 |
| | 10 | 11 | 12 | 13 | 14 | 15 | 16 | 17 | 18 |
| PAR | 3 | 5 | 4 | 4 | 4 | 4 | 3 | 4 | 4 |
| YARDS | 150 | 480 | 310 | 300 | 238 | 210 | 152 | 260 | 410 |

**Directions:** I-91 Southbound: take Exit 26 (Route 2 West) to Route 112 South. Left on Route 116 to course. Follow signs. I-91 Northbound: take Exit 24 (Route 116/South Deerfield) to Conway-Ashfield. Turn right in Ashfield at Baptist Corner Road. Follow signs.

# Edgewood Golf Club ✪✪

## 27

161 Sheep Pasture Road
Southwick, MA (413) 569-6826
www.edgewood4golf.com

**Club Pro:** Bob Hucha
**Payment:** Visa, MC
**Tee Times:** 4 days adv.

| Tees | Holes | Yards | Par | USGA | Slope |
|------|-------|-------|-----|------|-------|
| BACK | 18 | 6510 | 71 | 69.1 | 115 |
| MIDDLE | 18 | 6050 | 71 | 67.6 | 113 |
| FRONT | 18 | 5580 | 71 | 71.8 | 109 |

**Fee 9 Holes: Weekday:** $14      **Weekend:** $18
**Fee 18 Holes: Weekday:** $22      **Weekend:** $26
**Twilight Rates:** $6 after 6pm M-F; $10 after 5pm weekend
**Discounts:** Senior & Junior
**Cart Rental:** $16pp/18, $9.50pp/9      **Driving Range:** $7/lg, $4/sm bucket
**Lessons:** $40/half hour  **Schools:** No      **Junior Golf:** Yes, clinics
**Membership:** Yes      **Architect/Yr Open:** Geoffrey Cornish/1963
**Other:** Clubhouse / Showers / Snack Bar / Restaurant / Bar-Lounge

Picturesque, easy walk, fairly open.

**CTRL/ WEST MA**

|  | 1 | 2 | 3 | 4 | 5 | 6 | 7 | 8 | 9 |
|------|------|------|------|------|------|------|------|------|------|
| PAR | 5 | 4 | 4 | 5 | 4 | 3 | 4 | 3 | 4 |
| YARDS | 450 | 415 | 315 | 523 | 385 | 170 | 390 | 205 | 340 |
|  | 10 | 11 | 12 | 13 | 14 | 15 | 16 | 17 | 18 |
| PAR | 4 | 3 | 4 | 3 | 5 | 5 | 4 | 3 | 4 |
| YARDS | 295 | 160 | 375 | 150 | 545 | 480 | 355 | 150 | 340 |

**Directions:** I-90 (Mass Pike) to Exit 3 (Springfield). Route 57 to Southwick. Route 57 goes through Routes 10 and 202. Go through center of town. Take a left on Depot. Right onto Sheep Pasture Road, follow it around to the right.

# Egremont Country Club ✪✪½

## 28

Route 23
Great Barrington, MA
(413) 528-4222
www.egremontcountryclub.com

**Club Pro:** Frank Mazzarelli, GM
**Payment:** Cash, MC, Visa, Amex
**Tee Times:** 7 days adv. 413-528-4222 x1

| Tees | Holes | Yards | Par | USGA | Slope |
|------|-------|-------|-----|------|-------|
| BACK | 18 | 6036 | 71 | 69.5 | 124 |
| MIDDLE | 18 | 5771 | 71 | 67.5 | 121 |
| FRONT | 18 | 4894 | 71 | 68.1 | 119 |

**Fee 9 Holes: Weekday:** $20      **Weekend:** $32
**Fee 18 Holes: Weekday:** $28      **Weekend:** $45
**Twilight Rates:** After 4pm      **Discounts:** Senior & Junior
**Cart Rental:** $18pp/18, $10pp/9      **Driving Range:** Yes
**Lessons:** Yes **Schools:** Yes      **Junior Golf:** Yes
**Membership:** Yes      **Architect/Yr Open:** 1920
**Other:** Clubhouse / Lockers / Showers / Snack Bar / Restaurant / Bar-Lounge

COUPON

Signature hole #18: double-tiered, elevated tee area, framed by large maples. Some claim the feel of #18th hole 'chute' at Augusta. Green guarded by 2 bunkers. Accurate approach shots a must. Tanglewood nearby.

|  | 1 | 2 | 3 | 4 | 5 | 6 | 7 | 8 | 9 |
|------|------|------|------|------|------|------|------|------|------|
| PAR | 4 | 4 | 3 | 4 | 5 | 3 | 4 | 4 | 3 |
| YARDS | 335 | 245 | 175 | 389 | 497 | 140 | 320 | 325 | 151 |
|  | 10 | 11 | 12 | 13 | 14 | 15 | 16 | 17 | 18 |
| PAR | 4 | 4 | 5 | 5 | 3 | 4 | 4 | 4 | 4 |
| YARDS | 338 | 275 | 532 | 538 | 152 | 320 | 325 | 353 | 361 |

**Directions:** I-90 (Mass Pike) to Exit 2 (Lee) Route 7. Follow Route 102 West to Route 7 South. Turn right on Route 23 for 3 miles.

# Ellinwood Country Club

**1928 Pleasant Street**
**Athol, MA (978) 249-7460**
www.ellinwoodgolf.com

| Tees | Holes | Yards | Par | USGA | Slope |
|------|-------|-------|-----|------|-------|
| BACK | 18 | 6195 | 71 | 69.5 | 123 |
| MIDDLE | 18 | 5891 | 71 | 68.8 | 119 |
| FRONT | 18 | 5031 | 72 | 69.1 | 118 |

**Club Pro:** Jason Goodhind, PGA
**Payment:** Visa, MC, Cash
**Tee Times:** Yes
**Fee 9 Holes: Weekday:** $20 **Weekend:** $25
**Fee 18 Holes: Weekday:** $30 **Weekend:** $40
**Twilight Rates:** After 5pm **Discounts:** Junior
**Cart Rental:** Yes **Driving Range:** No
**Lessons:** Yes **Schools:** No **Junior Golf:** Yes
**Membership:** Yes **Architect/Yr Open:** Ross/1929; Cornish/1968
**Other:** Clubhouse / Snack Bar / Bar-Lounge / Banquet Hall

*COUPON*

Immaculate, fast greens. No back and forth holes. Every hole offers a different challenge. 9 holes by Donald Ross in 1929. 9 holes by Geoff Cornish in 1968. Fully irrigated in 2004. "A Hidden Gem of Worcester County."

| | 1 | 2 | 3 | 4 | 5 | 6 | 7 | 8 | 9 |
|------|-----|-----|-----|-----|-----|-----|-----|-----|-----|
| PAR | 4 | 4 | 3 | 5 | 5 | 3 | 4 | 3 | 4 |
| YARDS | 400 | 321 | 148 | 477 | 414 | 158 | 405 | 150 | 369 |
| | 10 | 11 | 12 | 13 | 14 | 15 | 16 | 17 | 18 |
| PAR | 3 | 4 | 3 | 5 | 3 | 4 | 5 | 4 | 4 |
| YARDS | 215 | 278 | 150 | 441 | 136 | 398 | 472 | 416 | 517 |

**Directions:** Route 2 to Exit 17. Take right off exit, follow ½ mile on right to Woodlawn Road. Go all the way to the end; clubhouse is on the right.

# Elmcrest Country Club

**105 Somersville Road**
**East Longmeadow, MA**
**(413) 525-4653**
www.elmcrestcc.com

| Tees | Holes | Yards | Par | USGA | Slope |
|------|-------|-------|-----|------|-------|
| BACK | 18 | 6347 | 70 | 70.5 | 131 |
| MIDDLE | 18 | 5904 | 70 | 68.9 | 128 |
| FRONT | 18 | 5363 | 72 | 71.4 | 122 |

**Club Pro:** Rick Fleury, PGA
**Payment:** All Types
**Tee Times:** Yes
**Fee 9 Holes: Weekday:** $21 **Weekend:** $24 (F/S/S)
**Fee 18 Holes: Weekday:** $35 **Weekend:** $40 (F/S/S)
**Twilight Rates:** Available **Discounts:** Senior, Military
**Cart Rental:** $18pp/18 **Driving Range:** No
**Lessons:** Yes **Schools:** No **Junior Golf:** No
**Membership:** Yes **Architect/Yr Open:** 1964
**Other:** Restaurant / Clubhouse / Lockers / Showers / Bar-Lounge / Banquet Facilities

*COUPON*

A course dedicated to its members, the local community and the game of golf. One of the best values in Western Massachusetts.

| | 1 | 2 | 3 | 4 | 5 | 6 | 7 | 8 | 9 |
|------|-----|-----|-----|-----|-----|-----|-----|-----|-----|
| PAR | 4 | 4 | 4 | 3 | 5 | 4 | 3 | 4 | 4 |
| YARDS | 331 | 366 | 328 | 184 | 445 | 341 | 142 | 295 | 344 |
| | 10 | 11 | 12 | 13 | 14 | 15 | 16 | 17 | 18 |
| PAR | 4 | 3 | 4 | 4 | 4 | 4 | 5 | 3 | 4 |
| YARDS | 322 | 180 | 368 | 387 | 379 | 413 | 489 | 156 | 424 |

**Directions:** I-90 (Mass Pike) to Exit 6 (I-91 South) to Exit 4 (Route 83 South). Stay on Route 83 South and go through the center of East Longmeadow and through the rotary, continue on 83 South for 3 miles to Somersville Road on your right.

# Forest Park Country Club

NR · **31** ▶

1928 Pleasant Street
Adams, MA (413) 743-3311
www.forestparkadams.com

| Tees | Holes | Yards | Par | USGA | Slope |
|------|-------|-------|-----|------|-------|
| BACK | | | | | |
| MIDDLE | 9 | 2555 | 34 | 63.8 | 110 |
| FRONT | 9 | 2323 | 34 | 63.8 | 110 |

**Club Pro:** Bruce Cardin, Manager
**Payment:** Cash or Check Only
**Tee Times:** No
**Fee 9 Holes: Weekday:** $15    **Weekend:** $15
**Fee 18 Holes: Weekday:** $20    **Weekend:** $20
**Twilight Rates:** No    **Discounts:** None
**Cart Rental:** $13.50pp/18, $7.50pp/9    **Driving Range:** No
**Lessons:** No **Schools:** No    **Junior Golf:** Yes
**Membership:** Yes    **Architect/Yr Open:** Alex Findlay/1900
**Other:** Clubhouse / Lockers / Showers / Snack Bar / Bar-Lounge/ Banquet Hall

COUPON

Sig. Hole: #5 is a 157-yard par 3: all carry, well bunkered, small sloping green. Tricky to birdie. Ongoing clubhouse renovations. Scenic 9 holes at the foot of Mt. Greylock.

|  | 1 | 2 | 3 | 4 | 5 | 6 | 7 | 8 | 9 |
|------|------|------|------|------|------|------|------|------|------|
| PAR | 4 | 4 | 3 | 4 | 3 | 4 | 4 | 4 | 4 |
| YARDS | 270 | 341 | 157 | 327 | 147 | 333 | 314 | 389 | 277 |

| PAR | | | | | | | | | |
|------|------|------|------|------|------|------|------|------|------|
| YARDS | | | | | | | | | |

**Directions:** I-90 (Mass Pike) to Exit 2 (Lee). Take Route 20 East to Route 8 to Adams. Take left at statue on Park Street to Maple Street. Take first left onto Forest Park Avenue.

# Franconia Municipal Golf Course ✪✪✪ · **32** ▶

618 Dwight Road
Springfield, MA (413) 734-9334
www.franconiagolfcourse.com

| Tees | Holes | Yards | Par | USGA | Slope |
|------|-------|-------|-----|------|-------|
| BACK | 18 | 6153 | 71 | 68.7 | 118 |
| MIDDLE | 18 | 5825 | 71 | 67.1 | 115 |
| FRONT | 18 | 5348 | 71 | 67.1 | 115 |

**Club Pro:** Kevin Kennedy, PGA
**Payment:** Most Major Credit Cards
**Tee Times:** Weekends
**Fee 9 Holes: Weekday:**    **Weekend:**
**Fee 18 Holes: Weekday:** $24    **Weekend:** $25
**Twilight Rates:** After 3pm    **Discounts:** Sr. & Jr. Weekdays
**Cart Rental:** $15pp/18, $7.50pp/9    **Driving Range:** No
**Lessons:** $24/half hour **Schools:** No    **Junior Golf:** Yes
**Membership:** Yes    **Architect/Yr Open:** Stiles & Van Kleek/1929
**Other:** Clubhouse / Snack Bar / Restaurant / Bar-Lounge

Rates are for all-day play. Several challenging par 5s. Good mix of holes. Discount for town residents. Great shape. Re-landscaped in 2001. Well maintained.

|  | 1 | 2 | 3 | 4 | 5 | 6 | 7 | 8 | 9 |
|------|------|------|------|------|------|------|------|------|------|
| PAR | 4 | 4 | 4 | 5 | 3 | 4 | 4 | 3 | 4 |
| YARDS | 314 | 307 | 349 | 557 | 124 | 412 | 360 | 162 | 387 |

|  | 10 | 11 | 12 | 13 | 14 | 15 | 16 | 17 | 18 |
|------|------|------|------|------|------|------|------|------|------|
| PAR | 5 | 4 | 5 | 4 | 3 | 4 | 4 | 3 | 4 |
| YARDS | 491 | 307 | 468 | 368 | 132 | 350 | 282 | 173 | 282 |

**Directions:** I-91 to Longmeadow exit. At 2nd light take a left onto Converse Street. At end, take left onto Dwight Road. Follow to course.

# Gardner Municipal Golf Course ✪✪½   ▶ 33

**152 Eaton Street**
**Gardner, MA (978) 632-9703**
**www.gardnergolfcourse.com**

| Tees | Holes | Yards | Par | USGA | Slope |
|------|-------|-------|-----|------|-------|
| BACK | 18 | 6131 | 71 | 70.3 | 133 |
| MIDDLE | 18 | 5857 | 71 | 69.0 | 127 |
| FRONT | 18 | 5524 | 75 | 72.1 | 129 |

**Club Pro:** Dan Berry
**Payment:** Cash and Credit
**Tee Times:** Weekends, Holidays
**Fee 9 Holes: Weekday:** $15    **Weekend:** $20
**Fee 18 Holes: Weekday:** $30    **Weekend:** $35
**Twilight Rates:** After 4pm weekday; after 3pm weekend
**Discounts:** Junior
**Cart Rental:** $18pp/18, $10pp/9    **Driving Range:** Yes
**Lessons:** Yes **Schools:**    **Junior Golf:** Yes
**Membership:** Yes    **Architect/Yr Open:** 1936
**Other:** Clubhouse / Snack Bar / Restaurant / Bar-Lounge

COUPON

Player Comments: "Lesser known to those outside the area, but well worth the trip." New tee on #8, provides new angle of approach to green, requires carry over bunker. 4th set of tees has been added (4898 yards).

|  | 1 | 2 | 3 | 4 | 5 | 6 | 7 | 8 | 9 |
|------|------|------|------|------|------|------|------|------|------|
| PAR | 4 | 4 | 3 | 4 | 5 | 3 | 5 | 3 | 4 |
| YARDS | 320 | 297 | 215 | 316 | 525 | 137 | 530 | 142 | 406 |
|  | **10** | **11** | **12** | **13** | **14** | **15** | **16** | **17** | **18** |
| PAR | 4 | 5 | 4 | 4 | 3 | 5 | 3 | 4 | 4 |
| YARDS | 300 | 450 | 323 | 370 | 136 | 478 | 207 | 352 | 353 |

**Directions:** Route 2 to Exit 24B (Route 140 North). Follow signs to Mount Wachusett Community College. Course is across street from front of college.

# GEAA Golf Club   NR   ▶ 34

**303 Crane Avenue**
**Pittsfield, MA (413) 443-5746**
**www.geaagolf.com**

| Tees | Holes | Yards | Par | USGA | Slope |
|------|-------|-------|-----|------|-------|
| BACK | 9 | 3180 | 36 | 70.0 | 118 |
| MIDDLE | 9 | 3079 | 36 | 69.6 | 115 |
| FRONT | 9 | 2637 | 36 | 69.4 | 110 |

**Club Pro:** Jay Abir, PGA
**Payment:** All Types
**Tee Times:** Yes
**Fee 9 Holes: Weekday:** $15    **Weekend:** $15
**Fee 18 Holes: Weekday:** $27    **Weekend:** $27
**Twilight Rates:** No    **Discounts:** None
**Cart Rental:** $15pp/18, $10pp/9    **Driving Range:** For Members
**Lessons:** Yes **Schools:** No    **Junior Golf:** Yes
**Membership:** Yes    **Architect/Yr Open:** Rowland Armacost/1930
**Other:** Restaurant / Clubhouse / Snack Bar / Bar-Lounge / Lockers / Showers

Gently rolling hills and windy all year round. Tree-lined fairways with beautiful view of Mt. Greylock.

|  | 1 | 2 | 3 | 4 | 5 | 6 | 7 | 8 | 9 |
|------|------|------|------|------|------|------|------|------|------|
| PAR | 3 | 4 | 4 | 4 | 5 | 5 | 4 | 3 | 4 |
| YARDS | 170 | 379 | 348 | 276 | 443 | 539 | 332 | 134 | 391 |
| PAR |  |  |  |  |  |  |  |  |  |
| YARDS |  |  |  |  |  |  |  |  |  |

**Directions:** I-90 (Mass Pike) to Lee exit. Follow Route 7 North through Lee and Lenox. ½ mile past Reed Middle School is Crane Street; take right to the course.

# Grandview Golf Course ✪✪

## 35

449 Wachusett Street
Leominster, MA (978) 537-9151
www.grandviewgolfleominster.com

**Club Pro:** Sue Tourigny, Golf Manager
**Payment:** Visa, MC, Disc, Check, Cash
**Tee Times:** 7 days adv.
**Fee 9 Holes: Weekday:** $14
**Fee 18 Holes: Weekday:** $23
**Twilight Rates:** No
**Cart Rental:** $13pp/18, $10pp/9
**Lessons:** No **Schools:** No
**Membership:** Yes
**Other:** Snack Bar

| Tees | Holes | Yards | Par | USGA | Slope |
|------|-------|-------|-----|------|-------|
| BACK | | | | | |
| MIDDLE | 9 | 3357 | 36 | 68.8 | 113 |
| FRONT | 9 | 3103 | 36 | | |

**Weekend:** $17
**Weekend:** $26
**Discounts:** Senior and Junior
**Driving Range:** No
**Junior Golf:** No
**Architect/Yr Open:**

Grandview is a scenic, public golf course that has been owned and operated by the Vachon Family since 1965. The 9 hole course is friendly, yet challenging for players of all levels. The course offers beautiful views of Wachusett Mountain and borders the Vachon Wildlife Sanctuary.

| | 1 | 2 | 3 | 4 | 5 | 6 | 7 | 8 | 9 |
|------|-----|-----|-----|-----|-----|-----|-----|-----|-----|
| PAR | 4 | 4 | 3 | 4 | 3 | 4 | 5 | 4 | 5 |
| YARDS | 337 | 358 | 195 | 425 | 175 | 440 | 491 | 397 | 539 |
| PAR | | | | | | | | | |
| YARDS | | | | | | | | | |

**Directions:** Route 2 West to Exit 33 (I-190 South). Left onto Route 12. Straight onto Pleasant Street. Travel 2.1 miles and take a right onto Wachusett Street. Course is 1.3 miles on right.

CTRL/
WEST
MA

# Green Hill Municipal Golf Course ✪✪✪½

## 36

1929 Skyline Drive
Worcester, MA (508) 799-1359
www.greenhillgc.com

**Club Pro:** Matthew Moison, PGA
**Payment:** Visa, MC, Disc, Check, Cash
**Tee Times:** 7 days (508) 799-1545
**Fee 9 Holes: Weekday:** $20
**Fee 18 Holes: Weekday:** $35
**Twilight Rates:** No
**Cart Rental:** $15pp/18, $10pp/9
**Lessons:** No **Schools:** Yes
**Membership:** Yes
**Other:** Clubhouse / Bar-Lounge / Snack Bar

| Tees | Holes | Yards | Par | USGA | Slope |
|------|-------|-------|-----|------|-------|
| BACK | 18 | 6485 | 72 | 71.4 | 130 |
| MIDDLE | 18 | 6054 | 72 | 69.6 | 127 |
| FRONT | 18 | 5424 | 72 | 66.5 | 122 |

**Weekend:** $30
**Weekend:** $40
**Discounts:** Seniors (62), Juniors (under 18)
**Driving Range:** No
**Junior Golf:** Yes
**Architect/Yr Open:** Ted Robinson/1929

Green Hill Golf Course is one of the older courses in the area. Our sloping greens and classic layout are attractive to golfers of many different styles and skill levels. Sitting atop one of Worcester's Seven Hills contributes a scenic pleasure to your golf game.

| | 1 | 2 | 3 | 4 | 5 | 6 | 7 | 8 | 9 |
|-------|-----|-----|-----|-----|-----|-----|-----|-----|-----|
| PAR | 4 | 4 | 5 | 4 | 4 | 3 | 4 | 3 | 5 |
| YARDS | 375 | 334 | 418 | 347 | 342 | 190 | 330 | 157 | 452 |
| | 10 | 11 | 12 | 13 | 14 | 15 | 16 | 17 | 18 |
| PAR | 4 | 3 | 4 | 5 | 4 | 3 | 5 | 4 | 4 |
| YARDS | 358 | 198 | 328 | 482 | 385 | 140 | 458 | 371 | 389 |

**Directions:** From Rt. 9 - East or West - Turn into Green Hill Park at Skyline Drive.

# Greenock Country Club

 37

220 West Park Street
Lee, MA (413) 243-3323
www.greenockcc.com

Club Pro: Ryan Butterick, PGA
Payment: Visa, MC, Cash, Check
Tee Times: Yes

| Tees | Holes | Yards | Par | USGA | Slope |
|------|-------|-------|-----|------|-------|
| BACK | | | | | |
| MIDDLE | 9 | 3070 | 35 | 68.9 | 120 |
| FRONT | 9 | 2843 | 37 | 72.2 | 123 |

Fee 9 Holes: Weekday: $25
Fee 18 Holes: Weekday: $35
Twilight Rates: No
Cart Rental: $21 pp/18, $12pp/9
Lessons: Yes  Schools: No
Membership: Yes

Weekend: $32
Weekend: $45
Discounts: Senior & Junior
Driving Range: No
Junior Golf: Yes
Architect/Yr Open: Donald Ross/1927

Other: Clubhouse / Lockers / Showers / Snack Bar / Restaurant / Bar-Lounge

Postage stamp-size greens. Donald Ross design, one of the first 100 courses built in the United States. New irrigation.

| | 1 | 2 | 3 | 4 | 5 | 6 | 7 | 8 | 9 |
|---|---|---|---|---|---|---|---|---|---|
| PAR | 4 | 3 | 4 | 4 | 4 | 5 | 3 | 4 | 4 |
| YARDS | 330 | 158 | 391 | 300 | 423 | 464 | 168 | 360 | 364 |
| PAR | | | | | | | | | |
| YARDS | | | | | | | | | |

Directions: I-90 (Mass Pike) to Exit 2 (Lee). Take right on Housatonic Street to the center of Lee. Come to the stop sign next to town park. Take West Park Street up the hill over the RR tracks. Course on right.

# Groton Country Club

 38

94 Lovers Lane
Groton, MA (978) 448-2564
www.grotoncountryclub.com

Club Pro: Rod Van Guilder
Payment: Most Major Credit Cards
Tee Times: 7 days adv.

| Tees | Holes | Yards | Par | USGA | Slope |
|------|-------|-------|-----|------|-------|
| BACK | 9 | 3003 | 35 | 66.5 | 116 |
| MIDDLE | 9 | 2709 | 35 | 66.5 | 116 |
| FRONT | 9 | 2409 | 36 | | |

Fee 9 Holes: Weekday: $19
Fee 18 Holes: Weekday: $27
Twilight Rates: 6pm wkday/5pm wknd ($10)
Cart Rental: $15pp/18, $9pp/9
Lessons: Yes  Schools: Yes
Membership: Yes

Weekend: $20
Weekend: $32
Discounts: Senior & Junior
Driving Range:
Junior Golf: Yes
Architect/Yr Open: 1950

Other: Full Restaurant / Clubhouse / Bar-Lounge / Snack Bar / Showers

Resident-discounted rates. Collared shirts are required. New Golf Cart and Cart Paths. Open April - November.

| | 1 | 2 | 3 | 4 | 5 | 6 | 7 | 8 | 9 |
|---|---|---|---|---|---|---|---|---|---|
| PAR | 4 | 4 | 4 | 3 | 3 | 4 | 4 | 5 | 4 |
| YARDS | 330 | 260 | 325 | 140 | 210 | 326 | 335 | 450 | 300 |
| PAR | | | | | | | | | |
| YARDS | | | | | | | | | |

Directions: I-495 to Route 119 West to Groton.

# Hemlock Ridge Golf Course ✪✪½ 39

220 Holland Road
Fiskdale, MA (508) 347-9935
www.hemlockridgegolfcourse.com

| Tees | Holes | Yards | Par | USGA | Slope |
|------|-------|-------|-----|------|-------|
| BACK | | | | | |
| MIDDLE | 9 | 3136 | 36 | 70.6 | 117 |
| FRONT | 9 | 2603 | 36 | 69.0 | 109 |

**Club Pro:** Ward Palmer, Manger
**Payment:** Visa, MC
**Tee Times:** Weekends Only
**Fee 9 Holes: Weekday:** $16          **Weekend:** $18
**Fee 18 Holes: Weekday:** $24         **Weekend:** $27
**Twilight Rates:** No                  **Discounts:** Senior $1 off
**Cart Rental:** $16pp/18, $8pp/9       **Driving Range:** No
**Lessons:** No  **Schools:** No        **Junior Golf:** Yes
**Membership:** Yes                     **Architect/Yr Open:** Philip Wogan/1965
**Other:** Clubhouse / Snack Bar / Showers    **GPS:**

CTRL/ WEST MA

Hilly and scenic. Conditions good for both fairways and greens. Dress code. Open April 1 - November 1.
"Great country course, worth the trip." –FP

| | 1 | 2 | 3 | 4 | 5 | 6 | 7 | 8 | 9 |
|------|----|----|----|----|----|----|----|----|----|
| PAR | 4 | 4 | 3 | 4 | 4 | 5 | 4 | 3 | 5 |
| YARDS | 308 | 382 | 154 | 449 | 370 | 471 | 317 | 170 | 515 |
| PAR | | | | | | | | | |
| YARDS | | | | | | | | | |

**Directions:** Mass Pike to Route 20 West through Sturbridge to Holland Road (at the junction of Route 148), turn left. Course is 1 mile up Holland Road.

# Heritage Country Club ✪✪½ 40

85 Sampson Road
Charlton, MA (508) 248-5111
www.heritagecountryclub.com

| Tees | Holes | Yards | Par | USGA | Slope |
|------|-------|-------|-----|------|-------|
| BACK | 18 | 6796 | 71 | 69.3 | 118 |
| MIDDLE | 18 | 6138 | 71 | 67.3 | 113 |
| FRONT | 18 | 5415 | 72 | 70.3 | 114 |

**Club Pro:** Shane Bayer
**Payment:** Cash, Credit Cards
**Tee Times:** 7 days adv.
**Fee 9 Holes: Weekday:** $21          **Weekend:** $25 after 3pm
**Fee 18 Holes: Weekday:** $35         **Weekend:** $43
**Twilight Rates:** After 4pm          **Discounts:** Senior & Junior
**Cart Rental:** $15pp/18, $9pp/9      **Driving Range:** $7/bucket
**Lessons:** $35/half hour **Schools:** Yes    **Junior Golf:** Yes
**Membership:** Yes                    **Architect/Yr Open:** Don Hoeing/1963
**Other:** Clubhouse / Lockers / Showers / Snack Bar / Bar-Lounge

COUPON

Player comments: "Good value. Hilly but fun and fair. Enjoy the views." "Worth a new visit."
Early-bird and late-afternoon specials. Weekend after 6pm – $10/walk, $15/ride, unlimited. New man-made
pond and new trees, bunkers, and tees.

| | 1 | 2 | 3 | 4 | 5 | 6 | 7 | 8 | 9 |
|------|----|----|----|----|----|----|----|----|----|
| PAR | 4 | 4 | 3 | 4 | 4 | 5 | 3 | 4 | 4 |
| YARDS | 365 | 372 | 176 | 360 | 352 | 525 | 166 | 319 | 443 |
| | 10 | 11 | 12 | 13 | 14 | 15 | 16 | 17 | 18 |
| PAR | 4 | 4 | 5 | 3 | 4 | 4 | 3 | 5 | 4 |
| YARDS | 393 | 364 | 580 | 155 | 297 | 381 | 175 | 564 | 360 |

**Directions:** Located on Route 20 in Charlton. 3 miles east of Old Sturbridge Village. Easy to reach
from Worcester, Boston, Springfield, Hartford, or Providence.

# Hickory Ridge Golf Club    ✪✪✪½

**191 West Pomeroy Lane**
**Amherst, MA (413) 230-3360**
www.hickoryridgecc.com

| Tees | Holes | Yards | Par | USGA | Slope |
|------|-------|-------|-----|------|-------|
| BACK | 18 | 6704 | 72 | 72.8 | 130 |
| MIDDLE | 18 | 6311 | 72 | 71.1 | 126 |
| FRONT | 18 | 5272 | 74 | 71.1 | 122 |

**Club Pro:** Jim McDonald, Jr., PGA
**Payment:** Visa, Amex, MC, Disc
**Tee Times:** 6 days adv.
**Fee 9 Holes: Weekday:** $18    **Weekend:** $18 after 2pm
**Fee 18 Holes: Weekday:** $25    **Weekend:** $27
**Twilight Rates:** After 2pm    **Discounts:** Junior/Senior
**Cart Rental:** $17pp/18, $10pp/9    **Driving Range:** $5 /bucket
**Lessons:** Yes **Schools:** No    **Junior Golf:** Yes
**Membership:** Yes    **Architect/Yr Open:** Cornish & Robinson/1970
**Other:** Clubhouse / Lockers / Showers / Snack Bar / Restaurant
**GPS:** No

*COUPON*

Generous landing areas, big greens, challenge for all playing abilities.

| | 1 | 2 | 3 | 4 | 5 | 6 | 7 | 8 | 9 |
|-----|-----|-----|-----|-----|-----|-----|-----|-----|-----|
| PAR | 5 | 4 | 4 | 4 | 3 | 5 | 4 | 3 | 4 |
| YARDS | 501 | 380 | 329 | 394 | 193 | 500 | 344 | 158 | 405 |
| | 10 | 11 | 12 | 13 | 14 | 15 | 16 | 17 | 18 |
| PAR | 4 | 5 | 4 | 4 | 4 | 3 | 5 | 3 | 4 |
| YARDS | 372 | 447 | 401 | 342 | 349 | 140 | 466 | 182 | 438 |

**Directions:** I-91 to Route 9 East from Northampton to Route 116 in Amherst. Go South on Route 116 for 2.5 miles to West Pomeroy Lane. Right onto West Pomeroy for ½ mile.

# Highfields Golf & Country Club   ✪✪✪✪   42

**42 Magill Drive (off Route 122)**
**Grafton, MA (508) 839-1945**
www.highfieldsgolfcc.com

| Tees | Holes | Yards | Par | USGA | Slope |
|------|-------|-------|-----|------|-------|
| BACK | 18 | 7021 | 72 | 74.5 | 140 |
| MIDDLE | 18 | 6474 | 72 | 72.2 | 136 |
| FRONT | 18 | 6024 | 72 | 69.9 | 131 |

**Club Pro:** Roger Adams, PGA
**Payment:** Visa, MC, Amex, Disc
**Tee Times:** Yes
**Fee 9 Holes: Weekday:** $29 walk, $38 ride    **Weekend:** $29 walk, $38 ride
**Fee 18 Holes: Weekday:** $57 inc cart    **Weekend:** $65 incl cart
**Twilight Rates:** No    **Discounts:** Senior & Junior M-F
**Cart Rental:** Included    **Driving Range:** Irons only
**Lessons:** Yes **Schools:** Yes    **Junior Golf:** Yes
**Membership:** Many levels    **Architect/Yr:** Cornish, Silva, & Mungeam/2002
**Other:** Clubhouse / Lockers / Showers / Snack Bar / Restaurant / Bar-Lounge

*COUPON*

Championship course designed by Cornish, Silva and Mungeam complements a beautiful residential project. Breathtaking views all around. Playable for all skill levels and abilities. Great conditions. Beautiful new clubhouse.

| | 1 | 2 | 3 | 4 | 5 | 6 | 7 | 8 | 9 |
|-----|-----|-----|-----|-----|-----|-----|-----|-----|-----|
| PAR | 5 | 3 | 4 | 4 | 3 | 4 | 4 | 4 | 5 |
| YARDS | 516 | 138 | 399 | 365 | 218 | 389 | 383 | 339 | 570 |
| | 10 | 11 | 12 | 13 | 14 | 15 | 16 | 17 | 18 |
| PAR | 4 | 3 | 4 | 4 | 4 | 5 | 4 | 3 | 5 |
| YARDS | 411 | 145 | 325 | 385 | 321 | 501 | 441 | 121 | 507 |

**Directions:** I-90 (Mass Pike) to Exit 11 (Route 122). Go right off ramp (122 South). 4.5 miles to Magill Drive on left. Follow Magill Drive 1.5 miles to clubhouse on left.

# Hillcrest Country Club ★½  43

325 Pleasant Street
Leicester, MA  (508) 892-0963

| Tees | Holes | Yards | Par | USGA | Slope |
|------|-------|-------|-----|------|-------|
| BACK | 9 | 3068 | 35 | 67.1 | 103 |
| MIDDLE | 9 | 3138 | 35 | 67.1 | 103 |
| FRONT | 9 | 2388 | 36 | 67.2 | 113 |

**Club Pro:** George Poaskis
**Payment:** Cash Only
**Tee Times:** Recommended
**Fee  9 Holes: Weekday:** $14        **Weekend:** $14
**Fee 18 Holes: Weekday:** $18        **Weekend:** $18
**Twilight Rates:** No        **Discounts:** Junior
**Cart Rental:** $16pp/18, $8pp/9        **Driving Range:** No
**Lessons:** No  **Schools:** No        **Junior Golf:** No
**Membership:** No        **Architect/Yr Open:** Robert B. Harris/1964
**Other:** Clubhouse / Snack Bar / Restaurant / Bar-Lounge

Ongoing improvements. Friendly staff and personnel. Under new management.

CTRL/
WEST
MA

|  | 1 | 2 | 3 | 4 | 5 | 6 | 7 | 8 | 9 |
|------|---|---|---|---|---|---|---|---|---|
| PAR | 5 | 4 | 4 | 4 | 3 | 5 | 3 | 3 | 4 |
| YARDS | 500 | 402 | 345 | 340 | 355 | 475 | 110 | 136 | 475 |
| PAR | | | | | | | | | |
| YARDS | | | | | | | | | |

**Directions:** I-90 (Mass Pike) to Exit 10 (Auburn). Take right onto Route 12, follow 3 miles. Take right onto Route 20, follow 3 miles; take right onto Route 56, 4 miles.

# Holden Hills Country Club ★★ 44

1800 Main Street
Jefferson, MA  (508) 829-3129
www.holdenhillsgolf.com

| Tees | Holes | Yards | Par | USGA | Slope |
|------|-------|-------|-----|------|-------|
| BACK | 18 | 6088 | 71 | 70.7 | 132 |
| MIDDLE | 18 | 5878 | 71 | 69.4 | 129 |
| FRONT | 18 | 5390 | 74 | 73.0 | 128 |

**Club Pro:** Jeff Bailey, PGA
**Payment:** MC, Visa, Amex
**Tee Times:** Weekends, 1 week adv.
**Fee  9 Holes: Weekday:** $25 w/cart        **Weekend:** $25 w/cart
**Fee 18 Holes: Weekday:** $35 w/cart        **Weekend:** $42 w/cart
**Twilight Rates:** After 5pm        **Discounts:** $15 after 5pm, $25 w/cart
**Car Rental:** $18pp/18, $10pp/9        **Driving Range:** No
**Lessons:** Yes  **Schools:** No        **Junior Golf:** Yes
**Membership:** Yes        **Architect/Yr Open:** William F. Mitchell/1957
**Other:** Clubhouse / Snack Bar / Restaurant / Bar-Lounge

Picturesque course set among hills, ponds, and streams. New cart path and bunkers. While not long, the holes demand good placement and are challenging. Renovated Clubhouse.

|  | 1 | 2 | 3 | 4 | 5 | 6 | 7 | 8 | 9 |
|------|---|---|---|---|---|---|---|---|---|
| PAR | 4 | 5 | 3 | 4 | 4 | 3 | 4 | 5 | 4 |
| YARDS | 354 | 592 | 170 | 309 | 312 | 147 | 340 | 484 | 348 |
|  | **10** | **11** | **12** | **13** | **14** | **15** | **16** | **17** | **18** |
| PAR | 3 | 4 | 4 | 5 | 4 | 4 | 4 | 4 | 3 |
| YARDS | 164 | 269 | 256 | 444 | 369 | 348 | 425 | 327 | 220 |

**Directions:** I-290 to Route 190 North. Take second exit (Holden). Go straight through lights, then bear right. Bear left at next light, up hill. Right on Main Street to Route 122A North. Course is 5 miles on right.

# Holyoke Country Club

NR ▶ **45**

Route 5 at Delaney House
Holyoke, MA (413) 534-1933
www.holyokecountryclub.com

| Tees | Holes | Yards | Par | USGA | Slope |
|------|-------|-------|-----|------|-------|
| BACK | | | | | |
| MIDDLE | 9 | 3495 | 36 | 71 | 118 |
| FRONT | 9 | 2723 | 37 | N/A | N/A |

**Club Pro:** Via Whightman, PGA
**Payment:** Visa, MC
**Tee Times:** S/S Members
**Fee 9 Holes: Weekday:** $12    **Weekend:** $12
**Fee 18 Holes: Weekday:** $20    **Weekend:** $20
**Twilight Rates:** No    **Discounts:** Please call
**Cart Rental:** $18pp/18, $9pp/9    **Driving Range:** No
**Lessons:** $30/45 min. **Schools:** Yes    **Junior Golf:** Yes
**Membership:** No    **Architect/Yr Open:** 1896
**Other:** Clubhouse / Lockers / Showers / Snack Bar / Restaurant / Bar-Lounge

Second hole is difficult with a quick green, hitting up 2 levels. If you are on the top level of the green, and flag is on the bottom, easy to bogey or double bogey.

| | 1 | 2 | 3 | 4 | 5 | 6 | 7 | 8 | 9 |
|------|-----|-----|-----|-----|-----|-----|-----|-----|-----|
| PAR | 4 | 4 | 4 | 4 | 5 | 4 | 4 | 3 | 4 |
| YARDS | 343 | 356 | 409 | 292 | 472 | 407 | 323 | 121 | 347 |
| PAR | | | | | | | | | |
| YARDS | | | | | | | | | |

**Directions:** I-91 to Exit 17A to traffic light. Turn left onto Route 5, approximately 2½ miles. At the Delaney Restaurant go through entrance, past restaurant 50 yards, then turn left to country club.

# Hopedale Country Club

✪✪✪ ▶ **46**

90 Mill Street
Hopedale, MA (508) 473-9876
www.hopedalecc.com

| Tees | Holes | Yards | Par | USGA | Slope |
|------|-------|-------|-----|------|-------|
| BACK | 9 | 3050 | 35 | 69 | 125 |
| MIDDLE | 9 | 2972 | 35 | 69 | 118 |
| FRONT | 9 | 2741 | 35 | 70.8 | 121 |

**Club Pro:** Craig Coombes, PGA
**Payment:** Visa, MC, Cash
**Tee Times:** No
**Fee 9 Holes: Weekday:** $20 before 3pm    **Weekend:** No public play
**Fee 18 Holes: Weekday:** $35 before 1pm M-Th    **Weekend:** No public play
**Twilight Rates:** No    **Discounts:** None
**Cart Rental:** $14pp/18, $7pp/9    **Driving Range:** No
**Lessons:** $40/half hour **Schools:** No    **Junior Golf:** Yes
**Membership:** Yes    **Architect/Yr Open:** Geoffrey Cornish/1953
**Other:** Clubhouse / Bar-Lounge / Snack Bar    **GPS:**

New clubhouse. 9 holes, 2 sets of tees. Public play welcome on weekdays, except holidays.

| | 1 | 2 | 3 | 4 | 5 | 6 | 7 | 8 | 9 |
|------|-----|-----|-----|-----|-----|-----|-----|-----|-----|
| PAR | 4 | 5 | 3 | 4 | 4 | 4 | 4 | 4 | 3 |
| YARDS | 374 | 508 | 140 | 371 | 362 | 316 | 304 | 381 | 216 |
| PAR | | | | | | | | | |
| YARDS | | | | | | | | | |

**Directions:** I-495 to Route 85 Milford. Turn right onto Route 85 and right onto Route 16 through center of Milford to Hopedale. At lights go left onto Hopedale Street to end. Take right onto Green Street to course.

# Indian Meadows Golf Club  ✪✪   47

275 Turnpike Road
Westboro, MA  (508) 836-5460
www.indianmeadowsgolf.com

| Tees | Holes | Yards | Par | USGA | Slope |
|------|-------|-------|-----|------|-------|
| BACK | 9 | 3265 | 36 | 71.7 | 124 |
| MIDDLE | 9 | 3019 | 36 | 69.4 | 119 |
| FRONT | 9 | 2468 | 36 | 67.0 | 107 |

**Club Pro:** Art Billingham
**Payment:** Cash, Visa, MC, Disc
**Tee Times:** 1 day adv.
**Fee  9 Holes: Weekday:** $20          **Weekend:** $22
**Fee 18 Holes: Weekday:** $30          **Weekend:** $32
**Twilight Rates:** After 5pm          **Discounts:** Sr & Jr (weekday only)
**Cart Rental:** $16pp/18, $8pp/9          **Driving Range:** No
**Lessons:** Yes  **Schools:** No          **Junior Golf:** Yes
**Membership:** Yes          **Architect/Yr Open:** Art Billingham/1990
**Other:** Restaurant / Clubhouse / Bar-Lounge / Snack Bar

Great atmosphere. Water on every hole. Shirts with collars required. Open April - December. Semi-private.

**CTRL/ WEST MA**

|  | 1 | 2 | 3 | 4 | 5 | 6 | 7 | 8 | 9 |
|------|---|---|---|---|---|---|---|---|---|
| PAR | 5 | 4 | 4 | 4 | 3 | 5 | 4 | 3 | 4 |
| YARDS | 451 | 340 | 420 | 316 | 136 | 455 | 415 | 173 | 313 |
| PAR | | | | | | | | | |
| YARDS | | | | | | | | | |

**Directions:** I-495 to Route 9 West (Turnpike Road). Follow Route 9 for 3 miles West to Westboro.

# Juniper Hill Golf Club (Lakeside) ✪✪✪½ 48

202 Brigham Street
Northboro, MA (508) 393-2444
www.juniperhillgc.com

| Tees | Holes | Yards | Par | USGA | Slope |
|------|-------|-------|-----|------|-------|
| BACK | 18 | 6289 | 71 | 70.3 | 126 |
| MIDDLE | 18 | 5378 | 71 | 66.0 | 117 |
| FRONT | 18 | 5272 | 71 | 70.5 | 118 |

**Club Pro:** Ken Chrzan, PGA
**Payment:** Visa, MC, Amex, Cash, Debit
**Tee Times:** 7 days adv.
**Fee  9 Holes: Weekday:** $23 Mon-Fri          **Weekend:** $26 S/S/H
**Fee 18 Holes: Weekday:** $40 Mon-Fri          **Weekend:** $45 S/S/H
**Twilight Rates:** No          **Discounts:** Before 1pm, Sr. & Jr. (M-F)
**Cart Rental:** $20pp/18, $13pp/9          **Driving Range:** Practice green
**Lessons:** Yes  **Schools:** Jr. & Sr.          **Junior Golf:** Yes
**Membership:** No          **Architect/Yr:** Phil Wogan, Homer Darling/1991
**Other:** Clubhouse / Lockers / Showers / Snack Bar / Bar-Lounge / Teaching Facility

18 holes of championship caliber with a lot of character. Collared shirts required. Noted for golf professional and friendly staff. Better year after year.

|  | 1 | 2 | 3 | 4 | 5 | 6 | 7 | 8 | 9 |
|------|---|---|---|---|---|---|---|---|---|
| PAR | 3 | 5 | 4 | 4 | 3 | 4 | 5 | 3 | 4 |
| YARDS | 187 | 524 | 313 | 392 | 169 | 314 | 522 | 146 | 307 |
|  | 10 | 11 | 12 | 13 | 14 | 15 | 16 | 17 | 18 |
| PAR | 4 | 4 | 4 | 4 | 3 | 5 | 4 | 5 | 3 |
| YARDS | 377 | 365 | 336 | 420 | 206 | 482 | 441 | 602 | 179 |

**Directions:** I-90 (Mass Pike) to I-495 North. Exit to Route 9 West and continue onto Route 135 West. Follow for 1.4 miles. Right onto Brigham Street. Follow for 1 mile to course.

# Juniper Hill Golf Club (Riverside) ✪✪✪½ 49

**202 Brigham Street**
**Northboro, MA (508) 393-2444**
www.juniperhillgc.com

| Tees | Holes | Yards | Par | USGA | Slope |
|------|-------|-------|-----|------|-------|
| BACK | 18 | 6245 | 71 | 70.5 | 126 |
| MIDDLE | 18 | 5379 | 71 | 66.0 | 117 |
| FRONT | 18 | 5272 | 71 | 70.5 | 118 |

**Club Pro:** Ken Chrzan, PGA
**Payment:** Visa, MC, Amex, Cash, Debit
**Tee Times:** 7 days adv.
**Fee 9 Holes: Weekday:** $23 Mon-Fri  **Weekend:** $26 S/S/H
**Fee 18 Holes: Weekday:** $40 Mon-Fri  **Weekend:** $45 S/S/H
**Twilight Rates:** No  **Discounts:** Before 1pm, Sr. & Jr. (M-F)
**Cart Rental:** $20pp/18, $13pp/9  **Driving Range:** Practice green
**Lessons:** Yes  **Schools:** Jr. & Sr.  **Junior Golf:** Yes
**Membership:** No
**Architect/Yr Open:** Homer Darling & Geoff Cornish/1931
**Other:** Clubhouse / Lockers / Showers / Snack Bar / Bar-Lounge / Teaching Facility

Player comments: "36 holes well-maintained for public play." "Some open fairways are inviting for your driver. Lots of variety." "Short overall but that doesn't mean easy. Number 17 is a dangerous and daunting par 3." Continually upgrading the facilities.

| | 1 | 2 | 3 | 4 | 5 | 6 | 7 | 8 | 9 |
|---|---|---|---|---|---|---|---|---|---|
| PAR | 4 | 4 | 5 | 4 | 3 | 4 | 3 | 4 | 4 |
| YARDS | 370 | 336 | 495 | 387 | 193 | 330 | 156 | 405 | 350 |
| | 10 | 11 | 12 | 13 | 14 | 15 | 16 | 17 | 18 |
| PAR | 5 | 4 | 4 | 4 | 4 | 3 | 4 | 3 | 5 |
| YARDS | 490 | 391 | 367 | 381 | 371 | 157 | 391 | 220 | 476 |

**Directions:** I-90 (Mass Pike) to I-495 North. Exit to Route 9 West and continue onto Route 135 West. Follow for 1.4 miles. Right onto Brigham Street. Follow for 1 mile to course.

# Kettle Brook Golf Club ✪✪✪½ 50

**136 Marshall Street**
**Paxton, MA (508) 799-4653**
www.kettlebrookgolfclub.com

| Tees | Holes | Yards | Par | USGA | Slope |
|------|-------|-------|-----|------|-------|
| BACK | 18 | 6912 | 72 | 73.1 | 125 |
| MIDDLE | 18 | 6203 | 72 | 70.3 | 121 |
| FRONT | 18 | 5105 | 72 | 70.2 | 118 |

**Club Pro:** Nick Marrone, PGA
**Payment:** Visa, MC, Amex, Cash, Checks
**Tee Times:** 7 days adv.
**Fee 9/12 Holes: Weekday:** $35 w/cart  **Weekend:**
**Fee 18 Holes: Weekday:** $55 w/cart M-F  **Weekend:** $60 w/cart
**Twilight Rates:** After 2pm  **Discounts:** Senior & Junior
**Cart Rental:** $18pp  **Driving Range:** No
**Lessons:** No  **Schools:** No  **Junior Golf:** No
**Membership:** Inner club  **Architect/Yr Open:** Brian Silva/1999
**Other:** Clubhouse / Bar / Snack Bar / Function Room for Outings

Player Comments: "Very good course—another Brian Silva gem. 3 of the best opening holes and 2 of the best closing holes anywhere." "Challenging but fun. Playable and friendly." "Awesome test of golf. Plays tougher than the slope rating. All they lack is a practice range."

| | 1 | 2 | 3 | 4 | 5 | 6 | 7 | 8 | 9 |
|---|---|---|---|---|---|---|---|---|---|
| PAR | 4 | 5 | 4 | 4 | 4 | 3 | 5 | 3 | 4 |
| YARDS | 366 | 522 | 359 | 327 | 339 | 170 | 485 | 132 | 452 |
| | 10 | 11 | 12 | 13 | 14 | 15 | 16 | 17 | 18 |
| PAR | 4 | 5 | 3 | 4 | 5 | 4 | 4 | 3 | 4 |
| YARDS | 346 | 485 | 164 | 251 | 481 | 338 | 379 | 196 | 411 |

**Directions:** I-290, exit to Route 9 to Worcester Center. Follow signs to Worcester airport. Take left off of Route 122 into airport rotary. First right to Bailey Street. Go 3 miles - course on right.

# Ledges Golf Club ✪✪½ 51 ▶

**18 Mulligan Drive**
**South Hadley, MA** (413) 532-2307
www.ledgesgc.com

**Club Pro:** Jim Falco, PGA
**Payment:** Visa, MC, Amex, Disc
**Tee Times:** 7 days adv.

| Tees | Holes | Yards | Par | USGA | Slope |
|------|-------|-------|-----|------|-------|
| BACK | 18 | 6507 | 72 | 72.2 | 133 |
| MIDDLE | 18 | 6110 | 72 | 70.9 | 129 |
| FRONT | 18 | 5001 | 72 | 69.5 | 125 |

**Fee 9 Holes: Weekday:** $21
**Fee 18 Holes: Weekday:** $31
**Twilight Rates:** After 2pm Sat/Sun
**Cart Rental:** $11pp/18, $7pp/9
**Lessons:** Yes **Schools:** Yes
**Membership:** Yes
**Other:** Snack Bar / Bar / Restaurant

**Weekend:** $23
**Weekend:** $39
**Discounts:** Sr./Jr./Military/Student
**Driving Range:** No
**Junior Golf:** Yes
**Architect/Yr Open:** Howard Maurer/2001
**GPS:**

COUPON

Picturesque championship golf course. 78 strategically placed bunkers, 4 sets of tees. Well-maintained with thick rough and fast greens. New pro shop and a full-service restaurant.

|  | 1 | 2 | 3 | 4 | 5 | 6 | 7 | 8 | 9 |
|------|------|------|------|------|------|------|------|------|------|
| PAR | 4 | 4 | 3 | 4 | 5 | 4 | 3 | 4 | 5 |
| YARDS | 386 | 424 | 96 | 276 | 456 | 300 | 123 | 349 | 528 |
|  | 10 | 11 | 12 | 13 | 14 | 15 | 16 | 17 | 18 |
| PAR | 5 | 4 | 3 | 4 | 3 | 4 | 4 | 4 | 5 |
| YARDS | 564 | 405 | 215 | 397 | 176 | 270 | 273 | 372 | 500 |

**Directions:** I-91 to Exit 16. Follow signs for Route 202 toward South Hadley. At rotary, take 3rd right onto West Summit Street. Follow signs.

# Leicester Country Club ✪✪✪ 52 ▶

**1430 Main Street**
**Leicester, MA** (508) 892-1390
www.leicestercc.com

**Club Pro:** Cheryl Orrico, PGA
**Payment:** Visa, MC, Amex
**Tee Times:** 7 days adv.

| Tees | Holes | Yards | Par | USGA | Slope |
|------|-------|-------|-----|------|-------|
| BACK | | | | | |
| MIDDLE | 18 | 6026 | 70 | 69.8 | 126 |
| FRONT | 18 | 4559 | 70 | 67.4 | 121 |

**Fee 9 Holes: Weekday:** $20
**Fee 18 Holes: Weekday:** $30
**Twilight Rates:** After 6pm
**Cart Rental:** $16pp/18, $8pp/9
**Lessons:** No **Schools:** No
**Membership:** Yes
**Other:** Snack Bar / Bar-Lounge / Banquet Facility

**Weekend:** $24
**Weekend:** $36
**Discounts:** Junior
**Driving Range:** No
**Junior Golf:** Yes
**Architect/Yr Open:** 1864

COUPON

Noted for excellent greens and some new ladies tees. Pro customer service and very friendly.

|  | 1 | 2 | 3 | 4 | 5 | 6 | 7 | 8 | 9 |
|------|------|------|------|------|------|------|------|------|------|
| PAR | 4 | 5 | 3 | 4 | 4 | 4 | 3 | 4 | 3 |
| YARDS | 437 | 489 | 201 | 345 | 371 | 328 | 179 | 309 | 173 |
|  | 10 | 11 | 12 | 13 | 14 | 15 | 16 | 17 | 18 |
| PAR | 4 | 4 | 3 | 4 | 5 | 4 | 5 | 3 | 4 |
| YARDS | 314 | 317 | 165 | 411 | 545 | 403 | 515 | 183 | 341 |

**Directions:** I-90 (Mass Pike) to Exit 10 (Auburn). Take Route 12 West to Route 20 to Route 56 North. Follow Route 56 for 7 miles to Route 9. Turn left (west) at the light and continue for 1 mile. Club is on the right at the top of the hill ¼ mile past the Castle Restaurant.

# Links at Lancaster Golf, The

438 Old Union Turnpike
Lancaster, MA (978) 537-8922
www.lancastergolfcenter.com

| Tees | Holes | Yards | Par | USGA | Slope |
|------|-------|-------|-----|------|-------|
| BACK | | | | | |
| MIDDLE | 9 | 1125 | 27 | | |
| FRONT | | | | | |

**Club Pro:** Dennis Lanciani
**Payment:** Visa, MC, Amex, Disc, Checks
**Tee Times:**
**Fee 9 Holes: Weekday:** $10    **Weekend:** $13
**Fee 18 Holes: Weekday:** $13    **Weekend:** $16
**Twilight Rates:** No    **Discounts:** Senior & Junior
**Cart Rental:**    **Driving Range:** Yes
**Lessons:** $45/half hour **Schools:**    **Junior Golf:** League & Summer Program
**Membership:** Yes    **Architect/Yr Open:** Gurall and Cronin/1996
**Other:**    **GPS:**

*COUPON*

Our range is rated a top 100 in USA by Golf Range Association. New longer first hole. We welcome beginners and junior golfers every day. Seniors pay ½ price greens fees Monday until 3pm. Women pay ½ price greens fees Tuesday until 3pm. Junior rate is $8 M-F. Excellent range.

| | 1 | 2 | 3 | 4 | 5 | 6 | 7 | 8 | 9 |
|------|-----|-----|-----|-----|-----|-----|-----|-----|-----|
| PAR | 3 | 3 | 3 | 3 | 3 | 3 | 3 | 3 | 3 |
| YARDS | 133 | 69 | 98 | 64 | 150 | 206 | 170 | 105 | 130 |
| PAR | | | | | | | | | |
| YARDS | | | | | | | | | |

**Directions:** Exit 34 off Route 2.

# Meadows Golf Club, The

398 Deerfield Street
Greenfield, MA (413)773-9047
www.meadowsgreenfield.com

| Tees | Holes | Yards | Par | USGA | Slope |
|------|-------|-------|-----|------|-------|
| BACK | 9 | 2858 | 36 | 66.6 | 106 |
| MIDDLE | 9 | 2800 | 36 | 66.6 | 106 |
| FRONT | 9 | 2547 | 36 | 66.6 | 106 |

**Club Pro:**
**Payment:** Visa, MC
**Tee Times:** No
**Fee 9 Holes: Weekday:** $14    **Weekend:** $17
**Fee 18 Holes: Weekday:** $20    **Weekend:** $22
**Twilight Rates:** No    **Discounts:** Seniors every day
**Cart Rental:** $14pp/18, $10pp/9    **Driving Range:** No
**Lessons:** No **Schools:** No    **Junior Golf:** $10/14 yrs. old or under
**Membership:** Yes    **Architect/Yr Open:** 1933
**Other:** Bar-Lounge / Restaurant Open All Year    **GPS:**

*COUPON*

New ownership has implemented a 3 year improvement plan. Now offering Fling Golf and Kick Golf. Great golf course for beginners. Extremely friendly and helpful staff.

| | 1 | 2 | 3 | 4 | 5 | 6 | 7 | 8 | 9 |
|------|-----|-----|-----|-----|-----|-----|-----|-----|-----|
| PAR | 5 | 3 | 4 | 4 | 4 | 3 | 5 | 4 | 4 |
| YARDS | 475 | 155 | 320 | 280 | 255 | 135 | 470 | 365 | 345 |
| PAR | | | | | | | | | |
| YARDS | | | | | | | | | |

**Directions:** I-91 to Route 2. Take Route 5 South, through Greenfield Center. Course is 1½ - 2 miles on right after Greenfield Center.

# Mill Valley Golf Links ★★ 55

380 Mill Valley Road
Belchertown, MA (413) 323-4079
www.millvalleygolflinks.com

**Club Pro:**
**Payment:** MC, Visa
**Tee Times:** 1 day adv.
**Fee 9 Holes: Weekday:** $15
**Fee 18 Holes: Weekday:** $20
**Twilight Rates:** No
**Cart Rental:** $14pp/18, $7pp/9
**Lessons:** No **Schools:** Yes
**Membership:** Yes
**Architect/Yr Open:** Armstrong Golf Associates/1963
**Other:** Restaurant / Bar-Lounge / Clubhouse

**Weekend:** $15
**Weekend:** $25
**Discounts:** Sr., Jr. before 12pm, M-F
**Driving Range:** No
**Junior Golf:** Yes

**GPS:** Garmin

| Tees | Holes | Yards | Par | USGA | Slope |
|------|-------|-------|-----|------|-------|
| BACK | 18 | 6583 | 72 | 72.2 | 131 |
| MIDDLE | 18 | 6076 | 72 | 70.5 | 125 |
| FRONT | 18 | 5546 | 72 | 72.0 | 131 |

COUPON

Scenic challenging golf course with tree-lined fairways. 14th hole features 200 feet drop from tee to fairway. Play our double dog-leg 16th, and the 17th is the hardest par 4 in Western Massachusetts.

| | 1 | 2 | 3 | 4 | 5 | 6 | 7 | 8 | 9 |
|------|---|---|---|---|---|---|---|---|---|
| PAR | 3 | 4 | 4 | 4 | 4 | 4 | 5 | 4 | 4 |
| YARDS | 206 | 319 | 382 | 316 | 468 | 362 | 552 | 422 | 323 |
| | 10 | 11 | 12 | 13 | 14 | 15 | 16 | 17 | 18 |
| PAR | 5 | 5 | 4 | 4 | 3 | 4 | 4 | 4 | 3 |
| YARDS | 500 | 517 | 331 | 311 | 240 | 321 | 400 | 400 | 172 |

**Directions:** I-90 (Mass Pike) to Route 32 to Route 181 North. Course is about 2 miles on right.

# Monoosnock Country Club ★★★ 56

40 Monoosnock Avenue
Leominster, MA (978) 537-1872
www.monoosnockcountryclub.com

**Club Pro:** John M. Novak
**Payment:** Visa, MC
**Tee Times:** No
**Fee 9 Holes: Weekday:** $16
**Fee 18 Holes: Weekday:** $26
**Twilight Rates:** No
**Cart Rental:** $16pp/18, $8pp/9
**Lessons:** Yes **Schools:** Night classes
**Membership:** Yes
**Other:** Clubhouse / Restaurant / Bar-Lounge

**Weekend:** $18 after 2pm
**Weekend:** $30 after 2pm
**Discounts:** None
**Driving Range:** $11/jumbo, $6/large
**Junior Golf:** Yes
**Architect/Yr Open:** 1919
**GPS:**

| Tees | Holes | Yards | Par | USGA | Slope |
|------|-------|-------|-----|------|-------|
| BACK | | | | | |
| MIDDLE | 9 | 3051 | 35 | 69.5 | 120 |
| FRONT | 9 | 2823 | 36 | 71.0 | 115 |

Course is open to public play on Monday - Friday until 3pm (except holidays). The fairways are narrow and brooks cross through 5 holes. 2 new bunkers on 5th hole and greens are in great shape. Full practice area with grass tees. Open April 1 - November 30.

| | 1 | 2 | 3 | 4 | 5 | 6 | 7 | 8 | 9 |
|------|---|---|---|---|---|---|---|---|---|
| PAR | 4 | 5 | 4 | 3 | 3 | 5 | 4 | 3 | 4 |
| YARDS | 335 | 515 | 378 | 158 | 235 | 450 | 387 | 214 | 379 |
| PAR | | | | | | | | | |
| YARDS | | | | | | | | | |

**Directions:** Route 2 to Route 13 North. Go north 1 mile and take right onto Monoosnock Avenue. Follow to pro shop.

# Northfield Golf Club
✪✪½ 57 ►

31 Holton Street
East Northfield, MA
(413) 498-2432
www.northfieldgolfcourse.com
**Club Pro:**
**Payment:** Visa, MC, Amex
**Tee Times:** No
**Fee 9 Holes: Weekday:** $12
**Fee 18 Holes: Weekday:** $20
**Twilight Rates:** No
**Cart Rental:** $24pp/18, $12pp/9
**Lessons:** No **Schools:** No
**Membership:** Yes
**Other:** Snack Bar / Clubhouse

| Tees | Holes | Yards | Par | USGA | Slope |
|------|-------|-------|-----|------|-------|
| BACK |  |  |  |  |  |
| MIDDLE | 9 | 2760 | 36 | 66.2 | 121 |
| FRONT | 9 | 2405 | 36 | 68.0 | 121 |

**Weekend:** $15
**Weekend:** $25
**Discounts:** None
**Driving Range:** Net hitting area
**Junior Golf:** Yes
**Architect/Yr Open:** Alex Findlay/1912
**GPS:**

Challenging layout. Very difficult to shoot the course rating. Open April - November. "Terrific greens" –FP

|  | 1 | 2 | 3 | 4 | 5 | 6 | 7 | 8 | 9 |
|------|---|---|---|---|---|---|---|---|---|
| PAR | 5 | 4 | 4 | 4 | 5 | 3 | 3 | 4 | 4 |
| YARDS | 430 | 300 | 370 | 260 | 450 | 170 | 130 | 270 | 380 |
| PAR |  |  |  |  |  |  |  |  |  |
| YARDS |  |  |  |  |  |  |  |  |  |

**Directions:** I-91 to Route 2 East to Routes 10 and 63 North, 1 mile north of the center of Northfield. Take Holton Street, turn right into parking lot.

# Oak Ridge Golf Club
✪✪ 58 ►

850 South Westfield Street
Feeding Hills, MA (413) 789-7307
www.oakridgegc.com
**Club Pro:** Tony Strycharz
**Payment:** MC, Visa, Amex, Disc
**Tee Times:** 7 days adv.
**Fee 9 Holes: Weekday:** $17
**Fee 18 Holes: Weekday:** $26
**Twilight Rates:** After 2pm
**Cart Rental:** $14pp/18 $8pp/9
**Lessons:** Yes **Schools:** No
**Membership:** Yes
**Other:** Clubhouse / Lockers / Showers / Bar-Lounge / Snack Bar

| Tees | Holes | Yards | Par | USGA | Slope |
|------|-------|-------|-----|------|-------|
| BACK | 18 | 6702 | 70 | 72.2 | 124 |
| MIDDLE | 18 | 6390 | 70 | 70.2 | 121 |
| FRONT | 18 | 5297 | 70 | 70.8 | 124 |

**Weekend:**
**Weekend:** $35
**Discounts:** Senior weekdays
**Driving Range:**
**Junior Golf:** Yes
**Architect/Yr Open:** Tom Fazio/1974

Excellent condition, flowers throughout course make for a real New England beauty. Open March 1 to December 1. Reduced rates after 2pm on weekends.

|  | 1 | 2 | 3 | 4 | 5 | 6 | 7 | 8 | 9 |
|------|---|---|---|---|---|---|---|---|---|
| PAR | 4 | 4 | 4 | 3 | 4 | 5 | 4 | 3 | 4 |
| YARDS | 379 | 379 | 395 | 191 | 378 | 570 | 385 | 151 | 387 |
|  | 10 | 11 | 12 | 13 | 14 | 15 | 16 | 17 | 18 |
| PAR | 4 | 3 | 5 | 3 | 4 | 4 | 5 | 3 | 4 |
| YARDS | 431 | 195 | 559 | 176 | 352 | 363 | 493 | 200 | 406 |

**Directions:** I-91 to Exit 3 Agawam/Southwick. Take Route 57 West to end. Take left onto Route 187 South then first left at Oak Ridge sign. Course ¼ mile on right.

# Oak Ridge Golf Club-Gill

231 West Gill Road
Gill, MA (413) 863-9693
www.oakridgegolfclub.net

**Club Pro:** Janis Giverson, Manager
**Payment:** Visa, MC
**Tee Times:** No

| Tees | Holes | Yards | Par | USGA | Slope |
|------|-------|-------|-----|------|-------|
| BACK | 9 | 2952 | 36 | 68.7 | 117 |
| MIDDLE | 9 | 2861 | 36 | 68.7 | 117 |
| FRONT | 9 | 2595 | 36 | 70.0 | 117 |

**Fee 9 Holes: Weekday:** $14    **Weekend:** $16
**Fee 18 Holes: Weekday:** $18    **Weekend:** $22
**Twilight Rates:** No    **Discounts:** Senior & Junior
**Cart Rental:** $12pp/18, $8pp/9    **Driving Range:** No
**Lessons:** No **Schools:** No    **Junior Golf:** No
**Membership:** Yes    **Architect/Yr Open:** 1963
**Other:** Full Restaurant/Clubhouse / Bar-Lounge / New Deck for Patio Dining

Scenic rolling hills, well groomed. Special rates for seniors (60+) and weekdays prior to 11am. Open March - November.

| | 1 | 2 | 3 | 4 | 5 | 6 | 7 | 8 | 9 |
|-----|-----|-----|-----|-----|-----|-----|-----|-----|-----|
| PAR | 4 | 4 | 5 | 4 | 4 | 4 | 4 | 4 | 3 |
| YARDS | 290 | 319 | 481 | 364 | 300 | 329 | 410 | 240 | 128 |
| PAR | | | | | | | | | |
| YARDS | | | | | | | | | |

**Directions:** I-91 to Exit 27 East and follow signs to golf course.

# Pakachoag Golf Course

15 Upland Street
Auburn, MA (508) 755-3291
www.pakachoaggolfcourse.com

**Club Pro:** Doug Johnson, GM
**Payment:** Cash or Credit Card
**Tee Times:** Weekends & Holidays am only

| Tees | Holes | Yards | Par | USGA | Slope |
|------|-------|-------|-----|------|-------|
| BACK | | | | | |
| MIDDLE | 9 | 3255 | 36 | 70.0 | 119 |
| FRONT | | | | | |

**Fee 9 Holes: Weekday:** $17    **Weekend:** $20
**Fee 18 Holes: Weekday:** $28    **Weekend:** $34
**Twilight Rates:** No    **Discounts:** Senior & Junior
**Cart Rental:** $30/18, $15/9 per cart    **Driving Range:** No
**Lessons:** Yes **Schools:** No    **Junior Golf:** Yes
**Membership:** Yes    **Architect/Yr Open:** 1932
**Other:** Snack Bar    **GPS:**

Sig. Hole: #9, a dogleg left, has 3 ways to play. Short hitters - right of pond. Medium hitters - 180 yard carry. Big hitters - 270 yards over stone wall. "Nice greens, some very challenging holes." –GM

| | 1 | 2 | 3 | 4 | 5 | 6 | 7 | 8 | 9 |
|-----|-----|-----|-----|-----|-----|-----|-----|-----|-----|
| PAR | 4 | 4 | 4 | 3 | 5 | 4 | 4 | 3 | 5 |
| YARDS | 376 | 329 | 395 | 143 | 563 | 372 | 377 | 189 | 511 |
| PAR | | | | | | | | | |
| YARDS | | | | | | | | | |

**Directions:** From Route 20 to Greenwood Street to Upland Street. From I-290 use Auburn Street exit to Route 12 (Southbridge Street). Left at lights. ¼ mile right, take Burnap Street up hill to Pakachoag Street and go left. 2 miles to Upland Street.

# Pine Grove Golf Club  ✪✪  61 ▶

254 Old Wilson Road
Florence, MA (413) 584-4570
www.pinegrovegolfma.com

**Club Pro:** Gill Verillo, Manager
**Payment:** Cash Only
**Tee Times:** 1 day adv.
**Fee  9 Holes: Weekday:** $15
**Fee 18 Holes: Weekday:** $24
**Twilight Rates:** After 4pm
**Cart Rental:** $16pp/18, $8 pp/9 per cart
**Lessons:** Yes  **Schools:** Yes
**Membership:** Yes
**Other:** Clubhouse / Snack Bar / Bar-Lounge

| Tees | Holes | Yards | Par | USGA | Slope |
|------|-------|-------|-----|------|-------|
| BACK | | | | | |
| MIDDLE | 18 | 6115 | 72 | 69.0 | 122 |
| FRONT | 18 | 4890 | 72 | 68.4 | 110 |

**Weekend:** $18
**Weekend:** $27
**Discounts:** Senior & Junior
**Driving Range:** No
**Junior Golf:** No
**Architect/Yr Open:** 1972
**GPS:**

COUPON

A scenic and challenging 18 hole public golf course in a beautiful New England setting.

| | 1 | 2 | 3 | 4 | 5 | 6 | 7 | 8 | 9 |
|---|---|---|---|---|---|---|---|---|---|
| PAR | 4 | 5 | 5 | 3 | 4 | 3 | 4 | 4 | 4 |
| YARDS | 315 | 475 | 500 | 140 | 350 | 165 | 370 | 385 | 335 |
| | 10 | 11 | 12 | 13 | 14 | 15 | 16 | 17 | 18 |
| PAR | 4 | 3 | 4 | 4 | 5 | 3 | 4 | 5 | 4 |
| YARDS | 375 | 125 | 370 | 330 | 470 | 140 | 360 | 600 | 310 |

**Directions:** I-91 to Exit 18. Left off exit, Route 5 North about 1.5 miles to light. Left onto Route 9 West to next light. Straight through light, then bear left onto Route 66 for 3 miles, and bear left onto Wilson Road.

# Pine Knoll Par 3 Golf Course  ✪✪  62 ▶

380 Porter Road
East Longmeadow, MA
(413) 525-4444 x5

**Club Pro:**
**Payment:** Cash or Credit
**Tee Times:** No
**Fee  9 Holes:** No rate
**Fee 18 Holes: Weekday:** $12
**Twilight Rates:** No
**Cart Rental:** $2/pull
**Lessons:** Yes  **Schools:** No
**Membership:** No
**Other:** First Tee Facility

| Tees | Holes | Yards | Par | USGA | Slope |
|------|-------|-------|-----|------|-------|
| BACK | | | | | |
| MIDDLE | 18 | 1567 | 54 | | |
| FRONT | | | | | |

**Weekend:**
**Weekend:** $13
**Discounts:** Senior & Junior
**Driving Range:** Yes
**Junior Golf:** No
**Architect/Yr Open:** Ralph Fisk/1940
**GPS:**

COUPON

Easy walker. Great for short game practice. Very scenic. Open March - November. At Fenway Batting cages complex.

| | 1 | 2 | 3 | 4 | 5 | 6 | 7 | 8 | 9 |
|---|---|---|---|---|---|---|---|---|---|
| PAR | 3 | 3 | 3 | 3 | 3 | 3 | 3 | 3 | 3 |
| YARDS | 86 | 64 | 80 | 92 | 78 | 60 | 72 | 60 | 102 |
| | 10 | 11 | 12 | 13 | 14 | 15 | 16 | 17 | 18 |
| PAR | 3 | 3 | 3 | 3 | 3 | 3 | 3 | 3 | 3 |
| YARDS | 74 | 96 | 48 | 130 | 114 | 124 | 115 | 85 | 87 |

**Directions:** I-91 to Exit 4. Sumner Avenue (Route 21) East. Go to end of Sumner Avenue, bear right by McDonald's onto Allen Street. ½ mile to Porter Road. Left turn onto Porter to course entrance on left.

# Pine Ridge Country Club ✪✪½ 63 ▶

28 Pleasant Street
North Oxford, MA (508) 892-9188
www.pineridgegolf.net
**Club Pro:** Betty Donovan, LPGA
**Payment:** Visa, MC, Amex, Disc
**Tee Times:** 7 days adv.

| Tees | Holes | Yards | Par | USGA | Slope |
|------|-------|-------|-----|------|-------|
| BACK | 18 | 6041 | 71 | 70.0 | 121 |
| MIDDLE | 18 | 5763 | 71 | 68.3 | 117 |
| FRONT | 18 | 5333 | 71 | 69.6 | 116 |

**Fee 9 Holes: Weekday:** $17    **Weekend:** $20
**Fee 18 Holes: Weekday:** $24    **Weekend:** $34
**Twilight Rates:** After 5pm    **Discounts:** Senior & Junior
**Cart Rental:** $17pp/18, $10pp/9    **Driving Range:** No
**Lessons:** $50/hour  **Schools:** No    **Junior Golf:** No
**Membership:** Yes    **Architect/Yr Open:** Phil Wogan/1969
**Other:** Clubhouse / Lockers / Showers / Snack Bar / Restaurant / Bar-Lounge

COUPON

Tournament friendly. Great value. New outdoor patio with access to the lounge. Great course for business outings with complete amenities.

|  | 1 | 2 | 3 | 4 | 5 | 6 | 7 | 8 | 9 |
|------|---|---|---|---|---|---|---|---|---|
| PAR | 4 | 3 | 4 | 3 | 4 | 5 | 4 | 4 | 3 |
| YARDS | 295 | 144 | 437 | 161 | 382 | 390 | 330 | 358 | 148 |
|  | 10 | 11 | 12 | 13 | 14 | 15 | 16 | 17 | 18 |
| PAR | 4 | 3 | 5 | 4 | 5 | 3 | 4 | 4 | 5 |
| YARDS | 270 | 188 | 431 | 403 | 482 | 166 | 354 | 344 | 480 |

**Directions:** I-90 (Mass Pike) Exit 10 or I-290 Exit 6B. Route 20 West to Route 56 North, go right. Take Route 56 North for 1 mile, club on left.

# Pontoosuc Lake Country Club ✪✪ 64 ▶

Kirkwood Drive
Pittsfield, MA (413) 445-4217
www.pontoosuclakecc.com
**Club Pro:** Bob Dastoli, PGA
**Payment:** Cash, Check
**Tee Times:** Weekends & Holidays

| Tees | Holes | Yards | Par | USGA | Slope |
|------|-------|-------|-----|------|-------|
| BACK | | | | | |
| MIDDLE | 18 | 6207 | 70 | 68.1 | 114 |
| FRONT | | | | | |

**Fee 9 Holes: Weekday:** $18    **Weekend:** $20
**Fee 18 Holes: Weekday:** $25    **Weekend:** $29
**Twilight Rates:** After 5pm    **Discounts:** Jr. & Sr., weekdays only
**Cart Rental:** $12.50pp/18, $8pp/9    **Driving Range:** No
**Lessons:** Yes  **Schools:** No    **Junior Golf:** Yes
**Membership:** Yes    **Architect/Yr Open:** Wayne Stiles/1935
**Other:** Snack Bar / Bar-Lounge / Hot Dogs    **GPS:**

COUPON

Sig. Hole: #9 links hole with large mounds and hills leading to a highly elevated green. Considered moderately difficult. No one under 14 unless accompanied by an adult. Prices subject to change.

|  | 1 | 2 | 3 | 4 | 5 | 6 | 7 | 8 | 9 |
|------|---|---|---|---|---|---|---|---|---|
| PAR | 4 | 4 | 5 | 3 | 4 | 4 | 4 | 3 | 4 |
| YARDS | 367 | 295 | 597 | 137 | 372 | 284 | 404 | 223 | 361 |
|  | 10 | 11 | 12 | 13 | 14 | 15 | 16 | 17 | 18 |
| PAR | 4 | 3 | 4 | 4 | 3 | 5 | 3 | 4 | 5 |
| YARDS | 411 | 152 | 386 | 355 | 173 | 593 | 196 | 360 | 541 |

**Directions:** I-90 (Mass Pike) to Route 7 North to Hancock Road (left). Approximately 1 mile to Ridge Avenue (right), turn left on Kirkwood Drive.

**CTRL/ WEST MA**

# Quaboag Country Club

Route 32
Monson, MA (413) 267-5294
www.quaboagcountryclub.com

| Tees | Holes | Yards | Par | USGA | Slope |
|------|-------|-------|-----|------|-------|
| BACK | | | | | |
| MIDDLE | 9 | 2880 | 34 | 67.2 | 116 |
| FRONT | 9 | 2610 | 35 | 69.2 | 113 |

**Club Pro:** Greg Farland
**Payment:** Cash, Credit
**Tee Times:** 7 days adv.
**Fee 9 Holes: Weekday:** $18
**Fee 18 Holes: Weekday:** $25
**Twilight Rates:** After 2pm weekends
**Cart Rental:** $10pp/9, $15pp/18
**Lessons:** $40/half hour  **Schools:** No
**Membership:** $595/year
**Other:** Bar-Lounge / Banquet / Snack Bar / Lockers / Showers

**Weekend:** $30 w/cart
**Weekend:** $45 w/cart
**Discounts:** Senior & Junior
**Driving Range:** No
**Junior Golf:** Yes
**Architect/Yr Open:** 1900

COUPON

Course is over 100 years old. Brimfield Flea Market and the Big "E" are area attractions.

| | 1 | 2 | 3 | 4 | 5 | 6 | 7 | 8 | 9 |
|------|-----|-----|-----|-----|-----|-----|-----|-----|-----|
| PAR | 4 | 3 | 4 | 4 | 4 | 4 | 4 | 3 | 4 |
| YARDS | 350 | 225 | 435 | 430 | 360 | 350 | 250 | 130 | 350 |
| PAR | | | | | | | | | |
| YARDS | | | | | | | | | |

**Directions:** I-90 to Exit 8 in Palmer. Turn right onto Route 32 South. Go 2 lights, turn left. Go 3 miles to golf course on right.

# Quail Hollow Golf & CC

1822 Old Turnpike Road
Oakham, MA (508) 882-5516
www.quailhollowgolf.net

| Tees | Holes | Yards | Par | USGA | Slope |
|------|-------|-------|-----|------|-------|
| BACK | 18 | 5809 | 70 | 68.6 | 123 |
| MIDDLE | 18 | 5439 | 70 | 67.0 | 120 |
| FRONT | 18 | 4441 | 70 | 68.9 | 120 |

**Club Pro:** Larry Hanch
**Payment:** Visa, MC, Cash
**Tee Times:** Recommended
**Fee 9 Holes: Weekday:** $12
**Fee 18 Holes: Weekday:** $17
**Twilight Rate:** No
**Cart Rental:** $16pp/18, $8pp/9
**Lessons:** Yes  **Schools:** No
**Membership:** Yes
**Other:** Clubhouse/ Bar-Lounge / Snack Bar

**Weekend:** $17
**Weekend:** $26
**Discounts:** Junior
**Driving Range:** Yes
**Junior Golf:** Yes
**Architect/Yr Open:** Philip Wogan/1990
**GPS:** Yes - Skycaddie

Cart paths are complete. Beautiful view. Hole #10 is a great short par 4. Super early morning weekday specials.

| | 1 | 2 | 3 | 4 | 5 | 6 | 7 | 8 | 9 |
|------|-----|-----|-----|-----|-----|-----|-----|-----|-----|
| PAR | 4 | 4 | 4 | 3 | 5 | 3 | 4 | 4 | 4 |
| YARDS | 302 | 315 | 249 | 182 | 510 | 487 | 410 | 300 | 331 |
| | 10 | 11 | 12 | 13 | 14 | 15 | 16 | 17 | 18 |
| PAR | 4 | 3 | 4 | 4 | 4 | 4 | 5 | 3 | 4 |
| YARDS | 351 | 177 | 376 | 371 | 363 | 420 | 510 | 130 | 325 |

**Directions:** I-290 to Worcester to Route 122 North to Oakham to Old Turnpike Road. Course is 3.5 miles off Route 122.

# Ranch Golf Club, The ✪✪✪✪  67

65 Sunnyside Road
Southwick, MA  (413) 569-9333
www.theranchgolfclub.com

| Tees | Holes | Yards | Par | USGA | Slope |
|---|---|---|---|---|---|
| BACK | 18 | 7174 | 72 | 75.0 | 139 |
| MIDDLE | 18 | 6103 | 72 | 69.6 | 130 |
| FRONT | 18 | 4983 | 72 | 69.7 | 125 |

**Club Pro:** Bill Rosemblum, PGA
**Payment:** Visa, MC, Amex, Checks, Cash
**Tee Times:** 7 days adv.
**Fee  9 Holes: Weekday:** $35       **Weekend:** $40
**Fee 18 Holes: Weekday:** $55 M-Th   **Weekend:** $75 F/S/S/H
**Twilight Rates:** After 2pm        **Discounts:** Senior & Junior
**Cart Rental:** $20pp/18; $15pp/9   **Driving Range:** Yes
**Lessons:** $45/30min., $80/50min.  **Schools:** Jr. **Junior Golf:** Yes
**Membership:** Yes                  **Architect/Yr Open:** Damian Pacuzzo/2001
**Other:** Clubhouse / Lockers / Showers / Bar-Lounge / Restaurant / Golf Shop
**GPS:** Yes

*COUPON*

One of *Golf Digest's* "Best Places to Play". Great condition, great layout, great service — great fun!

CTRL/
WEST
MA

|  | 1 | 2 | 3 | 4 | 5 | 6 | 7 | 8 | 9 |
|---|---|---|---|---|---|---|---|---|---|
| PAR | 5 | 4 | 4 | 4 | 3 | 4 | 4 | 3 | 5 |
| YARDS | 480 | 341 | 365 | 404 | 146 | 334 | 369 | 180 | 502 |
|  | 10 | 11 | 12 | 13 | 14 | 15 | 16 | 17 | 18 |
| PAR | 4 | 3 | 3 | 5 | 4 | 4 | 5 | 3 | 4 |
| YARDS | 406 | 366 | 181 | 540 | 419 | 357 | 578 | 170 | 404 |

**Directions:** I-90 (Mass Pike) to Exit 3. Go South on Routes 10/202 to Southwick. After Southwick
Country Club, take right on Sunnyside Road. Club is 1 mile on left.

# Red Tail Golf Club ✪✪✪✪✪ 68

15 Bulge Road
Devens, MA  (978) 772-3273
www.redtailgolf.net

| Tees | Holes | Yards | Par | USGA | Slope |
|---|---|---|---|---|---|
| BACK | 18 | 7006 | 72 | 72.7 | 135 |
| MIDDLE | 18 | 6292 | 72 | 68.5 | 126 |
| FRONT | 18 | 5049 | 72 | 69.2 | 123 |

**Club Pro:** Jim Pavlik, PGA
**Payment:** Visa, MC, Amex, Disc, Checks, Cash
**Tee Times:** 7 days adv.
**Fee  9 Holes: Weekday:**              **Weekend:**
**Fee 18 Holes: Weekday:** $89 cart incl. M-Th  **Weekend:** $105 cart incl. F/S/S
**Twilight Rates:** After 2pm           **Discounts:** Senior (62+) $59 cart incl. M-Th
**Cart Rental:** Yes                    **Driving Range:** Yes
**Lessons:** Yes **Schools:** Sr. & Jr.  **Junior Golf:** Yes
**Membership:** No                      **Architect/Yr:** Brian Silva/2002
**Other:** Bar-Lounge / Restaurants / Clubhouse / Showers / Spring Hill Suites - Devens
**GPS:**

Site of 2009 U.S.G.A. Women's Amateur National Public Links Championship, the 2015 and 2016
MGA Amateur Public Links Championship and the 2017 MGA Senior Four Ball State Championship.
"Top 50 Public Course in America," *Golf World*. A true championship course.

|  | 1 | 2 | 3 | 4 | 5 | 6 | 7 | 8 | 9 |
|---|---|---|---|---|---|---|---|---|---|
| PAR | 4 | 5 | 3 | 5 | 3 | 4 | 4 | 4 | 4 |
| YARDS | 354 | 516 | 170 | 512 | 161 | 331 | 400 | 306 | 374 |
|  | 10 | 11 | 12 | 13 | 14 | 15 | 16 | 17 | 18 |
| PAR | 5 | 3 | 4 | 4 | 4 | 3 | 4 | 4 | 5 |
| YARDS | 507 | 154 | 352 | 342 | 380 | 157 | 329 | 385 | 499 |

**Directions:** I-495 to Route 2 West to Jackson Road, Devens exit. North on Jackson Road to Patton
Road. Right on Patton Road to Bulge Road. Left on Bulge to clubhouse.

# Settlers Crossing Golf Course   ✪½  69

994 Northfield Road
Lunenburg, MA  (978) 582-6694
www.settlersgolf.com

Club Pro: Don Lyons, PGA
Payment: Visa, MC, Amex, Disc, Cash
Tee Times:
Fee  9 Holes: Weekday: $16
Fee 18 Holes: Weekday: $26
Twilight Rates: After 6pm
Cart Rental: $15pp/18, $9 pp/9
Lessons: $45/40 min.  Schools: No
Membership: Yes:

| Tees | Holes | Yards | Par | USGA | Slope |
|------|-------|-------|-----|------|-------|
| BACK | | | | | |
| MIDDLE | 9 | 2685 | 35 | 63.9 | 106 |
| FRONT | 9 | 2520 | 35 | 66.5 | 105 |

Weekend: $18
Weekend: $28
Discounts: Senior/Junior/Military
Driving Range: No
Junior Golf: Yes
Architect/Yr Open: 1961

Other: Clubhouse / Snack Bar / Restaurant / Bar-Lounge / Putting Course

Junior and family friendly. "Friendly staff, new management. Improvements ongoing." –GM

| | 1 | 2 | 3 | 4 | 5 | 6 | 7 | 8 | 9 |
|-----|-----|-----|-----|-----|-----|-----|-----|-----|-----|
| PAR | 4 | 3 | 4 | 4 | 4 | 4 | 3 | 4 | 5 |
| YARDS | 230 | 130 | 350 | 320 | 310 | 340 | 175 | 350 | 490 |
| PAR | | | | | | | | | |
| YARDS | | | | | | | | | |

Directions: Route 2 to Route 13 North. Take right, ⅛ mile to top of hill. Take left back on Route 13 North, go 2 miles to Northfield Road. Take left, go 1 mile. Clubhouse on right.

# Shaker Farms Country Club   ✪✪  70

866 Shaker Road
Westfield, MA (413) 568-4087
www.shakerfarmscc.com

Club Pro: Eric Nelson, PGA
Payment: Visa, MC, Amex, Check
Tee Times: 1-7 days adv.

| Tees | Holes | Yards | Par | USGA | Slope |
|------|-------|-------|-----|------|-------|
| BACK | 18 | 6285 | 72 | 69.4 | 119 |
| MIDDLE | 18 | 6096 | 72 | 68.3 | 116 |
| FRONT | 18 | 5271 | 72 | 70.2 | 119 |

Fee  9 Holes: Weekday: $15 walk, $21 ride
Fee 18 Holes: Weekday: $21 walk, $29 ride
Twilight Rates: After 5pm
Cart Rental: Included
Lessons: Yes  Schools: Yes
Membership: Yes
Other: Restaurant / Clubhouse / Lockers / Showers / Bar-Lounge
GPS:

Weekend: $17 walk, $25 ride
Weekend: $25 walk, $36 ride
Discounts: Junior
Driving Range: Yes
Junior Golf: Yes
Architect/Yr Open: Geoffrey Cornish/1953

Each hole has its own personality with natural slopes, breathtaking scenery, doglegs, and strategically placed bunkers. The back 9 is Cornish at his very best.

| | 1 | 2 | 3 | 4 | 5 | 6 | 7 | 8 | 9 |
|-----|-----|-----|-----|-----|-----|-----|-----|-----|-----|
| PAR | 5 | 4 | 4 | 5 | 4 | 5 | 3 | 4 | 3 |
| YARDS | 510 | 340 | 329 | 461 | 388 | 577 | 215 | 375 | 156 |
| | 10 | 11 | 12 | 13 | 14 | 15 | 16 | 17 | 18 |
| PAR | 4 | 4 | 3 | 4 | 3 | 4 | 4 | 5 | 4 |
| YARDS | 311 | 360 | 140 | 314 | 137 | 342 | 405 | 447 | 290 |

Directions: I-90 (Mass Pike) to Exit 3 Westfield. Follow Routes 10 and 202 South to Route 20. Stay on Route 20 East passing Westfield shops. Turn right on Route 187 at blinking light. Follow to course.

# Shaker Hills Country Club ✪✪✪✪✪

146 Shaker Road
Harvard, MA (978) 772-3330 x1
www.shakerhills.com

**Club Pro:** Andy Jordan, PGA
**Payment:** MC, Visa, Amex, Disc, Cash
**Tee Times:** 7 days adv.

| Tees | Holes | Yards | Par | USGA | Slope |
|------|-------|-------|-----|------|-------|
| BACK | 18 | 6952 | 72 | 74.0 | 136 |
| MIDDLE | 18 | 6020 | 72 | 71.2 | 126 |
| FRONT | 18 | 5100 | 72 | 69.4 | 126 |

**Fee 9 Holes:** $45 Mon.-Thurs.
**Fee 18 Holes: Weekday:** $75
**Twilight Rates:** After 12pm
**Cart Rental:** Included
**Lessons:** Yes  **Schools:** No
**Membership:** Available
**Other:** Clubhouse / Restaurant / Bar-Lounge / Lockers / Showers

**Weekend:** $45 after 12pm
**Weekend:** $89
**Discounts:** Senior, Junior, Military
**Driving Range:** Yes, $6/bucket
**Junior Golf:** No
**Architect/Yr Open:** Silva & Mungeam/1991

**CTRL/
WEST
MA**

A true test at golf for players of all abilities. Tremendous new renovations to the 18th hole and clubhouse. Great conditions and a great layout. Shaker Hill staff makes everyone feel like a member at a private course for the day. Check out Shaker Hills' unique 10 play discount.

| | 1 | 2 | 3 | 4 | 5 | 6 | 7 | 8 | 9 |
|---|---|---|---|---|---|---|---|---|---|
| **PAR** | 4 | 5 | 3 | 4 | 5 | 3 | 4 | 4 | 4 |
| **YARDS** | 342 | 506 | 186 | 449 | 558 | 172 | 333 | 390 | 347 |
| | **10** | **11** | **12** | **13** | **14** | **15** | **16** | **17** | **18** |
| **PAR** | 4 | 4 | 4 | 3 | 4 | 5 | 3 | 4 | 5 |
| **YARDS** | 396 | 387 | 380 | 149 | 300 | 538 | 224 | 315 | 537 |

**Directions:** I-495 to Exit 30 (Route 2A West). 4 miles left onto Shaker Road. Course is ½ mile on left.

# Skyline Country Club

NR  **72**

405 South Main Street (Route 7)
Lanesborough, MA (413) 445-5584
www.skyline-cc.com

**Club Pro:** Jim Mitus
**Payment:** MC, Visa, Cash
**Tee Times:** 1 week adv.

| Tees | Holes | Yards | Par | USGA | Slope |
|------|-------|-------|-----|------|-------|
| BACK | 18 | 6250 | 71 | 68.8 | 117 |
| MIDDLE | 18 | 6100 | 72 | 66.9 | 113 |
| FRONT | 18 | 4900 | 71 | 67.5 | 114 |

**Fee 9 Holes: Weekday:** $16
**Fee 18 Holes: Weekday:** $25
**Twilight Rates:** After 3pm
**Cart Rental:** $15pp/18, $8pp/9 per cart
**Lessons:** $40/half hour  **Schools:** No
**Membership:** Yes
**Other:** Snack Bar / Bar-Lounge

**Weekend:** $17
**Weekend:** $27
**Discounts:** None
**Driving Range:** Yes
**Junior Golf:** Yes
**Architect/Yr Open:** Rowland Armacost/1962
**GPS:**

The course is somewhat hilly; considered moderately difficult.

| | 1 | 2 | 3 | 4 | 5 | 6 | 7 | 8 | 9 |
|---|---|---|---|---|---|---|---|---|---|
| **PAR** | 4 | 5 | 3 | 4 | 4 | 4 | 3 | 5 | 4 |
| **YARDS** | 369 | 487 | 127 | 331 | 363 | 390 | 196 | 540 | 379 |
| | **10** | **11** | **12** | **13** | **14** | **15** | **16** | **17** | **18** |
| **PAR** | 4 | 3 | 5 | 4 | 4 | 3 | 5 | 4 | 4 |
| **YARDS** | 395 | 167 | 490 | 343 | 295 | 167 | 432 | 362 | 379 |

**Directions:** I-90 (Mass Pike) to Exit 2 (Lee). Go North on Route 7. Course is approximately 20 miles on right.

# Southampton Country Club ✪✪½  73 ▶

329 College Highway (Route 10)
Southampton, MA  (413) 527-9815

| Tees | Holes | Yards | Par | USGA | Slope |
|------|-------|-------|-----|------|-------|
| BACK | 18 | 6585 | 72 | 72.6 | 126 |
| MIDDLE | 18 | 6135 | 72 | 69.1 | 120 |
| FRONT | 18 | 5422 | 72 | 66.6 | 116 |

**Club Pro:** Dennis Nolan, GM
**Payment:** Cash, Check
**Tee Times:** S/S 1 wk. adv.
**Fee 9 Holes: Weekday:** $13       **Weekend:** $16
**Fee 18 Holes: Weekday:** $19      **Weekend:** $26
**Twilight Rates:** After 4pm       **Discounts:** None
**Cart Rental:** $14pp/18, $8pp/9   **Driving Range:** No
**Lessons:** No  **Schools:** No    **Junior Golf:** No
**Membership:** Yes                 **Architect/Yr Open:** John Strychary/1950
**Other:** Snack Bar / Restaurant / Bar-Lounge   **GPS:**

Sig. Hole: #4, 165-yard par 3. This meticulously maintained course is moderately easy with large greens, rolling hills and panoramic views. Rated 3½ stars by *Golf Digest*. New clubhouse completed in 2010.

|  | 1 | 2 | 3 | 4 | 5 | 6 | 7 | 8 | 9 |
|--|---|---|---|---|---|---|---|---|---|
| PAR | 4 | 3 | 4 | 3 | 4 | 5 | 4 | 4 | 5 |
| YARDS | 325 | 165 | 380 | 165 | 310 | 455 | 400 | 390 | 460 |
|  | 10 | 11 | 12 | 13 | 14 | 15 | 16 | 17 | 18 |
| PAR | 3 | 5 | 5 | 3 | 4 | 4 | 4 | 4 | 4 |
| YARDS | 140 | 485 | 460 | 200 | 340 | 365 | 405 | 325 | 365 |

**Directions:** I-90 (Mass Pike) to Exit 3 West (Westfield exit). Take left onto Route 10/Route 202, course is 5 miles on right.

# Southwick Country Club ✪✪✪  74 ▶

739 College Highway
Southwick, MA  (413) 569-0136
www.southwickcountryclub.com

| Tees | Holes | Yards | Par | USGA | Slope |
|------|-------|-------|-----|------|-------|
| BACK |  |  |  |  |  |
| MIDDLE | 18 | 6100 | 71 | 64.8 | 102 |
| FRONT | 18 | 5570 | 71 | 64.7 | 103 |

**Club Pro:** Frank Powers, Manager
**Payment:** Cash, Credit Cards
**Tee Times:** 1 day adv.
**Fee 9 Holes: Weekday:** $15       **Weekend:** $20
**Fee 18 Holes: Weekday:** $22      **Weekend:** $26
**Twilight Rates:** After 6pm       **Discounts:** Senior & Junior
**Cart Rental:** $16pp/18, $9.50pp/9   **Driving Range:** No
**Lessons:** Yes  **Schools:** No   **Junior Golf:** Yes
**Membership:** Yes                 **Architect/Yr Open:** 1928
**Other:** Snack Bar / Restaurant / Lounge / Weekday Specials

COUPON

The other course in Southwick. The course is flat and wide open; considered an easy walker. Greens and course in excellent condition.

|  | 1 | 2 | 3 | 4 | 5 | 6 | 7 | 8 | 9 |
|--|---|---|---|---|---|---|---|---|---|
| PAR | 4 | 5 | 3 | 4 | 4 | 3 | 4 | 4 | 4 |
| YARDS | 410 | 525 | 175 | 400 | 430 | 120 | 325 | 300 | 355 |
|  | 10 | 11 | 12 | 13 | 14 | 15 | 16 | 17 | 18 |
| PAR | 5 | 4 | 4 | 4 | 3 | 4 | 4 | 4 | 4 |
| YARDS | 490 | 290 | 320 | 315 | 125 | 450 | 415 | 310 | 345 |

**Directions:** I-90 (Mass Pike) Exit 3, Westfield; turn right onto Route 202. Course is approximately 4 miles south of Westfield.

# St. Anne Country Club ✪✪½  75 ▶

781 Shoemaker Lane
Feeding Hills, MA (413) 786-2088
www.stannecc.com

| Tees | Holes | Yards | Par | USGA | Slope |
|------|-------|-------|-----|------|-------|
| BACK | 18 | 6608 | 72 | 70.8 | 120 |
| MIDDLE | 18 | 5927 | 72 | 69.5 | 118 |
| FRONT | 18 | 5566 | 72 | 70.0 | 118 |

**Club Pro:** Paul Napolitan
**Payment:** Most Major
**Tee Times:** 1 week adv.
**Fee 9 Holes: Weekday:** $18
**Fee 18 Holes: Weekday:** $23
**Twilight Rates:** No
**Cart Rental:** $28/18, $14/9 per cart
**Lessons:** Yes **Schools:** No
**Membership:** Open
**Other:** Snack Bar / Bar-Lounge

**Weekend:** $21
**Weekend:** $27
**Discounts:** Senior
**Driving Range:** No
**Junior Golf:** No
**Architect/Yr Open:** Joe Napolitan/1963
**GPS:**

**CTRL/ WEST MA**

"Looks and feels like an arboretum with overviews of the course from elevated tees and level fairways. Easy layout that is great for beginners." –GG

| | 1 | 2 | 3 | 4 | 5 | 6 | 7 | 8 | 9 |
|------|---|---|---|---|---|---|---|---|---|
| PAR | 4 | 4 | 3 | 4 | 5 | 4 | 4 | 5 | 3 |
| YARDS | 385 | 312 | 141 | 342 | 500 | 381 | 394 | 420 | 171 |
| | 10 | 11 | 12 | 13 | 14 | 15 | 16 | 17 | 18 |
| PAR | 4 | 3 | 4 | 4 | 4 | 3 | 5 | 4 | 5 |
| YARDS | 310 | 133 | 315 | 315 | 273 | 185 | 467 | 360 | 523 |

**Directions:** I-91 to Route 57 West to Route 187. Turn right. First right is Shoemaker Lane, The club is ½ mile on the right.

# St. Mark's Golf Club ✪✪ 76 ▶

32 Cordaville Road
Southborough, MA (508) 460-0946
www.stmarksgolfclub.com

| Tees | Holes | Yards | Par | USGA | Slope |
|------|-------|-------|-----|------|-------|
| BACK | | | | | |
| MIDDLE | 9 | 2905 | 35 | 67.1 | 117 |
| FRONT | 9 | 2670 | 35 | 67.1 | 117 |

**Club Pro:**
**Payment:** Cash or Credit
**Tee Times:** Weekends, Holidays
**Fee 9 Holes: Weekday:** $18
**Fee 18 Holes: Weekday:** $28
**Twilight Rates:** Yes
**Cart Rental:** $13pp/18, $8pp/9
**Lessons:** No **Schools:** No
**Membership:** Yes
**Other:** Leagues welcome

**Weekend:** $20
**Weekend:** $30
**Discounts:** Senior & Junior
**Driving Range:** Practice area
**Junior Golf:** No
**Architect/Yr Open:** 1895
**GPS:**

Scottish links styling, rolling terrain, long grass and sand pot bunkers, adjacent to scenic Sudbury reservoir.

| | 1 | 2 | 3 | 4 | 5 | 6 | 7 | 8 | 9 |
|------|---|---|---|---|---|---|---|---|---|
| PAR | 4 | 3 | 5 | 4 | 4 | 4 | 3 | 4 | 4 |
| YARDS | 325 | 155 | 445 | 345 | 375 | 335 | 195 | 320 | 410 |
| PAR | | | | | | | | | |
| YARDS | | | | | | | | | |

**Directions:** Route 9 to Route 85 North. Course is .8 mile after intersection.

# Taconic Golf Club

19 Meachum Street
Williamstown, MA (413) 458-3997
www.taconicgolf.com

| Tees | Holes | Yards | Par | USGA | Slope |
|---|---|---|---|---|---|
| BACK | 18 | 6808 | 71 | 73.5 | 136 |
| MIDDLE | 18 | 6410 | 71 | 72.1 | 127 |
| FRONT | 18 | 5143 | 71 | 71.4 | 122 |

**Club Pro:** Rick Pohle, PGA
**Payment:** Credit Cards, Checks, Cash
**Tee Times:** 7 days adv.
**Fee 9 Holes: Weekday:** No    **Weekend:** No
**Fee 18 Holes: Weekday:** $145 (incl. cart)    **Weekend:** $145 (incl. cart)
**Twilight Rates:** No    **Discounts:** None
**Cart Rental:** Included in greens fee    **Driving Range:** Yes
**Lessons:** $50/45 min. **Schools:**    **Junior Golf:** Yes
**Membership:** No    **Architect/Yr Open:** Stiles & Van Kleek/1896
**Other:** Clubhouse / Lockers / Showers / Snack Bar / Bar-Lounge

Player Comments: "Outstanding course. Worth high rating. Nice people. Course was in super shape."
"If you come to golf in Western New England or Eastern New York, you need to come to Taconic." –ER

| | 1 | 2 | 3 | 4 | 5 | 6 | 7 | 8 | 9 |
|---|---|---|---|---|---|---|---|---|---|
| PAR | 5 | 4 | 4 | 4 | 3 | 4 | 4 | 4 | 3 |
| YARDS | 470 | 355 | 383 | 346 | 157 | 356 | 368 | 382 | 167 |
| | 10 | 11 | 12 | 13 | 14 | 15 | 16 | 17 | 18 |
| PAR | 5 | 4 | 4 | 4 | 3 | 4 | 4 | 3 | 5 |
| YARDS | 498 | 449 | 363 | 377 | 152 | 426 | 430 | 221 | 510 |

**Directions:** Route 2 to Williamstown; left on Route 43 South; 3rd street on right.

# Tekoa Country Club

459 Russell Road
Westfield, MA (413) 568-1064
www.tekoacc.com

| Tees | Holes | Yards | Par | USGA | Slope |
|---|---|---|---|---|---|
| BACK | 18 | 6438 | 71 | 70.1 | 123 |
| MIDDLE | 18 | 5917 | 71 | 69.2 | 121 |
| FRONT | 18 | 5201 | 71 | 69.3 | 112 |

**Club Pro:** E.J. Altobello
**Payment:** Visa, MC, Amex, Disc
**Tee Times:** 7 days adv.
**Fee 9 Holes: Weekday:** $16    **Weekend:** $20
**Fee 18 Holes: Weekday:** $25    **Weekend:** $28
**Twilight Rates:** After 5pm    **Discounts:** Senior & Junior
**Cart Rental:** $10pp/18, $6pp/9    **Driving Range:** No
**Lessons:** $35/half hour, $50/hour **Schools:** No **Junior Golf:** Yes
**Membership:** Yes    **Architect/Yr Open:** Donald Ross/1923
**Other:** Clubhouse / Restaurant / Sports Bar / Banquet Facilities

Donald Ross design. Scenic views of Tekoa Mountain and Westfield River. Easy walking, short but challenging.

| | 1 | 2 | 3 | 4 | 5 | 6 | 7 | 8 | 9 |
|---|---|---|---|---|---|---|---|---|---|
| PAR | 4 | 4 | 3 | 5 | 4 | 3 | 5 | 4 | 4 |
| YARDS | 356 | 398 | 157 | 461 | 342 | 202 | 445 | 377 | 346 |
| | 10 | 11 | 12 | 13 | 14 | 15 | 16 | 17 | 18 |
| PAR | 4 | 3 | 5 | 4 | 5 | 4 | 3 | 4 | 3 |
| YARDS | 361 | 146 | 477 | 389 | 479 | 339 | 145 | 415 | 187 |

**Directions:** Take Mass Pike to Exit 3. Bear right onto Routes 10/202 South. Travel 2 miles into the center of Westfield. Bear right onto Route 20 West. Course is 2 miles on the right.

# Templewood Golf Course ✪✪½  79 ▶

160 Brooks Road
Templeton, MA (978) 939-5031
www.templewoodgolfcourse.com

**Club Pro:** John Ross
**Payment:** Visa, MC, Disc, Check, Cash
**Tee Times:** 1 week adv.
**Fee 9 Holes: Weekday:** $14
**Fee 18 Holes: Weekday:** $20
**Twilight Rates:** After 1pm
**Cart Rental:** $16pp/18, $12pp/9
**Lessons:** Yes **Schools:** No
**Membership:** Yes
**Other:** Clubhouse / Lounge / New Pavillion

| Tees | Holes | Yards | Par | USGA | Slope |
|------|-------|-------|-----|------|-------|
| BACK | 18 | 6067 | 70 | | |
| MIDDLE | 18 | 5691 | 70 | | |
| FRONT | 18 | 4882 | 70 | | |

**Weekend:** $22
**Weekend:** $35
**Discounts:** No
**Driving Range:** No - practice nets
**Junior Golf:** Yes
**Architect/Yr Open:** Cornish/Maurer/1998

COUPON

CTRL/
WEST
MA

Inspiring views of surrounding terrain. Panoramic view of Mt. Monadnock. Friendly staff. Beautiful course.

| | 1 | 2 | 3 | 4 | 5 | 6 | 7 | 8 | 9 |
|------|----|----|----|----|----|----|----|----|----|
| PAR | 5 | 3 | 4 | 3 | 5 | 4 | 3 | 4 | 4 |
| YARDS | 515 | 135 | 375 | 135 | 455 | 405 | 135 | 245 | 345 |
| | 10 | 11 | 12 | 13 | 14 | 15 | 16 | 17 | 18 |
| PAR | 5 | 3 | 4 | 4 | 3 | 4 | 3 | 4 | 5 |
| YARDS | 479 | 158 | 373 | 262 | 154 | 382 | 186 | 400 | 552 |

**Directions:** Route 2 to Exit 20. Follow Trailblazing signs.

# Thomas Memorial Golf & CC ✪✪ 80 ▶

29 Country Club Lane
Turners Falls, MA (413) 863-8003

**Club Pro:** Pam Pierney, GM
**Payment:** Visa, MC, Disc
**Tee Times:** No
**Fee 9 Holes: Weekday:** $15
**Fee 18 Holes: Weekday:** $21
**Twilight Rates:** No
**Cart Rental:** $12.50pp/18, $8.50pp/9
**Lessons:** **Schools:** No
**Membership:** Yes
**Other:** Bar-Lounge / Snack Bar

| Tees | Holes | Yards | Par | USGA | Slope |
|------|-------|-------|-----|------|-------|
| BACK | | | | | |
| MIDDLE | 9 | 2688 | 35 | 66.0 | 113 |
| FRONT | 9 | 2424 | 35 | 68.0 | 113 |

**Weekend:** $17
**Weekend:** $23
**Discounts:** None
**Driving Range:** No
**Junior Golf:** Yes
**Architect/Yr Open:** Walter B. Hatch/1959
**GPS:**

COUPON

Course layout is interesting: hilly, several blind holes, narrow fairways, and some water hazards, 2 holes have 2 separate greens.

| | 1 | 2 | 3 | 4 | 5 | 6 | 7 | 8 | 9 |
|------|----|----|----|----|----|----|----|----|----|
| PAR | 4 | 4 | 4 | 4 | 5 | 4 | 3 | 4 | 3 |
| YARDS | 360 | 323 | 235 | 280 | 460 | 352 | 128 | 256 | 145 |
| PAR | | | | | | | | | |
| YARDS | | | | | | | | | |

**Directions:** Route 2 to lights at Turners Falls. Turn South on Avenue A to Turners Falls, left on 3rd Street. Right on L Street. At fork, bear left onto Montague. Right onto Griswold. Course .25 mile on right.

# Townsend Ridge Country Club ✪✪✪✪ 81

40 Scales Lane
Townsend, MA (978) 597-8400
www.townsendridge.com

**Club Pro:** Derick Fors
**Payment:** Visa, MC, Amex
**Tee Times:** 7 days adv.

| Tees | Holes | Yards | Par | USGA | Slope |
|------|-------|-------|-----|------|-------|
| BACK | 18 | 6231 | 70 | 70.4 | 126 |
| MIDDLE | 18 | 5819 | 70 | 68.6 | 121 |
| FRONT | 18 | 4685 | 71 | 68.5 | 115 |

**Fee 9 Holes: Weekday:** $19       **Weekend:** $22 (after 12pm)
**Fee 18 Holes: Weekday:** $35      **Weekend:** $45
**Twilight Rates:** After 2pm wkdy; after 12pm wknd   **Discounts:** Sr., 55+ & Jr.,18-
**Cart Rental:** $20pp/18, $10pp/9   **Driving Range:** $5/sm, $8/lg
**Lessons:** $55/half hour; $95/hour  **Schools:** Yes  **Junior Golf:** Yes
**Membership:** Yes                   **Architect/Yr:** T. Manning & Mary Mills/1996
**Other:** Clubhouse / 19th Hole Lounge / Full Bar / Restaurant

COUPON

Picturesque and well groomed course. Challenging for players of all ability levels with a wide variety of holes ranging in difficulty. Gets better every year. Membership and outings encouraged!

| | 1 | 2 | 3 | 4 | 5 | 6 | 7 | 8 | 9 |
|---|---|---|---|---|---|---|---|---|---|
| PAR | 4 | 4 | 3 | 4 | 5 | 4 | 3 | 4 | 4 |
| YARDS | 312 | 375 | 126 | 390 | 469 | 308 | 156 | 349 | 351 |
| | 10 | 11 | 12 | 13 | 14 | 15 | 16 | 17 | 18 |
| PAR | 4 | 4 | 5 | 4 | 4 | 3 | 4 | 3 | 4 |
| YARDS | 375 | 377 | 460 | 328 | 407 | 135 | 367 | 170 | 364 |

**Directions:** I-495 to Exit 31. Go west on Route 119 for 15 miles. Take first left after Townsend Ford onto Scales Lane.

# Twin Springs Golf Club ✪✪ 82

295 Wilder Road
Bolton, MA (978) 779-5020
www.twinspringsgolf.com

**Club Pro:** Robert Keene, PGA
**Payment:** MC, Visa, Amex
**Tee Times:** 1 week adv.

| Tees | Holes | Yards | Par | USGA | Slope |
|------|-------|-------|-----|------|-------|
| BACK | | | | | |
| MIDDLE | 9 | 2592 | 34 | 64.8 | 113 |
| FRONT | 9 | 2432 | 35 | 67.2 | 106 |

**Fee 9 Holes: Weekday:** $16       **Weekend:** $18
**Fee 18 Holes: Weekday:** $24      **Weekend:** $28
**Twilight Rates:** No               **Discounts:** Sr. & Jr. wkdy; Jr. wknd
**Cart Rental:** $12.75pp/18, $7.75pp/9
**Driving Range:** Sm./$3.50, Med./$7, Jumbo/$10.50
**Lessons:** $60/hour  **Schools:** Yes    **Junior Golf:** Yes
**Membership:** Senior & Junior      **Architect/Yr Open:** 1932
**Other:** Snack Bar/ Range          **GPS:**

COUPON

Sig. Hole: #4 is a devilish par 3 with a great view of Wachusett Mountain, fronted by a creek. "Fun for all levels of golfers." –FP

| | 1 | 2 | 3 | 4 | 5 | 6 | 7 | 8 | 9 |
|---|---|---|---|---|---|---|---|---|---|
| PAR | 4 | 4 | 4 | 3 | 3 | 4 | 4 | 4 | 4 |
| YARDS | 327 | 294 | 300 | 140 | 161 | 318 | 368 | 320 | 384 |
| PAR | | | | | | | | | |
| YARDS | | | | | | | | | |

**Directions:** I-495 to Exit 27 to Route 117 West into center of Bolton. Go straight for .7 mile. Turn left up hill at Wilder Road. Course is 2 miles on right.

# Tyngsboro Country Club  ✪½  ▶ 83

48 Sherburne Avenue
Tyngsboro, MA  (978) 649-7334

| Tees | Holes | Yards | Par | USGA | Slope |
|------|-------|-------|-----|------|-------|
| BACK | 9 | 2590 | 35 | 65.2 | 104 |
| MIDDLE | 9 | 2397 | 35 | 63.2 | 104 |
| FRONT | 9 | 2023 | 35 | 62.6 | 97 |

**Club Pro:** Allan Pottle
**Payment:** Cash Only
**Tee Times:** 5 days adv. weekends
**Fee  9 Holes: Weekday:** $17
**Fee 18 Holes: Weekday:** $28
**Twilight Rates:** No
**Cart Rental:** $25/18, $14/9 per cart
**Lessons:** No  **Schools:** Yes
**Membership:** 7 day and weekday available
**Other:** Snack Bar / Bar-Lounge

**Weekend:** $19
**Weekend:** $31
**Discounts:** None
**Driving Range:** No
**Junior Golf:** No
**Architect/Yr Open:** 1933
**GPS:**

CTRL/ WEST MA

The course requires accurate shots and is easy to walk. Dress code required. Specials: Wednesday after 2pm - $12 for 9 holes; Tuesday, Thursday, and Friday after 6pm - $15 for 9 holes; Saturday and Sunday after 2pm - $15 for 9 holes.

|  | 1 | 2 | 3 | 4 | 5 | 6 | 7 | 8 | 9 |
|------|---|---|---|---|---|---|---|---|---|
| PAR | 4 | 4 | 3 | 5 | 3 | 5 | 4 | 4 | 3 |
| YARDS | 320 | 314 | 216 | 446 | 160 | 463 | 282 | 249 | 140 |

|  |
|------|
| PAR |
| YARDS |

**Directions:** I-95 to Route 3 North to Exit 35 (onto Route 113 East); go approximately 2.5 miles to course.

# Veteran's Memorial Golf Course  ✪✪½  ▶ 84

1059 South Branch Pkwy
Springfield, MA (413) 787-6449
www.veteransgolfcourse.com

| Tees | Holes | Yards | Par | USGA | Slope |
|------|-------|-------|-----|------|-------|
| BACK | 18 | 6433 | 72 | 71.7 | 126 |
| MIDDLE | 18 | 5901 | 72 | 68.7 | 121 |
| FRONT | 18 | 4810 | 72 | 68.3 | 121 |

**Club Pro:** Kevin Kennedy, PGA
**Payment:** Cash, Visa, MC
**Tee Times:** Wknd, call Wed.
**Fee  9 Holes: Weekday:**
**Fee 18 Holes: Weekday:** $24
**Twilight Rates:** After 3pm
**Cart Rental:** $14pp/18, $7pp/9
**Lessons:** Yes  **Schools:**
**Membership:** No
**Other:** Restaurant / Bar-Lounge

**Weekend:**
**Weekend:** $25
**Discounts:** Senior & Junior
**Driving Range:** No
**Junior Golf:** No
**Architect/Yr Open:** Geoffrey Cornish/1963
**GPS:**

Good value. Worth exploring.

|  | 1 | 2 | 3 | 4 | 5 | 6 | 7 | 8 | 9 |
|------|---|---|---|---|---|---|---|---|---|
| PAR | 4 | 4 | 5 | 4 | 3 | 4 | 3 | 4 | 5 |
| YARDS | 261 | 341 | 431 | 331 | 194 | 343 | 145 | 273 | 485 |
|  | **10** | **11** | **12** | **13** | **14** | **15** | **16** | **17** | **18** |
| PAR | 4 | 4 | 5 | 4 | 5 | 3 | 4 | 4 | 3 |
| YARDS | 362 | 405 | 498 | 345 | 472 | 166 | 288 | 324 | 157 |

**Directions:** I-95 (Exit 2), Sumner Ave. (3.8 miles), left on Bradley Road (0.4 miles). Right onto South Branch Parkway. Course is on left.

# Wachusett Country Club  ✪✪✪¹/₂  85 ▶

187 Prospect Street
West Boylston, MA (508) 835-2264
www.wachusettcc.com

**Club Pro:** Nick Marrone, PGA
**Payment:** Visa, MC, Amex, Disc
**Tee Times:** 7 days adv.

| Tees | Holes | Yards | Par | USGA | Slope |
|------|-------|-------|-----|------|-------|
| BACK | 18 | 6608 | 72 | 71.4 | 124 |
| MIDDLE | 18 | 6206 | 72 | 71.7 | 123 |
| FRONT | 18 | 5573 | 72 | 68.6 | 115 |

**Fee  9 Holes: Weekday:** $20/walk, $30/ride M-Th (9am-3pm)
**Fee 18 Holes: Weekday:** $40/walk, $57/ride  **Weekend:** $45/walk (after 12pm), $62/ride
**Twilight Rates:** After 3pm & before 9am M-F  **Discounts:** Jr. after 3pm M-F
**Cart Rental:** $17pp/18, $12pp/9  **Driving Range:** Yes
**Lessons:** Yes  **Schools:** Junior Camp  **Junior Golf:** Yes
**Membership:** Yes, wait list  **Architect/Yr Open:** Donald Ross/1927
**Other:** Snack Bar / Bar-Lounge / Banquet Facilities

Donald Ross design. Reduced rates after 3pm on weekdays. "Beautifully maintained with nice views. Definitely give this course a try." –FP

|  | 1 | 2 | 3 | 4 | 5 | 6 | 7 | 8 | 9 |
|------|---|---|---|---|---|---|---|---|---|
| PAR | 4 | 5 | 4 | 3 | 5 | 3 | 4 | 4 | 4 |
| YARDS | 388 | 518 | 380 | 145 | 507 | 175 | 360 | 436 | 426 |
|  | 10 | 11 | 12 | 13 | 14 | 15 | 16 | 17 | 18 |
| PAR | 5 | 4 | 4 | 3 | 4 | 5 | 4 | 4 | 3 |
| YARDS | 494 | 430 | 426 | 203 | 330 | 508 | 316 | 374 | 192 |

**Directions:** I-90 (Mass Pike) to I-290 to I-190, Exit 4 onto Route 12 North. Approximately 2 miles to Franklin Street, turn left. At end of road turn left onto Prospect.

# Wahconah Country Club  ✪✪✪  86 ▶

15 Orchard Road
Dalton, MA (413) 684-1333
www.wahconahcountryclub.com

**Club Pro:** Peter Egazarian, PGA
**Payment:** Cash, Check, Visa, MC
**Tee Times:** 5 days adv.

| Tees | Holes | Yards | Par | USGA | Slope |
|------|-------|-------|-----|------|-------|
| BACK | 18 | 6553 | 71 | 72.5 | 135 |
| MIDDLE | 18 | 6229 | 71 | 71.6 | 132 |
| FRONT | 18 | 5831 | 73 | 73 | 128 |

**Fee  9 Holes: Weekday:** $40  **Weekend:** $45
**Fee 18 Holes: Weekday:** $70  **Weekend:** $80
**Twilight Rates:** No  **Discounts:** None
**Cart Rental:** $15pp/18, 2 riders  **Driving Range:** $5/lg., $3/sm.
**Lessons:** $40/half hour  **Schools:** Yes  **Junior Golf:** Yes
**Membership:** Yes  **Architect/Yr Open:** Wayne Stiles/1930
**Other:** Clubhouse / Restaurant / Bar-Lounge / Landscaped Patio

A beautiful, very challenging, semi-private course with fast greens. Considered to be moderately difficult. Open April 15 - November 15. "Excellent conditions." –FP

|  | 1 | 2 | 3 | 4 | 5 | 6 | 7 | 8 | 9 |
|------|---|---|---|---|---|---|---|---|---|
| PAR | 4 | 3 | 4 | 4 | 4 | 3 | 5 | 4 | 4 |
| YARDS | 382 | 206 | 398 | 300 | 360 | 147 | 476 | 390 | 388 |
|  | 10 | 11 | 12 | 13 | 14 | 15 | 16 | 17 | 18 |
| PAR | 4 | 4 | 4 | 3 | 5 | 4 | 4 | 3 | 5 |
| YARDS | 368 | 340 | 371 | 203 | 480 | 349 | 430 | 177 | 458 |

**Directions:** I-90 (Mass Pike) to Exit 2. Follow Route 9 North from Amherst into Dalton. In Dalton, take left onto Orchard Road. Course is approximately ½ mile on left.

# Waubeeka Golf Links

✪✪✪✪½  ▶ 87

137 New Ashford Road (Route 7)
South Williamstown, MA
(413) 458-8355
www.waubeeka.com

| Tees | Holes | Yards | Par | USGA | Slope |
|------|-------|-------|-----|------|-------|
| BACK | 18 | 6403 | 71 | 71.0 | 124 |
| MIDDLE | 18 | 5972 | 71 | 68.8 | 121 |
| FRONT | 18 | 4845 | 70 | 68.1 | 112 |

**Club Pro:** Vicki Richardello, GM
**Payment:** Cash, Amex, MC, Visa, Disc
**Tee Times:** 7 days adv.
**Fee 9 Holes: Weekday:** $26    **Weekend:** $30
**Fee 18 Holes: Weekday:** $50    **Weekend:** $65
**Twilight Rates:** After 4pm, S/S/M/T    **Discounts:** Junior & Senior
**Cart Rental:** $20pp/18, $11pp/9
**Lessons:** $60/hour    **Driving Range:** New, plus practice facility
**Schools:** Jr./Women    **Junior Golf:** Yes
**Membership:** Yes    **Architect:** Redesign Mungeam 2009/2010
**Other:** Clubhouse / Lockers / Showers / Snack Bar / Restaurant / Bar-Lounge

COUPON

Well-groomed, scenic, Audubon Society member. Hosted the 2015 Public Links Qualifier. Hosted the 2016 MGA Amateur Public Links Championship. "Rolling hills with scenic views. Great condition." –GM

|  | 1 | 2 | 3 | 4 | 5 | 6 | 7 | 8 | 9 |
|------|-----|-----|-----|-----|-----|-----|-----|-----|-----|
| PAR | 4 | 4 | 3 | 5 | 4 | 4 | 3 | 5 | 4 |
| YARDS | 351 | 410 | 167 | 480 | 410 | 342 | 176 | 453 | 360 |
|  | 10 | 11 | 12 | 13 | 14 | 15 | 16 | 17 | 18 |
| PAR | 3 | 4 | 4 | 4 | 3 | 5 | 3 | 5 | 4 |
| YARDS | 197 | 386 | 340 | 305 | 138 | 515 | 145 | 485 | 318 |

**Directions:** I-90 (Mass Pike) to Exit 2 (Lee) to Route 20 North to Route 7 North. Go north about 45 minutes. Course is on left.

# Westborough Country Club

✪✪½  ▶ 88

121 West Main Street
Westborough, MA (508) 366-9947
www.westborocountryclub.com

| Tees | Holes | Yards | Par | USGA | Slope |
|------|-------|-------|-----|------|-------|
| BACK | 9 | 3172 | 36 | 35.5 | 123 |
| MIDDLE | 9 | 2978 | 36 | 34.3 | 119 |
| FRONT | 9 | 2706 | 36 | 33.3 | 115 |

**Club Pro:** Jack A. Negoshian, PGA
**Payment:** Visa, MC, Amex, Disc
**Tee Times:** Weekends/Holidays, call Friday
**Fee 9 Holes: Weekday:** $22    **Weekend:** $24
**Fee 18 Holes: Weekday:** $33    **Weekend:** $35
**Twilight Rates:** After 6pm    **Discounts:** Senior & Junior
**Cart Rental:** $18pp/18, $9pp/9    **Driving Range:** No
**Lessons:** Yes   Schools: No    **Junior Golf:** No
**Membership:** Yes    **Architect/Yr Open:** Howe/1921
**Other:** Restaurant / Bar-Lounge / Clubhouse / Showers/Pro Shop / Putting Course

COUPON

Expanded Fairways in front of greens for easy run-ups. Hilly Course.

|  | 1 | 2 | 3 | 4 | 5 | 6 | 7 | 8 | 9 |
|------|-----|-----|-----|-----|-----|-----|-----|-----|-----|
| PAR | 5 | 4 | 5 | 4 | 3 | 4 | 3 | 4 | 4 |
| YARDS | 412 | 262 | 491 | 325 | 169 | 345 | 150 | 409 | 415 |
| PAR |  |  |  |  |  |  |  |  |  |
| YARDS |  |  |  |  |  |  |  |  |  |

**Directions:** Route 9 to Route 30 toward Westborough. Take a right at the stop sign. Course is 1 mile past center of town on the right. From 495, Exit 23B, Route. 9 West - Worcester - right onto Route 30. West toward Westborough/North Grafton - straight through Rotary, club is 1 mile on right.

# Westminster Country Club ✪✪✪

## 89

**51 Ellis Road**
**Westminster, MA (978) 874-5938**
www.westminstercountryclub.com

| Tees | Holes | Yards | Par | USGA | Slope |
|------|-------|-------|-----|------|-------|
| BACK | 18 | 6512 | 71 | 71.8 | 125 |
| MIDDLE | 18 | 6250 | 71 | 70.6 | 123 |
| FRONT | 18 | 5079 | 70 | 69.3 | 115 |

**Club Pro:** Michael Leblanc
**Payment:** Most Major
**Tee Times:** 4 days adv.
**Fee 9 Holes: Weekday:** $15     **Weekend:** $35
**Fee 18 Holes: Weekday:** $30     **Weekend:** $35
**Twilight Rates:** No     **Discounts:** Sr. & Jr. during "off" hrs.
**Cart Rental:** $16pp/18, $8pp/9     **Driving Range:** No
**Lessons:** Yes **Schools:** No     **Junior Golf:** Yes
**Membership:** Yes     **Architect/Yr Open:** LeBlanc and Francis/1957
**Other:** Clubhouse / Lockers / Showers / Snack Bar / Restaurant / Bar-Lounge / Lodging Partner

A great blue collar golf course with exceptional value. Site of the 2014 MGA Mid-Amateur Qualifier. "Friendly and fair with a good mix of holes." –FP

| | 1 | 2 | 3 | 4 | 5 | 6 | 7 | 8 | 9 |
|---|---|---|---|---|---|---|---|---|---|
| PAR | 4 | 4 | 4 | 4 | 4 | 4 | 4 | 4 | 3 |
| YARDS | 400 | 396 | 344 | 384 | 353 | 339 | 333 | 312 | 173 |
| | 10 | 11 | 12 | 13 | 14 | 15 | 16 | 17 | 18 |
| PAR | 3 | 4 | 3 | 4 | 5 | 4 | 5 | 3 | 5 |
| YARDS | 131 | 381 | 224 | 452 | 532 | 340 | 548 | 157 | 451 |

**Directions:** Route 2 to Route 140 East. Take an immediate right after bridge, through Westminster Center. Follow 2 miles. Left onto Nichols. Bear right at fork onto Ellis. Course is 1 mile on right.

# Westover Golf Course ✪✪

## 90

**181 South Street**
**Granby, MA (413) 547-8610**
www.westovergolfcourse.com

| Tees | Holes | Yards | Par | USGA | Slope |
|------|-------|-------|-----|------|-------|
| BACK | 18 | 7025 | 72 | 74.0 | 131 |
| MIDDLE | 18 | 6610 | 72 | 71.9 | 129 |
| FRONT | 18 | 5580 | 72 | 71.9 | 117 |

**Club Pro:** Bill Kubinski, PGA
**Payment:** Cash, Visa, MC, Amex, Disc
**Tee Times:** 7 days adv.
**Fee 9 Holes: Weekday:** $16     **Weekend:** $19
**Fee 18 Holes: Weekday:** $23     **Weekend:** $26
**Twilight Rates:** After 4pm     **Discounts:** Senior & Junior
**Cart Rental:** $13pp/18, $8pp/9     **Driving Range:** Yes
**Lessons:** $45/50 min. **Schools:** No     **Junior Golf:** Yes
**Membership:** No     **Architect/Yr Open:** Orin Smith/1959
**Other:** Clubhouse / Lockers / Snack Bar / Bar-Lounge

Player Comments: "A great challenge for a reasonable price." Fantastic layout, very challenging. Dress code: no cutoffs or tank tops. Lessons for all ages and abilities. Open April 1 - December.

| | 1 | 2 | 3 | 4 | 5 | 6 | 7 | 8 | 9 |
|---|---|---|---|---|---|---|---|---|---|
| PAR | 4 | 4 | 4 | 3 | 4 | 4 | 5 | 3 | 5 |
| YARDS | 390 | 410 | 335 | 207 | 396 | 419 | 489 | 163 | 532 |
| | 10 | 11 | 12 | 13 | 14 | 15 | 16 | 17 | 18 |
| PAR | 3 | 4 | 5 | 3 | 4 | 4 | 4 | 4 | 5 |
| YARDS | 160 | 422 | 490 | 160 | 364 | 405 | 373 | 354 | 541 |

**Directions:** I-90 to Exit 5. Go left on Route 33 North, follow for approximately 5 miles to New Ludlow Road. Take right and go 3 miles to South Street.

# Winchendon Golf Club

**★★1/2**   **91**

435 Spring Street
Winchendon, MA (978) 297-9897
www.winchgolf.com

**Club Pro:** Tom Borden, PGA
**Payment:** Visa, MC, Check, Cash
**Tee Times:** 7 days adv.

| Tees | Holes | Yards | Par | USGA | Slope |
|------|-------|-------|-----|------|-------|
| BACK | 18 | 5512 | 70 | 67.8 | 122 |
| MIDDLE | 18 | 5348 | 70 | 67.2 | 119 |
| FRONT | 18 | 4693 | 72 | 70.5 | 124 |

**Fee  9 Holes: Weekday:** $15
**Fee 18 Holes: Weekday:** $22
**Twilight Rates:** After 2pm
**Cart Rental:** $17pp/18, $11pp/9
**Lessons:** Yes **Schools:** Yes
**Membership:** Yes
**Other:** Clubhouse / Zoe's Restaurant / Snack Bar / Banquets / Outings Welcome

**Weekend:** $18
**Weekend:** $26
**Discounts:** Sr, Jr, College, Military
**Driving Range:** Yes
**Junior Golf:** Yes
**Architect/Yr Open:** Donald Ross/1926

Improvements include a new clubhouse and pro shop. New driving range. Some short par 4's and long par 3's. "Nice, friendly staff." –FP

CTRL/ WEST MA

|  | 1 | 2 | 3 | 4 | 5 | 6 | 7 | 8 | 9 |
|------|---|---|---|---|---|---|---|---|---|
| PAR | 4 | 5 | 4 | 4 | 3 | 4 | 3 | 3 | 4 |
| YARDS | 278 | 423 | 242 | 288 | 245 | 233 | 211 | 175 | 314 |
|  | 10 | 11 | 12 | 13 | 14 | 15 | 16 | 17 | 18 |
| PAR | 5 | 4 | 4 | 4 | 4 | 4 | 3 | 5 | 3 |
| YARDS | 472 | 388 | 381 | 377 | 372 | 285 | 161 | 502 | 165 |

**Directions:** Route 2 to Route 140 North to Route 12 North. 1/2 mile down on your left.

# Woods of Westminster

**★★★**   **92**

90 Bean Porridge Hill Road
Westminster, MA (978) 874-0500
www.woodsofwestminster.com

**Club Pro:** Dan Bartkus
**Payment:** Visa, MC
**Tee Times:** 5 days adv.

| Tees | Holes | Yards | Par | USGA | Slope |
|------|-------|-------|-----|------|-------|
| BACK | 18 | 6060 | 72 | 67.2 | 121 |
| MIDDLE | 18 | 5505 | 72 | 65.7 | 117 |
| FRONT | 18 | 4765 | 72 | 66.6 | 111 |

**Fee  9 Holes: Weekday:** $16
**Fee 18 Holes: Weekday:** $24
**Twilight Rates:** No
**Cart Rental:** $16pp/18, $10pp/9
**Lessons:** Yes **Schools:** Yes
**Membership:** Yes
**Other:** Bar-Lounge

**Weekend:** $18
**Weekend:** $34
**Discounts:** Senior & Junior
**Driving Range:** $7/lg., $5/sm.
**Junior Golf:** Yes
**Architect/Yr Open:** Al Zikorus/1998
**GPS:**

The best course and the friendliest people you'll ever play and meet.

|  | 1 | 2 | 3 | 4 | 5 | 6 | 7 | 8 | 9 |
|------|---|---|---|---|---|---|---|---|---|
| PAR | 5 | 4 | 5 | 4 | 4 | 3 | 4 | 3 | 4 |
| YARDS | 460 | 275 | 525 | 295 | 345 | 175 | 405 | 145 | 320 |
|  | 10 | 11 | 12 | 13 | 14 | 15 | 16 | 17 | 18 |
| PAR | 5 | 4 | 4 | 5 | 3 | 4 | 3 | 4 | 4 |
| YARDS | 345 | 220 | 330 | 435 | 145 | 315 | 130 | 300 | 340 |

**Directions:** From Routes I-95, I-495 or I-190: take Route 2 West, turn left off ramp onto 2A. Follow 2 miles, turn left onto South Ashburnham Road, follow for 1 mile. Turn right onto Bean Porridge Hill Road for 1 mile. Woods of Westminster is on the left at the top of the hill.

# Worthington Golf Course

113 Ridge Road
Worthington, MA (413) 238-4464
www.worthingtongolfclub.net

| Tees | Holes | Yards | Par | USGA | Slope |
|------|-------|-------|-----|------|-------|
| BACK | 9 | 2782 | 35 | 33.3 | 115 |
| MIDDLE | 9 | 2797 | 70 | 66.8 | 116 |
| FRONT | 9 | 2797 | 35 | 33.5 | 121 |

**Club Pro:** Karl Enroth, PGA
**Payment:** Cash, Credit
**Tee Times:** 1 week adv.
**Fee 9 Holes: Weekday:** $13
**Fee 18 Holes: Weekday:** $26
**Twilight Rates:** No
**Cart Rental:** $30/18, $18/9 per cart
**Lessons:** Yes **Schools:** Yes
**Membership:** Yes
**Other:** Clubhouse / Snack Bar / Restaurant / Bar-Lounge

**Weekend:** $17
**Weekend:** $30
**Discounts:** None
**Driving Range:** Yes
**Junior Golf:** Yes
**Architect/Yr Open:** A.P. Taylor/1904

COUPON

Sig. Hole: #6, par 3, 2 trees guarding fairway. 2 sand traps in front and 2-tiered green. Call ahead for tee times. 2 sets of tees makes an interesting 18. The 8th hole is the highest elevated golf hole in all of Massachusetts.

| | 1 | 2 | 3 | 4 | 5 | 6 | 7 | 8 | 9 |
|------|-----|-----|-----|-----|-----|-----|-----|-----|-----|
| PAR | 4 | 4 | 4 | 4 | 3 | 3 | 5 | 5 | 3 |
| YARDS | 333 | 322 | 340 | 301 | 201 | 148 | 528 | 476 | 148 |
| PAR | | | | | | | | | |
| YARDS | | | | | | | | | |

**Directions:** I-91 to Northampton. Exit 19, depart Route 9 West toward Williamsburg, turn left onto Route 143 West. Follow to the traffic light at Worthington Four Corners. Go straight through intersection up Buffington Hill Road. Turn left onto Ridge Road to the course.

# CHAPTER 5 New Hampshire

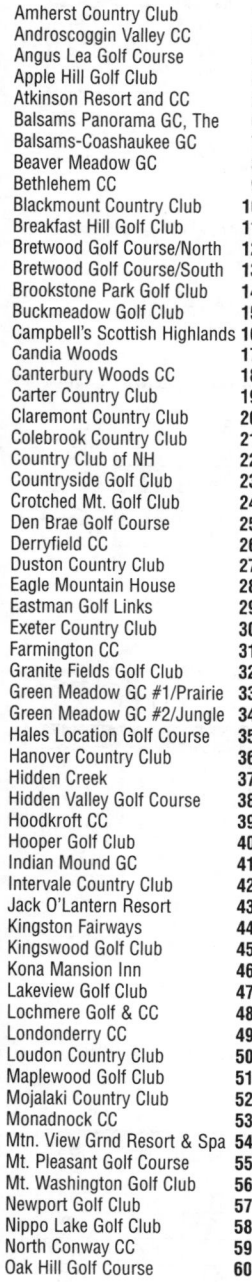

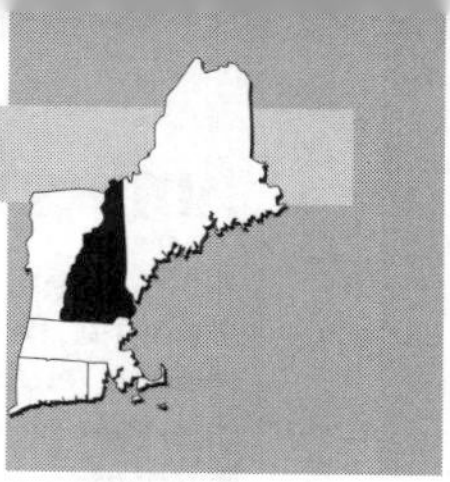

| | |
|---|---|
| Amherst Country Club | 1 |
| Androscoggin Valley CC | 2 |
| Angus Lea Golf Course | 3 |
| Apple Hill Golf Club | 4 |
| Atkinson Resort and CC | 5 |
| Balsams Panorama GC, The | 6 |
| Balsams-Coashaukee GC | 7 |
| Beaver Meadow GC | 8 |
| Bethlehem CC | 9 |
| Blackmount Country Club | 10 |
| Breakfast Hill Golf Club | 11 |
| Bretwood Golf Course/North | 12 |
| Bretwood Golf Course/South | 13 |
| Brookstone Park Golf Club | 14 |
| Buckmeadow Golf Club | 15 |
| Campbell's Scottish Highlands | 16 |
| Candia Woods | 17 |
| Canterbury Woods CC | 18 |
| Carter Country Club | 19 |
| Claremont Country Club | 20 |
| Colebrook Country Club | 21 |
| Country Club of NH | 22 |
| Countryside Golf Club | 23 |
| Crotched Mt. Golf Club | 24 |
| Den Brae Golf Course | 25 |
| Derryfield CC | 26 |
| Duston Country Club | 27 |
| Eagle Mountain House | 28 |
| Eastman Golf Links | 29 |
| Exeter Country Club | 30 |
| Farmington CC | 31 |
| Granite Fields Golf Club | 32 |
| Green Meadow GC #1/Prairie | 33 |
| Green Meadow GC #2/Jungle | 34 |
| Hales Location Golf Course | 35 |
| Hanover Country Club | 36 |
| Hidden Creek | 37 |
| Hidden Valley Golf Course | 38 |
| Hoodkroft CC | 39 |
| Hooper Golf Club | 40 |
| Indian Mound GC | 41 |
| Intervale Country Club | 42 |
| Jack O'Lantern Resort | 43 |
| Kingston Fairways | 44 |
| Kingswood Golf Club | 45 |
| Kona Mansion Inn | 46 |
| Lakeview Golf Club | 47 |
| Lochmere Golf & CC | 48 |
| Londonderry CC | 49 |
| Loudon Country Club | 50 |
| Maplewood Golf Club | 51 |
| Mojalaki Country Club | 52 |
| Monadnock CC | 53 |
| Mtn. View Grnd Resort & Spa | 54 |
| Mt. Pleasant Golf Course | 55 |
| Mt. Washington Golf Club | 56 |
| Newport Golf Club | 57 |
| Nippo Lake Golf Club | 58 |
| North Conway CC | 59 |
| Oak Hill Golf Course | 60 |
| Oaks Golf Links, The | 61 |
| Overlook GC | 62 |
| Owl's Nest Golf Club | 63 |
| Passaconaway CC | 64 |
| Pease Golf Course | 65 |
| Pembroke Pines CC | 66 |
| Pheasant Ridge CC | 67 |
| Pine Grove Springs CC | 68 |
| Pine Valley Golf Links | 69 |
| Ponemah Green Family Center | 70 |
| Portsmouth CC | 71 |
| Ragged Mountain Resort | 72 |
| Ridgewood Country Club | 73 |
| Rochester Country Club | 74 |
| Rockingham CC | 75 |
| Sagamore-Hampton GC | 76 |
| Shattuck GC, The | 77 |
| Souhegan Woods GC | 78 |
| Stonebridge Country Club | 79 |
| Sunset Hill Golf Course | 80 |
| Twin Lake Villa Golf Course | 81 |
| Waterville Valley | 82 |
| Waukewan Golf Club | 83 |
| Waumbek Golf Club | 84 |
| Wentworth Resort GC | 85 |
| Whip-Poor-Will GC | 86 |
| White Mountain CC | 87 |
| Windham Country Club | 88 |

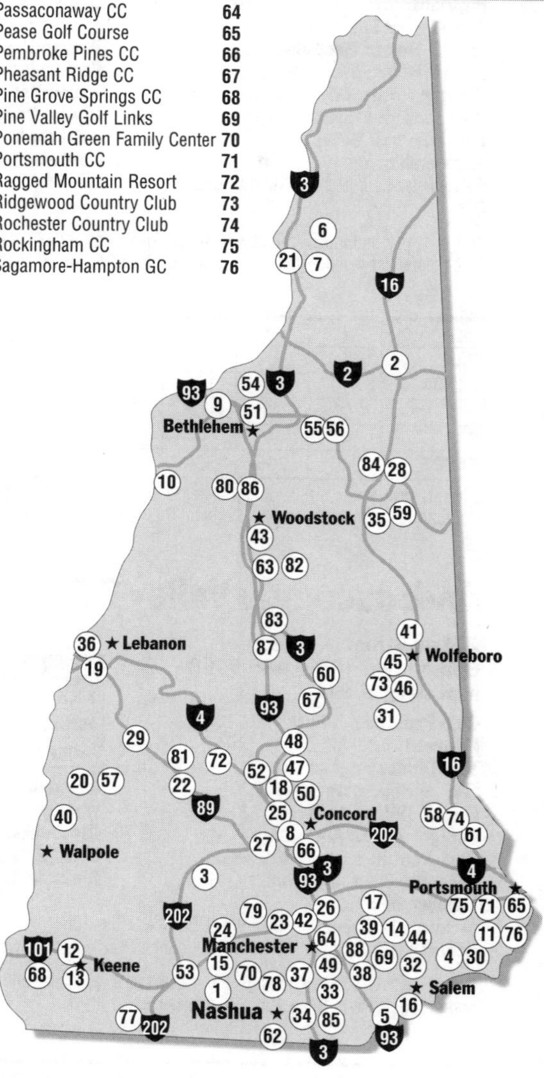


**KEY TO THE STAR RATINGS:**
**5✪** = Outstanding **4✪** = Excellent **3✪** = Very Good **2✪** = Good **1✪** = Average **NR** = Not Rated

# Amherst Country Club ✪✪✪

72 Ponemah Road
Amherst, NH (603) 673-9908
www.amherstcountryclub.com

| Tees | Holes | Yards | Par | USGA | Slope |
|------|-------|-------|-----|------|-------|
| BACK | 18 | 6462 | 72 | 70.8 | 124 |
| MIDDLE | 18 | 6052 | 72 | 67.3 | 118 |
| FRONT | 18 | 5518 | 74 | 71.0 | 111 |

**Club Pro:** Chad Gonzales
**Payment:** Visa, MC, Amex, Disc, Cash, Check
**Tee Times:** 5 days adv.
**Fee 9 Holes: Weekday:** $25    **Weekend:** $27
**Fee 18 Holes: Weekday:** $40    **Weekend:** $50
**Twilight Rates:** Check for availability    **Discounts:** Senior (wkdys) & Junior (after 12pm)
**Cart Rental:** $15pp/18, $8pp/9    **Driving Range:** Yes
**Lessons:** Yes **Schools:** Yes    **Junior Golf:** Yes
**Membership:** Yes    **Architect/Yr Open:** William Mitchell/1965
**Other:** Bar-Lounge / Restaurant / Clubhouse / Showers
**GPS:**

With a reputation for excellent conditions and quality customer service, Amherst Country Club is an 18-hole premier golf destination for all levels of play. Accomodates all levels of play with 4 sets of tees.

| | 1 | 2 | 3 | 4 | 5 | 6 | 7 | 8 | 9 |
|------|-----|-----|-----|-----|-----|-----|-----|-----|-----|
| PAR | 4 | 5 | 3 | 5 | 4 | 4 | 3 | 4 | 4 |
| YARDS | 312 | 472 | 188 | 465 | 374 | 340 | 183 | 383 | 363 |
| | 10 | 11 | 12 | 13 | 14 | 15 | 16 | 17 | 18 |
| PAR | 4 | 4 | 4 | 3 | 5 | 3 | 4 | 4 | 5 |
| YARDS | 345 | 255 | 369 | 135 | 436 | 135 | 390 | 399 | 508 |

**Directions:** Route 3 (Everett Turnpike) to Exit 7W-Rowe 101A West; Go 7 miles on Route 101A West to Route 122; turn right on 122. Amherst Country Club is ½ mile on right.

# Androscoggin Valley CC ✪✪✪½

2 Main Street (Route 2)
Gorham, NH (603) 466-9468
www.avccgolf.com

| Tees | Holes | Yards | Par | USGA | Slope |
|------|-------|-------|-----|------|-------|
| BACK | 18 | 6110 | 70 | 67.9 | 118 |
| MIDDLE | 18 | 5715 | 70 | 66.5 | 115 |
| FRONT | 18 | 5131 | 70 | 71.0 | 122 |

**Club Pro:** Gary A. Riff
**Payment:** Visa, MC, Amex, Disc
**Tee Times:** 1 day adv.
**Fee 9 Holes: Weekday:** $20    **Weekend:** $25
**Fee 18 Holes: Weekday:** $30    **Weekend:** $35
**Twilight Rates:** After 1pm    **Discounts:** Junior
**Cart Rental:** $50/18, $30/9 per cart    **Driving Range:** $10/lg, $5/sm
**Lessons:** $50/hour **Schools:**    **Junior Golf:** Yes, $1/hole
**Membership:** Yes
**Architect/Yr Open:** Alex Chisolm & Horace Smith/2004
**Other:** Clubhouse / Snack Bar / Bar-Lounge / Lockers / Showers

COUPON

Scenic, open layout with good greens makes this a joy to play and score on. Some holes border the Androscoggin River. Open April 20 - October 31.

| | 1 | 2 | 3 | 4 | 5 | 6 | 7 | 8 | 9 |
|------|-----|-----|-----|-----|-----|-----|-----|-----|-----|
| PAR | 5 | 4 | 3 | 5 | 4 | 3 | 3 | 4 | 5 |
| YARDS | 475 | 375 | 165 | 475 | 310 | 190 | 170 | 325 | 520 |
| | 10 | 11 | 12 | 13 | 14 | 15 | 16 | 17 | 18 |
| PAR | 4 | 4 | 4 | 3 | 5 | 3 | 4 | 3 | 4 |
| YARDS | 375 | 370 | 350 | 145 | 480 | 155 | 290 | 195 | 350 |

**Directions:** I-93 to Route 3 through Twin Mountain to Route 115 East to Route 2. Take Route 2 to Gorham. At light, take a right through town. Cross bridge, club is on left.

# Angus Lea Golf Course

NR ▶ 3

126 West Main Street
Hillsboro, NH (603) 464-5404
www.anguslea.com

**Club Pro:** Curtis R. Niven, PGA
**Payment:** Visa, MC
**Tee Times:** Weekends/Holidays
**Fee 9 Holes: Weekday:** $18.95
**Fee 18 Holes: Weekday:** $33
**Twilight Rates:** No
**Discounts:** M-Th 11-2pm $16/Student (w/proper ID); $15/Junior
**Cart Rental:** $28/18, $16/9 per cart
**Lessons:** $45/hour **Schools:** No
**Membership:** Yes
**Other:** Snack Bar / Bar-Lounge / Full Pro Shop

| Tees | Holes | Yards | Par | USGA | Slope |
|---|---|---|---|---|---|
| BACK | | | | | |
| MIDDLE | 9 | 2319 | 33 | 60.0 | 94 |
| FRONT | 9 | 2097 | 33 | 62.3 | 104 |

**Weekend:** $18.95
**Weekend:** $33

**Driving Range:** No
**Junior Golf:** Yes
**Architect/Yr Open:** Ed Bedell/1964
**GPS:**

Bordered by the Contoocook River, the course plays around water and through the woods. Beautiful view from large screened porch.

|  | 1 | 2 | 3 | 4 | 5 | 6 | 7 | 8 | 9 |
|---|---|---|---|---|---|---|---|---|---|
| PAR | 4 | 3 | 3 | 4 | 4 | 4 | 4 | 3 | 4 |
| YARDS | 283 | 150 | 160 | 300 | 310 | 435 | 245 | 161 | 275 |
| PAR | | | | | | | | | |
| YARDS | | | | | | | | | |

**Directions:** I-89 to Exit #5. Located on Main Street (Route 202/9) in Hillsboro. ½ mile on left after traffic light in downtown.

# Apple Hill Golf Club

✪✪ ▶ 4

69 East Road (Route 107)
E. Kingston, NH (603) 642-4414
www.applehillgolf.com

**Club Pro:** Steve Lundquist, PGA
**Payment:** Visa, MC, Disc, Checks
**Tee Times:** 1 week adv.
**Fee 9 Holes:** $20 Mon-Thurs
**Fee 18 Holes:** $35 Mon-Thurs
**Twilight Rates:** Sunday after 2pm
**Cart Rental:** $15pp/18, $8pp/9
**Lessons:** Yes **Schools:** No
**Membership:** Yes
**Other:** Clubhouse / Snack Bar / Bar-Lounge

| Tees | Holes | Yards | Par | USGA | Slope |
|---|---|---|---|---|---|
| BACK | 18 | 6184 | 70 | 68.6 | 124 |
| MIDDLE | 18 | 5875 | 70 | 67.2 | 119 |
| FRONT | 18 | 4767 | 70 | 68.4 | 118 |

**Weekend:** $22 Fri, Sat, Sun
**Weekend:** $40 Fri, Sat, Sun
**Discounts:** Senior & Junior
**Driving Range:** No
**Junior Golf:** Yes
**Architect/Yr Open:**
**GPS:**

COUPON

Now 27 holes, including Apple Hill 9-hole par 3 course, 715 yards. Both courses are well maintained. Rates for the 9 hole course are $12 every day.

|  | 1 | 2 | 3 | 4 | 5 | 6 | 7 | 8 | 9 |
|---|---|---|---|---|---|---|---|---|---|
| PAR | 4 | 3 | 4 | 3 | 5 | 4 | 4 | 4 | 4 |
| YARDS | 365 | 145 | 389 | 165 | 479 | 415 | 383 | 358 | 367 |
|  | **10** | **11** | **12** | **13** | **14** | **15** | **16** | **17** | **18** |
| PAR | 5 | 3 | 4 | 5 | 3 | 4 | 4 | 3 | 4 |
| YARDS | 465 | 181 | 363 | 420 | 169 | 294 | 356 | 136 | 425 |

**Directions:** I-95 to Exit 1 in New Hampshire (Route 107 North). The course is 6 miles on right. From Route 125 Kingston take Route 107 South, go 3½ miles.

NH

# Atkinson Resort and CC ✪✪✪✪✪ ▶ 5

85 Country Club Drive
Atkinson, NH (603) 362-8700
www.atkinsonresort.com

| Tees | Holes | Yards | Par | USGA | Slope |
|------|-------|-------|-----|------|-------|
| BACK | 18 | 6580 | 72 | 72.9 | 136 |
| MIDDLE | 18 | 6088 | 72 | 70.1 | 131 |
| FRONT | 18 | 4867 | 72 | 69.2 | 119 |

**Club Pro:** Peter Doherty, PGA
**Payment:** Visa, MC, Amex, Checks
**Tee Times:** 5 days adv.
**Fee  9 Holes: Weekday:** $32 (inc. range balls) **Weekend:** $37 (inc. range balls)
**Fee 18 Holes: Weekday:** $58 (inc. range balls) **Weekend:** $68 (inc. range balls)
**Twilight Rates:** After 5:30pm weekdays      **Discounts:** Sr, Jr, Military
**Cart Rental:** $22pp/18, $13pp/9      **Driving Range:** Yes
**Lessons:** Yes **Schools:** Yes      **Junior Golf:** Yes
**Membership:** Yes      **Architect/Yr Open:** Lewis Group/1996
**Other:** Snack Bar / Clubhouse / Lockers / Showers / Restaurant / Bar-Lounge / Hotel / Golf Academy

*COUPON*

A championship 18-hole golf course with a fully equipped pro shop. A state-of-the-art practice facility, the area's most sophisticated indoor virtual golf simulators, family-friendly 9-hole Par 3 course, and the Willowcreek Golf Academy—all open to the public seven days a week. 2015 NGCOA National Golf Course of the Year.

| | 1 | 2 | 3 | 4 | 5 | 6 | 7 | 8 | 9 |
|---|---|---|---|---|---|---|---|---|---|
| PAR | 4 | 5 | 3 | 4 | 4 | 5 | 4 | 3 | 4 |
| YARDS | 310 | 485 | 180 | 350 | 400 | 481 | 366 | 185 | 380 |
| | 10 | 11 | 12 | 13 | 14 | 15 | 16 | 17 | 18 |
| PAR | 4 | 3 | 5 | 4 | 3 | 4 | 5 | 4 | 4 |
| YARDS | 346 | 144 | 477 | 317 | 127 | 370 | 466 | 370 | 334 |

**Directions:** Route 495 to Exit 50 (Route 97). Left off exit, follow 4 miles, take right onto Hampstead Road. Course is 2.3 miles on right.

# Balsams Panorama Golf Club NR ▶ 6

1000 Cold Spring Road
Dixville Notch, NH (603) 255-2500
www.thebalsams.com

| Tees | Holes | Yards | Par | USGA | Slope |
|------|-------|-------|-----|------|-------|
| BACK | 18 | 6804 | 72 | 72.8 | 130 |
| MIDDLE | 18 | 6097 | 72 | 69.1 | 122 |
| FRONT | 18 | 5069 | 72 | 67.8 | 115 |

**Club Pro:** Douglas A. Ruttle, PGA
**Payment:** Visa, MC, Amex, Disc
**Tee Times:** 7 days adv.
**Fee  9 Holes: Weekday:** $52      **Weekend:** $52
**Fee 18 Holes: Weekday:** $99      **Weekend:** $99
**Twilight Rates:** $65 after 2pm      **Discounts:** Afternoon only
**Cart Rental:** Included      **Driving Range:** $5/lg
**Lessons:** $85/hour **Schools:** Yes      **Junior Golf:** No
**Membership:** Yes      **Architect/Yr Open:** Donald Ross/1912
**Other:** Clubhouse / Restaurant / Lockers / Showers / Bar-Lounge / Resort Hotel

Closed for renovations. Expected to open summer 2017.

| | 1 | 2 | 3 | 4 | 5 | 6 | 7 | 8 | 9 |
|---|---|---|---|---|---|---|---|---|---|
| PAR | 4 | 5 | 4 | 4 | 3 | 5 | 3 | 4 | 4 |
| YARDS | 366 | 457 | 376 | 363 | 175 | 463 | 157 | 346 | 316 |
| | 10 | 11 | 12 | 13 | 14 | 15 | 16 | 17 | 18 |
| PAR | 4 | 4 | 4 | 4 | 3 | 5 | 3 | 4 | 5 |
| YARDS | 320 | 302 | 323 | 423 | 191 | 501 | 173 | 365 | 480 |

**Directions:** 1) Take I-93 North to Exit 35, Route 3 North to Colebrook, east on Route 26 for 10 miles; or 2) Take I-91 to exit at St. Johnsbury, Route 2. Go east on Route 2 to Lancaster. Take Route 3 North to Colebrook, and east on Route 26 for 10 miles.

# Balsams-Coashaukee Golf Course  NR  7

1000 Cold Spring Road
Dixville Notch, NH (603) 255-4961
www.thebalsams.com

| Tees | Holes | Yards | Par | USGA | Slope |
|------|-------|-------|-----|------|-------|
| BACK | | | | | |
| MIDDLE | 9 | 1917 | 32 | 59.1 | 87 |
| FRONT | | | | | |

**Club Pro:** Douglas A. Ruttle
**Payment:** MC, Visa, Disc, Amex
**Tee Times:** None required
**Fee 9 Holes: Weekday:**
**Fee 18 Holes: Weekday:** $25
**Twilight Rates:** No
**Cart Rental:** $25pp/18, $17pp/9
**Lessons:** Yes **Schools:** Sr.
**Membership:** Yes
**Other:**

**Weekend:**
**Weekend:** $25
**Discounts:** None
**Driving Range:** No
**Junior Golf:** No
**Architect/Yr Open:** James Smith/1965
**GPS:**

Closed for renovations. Expected to open summer 2016.

|  | 1 | 2 | 3 | 4 | 5 | 6 | 7 | 8 | 9 |
|-----|-----|-----|-----|-----|-----|-----|-----|-----|-----|
| PAR | 4 | 3 | 3 | 4 | 4 | 4 | 3 | 4 | 3 |
| YARDS | 304 | 147 | 174 | 223 | 265 | 236 | 145 | 313 | 110 |
| PAR | | | | | | | | | |
| YARDS | | | | | | | | | |

**Directions:** 1) Take I-93 North to Exit 35, Route 3 North to Colebrook, east on Route 26 for 10 miles; or 2) Take I-91 to exit at St. Johnsbury, Route 2. Go east on Route 2 to Lancaster. Take Route 3 North to Colebrook, and east on Route 26 for 10 miles.

# Beaver Meadow Golf Club  ✪✪½  8

1 Beaver Meadow Drive
Concord, NH (603) 228-8954
www.beavermeadowgolfcourse.com

| Tees | Holes | Yards | Par | USGA | Slope |
|------|-------|-------|-----|------|-------|
| BACK | 18 | 6356 | 72 | 70.8 | 127 |
| MIDDLE | 18 | 6034 | 72 | 69.2 | 121 |
| FRONT | 18 | 6519 | 72 | 71.8 | 123 |

**Club Pro:** Phil Davis, PGA
**Payment:** Visa, MC
**Tee Times:** Weekends, 2 days adv.
**Fee 9 Holes: Weekday:** $25
**Fee 18 Holes: Weekday:** $40
**Twilight Rates:** After 3pm
**Cart Rental:** $16pp/18, $8pp/9
**Lessons:** $50/45 min. **Schools:** No
**Membership:** Yes
**Other:** Clubhouse / Snack Bar / Bar-Lounge

**Weekend:** $25
**Weekend:** $40
**Discounts:** Srs. on annual basis
**Driving Range:** Yes
**Junior Golf:** City Rec. Dept.
**Architect/Yr Open:** Willie Campbell/1896
**GPS:**

COUPON

Newly renovated practice facility with grass tee. Host site 2009 USI Championship. An official event on the Duramed Futures Tour, road to the LPGA.

|  | 1 | 2 | 3 | 4 | 5 | 6 | 7 | 8 | 9 |
|-----|-----|-----|-----|-----|-----|-----|-----|-----|-----|
| PAR | 4 | 5 | 3 | 5 | 4 | 3 | 4 | 4 | 4 |
| YARDS | 341 | 480 | 153 | 474 | 336 | 138 | 366 | 414 | 315 |
|  | 10 | 11 | 12 | 13 | 14 | 15 | 16 | 17 | 18 |
| PAR | 5 | 4 | 4 | 3 | 4 | 4 | 5 | 3 | 4 |
| YARDS | 527 | 320 | 301 | 130 | 347 | 400 | 560 | 156 | 276 |

**Directions:** I-93 to Exit 15 West (North Main Street). At second light, take right onto Route 3 North. Course is 3.1 miles on right.

# Bethlehem Country Club

NR ▶ 9

1901 Main Street
Bethlehem, NH (603) 869-5745
www.bethlehemccnhgolf.com

**Club Pro:** Darren Perkins, GM
**Payment:** Visa, MC, Cash
**Tee Times:** Required
**Fee 9 Holes: Weekday:** $20 (12 holes)
**Fee 18 Holes: Weekday:** $30
**Twilight Rates:** After 2pm
**Cart Rental:** $16pp/18, $12pp/12
**Lessons:** Yes **Schools:** No
**Membership:** Yes
**Other:** Restaurant/ Snack Bar / Retail

| Tees | Holes | Yards | Par | USGA | Slope |
|------|-------|-------|-----|------|-------|
| BACK | 18 | 5808 | 70 | 67.9 | 110 |
| MIDDLE | 18 | 5586 | 70 | 66.6 | 110 |
| FRONT | 18 | 5008 | 70 | 63.0 | 98 |

**Weekend:** $25 (12 holes)
**Weekend:** $35
**Discounts:** Junior
**Driving Range:** No
**Junior Golf:** Yes
**Architect/Yr:** W. Lilywhite/1898; D. Ross/1910
**GPS:**

COUPON

Player Comments: "Generous fairways and light rough will have you blasting your driver on all long holes. Accuracy is required on the 4 par 3 holes." –AP

| | 1 | 2 | 3 | 4 | 5 | 6 | 7 | 8 | 9 |
|---|---|---|---|---|---|---|---|---|---|
| PAR | 4 | 4 | 3 | 4 | 4 | 4 | 3 | 4 | 4 |
| YARDS | 413 | 319 | 210 | 264 | 402 | 399 | 157 | 328 | 288 |
| | 10 | 11 | 12 | 13 | 14 | 15 | 16 | 17 | 18 |
| PAR | 3 | 5 | 3 | 4 | 4 | 5 | 4 | 4 | 4 |
| YARDS | 95 | 487 | 153 | 417 | 260 | 501 | 270 | 296 | 360 |

**Directions:** I-93 to Exit 40 East. 2.5 miles on Route 302 East.

# Blackmount Country Club

✪✪ ▶ 10

400 Clark Pond Road
North Haverhill, NH (603) 787-6564
www.blackmountcountryclub.com

**Club Pro:** Bill Grimes
**Payment:** Cash or Check
**Tee Times:** No
**Fee 9 Holes: Weekday:** $12
**Fee 18 Holes: Weekday:** $20
**Twilight Rates:** No
**Cart Rental:** $24/18, $15/9 per cart
**Lessons:** Yes **Schools:** No
**Membership:** Yes
**Other:** Clubhouse / Snack Bar / Gazebo / Beer & Wine

| Tees | Holes | Yards | Par | USGA | Slope |
|------|-------|-------|-----|------|-------|
| BACK | 9 | 3015 | 36 | 34.8 | 114 |
| MIDDLE | 9 | 2658 | 36 | 33.3 | 110 |
| FRONT | 9 | 2316 | 36 | 35.7 | 121 |

**Weekend:** $16
**Weekend:** $24
**Discounts:** Senior, Junior, Ladies
**Driving Range:** Yes
**Junior Golf:** No
**Architect/Yr Open:** Robert Stoddard

COUPON

Outstanding greens. Beautiful course. Play & Stay package with the Hayloft Inn B&B adjacent to 1st hole.

| | 1 | 2 | 3 | 4 | 5 | 6 | 7 | 8 | 9 |
|---|---|---|---|---|---|---|---|---|---|
| PAR | 3 | 5 | 4 | 5 | 4 | 4 | 4 | 3 | 4 |
| YARDS | 150 | 400 | 333 | 383 | 217 | 317 | 350 | 142 | 366 |
| PAR | | | | | | | | | |
| YARDS | | | | | | | | | |

**Directions:** I-91 to Bradford, VT. Exit to NH Route 10 to village of North Haverhill, NH. Turn onto Clark Pond Road, across from Aldrich's General Store. Bear right for 1.5 miles.

# Breakfast Hill Golf Club ✪✪✪  ▶11

399 Breakfast Hill Road
Greenland, NH (603) 436-5001
www.breakfasthill.com

| Tees | Holes | Yards | Par | USGA | Slope |
|------|-------|-------|-----|------|-------|
| BACK | 18 | 6493 | 71 | 71.5 | 130 |
| MIDDLE | 18 | 5864 | 71 | 68.4 | 125 |
| FRONT | 18 | 5002 | 72 | 69.3 | 121 |

**Club Pro:** Nathan Bridges, Dir. of Golf
**Payment:** Visa, MC, Disc, Checks
**Tee Times:** 7 days adv.
**Fee 9 Holes: Weekday:** $33
**Fee 18 Holes: Weekday:** $49
**Twilight Rates:** After 3pm
**Cart Rental:** $20pp/18, $14pp/9
**Lessons:** Yes **Schools:** No
**Membership:** Yes, Season Pass
**Other:** Restaurant / Clubhouse / Bar-Lounge

**Weekend:** $33
**Weekend:** $59
**Discounts:** Senior and Junior
**Driving Range:** Yes
**Junior Golf:** Yes, pay your age under 18
**Architect/Yr Open:** Brian Silva/2000
**GPS:**

*COUPON*

18 unique championship holes with rolling fairways and contoured greens. Brian Silva design. Rated Top public course in New Hampshire by *Golfweek, Golf* magazine, *Golf Digest* and Golf.com.

|  | 1 | 2 | 3 | 4 | 5 | 6 | 7 | 8 | 9 |
|------|---|---|---|---|---|---|---|---|---|
| PAR | 4 | 5 | 4 | 3 | 5 | 3 | 4 | 4 | 4 |
| YARDS | 335 | 465 | 362 | 140 | 484 | 126 | 368 | 328 | 341 |
|  | 10 | 11 | 12 | 13 | 14 | 15 | 16 | 17 | 18 |
| PAR | 4 | 4 | 5 | 4 | 3 | 4 | 4 | 3 | 4 |
| YARDS | 302 | 455 | 526 | 289 | 145 | 319 | 364 | 131 | 384 |

**Directions:** I-95 to Exit 3 (Greenland/Portsmouth). Left onto Route 33. Left onto Route 151 South for 1.4 miles. Go left onto Breakfast Hill Road. Course is 1 mile on left.

# Bretwood Golf Course (North) ✪✪✪½  ▶12

635 East Surry Road
Keene, NH (603) 352-7626
www.bretwoodgolf.com

| Tees | Holes | Yards | Par | USGA | Slope |
|------|-------|-------|-----|------|-------|
| BACK | 18 | 6974 | 72 | 73.9 | 132 |
| MIDDLE | 18 | 6434 | 72 | 71.5 | 129 |
| FRONT | 18 | 5822 | 72 | 68.9 | 125 |

**Club Pro:** Matt Barrett, PGA
**Payment:** Visa, MC, Disc
**Tee Times:** Weekends, 3 days adv.
**Fee 9 Holes: Weekday:** $20
**Fee 18 Holes: Weekday:** $38
**Twilight Rates:** No
**Cart Rental:** $13pp/18, $8pp/9 (all day $24)
**Lessons:** Yes **Schools:** No
**Membership:** Yes
**Other:** Clubhouse / Snack Bar / Group Outings for all Sizes.

**Weekend:** $24
**Weekend:** $42
**Discounts:** None
**Driving Range:** $8/lg., $6/med., $4/sm.
**Junior Golf:** Yes
**Architect/Yr Open:** Hugh Barrett/1968

Player Comments: "Gets better every year. Favorite hole # 13 island green." "Scenic. Great layouts." "Excellent fairways and greens. River meanders through course and comes into play often. Covered bridges, great value." –GG

|  | 1 | 2 | 3 | 4 | 5 | 6 | 7 | 8 | 9 |
|------|---|---|---|---|---|---|---|---|---|
| PAR | 4 | 5 | 3 | 4 | 5 | 4 | 5 | 3 | 4 |
| YARDS | 413 | 552 | 187 | 340 | 505 | 390 | 480 | 138 | 400 |
|  | 10 | 11 | 12 | 13 | 14 | 15 | 16 | 17 | 18 |
| PAR | 4 | 4 | 4 | 3 | 4 | 4 | 3 | 5 | 4 |
| YARDS | 400 | 340 | 372 | 130 | 380 | 379 | 154 | 501 | 373 |

**Directions:** I-91 North to Route 9 East to Keene. Follow hospital signs to Court Street. East Surry Road is off Upper Court Street. 1.5 miles to course.

# Bretwood Golf Course (South) ✪✪✪  13 ▶

**635 East Surry Road**
**Keene, NH (603) 352-7626**
www.bretwoodgolf.com

**Club Pro:** Matt Barrett, PGA
**Payment:** Visa, MC, Disc
**Tee Times:** Weekends, 3 days adv.
**Fee 9 Holes: Weekday:** $20
**Fee 18 Holes: Weekday:** $38
**Twilight Rates:** No
**Cart Rental:** $13pp/18, $8pp/9 (all day $24)
**Lessons:** Yes **Schools:** No
**Membership:** Yes
**Other:** Clubhouse / Snack Bar / Group Outings for all Sizes
**GPS:** Yes

| Tees | Holes | Yards | Par | USGA | Slope |
|------|-------|-------|-----|------|-------|
| BACK | 18 | 6952 | 72 | 73.2 | 133 |
| MIDDLE | 18 | 6345 | 72 | 70.7 | 124 |
| FRONT | 18 | 5645 | 70 | 68.0 | 119 |

**Weekend:** $24
**Weekend:** $42
**Discounts:** None
**Driving Range:** $8/lg., $6/med., $4/sm. bucket
**Junior Golf:** Yes
**Architect/Yr:** Geoffrey Cornish, Hugh Barrett/1968

Front nine lulls you into submission as the back nine tests you metal as you wind your way through Jurasic Park (holes #15, #17).

|  | 1 | 2 | 3 | 4 | 5 | 6 | 7 | 8 | 9 |
|------|---|---|---|---|---|---|---|---|---|
| PAR | 5 | 5 | 3 | 4 | 4 | 4 | 3 | 4 | 4 |
| YARDS | 477 | 530 | 168 | 364 | 288 | 305 | 181 | 394 | 383 |
|  | **10** | **11** | **12** | **13** | **14** | **15** | **16** | **17** | **18** |
| PAR | 5 | 4 | 3 | 5 | 4 | 4 | 3 | 4 | 4 |
| YARDS | 472 | 372 | 133 | 536 | 371 | 340 | 176 | 410 | 445 |

**Directions:** I-91 North to Route 9 East to Keene. Follow hospital signs to Court Street. East Surry Road is off Upper Court Street. 1.5 miles to course.

# Brookstone Park Golf Course  NR  14 ▶

**14 Route 111**
**Derry, NH (603) 894-7336**
www.brookstone-park.com

**Club Pro:** Joe Kobrenski, Manager
**Payment:** All Types
**Tee Times:** 7 days adv.
**Fee 9 Holes: Weekday:** $13
**Fee 18 Holes: Weekday:** $23
**Twilight Rates:** No
**Cart Rental:** $12pp/18, $7pp/9
**Lessons:** Yes **Schools:** Yes
**Membership:** Yes
**Other:** Clubhouse / Snack Bar

| Tees | Holes | Yards | Par | USGA | Slope |
|------|-------|-------|-----|------|-------|
| BACK | 9 | 1211 | 27 | | |
| MIDDLE | 9 | 946 | 27 | | |
| FRONT | 9 | 751 | 27 | | |

**Weekend:** $15
**Weekend:** $26
**Discounts:** Senior & Junior
**Driving Range:** Yes
**Junior Golf:** Yes
**Architect/Yr Open:** Howard Maurer/2005
**GPS:**

The course has large greens, sand traps, rolling hills and water hazards that are strategically placed to create "target style" greens.

|  | 1 | 2 | 3 | 4 | 5 | 6 | 7 | 8 | 9 |
|------|---|---|---|---|---|---|---|---|---|
| PAR | 3 | 3 | 3 | 3 | 3 | 3 | 3 | 3 | 3 |
| YARDS | 96 | 119 | 125 | 84 | 125 | 116 | 76 | 72 | 133 |
| PAR | | | | | | | | | |
| YARDS | | | | | | | | | |

**Directions:** I-93 to Exit 3 in NH, head east on Route 111. Go about 4.5 miles. Golf course is on left.

# Buckmeadow Golf Club ✪½ ▶ 15

30 Route 101A
Amherst, NH (603) 673-7077

**Club Pro:** Ken Young, Manager
**Payment:** Cash, Check
**Tee Times:** Public/Members
**Fee 9 Holes: Weekday:** $14
**Fee 18 Holes: Weekday:** $26
**Twilight Rates:** No
**Cart Rental:** $14pp/18, $7pp/9
**Lessons:** Yes **Schools:** No
**Membership:** Limited/100 max.
**Other:** Bar-Lounge / Snack Bar

| Tees | Holes | Yards | Par | USGA | Slope |
|------|-------|-------|-----|------|-------|
| BACK | 9 | 2425 | 33 | 61.8 | 101 |
| MIDDLE | 9 | 2340 | 33 | 60.9 | 100 |
| FRONT | 9 | 2280 | 34 | 66.2 | 103 |

**Weekend:** $16
**Weekend:** $28
**Discounts:** Senior & Junior
**Driving Range:** No
**Junior Golf:** No
**Architect/Yr Open:** M.E. Young/1979
**GPS:**

"Six dogleg par 4s and 3 interesting 1-shot holes make for a challenging round on this nicely maintained venue." –AP

NH

|  | 1 | 2 | 3 | 4 | 5 | 6 | 7 | 8 | 9 |
|------|-----|-----|-----|-----|-----|-----|-----|-----|-----|
| PAR | 4 | 3 | 4 | 4 | 4 | 3 | 4 | 3 | 4 |
| YARDS | 320 | 120 | 190 | 335 | 345 | 175 | 330 | 185 | 340 |
| PAR |  |  |  |  |  |  |  |  |  |
| YARDS |  |  |  |  |  |  |  |  |  |

**Directions:** Route 3 to Route 101A West. Course is 1.5 miles off Route 101 outside of Milford.


# Campbell's Scottish Highlands ✪✪✪½ ▶ 16

79 Brady Avenue
Salem, NH (603) 894-4653
www.scottishhighlandsgolf.com

**Club Pro:** Geoff Williams
**Payment:** Visa, MC, Disc, Amex
**Tee Times:** 5 days adv. 603-894-4653 x13
**Fee 9 Holes: Weekday:** $24
**Fee 18 Holes: Weekday:** $40
**Twilight Rates:** Yes
**Cart Rental:** $18pp/18, $10pp/9
**Lessons:** $60/half hour **Schools:**
**Membership:** Season Passes
**Other:** Clubhouse / Bar-Lounge / Lockers / Shower / Snack Bar

| Tees | Holes | Yards | Par | USGA | Slope |
|------|-------|-------|-----|------|-------|
| BACK | 18 | 6249 | 71 | 70.1 | 121 |
| MIDDLE | 18 | 5746 | 71 | 67.6 | 113 |
| FRONT | 18 | 5056 | 71 | 68.1 | 109 |

**Weekend:** $29
**Weekend:** $50
**Discounts:** Sr. cart; Jr. twilgt. w/adult
**Driving Range:** Yes
**Junior Golf:** Yes
**Architect/Yr:** MHF Design & G. Sargent/1994

COUPON

NGCOA - Beginner-friendly certified. Noted for friendly staff, well-maintained turf. Open, rolling fairways and 'true rolling' velvet greens, some of them very large. Links-style course with well-placed hazards.

|  | 1 | 2 | 3 | 4 | 5 | 6 | 7 | 8 | 9 |
|------|-----|-----|-----|-----|-----|-----|-----|-----|-----|
| PAR | 4 | 5 | 3 | 4 | 5 | 4 | 3 | 4 | 4 |
| YARDS | 341 | 454 | 185 | 418 | 482 | 358 | 167 | 260 | 352 |
|  | 10 | 11 | 12 | 13 | 14 | 15 | 16 | 17 | 18 |
| PAR | 4 | 3 | 4 | 4 | 4 | 3 | 4 | 4 | 5 |
| YARDS | 295 | 162 | 330 | 322 | 395 | 125 | 303 | 305 | 492 |

**Directions:** I-93 to Exit 2 (bear left if exiting I-93 South or bear right if exiting I-93 North). Turn right onto South Policy Street. At the 2nd light turn right onto Route 38. Straight through next set of lights, left onto Brady Avenue for .5 miles.

# Candia Woods ✪✪½ 17 ▶

**313 South Road**
**Candia, NH (603) 483-2307**
www.candiawoods.com

| Tees | Holes | Yards | Par | USGA | Slope |
|------|-------|-------|-----|------|-------|
| BACK | 18 | 6540 | 71 | 70.9 | 118 |
| MIDDLE | 18 | 6317 | 71 | 69.8 | 117 |
| FRONT | 18 | 5367 | 71 | 69.8 | 116 |

**Club Pro:** Craig McLaughlin, PGA
**Payment:** Visa, MC, Disc, Amex
**Tee Times:** 5 days adv.
**Fee 9 Holes: Weekday:** $27
**Fee 18 Holes: Weekday:** $46
**Twilight Rates:** $20 after 3pm
**Cart Rental:** $19pp/18, $10pp/9
**Lessons:** $60/45 min. **Schools:** No
**Membership:** Yes
**Weekend:** $28
**Weekend:** $56
**Discounts:** Senior, Junior, Military
**Driving Range:** $9/sm., $12/lg. bucket
**Junior Golf:** Yes
**Architect/Yr Open:** Phil Wogan/1964
**Other:** Restaurant / Bar-Lounge / Lockers / Showers / Snack Bar / Pavilion / Outings

10 minutes from Manchester Airport and Mall of NH. Multiple tees allow for all skill levels, user-friendly layout. Private club conditions and service.

| | 1 | 2 | 3 | 4 | 5 | 6 | 7 | 8 | 9 |
|------|-----|-----|-----|-----|-----|-----|-----|-----|-----|
| PAR | 4 | 4 | 4 | 4 | 3 | 4 | 4 | 3 | 5 |
| YARDS | 409 | 359 | 355 | 389 | 183 | 357 | 382 | 195 | 521 |
| | 10 | 11 | 12 | 13 | 14 | 15 | 16 | 17 | 18 |
| PAR | 5 | 4 | 4 | 4 | 4 | 3 | 5 | 3 | 4 |
| YARDS | 464 | 443 | 394 | 309 | 308 | 158 | 540 | 146 | 405 |

**Directions:** I-93, Exit 7 to Route 101 East. Take Exit 3. Straight at stop sign, right at next stop sign. Club is ⅛ mile on left at top of hill.

# Canterbury Woods Country Club ✪✪✪ 18 ▶

**15 West Road**
**Canterbury, NH (603) 783-9400**
www.canterburywoodscc.com

| Tees | Holes | Yards | Par | USGA | Slope |
|------|-------|-------|-----|------|-------|
| BACK | 18 | 6650 | 72 | 71.7 | 136 |
| MIDDLE | 18 | 6134 | 72 | 69.2 | 130 |
| FRONT | 18 | 5535 | 72 | 66.1 | 118 |

**Club Pro:** Walter Reeves, PGA
**Payment:** Visa, MC
**Tee Times:** 5 days adv.
**Fee 9 Holes: Weekday:** $20 walk, $30 ride after 12pm
**Weekend:** $25 walk, $35 ride after 12pm
**Fee 18 Holes: Weekday:** $35 walk, $50 ride **Weekend:** $42 walk, $58 ride
**Twilight Rates:** Yes
**Cart Rental:** $15pp/18, $10pp/9
**Lessons:** Yes **Schools:** Yes
**Membership:** Yes
**Discounts:** Senior & Junior
**Driving Range:** Yes
**Junior Golf:** Clinics
**Architect/Yr Open:** Ross Forbes/2003
**Other:** Restaurant / Clubhouse/ Snack Bar / Bar-Lounge

COUPON

Site of the 2006 NH State Amateur Championship. Bent grass greens, tees, and fairways. Outstanding playing conditions. New tee box #7 and drainage in fairways.

| | 1 | 2 | 3 | 4 | 5 | 6 | 7 | 8 | 9 |
|------|-----|-----|-----|-----|-----|-----|-----|-----|-----|
| PAR | 4 | 5 | 4 | 5 | 4 | 3 | 4 | 3 | 4 |
| YARDS | 394 | 488 | 364 | 518 | 264 | 128 | 353 | 208 | 347 |
| | 10 | 11 | 12 | 13 | 14 | 15 | 16 | 17 | 18 |
| PAR | 5 | 3 | 4 | 3 | 4 | 5 | 5 | 3 | 4 |
| YARDS | 456 | 180 | 381 | 176 | 340 | 516 | 474 | 138 | 409 |

**Directions:** I-93 to Exit 18. Turn left on to West Road. Continue left at fork ½ mile from exit ramp. Course entrance is on the left just beyond Sloping Acres Farm (approximately ½ mile) from fork.

# Carter Country Club

NR 19

257 Mechanic Street
Lebanon, NH (603) 448-4483
www.cartercc.com

**Club Pro:** Rich Parker, PGA
**Payment:** Most Major
**Tee Times:** No
**Fee 9 Holes: Weekday:** $15
**Fee 18 Holes: Weekday:** $24
**Twilight Rates:** No
**Cart Rental:** $13pp/18, $7pp/9
**Lessons:** Yes **Schools:** No
**Membership:** Yes
**Other:** Restaurant / Clubhouse / Bar-Lounge

| Tees | Holes | Yards | Par | USGA | Slope |
|------|-------|-------|-----|------|-------|
| BACK | 9 | 2800 | 36 | 68.1 | 116 |
| MIDDLE | 9 | 2760 | 36 | 66.1 | 114 |
| FRONT | 9 | 2565 | 36 | 71.7 | 127 |

**Weekend:** $15
**Weekend:** $24
**Discounts:** None
**Driving Range:** No
**Junior Golf:** Yes
**Architect/Yr Open:** Donald Ross/1923
**GPS:**

Semi-hilly course, very scenic, especially nice in the Fall, small greens, very sloped. Men's League on Thursday. Open April - November. New drainage makes the course much drier.

|  | 1 | 2 | 3 | 4 | 5 | 6 | 7 | 8 | 9 |
|------|---|---|---|---|---|---|---|---|---|
| PAR | 4 | 3 | 5 | 4 | 4 | 5 | 4 | 4 | 3 |
| YARDS | 350 | 155 | 470 | 365 | 280 | 480 | 265 | 285 | 110 |
| PAR | | | | | | | | | |
| YARDS | | | | | | | | | |

**Directions:** Just a short pitch off I-89, Exit 19.

# Claremont Country Club

NR 20

Maple Avenue
Claremont, NH (603) 542-9550
www.claremontcountryclubnh.com

**Club Pro:**
**Payment:** Cash or Check
**Tee Times:** No
**Fee 9 Holes: Weekday:** $16
**Fee 18 Holes: Weekday:** $25
**Twilight Rates:** No
**Cart Rental:** $25pp/18, $15pp/9
**Lessons:** **Schools:** No
**Membership:** Yes
**Other:** Clubhouse / Bar-Lounge / Snack Bar / Lockers / Showers

| Tees | Holes | Yards | Par | USGA | Slope |
|------|-------|-------|-----|------|-------|
| BACK | 9 | 2647 | 34 | 64.7 | 104 |
| MIDDLE | 9 | 2415 | 34 | | |
| FRONT | 9 | 2335 | 34 | | |

**Weekend:** $18
**Weekend:** $28
**Discounts:** None
**Driving Range:** Yes
**Junior Golf:** Yes
**Architect/Yr Open:** 1917

Old-style course. Small greens. Hilly, with woods.

|  | 1 | 2 | 3 | 4 | 5 | 6 | 7 | 8 | 9 |
|------|---|---|---|---|---|---|---|---|---|
| PAR | 4 | 4 | 4 | 4 | 4 | 3 | 4 | 3 | 4 |
| YARDS | 420 | 328 | 273 | 262 | 275 | 174 | 434 | 169 | 312 |
| PAR | | | | | | | | | |
| YARDS | | | | | | | | | |

**Directions:** I-91 to Claremont exit. Follow signs to downtown Claremont. Take Pleasant Street to Maple Avenue. Right onto Maple. Go ½ mile to course.

NH

# Colebrook Country Club NR ▶ 21

15 Abenaki Lane
Colebrook, NH (603) 237-5566
www.colebrookcountryclub.com

**Club Pro:** Clayton Hinds, Manager
**Payment:** Visa, MC, Amex, Disc
**Tee Times:** No
**Fee 9 Holes: Weekday:** $22
**Fee 18 Holes: Weekday:** $22
**Twilight Rates:** After 3pm
**Cart Rental:** $34/18, $20/9 per cart
**Lessons:** No  **Schools:** Yes
**Membership:** Yes
**Other:** Restaurant / Bar-Lounge / Motel

| Tees | Holes | Yards | Par | USGA | Slope |
|------|-------|-------|-----|------|-------|
| BACK | 9 | 3001 | 36 | 67.1 | 114 |
| MIDDLE | 9 | 2897 | 36 | 67.1 | 114 |
| FRONT | 9 | 2114 | 36 | 72.3 | 114 |

**Weekend:** $25
**Weekend:** $25
**Discounts:** Senior, Junior, Women
**Driving Range:** No
**Junior Golf:** Yes
**Architect/Yr Open:** 1927
**GPS:**

*COUPON*

Tee #3 rebuilt August, 2010. Beautifully maintained. Hole #5 is 612 yards. Discounts after 3pm daily and on Mondays and Wednesdays. 9 holes with 2 sets of tees. Hole #7 has been rebuilt in June 2007.

|  | 1 | 2 | 3 | 4 | 5 | 6 | 7 | 8 | 9 |
|------|---|---|---|---|---|---|---|---|---|
| PAR | 4 | 4 | 3 | 4 | 6 | 3 | 5 | 3 | 4 |
| YARDS | 345 | 328 | 191 | 289 | 612 | 192 | 518 | 122 | 300 |
| PAR |  |  |  |  |  |  |  |  |  |
| YARDS |  |  |  |  |  |  |  |  |  |

**Directions:** From I-93 or I-91, take Route 3 North from Littleton, NH. When in Colebrook, take right onto Route 26 East about ½ mile. Club is on left.

# Country Club of New Hampshire ○○½ ▶ 22

178 Kearsarge Road
North Sutton, NH (603) 927-4246
www.playgolfne.com

**Club Pro:** Dave Krumenacker
**Payment:** Visa, MC, Amex, Disc, Checks, Cash
**Tee Times:** 1 week adv.
**Fee 9 Holes: Weekday:** $18
**Fee 18 Holes: Weekday:** $35
**Twilight Rates:** After 2pm
**Cart Rental:** $17pp/18, $10pp/9
**Lessons:** $45/half hour  **Schools:** No
**Membership:** Yes
**Other:** Clubhouse / Showers / Snack Bar / Restaurant / Bar-Lounge / Hotel

| Tees | Holes | Yards | Par | USGA | Slope |
|------|-------|-------|-----|------|-------|
| BACK | 18 | 6743 | 72 | 72.5 | 134 |
| MIDDLE | 18 | 6256 | 72 | 70.3 | 126 |
| FRONT | 18 | 5416 | 72 | 71.7 | 127 |

**Weekend:** $25
**Weekend:** $43
**Discounts:** None
**Driving Range:** $12/lg,$6/md,$4/sm
**Junior Golf:** Yes
**Architect/Yr Open:** Stiles & Van Kleek/1930

*COUPON*

The front 9 is level, the back is hilly. Located at the base of 3000 ft, Mt. Kearsarge.

|  | 1 | 2 | 3 | 4 | 5 | 6 | 7 | 8 | 9 |
|------|---|---|---|---|---|---|---|---|---|
| PAR | 4 | 3 | 5 | 4 | 4 | 3 | 4 | 5 | 4 |
| YARDS | 380 | 160 | 495 | 330 | 346 | 169 | 376 | 452 | 380 |
|  | **10** | **11** | **12** | **13** | **14** | **15** | **16** | **17** | **18** |
| PAR | 4 | 3 | 4 | 5 | 4 | 3 | 4 | 4 | 5 |
| YARDS | 410 | 124 | 351 | 471 | 366 | 169 | 412 | 400 | 465 |

**Directions:** One mile off I-89 at Exit 10. Follow signs to Winslow State Park.

# Countryside Golf Club

NR **23** ▶

20 Country Club Drive (Route 13)
Dunbarton, NH (603) 774-5031
www.golfcountryside.net

**Club Pro:** Dan Minoughan, Manager
**Payment:** Visa, MC, Cash
**Tee Times:** Weekends only
**Fee 9 Holes: Weekday:** $16
**Fee 18 Holes: Weekday:** $26
**Twilight Rates:** No
**Cart Rental:** Per person, call for price
**Lessons:** Yes **Schools:** No
**Membership:** Yes
**Other:** Clubhouse / Snack Bar / Bar-Lounge / Deck

| Tees | Holes | Yards | Par | USGA | Slope |
|------|-------|-------|-----|------|-------|
| BACK | 9 | 3157 | 36 | 69.3 | 128 |
| MIDDLE | 9 | 3001 | 36 | 69.2 | 126 |
| FRONT | 9 | 2758 | 36 | 71.5 | 126 |

**Weekend:** $19
**Weekend:** $29
**Discounts:** Sr & Jr weekdays
**Driving Range:** Yes
**Junior Golf:** Yes
**Architect/Yr Open:** Bill Mitchell/1964

COUPON

Scenic views and friendly staff under new management/ownership.

NH

| | 1 | 2 | 3 | 4 | 5 | 6 | 7 | 8 | 9 |
|-----|-----|-----|-----|-----|-----|-----|-----|-----|-----|
| PAR | 4 | 4 | 3 | 5 | 4 | 4 | 4 | 3 | 5 |
| YARDS | 305 | 369 | 138 | 485 | 386 | 365 | 344 | 143 | 466 |
| PAR | | | | | | | | | |
| YARDS | | | | | | | | | |

**Directions:** Route 101 to Route 114 toward Goffstown. Take Route 13 North at Sully's Superette. Go 4 miles. Club is on left.

# Crotched Mountain Golf Club ✪✪✪½

**24** ▶

740 2nd NH Turnpike North
Francestown, NH (603) 588-2923
www.crotchedmountaingolfclub.com

**Club Pro:** Matthew Bradbury, PGA
**Payment:** Visa, MC, Amex, Disc, Check, Cash
**Tee Times:** 10 days adv.
**Fee 9 Holes: Weekday:** $18
**Fee 18 Holes: Weekday:** $25
**Twilight Rates:** After 2pm
**Cart Rental:** $14pp/18, $8pp/9
**Lessons:** $45/30 min. **Schools:** Yes
**Membership:** Yes
**Other:** Restaurant / Clubhouse / Bar-Lounge / Function Room / Lodging Partner

| Tees | Holes | Yards | Par | USGA | Slope |
|------|-------|-------|-----|------|-------|
| BACK | 18 | 6111 | 71 | 69.2 | 125 |
| MIDDLE | 18 | 5530 | 71 | 66.7 | 118 |
| FRONT | 18 | 4604 | 71 | 67.4 | 117 |

**Weekend:** $18
**Weekend:** $35
**Discounts:** None
**Driving Range:** Yes
**Junior Golf:** Yes
**Architect/Yr Open:** Donald Ross/1929

COUPON

A scenic NH Mountain course. Beautifully manicured. Small sloping greens. A hidden gem. CMGC has a dress code – no denims, proper golf shirt.

| | 1 | 2 | 3 | 4 | 5 | 6 | 7 | 8 | 9 |
|-----|-----|-----|-----|-----|-----|-----|-----|-----|-----|
| PAR | 4 | 4 | 3 | 5 | 4 | 3 | 5 | 4 | 4 |
| YARDS | 338 | 310 | 145 | 479 | 339 | 184 | 416 | 333 | 374 |
| | 10 | 11 | 12 | 13 | 14 | 15 | 16 | 17 | 18 |
| PAR | 4 | 4 | 4 | 5 | 4 | 4 | 3 | 4 | 3 |
| YARDS | 347 | 289 | 342 | 383 | 328 | 277 | 186 | 290 | 170 |

**Directions:** From I-93, Route 114 to Route 13 South. In New Boston take 136 to Francestown. In Francestown take 47 West, 4 miles on right is Crotched Mountain Resort.

# Den Brae Golf Course

✪✪½  **25**

80 Prescott Road
Sanbornton, NH  (603) 934-9818
www.denbrae.com

**Club Pro:** Tom Gilley
**Payment:** Visa, MC
**Tee Times:** Weekends, Holidays
**Fee 9 Holes: Weekday:** $15
**Fee 18 Holes: Weekday:** $25
**Twilight Rates:** After 3pm
**Cart Rental:** $14pp/18, $8pp/9
**Lessons:** $27/hour  **Schools:** No
**Membership:** Yes
**Other:** Clubhouse / Snack Bar / Bar-Lounge

| Tees | Holes | Yards | Par | USGA | Slope |
|------|-------|-------|-----|------|-------|
| BACK | 9 | 3095 | 36 | | |
| MIDDLE | 9 | 2959 | 36 | 67.0 | 112 |
| FRONT | 9 | 2663 | 36 | 70.0 | 123 |

**Weekend:** $16
**Weekend:** $27
**Discounts:** None
**Driving Range:** $6.50/lg., grass tees
**Junior Golf:** Yes
**Architect/Yr Open:** Henry Homan/1958
**GPS:**

COUPON

New 6500-square-foot 7th green is pure putting purgatory! Open April - October. New women's tees make course more woman-friendly. New greens on course. New target greens on driving range.

| | 1 | 2 | 3 | 4 | 5 | 6 | 7 | 8 | 9 |
|---|---|---|---|---|---|---|---|---|---|
| PAR | 4 | 4 | 3 | 5 | 4 | 4 | 4 | 4 | 4 |
| YARDS | 380 | 241 | 170 | 490 | 270 | 370 | 288 | 355 | 395 |
| PAR | | | | | | | | | |
| YARDS | | | | | | | | | |

**Directions:** I-93 to Exit 22, go south on Route 127 for 1.1 miles. Right on Prescott Road, .3 miles on left.

# Derryfield Country Club

✪✪  **26**

625 Mammoth Road
Manchester, NH  (603) 669-0235
www.derryfieldgolf.com

**Club Pro:** Mike Ryan, PGA
**Payment:** Cash, Visa, MC, Disc
**Tee Times:** 7 days a week
**Fee 9 Holes: Weekday:** $27
**Fee 18 Holes: Weekday:** $43
**Twilight Rates:** After 5pm
**Cart Rental:** $16pp/18, $9pp/9
**Lessons:** $40/half hour  **Schools:** No
**Membership:** Yes
**Other:** Snack Bar / Restaurant / Bar-Lounge

| Tees | Holes | Yards | Par | USGA | Slope |
|------|-------|-------|-----|------|-------|
| BACK | 18 | 6143 | 70 | 69.1 | 121 |
| MIDDLE | 18 | 5852 | 70 | 67.9 | 118 |
| FRONT | 18 | 5174 | 70 | 69.1 | 111 |

**Weekend:** $27
**Weekend:** $43
**Discounts:** None
**Driving Range:** No
**Junior Golf:** Yes
**Architect/Yr Open:** 1932
**GPS:**

COUPON

Because course is hilly with small greens, approach shots are key. Wide-open fairways let you open up. Major improvements completed in 2014.

| | 1 | 2 | 3 | 4 | 5 | 6 | 7 | 8 | 9 |
|---|---|---|---|---|---|---|---|---|---|
| PAR | 4 | 4 | 3 | 4 | 4 | 4 | 4 | 3 | 4 |
| YARDS | 302 | 386 | 176 | 349 | 361 | 363 | 349 | 159 | 313 |
| | 10 | 11 | 12 | 13 | 14 | 15 | 16 | 17 | 18 |
| PAR | 4 | 4 | 3 | 4 | 4 | 4 | 4 | 5 | 4 |
| YARDS | 312 | 409 | 146 | 238 | 327 | 327 | 320 | 504 | 374 |

**Directions:** I-93 to Exit 8. Bear right at the bottom of the ramp. At second set of lights, take a left. Course is on the left.

# Duston Country Club

○½ **27** ▶

40 Country Club Road
Hopkinton, NH (603) 746-4234
www.dustoncc.com

| Tees | Holes | Yards | Par | USGA | Slope |
|------|-------|-------|-----|------|-------|
| BACK | | | | | |
| MIDDLE | 9 | 2109 | 32 | 61.4 | 100 |
| FRONT | 9 | 2065 | 33 | 64.4 | 106 |

**Club Pro:**
**Payment:** Visa, MC, Disc
**Tee Times:** Weekends & Holidays
**Fee 9 Holes: Weekday:** $15
**Fee 18 Holes: Weekday:** $24
**Twilight Rates:** After Labor Day
**Cart Rental:** $24/18, $15/9 per cart
**Lessons: Schools:** No
**Membership:** Yes
**Other:** Clubhouse / Grill / Bar-Lounge

**Weekend:** $16
**Weekend:** $26
**Discounts:** Senior & Junior
**Driving Range:** No
**Junior Golf:** Yes
**Architect/Yr Open:** 1926
**GPS:**

COUPON

Scottish-style bunkers and lush greens. Some hills. Greens are small to medium in size. Open April - November. Family run.

| | 1 | 2 | 3 | 4 | 5 | 6 | 7 | 8 | 9 |
|---|---|---|---|---|---|---|---|---|---|
| PAR | 4 | 3 | 4 | 3 | 4 | 4 | 3 | 4 | 3 |
| YARDS | 295 | 117 | 353 | 133 | 265 | 299 | 194 | 273 | 180 |
| PAR | | | | | | | | | |
| YARDS | | | | | | | | | |

**Directions:** I-89 to Exit 5 onto Routes 202 & 9 for 3 miles. Take Country Club Road exit.

# Eagle Mountain House

NR **28** ▶

Carter Notch Road
Jackson, NH (603) 383-9090
www.eaglemt.com

| Tees | Holes | Yards | Par | USGA | Slope |
|------|-------|-------|-----|------|-------|
| BACK | | | | | |
| MIDDLE | 9 | 2120 | 32 | 61 | 102 |
| FRONT | 9 | 1539 | 32 | 61 | 102 |

**Club Pro:** Bob McGraw PGA
**Payment:** Cash, Visa, MC, Amex, Disc
**Tee Times:** 1 week adv.
**Fee 9 Holes: Weekday:** $22
**Fee 18 Holes: Weekday:** $32
**Twilight Rates:** After 3pm
**Cart Rental:** $15pp/18, $10pp/9
**Lessons:** Yes **Schools:** No
**Membership:** Yes
**Other:** Hotel / Lockers / Showers / Snack Bar / Restaurant / Bar-Lounge

**Weekend:** $22
**Weekend:** $32
**Discounts:** Junior
**Driving Range:** Full
**Junior Golf:** Yes
**Architect/Yr Open:** Arthur Gae/1931

Family Friendly. Breathtaking views of mountains and river. Grass driving range. Always improving. Open early May - end of October.

| | 1 | 2 | 3 | 4 | 5 | 6 | 7 | 8 | 9 |
|---|---|---|---|---|---|---|---|---|---|
| PAR | 4 | 3 | 4 | 5 | 3 | 3 | 3 | 3 | 4 |
| YARDS | 270 | 188 | 331 | 395 | 143 | 152 | 160 | 188 | 293 |
| PAR | | | | | | | | | |
| YARDS | | | | | | | | | |

**Directions:** I-95 to Route 16 North. 9 miles north of North Conway. Continue through covered bridge into Jackson, ½ mile up Carter Notch Road.

# Eastman Golf Links

✪✪✪✪

29

6 Clubhouse Lane
Grantham, NH (603) 863-4500
www.eastmangolflinks.com

**Club Pro:** Mark Larrabee, PGA
**Payment:** Visa, MC, Amex, Disc, Checks
**Tee Times:** Up to 5 days adv.

| Tees | Holes | Yards | Par | USGA | Slope |
|------|-------|-------|-----|------|-------|
| BACK | 18 | 6731 | 71 | 72.8 | 129 |
| MIDDLE | 18 | 6338 | 71 | 71.0 | 127 |
| FRONT | 18 | 5499 | 73 | 72.7 | 125 |

**Fee 9 Holes: Weekday:** $30    **Weekend:** $30
**Fee 18 Holes: Weekday:** $49    **Weekend:** $49
**Twilight Rates:** No    **Discounts:** Junior after 2pm
**Cart Rental:** $20pp/18, $12pp/9    **Driving Range:** $6/bucket
**Lessons:** Yes, 3 teachers   **Schools:** No    **Junior Golf:** Yes - PGA Jr. League Team
**Membership:** Limited - Five Options    **Architect/Yr Open:** Geoffrey Cornish/1973
**Other:** Clubhouse / Lockers / Showers / Snack Bar / Restaurant / Bar-Lounge

*COUPON*

Golf carts are required Friday, Saturday and Sunday before 2pm. Hosted 2010 NHGA Men's State Amateur. NHWGA Womens State Open in 2017. Book tee times online and by mobile device @ www.eastmangolflinks.com/mobile. New Clubhouse in 2016. New forward tees 2016 silver and green. "A great public golf course with the feel of a private club." –FP

| | 1 | 2 | 3 | 4 | 5 | 6 | 7 | 8 | 9 |
|------|---|---|---|---|---|---|---|---|---|
| PAR | 4 | 5 | 3 | 4 | 4 | 4 | 3 | 5 | 4 |
| YARDS | 354 | 544 | 167 | 353 | 389 | 409 | 189 | 493 | 395 |
| | 10 | 11 | 12 | 13 | 14 | 15 | 16 | 17 | 18 |
| PAR | 4 | 4 | 4 | 3 | 4 | 3 | 5 | 4 | 4 |
| YARDS | 322 | 384 | 443 | 189 | 384 | 113 | 441 | 385 | 384 |

**Directions:** Take I-89 to Exit 13; left off ramp from North, right off ramp from South. ¼ mile on right is entrance to course.

# Exeter Country Club

✪✪

30

58 Jady Hill Avenue
Exeter, NH (603) 772-4752
www.exetercountryclub.com

**Club Pro:** Bill Cassell, PGA
**Payment:** Visa, MC, Disc
**Tee Times:** Yes

| Tees | Holes | Yards | Par | USGA | Slope |
|------|-------|-------|-----|------|-------|
| BACK | | | | | |
| MIDDLE | 9 | 2721 | 35 | 70.1 | 117 |
| FRONT | 9 | 2553 | 35 | 68.9 | 114 |

**Fee 9 Holes: Weekday:** $20    **Weekend:** $25
**Fee 18 Holes: Weekday:** $35    **Weekend:** $40
**Twilight Rates:** After 5pm    **Discounts:** None
**Cart Rental:** $18pp/18, $9pp/9    **Driving Range:** Yes
**Lessons:** $45/half hour   **Schools:** Yes    **Junior Golf:** Yes
**Membership:** $1200/$249 Junior    **Architect/Yr Open:** 1889; M. Francis/1950
**Other:** Restaurant / Clubhouse / Snack Bar / Showers / Bar-Lounge

*COUPON*

Player Comments: "A placement course. Makes you think about each shot." Rolling terrain with a variety of challenges. Not overly difficult. Open April 1 - December 1.

| | 1 | 2 | 3 | 4 | 5 | 6 | 7 | 8 | 9 |
|------|---|---|---|---|---|---|---|---|---|
| PAR | 4 | 3 | 5 | 4 | 4 | 4 | 4 | 3 | 4 |
| YARDS | 379 | 160 | 460 | 361 | 365 | 250 | 281 | 165 | 300 |
| PAR | | | | | | | | | |
| YARDS | | | | | | | | | |

**Directions:** I-95 to Hampton, NH exit to Route 101 West, exit to Route 108 to Stratham, Exeter. Bear left. Go right at 3rd light, take 1st left, then the next right.

# Farmington Country Club

NR

**188 Main Street (Route 153)**
**Farmington, NH (603) 755-2412**
www.farmingtoncountryclubnh.com

| Tees | Holes | Yards | Par | USGA | Slope |
|------|-------|-------|-----|------|-------|
| BACK | | | | | |
| MIDDLE | 9 | 3152 | 36 | 69.7 | 125 |
| FRONT | 9 | 2739 | 36 | 70.7 | 123 |

**Club Pro:** James Pollini, PGA
**Payment:** Visa, MC
**Tee Times:** Weekends
**Fee 9 Holes: Weekday:** $17 **Weekend:** $21
**Fee 18 Holes: Weekday:** $25 **Weekend:** $31
**Twilight Rates:** No **Discounts:** None
**Cart Rental:** $25/18, $17/9 per cart **Driving Range:** Yes
**Lessons:** $40/half hour **Schools:** Yes **Junior Golf:** Yes
**Membership:** Yes **Architect/Yr Open:** 1924, 1996
**Other:** Clubhouse / Snack Bar/ Bar-Lounge / Beverage Cart

Challenging redesigned course. 9 holes, 2 sets of tees. Highly improved conditions.

|  | 1 | 2 | 3 | 4 | 5 | 6 | 7 | 8 | 9 |
|---|---|---|---|---|---|---|---|---|---|
| PAR | 4 | 4 | 3 | 5 | 4 | 3 | 5 | 4 | 4 |
| YARDS | 350 | 350 | 140 | 491 | 375 | 135 | 516 | 406 | 345 |
| PAR | | | | | | | | | |
| YARDS | | | | | | | | | |

**Directions:** From Spaulding Turnpike (Route 16), take Route 11 West. Then to Route 153 North. Approximately 1.5 miles on the right is club.

# Granite Fields Golf Club

★★½

**7 Route 125**
**Kingston, NH (603) 642-9977**
www.granitefields.com

| Tees | Holes | Yards | Par | USGA | Slope |
|------|-------|-------|-----|------|-------|
| BACK | 18 | 6518 | 72 | 71.6 | 131 |
| MIDDLE | 18 | 6018 | 72 | 68.7 | 124 |
| FRONT | 18 | 4695 | 72 | 116 | 68.0 |

**Club Pro:** Jim Dufresne, Manager
**Payment:** Most Major Credit Cards
**Tee Times:** 5 days adv.
**Fee 9 Holes: Weekday:** $20 **Weekend:** $25
**Fee 18 Holes: Weekday:** $30 **Weekend:** $44
**Twilight Rates:** After 4pm **Discounts:** Senior & Junior
**Cart Rental:** $15pp/18, $10pp/9 **Driving Range:** Yes (Net)
**Lessons:** Yes **Schools:** No **Junior Golf:**
**Membership:** Yes **Architect/Yr Open:** Steve Cummings/2005
**Other:** Clubhouse / Bar-Lounge **GPS:**

COUPON

Has matured into a real winner. Very scenic and challenging. Distances below are from the Blue tees.

|  | 1 | 2 | 3 | 4 | 5 | 6 | 7 | 8 | 9 |
|---|---|---|---|---|---|---|---|---|---|
| PAR | 4 | 4 | 4 | 3 | 4 | 5 | 4 | 3 | 5 |
| YARDS | 356 | 323 | 305 | 175 | 354 | 493 | 380 | 150 | 450 |
|  | 10 | 11 | 12 | 13 | 14 | 15 | 16 | 17 | 18 |
| PAR | 4 | 3 | 4 | 3 | 5 | 5 | 4 | 4 | 4 |
| YARDS | 344 | 133 | 369 | 151 | 479 | 478 | 387 | 319 | 352 |

**Directions:** I-495 to Exit 51B. North on Route 125. 5.3 miles on right. From 101: take 125 South. Approximately 11 miles on left.

# Green Meadow GC #1, The Prairie ✪✪½

33 ▶

59 Steele Road
Hudson, NH (603) 889-1555
www.greenmeadowgolfclub.com

| Tees | Holes | Yards | Par | USGA | Slope |
|------|-------|-------|-----|------|-------|
| BACK | 18 | 6160 | 70 | 68.4 | 113 |
| MIDDLE | 18 | 5810 | 70 | 66.7 | 110 |
| FRONT | 18 | 4877 | 70 | 66.6 | 106 |

**Club Pro:** Peter Dupuis, PGA
**Payment:** Cash, MC, Visa, Disc, Amex
**Tee Times:** 7 days a week, 1 week adv.
**Fee  9 Holes: Weekday:** $25
**Fee 18 Holes: Weekday:** $36
**Twilight Rates:** After 12pm
**Cart Rental:** $16pp/18, $11pp/9
**Lessons:** Yes **Schools:** No
**Membership:** No
**Other:** Clubhouse / Snack Bar / Bar-Lounge / Showers

**Weekend:**
**Weekend:** $44
**Discounts:** Senior/$31, Junior/$15
**Driving Range:** $8/lg. bucket
**Junior Golf:** Yes
**Architect/Yr Open:** Philip Friel/1959

Lots of room and very forgiving. Junior discounts.

| | 1 | 2 | 3 | 4 | 5 | 6 | 7 | 8 | 9 |
|------|---|---|---|---|---|---|---|---|---|
| PAR | 4 | 4 | 3 | 4 | 4 | 3 | 5 | 4 | 4 |
| YARDS | 334 | 328 | 141 | 376 | 341 | 169 | 471 | 411 | 364 |
| | 10 | 11 | 12 | 13 | 14 | 15 | 16 | 17 | 18 |
| PAR | 4 | 3 | 4 | 3 | 4 | 4 | 4 | 4 | 5 |
| YARDS | 353 | 158 | 324 | 153 | 329 | 410 | 313 | 329 | 506 |

**Directions:** Take Route 3 to Exit 2. Follow the signs toward Hudson, NH. At the end of the bridge bear to the right onto Route 3A South. At the third set of lights, which is Steele Road, take a right. This road leads directly into the Green Meadow parking lot.

# Green Meadow GC #2, The Jungle ✪✪✪

34 ▶

59 Steele Road
Hudson, NH (603) 889-1555
www.greenmeadowgolfclub.com

| Tees | Holes | Yards | Par | USGA | Slope |
|------|-------|-------|-----|------|-------|
| BACK | 18 | 6940 | 72 | 71.5 | 124 |
| MIDDLE | 18 | 6394 | 72 | 68.9 | 120 |
| FRONT | 18 | 5352 | 72 | 69.7 | 114 |

**Club Pro:** Peter Dupuis, PGA
**Payment:** Cash, MC, Visa, Disc, Amex
**Tee Times:** 7 days a week, 1 week adv.
**Fee  9 Holes: Weekday:** $25
**Fee 18 Holes: Weekday:** $36
**Twilight Rates:** After 12pm
**Cart Rental:** $16pp/18, $11pp/9
**Lessons:** Yes **Schools:** No
**Membership:** No
**Other:** Clubhouse / Snack Bar / Bar-Lounge / Showers

**Weekend:**
**Weekend:** $44
**Discounts:** Senior/$31; Junior/$15
**Driving Range:** $8/lg.
**Junior Golf:** Yes
**Architect/Yr Open:** Philip Friel/1959

Junior discounts 7 days a week. Course set along the Merrimac River. More challenging than the Prairie Course. Junior discounts with no restrictions.

| | 1 | 2 | 3 | 4 | 5 | 6 | 7 | 8 | 9 |
|------|---|---|---|---|---|---|---|---|---|
| PAR | 4 | 4 | 5 | 3 | 4 | 4 | 4 | 3 | 5 |
| YARDS | 368 | 341 | 513 | 164 | 351 | 405 | 366 | 185 | 479 |
| | 10 | 11 | 12 | 13 | 14 | 15 | 16 | 17 | 18 |
| PAR | 4 | 3 | 4 | 5 | 4 | 4 | 3 | 4 | 5 |
| YARDS | 358 | 137 | 370 | 538 | 382 | 368 | 142 | 415 | 512 |

**Directions:** Take Route 3 to Exit 2. Follow the signs toward Hudson, NH. At the end of the bridge bear to the right onto Route 3A South. At the third set of lights, which is Steele Road, take a right. This road leads directly into the Green Meadow parking lot.

**244  New Hampshire**                    **NEW ENGLAND GOLFGUIDE**

# Hales Location Golf Course  ✪✪½  ▶ 35

87 Fairway Drive
North Conway, NH  (603) 356-2140
www.haleslocationgolf.com
**Club Pro:** Wayne Sprouse, Dir. of Golf
**Payment:** Visa, MC, Disc
**Tee Times:** May 1st for season
**Fee  9 Holes: Weekday:** $35
**Fee 18 Holes: Weekday:** $47
**Twilight Rates:** After 3pm
**Cart Rental:** $17pp/18, $11pp/9
**Lessons:** Yes  **Schools:** Yes
**Membership:** Yes

| Tees | Holes | Yards | Par | USGA | Slope |
|---|---|---|---|---|---|
| BACK | 9 | 3025 | 36 | 68.8 | 122 |
| MIDDLE | 9 | 2816 | 36 | 66.8 | 115 |
| FRONT | 9 | 2508 | 36 | 67.4 | 113 |

**Weekend:** $38 (F/S/S)
**Weekend:** $50 (F/S/S)
**Discounts:** Senior and Junior
**Driving Range:** No
**Junior Golf:** Yes
**Architect/Yr Open:** Al Zikorus/1990

COUPON

**Other:** Clubhouse / Hotel / Restaurant / Bar-Lounge / Snack Bar / Lockers / Showers
**GPS:** Yes

Special holes: #1 and #9. Great 9-hole layout with breathtaking views of the White Mountains. Bent grass fairways and greens. Golf rates vary seasonally. Open May-November.

|  | 1 | 2 | 3 | 4 | 5 | 6 | 7 | 8 | 9 |
|---|---|---|---|---|---|---|---|---|---|
| PAR | 5 | 4 | 3 | 4 | 5 | 3 | 4 | 4 | 4 |
| YARDS | 458 | 312 | 148 | 256 | 468 | 130 | 334 | 368 | 342 |

|  |
|---|
| PAR |
| YARDS |

**Directions:** Route 16 to traffic light in Conway. Turn onto Washington Street, then right onto West Side Road; 5 miles on left.

# Hanover Country Club  ✪✪✪½  ▶ 36

36 Hilton Field Lane
Hanover, NH  (603) 646-2000
www.golf.dartmouth.edu
**Club Pro:** Alex Kirk, PGA
**Payment:** Visa, MC, Amex
**Tee Times:** 3 days adv.
**Fee  9 Holes: Weekday:**
**Fee 18 Holes: Weekday:** $49
**Twilight Rates:** $30 after 3pm
**Cart Rental:** $16pp/18
**Lessons:** $40/half hour  **Schools:** No
**Membership:** Yes
**Other:** Clubhouse / Snack Bar / Leagues

| Tees | Holes | Yards | Par | USGA | Slope |
|---|---|---|---|---|---|
| BACK | 18 | 6472 | 71 | 70.8 | 131 |
| MIDDLE | 18 | 6142 | 71 | 70.8 | 131 |
| FRONT | 18 | 5330 | 72 | 71.5 | 128 |

**Weekend:**
**Weekend:** $59
**Discounts:** Junior
**Driving Range:** Yes
**Junior Golf:** Yes
**Architect/Yr Open:** O. Smith/1899
**GPS:**

COUPON

Home of Dartmouth golf team. Parkland-style with old-growth trees. "Course greens in great shape, fast, challenging, and fun."

|  | 1 | 2 | 3 | 4 | 5 | 6 | 7 | 8 | 9 |
|---|---|---|---|---|---|---|---|---|---|
| PAR | 4 | 4 | 4 | 3 | 3 | 4 | 4 | 4 | 5 |
| YARDS | 400 | 408 | 290 | 115 | 183 | 341 | 405 | 283 | 572 |
|  | 10 | 11 | 12 | 13 | 14 | 15 | 16 | 17 | 18 |
| PAR | 4 | 4 | 3 | 4 | 3 | 4 | 4 | 5 | 5 |
| YARDS | 385 | 315 | 177 | 308 | 142 | 425 | 358 | 467 | 457 |

**Directions:** I-91 to bridge into Hanover. 1st left after lights, then 2nd left onto Maynard Street. Next right onto Rope Ferry Road. Follow to end.

# Hidden Creek Golf Course ✪✪✪   37▶

17 Morgan Road
Litchfield, NH (603) 262-9272
www.hiddencreekgolfnh.com

| Tees | Holes | Yards | Par | USGA | Slope |
|------|-------|-------|-----|------|-------|
| BACK | 9 | 3252 | 36 | 70.5 | 127 |
| MIDDLE | 9 | 3114 | 36 | 68.5 | 126 |
| FRONT | 9 | 2858 | 36 | 68.0 | 124 |

Club Pro: Frank Carpentino, Pro Shop Mgr.
Payment: Visa, MC
Tee Times: Yes
Fee  9 Holes: Weekday: $30   Weekend: $33
Fee 18 Holes: Weekday: $39   Weekend: $45
Twilight Rates: After 6pm   Discounts: Senior
Cart Rental: $15pp/18, $10pp/9   Driving Range: Yes
Lessons: No  Schools: No   Junior Golf: No
Membership: Yes   Architect/Yr Open: 2005
Other:   GPS:

Sister course to Passaconaway. Some wide open fairways with large greens. Private course feel. "Nice layout for all levels of play." –FP

| | 1 | 2 | 3 | 4 | 5 | 6 | 7 | 8 | 9 |
|-----|---|---|---|---|---|---|---|---|---|
| PAR | 4 | 4 | 3 | 5 | 4 | 4 | 3 | 5 | 4 |
| YARDS | 371 | 345 | 190 | 565 | 330 | 283 | 140 | 500 | 390 |
| PAR | | | | | | | | | |
| YARDS | | | | | | | | | |

Directions: I-93 North to Exit 5 (Route 28). Go South 1.3 miles, turn right at Stonehenge Road. Go left at Bartley Hill Road for 3.5 miles (becomes Corning Road). Turn left at Charles Bancroft Highway (Route 3A), turn left at Albuquerque Avenue and left at Morgan Road.

# Hidden Valley Golf Course   ✪½   38▶

81 Damren Road
Derry, NH (603) 887-7888
www.hiddenvalleyrv.com

| Tees | Holes | Yards | Par | USGA | Slope |
|------|-------|-------|-----|------|-------|
| BACK | 18 | 6280 | 72 | 70.8 | 126 |
| MIDDLE | 18 | 5823 | 72 | 67.8 | 124 |
| FRONT | 18 | 5175 | 72 | 65.3 | 109 |

Club Pro: Ed Simonsen, Manager
Payment: Visa, MC, Cash
Tee Times: 7 days adv.
Fee  9 Holes: Weekday: $20   Weekend: $25
Fee 18 Holes: Weekday: $30   Weekend: $40
Twilight Rates: After 4pm   Discounts: Senior & Junior
Cart Rental: $15pp/18, $10pp/9   Driving Range: No
Lessons: Yes  Schools: No   Junior Golf: Yes
Membership: $1300   Architect/Yr Open: Ed Simonsen/1993
Other: RV Campsites / Canobie Lake Park   GPS:

COUPON

Rates subject to change for 2017 season. RV sites at course. Nice big greens. Added 9-hole par 3 courses. Southern NH's most scenic, well-maintained 18-hole championship course. Friendly staff, leagues, tournaments.

| | 1 | 2 | 3 | 4 | 5 | 6 | 7 | 8 | 9 |
|-----|---|---|---|---|---|---|---|---|---|
| PAR | 3 | 4 | 3 | 5 | 4 | 4 | 4 | 5 | 4 |
| YARDS | 150 | 310 | 155 | 420 | 355 | 345 | 345 | 505 | 275 |
| | 10 | 11 | 12 | 13 | 14 | 15 | 16 | 17 | 18 |
| PAR | 5 | 4 | 3 | 5 | 4 | 4 | 3 | 4 | 4 |
| YARDS | 420 | 325 | 190 | 530 | 365 | 308 | 155 | 355 | 330 |

Directions: Take Exit 4 on Route 93. Go east until the Derry Rotary Circle. Take East Derry Road for 4½ miles. Go left onto Damren Road to Course.

# Hoodkroft Country Club  ✪✪  ▶39

121 East Broadway
Derry, NH (603) 434-0651
www.hoodkroftcc.com

| Tees | Holes | Yards | Par | USGA | Slope |
|------|-------|-------|-----|------|-------|
| BACK | 9 | 3283 | 36 | 35.5 | 125 |
| MIDDLE | 9 | 3186 | 36 | 33.4 | 116 |
| FRONT | 9 | 2434 | 36 | 33.9 | 110 |

Club Pro: Tony Zdunko, PGA
Payment: Visa, MC, Disc, Amex
Tee Times: 7 days a week
Fee 9 Holes: Weekday: $24   Weekend: $25
Fee 18 Holes: Weekday: $29   Weekend: $35
Twilight Rates: After 5pm   Discounts: Sr/Jr/Military/Weekdays
Cart Rental: $18pp/18, $10pp/9   Driving Range: No
Lessons: Yes  Schools: No   Junior Golf: Yes
Membership: Available   Architect/Yr Open: Philip Wogan/1971
Other: Clubhouse / Bar-Lounge / Snack Bar / Showers

Mostly flat, open fairways, lots of water. Large open greens. New chipping area. Open April 1 - November 30 (or snow).

|  | 1 | 2 | 3 | 4 | 5 | 6 | 7 | 8 | 9 |
|------|---|---|---|---|---|---|---|---|---|
| PAR | 4 | 4 | 3 | 5 | 4 | 4 | 4 | 3 | 5 |
| YARDS | 335 | 420 | 187 | 538 | 355 | 380 | 340 | 155 | 456 |
| PAR | | | | | | | | | |
| YARDS | | | | | | | | | |

Directions: I-93 to Exit 4 in NH, head east on Route 102. Go about 2 miles. Golf course is on right-hand side.

# Hooper Golf Club  ✪✪✪  ▶40

166 Prospect Hill
Walpole, NH (603) 756-4080
www.hoopergolfclub.com

| Tees | Holes | Yards | Par | USGA | Slope |
|------|-------|-------|-----|------|-------|
| BACK | | | | | |
| MIDDLE | 9 | 3033 | 71 | 68.9 | 123 |
| FRONT | 9 | 2709 | 36 | 71.2 | 121 |

Club Pro: Ron Rosko, PGA
Payment: Visa, MC, Amex, Cash
Tee Times: Yes
Fee 9 Holes: Weekday: $22   Weekend: $22
Fee 18 Holes: Weekday: $41   Weekend: $41
Twilight Rates: No   Discounts: None
Cart Rental: $19pp/18, $11pp/9   Driving Range: No
Lessons: Yes  Schools: No   Junior Golf: No
Membership: $670/Adult, $1050/Couple   Architect/Yr Open: Stiles & Van Kleek/1927
Other: Full Restaurant / Clubhouse / Bed and Breakfast Hotel

Named 11th best 9 hole course in US by "Golf World." Historic clubhouse and bed & breakfast. Call ahead to this busy course. Open April - October. On weekends opens at 10:30am to non-members.

|  | 1 | 2 | 3 | 4 | 5 | 6 | 7 | 8 | 9 |
|------|---|---|---|---|---|---|---|---|---|
| PAR | 5 | 4 | 4 | 3 | 5 | 3 | 4 | 4 | 4 |
| YARDS | 456 | 427 | 285 | 155 | 474 | 194 | 311 | 381 | 350 |
| PAR | | | | | | | | | |
| YARDS | | | | | | | | | |

Directions: I-91 to Exit 5. Take Route 5 South to 1st left, onto Route 123 to Route 12. Turn right onto Route 12 South, take 1st left onto South Street to Prospect Hill Road, ¾ mile on Prospect. Golf course on right.

NH

# Indian Mound Golf Club  ✪✪

## 41

Route 16B
Center Ossipee, NH (603) 539-7733
www.indianmoundgc.com
**Club Pro:** Julie/Jonathan Rivers
**Payment:** Most Major Credit Cards, Checks
**Tee Times:** Yes
**Fee 9 Holes: Weekday:** $29 **Weekend:** $39
**Fee 18 Holes: Weekday:** $49 **Weekend:** $59
**Twilight Rates:** After 3pm **Discounts:** Senior & Junior
**Cart Rental:** $16pp/18, $10pp/9 **Driving Range:** No
**Lessons:** Yes **Schools:** No **Junior Golf:** Yes
**Membership:** Yes **Architect/Yr Open:** Sargent/1966
**Other:** Clubhouse / Restaurant / Bar-Lounge / Lodging Partner

| Tees | Holes | Yards | Par | USGA | Slope |
|---|---|---|---|---|---|
| BACK | 18 | 5675 | 70 | 68.1 | 120 |
| MIDDLE | 18 | 5360 | 70 | 67.1 | 118 |
| FRONT | 18 | 4713 | 70 | 67.5 | 117 |

COUPON

Lots of upgrades, great course for all abilities, groups. Tournaments welcome, great food and beverage, very friendly staff. Newly renovated 1st hole and great finishing hole. Course is in the best shape ever.

| | 1 | 2 | 3 | 4 | 5 | 6 | 7 | 8 | 9 |
|---|---|---|---|---|---|---|---|---|---|
| PAR | 4 | 5 | 4 | 3 | 4 | 4 | 4 | 3 | 4 |
| YARDS | 295 | 465 | 355 | 118 | 288 | 276 | 295 | 170 | 365 |
| | 10 | 11 | 12 | 13 | 14 | 15 | 16 | 17 | 18 |
| PAR | 4 | 3 | 4 | 4 | 5 | 4 | 3 | 5 | 3 |
| YARDS | 340 | 113 | 303 | 400 | 433 | 360 | 104 | 495 | 185 |

**Directions:** From West or East, Route 25 or Route 28 to Route 16 to Center Ossipee exit. Course is .5 mile on left. 20 minutes south of North Conway on Route 16.

# Intervale Country Club  ✪✪½

## 42

1491 Front Street
Manchester, NH (603) 647-6811
www.intervalecc.com
**Club Pro:** Matt Thibeault, PGA
**Payment:** Credit Cards, Cash or Check
**Tee Times:** No
**Fee 9 Holes: Weekday:** $25 **Weekend:** $25
**Fee 18 Holes: Weekday:** $35 **Weekend:** $35
**Twilight Rates:** No **Discounts:** Junior
**Cart Rental:** $13pp/18, $7pp/9 **Driving Range:** No
**Lessons:** $50/hour **Schools:** No **Junior Golf:** Yes
**Membership:** Yes
**Architect/Yr Open:** A. Findlay/1903; W.B. Booth/2004
**Other:** Restaurant / Bar-Lounge

| Tees | Holes | Yards | Par | USGA | Slope |
|---|---|---|---|---|---|
| BACK | | | | | |
| MIDDLE | 9 | 3086 | 36 | 69.6 | 115 |
| FRONT | 9 | 2740 | 36 | 71.0 | 120 |

COUPON

Semi-private. Call for details. Open April - November. Classic design, course is over 100 years old. New green added over water hazard. Tee enlargement #2, #7, #9. Host of NHPGA Pro-Pro Championship. Toughest starting hole in the state!

| | 1 | 2 | 3 | 4 | 5 | 6 | 7 | 8 | 9 |
|---|---|---|---|---|---|---|---|---|---|
| PAR | 3 | 4 | 4 | 5 | 4 | 4 | 4 | 3 | 5 |
| YARDS | 222 | 338 | 334 | 463 | 441 | 342 | 284 | 137 | 516 |
| PAR | | | | | | | | | |
| YARDS | | | | | | | | | |

**Directions:** I-293 North to Exit 7. Course is ½ mile on right. From the north take Exit 10 off I-93. Take left and course is 2 miles on left.

# Jack O'Lantern Resort ✪✪ 43

Route 3
Woodstock, NH (603) 745-3636
www.jackolanternresort.com

| Tees | Holes | Yards | Par | USGA | Slope |
|---|---|---|---|---|---|
| BACK | | | | | |
| MIDDLE | 18 | 6003 | 70 | 68.6 | 117 |
| FRONT | 18 | 4917 | 71 | 67.0 | 113 |

**Club Pro:** Gary Clement
**Payment:** Visa, MC, Amex, Disc
**Tee Times:** 24 hours adv.
**Fee 9 Holes: Weekday:** $35
**Fee 18 Holes: Weekday:** $40
**Twilight Rates:**
**Cart Rental:** $18pp/18, $11pp/9
**Lessons:** $30/half hour **Schools:** Yes
**Membership:** Yes
**Other:** Restaurant / Hotel / Bar-Lounge / Snack Bar / Horses / Bear Shows / Parks

**Weekend:** $55
**Weekend:** $60
**Discounts:** Junior
**Driving Range:** No
**Junior Golf:** Yes
**Architect/Yr Open:** Bob Keating/1948

COUPON

Players enjoy and are challenged by dogleg turns and narrow fairways. River golf holes and Bridge over water, 360 degree views of mountains. Maintained by golf professionals.

| | 1 | 2 | 3 | 4 | 5 | 6 | 7 | 8 | 9 |
|---|---|---|---|---|---|---|---|---|---|
| PAR | 4 | 4 | 4 | 4 | 3 | 4 | 4 | 4 | 3 |
| YARDS | 370 | 365 | 414 | 362 | 175 | 421 | 335 | 395 | 160 |
| | 10 | 11 | 12 | 13 | 14 | 15 | 16 | 17 | 18 |
| PAR | 5 | 4 | 4 | 3 | 4 | 5 | 4 | 3 | 4 |
| YARDS | 519 | 292 | 305 | 140 | 410 | 520 | 320 | 175 | 325 |

**Directions:** I-93 to Exit 30, right there on the right!

# Kingston Fairways Golf Club ✪✪ 44

65 Depot Road (Route 107)
Kingston, NH (603) 642-7722
www.kingstonfairwaysgolf.com

| Tees | Holes | Yards | Par | USGA | Slope |
|---|---|---|---|---|---|
| BACK | | | | | |
| MIDDLE | 18 | 5670 | 71 | 67.4 | 114 |
| FRONT | 18 | 5078 | 71 | | |

**Club Pro:** Tom Augusta
**Payment:** Cash, Visa, MC
**Tee Times:** No
**Fee 9 Holes: Weekday:** $16
**Fee 18 Holes: Weekday:** $27
**Twilight Rates:** After 4:30pm
**Cart Rental:** $28/18, $14/9 per cart
**Lessons:** No **Schools:** No
**Membership:** No
**Other:** Clubhouse / Snack Bar/ Improved bunkers

**Weekend:** $19
**Weekend:** $33
**Discounts:** Senior & Junior
**Driving Range:** No
**Junior Golf:** Yes
**Architect/Yr Open:** Frank Colanton/1994

COUPON

| | 1 | 2 | 3 | 4 | 5 | 6 | 7 | 8 | 9 |
|---|---|---|---|---|---|---|---|---|---|
| PAR | 3 | 5 | 4 | 4 | 4 | 4 | 4 | 4 | 4 |
| YARDS | 125 | 505 | 315 | 329 | 347 | 300 | 300 | 330 | 381 |
| | 10 | 11 | 12 | 13 | 14 | 15 | 16 | 17 | 18 |
| PAR | 3 | 4 | 4 | 3 | 4 | 4 | 5 | 4 | 4 |
| YARDS | 154 | 429 | 300 | 135 | 240 | 380 | 470 | 252 | 378 |

**Directions:** Route 107 off Route 125 in Kingston, ¼ of a mile. Or Exit 1 in Seabrook off of Route I-95. Go 10 miles West on Route 107.

NH

# Kingswood Golf Club

★★½  45 ▶

37 Kingswood Road
Wolfeboro, NH (603) 569-3569
www.kingswoodgolfclub.com
**Club Pro:** Kristy Gleason
**Payment:** Visa, MC, Amex, Disc
**Tee Times:** 7 days adv.

| Tees | Holes | Yards | Par | USGA | Slope |
|------|-------|-------|-----|------|-------|
| BACK | 18 | 6366 | 72 | 71.4 | 134 |
| MIDDLE | 18 | 5934 | 72 | 69.3 | 128 |
| FRONT | 18 | 5448 | 72 | 69.7 | 118 |

**Fee 9 Holes:** Contact Pro Shop    **Weekend:** Contact Pro Shop
**Fee 18 Holes:** Contact Pro Shop    **Weekend:** Contact Pro Shop
**Twilight Rates:** After 2pm    **Discounts:** None
**Cart Rental:** $22pp/18, $12pp/9    **Driving Range:** $6.50/bucket
**Lessons:** $90/hour, $50/half hour **Schools:** No    **Junior Golf:** Yes
**Membership:** Yes    **Architect/Yr Open:** Donald Ross/1915
**Other:** Snack Bar / Bar-Lounge    **GPS:**

Classic New England mountain course with great views. The course is hilly with 5 ponds. Has an excellent new range (230-yard range) and new instruction area. Reduced fees after 3pm with or without cart. Open April - October 31. Membership – $1250 Try and Buy Special (1 year only).

| | 1 | 2 | 3 | 4 | 5 | 6 | 7 | 8 | 9 |
|-----|-----|-----|-----|-----|-----|-----|-----|-----|-----|
| PAR | 4 | 5 | 3 | 4 | 4 | 3 | 4 | 4 | 4 |
| YARDS | 380 | 420 | 163 | 372 | 310 | 138 | 367 | 297 | 337 |
| | 10 | 11 | 12 | 13 | 14 | 15 | 16 | 17 | 18 |
| PAR | 4 | 5 | 4 | 3 | 4 | 4 | 5 | 4 | 4 |
| YARDS | 334 | 461 | 367 | 175 | 349 | 284 | 464 | 360 | 356 |

**Directions:** Route 28 North .25 mile past Kingswood High School. Turn left onto Kingswood Road.

# Kona Mansion Inn

NR  46 ▶

Moultonborough Neck Road
Center Harbor, NH (603) 253-4900

| Tees | Holes | Yards | Par | USGA | Slope |
|------|-------|-------|-----|------|-------|
| BACK | | | | | |
| MIDDLE | 9 | 1170 | 27 | | |
| FRONT | | | | | |

**Club Pro:**
**Payment:** Visa, MC, Disc
**Tee Times:** No
**Fee 9 Holes: Weekday:** $15    **Weekend:** $15
**Fee 18 Holes: Weekday:** $15    **Weekend:** $15
**Twilight Rates:** No    **Discounts:** None
**Cart Rental:** $3/pull    **Driving Range:** Yes
**Lessons:** No **Schools:** No    **Junior Golf:** No
**Membership:** Yes, seasonal    **Architect/Yr Open:** N.P. Nelson/1903
**Other:** Hotel / Full-Service Restaurant    **GPS:**

A resort on Lake Winnipesaukee. Par 3 course. New driving range.

| | 1 | 2 | 3 | 4 | 5 | 6 | 7 | 8 | 9 |
|-----|-----|-----|-----|-----|-----|-----|-----|-----|-----|
| PAR | 3 | 3 | 3 | 3 | 3 | 3 | 3 | 3 | 3 |
| YARDS | 105 | 150 | 130 | 135 | 128 | 150 | 162 | 125 | 85 |
| PAR | | | | | | | | | |
| YARDS | | | | | | | | | |

**Directions:** I-93 to Exit 23 (Meredith). Go 11 miles, take a left on Route 3 to lights, take right on Route 25. Go 9 miles to Moultonboro Neck Road on right. Go right, 2.5 miles to Kona Road on right. Follow signs.

# Lakeview Golf Club

NR 47 ▶

89 Ladd Hill Road
Belmont, NH (603) 524-2220

| Tees | Holes | Yards | Par | USGA | Slope |
|------|-------|-------|-----|------|-------|
| BACK | | | | | |
| MIDDLE | 9 | 3615 | 35 | 69 | |
| FRONT | 9 | 2270 | 37 | 72.0 | |

**Club Pro:** Tony Speradino, Manager
**Payment:** Cash or Check
**Tee Times:** No
**Fee 9 Holes: Weekday:** $15 **Weekend:** $15
**Fee 18 Holes: Weekday:** $22 **Weekend:** $22
**Twilight Rates:** After 3pm $13pp/9 M-F **Discounts:** None
**Cart Rental:** $10pp/18, $6pp/9 **Driving Range:** No
**Lessons:** No **Schools:** No **Junior Golf:** No
**Membership:** Yes **Architect/Yr Open:** 1925

Beautiful 9-hole golf course overlooks a panorama of lakes and mountains. Good walking course. Dress code. Twilight rates for 9 holes after 3pm - $12.

| | 1 | 2 | 3 | 4 | 5 | 6 | 7 | 8 | 9 |
|---|---|---|---|---|---|---|---|---|---|
| PAR | 5 | 4 | 4 | 4 | 3 | 4 | 3 | 5 | 3 |
| YARDS | 505 | 315 | 290 | 425 | 220 | 435 | 175 | 550 | 195 |

| | | | | | | | | | |
|---|---|---|---|---|---|---|---|---|---|
| PAR | | | | | | | | | |
| YARDS | | | | | | | | | |

**Directions:** I-93 North to Exit 20, then East toward Laconia on Routes 3 & 11. Cross Winnisquam bridge and follow 1 mile to set of lights. Take right, across from Belknap Mall.

# Lochmere Golf & Country Club ✪✪✪½ 48 ▶

360 Laconia Road
Tilton, NH (603) 528-4653
www.lochmeregolf.com

| Tees | Holes | Yards | Par | USGA | Slope |
|------|-------|-------|-----|------|-------|
| BACK | 18 | 6660 | 72 | 71.7 | 128 |
| MIDDLE | 18 | 6227 | 72 | 69.4 | 123 |
| FRONT | 18 | 5227 | 72 | 68.9 | 120 |

**Club Pro:** Vic Stanfield, PGA
**Payment:** Visa, MC
**Tee Times:** 7 days adv.
**Fee 9 Holes: Weekday:** $18 **Weekend:** $25
**Fee 18 Holes: Weekday:** $32, $47 w/cart **Weekend:** $45, $61 w/cart
**Twilight Rates:** After 4pm **Discounts:** Seasonal specials
**Cart Rental:** $16pp/18, $9pp/9 **Driving Range:** $3/$5/$7 bucket
**Lessons:** $45/half hour **Schools:** No **Junior Golf:** Yes
**Membership:** Yes **Architect/Yr Open:** Wogan & Sargent/1992
**Other:** Restaurant / Clubhouse / Bar-Lounge / Snack Bar / Function Room / Gazebo
**GPS:** Yes

Player Comments: "Great challenging course, friendly staff, just gets better every visit." –FP
Renovated hole #5 has greater landing area. Tuesday is senior citizen day. Four-Star *Golf Digest* facility.

| | 1 | 2 | 3 | 4 | 5 | 6 | 7 | 8 | 9 |
|---|---|---|---|---|---|---|---|---|---|
| PAR | 4 | 4 | 3 | 4 | 4 | 4 | 5 | 3 | 4 |
| YARDS | 330 | 340 | 140 | 350 | 368 | 363 | 480 | 163 | 390 |
| | 10 | 11 | 12 | 13 | 14 | 15 | 16 | 17 | 18 |
| PAR | 4 | 5 | 4 | 3 | 4 | 4 | 4 | 4 | 5 |
| YARDS | 350 | 500 | 310 | 160 | 410 | 401 | 377 | 323 | 472 |

**Directions:** I-93 to Exit 20 (Laconia/Tilton). Go 1.5 miles East on Route 3. Course is on left.

# Londonderry Country Club ✪✪ 49

56 Kimball Road
Londonderry, NH (603) 432-9789
www.londonderrycountryclub.com

Club Pro: Helga Kimball, GM
Payment: Cash, Visa, MC
Tee Times: Thurs. am for weekend

| Tees | Holes | Yards | Par | USGA | Slope |
|---|---|---|---|---|---|
| BACK | | | | | |
| MIDDLE | 18 | 3897 | 62 | 60.7 | 102 |
| FRONT | 18 | 3258 | 62 | 58.5 | 92 |

Fee 9 Holes: Weekday: $20          Weekend: $24
Fee 18 Holes: Weekday: $30          Weekend: $34
Twilight Rates: No          Discounts: Senior & Junior
Cart Rental: $22/18, $14pp/9 per cart          Driving Range: No
Lessons: Yes  Schools: No          Junior Golf: Yes
Membership: No          Architect/Yr Open: Forrest & Tom Kimball/1969
Other: Nuttfield Lounge and Snack Bar          GPS:

Lots of improvements in last two years. Beautiful condition due to the new improvements! Friendly staff. "Great course for your irons." –FP

| | 1 | 2 | 3 | 4 | 5 | 6 | 7 | 8 | 9 |
|---|---|---|---|---|---|---|---|---|---|
| PAR | 3 | 3 | 4 | 4 | 3 | 3 | 3 | 3 | 3 |
| YARDS | 210 | 165 | 235 | 215 | 135 | 165 | 177 | 123 | 165 |
| | 10 | 11 | 12 | 13 | 14 | 15 | 16 | 17 | 18 |
| PAR | 3 | 3 | 4 | 4 | 4 | 4 | 4 | 4 | 3 |
| YARDS | 155 | 115 | 300 | 310 | 340 | 235 | 370 | 345 | 135 |

Directions: I-93 to Exit 4, left onto Route 102 West, follow to Route 128 North. Follow 4 miles to traffic light. Left on Litchfield Road. Go 1.7 miles, take left onto Kimball Road. Club is 1 mile on right.

# Loudon Country Club ✪✪½ 50

653 Route 106
Loudon, NH (603) 783-3372
www.loudoncc.com

Club Pro: Bob Bean, PGA
Payment: Most Major Credit Cards, Cash
Tee Times: 6 days adv.

| Tees | Holes | Yards | Par | USGA | Slope |
|---|---|---|---|---|---|
| BACK | 18 | 6298 | 72 | 70.4 | 120 |
| MIDDLE | 18 | 5959 | 72 | 68.7 | 115 |
| FRONT | 18 | 5132 | 72 | 69 | 118 |

Fee 9 Holes: Weekday: $20          Weekend: $24
Fee 18 Holes: Weekday: $34          Weekend: $40
Twilight Rates: After 3:30pm          Discounts: Senior & Junior M-W
Cart Rental: $16pp/18, $10pp/9          Driving Range: $7/lg., $5/sm.
Lessons: Yes  Schools: Yes          Junior Golf: Yes
Membership: Yes          Architect/Yr Open: William Leombruno/1993
Other: Full Restaurant / Bar-Lounge / Clubhouse

COUPON

Challenging, yet playable. Very scenic and great conditions.

| | 1 | 2 | 3 | 4 | 5 | 6 | 7 | 8 | 9 |
|---|---|---|---|---|---|---|---|---|---|
| PAR | 4 | 5 | 4 | 3 | 4 | 5 | 4 | 3 | 4 |
| YARDS | 271 | 497 | 365 | 169 | 389 | 484 | 404 | 168 | 429 |
| | 10 | 11 | 12 | 13 | 14 | 15 | 16 | 17 | 18 |
| PAR | 4 | 3 | 5 | 3 | 4 | 4 | 4 | 4 | 4 |
| YARDS | 339 | 210 | 485 | 166 | 298 | 359 | 482 | 415 | 381 |

Directions: From Route I-93 North or South: Exit 15 East (Route 4) – go 3 miles to Exit 3 (Route 106). Take left – approximately 6 miles on left.

# Maplewood Golf Club

✪✪½  **51** ▶

Route 302
Bethlehem, NH (603) 869-3335
www.maplewoodgolfresort.com

Club Pro: Trevor Howard, Golf Dir.
Payment: Most Major Credit Cards
Tee Times: Yes
Fee 9 Holes: Weekday: $22
Fee 18 Holes: Weekday: $39
Twilight Rates: After 4pm wkdy, 5pm wknd
Cart Rental: $16pp/18, $10pp/9
Lessons: No  Schools: No
Membership: Yes

| Tees | Holes | Yards | Par | USGA | Slope |
|------|-------|-------|-----|------|-------|
| BACK | 18 | 6200 | 72 | 69.2 | 125 |
| MIDDLE | 18 | 6001 | 72 | 69.2 | 123 |
| FRONT | 18 | 5013 | 71 | 68.8 | 113 |

Weekend: $28
Weekend: $49
Discounts: Junior
Driving Range:
Junior Golf: No
Architect/Yr Open: Donald Ross/1914

Other: 1890 Restored Clubhouse / Showers / Lockers / Bar-Lounge / Hotel

Recently restored classic Donald Ross course. Stay and Play packages. Ladies' Day on Wednesday.
Cart required 8am - 2pm on weekends. New tees on holes 3 and 6.

**NH**

| | 1 | 2 | 3 | 4 | 5 | 6 | 7 | 8 | 9 |
|---|---|---|---|---|---|---|---|---|---|
| PAR | 5 | 4 | 4 | 4 | 4 | 4 | 4 | 3 | 4 |
| YARDS | 445 | 399 | 277 | 388 | 367 | 373 | 319 | 150 | 355 |
| | 10 | 11 | 12 | 13 | 14 | 15 | 16 | 17 | 18 |
| PAR | 4 | 3 | 3 | 4 | 4 | 5 | 6 | 4 | 3 |
| YARDS | 355 | 163 | 201 | 321 | 279 | 527 | 651 | 287 | 144 |

Directions: I-93 Exit 40 onto Route 302 East. Approximately 5 miles.

# Mojalaki Country Club

✪½  **52** ▶

321 Prospect Street
Franklin, NH (603) 934-3033
www.mojalaki.com

Club Pro: Bob Warren
Payment: Visa, MC, Disc
Tee Times: 5 days adv.
Fee 9 Holes: Weekday: $15
Fee 18 Holes: Weekday: $23
Twilight Rates: After 2pm
Cart Rental: $17pp/18, $11pp/9
Lessons: Yes  Schools: Yes
Membership: Yes

| Tees | Holes | Yards | Par | USGA | Slope |
|------|-------|-------|-----|------|-------|
| BACK | 18 | 5820 | 70 | 69.9 | 113 |
| MIDDLE | 18 | 5342 | 70 | 66.2 | 106 |
| FRONT | 18 | 4802 | 70 | 63.5 | 104 |

Weekend: $15
Weekend: $23
Discounts: Senior & Junior
Driving Range: Yes
Junior Golf: Yes
Architect/Yr Open: Stiles & Sargent/1920, 2003

Other: Complete Function Facility Holds 180 / Snack Bar / Large Outings Welcome /
Gazebo Available For Weddings

Beautiful views and a combination of contemporary and traditional design with tees to complement every
skill level. Driving range, putting and chipping green. "Friendly owner, great staff, very good value." –FP

| | 1 | 2 | 3 | 4 | 5 | 6 | 7 | 8 | 9 |
|---|---|---|---|---|---|---|---|---|---|
| PAR | 4 | 3 | 4 | 3 | 5 | 4 | 3 | 4 | 4 |
| YARDS | 312 | 93 | 352 | 135 | 465 | 344 | 140 | 307 | 250 |
| | 10 | 11 | 12 | 13 | 14 | 15 | 16 | 17 | 18 |
| PAR | 4 | 4 | 3 | 5 | 4 | 4 | 5 | 3 | 4 |
| YARDS | 258 | 322 | 140 | 478 | 407 | 319 | 454 | 179 | 387 |

Directions: I-93 to Exit 19 traveling North, Exit 20 traveling South. Route 3 South to downtown
Franklin, left onto Prospect Street. Golf course 1 mile on right.

# Monadnock Country Club ✪✪ 53 ▶

49 High Street
Peterborough, NH (603) 924-7769
www.monadnockcc.com
**Club Pro:** Dana Hennessey
**Payment:** Visa, MC
**Tee Times:** No
**Fee 9 Holes: Weekday:** $15
**Fee 18 Holes: Weekday:** $24
**Twilight Rates:** After 4pm
**Cart Rental:** $25/18, $14/9 per cart
**Lessons:** Yes **Schools:** Yes
**Membership:** Yes

**Weekend:** $16
**Weekend:** $26
**Discounts:** Senior & Junior
**Driving Range:** No
**Junior Golf:** Yes
**Architect/Yr Open:** S. Anderson & Son/1901
**Other:** Clubhouse / Snack Bar / Bar-Lounge / Banquet Facility

| Tees | Holes | Yards | Par | USGA | Slope |
|------|-------|-------|-----|------|-------|
| BACK | | | | | |
| MIDDLE | 9 | 3250 | 29 | 58.4 | 90 |
| FRONT | 9 | 2822 | 29 | | |

This course can be challenging for both veterans and beginners. The scenic beauty alone is worth the trip. Clubhouse has been recently renovated.

| | 1 | 2 | 3 | 4 | 5 | 6 | 7 | 8 | 9 |
|------|-----|-----|-----|-----|-----|-----|-----|-----|-----|
| PAR | 3 | 4 | 3 | 3 | 3 | 4 | 3 | 3 | 3 |
| YARDS | 155 | 300 | 110 | 205 | 135 | 265 | 135 | 165 | 155 |
| PAR | | | | | | | | | |
| YARDS | | | | | | | | | |

**Directions:** From East or West, take Route 101. From North or South, take Route 202. Located on High Street.

# Mountain View Grand Resort & Spa ✪½ 54 ▶

101 Mountain View Road
Whitefield, NH (603) 837-0076
www.mountainviewgrand.com
**Club Pro:**
**Payment:** Visa, MC, Amex, Disc
**Tee Times:** 7 days adv.
**Fee 9 Holes: Weekday:** $20
**Fee 18 Holes: Weekday:** $30
**Twilight Rates:** After 3pm
**Cart Rental:** $30/18, $20/9 per cart
**Lessons:** No **Schools:** No
**Membership:** Yes

**Weekend:** $25
**Weekend:** $35
**Discounts:** Senior
**Driving Range:** No
**Junior Golf:**
**Architect/Yr Open:** Ralph Barton/1900
**Other:** Restaurant / Clubhouse / Showers / Hotel / Bar / Lounge / Tennis

| Tees | Holes | Yards | Par | USGA | Slope |
|------|-------|-------|-----|------|-------|
| BACK | | | | | |
| MIDDLE | 9 | 2930 | 35 | 66 | 112 |
| FRONT | 9 | 2873 | 35 | 66 | 112 |

Challenging course in the heart of the White Mountains. Majestic views 360 degrees and historic hotel with great accommodations. Historic 9 holes completely renovated in 1998. Additional holes in planning stage.

| | 1 | 2 | 3 | 4 | 5 | 6 | 7 | 8 | 9 |
|------|-----|-----|-----|-----|-----|-----|-----|-----|-----|
| PAR | 4 | 4 | 5 | 4 | 4 | 3 | 4 | 3 | 4 |
| YARDS | 449 | 398 | 472 | 326 | 316 | 126 | 342 | 123 | 321 |
| PAR | | | | | | | | | |
| YARDS | | | | | | | | | |

**Directions:** I-93 North to Exit 35. Go 21 miles north on Route 3.

# Mt. Pleasant Golf Course

NR  55 ▶

**210 Mt. Washington Hotel Road**
**Bretton Woods, NH (603) 278-4653**
**www.mountwashingtonresort.com**

| Tees | Holes | Yards | Par | USGA | Slope |
|------|-------|-------|-----|------|-------|
| BACK | 9 | 3212 | 35 | 68.6 | 124 |
| MIDDLE | 9 | 2990 | 35 | 67.4 | 122 |
| FRONT | 9 | 2451 | 35 | 67.6 | 109 |

**Club Pro:** John Pawlak
**Payment:** Visa, MC, Amex, Disc, Checks
**Tee Times:** Yes, 603-278-GOLF
**Fee 9 Holes: Weekday:** $54 ($49 resort)    **Weekend:** $64 ($59 resort)
**Fee 18 Holes: Weekday:**      **Weekend:**
**Twilight Rates:** $44 ($39 resort) after 1pm weekdays, $51 ($39 resort) after 3pm weekends
**Discounts:** Senior & Junior
**Cart Rental:** Included    **Driving Range:** Yes
**Lessons:** Private and Group **Schools:** Yes    **Junior Golf:** Yes
**Membership:** Yes
**Architect/Yr Open:** Alex Findlay/1895; Reconstuction - Brian Silva/1989
**Other:** Resort / Golf Packages / Restaurant / Clubhouse / Bar-Lounge / Lockers / Showers

Spectacular Alex Findlay layout set at the foot of the Presidential Mountains. Challenging 9-hole course alongside New Hampshire's scenic Ammonoosuc River. Part of the Mt. Washington Hotel complex.

|  | 1 | 2 | 3 | 4 | 5 | 6 | 7 | 8 | 9 |
|------|---|---|---|---|---|---|---|---|---|
| PAR | 5 | 4 | 4 | 4 | 3 | 4 | 4 | 3 | 4 |
| YARDS | 500 | 330 | 380 | 370 | 120 | 415 | 385 | 140 | 350 |
| PAR | | | | | | | | | |
| YARDS | | | | | | | | | |

**Directions:** From I-93 take Exit 35 to Route 3N. Follow to Twin Mountain. Turn right at Route 302 and follow to Mount Washington Resort.

# Mt. Washington Golf Club

✪✪✪✪✪ 56 ▶

**210 Mt. Washington Hotel Road**
**Bretton Woods, NH (603) 278-4653**
**www.mountwashingtonresort.com**

| Tees | Holes | Yards | Par | USGA | Slope |
|------|-------|-------|-----|------|-------|
| BACK | 18 | 7004 | 72 | 73.7 | 124 |
| MIDDLE | 18 | 6400 | 72 | 67.0 | 122 |
| FRONT | 18 | 5246 | 71 | 70.2 | 120 |

**Club Pro:** John Pawlak
**Payment:** Visa, MC, Amex, Disc, Checks
**Tee Times:** Yes, 603-278-GOLF
**Fee 9 Holes: Weekday:**    **Weekend:**
**Fee 18 Holes: Weekday:** $89    **Weekend:** $99
**Twilight Rates:** After 2pm    **Discounts:** Senior & Junior
**Cart Rental:** Included    **Driving Range:** Yes
**Lessons:** Private and Group **Schools:** Yes    **Junior Golf:** Yes
**Membership:** Yes
**Architect/Yr Open:** Donald Ross/1915, Reconstuction - Brian Silva/2008
**Other:** Resort / Golf Packages / Restaurant / Clubhouse / Bar-Lounge / Lockers / Showers

*COUPON*

Spectacular Donald Ross layout set at the foot of the Presidential Mountains. Brilliant design fully restored by Brian Silva in 2008. *Golfweek's* #1 Course You Can Play in NH. 100th anniversary in 2015.

|  | 1 | 2 | 3 | 4 | 5 | 6 | 7 | 8 | 9 |
|------|---|---|---|---|---|---|---|---|---|
| PAR | 4 | 4 | 4 | 4 | 3 | 5 | 4 | 4 | 4 |
| YARDS | 377 | 395 | 379 | 309 | 193 | 501 | 318 | 410 | 394 |
|  | **10** | **11** | **12** | **13** | **14** | **15** | **16** | **17** | **18** |
| PAR | 5 | 5 | 4 | 4 | 3 | 4 | 3 | 4 | 4 |
| YARDS | 522 | 508 | 313 | 374 | 204 | 293 | 186 | 371 | 353 |

**Directions:** From I-93 take Exit 35 to Route 3N. Follow to Twin Mountain. Turn right at Route 302 and follow to Mount Washington Resort.

**NH**

# Newport Golf Club  ✪✪  57

**112 Unity Road**
**Newport, NH (603) 863-7787**
www.newport-golf.com

**Club Pro:** Vince Molesky, Dir. of Golf
**Payment:** Visa, MC, Cash
**Tee Times:** 3 days adv.
**Fee  9 Holes: Weekday:** $20
**Fee 18 Holes: Weekday:** $34
**Twilight Rates:** After 2pm
**Cart Rental:** $15pp/18, $10pp/9
**Lessons:** $35/half hour  **Schools:** No
**Membership:** Yes
**Other:** Clubhouse / Snack Bar / Bar-Lounge / Lockers

| Tees | Holes | Yards | Par | USGA | Slope |
|------|-------|-------|-----|------|-------|
| BACK | 18 | 6509 | 71 | 72.7 | 126 |
| MIDDLE | 18 | 6083 | 71 | 70.4 | 125 |
| FRONT | 18 | 4738 | 71 | 62.7 | 108 |

**Weekend:** $38 includes cart
**Weekend:** $59 includes cart
**Discounts:** Junior
**Driving Range:** Yes
**Junior Golf:** Yes
**Architect/Yr Open:** Raph Barton/1922

Improvements: recently completed full renovations. New hole number 5. Area attractions include, Mt. Sunapee, great hiking, and stream fishing.

| | 1 | 2 | 3 | 4 | 5 | 6 | 7 | 8 | 9 |
|------|-----|-----|-----|-----|-----|-----|-----|-----|-----|
| PAR | 5 | 4 | 4 | 3 | 4 | 4 | 3 | 4 | 4 |
| YARDS | 511 | 326 | 388 | 179 | 373 | 375 | 145 | 269 | 369 |
| | 10 | 11 | 12 | 13 | 14 | 15 | 16 | 17 | 18 |
| PAR | 5 | 3 | 4 | 4 | 4 | 4 | 3 | 4 | 5 |
| YARDS | 477 | 138 | 387 | 379 | 375 | 341 | 169 | 375 | 507 |

**Directions:** I-91 to Exit 8. East to Claremont, then Route 11 toward Newport, ¾ mile take right onto Unity Road. Or, I-89 North to Exit 9. Follow Route 103 to Route 11 to center of town on Route 11 & 10 to lights, take right toward Claremont, first left after next light onto Unity Road, ¾ mile on left.

# Nippo Lake Golf Club  ✪✪✪  58

**88 Stagecoach Road**
**Barrington, NH (603) 664-7616**
www.nippolake.com

**Club Pro:** Chris Mowers, PGA
**Payment:** Visa, MC
**Tee Times:** 7 days adv.
**Fee  9 Holes: Weekday:** $20
**Fee 18 Holes: Weekday:** $35
**Twilight Rates:** After 4pm
**Cart Rental:** $16pp/18, $10pp/9
**Lessons:** $45/30 min.  **Schools:** Jr.
**Membership:** Yes
**Other:** Clubhouse / Snack Bar / Restaurant / Bar-Lounge / Video instruction

| Tees | Holes | Yards | Par | USGA | Slope |
|------|-------|-------|-----|------|-------|
| BACK | 18 | 5594 | 70 | 66.5 | 121 |
| MIDDLE | 18 | 5307 | 70 | 64.9 | 117 |
| FRONT | 18 | 4513 | 70 | 85.4 | 104 |

**Weekend:** $24
**Weekend:** $42
**Discounts:** Junior & Senior
**Driving Range:** Yes
**Junior Golf:** Yes
**Architect/Yr Open:**

You will enjoy the majestic beauty of this backwoods links through the serene mountain setting and the friendly staff.

| | 1 | 2 | 3 | 4 | 5 | 6 | 7 | 8 | 9 |
|------|-----|-----|-----|-----|-----|-----|-----|-----|-----|
| PAR | 4 | 5 | 3 | 5 | 4 | 3 | 4 | 4 | 3 |
| YARDS | 314 | 518 | 150 | 505 | 371 | 130 | 329 | 344 | 135 |
| | 10 | 11 | 12 | 13 | 14 | 15 | 16 | 17 | 18 |
| PAR | 5 | 4 | 3 | 4 | 4 | 4 | 4 | 3 | 4 |
| YARDS | 476 | 333 | 171 | 315 | 316 | 351 | 365 | 180 | 291 |

**Directions:** Spaulding Turnpike North to Exit 13 (Route 202 North). Take right onto Route 126. Go ¼ mile, then take a left onto Province Road.

# North Conway Country Club    ✪✪½  59 ▶

76 Norcross Circle
North Conway, NH (603) 356-9391
www.northconwaycountryclub.com

| Tees | Holes | Yards | Par | USGA | Slope |
|------|-------|-------|-----|------|-------|
| BACK | 18 | 6659 | 71 | 71.9 | 125 |
| MIDDLE | 18 | 6266 | 71 | 70.3 | 121 |
| FRONT | 18 | 5530 | 71 | 70.7 | 118 |

**Club Pro:** Larry Gallagher, PGA
**Payment:** Visa, MC, Disc
**Tee Times:** 5 days adv.
**Fee  9 Holes: Weekday:**
**Fee 18 Holes: Wkdy:** $46 walk, $60 ride, M-Th
**Twilight Rates:** After 4pm
**Cart Rental:** $14pp/18
**Lessons:** By appointment  **Schools:** Junior
**Membership:** Yes
**Other:** Restaurant / Bar-Lounge / Clubhouse

**Weekend:**
**Weekend:** $70 w/cart F/S/S/H
**Discounts:** Sr. & Jr. after 1pm M-Th
**Driving Range:** Yes, natural grass
**Junior Golf:** Yes
**Architect/Yr:** Alex Findlay & Phil Wogan/1895
**GPS:**

*COUPON*

Scenic and golfer friendly, well condition. Host to NH Ladies and Men Amateur, NH Open and NH PGA Championship.

|  | 1 | 2 | 3 | 4 | 5 | 6 | 7 | 8 | 9 |
|------|---|---|---|---|---|---|---|---|---|
| PAR | 4 | 4 | 4 | 3 | 4 | 4 | 3 | 5 | 4 |
| YARDS | 406 | 399 | 354 | 130 | 328 | 362 | 208 | 497 | 376 |
|  | 10 | 11 | 12 | 13 | 14 | 15 | 16 | 17 | 18 |
| PAR | 4 | 5 | 4 | 3 | 4 | 3 | 4 | 5 | 4 |
| YARDS | 349 | 475 | 385 | 150 | 420 | 147 | 357 | 528 | 337 |

**Directions:** Route 16 to Main Street, North Conway. Next to scenic railroad station.

# Oak Hill Golf Course    ✪✪  60 ▶

159 Pease Road
Meredith, NH  (603) 279-4438
www.oakhillgc.com

| Tees | Holes | Yards | Par | USGA | Slope |
|------|-------|-------|-----|------|-------|
| BACK | 9 | 2347 | 34 | 63.4 | 97 |
| MIDDLE | 9 | 2210 | 34 | 62.4 | 94 |
| FRONT | 9 | 1890 | 34 | 60.0 | 98 |

**Club Pro:** Barbara Jenkins, Manager
**Payment:** Cash, Visa, MC
**Tee Times:** No
**Fee  9 Holes: Weekday:** $14
**Fee 18 Holes: Weekday:** $24
**Twilight Rates:** After 3pm
**Cart Rental:** $24/18, $14/9 per cart
**Lessons:** No  **Schools:** No
**Membership:** Yes
**Other:** Snack Bar / Bar-Lounge

**Weekend:** $14
**Weekend:** $24
**Discounts:** None
**Driving Range:** No
**Junior Golf:** No
**Architect/Yr Open:** Harry Page/1963
**GPS:**

*COUPON*

Short regulation New England course. Good challenge for your irons. Wooded and scenic. Features such as stonewalls, scenic beauty, and its four hidden greens give Oak Hill an abundance of character. Our greens fees are the most reasonable around and our friendly atmosphere will tempt you to stay awhile. No tank tops. Open late April to November.

|  | 1 | 2 | 3 | 4 | 5 | 6 | 7 | 8 | 9 |
|------|---|---|---|---|---|---|---|---|---|
| PAR | 4 | 3 | 4 | 4 | 3 | 4 | 3 | 4 | 5 |
| YARDS | 255 | 136 | 258 | 298 | 159 | 229 | 118 | 300 | 457 |
| PAR |  |  |  |  |  |  |  |  |  |
| YARDS |  |  |  |  |  |  |  |  |  |

**Directions:** I-93 to Exit 23 Route 104 East, 7.5 miles to stop light. Turn right onto Pease Road 1.5 miles. Parking on left, golf course on right.

# Oaks Golf Links, The ✪✪✪½ 61

100 Hideaway Place
Somersworth, NH (603) 692-6257
www.theoaksgolflinks.com

| Tees | Holes | Yards | Par | USGA | Slope |
|------|-------|-------|-----|------|-------|
| BACK | 18 | 6825 | 71 | 72.1 | 126 |
| MIDDLE | 18 | 6165 | 71 | 69.4 | 123 |
| FRONT | 18 | 4880 | 71 | 69.7 | 112 |

**Club Pro:** Shaun Bishop
**Payment:** Most Major Credit Cards
**Tee Times:** 5 days adv.
**Fee 9 Holes: Weekday:** $30 **Weekend:** $35
**Fee 18 Holes: Weekday:** $50 **Weekend:** $60
**Twilight Rates:** Ater 5:30pm **Discounts:** Senior & Junior, wkdys only
**Cart Rental:** $18pp/18, $9pp/9 **Driving Range:** Yes
**Lessons:** Yes **Schools:** Yes **Junior Golf:** Yes
**Membership:** Yes **Architect/Yr Open:** Brad Booth/2005
**Other:** Restaurant / Bar and Grille / Clubhouse **GPS:**

Beautifully manicured tight fairways and fast greens make The Oaks a must play. Dual memberships available with our sister course, Candia Woods. A public course with the private club feel. Top notch practice facility.

| | 1 | 2 | 3 | 4 | 5 | 6 | 7 | 8 | 9 |
|------|----|----|----|----|----|----|----|----|----|
| PAR | 4 | 4 | 3 | 5 | 3 | 4 | 4 | 4 | 4 |
| YARDS | 346 | 320 | 169 | 555 | 149 | 400 | 398 | 324 | 390 |
| | 10 | 11 | 12 | 13 | 14 | 15 | 16 | 17 | 18 |
| PAR | 4 | 5 | 4 | 3 | 4 | 4 | 3 | 4 | 5 |
| YARDS | 360 | 518 | 306 | 133 | 359 | 327 | 150 | 392 | 562 |

**Directions:** I-95 in Portsmouth to Route 16 North (Spaulding Turnpike) to Exit 9. Bear right off ramp and then move to left lane at Weeks Crossings intersection (about .3 miles). North on Route 108 for 3.6 miles; club on right.

# Overlook Golf Club ✪✪✪½ 62

5 Overlook Drive
Hollis, NH (603) 465-2909
www.overlookgolfclub.com

| Tees | Holes | Yards | Par | USGA | Slope |
|------|-------|-------|-----|------|-------|
| BACK | 18 | 6624 | 71 | 70.1 | 126 |
| MIDDLE | 18 | 6103 | 71 | 68.2 | 119 |
| FRONT | 18 | 5255 | 72 | 69.2 | 114 |

**Club Pro:** John McNeill, Manager
**Payment:** Visa, MC, Amex, Disc
**Tee Times:** 7 days adv.
**Fee 9 Holes: Weekday:** $25 **Weekend:** $30
**Fee 18 Holes: Weekday:** $42 **Weekend:** $52
**Twilight Rates:** After 1pm **Discounts:** Senior & Junior
**Cart Rental:** $15pp/18, $10pp/9 **Driving Range:** No
**Lessons:** Yes **Schools:** No **Junior Golf:** Yes
**Membership:** Inner Club **Architect/Yr Open:** 1989
**Other:** Clubhouse / Snack Bar / Bar-Lounge **GPS:**

Player Comments: "Enjoyable for all abilities." "Use all clubs in bag." The front 9 are fairly hilly, back 9 are somewhat flat. New 6th hole. Front and back women's tees. Friendly atmosphere, great conditions. Nice practice area with bunkers and huge putting green.

| | 1 | 2 | 3 | 4 | 5 | 6 | 7 | 8 | 9 |
|------|----|----|----|----|----|----|----|----|----|
| PAR | 5 | 4 | 4 | 4 | 3 | 4 | 4 | 3 | 4 |
| YARDS | 535 | 299 | 433 | 390 | 177 | 371 | 292 | 167 | 326 |
| | 10 | 11 | 12 | 13 | 14 | 15 | 16 | 17 | 18 |
| PAR | 5 | 4 | 4 | 4 | 3 | 4 | 4 | 3 | 5 |
| YARDS | 522 | 376 | 346 | 390 | 164 | 341 | 320 | 138 | 516 |

**Directions:** From Route 495 take Exit to Route 3 North to Exit 5W (Route 111 West). Follow Route 111 West approximately 3½ miles. Course is on the right.

# Owl's Nest Golf Club

✪✪✪½  **63** ▶

40 Clubhouse Lane
Campton, NH (603) 726-3076
www.owlsnestgolf.com

| Tees | Holes | Yards | Par | USGA | Slope |
|------|-------|-------|-----|------|-------|
| BACK | 18 | 6818 | 72 | 74.0 | 133 |
| MIDDLE | 18 | 6110 | 72 | 69.7 | 124 |
| FRONT | 18 | 5174 | 72 | 67.8 | 117 |

**Club Pro:** Charles Wheeler, Dir. of Golf
**Payment:** Visa, MC, Amex, Disc
**Tee Times:** 7 days adv., 1-888-OWL-NEST
**Fee 9 Holes: Weekday:** $40
**Fee 18 Holes: Weekday:** $70
**Twilight Rates:** After 3pm
**Cart Rental:** Included
**Lessons:** $45/half hour; $75/hr. **Schools:** No
**Membership:** Yes
**Other:** Off-season rates as low as $44/18

**Weekend:** $50 (F/S/S)
**Weekend:** $85 (F/S/S)
**Discounts:** Junior 50% M-Th
**Driving Range:** $5
**Junior Golf:** Yes
**Architect/Yr Open:** Cornish & Mungeam/1998
**GPS:**

 COUPON

Player Comments: "Great greens" "Nice layout, well-maintained, courteous staff." "Excellent customer service." "A true destination course."
Discount rates in early and late seasons (call ahead). One of the best layouts in New England. Best scenic view around; staff will make you feel welcome.

| | 1 | 2 | 3 | 4 | 5 | 6 | 7 | 8 | 9 |
|-----|-----|-----|-----|-----|-----|-----|-----|-----|-----|
| PAR | 4 | 4 | 4 | 5 | 3 | 4 | 4 | 4 | 5 |
| YARDS | 370 | 366 | 395 | 503 | 160 | 311 | 350 | 335 | 483 |
| | 10 | 11 | 12 | 13 | 14 | 15 | 16 | 17 | 18 |
| PAR | 3 | 4 | 4 | 5 | 3 | 5 | 4 | 5 | 4 |
| YARDS | 127 | 316 | 391 | 489 | 160 | 259 | 435 | 488 | 348 |

**Directions:** I-93 to Exit 28, West on Route 49, then north on Owl Street.

# Passaconaway Country Club

✪✪✪½  **64** ▶

12 Midway Avenue (Route 3A)
Litchfield, NH (603) 424-4653
www.passaconawaycc.com

| Tees | Holes | Yards | Par | USGA | Slope |
|------|-------|-------|-----|------|-------|
| BACK | 18 | 6855 | 71 | 72.6 | 132 |
| MIDDLE | 18 | 6462 | 71 | 70.5 | 128 |
| FRONT | 18 | 5369 | 71 | 70.9 | 118 |

**Club Pro:** Joe Healey
**Payment:** Cash, Visa, MC
**Tee Times:** 5 days adv.
**Fee 9 Holes: Weekday:** $31
**Fee 18 Holes: Weekday:** $45
**Twilight Rates:** After 6pm
**Cart Rental:** $18pp/18, $11pp/9
**Lessons:** $45/half hour **Schools:** No
**Membership:** Yes, Inner Club
**Other:** Restaurant / Showers

**Weekend:** $34 after 10am only
**Weekend:** $56
**Discounts:** Sr., Jr., & Ladies wkdys
**Driving Range:** $10/lg., $5/sm.
**Junior Golf:** Yes
**Architect/Yr Open:** Cornish & Silva/1989
**GPS:**

Player Comments: "Links-style. Clubhouse staff very friendly. Course is well-maintained, very plush, greens outstanding and true. Plenty of water on the course. Bring the driver: long par 4's."

| | 1 | 2 | 3 | 4 | 5 | 6 | 7 | 8 | 9 |
|-----|-----|-----|-----|-----|-----|-----|-----|-----|-----|
| PAR | 5 | 3 | 4 | 3 | 5 | 4 | 4 | 3 | 4 |
| YARDS | 532 | 150 | 424 | 172 | 556 | 454 | 443 | 169 | 428 |
| | 10 | 11 | 12 | 13 | 14 | 15 | 16 | 17 | 18 |
| PAR | 4 | 4 | 4 | 3 | 5 | 4 | 4 | 4 | 4 |
| YARDS | 352 | 327 | 395 | 203 | 502 | 348 | 321 | 379 | 307 |

**Directions:** Route 93 North to Exit 4. Left on Route 102 for 5.5 miles to yellow blinking light. Take right on West Road, for 3 miles to the end. Left on Hillcrest for 3 miles, the course is straight ahead.

# Pease Golf Course ✪✪✪ 65

200 Grafton Road
Portsmouth, NH (603) 433-1331
www.peasegolf.com

| Tees | Holes | Yards | Par | USGA | Slope |
|------|-------|-------|-----|------|-------|
| BACK | 27/18 | 6292 | 71 | 70.1 | 120 |
| MIDDLE | 27/18 | 5784 | 71 | 67.4 | 117 |
| FRONT | 27/18 | 4963 | 71 | 68.3 | 114 |

**Club Pro:** Tim Riese, PGA
**Payment:** Visa, MC, Amex, Cash
**Tee Times:** 7 days adv.
**Fee 9 Holes: Weekday:** $27　　**Weekend:** $30
**Fee 18 Holes: Weekday:** $46 (F/S/S)　　**Weekend:** $50 (F/S/S)
**Twilight Rates:** After 1pm　　**Discounts:** Senior & Junior
**Cart Rental:** $16pp/18, $10pp/9　　**Driving Range:** $10/lg., $6/sm.
**Lessons:** Yes **Schools:** No　　**Junior Golf:** Yes
**Membership:** Yes　　**Architect/Yr Open:** Arthur Findlay/1901
**Other:** Clubhouse / Bar-Lounge / Snack Bar / Showers / Lockers

27 holes available. Blue course 9 demanding for all levels: rating, 35.0/slope/120. Carts mandatory only for new 9. New clubhouse and reconstruction of the original 18 holes.

| | 1 | 2 | 3 | 4 | 5 | 6 | 7 | 8 | 9 |
|---|---|---|---|---|---|---|---|---|---|
| PAR | 5 | 5 | 3 | 4 | 4 | 4 | 4 | 4 | 3 |
| YARDS | 465 | 471 | 160 | 280 | 375 | 308 | 356 | 265 | 150 |
| | 10 | 11 | 12 | 13 | 14 | 15 | 16 | 17 | 18 |
| PAR | 4 | 3 | 4 | 5 | 3 | 5 | 3 | 4 | 4 |
| YARDS | 322 | 185 | 385 | 532 | 140 | 498 | 162 | 365 | 375 |

**Directions:** I-95 North to Exit 3, at light turn left, take 1st right. From Route I-95 South take Exit 3A, at stop sign turn right.

# Pembroke Pines Country Club ✪✪½ 66

42 Whittemore Road
Pembroke, NH (603) 210-1365
www.pembrokecc.net

| Tees | Holes | Yards | Par | USGA | Slope |
|------|-------|-------|-----|------|-------|
| BACK | 18 | 6572 | 72 | 62.4 | 130 |
| MIDDLE | 18 | 6162 | 72 | 61.4 | 125 |
| FRONT | 18 | 5419 | 72 | 71.0 | 122 |

**Club Pro:** Eric Thompson, PGA
**Payment:**
**Tee Times:** 5 days adv.
**Fee 9 Holes: Weekday:** $24　　**Weekend:** $26
**Fee 18 Holes: Weekday:** $40　　**Weekend:** $45
**Twilight Rates:** After 4pm　　**Discounts:** Senior
**Cart Rental:** $16pp/18, $10pp/9　　**Driving Range:** Yes
**Lessons:** Yes **Schools:** No　　**Junior Golf:** Yes
**Membership:** Yes　　**Architect/Yr Open:** 1963
**Other:**　　**GPS:**

COUPON

Two different experiences at one course. A wide-open front 9 with room to recover from wayward shots. "While the back 9 with picturesque views and tight fairways are a shot-makers paradise." –FP

Red/White

| | 1 | 2 | 3 | 4 | 5 | 6 | 7 | 8 | 9 |
|---|---|---|---|---|---|---|---|---|---|
| PAR | 5 | 4 | 4 | 3 | 4 | 3 | 4 | 4 | 5 |
| YARDS | 451 | 393 | 343 | 148 | 441 | 165 | 346 | 386 | 474 |
| | 10 | 11 | 12 | 13 | 14 | 15 | 16 | 17 | 18 |
| PAR | 4 | 4 | 5 | 3 | 5 | 4 | 3 | 4 | 4 |
| YARDS | 387 | 399 | 545 | 164 | 516 | 306 | 125 | 328 | 245 |

**Directions:** I-293, to Route 101 West to Amherst. Then take Route 122 to the course located ½ mile past Amherst Country Club.

# Pheasant Ridge Country Club ✪✪

**140 Country Club Road**
**Gilford, NH (603) 524-7808**
www.playgolfne.com
**Club Pro:** Jim Swarthout, PGA
**Payment:** Visa, MC, Disc, Amex
**Tee Times:** 7 days adv.

| Tees | Holes | Yards | Par | USGA | Slope |
|------|-------|-------|-----|------|-------|
| BACK | 18 | 6402 | 70 | 69.3 | 115 |
| MIDDLE | 18 | 6004 | 70 | 67.2 | 112 |
| FRONT | 18 | 5192 | 70 | 68.6 | 112 |

**Fee 9 Holes: Weekday:** $20
**Fee 18 Holes: Weekday:** $34
**Twilight Rates:** After 2pm
**Cart Rental:** $32/18 per cart
**Lessons:** Yes **Schools:** No
**Membership:** Season Pass
**Other:** Snack Bar / Bar-Lounge / 400-Seat Function Hall

**Weekend:** $26
**Weekend:** $44
**Discounts:** None
**Driving Range:** Yes
**Junior Golf:** No
**Architect/Yr Open:** Geoffrey Cornish/1962

"Course reflects both the late Phil Friel's skill as a golfer and as a developer." –Paul Harber. Beautiful views. A Golf Management Company course.

|  | 1 | 2 | 3 | 4 | 5 | 6 | 7 | 8 | 9 |
|------|-----|-----|-----|-----|-----|-----|-----|-----|-----|
| PAR | 4 | 3 | 4 | 4 | 4 | 5 | 4 | 3 | 4 |
| YARDS | 340 | 150 | 370 | 410 | 290 | 535 | 329 | 163 | 370 |
|  | 10 | 11 | 12 | 13 | 14 | 15 | 16 | 17 | 18 |
| PAR | 5 | 4 | 4 | 3 | 4 | 4 | 4 | 4 | 3 |
| YARDS | 480 | 385 | 380 | 190 | 340 | 360 | 360 | 376 | 176 |

**Directions:** I-93 to Exit 20 (3 North), follow 9 miles onto Laconia Bypass. Take 2nd exit, right off ramp then next right onto Country Club Road. Course is ½ mile up hill on left.

# Pine Grove Springs Country Club NR 68

**292 Route 9A**
**Spofford, NH (603) 363-4433**
www.pgscc.com
**Club Pro:** Bob Maibusch
**Payment:** All Major Credit Cards, Check
**Tee Times:** No

| Tees | Holes | Yards | Par | USGA | Slope |
|------|-------|-------|-----|------|-------|
| BACK | | | | | |
| MIDDLE | 9 | 2924 | 36 | 69.7 | 124 |
| FRONT | 9 | 2630 | 36 | 72.2 | 120 |

**Fee 9 Holes: Weekday:** $15
**Fee 18 Holes: Weekday:** $25
**Twilight Rates:** After 4pm
**Cart Rental:** $15pp/18, $10pp/9
**Driving Range:** Yes
**Lessons:** Yes **Schools:** No
**Membership:** Yes
**Other:** Snack Bar / Bar-Lounge

**Weekend:** $15
**Weekend:** $25
**Discounts:** Senior over 65
           Junior 18 and under

**Junior Golf:** Yes
**Architect/Yr Open:** 1900

COUPON

Sig. Hole: #3 is a par 5 with 3 water hazards, dogleg right, rolling fairways, and elevated green. Open April – October. Plus 5-hole pitch and putt course. "Nice greens, great par 3 finishing hole." –GM

|  | 1 | 2 | 3 | 4 | 5 | 6 | 7 | 8 | 9 |
|------|-----|-----|-----|-----|-----|-----|-----|-----|-----|
| PAR | 4 | 4 | 5 | 4 | 3 | 4 | 5 | 4 | 3 |
| YARDS | 269 | 368 | 541 | 345 | 148 | 347 | 420 | 318 | 168 |
| PAR | | | | | | | | | |
| YARDS | | | | | | | | | |

**Directions:** I-91 to Exit 3, 6 miles east of Brattleboro, VT.

# Pine Valley Golf Links    ✪½   ▶69

247 Main Street
Pelham, NH 03076
(603) 635-7979, (603) 635-8305
www.pinevalleygolflinks.com

| Tees | Holes | Yards | Par | USGA | Slope |
|------|-------|-------|-----|------|-------|
| BACK | 9 | 3015 | 35 | 90 | 128 |
| MIDDLE | 9 | 2805 | 35 | 66.8 | 113 |
| FRONT | 9 | 2675 | 36 | 69 | 122 |

**Club Pro:** Todd Madden, PGA
**Payment:** All Cards Accepted
**Tee Times:** Weekends only
**Fee  9 Holes: Weekday:** $18    **Weekend:** $20
**Fee 18 Holes: Weekday:** $23    **Weekend:** $28
**Twilight Rates:** $18 after 3pm/wkdy; $20/wknd **Discounts:** None
**Cart Rental:** $14pp/18, $8pp/9    **Driving Range:** No
**Lessons:** Yes (by appointment) **Schools:** No   **Junior Golf:** Yes
**Membership:** Yes    **Architect/Yr Open:** Todd Madden/1961
**Other:** Snack Bar / Bar-Lounge    **GPS:**

*COUPON*

Course is well-trapped and wooded. Easy to walk. Extended tee on #7. Fast greens and lots of trees and water. Dress code. No tanktops.

| | 1 | 2 | 3 | 4 | 5 | 6 | 7 | 8 | 9 |
|------|-----|-----|-----|-----|-----|-----|-----|-----|-----|
| PAR | 4 | 3 | 5 | 4 | 4 | 4 | 4 | 4 | 3 |
| YARDS | 290 | 200 | 510 | 295 | 335 | 410 | 350 | 320 | 125 |
| PAR | | | | | | | | | |
| YARDS | | | | | | | | | |

**Directions:** I-93 to Exit 1 (Rockingham Park). Follow signs to Route 38 South (Pelham). Course is located 4 miles up on left.

# Ponemah Green Family Center   ✪✪½   ▶70

55 Ponemah Road
Amherst, NH (603) 672-4732
www.amherstcountryclub.com

| Tees | Holes | Yards | Par | USGA | Slope |
|------|-------|-------|-----|------|-------|
| BACK | 9 | 2210 | 34 | 62.4 | 110 |
| MIDDLE | 9 | 2160 | 34 | 61.4 | 107 |
| FRONT | 9 | 1804 | 34 | 71.0 | 106 |

**Club Pro:** Susan Currier, Manager
**Payment:** Visa, MC, Disc
**Tee Times:** 5 days adv.
**Fee  9 Holes: Weekday:** $16    **Weekend:** $16
**Fee 18 Holes: Weekday:** $25    **Weekend:** $25
**Twilight Rates:** After 4pm, weekends only **Discounts:** Junior
**Cart Rental:** $9pp/9    **Driving Range:** $5/sm., $8/lg.
**Lessons:** $69/hour, $40/half hour **Schools:** No   **Junior Golf:** Yes
**Membership:** Yes    **Architect/Yr Open:** Geoffrey Cornish/1989
**Other:** Clubhouse / Snack Shop    **GPS:**

Executive 9-hole golf course with small undulating greens. Accuracy a must. Open April until first snow. Now with mini-golf.

| | 1 | 2 | 3 | 4 | 5 | 6 | 7 | 8 | 9 |
|------|-----|-----|-----|-----|-----|-----|-----|-----|-----|
| PAR | 3 | 3 | 4 | 4 | 4 | 4 | 4 | 4 | 4 |
| YARDS | 111 | 129 | 252 | 238 | 394 | 251 | 292 | 229 | 314 |
| PAR | | | | | | | | | |
| YARDS | | | | | | | | | |

**Directions:** I-293, to Route 101 West to Amherst. Then take Route 122 to the course located ½ mile past Amherst Country Club.

# Portsmouth Country Club ✪✪✪✪ 71 ▶

80 Country Club Lane
Greenland, NH (603) 436-9719
www.portsmouthcc.net

**Club Pro:** Bill Andrews, PGA
**Payment:** Visa, MC, Amex, Disc, Cash
**Tee Times:** 3 day adv.

| Tees | Holes | Yards | Par | USGA | Slope |
|---|---|---|---|---|---|
| BACK | 18 | 7153 | 72 | 73.8 | 124 |
| MIDDLE | 18 | 6222 | 72 | 70.6 | 119 |
| FRONT | 18 | 5134 | 75 | 64.8 | 111 |

**Fee 9 Holes: Weekday:** $55
**Fee 18 Holes: Weekday:** $100
**Twilight Rates:** No
**Cart Rental:** $20pp/18, $14pp/9
**Lessons:** $80/hour **Schools:** No
**Membership:** Yes
**Weekend:** $55
**Weekend:** $100
**Discounts:** No
**Driving Range:** Yes
**Junior Golf:** No
**Architect/Yr Open:** Robert Trent Jones Jr./1957
**Other:** Clubhouse / Restaurant / Bar-Lounge / Lockers / Showers

Championship layout! 8 holes played along Great Bay. You will play shots over the ocean, around the ocean and often into the ocean! Magnificently manicured with traditional fast greens in excellent condition. You will not be disappointed.

|  | 1 | 2 | 3 | 4 | 5 | 6 | 7 | 8 | 9 |
|---|---|---|---|---|---|---|---|---|---|
| PAR | 4 | 4 | 4 | 5 | 3 | 4 | 5 | 3 | 4 |
| YARDS | 370 | 378 | 349 | 471 | 139 | 403 | 474 | 210 | 368 |
|  | 10 | 11 | 12 | 13 | 14 | 15 | 16 | 17 | 18 |
| PAR | 4 | 5 | 4 | 3 | 5 | 4 | 3 | 4 | 4 |
| YARDS | 395 | 483 | 423 | 130 | 432 | 310 | 117 | 376 | 394 |

**Directions:** I-95 to Route 33 West (Greenland exit). Follow (tiny) signs. Course is approximately 2 miles from I-95.

# Ragged Mountain Resort ✪✪½  72 ▶

620 Ragged Mountain Road
Danbury, NH (603) 768-3600
www.raggedmountainresort.com

**Club Pro:** Ian Willikens, PGA
**Payment:** Visa, MC
**Tee Times:** 7 days adv.

| Tees | Holes | Yards | Par | USGA | Slope |
|---|---|---|---|---|---|
| BACK | 18 | 6482 | 72 | 72.5 | 136 |
| MIDDLE | 18 | 5762 | 72 | 69.3 | 125 |
| FRONT | 18 | 4963 | 72 | 65.1 | 118 |

**Fee 9 Holes: Weekday:** $35 ride
**Fee 18 Holes: Weekday:** $49 ride
**Twilight Rates:** $35 after 3pm
**Cart Rental:** Included
**Lessons: Schools:** No
**Membership:** No
**Weekend:** $35 ride
**Weekend:** $59 ride
**Discounts:** None
**Driving Range:** $4.50/bucket
**Junior Golf:** No
**Architect/Yr Open:** Jeff Julian/1999
**Other:** Full Restaurant / Clubhouse / Bar Lounge

Player Comments: "Great mountain course. Beautiful setting." Spectacular views under 2 hours from Boston. 4 sets of tees. Ask about early season rates.

|  | 1 | 2 | 3 | 4 | 5 | 6 | 7 | 8 | 9 |
|---|---|---|---|---|---|---|---|---|---|
| PAR | 4 | 5 | 4 | 4 | 3 | 4 | 3 | 5 | 4 |
| YARDS | 305 | 432 | 377 | 290 | 143 | 302 | 112 | 497 | 302 |
|  | 10 | 11 | 12 | 13 | 14 | 15 | 16 | 17 | 18 |
| PAR | 4 | 5 | 4 | 3 | 4 | 3 | 4 | 5 | 4 |
| YARDS | 342 | 438 | 307 | 136 | 349 | 188 | 412 | 500 | 330 |

**Directions:** Route 93 North to Exit 23. Take Route 104 West for 20 minutes, through town of Bristol. Follow signs for Ragged Mountain access road on left. Follow road for 2 miles to course.

# Ridgewood Country Club ✪✪✪½ ▶ 73

258 Gov. Wentworth Highway
Moultonborough, NH
(603) 476-5930
www.ridgewoodcc.net

| Tees | Holes | Yards | Par | USGA | Slope |
|------|-------|-------|-----|------|-------|
| BACK | 18 | 6573 | 72 | 71.8 | 130 |
| MIDDLE | 18 | 6044 | 72 | 69.2 | 124 |
| FRONT | 18 | 4473 | 72 | 66.9 | 112 |

**Club Pro:** Mike Uhlman
**Payment:** Visa, MC, Amex, Disc
**Tee Times:** 5 days adv.
**Fee 9 Holes: Weekday:** $29
**Fee 18 Holes: Weekday:** $32
**Twilight Rates:** After 3pm
**Cart Rental:** $17pp/18, $10pp/9
**Lessons: Yes Schools:** Yes
**Membership:** Yes, yearly/monthly/weekly
**Other:** Full-Service Restaurant

**Weekend:** $39
**Weekend:** $42
**Discounts:** No
**Driving Range:** Yes
**Junior Golf:** Yes
**Architect/Yr Open:** John Ponko/1998
**GPS:**

COUPON

18 championship holes, full-service golf shop, custom club fitting, short game practice area.

| | 1 | 2 | 3 | 4 | 5 | 6 | 7 | 8 | 9 |
|-----|-----|-----|-----|-----|-----|-----|-----|-----|-----|
| PAR | 4 | 4 | 5 | 4 | 3 | 4 | 3 | 4 | |
| YARDS | 302 | 336 | 470 | 393 | 173 | 371 | 178 | 288 | 530 |
| | **10** | **11** | **12** | **13** | **14** | **15** | **16** | **17** | **18** |
| PAR | 3 | 5 | 4 | 4 | 4 | 4 | 4 | 3 | 5 |
| YARDS | 173 | 517 | 347 | 359 | 361 | 340 | 349 | 128 | 438 |

**Directions:** Route I-93, Exit 23 to Route 104. Left at Route 3 in Meredith to Route 25 East Moultonboro to Route 109 South. 1.5 mile on right. Please see website.

# Rochester Country Club ✪✪✪½ ▶ 74

94 Church Street
Rochester, NH (603) 332-9892
www.rochestercc.com

| Tees | Holes | Yards | Par | USGA | Slope |
|------|-------|-------|-----|------|-------|
| BACK | 18 | 6687 | 72 | 72.0 | 131 |
| MIDDLE | 18 | 6344 | 72 | 70.2 | 128 |
| FRONT | 18 | 5187 | 72 | 69.9 | 121 |

**Club Pro:** Jon Ellis, PGA
**Payment:** Visa, MC, Amex, Disc, Cash, Check
**Tee Times:** 7 days adv.
**Fee 9 Holes: Weekday:** $20
**Fee 18 Holes: Weekday:** $35
**Twilight Rates:** After 4pm
**Cart Rental:** $16pp/18, $10pp/9
**Lessons:** $45/30 min. **Schools:** Junior
**Membership:** Yes
**Architect/Yr Open:** William Mitchell & Philip Wogan/1939
**Other:** Restaurant / Lockers / Showers / Snack Bar / Bar-Lounge / Function Room

**Weekend:** $24
**Weekend:** $42
**Discounts:** Senior & Juniors
**Driving Range:** No
**Junior Golf:** Yes

COUPON

"Great public course with a private flair. Continued improvements being made all the time. Every hole is unique." –FP & MH

| | 1 | 2 | 3 | 4 | 5 | 6 | 7 | 8 | 9 |
|-----|-----|-----|-----|-----|-----|-----|-----|-----|-----|
| PAR | 4 | 5 | 4 | 3 | 4 | 5 | 3 | 4 | 4 |
| YARDS | 322 | 481 | 447 | 205 | 306 | 516 | 134 | 407 | 324 |
| | **10** | **11** | **12** | **13** | **14** | **15** | **16** | **17** | **18** |
| PAR | 4 | 5 | 3 | 4 | 4 | 5 | 3 | 4 | 4 |
| YARDS | 362 | 548 | 168 | 421 | 328 | 487 | 193 | 393 | 302 |

**Directions:** From Route 16 (Spaulding Turnpike): take 125 South for 2 miles and turn left onto Church Street.

# Rockingham Country Club

NR 75

200 Exeter Road
Newmarket, NH (603) 659-9956
www.rockinghamgolf.com

**Club Pro:** Robert Greene, Club Manager
**Payment:** Visa, MC, Cash
**Tee Times:** 3 days adv.
**Fee 9 Holes: Weekday:** $20
**Fee 18 Holes: Weekday:** $30
**Twilight Rates:** No
**Cart Rental:** $25/18, $15/9 per cart
**Lessons:** Yes **Schools:** No
**Membership:** Yes
**Other:**

| Tees | Holes | Yards | Par | USGA | Slope |
|------|-------|-------|-----|------|-------|
| BACK | | | | | |
| MIDDLE | 9 | 2875 | 35 | 65.3 | 104 |
| FRONT | 9 | 2622 | 37 | 69.4 | 104 |

**Weekend:** $25
**Weekend:** $35
**Discounts:**
**Driving Range:** No
**Junior Golf:** No
**Architect/Yr Open:** 1933

COUPON

The course is level and well-kept with 2 water holes. Renovated clubhouse. Under new management.

| | 1 | 2 | 3 | 4 | 5 | 6 | 7 | 8 | 9 |
|------|-----|-----|-----|-----|-----|-----|-----|-----|-----|
| PAR | 4 | 4 | 3 | 4 | 4 | 4 | 3 | 4 | 5 |
| YARDS | 386 | 315 | 175 | 393 | 315 | 380 | 125 | 306 | 480 |
| PAR | | | | | | | | | |
| YARDS | | | | | | | | | |

**Directions:** I-95 to Hampton Exit (Route 101 West) to Route 108. North to course.

# Sagamore-Hampton Golf Club ✪✪½ 76

101 North Road
North Hampton, NH (603) 964-5341
www.sagamoregolf.com

**Club Pro:** Laura Shanahan Rowe, LPGA
**Payment:** Visa, MC, Amex
**Tee Times:** 1 week adv.
**Fee 9 Holes: Weekday:** $26
**Fee 18 Holes: Weekday:** $42
**Twilight Rates:** After 3pm/wknds; 5pm/wkdys
**Cart Rental:** $17pp/18, $10pp/9
**Driving Range:** Off-site, 603-964-8393
**Lessons:** Yes **Schools:** No
**Membership:** No
**Other:**

| Tees | Holes | Yards | Par | USGA | Slope |
|------|-------|-------|-----|------|-------|
| BACK | 18 | 6041 | 71 | 68.6 | 118 |
| MIDDLE | 18 | 5647 | 71 | 67.1 | 115 |
| FRONT | 18 | 4886 | 71 | 67.5 | 112 |

**Weekend:** $28
**Weekend:** $47
**Discounts:** Senior/Junior/College

**Junior Golf:** Yes
**Architect/Yr Open:** Christopher Luff/1962

COUPON

A Seacoast favorite for 50 years, featuring great golf, a friendly staff, and unbeatable golf value. Rated a "4-star" course by *Golf Digest* and voted "Best on the Seacoast." New bunkers added to the 7th and 14th hole. An ideal course for any level of golfer, featuring a spacious Front 9 combined with a tree-lined Back 9.

| | 1 | 2 | 3 | 4 | 5 | 6 | 7 | 8 | 9 |
|------|-----|-----|-----|-----|-----|-----|-----|-----|-----|
| PAR | 4 | 4 | 4 | 3 | 4 | 5 | 3 | 5 | 3 |
| YARDS | 291 | 325 | 352 | 135 | 300 | 463 | 192 | 424 | 166 |
| | 10 | 11 | 12 | 13 | 14 | 15 | 16 | 17 | 18 |
| PAR | 5 | 3 | 4 | 5 | 3 | 4 | 5 | 3 | 4 |
| YARDS | 527 | 172 | 380 | 446 | 125 | 284 | 456 | 190 | 419 |

**Directions:** I-95 to Exit 2, right to 101 West. First exit, go right onto 111 East, then follow 2.5 miles. Left onto 151 North, follow 1 mile, right onto North Road.

NH

# Shattuck Golf Course, The ✪✪✪

 77

53 Dublin Road
Jaffrey, NH  (603) 532-4300
www.sterlinggolf.com

**Club Pro:** Tom Borden, PGA
**Payment:** MC, Visa, Amex, Cash
**Tee Times:** 7 days adv.

| Tees | Holes | Yards | Par | USGA | Slope |
|------|-------|-------|-----|------|-------|
| BACK | 18 | 6764 | 72 | 75.0 | 147 |
| MIDDLE | 18 | 6112 | 72 | 71.0 | 142 |
| FRONT | 18 | 4632 | 72 | 67.6 | 125 |

**Fee  9 Holes: Weekday:** $29 (includes cart)  **Weekend:** $35 (includes cart)
**Fee 18 Holes: Weekday:** $45 (includes cart)  **Weekend:** $49 (includes cart)
**Twilight Rates:** After 4pm          **Discounts:** Senior & Junior
**Cart Rental:**                       **Driving Range:** Yes
**Lessons:** Yes  **Schools:** Yes     **Junior Golf:** Yes
**Membership:** Yes                    **Architect/Yr Open:** Brian Silva/1991
**Other:** Bar-Lounge / Weddings / Large Functions

COUPON

Player Comments: "Every-club-in-the-bag course. Very challenging." "Believe the slope rating—this is a monster. Helpful Player's Guide on website. Uncrowded."
Under Sterling Golf Management. Created combo tees for softer side of Shattuck. *Golf Digest* ranked 43rd of the 50 toughest golf courses in the U.S.

|  | 1 | 2 | 3 | 4 | 5 | 6 | 7 | 8 | 9 |
|------|---|---|---|---|---|---|---|---|---|
| PAR | 4 | 3 | 4 | 4 | 5 | 5 | 3 | 4 | 4 |
| YARDS | 357 | 146 | 343 | 312 | 551 | 508 | 183 | 373 | 356 |
|  | 10 | 11 | 12 | 13 | 14 | 15 | 16 | 17 | 18 |
| PAR | 4 | 5 | 3 | 4 | 3 | 5 | 4 | 4 | 4 |
| YARDS | 394 | 407 | 190 | 303 | 121 | 508 | 367 | 313 | 380 |

**Directions:** I-90 (Mass Pike) to 495 North to Route 2 West. Take Exit 24B Route 140 North to Route 12 North. Take a left, go .9 mile. Go right on Route 202 North to Jaffrey, NH. Go left on Route 124. Follow West 2.2 miles. Go right at Mount Monadnock sign. Club is on the left.

# Souhegan Woods Golf Club ✪✪✪

 78

65 Thornton's Ferry Road
Amherst, NH  (603) 673-0200
www.playgolfne.com

**Club Pro:** John Wollen, PGA
**Payment:** Most Major
**Tee Times:** 7 days adv.

| Tees | Holes | Yards | Par | USGA | Slope |
|------|-------|-------|-----|------|-------|
| BACK | 18 | 6507 | 72 | 70.3 | 125 |
| MIDDLE | 18 | 6142 | 72 | 68.8 | 120 |
| FRONT | 18 | 5158 | 72 | 70.3 | 120 |

**Fee  9 Holes: Weekday:** $26      **Weekend:** $27
**Fee 18 Holes: Weekday:** $38      **Weekend:** $49
**Twilight Rates:** After 3pm       **Discounts:** Senior & Junior
**Cart Rental:** $16pp/18, $11pp/9  **Driving Range:** $10/lg, $6/sm bucket
**Lessons:** $80/hour  **Schools:** No  **Junior Golf:** Yes
**Membership:** No                  **Architect/Yr Open:** Phil Friel/1992
**Other:** Clubhouse / Bar-Lounge / Snack Bar / Showers

Designed to challenge all golfers. In very good condition and well spread out. Open April - November. A Golf Management Company course.

|  | 1 | 2 | 3 | 4 | 5 | 6 | 7 | 8 | 9 |
|------|---|---|---|---|---|---|---|---|---|
| PAR | 4 | 4 | 3 | 5 | 4 | 5 | 4 | 3 | 4 |
| YARDS | 375 | 312 | 168 | 445 | 402 | 501 | 337 | 149 | 355 |
|  | 10 | 11 | 12 | 13 | 14 | 15 | 16 | 17 | 18 |
| PAR | 4 | 3 | 4 | 4 | 5 | 4 | 4 | 3 | 5 |
| YARDS | 312 | 153 | 343 | 368 | 510 | 349 | 406 | 166 | 469 |

**Directions:** Route 3 (Everett Turnpike) in NH take Exit 11. Turn left at end of ramp and proceed under the highway. Take your very first right onto Amherst Road and proceed 4.3 miles. Take a right onto Stillwater Road. Course is a ¼ mile on the right.

# Stonebridge Country Club ✪✪✪½   79 ▶

161 Gorham Pond Road
Goffstown, NH (603) 497-8633
www.golfstonebridgecc.com
**Club Pro:** Ken Hamel, PGA
**Payment:** Visa, MC, Amex, Disc
**Tee Times:** 5 days adv.

| Tees | Holes | Yards | Par | USGA | Slope |
|------|-------|-------|-----|------|-------|
| BACK | 18 | 6808 | 72 | 72.9 | 136 |
| MIDDLE | 18 | 6388 | 72 | 71.0 | 133 |
| FRONT | 18 | 4747 | 72 | 67.6 | 116 |

**Fee 9 Holes: Weekday:** $29     **Weekend:** $39
**Fee 18 Holes: Weekday:** $44   **Weekend:** $55
**Twilight Rates:** $29 after 2pm; $20 after 6pm  **Discounts:** Jr., M-Th before 3pm
**Cart Rental:** $17pp/18, $12pp/9   **Driving Range:** $7/bucket
**Lessons:** $40/half hour  **Schools:** No   **Junior Golf:** Yes
**Membership:** Yes   **Architect/Yr Open:** Phil Wogan/1998
**Other:** Full Restaurant / Clubhouse / Lockers / Showers / Bar-Lounge

COUPON

Player Comments: "Challenging greens. Beautiful landscape." "Demanding layout from middle and back tees." Newly paved cart paths, new carts, and other renovations completed in 2008. Hole no. 6, the short but dangerous par 3, was voted number 1 golf hole in NH by WMUR-TV viewers.

|  | 1 | 2 | 3 | 4 | 5 | 6 | 7 | 8 | 9 |
|-------|-----|-----|-----|-----|-----|-----|-----|-----|-----|
| PAR | 5 | 4 | 4 | 3 | 4 | 3 | 4 | 4 | 4 |
| YARDS | 480 | 398 | 370 | 152 | 366 | 136 | 332 | 408 | 417 |
|  | **10** | **11** | **12** | **13** | **14** | **15** | **16** | **17** | **18** |
| PAR | 5 | 4 | 4 | 3 | 5 | 4 | 3 | 5 | 4 |
| YARDS | 496 | 325 | 349 | 193 | 526 | 369 | 150 | 521 | 400 |

**Directions:** I-93 to Route 101 West to Route 114 North for 9 miles, through Goffstown center. After Sully's Superette, go 1.5 mile and take right onto Parker Station Road. Immediate right onto Gorham Pond Road. Course is ¾ mile on left.

# Sunset Hill Golf Course   NR   80 ▶

234 Sunset Hill Road
Sugar Hill, NH (603) 823-7244

| Tees | Holes | Yards | Par | USGA | Slope |
|------|-------|-------|-----|------|-------|
| BACK |  |  |  |  |  |
| MIDDLE | 9 | 1977 | 29 |  |  |
| FRONT |  |  |  |  |  |

**Club Pro:** Lon Henderson, Manager
**Payment:** Visa, MC, Amex, Disc, Checks
**Tee Times:** Yes
**Fee 9 Holes: Weekday:** $15    **Weekend:** $20
**Fee 18 Holes: Weekday:** $20   **Weekend:** $30
**Twilight Rates:** After 5pm   **Discounts:** Junior
**Cart Rental:** $25pp/18, $15pp/9 weekday; $30pp/18, $20pp/9 weekend
**Driving Range:** No
**Lessons:** $30/half hour  **Schools:** Yes   **Junior Golf:** Yes
**Membership:** Yes   **Architect/Yr Open:** Ted Bonar/1897
**Other:** Snack Bar / Restaurant / Hotel Along 1st Hole / Functions

COUPON

Oldest 9-hole course in NH, built in 1897. Antique clubhouse restored in 2007. A really fun place to play golf. Player Comments: "Particularly friendly for families, beginners, and seniors. Hassle-free golf the way we remember it."

|  | 1 | 2 | 3 | 4 | 5 | 6 | 7 | 8 | 9 |
|-------|-----|-----|-----|-----|-----|-----|-----|-----|-----|
| PAR | 4 | 4 | 3 | 3 | 3 | 3 | 3 | 3 | 3 |
| YARDS | 240 | 256 | 217 | 176 | 168 | 143 | 150 | 182 | 158 |
| PAR |  |  |  |  |  |  |  |  |  |
| YARDS |  |  |  |  |  |  |  |  |  |

**Directions:** I-93 to Exit 38. Go left at bottom of ramp, take right at blinking light. Go ½ mile then left on Route 117. Go uphill for 2 miles and turn left onto Sunset Hill Road. Course is ½ mile on the left.

# Twin Lake Villa Golf Course

NR 81 ▶

164 Twin Lake Villa Road
New London, NH (603) 526-2034
www.twinlakevillage.com

**Club Pro:**
**Payment:** Cash, Personal Checks
**Tee Times:** 3 days adv.
**Fee 9 Holes: Weekday:** $12
**Fee 18 Holes: Weekday:** $16
**Twilight Rates:** No
**Cart Rental:** No
**Lessons:** No **Schools:** No
**Membership:** Yes
**Other:**

**Weekend:** $12
**Weekend:** $16
**Discounts:** Senior, $2 off
**Driving Range:** No
**Junior Golf:** No
**Architect/Yr Open:** Henry Kidder/1948
**GPS:**

| Tees | Holes | Yards | Par | USGA | Slope |
|------|-------|-------|-----|------|-------|
| BACK | 9 | 1515 | 27 | | |
| MIDDLE | 9 | 1356 | 27 | | |
| FRONT | 9 | 1149 | 27 | | |

Open May 1 - October 31.

| | 1 | 2 | 3 | 4 | 5 | 6 | 7 | 8 | 9 |
|------|---|---|---|---|---|---|---|---|---|
| PAR | 3 | 3 | 3 | 3 | 3 | 3 | 3 | 3 | 3 |
| YARDS | 141 | 113 | 118 | 109 | 190 | 197 | 180 | 177 | 131 |
| PAR | | | | | | | | | |
| YARDS | | | | | | | | | |

**Directions:** I-89 to Exit 12. Go East 2 miles to New London. At blinking light, turn left onto Country Road. At first stop sign, turn left onto Little Sunapee Road for 1 mile. Bear right onto Twin Lake Villa Road and follow up hill to Hotel and Golf Shop.

# Waterville Valley Golf Club

NR 82 ▶

3 Lost Pass Road
Waterville Valley, NH
(603) 236-4805
www.waterville.com

**Club Pro:**
**Payment:** Visa, MC, Amex, Disc
**Tee Times:** 48 hours adv.
**Fee 9 Holes: Weekday:** $25
**Fee 18 Holes: Weekday:** $35
**Twilight Rates:** No
**Cart Rental:** $26pp/18, $18pp/9
**Lessons:** Yes **Schools:** No
**Membership:** Yes
**Other:** Clubhouse / Snack Bar / Club Storage / Resort

**Weekend:** $25
**Weekend:** $35
**Discounts:** None
**Driving Range:** No
**Junior Golf:** Yes
**Architect/Yr Open:** 1898

| Tees | Holes | Yards | Par | USGA | Slope |
|------|-------|-------|-----|------|-------|
| BACK | | | | | |
| MIDDLE | 9 | 1700 | 30 | 63 | 105 |
| FRONT | | | | | |

Interesting, newly designed golf course with 3 holes on the top of the hill. Spectacular view. Mountain resort. Open May 27 - October 15. Inquire about junior clinics. New clubhouse.

| | 1 | 2 | 3 | 4 | 5 | 6 | 7 | 8 | 9 |
|------|---|---|---|---|---|---|---|---|---|
| PAR | 4 | 3 | 3 | 3 | 3 | 4 | 3 | 4 | 3 |
| YARDS | 294 | 185 | 105 | 128 | 118 | 317 | 136 | 312 | 105 |
| PAR | | | | | | | | | |
| YARDS | | | | | | | | | |

**Directions:** I-93 to Exit 28; follow Route 49 for 12 miles.

# Waukewan Golf Club

★★★½  83

166 Waukewan Road
Center Harbor, NH (603) 279-6661
www.waukewan.com

**Club Pro:** Chuck Yeager
**Payment:** Cash or Credit Card
**Tee Times:** Up to 7 days adv. 6am-3pm
**Fee 9 Holes: Weekday:** $25
**Fee 18 Holes: Weekday:** $40
**Twilight Rates:** $15 after 3pm walking
**Cart Rental:** $16pp/18, $10pp/9
**Lessons:** Available **Schools:** Yes
**Membership:** Yes
**Other:** Clubhouse / Snack Bar / Bar-Lounge

**Weekend:** $30
**Weekend:** $50
**Discounts:** None
**Driving Range:** $6/lg, $3/sm bucket
**Junior Golf:** Yes
**Architect/Yr Open:** Melvin D. Hale Sr./1958
**GPS:**

| Tees | Holes | Yards | Par | USGA | Slope |
|------|-------|-------|-----|------|-------|
| BACK | 18 | 5885 | 72 | 68.7 | 118 |
| MIDDLE | 18 | 5415 | 72 | 68.3 | 117 |
| FRONT | 18 | 4695 | 72 | 64.6 | 113 |

Located in the Lakes Region of New Hampshire, this scenic course is nestled within a beautiful mountain range. The redsigned 13th green is our latest accomplishment. The friendly staff will only add to your relaxing golf experience.

| | 1 | 2 | 3 | 4 | 5 | 6 | 7 | 8 | 9 |
|---|---|---|---|---|---|---|---|---|---|
| PAR | 4 | 4 | 3 | 4 | 4 | 5 | 3 | 5 | 4 |
| YARDS | 360 | 305 | 130 | 230 | 230 | 530 | 160 | 430 | 370 |
| | 10 | 11 | 12 | 13 | 14 | 15 | 16 | 17 | 18 |
| PAR | 4 | 3 | 4 | 4 | 4 | 5 | 3 | 5 | 4 |
| YARDS | 260 | 180 | 245 | 400 | 280 | 440 | 180 | 430 | 215 |

**Directions:** I-93 to Exit 23. Route 104 to Meredith. Route 3 North toward Plymouth. At 3 miles from Meredith traffic junction, left turn onto Waukewan Road.

NH

# Waumbek Golf Club

★★½  84

28 Waumbek Street
Jefferson, NH (603) 586-7777
www.playgolfne.com

**Club Pro:** Dianne L. Morneau, Gen. Manager
**Payment:** Visa, MC, Amex, Disc, Cash
**Tee Times:** Yes
**Fee 9 Holes: Weekday:** $17
**Fee 18 Holes: Weekday:** $26
**Twilight Rates:** After 3pm
**Cart Rental:** $15pp/18, $9pp/9
**Lessons:** No **Schools:** No
**Membership:** Yes
**Other:** Restaurant / Bar-Lounge / Lodging Patner

**Weekend:** $20
**Weekend:** $32
**Discounts:** Junior
**Driving Range:** No
**Junior Golf:** Yes
**Architect/Yr Open:** Willy Norton/1895
**GPS:**

| Tees | Holes | Yards | Par | USGA | Slope |
|------|-------|-------|-----|------|-------|
| BACK | 18 | 6128 | 71 | 67.0 | 117 |
| MIDDLE | 18 | 5792 | 71 | 65 | 111 |
| FRONT | 18 | 4772 | 71 | 67.8 | 111 |

COUPON

New Hampshire's oldest 18 hole course. Scottish link style course. 90% of greens slope toward Cherry Mountain. Located on back side of the Presidential Range Mountains. Breathtaking views on every hole.

| | 1 | 2 | 3 | 4 | 5 | 6 | 7 | 8 | 9 |
|---|---|---|---|---|---|---|---|---|---|
| PAR | 4 | 4 | 5 | 4 | 4 | 4 | 4 | 3 | 3 |
| YARDS | 333 | 370 | 500 | 310 | 320 | 390 | 290 | 200 | 195 |
| | 10 | 11 | 12 | 13 | 14 | 15 | 16 | 17 | 18 |
| PAR | 4 | 5 | 4 | 4 | 3 | 4 | 4 | 5 | 3 |
| YARDS | 310 | 465 | 387 | 280 | 110 | 340 | 335 | 490 | 170 |

**Directions:** I-93 to Exit 35 (Route 3 North). Follow Route 3 for 12 miles, then take a right onto Route 115 North. Follow Route 115 North for 6.7 miles. Take a left onto Route 115A. Golf course is 4 miles down on the right.

# Wentworth Resort Golf Club ✪✪ 85 ▶

Route 16A
Jackson, NH (603) 383-9641
www.wentworthgolf.com

| Tees | Holes | Yards | Par | USGA | Slope |
|------|-------|-------|-----|------|-------|
| BACK | | | | | |
| MIDDLE | 18 | 5581 | 69 | 66.0 | 115 |
| FRONT | 18 | 5087 | 70 | 66.7 | 114 |

**Club Pro:** Kevin Walker PGA
**Payment:** MC, Visa, Amex, Disc
**Tee Times:** Yes
**Fee 9 Holes: Weekday:**
**Fee 18 Holes: Weekday:** $35
**Twilight Rates:** After 3pm
**Cart Rental:** $15pp/18, $9pp/9
**Lessons:** $45/45 min **Schools:** No
**Membership:** Yes
**Other:** Snack Bar / Restaurant / Bar-Lounge

**Weekend:**
**Weekend:** $45 F/S/S/H
**Discounts:** Junior
**Driving Range:** No
**Junior Golf:** Yes
**Architect/Yr:** Wayne Stiles/1895, Arthur Hill/1998
**GPS:**

COUPON

Challenging course situated in Jackson Village. Enjoy the rolling hills and the covered bridge crossing the Ellis River on the White Mountains' 2nd oldest course.

| | 1 | 2 | 3 | 4 | 5 | 6 | 7 | 8 | 9 |
|---|---|---|---|---|---|---|---|---|---|
| PAR | 4 | 4 | 4 | 3 | 3 | 4 | 4 | 4 | 5 |
| YARDS | 305 | 337 | 349 | 304 | 147 | 411 | 291 | 307 | 479 |
| | 10 | 11 | 12 | 13 | 14 | 15 | 16 | 17 | 18 |
| PAR | 4 | 4 | 4 | 4 | 3 | 5 | 3 | 3 | 4 |
| YARDS | 333 | 359 | 336 | 365 | 185 | 454 | 180 | 144 | 295 |

**Directions:** I-95 to Spaulding Turnpike. Take Route 16 North to Jackson Village. Or I-93 to Route 25 to Route 16 North to Jackson Village.

# Whip-Poor-Will Golf Club ✪✪½ 86 ▶

55 Marsh Road
Hudson, NH (603) 889-9706

| Tees | Holes | Yards | Par | USGA | Slope |
|------|-------|-------|-----|------|-------|
| BACK | 9 | 3015 | 36 | 67.8 | 120 |
| MIDDLE | 9 | 2990 | 36 | 67.8 | 120 |
| FRONT | 9 | 2547 | 36 | 69.9 | 119 |

**Club Pro:** Jack Sullivan, PGA
**Payment:** Visa, MC, Amex, Disc
**Tee Times:** 7 days adv.
**Fee 9 Holes: Weekday:** $23
**Fee 18 Holes: Weekday:** $33
**Twilight Rates:** After 3pm wknds
**Cart Rental:** $8pp/9, $13pp/18
**Lessons:** Yes **Schools:** No
**Membership:** No
**Other:** Clubhouse / Snack Bar / Bar Lounge

**Weekend:** $25
**Weekend:** $37
**Discounts:** Senior & Junior
**Driving Range:** No
**Junior Golf:** Yes
**Architect/Yr Open:** Manuel Francis/1959
**GPS:**

An enjoyable well-maintained 9-hole course, perfect for an early afternoon off. A Golf Management Company course. New senior tees.

| | 1 | 2 | 3 | 4 | 5 | 6 | 7 | 8 | 9 |
|---|---|---|---|---|---|---|---|---|---|
| PAR | 4 | 3 | 4 | 4 | 5 | 4 | 4 | 5 | 3 |
| YARDS | 330 | 170 | 345 | 315 | 485 | 402 | 280 | 498 | 165 |
| PAR | | | | | | | | | |
| YARDS | | | | | | | | | |

**Directions:** I-93 to Exit 4 to Route 102 West approximately 7 miles. Course is on left at Marsh Road just after Alverine High School.

# White Mountain Country Club ✪✪½

North Ashland Road
Ashland, NH (603) 536-2227
www.playgolfne.com
**Club Pro:** Gregg Sufat
**Payment:** Visa, MC, Amex, Disc
**Tee Times:** 1 week adv.

| Tees | Holes | Yards | Par | USGA | Slope |
|------|-------|-------|-----|------|-------|
| BACK | 18 | 6428 | 71 | 70.4 | 122 |
| MIDDLE | 18 | 5963 | 112 | 67.9 | 119 |
| FRONT | 18 | 5350 | 72 | 69.6 | 118 |

**Fee  9 Holes: Weekday:** $20          **Weekend:** $32
**Fee 18 Holes: Weekday:** $33          **Weekend:** $43
**Twilight Rates:** After 3pm            **Discounts:** None
**Cart Rental:** $16pp/18, $9pp/9        **Driving Range:** $8/lg, $4/sm bucket
**Lessons:** $30/half hour, $50/hour  **Schools:** No   **Junior Golf:** No
**Membership:** No                       **Architect/Yr Open:** Cornish & Silva/1975
**Other:** Bar-Lounge / Snack Bar / Townhouse Rentals

Player Comments: "Great course in the Fall." Golfer-friendly, challenging, well-cared-for. Expanded driving range and recent reversal of dogleg on hole #2. A Golf Management Company course.

| | 1 | 2 | 3 | 4 | 5 | 6 | 7 | 8 | 9 |
|---|---|---|---|---|---|---|---|---|---|
| PAR | 4 | 4 | 4 | 3 | 5 | 4 | 3 | 5 | 4 |
| YARDS | 327 | 334 | 325 | 174 | 524 | 300 | 172 | 508 | 312 |
| | 10 | 11 | 12 | 13 | 14 | 15 | 16 | 17 | 18 |
| PAR | 4 | 3 | 4 | 4 | 4 | 4 | 4 | 4/5 | 4 |
| YARDS | 356 | 154 | 356 | 374 | 321 | 301 | 359 | 410 | 356 |

**Directions:** I-93 North to Exit 24, left off ramp for 1 mile. Right onto North Ashland Road, 2.5 miles on left.

# Windham Country Club ✪✪✪

1 Country Club Road
Windham, NH (603) 434-2093
www.windhamcc.com
**Club Pro:** Joanne Flynn, PGA
**Payment:** Visa, MC, Disc, Amex
**Tee Times:** 7 days adv.

| Tees | Holes | Yards | Par | USGA | Slope |
|------|-------|-------|-----|------|-------|
| BACK | 18 | 6442 | 72 | 71.2 | 135 |
| MIDDLE | 18 | 6033 | 72 | 69.1 | 129 |
| FRONT | 18 | 5584 | 72 | 67.4 | 122 |

**Fee  9 Holes: Weekday:** $24          **Weekend:** $29
**Fee 18 Holes: Weekday:** $42          **Weekend:** $50
**Twilight Rates:** Weekends after 1pm and 3pm    **Discounts:** Senior & Junior
**Cart Rental:** $18pp/18, $9pp/9        **Driving Range:** Yes
**Lessons:** $80/half hour  **Schools:** Yes   **Junior Golf:** Yes
**Membership:** Yes                      **Architect/Yr Open:** William Flynn/1995
**Other:** Clubhouse / Bar-Lounge

Noted for great overall condition and challenging layout. Open year round (when possible). Year round Golf Academy with 3 heated bays and professional golf technology. Reconstructed 3 tees and expanded the driving range.

| | 1 | 2 | 3 | 4 | 5 | 6 | 7 | 8 | 9 |
|---|---|---|---|---|---|---|---|---|---|
| PAR | 5 | 4 | 3 | 4 | 5 | 3 | 4 | 4 | 3 |
| YARDS | 522 | 374 | 158 | 365 | 578 | 136 | 398 | 369 | 165 |
| | 10 | 11 | 12 | 13 | 14 | 15 | 16 | 17 | 18 |
| PAR | 4 | 4 | 5 | 4 | 3 | 5 | 4 | 4 | 4 |
| YARDS | 280 | 354 | 440 | 304 | 166 | 444 | 382 | 335 | 306 |

**Directions:** I-93 to Exit 3. Take Route 111 West 1.5 miles. Then right on Church Street to fire station; then right onto North Lowell for 1 mile. Left onto Londonderry Road .5 mile and left on Country Club Road.

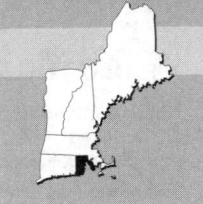

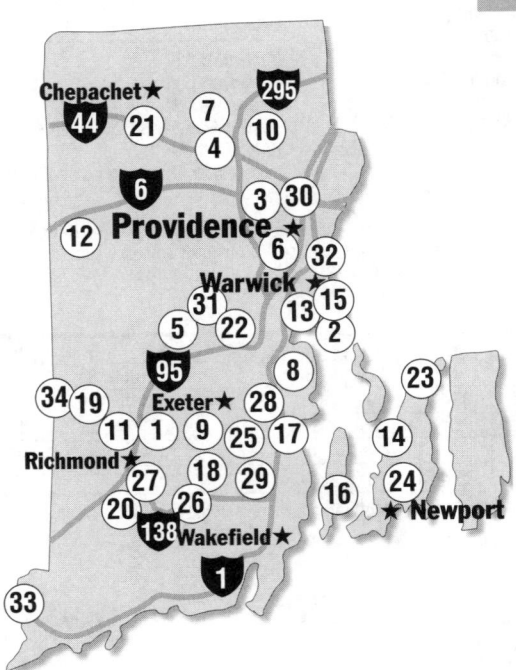

| | | | | | |
|---|---|---|---|---|---|
| Beaver River Golf Club | 1 | Goddard State Park GC | 13 | North Kingstown Muni. GC | 25 |
| Bristol Golf Club | 2 | Green Valley CC | 14 | Pinecrest Golf Course | 26 |
| Button Hole | 3 | Harbor Lights Golf & CC | 15 | Richmond Country Club | 27 |
| Country View Golf Club | 4 | Jamestown Golf & CC | 16 | Rolling Greens GC | 28 |
| Coventry Pines Golf Club | 5 | Kings Crossing GC | 17 | Rose Hill Golf Course | 29 |
| Cranston Country Club | 6 | Laurel Lane Country Club | 18 | Triggs Memorial GC | 30 |
| Crystal Lake GC of RI | 7 | Lindhbrook GC | 19 | West Warwick CC, The | 31 |
| East Greenwich CC | 8 | Meadow Brook | 20 | Windmill Hill Golf Course | 32 |
| Exeter Country Club | 9 | Melody Hill Golf Course | 21 | Winnapaug Golf Course | 33 |
| Fairlawn Golf Course | 10 | Midville Country Club | 22 | Wood River Golf | 34 |
| Fenner Hill Golf Club | 11 | Montaup Country Club | 23 | | |
| Foster Country Club | 12 | Newport National Golf Club | 24 | | |

**KEY TO THE STAR RATINGS:**
5✪ = Outstanding  4✪ = Excellent  3✪ = Very Good  2✪ = Good  1✪ = Average  **NR** = Not Rated

# Beaver River Golf Club   ✪✪½   ▶ 1

343 Kingstown Road
Richmond, RI (401) 539-2100
www.beaverrivergolf.com
**Club Pro:**
**Payment:** Visa, MC
**Tee Times:** 7 days adv.

| Tees | Holes | Yards | Par | USGA | Slope |
|------|-------|-------|-----|------|-------|
| BACK | 18 | 6086 | 70 | 67.1 | 123 |
| MIDDLE | 18 | 5802 | 70 | 65.7 | 123 |
| FRONT | 18 | 5410 | 70 | 70.8 | 115 |

**Fee 9 Holes: Weekday:** $20/Sr; $16/Jr
**Fee 18 Holes: Weekday:** $36
**Twilight Rates:** After 3pm
**Cart Rental:** $16pp/18, $8pp/9
**Lessons:** No **Schools:** Yes
**Membership:** Yes
**Other:** Clubhouse / Bar-Lounge

**Weekend:** $22
**Weekend:** $42
**Discounts:** Senior and Military
**Driving Range:** No
**Junior Golf:** Yes
**Architect/Yr Open:** Michael Weremay/2001
**GPS:**

COUPON

Bent grass from tee to green. Excellent conditions and service. South County course. New cosmetic improvements. Scenic fall views.

| | 1 | 2 | 3 | 4 | 5 | 6 | 7 | 8 | 9 |
|------|---|---|---|---|---|---|---|---|---|
| PAR | 5 | 4 | 3 | 4 | 4 | 5 | 3 | 4 | 4 |
| YARDS | 477 | 334 | 150 | 326 | 318 | 485 | 201 | 411 | 332 |
| | 10 | 11 | 12 | 13 | 14 | 15 | 16 | 17 | 18 |
| PAR | 4 | 3 | 4 | 4 | 4 | 3 | 4 | 4 | 4 |
| YARDS | 328 | 146 | 433 | 379 | 300 | 170 | 265 | 367 | 380 |

**Directions:** I-95 to Exit 3A. Take Route 138 E, 3 miles east.

**RI**

# Bristol Golf Club   NR   ▶ 2

95 Tupelo Road
Bristol, RI (401) 253-9844
www.bristolclubhouse.com
**Club Pro:** Patty Francis, GM
**Payment:** Cash, Credit
**Tee Times:** No

| Tees | Holes | Yards | Par | USGA | Slope |
|------|-------|-------|-----|------|-------|
| BACK | | | | | |
| MIDDLE | 9 | 2273 | 33 | 69.9 | 118 |
| FRONT | | | | | |

**Fee 9 Holes: Weekday:** $12
**Fee 18 Holes: Weekday:** $12
**Twilight Rates:** No
**Cart Rental:** $20pp/18, $5/pull
**Lessons:** No **Schools:** No
**Membership:** Yes
**Other:** Snack Bar / Bar-Lounge

**Weekend:** $14
**Weekend:** $14
**Discounts:**
**Driving Range:** No
**Junior Golf:** No
**Architect/Yr Open:** 1964
**GPS:**

A good course for beginners.

| | 1 | 2 | 3 | 4 | 5 | 6 | 7 | 8 | 9 |
|------|---|---|---|---|---|---|---|---|---|
| PAR | 3 | 4 | 3 | 3 | 3 | 4 | 5 | 4 | 4 |
| YARDS | 137 | 254 | 148 | 130 | 167 | 337 | 480 | 320 | 300 |
| PAR | | | | | | | | | |
| YARDS | | | | | | | | | |

**Directions:** I-195 East to Exit 2, follow Route 136 to Tupelo Street, take right and course is on left.

# Button Hole ✪✪ ▶3

1 Button Hole Drive
Providence, RI (401) 421-1664
www.buttonhole.org
Club Pro: Dan Gaughan
Payment: Visa, MC, Amex, Disc
Tee Times:

| Tees | Holes | Yards | Par | USGA | Slope |
|------|-------|-------|-----|------|-------|
| BACK | | | | | |
| MIDDLE | 9 | 1035 | 27 | 50.9 | |
| FRONT | 9 | 780 | 27 | 48.6 | |

Fee  9 Holes: Weekday: $10          Weekend: $10
Fee 18 Holes: Weekday: $15          Weekend: $15
Twilight Rates: No                  Discounts: Senior/Junior/Military
Cart Rental: $3/pull                Driving Range: $10/lg., $6/sm.
Lessons: Yes*  Schools: Yes         Junior Golf: Yes
Membership: Range and Course        Architect/Yr Open: Ron Pritchard, P.B. Dye/1998
Other: Clubhouse / Patio / Snacks / 16,000 sq ft Putting Green / Chipping Area

Short course and teaching center designed to lower cost, provide easy access and playing time. "Not just a beginner's layout. Shots and putts have to be made to score." –RW

*Lessons priced according to age. Inquire!

| | 1 | 2 | 3 | 4 | 5 | 6 | 7 | 8 | 9 |
|------|----|----|----|----|----|----|----|----|----|
| PAR | 3 | 3 | 3 | 3 | 3 | 3 | 3 | 3 | 3 |
| YARDS | 70 | 118 | 60 | 90 | 95 | 62 | 110 | 90 | 85 |
| PAR | | | | | | | | | |
| YARDS | | | | | | | | | |

Directions: I-95 to Route 6 West to Route 6A West-Hartford Avenue exit. Take left (East) on Hartford Avenue. Go .7 miles and take right on Glenbridge Avenue. Go .3 miles and take left on Button Hole Drive. Facility on right.

# Country View Golf Club ✪✪½ ▶4

49 Club Lane
Harrisville, RI (401) 568-7157
www.countryviewgolf.net
Club Pro: Rick Finlayson, PGA
Payment: Visa, MC, Disc, Cash
Tee Times: 7 days adv.

| Tees | Holes | Yards | Par | USGA | Slope |
|------|-------|-------|-----|------|-------|
| BACK | 18 | 6067 | 70 | 68.2 | 117 |
| MIDDLE | 18 | 5721 | 70 | 66.5 | 113 |
| FRONT | 18 | 5060 | 70 | 67.4 | 108 |

Fee  9 Holes: Weekday: $18          Weekend: $25
Fee 18 Holes: Weekday: $30          Weekend: $38
Twilight Rates: After 5:30pm        Discounts: Senior & Junior
Cart Rental: $17pp/18, $9pp/9       Driving Range: No
Lessons: $35/half hour  Schools: No Junior Golf: No
Membership: Yes                     Architect/Yr Open: Carl Dexter/1965
Other: Clubhouse / Lockers / Showers / Snack Bar / Restaurant / Bar-Lounge

With a great mixture of holes, Country View provides a challenge for all players. Improved drainage on the front 9. New ladies tees (4, 6, 18). New, redesigned holes (12, 14, 17). Quiet country atmosphere to enjoy your round.

| | 1 | 2 | 3 | 4 | 5 | 6 | 7 | 8 | 9 |
|------|----|----|----|----|----|----|----|----|----|
| PAR | 4 | 3 | 4 | 4 | 4 | 5 | 3 | 4 | 4 |
| YARDS | 318 | 126 | 341 | 347 | 315 | 461 | 137 | 344 | 348 |
| | 10 | 11 | 12 | 13 | 14 | 15 | 16 | 17 | 18 |
| PAR | 4 | 4 | 5 | 3 | 4 | 4 | 4 | 3 | 4 |
| YARDS | 379 | 281 | 485 | 178 | 332 | 392 | 386 | 184 | 367 |

Directions: I-295 to Exit 8 (Route 7 North). Follow 5 miles past Bryant University, take left onto Mattity Road follow to end. Take left onto Tarkiln Road. Follow 600 yards take left onto Colewell Road, entrance is ½ mile on right.

# Coventry Pines Golf Club

NR ▶ 5

**1065 Harkney Hill Road**
**Coventry, RI (401) 397-9482**
www.coventrypines.com

| Tees | Holes | Yards | Par | USGA | Slope |
|------|-------|-------|-----|------|-------|
| BACK | | | | | |
| MIDDLE | 9 | 3170 | 36 | 68.0 | 113 |
| FRONT | 9 | 3120 | 36 | 70.0 | 113 |

**Club Pro:** Christopher Anderson, GM
**Payment:** Cash Only
**Tee Times:** No
**Fee 9 Holes: Weekday:** $16    **Weekend:** $16
**Fee 18 Holes: Weekday:** $25    **Weekend:** $25
**Twilight Rates:** $10 after 6pm    **Discounts:** Senior/Junior
**Cart Rental:** $10pp or $14 per cart    **Driving Range:** Practice field
**Lessons:** By arrangement   **Schools:** No    **Junior Golf:** $7/9 holes
**Membership:** No    **Architect/Yr Open:** Anderson Brothers/1959
**Other:** Snack Bar / Club Rental / Pull Carts    **GPS:**

A very scenic course with rolling hills and tree-lined fairways. 3 water holes. Noted for the par 5 sixth which has 2 different greens, men's and women's. South County course. Open March - December.

| | 1 | 2 | 3 | 4 | 5 | 6 | 7 | 8 | 9 |
|------|-----|-----|-----|-----|-----|-----|-----|-----|-----|
| PAR | 4 | 4 | 3 | 5 | 4 | 5 | 4 | 3 | 4 |
| YARDS | 375 | 308 | 169 | 484 | 408 | 520 | 357 | 187 | 362 |
| PAR | | | | | | | | | |
| YARDS | | | | | | | | | |

**Directions:** I-95 to RI Exit 6 (Route 3). Continue north on Route 3 for 1 mile. Take a left on Harkney Hill Road. The course is 2 miles on the left.

**RI**

# Cranston Country Club

✪✪✪½ ▶ 6

**69 Burlingame Road**
**Cranston, RI (401) 826-1683**
www.cranstoncc.com

| Tees | Holes | Yards | Par | USGA | Slope |
|------|-------|-------|-----|------|-------|
| BACK | 18 | 6914 | 71 | 73.5 | 130 |
| MIDDLE | 18 | 6493 | 71 | 70.8 | 125 |
| FRONT | 18 | 6109 | 71 | 69.1 | 122 |

**Club Pro:** Tom Palmer, Dir. of Golf
       Isaac Moniz, PGA
**Payment:** Visa, MC, Cash
**Tee Times:** Yes
**Fee 9 Holes: Weekday:** $27    **Weekend:** $28
**Fee 18 Holes: Weekday:** $41    **Weekend:** $47
**Twilight Rates:** $28 after 2pm wknds    **Discounts:** Senior M-F $30
**Cart Rental:** $18pp/18, $9pp/9    **Driving Range:** Grass
**Lessons:** Yes **Schools:** No    **Junior Golf:** Yes
**Membership:** Yes    **Architect/Yr Open:** Geoffrey Cornish/1974
**Other:** Clubhouse / Lockers / Showers / Snack Bar / Bar / Banquet Facilities

*COUPON*

Hole #8 is an island green. Scenic country setting. W-i-d-e fairways. Lots of room to hit driver. 4 finishing holes are a fun challenge!

| | 1 | 2 | 3 | 4 | 5 | 6 | 7 | 8 | 9 |
|------|-----|-----|-----|-----|-----|-----|-----|-----|-----|
| PAR | 5 | 4 | 4 | 3 | 4 | 4 | 4 | 3 | 4 |
| YARDS | 529 | 348 | 375 | 180 | 338 | 346 | 344 | 173 | 410 |
| | **10** | **11** | **12** | **13** | **14** | **15** | **16** | **17** | **18** |
| PAR | 4 | 4 | 3 | 5 | 4 | 3 | 4 | 5 | 4 |
| YARDS | 345 | 377 | 125 | 475 | 349 | 166 | 369 | 545 | 355 |

**Directions:** I-95 to Route 37 West (Exit 14). Go to end of Route 37, turn left. Go .2 mile to intersection, turn right; .4 mile to stop sign, bear right. Proceed .2 mile to crossroads and turn left (Phoenix Avenue). Go 2 miles to golf course.

# Crystal Lake Golf Club ✪✪✪

**7**

**100 Broncos Highway (Route 102)**
**Mapleville, RI (401) 567-4500**
www.crystallakegolfclub.com

| Tees | Holes | Yards | Par | USGA | Slope |
|------|-------|-------|-----|------|-------|
| BACK | 18 | 6249 | 71 | 69.8 | 121 |
| MIDDLE | 18 | 5966 | 71 | 69.1 | 119 |
| FRONT | 18 | 5590 | 71 | 66.6 | 116 |

**Club Pro:** Tony DiGiorgio, PGA
**Payment:** Cash, MC, Visa, Amex, Disc
**Tee Times:** 6 days adv.
**Fee 9 Holes:** $19 Mon-Thurs
**Fee 18 Holes:** $33 Mon-Thurs
**Twilight Rates:** After 6pm
**Cart Rental:** $17pp/18, $10pp/9
**Lessons:** Yes **Schools:**
**Membership:** Yes
**Other:** Clubhouse / Restaurant / Bar / Function Facility

**Weekend:** $21/Fri; $25/Wknd, Hldy
**Weekend:** $39/Fri; $45Wknd, Hldy
**Discounts:** Senior
**Driving Range:** Yes
**Junior Golf:** Yes
**Architect/Yr Open:** Howard Maurer/2003

*COUPON*

"18-hole course with great variety of holes wrapped around Crystal Lake. Lots of elevation changes and doglegs make for interesting round." –JD
Clubhouse with 4-star restaurant. Lunch Special: $46 for 18 holes, cart, $5 lunch voucher. Great views and better greens.

|  | 1 | 2 | 3 | 4 | 5 | 6 | 7 | 8 | 9 |
|------|-----|-----|-----|-----|-----|-----|-----|-----|-----|
| **PAR** | 4 | 3 | 4 | 4 | 5 | 5 | 4 | 3 | 4 |
| **YARDS** | 353 | 163 | 377 | 390 | 478 | 438 | 420 | 175 | 294 |
|  | **10** | **11** | **12** | **13** | **14** | **15** | **16** | **17** | **18** |
| **PAR** | 4 | 3 | 4 | 4 | 5 | 3 | 4 | 4 | 4 |
| **YARDS** | 406 | 181 | 299 | 280 | 501 | 148 | 313 | 378 | 372 |

**Directions:** 146 North or South to Route 102 West, 8 miles to Crystal Lake on right.

# East Greenwich Country Club ✪✪½

**8**

**1646 Division Street**
**East Greenwich, RI (401) 884-5656**
www.eastgreenwichgolfclub.com

| Tees | Holes | Yards | Par | USGA | Slope |
|------|-------|-------|-----|------|-------|
| BACK | 9 | 3315 | 36 | | 127 |
| MIDDLE | 9 | 3125 | 36 | | 124 |
| FRONT | 9 | 2875 | 36 | | 119 |

**Club Pro:** Larry Rittmann
**Payment:** Cash, Visa, MC, Amex
**Tee Times:** No
**Fee 9 Holes: Weekday:** $19
**Fee 18 Holes: Weekday:** $29
**Twilight Rates:** After 5pm
**Cart Rental:** $15pp/18, $12pp/9
**Lessons:** Yes **Schools:** Yes
**Membership:** Yes
**Other:** Snack Bar / Bar-Lounge / Restaurant

**Weekend:** $24
**Weekend:** $34
**Discounts:** Senior
**Driving Range:** No
**Junior Golf:** Yes
**Architect/Yr Open:** Michael Kroian/1963
**GPS:**

Rated as one of the more challenging 9-hole courses in N.E. Private club conditions. Fantastic greens, trees, and scenic ponds.

|  | 1 | 2 | 3 | 4 | 5 | 6 | 7 | 8 | 9 |
|------|-----|-----|-----|-----|-----|-----|-----|-----|-----|
| **PAR** | 4 | 4 | 5 | 4 | 4 | 3 | 5 | 4 | 3 |
| **YARDS** | 365 | 325 | 500 | 360 | 385 | 160 | 475 | 380 | 175 |
| **PAR** | | | | | | | | | |
| **YARDS** | | | | | | | | | |

**Directions:** I-95 to Exit 8 (East Greenwich). Take right off exit (Route 2). Head South for 300 yards to traffic light. Take right (Division Road). Course is ½ mile on left.

# Exeter Country Club

**★★½**  9

320 Pen Rod Road
Exeter, RI (401) 295-8212
www.exetercc.com

| Tees | Holes | Yards | Par | USGA | Slope |
|------|-------|-------|-----|------|-------|
| BACK | 18 | 6919 | 72 | 72.3 | 123 |
| MIDDLE | 18 | 6390 | 72 | 69.9 | 116 |
| FRONT | 18 | 5733 | 72 | 72.1 | 115 |

**Club Pro:** Justin Scott, PGA
**Payment:** Visa, MC ($15 Minimum)
**Tee Times:** 1 day adv., call after 8am
**Fee 9 Holes: Weekday:** $20 M-Th 1pm **Weekend:** $25 F/S/S/H 3:30pm
**Fee 18 Holes: Weekday:** $35 walk/$50 ride **Weekend:** $40 walk/$55 ride F/S/S/H
**Twilight Rates:** After 4pm **Discounts:** Junior
**Cart Rental:** $15pp/18, $9pp/9 **Driving Range:** $8/lg., $5/med.
**Lessons:** No **Schools:** No **Junior Golf:** No
**Membership:** Yes, waiting list **Architect/Yr Open:** Geoffrey Cornish/1969
**Other:** Clubhouse / Snack Bar / Lockers / Bar-Lounge / Full Restaurant

Course has a beautiful layout with strategically placed hazards. Wide fairways – bring your driver. Friendly staff. Open March - November. South County course.

| | 1 | 2 | 3 | 4 | 5 | 6 | 7 | 8 | 9 |
|---|---|---|---|---|---|---|---|---|---|
| PAR | 4 | 5 | 3 | 5 | 3 | 4 | 4 | 4 | 4 |
| YARDS | 350 | 530 | 190 | 510 | 180 | 360 | 420 | 370 | 400 |
| | 10 | 11 | 12 | 13 | 14 | 15 | 16 | 17 | 18 |
| PAR | 4 | 3 | 4 | 4 | 5 | 4 | 4 | 3 | 5 |
| YARDS | 400 | 150 | 330 | 310 | 480 | 350 | 370 | 200 | 490 |

**Directions:** I-95 to Route 4 (Exit 5B South) into Exeter (approximately 4-5 miles), take Route 102 North. Course is 2.5 miles on left. From South, take I-95 North to Exit 4. Take Route 3 North; at intersection of Route 102, go right. Course is 5 miles on right side.

**RI**

# Fairlawn Golf Course

**NR**  10

3 Sherman Avenue
Lincoln, RI (401) 334-3937
www.fairlawngolfcourse.com

| Tees | Holes | Yards | Par | USGA | Slope |
|------|-------|-------|-----|------|-------|
| BACK | | | | | |
| MIDDLE | 9 | 2534 | 27 | 52.2 | N/A |
| FRONT | | | | | |

**Club Pro:** Sabrina Roberts, Manager
**Payment:** Cash Only
**Tee Times:** No
**Fee 9 Holes: Weekday:** $13 **Weekend:** $15
**Fee 18 Holes: Weekday:** $18 **Weekend:** $20
**Twilight Rates:** **Discounts:** Military, Public Safety
**Cart Rental:** $13pp/18; $6.50pp/9 **Driving Range:** No
**Lessons:** No **Schools:** No **Junior Golf:** No
**Membership:** Yes **Architect/Yr Open:** Adams/1963
**Other:** Clubhouse / Beer and Wine **GPS:**

COUPON

Beautiful and affordable course.

| | 1 | 2 | 3 | 4 | 5 | 6 | 7 | 8 | 9 |
|---|---|---|---|---|---|---|---|---|---|
| PAR | 3 | 3 | 3 | 3 | 3 | 3 | 3 | 3 | 3 |
| YARDS | 133 | 181 | 121 | 167 | 91 | 110 | 110 | 161 | 193 |
| PAR | | | | | | | | | |
| YARDS | | | | | | | | | |

**Directions:** I-95 North to Route 146 North to Sherman Avenue exit. Course is on right — you can't miss it.

# Fenner Hill Golf Club

 ★★½ 11

33 Wheeler Lane
Hope Valley, RI (401) 539-8000
www.fennerhill.com

| Tees | Holes | Yards | Par | USGA | Slope |
|------|-------|-------|-----|------|-------|
| BACK | 18 | 6636 | 72 | 71.8 | 129 |
| MIDDLE | 18 | 6262 | 72 | 70.1 | 126 |
| FRONT | 18 | 5724 | 72 | 67.4 | 118 |

**Club Pro:** Fred DiMeo, Dir. of Golf
**Payment:** Visa, MC
**Tee Times:** 3 days adv.
**Fee 9 Holes: Weekday:** $25 · **Weekend:** Variable by time
**Fee 18 Holes: Weekday:** $35 · **Weekend:** Variable by time
**Twilight Rates:** After 1pm · **Discounts:** Sr. & Jr. Weekdays
**Cart Rental:** $17pp/18, $10pp/9 · **Driving Range:** No
**Lessons:** No **Schools:** No · **Junior Golf:** No
**Membership:** Full, Weekday, Inner Club · **Architect/Yr Open:** Ron & Dennis Levesque/1999
**Other:** Restaurant / Bar-Lounge / Banquet Facilities / Corporate Outings

Player Comments: "Looks easy from the road, but watch out. Walkable." The beauty of the landscape pleases and challenges all levels. Greens #16 and #18 have been rebuilt. Foxwoods nearby.

| | 1 | 2 | 3 | 4 | 5 | 6 | 7 | 8 | 9 |
|---|---|---|---|---|---|---|---|---|---|
| PAR | 4 | 4 | 5 | 3 | 4 | 3 | 4 | 5 | 4 |
| YARDS | 366 | 347 | 486 | 152 | 352 | 158 | 394 | 520 | 355 |
| | 10 | 11 | 12 | 13 | 14 | 15 | 16 | 17 | 18 |
| PAR | 5 | 3 | 4 | 4 | 5 | 4 | 3 | 4 | 4 |
| YARDS | 468 | 164 | 440 | 338 | 525 | 309 | 166 | 297 | 425 |

**Directions:** I-95 to Exit 2. From the south take right at stop sign. Course is ¾ mile on right. From the north take left at stop sign. Course is ¾ mile on right.

# Foster Country Club

 ★★ 12

67 Johnson Road
Foster, RI (401) 397-7750
www.fostercountryclub.com

| Tees | Holes | Yards | Par | USGA | Slope |
|------|-------|-------|-----|------|-------|
| BACK | 18 | 6221 | 72 | 70.9 | 116 |
| MIDDLE | 18 | 5754 | 72 | 68.8 | 114 |
| FRONT | 18 | 5130 | 72 | 66.6 | 108 |

**Club Pro:** Brian Benson
**Payment:** Visa, MC
**Tee Times:** 7 days adv.
**Fee 9 Holes: Weekday:** $19 · **Weekend:** $22
**Fee 18 Holes: Weekday:** $28 · **Weekend:** $38
**Twilight Rates:** After 12pm · **Discounts:** Juniors and seniors
**Cart Rental:** $20pp/18, $10pp/9 · **Driving Range:** Practice nets
**Lessons:** Yes **Schools:** No · **Junior Golf:** Yes
**Membership:** Yes · **Architect/Yr Open:** Geoffrey Cornish/1962
**Other:** Clubhouse / Snack Bar / Restaurant / Bar-Lounge / 180-Seat Banquet Hall

COUPON

"Friendly atmosphere, nice clubhouse, challenging layout, back nine a bit quirky." –GM

| | 1 | 2 | 3 | 4 | 5 | 6 | 7 | 8 | 9 |
|---|---|---|---|---|---|---|---|---|---|
| PAR | 4 | 4 | 3 | 5 | 4 | 4 | 3 | 5 | 4 |
| YARDS | 356 | 340 | 241 | 595 | 295 | 425 | 130 | 485 | 310 |
| | 10 | 11 | 12 | 13 | 14 | 15 | 16 | 17 | 18 |
| PAR | 4 | 4 | 5 | 4 | 5 | 4 | 4 | 3 | 3 |
| YARDS | 405 | 310 | 495 | 375 | 450 | 295 | 315 | 170 | 195 |

**Directions:** Take I-95 to Route 102 North to Route 14. Left on Route 14 to Moosup Valley Road (on right) to Johnson Road (on right). Follow to course.

# Goddard State Park Golf Course NR 13 ▶

Ives Road
Warwick, RI (401) 884-9834
www.riparks.com

| Tees | Holes | Yards | Par | USGA | Slope |
|------|-------|-------|-----|------|-------|
| BACK | 9 | 3250 | 36 | 34.2 | 111 |
| MIDDLE | 9 | 3032 | 36 | 33.8 | 109 |
| FRONT | | | | | |

**Club Pro:**
**Payment:** Cash or Check
**Tee Times:** No
**Fee 9 Holes: Weekday:** $12    **Weekend:** $14
**Fee 18 Holes: Weekday:**    **Weekend:**
**Twilight Rates:** No    **Discounts:** Senior ½ price
**Cart Rental:** $15pp/9    **Driving Range:** No
**Lessons:** No **Schools:** No    **Junior Golf:** No
**Membership:** No    **Architect/Yr Open:** 1939
**Other:** Clubhouse / Snack Bar / Picnic Facilities / Beach / Showers

The course, located inside Goddard State Park, is open and very walkable. Horse paths and jogging trails are also available. 300 trees have been added to the course, resulting in more of a challenge.

| | 1 | 2 | 3 | 4 | 5 | 6 | 7 | 8 | 9 |
|------|-----|-----|-----|-----|-----|-----|-----|-----|-----|
| PAR | 5 | 4 | 3 | 4 | 5 | 4 | 3 | 4 | 4 |
| YARDS | 503 | 377 | 180 | 292 | 500 | 301 | 168 | 390 | 321 |
| PAR | | | | | | | | | |
| YARDS | | | | | | | | | |

**Directions:** I-95 to Route 4 cutoff, take first exit (East Greenwich). Take Route 401 and follow signs to course.

# Green Valley Country Club ✪✪½ 14 ▶

371 Union Street
Portsmouth, RI (401) 847-9543
www.greenvalleyccofri.com

| Tees | Holes | Yards | Par | USGA | Slope |
|------|-------|-------|-----|------|-------|
| BACK | 18 | 6830 | 71 | 72.1 | 125 |
| MIDDLE | 18 | 6721 | 71 | 71.6 | 122 |
| FRONT | 18 | 5459 | 71 | 69.5 | 120 |

**Club Pro:** Gary P. Dorsi, PGA
**Payment:** Visa, MC, Amex
**Tee Times:** 3 days adv.
**Fee 9 Holes: Weekday:**    **Weekend:**
**Fee 18 Holes: Weekday:** $38    **Weekend:** $48
**Twilight Rates:** After 3pm    **Discounts:** None
**Cart Rental:** $16pp/18    **Driving Range:** $3/bucket
**Lessons:** $35/half hour **Schools:** Yes    **Junior Golf:** Yes
**Membership:** Yes, Junior    **Architect/Yr Open:** Manuel Raposa/1957
**Other:** Snack Bar / Clubhouse / Outings    **GPS:**

Hosted USGA Qualifiers, RI Amateur, RI Open. May book large or small outings. Nice character with old stone walls. Ideal for tournaments and outings and an afternoon of golf.

| | 1 | 2 | 3 | 4 | 5 | 6 | 7 | 8 | 9 |
|------|-----|-----|-----|-----|-----|-----|-----|-----|-----|
| PAR | 4 | 4 | 4 | 5 | 3 | 4 | 4 | 3 | 4 |
| YARDS | 361 | 454 | 386 | 541 | 175 | 392 | 354 | 201 | 424 |
| | 10 | 11 | 12 | 13 | 14 | 15 | 16 | 17 | 18 |
| PAR | 5 | 3 | 3 | 4 | 4 | 4 | 4 | 5 | 4 |
| YARDS | 605 | 220 | 125 | 327 | 440 | 334 | 394 | 540 | 368 |

**Directions:** I-195 to Route 24 South, follow Route 114 South, Raytheon Corporation is on right. Take left on Union Street (2nd light after Raytheon Corporation).

# Harbor Lights Golf & Country Club ✪✪✪  ▶15

**150 Gray Street**
**Warwick, RI (401) 737-6353**
www.harborlightsri.com

**Club Pro:** Al Vallante, PGA
**Payment:** Most Credit Cards
**Tee Times:** No
**Fee 9 Holes: Weekday:** $19
**Fee 18 Holes: Weekday:** $29
**Twilight Rates:** No
**Cart Rental:** $14pp/18, $7pp/9
**Lessons:** Yes **Schools:** No
**Membership:** Yes
**Other:** Clubhouse / Snack Bar / Bar-Lounge

| Tees | Holes | Yards | Par | USGA | Slope |
|------|-------|-------|-----|------|-------|
| BACK | 9 | 2777 | 36 | 67.0 | 118 |
| MIDDLE | 9 | 2488 | 34 | 66.3 | 116 |
| FRONT | 9 | 2152 | 33 | 65.8 | 114 |

**Weekend:** $20
**Weekend:** $31
**Discounts:** Senior
**Driving Range:** Yes, irons only
**Junior Golf:** Yes
**Architect/Yr Open:** Geoffrey Cornish
**GPS:**

The scenic and beautifully manicured Harbor Lights Golf & Country Club is the former Seaview Country Club — reclaimed, redesigned and reconditioned to a quality befitting its prime seaside location.

| | 1 | 2 | 3 | 4 | 5 | 6 | 7 | 8 | 9 |
|------|-----|-----|-----|-----|-----|-----|-----|-----|-----|
| PAR | 4 | 4 | 3 | 5 | 3 | 3 | 4 | 4 | 4 |
| YARDS | 313 | 233 | 195 | 501 | 124 | 167 | 286 | 256 | 413 |
| PAR | | | | | | | | | |
| YARDS | | | | | | | | | |

**Directions:** From I-95, take Exit 10E onto Route 117 East. Follow Route 117 for 4 miles to Warwick Neck Ave (Sunoco station) on right. Turn onto Warwick Neck Ave for .6 miles to Meadow View Avenue on right. Turn onto Meadow View Avenue and follow the signs to Harbor Lights.

# Jamestown Golf Course ✪✪✪½  ▶16

**245 Conanicus Ave**
**Jamestown, RI (401) 423-9930**
www.jamestowngolf.com

**Club Pro:** Jon Mistowski, Manager
**Payment:** All Types
**Tee Times:** No
**Fee 9 Holes: Weekday:** $17
**Fee 18 Holes: Weekday:** $27
**Twilight Rates:** No
**Cart Rental:** $12pp/18, $7pp/9
**Lessons:** No **Schools:** No
**Membership:** No
**Other:** Clubhouse / Snack Bar / Bar-Lounge

| Tees | Holes | Yards | Par | USGA | Slope |
|------|-------|-------|-----|------|-------|
| BACK | 9 | 3048 | 36 | 69.7 | 110 |
| MIDDLE | 9 | 2751 | 36 | 69.7 | 110 |
| FRONT | 9 | 2421 | 38 | | |

**Weekend:** $19
**Weekend:** $29
**Discounts:** None
**Driving Range:** No
**Junior Golf:** Yes
**Architect/Yr Open:** 1901
**GPS:**

Course is completely watered by irrigation. Open April - November. "Great views, great condition." –FP

| | 1 | 2 | 3 | 4 | 5 | 6 | 7 | 8 | 9 |
|------|-----|-----|-----|-----|-----|-----|-----|-----|-----|
| PAR | 4 | 5 | 4 | 4 | 3 | 5 | 3 | 4 | 4 |
| YARDS | 270 | 484 | 279 | 375 | 114 | 379 | 141 | 368 | 328 |
| PAR | | | | | | | | | |
| YARDS | | | | | | | | | |

**Directions:** I-95 to Route 138 East. Go over Jamestown Bridge. Cross the island and follow signs to the Newport Bridge. When toll booths are in sight, take last exit before toll. Course is on right.

# Kings Crossing Golf Club

✪½ **17** ▶

655 Old Baptist Road
North Kingstown, RI (401) 294-2872
www.kingscrossinggolfclub.com

**Club Pro:** Robert McNeil, Manager
**Payment:** Visa, MC, Amex, Disc
**Tee Times:** Yes

| Tees | Holes | Yards | Par | USGA | Slope |
|------|-------|-------|-----|------|-------|
| BACK | 9 | 3023 | 35 | 68.5 | |
| MIDDLE | 9 | 2872 | 35 | 68.5 | 124 |
| FRONT | 9 | 2417 | 36 | | |

**Fee 9 Holes: Weekday:** $22
**Fee 18 Holes: Weekday:** $30
**Twilight Rates:** After 2pm
**Cart Rental:** $20pp/18, $10pp/9
**Lessons:** Yes **Schools:** Yes
**Membership:** Yes
**Other:** Snack Bar / Bar-Lounge / Restaurant / Function Room

**Weekend:** $24
**Weekend:** $32
**Discounts:** Senior and Junior
**Driving Range:** No
**Junior Golf:** Yes
**Architect/Yr Open:** Geoffrey Cornish/1963

COUPON

Player Comments: "The course has tight fairways and fast greens." Open March - December. South County course. Kings Crossing is uniquely laid out to allow players to enjoy a round of 4 holes, 9 holes, or 18 holes with ae flexible tee system.

| | 1 | 2 | 3 | 4 | 5 | 6 | 7 | 8 | 9 |
|------|-----|-----|-----|-----|-----|-----|-----|-----|-----|
| PAR | 4 | 5 | 3 | 5 | 3 | 4 | 4 | 3 | 4 |
| YARDS | 360 | 413 | 198 | 505 | 152 | 330 | 297 | 203 | 414 |
| PAR | | | | | | | | | |
| YARDS | | | | | | | | | |

**Directions:** I-95 to Route 4 South. Take Exit 5 (Wickford); turn right off exit. Take left at 3rd light onto Old Baptist Road. Course is ⅛ mile on left.

**RI**

# Laurel Lane Country Club

✪✪✪ **18** ▶

309 Laurel Lane
West Kingston, RI (401) 783-3844
www.laurellanecountryclub.com

**Club Pro:** Pat O'Brien
**Payment:** Cash, Visa, MC, Amex
**Tee Times:** 7 days adv.

| Tees | Holes | Yards | Par | USGA | Slope |
|------|-------|-------|-----|------|-------|
| BACK | 18 | 6177 | 71 | 69.1 | 124 |
| MIDDLE | 18 | 6010 | 71 | 67.8 | 117 |
| FRONT | 18 | 4966 | 70 | 69.2 | 120 |

**Fee 9 Holes: Weekday:** $23
**Fee 18 Holes: Weekday:** $33
**Twilight Rates:** After 2pm
**Cart Rental:** $18pp/18, $10pp/9
**Lessons:** Yes **Schools:** Jr.
**Membership:** Yes
**Other:** Clubhouse / Snack Bar / Bar-Lounge

**Weekend:** $25
**Weekend:** $38
**Discounts:** Senior & Junior
**Driving Range:** Yes
**Junior Golf:** Yes
**Architect/Yr:** Holley, Sr., Thoren, Bota/1961
**GPS:**

COUPON

Fun course for all. Easy to walk. Excellent greens. Friendly staff. Fabulous practice facilities including driving range, 4 tier putting green, chipping area and bunkers. Check out the restaurant — great food!

| | 1 | 2 | 3 | 4 | 5 | 6 | 7 | 8 | 9 |
|------|-----|-----|-----|-----|-----|-----|-----|-----|-----|
| PAR | 4 | 5 | 3 | 4 | 4 | 4 | 3 | 4 | 4 |
| YARDS | 410 | 470 | 177 | 362 | 347 | 236 | 207 | 363 | 372 |
| | 10 | 11 | 12 | 13 | 14 | 15 | 16 | 17 | 18 |
| PAR | 4 | 4 | 4 | 4 | 4 | 3 | 5 | 3 | 5 |
| YARDS | 390 | 306 | 319 | 340 | 384 | 150 | 475 | 162 | 540 |

**Directions:** I-95 to Exit 3A. Go approximately 6 miles east on Route 138. Right on Laurel Lane.

# Lindhbrook Golf Course

NR 19 ▶

299 Woodville Alton Road
Hope Valley, RI (401) 539-8700

| Tees | Holes | Yards | Par | USGA | Slope |
|------|-------|-------|-----|------|-------|
| BACK | 18 | 3000 | 54 | | |
| MIDDLE | 18 | 2869 | 54 | | |
| FRONT | 18 | 2600 | 54 | | |

**Club Pro:** Bill Patnoad
**Payment:** Visa, MC, Amex
**Tee Times:** Yes
**Fee  9 Holes: Weekday:** $15    **Weekend:** $15
**Fee 18 Holes: Weekday:** $20    **Weekend:** $25
**Twilight Rates:** After 5:30pm    **Discounts:** Senior & Junior
**Cart Rental:** $18pp/18, $12pp/9    **Driving Range:** No
**Lessons:** Yes  **Schools:** No    **Junior Golf:** Yes
**Membership:** Yes    **Architect/Yr Open:** 1954
**Other:** Snack Bar / Restaurant / Bar-Lounge    **GPS:**

South County course.

| | 1 | 2 | 3 | 4 | 5 | 6 | 7 | 8 | 9 |
|------|-----|-----|-----|-----|-----|-----|-----|-----|-----|
| PAR | 3 | 3 | 3 | 3 | 3 | 3 | 3 | 3 | 3 |
| YARDS | 132 | 146 | 171 | 172 | 150 | 168 | 158 | 175 | 125 |
| | 10 | 11 | 12 | 13 | 14 | 15 | 16 | 17 | 18 |
| PAR | 3 | 3 | 3 | 3 | 3 | 3 | 3 | 3 | 3 |
| YARDS | 139 | 143 | 127 | 180 | 181 | 192 | 143 | 183 | 184 |

**Directions:** I-95 to Exit 2. If Northbound, bear right; if Southbound, turn left. Course 800 yards from I-95 on right.

# Meadow Brook

✪✪✪✪ 20 ▶

163 Kingstown Road
Richmond, RI (401) 539-8491
www.meadowbrookgolfri.com

| Tees | Holes | Yards | Par | USGA | Slope |
|------|-------|-------|-----|------|-------|
| BACK | 18 | 7468 | 72 | 74.4 | 130 |
| MIDDLE | 18 | 6532 | 72 | 69.9 | 119 |
| FRONT | 18 | 5308 | 72 | 68.9 | 117 |

**Club Pro:** John Grimley, PGA
**Payment:** Visa, MC
**Tee Times:** 2 days adv.
**Fee  9 Holes: Weekday:**    **Weekend:**
**Fee 18 Holes: Weekday:** $50    **Weekend:** $60
**Twilight Rates:** Available    **Discounts:** Senior
**Cart Rental:** $15pp/18    **Driving Range:** No
**Lessons:** Yes  **Schools:** No    **Junior Golf:** No
**Membership:** No    **Architect/Yr Open:** Rulewich & Fleury/2010
**Other:** Clubhouse / Restaurant / Bar-Lounge    **GPS:**

Located 2 miles off of I-95 on Route 138. Meadow Brook is 30 minutes from Providence, the beaches and the casinos. Stretching over 7400 yards, Meadow Brook is the longest golf course in RI. Beautiful yet challenging and playable for golfers at all levels offering 5 sets of tees.

| | 1 | 2 | 3 | 4 | 5 | 6 | 7 | 8 | 9 |
|------|-----|-----|-----|-----|-----|-----|-----|-----|-----|
| PAR | 4 | 5 | 4 | 3 | 4 | 3 | 4 | 5 | 4 |
| YARDS | 374 | 486 | 359 | 178 | 432 | 139 | 371 | 506 | 361 |
| | 10 | 11 | 12 | 13 | 14 | 15 | 16 | 17 | 18 |
| PAR | 3 | 4 | 5 | 4 | 4 | 5 | 4 | 3 | 4 |
| YARDS | 151 | 376 | 538 | 362 | 399 | 569 | 404 | 159 | 368 |

**Directions:** I-95 to Exit 3A in RI. Continue on Route 138 East. Course is 1 mile east of I-95.

# Melody Hill Golf Course

NR ▶ **21**

55 Melody Hill Lane
Harmony, RI (401) 949-9851
www.melodyhillcc.com

**Club Pro:** Steve Lauzier, PGA
**Payment:** Cash Only
**Tee Times:** No

| Tees | Holes | Yards | Par | USGA | Slope |
|------|-------|-------|-----|------|-------|
| BACK | 18 | 6004 | 71 | 68.4 | 109 |
| MIDDLE | 18 | 5801 | 71 | 67.5 | 108 |
| FRONT | 18 | 5363 | 71 | 70.4 | 113 |

**Fee  9 Holes: Weekday:** $19 **Weekend:** $20
**Fee 18 Holes: Weekday:** $27 **Weekend:** $31
**Twilight Rates:** $18 after 4pm; $16 after 5pm **Discounts:** Senior $21pp/18, $17pp/9 (M-F)
**Cart Rental:** $28/18, $14/9 per cart **Driving Range:** No
**Lessons:** Yes **Schools:** No **Junior/Senior Golf:** Senior Rates
**Membership:** Limited **Architect/Yr Open:** Sam Mitchell/1967
**Other:** Clubhouse / Snack Bar / Bar-Lounge **GPS:**

Lessons by certified teacher of golf. Twilight rates: 9 holes only $15 after 5pm weekdays; $17 after 4pm weekends. Seniors M-F 9 holes $17, 18 holes $21.

| | 1 | 2 | 3 | 4 | 5 | 6 | 7 | 8 | 9 |
|---|---|---|---|---|---|---|---|---|---|
| PAR | 4 | 4 | 4 | 3 | 4 | 3 | 4 | 5 | 4 |
| YARDS | 360 | 315 | 385 | 95 | 465 | 145 | 425 | 500 | 235 |
| | **10** | **11** | **12** | **13** | **14** | **15** | **16** | **17** | **18** |
| PAR | 5 | 4 | 5 | 3 | 4 | 3 | 4 | 4 | 4 |
| YARDS | 445 | 405 | 535 | 185 | 360 | 165 | 355 | 400 | 410 |

**Directions:** Route 44 West toward CT, take first left after fire station in Harmony Center onto Saw Mill Road.

**RI**

# Midville Country Club

✪✪½ ▶ **22**

100 Lombardi Lane
West Warwick, RI (401) 828-9215
www.midvillegolfclub.com

**Club Pro:** Ron Lombardi, GM
**Payment:** Visa, MC
**Tee Times:** Yes

| Tees | Holes | Yards | Par | USGA | Slope |
|------|-------|-------|-----|------|-------|
| BACK | 9 | 2910 | 35 | 67.0 | 118 |
| MIDDLE | 9 | 2755 | 35 | 65.6 | 115 |
| FRONT | 9 | 2345 | 35 | 65.0 | 115 |

**Fee  9 Holes: Weekday:** $25 **Weekend:** $26
**Fee 18 Holes: Weekday:** $39 **Weekend:** $43
**Twilight Rates:** No
**Discounts:** Senior & Junior (before 2pm wkdy, after 2pm wknd)
**Cart Rental:** $10pp/9, pull cart: $2 **Driving Range:** No
**Lessons:** No **Schools:** No **Junior Golf:** Yes
**Membership:** No **Architect/Yr Open:** Carmine Lombardi/1962
**Other:** Clubhouse / Snack Bar / Bar-Lounge **GPS:**

COUPON

Scenic 9-hole layout. Well-conditioned public course. April - December.

| | 1 | 2 | 3 | 4 | 5 | 6 | 7 | 8 | 9 |
|---|---|---|---|---|---|---|---|---|---|
| PAR | 4 | 4 | 4 | 4 | 3 | 5 | 3 | 4 | 4 |
| YARDS | 345 | 295 | 335 | 345 | 145 | 525 | 145 | 290 | 330 |
| PAR | | | | | | | | | |
| YARDS | | | | | | | | | |

**Directions:** I-95 to Route 113 West exit. Go straight through 3 sets of lights. Cross bridge, bear right and then straight through the 4th light. Course is 1 mile on left.

# Montaup Country Club  ✪✪✪½  ▸ 23

500 Anthony Road
Portsmouth, RI (401) 683-0955
www.montaupcc.com

**Club Pro:** Steve Diemoz
**Payment:** Cash, Visa, MC, Check
**Tee Times:** 3 days adv.

| Tees | Holes | Yards | Par | USGA | Slope |
|------|-------|-------|-----|------|-------|
| BACK | 18 | 6321 | 71 | 70.9 | 125 |
| MIDDLE | 18 | 5807 | 71 | 68.1 | 122 |
| FRONT | 18 | 5359 | 73 | 71.6 | 122 |

**Fee 9 Holes: Weekday:**
**Fee 18 Holes: Weekday:** $47
**Twilight Rates:** After 3:30pm wknds only
**Cart Rental:** $20pp/18
**Lessons:** Yes **Schools:** No
**Membership:** No
**Weekend:**
**Weekend:** $47
**Discounts:** None
**Driving Range:** No
**Junior Golf:** Yes
**Architect/Yr Open:** 1923
**Other:** Clubhouse / Snack Bar / Restaurant / Bar-Lounge

Player Comments: "Always in excellent shape and great to walk." "Excellent greens, lots of room to hit away." Open April - December.

| | 1 | 2 | 3 | 4 | 5 | 6 | 7 | 8 | 9 |
|------|-----|-----|-----|-----|-----|-----|-----|-----|-----|
| PAR | 4 | 4 | 3 | 4 | 5 | 4 | 5 | 3 | 4 |
| YARDS | 414 | 405 | 213 | 386 | 503 | 351 | 521 | 145 | 339 |
| | 10 | 11 | 12 | 13 | 14 | 15 | 16 | 17 | 18 |
| PAR | 3 | 4 | 3 | 5 | 3 | 4 | 5 | 4 | 4 |
| YARDS | 154 | 398 | 184 | 503 | 163 | 424 | 519 | 399 | 300 |

**Directions:** Exit 3 from Route 24 South, left on Anthony Road to entrance. Exit 4 from 24 North, left on Boyd Lane, right on Anthony Road to entrance.

# Newport National Golf Club  ✪✪✪✪  ▸ 24

324 Mitchell's Lane
Middletown, RI (401) 848-9690
www.newportnational.com

**Club Pro:** Andy Farrea
**Payment:** Cash, All Major Cards
**Tee Times:** 7 days adv.

| Tees | Holes | Yards | Par | USGA | Slope |
|------|-------|-------|-----|------|-------|
| BACK | 18 | 7244 | 72 | 74.4 | 138 |
| MIDDLE | 18 | 6553 | 72 | 71.9 | 130 |
| FRONT | 18 | 5217 | 71 | 68.8 | 119 |

**Fee 9 Holes: Weekday:**
**Fee 18 Holes: Weekday:** $125 w/cart
**Twilight Rates:** After 1pm
**Cart Rental:** Included
**Lessons:** Yes **Schools:** No
**Membership:** Yes
**Other:** Restaurant / Bar-Lounge
**Weekend:**
**Weekend:** $150 w/cart F/S/S
**Discounts:** No
**Driving Range:** None
**Junior Golf:** Yes
**Architect/Yr Open:** Arthur Hills, Drew Rogers/2002
**GPS:**

Named the "Best Course that You Can Play" by *Golf Digest, Golf Week* and *Golf Magazine* for Rhode Island. #1 slope and rated course in the State.

| | 1 | 2 | 3 | 4 | 5 | 6 | 7 | 8 | 9 |
|------|-----|-----|-----|-----|-----|-----|-----|-----|-----|
| PAR | 5 | 4 | 3 | 3 | 4 | 4 | 4 | 5 | 4 |
| YARDS | 486 | 400 | 168 | 154 | 296 | 449 | 444 | 495 | 348 |
| | 10 | 11 | 12 | 13 | 14 | 15 | 16 | 17 | 18 |
| PAR | 4 | 5 | 4 | 3 | 5 | 4 | 3 | 4 | 4 |
| YARDS | 383 | 505 | 326 | 148 | 523 | 396 | 212 | 439 | 381 |

**Directions:** I-195 to MA Route 24 South or RI 138 or RI 114 South. Follow signs to Newport. Take 138 South (East Main Road) through Portsmouth. Watch for Mitchell's Lane on the left. Newport Airport? You went too far.

# North Kingstown Munipal GC ✪✪✪

## 25

615 Callahan Road
North Kingstown, RI (401) 294-0684
www.nkgc.com

**Club Pro:** John Rainone, Head Pro
**Payment:** Cash, Visa, MC
**Tee Times:** 2 days adv.

| Tees | Holes | Yards | Par | USGA | Slope |
|------|-------|-------|-----|------|-------|
| BACK | 18 | 6161 | 70 | 69.3 | 123 |
| MIDDLE | 18 | 5848 | 70 | 67.8 | 121 |
| FRONT | 18 | 5227 | 70 | 69.5 | 115 |

**Fee 9 Holes: Weekday:** $26 **Weekend:** $26
**Fee 18 Holes: Weekday:** $33 **Weekend:** $41
**Twilight Rates:** $25 after 4pm (weekends only)
**Discounts:** Senior
**Cart Rental:** $36/18, $20/9 per cart **Driving Range:** $10/lg, $6/sm
**Lessons:** Yes **Schools:** Yes **Junior Golf:** Yes
**Membership:** Yes **Architect/Yr Open:** Walter Johnson/1943
**Other:** Restaurant / Lounge / Clubhouse **GPS:**

Player Comments: "Just plain enjoyable. Redefines what a muncipal can be." Hosted 2006 and 2016 US Open Qualifier. Links-style overlooking Narragansett Bay. South County course.

| | 1 | 2 | 3 | 4 | 5 | 6 | 7 | 8 | 9 |
|------|---|---|---|---|---|---|---|---|---|
| PAR | 4 | 4 | 3 | 5 | 4 | 4 | 5 | 3 | 4 |
| YARDS | 369 | 411 | 185 | 499 | 375 | 353 | 545 | 197 | 283 |
| | 10 | 11 | 12 | 13 | 14 | 15 | 16 | 17 | 18 |
| PAR | 3 | 5 | 4 | 4 | 3 | 4 | 4 | 4 | 3 |
| YARDS | 171 | 559 | 333 | 403 | 194 | 413 | 398 | 315 | 158 |

**Directions:** I-95 South to Route 45. Exit 7A off Route 45 (403E). Follow approximately 4.5 miles. Go left at 1st light. First right. Clubhouse on the right.

# Pinecrest Golf Course ✪✪½

25 Pinehurst Drive
Carolina, RI (401) 364-8600
www.pinecrestri.com

**Club Pro:** Joseph Scott
**Payment:** Visa, MC, Personal Cks, Cash
**Tee Times:** 4 day adv./Wed. for nonmembers

| Tees | Holes | Yards | Par | USGA | Slope |
|------|-------|-------|-----|------|-------|
| BACK | 9 | 2900 | 35 | 67.7 | 131 |
| MIDDLE | 9 | 2611 | 35 | 66.2 | 123 |
| FRONT | 9 | 2309 | 35 | 69.4 | 123 |

**Fee 9 Holes: Weekday:** $20 **Weekend:** $22
**Fee 18 Holes: Weekday:** $30 **Weekend:** $32
**Twilight Rates:** After 3pm **Discounts:** Senior & Junior
**Cart Rental:** $13pp/18, $8pp/9 **Driving Range:** No
**Lessons:** No **Schools:** No **Junior Golf:** No
**Membership:** Yes
**Architect/Yr Open:** Beakman-Wermy/Intergolf Design/2002
**Other:** Bar / Grille / Clubhouse

"Short 9 holes with one par 5. Very playable for all levels of golfing ability. 2nd is the signature hole." –RW

| | 1 | 2 | 3 | 4 | 5 | 6 | 7 | 8 | 9 |
|------|---|---|---|---|---|---|---|---|---|
| PAR | 4 | 4 | 4 | 5 | 3 | 4 | 4 | 3 | 4 |
| YARDS | 320 | 385 | 348 | 540 | 129 | 382 | 337 | 145 | 314 |
| PAR | | | | | | | | | |
| YARDS | | | | | | | | | |

**Directions:** I-95 to Exit 3 to Route 138 East to Route 112. 2.4 miles to Pinehurst Drive on left.

**RI**

# Richmond Country Club

74 Sandy Pond Road
Richmond, RI (401) 364-9200
www.richmondcountryclub.net
**Club Pro:** Jonathan Rapoza
**Payment:** Visa, MC
**Tee Times:** 3 days adv.
**Fee  9 Holes: Weekday:** $22
**Fee 18 Holes: Weekday:** $37
**Twilight Rates:** After 3pm
**Cart Rental:** $15pp/18
**Lessons:** No  **Schools:** No
**Membership:** No

| Tees | Holes | Yards | Par | USGA | Slope |
|------|-------|-------|-----|------|-------|
| BACK | 18 | 6515 | 71 | 69.9 | 117 |
| MIDDLE | 18 | 5827 | 71 | 68.5 | 114 |
| FRONT | 18 | 4974 | 71 | 70.4 | 113 |

**Weekend:**
**Weekend:** $42
**Discounts:** Senior & Junior
**Driving Range:** Yes
**Junior Golf:** No
**Architect/Yr Open:** Cornish & Silva/1992
**Other:** Restaurant / Clubhouse / Bar-Lounge / Banquet Facilities

Player Comments: "Plush fairways. Pure greens. Aesthetically pleasant." South County course.
Look for new tee box locations for more challenging play. Rates subject to change.

|  | 1 | 2 | 3 | 4 | 5 | 6 | 7 | 8 | 9 |
|------|---|---|---|---|---|---|---|---|---|
| PAR | 4 | 4 | 3 | 5 | 3 | 4 | 5 | 4 | 4 |
| YARDS | 318 | 353 | 204 | 504 | 165 | 428 | 450 | 277 | 285 |
|  | 10 | 11 | 12 | 13 | 14 | 15 | 16 | 17 | 18 |
| PAR | 4 | 5 | 3 | 4 | 4 | 3 | 5 | 4 | 3 |
| YARDS | 320 | 431 | 184 | 408 | 368 | 176 | 474 | 154 | 328 |

**Directions:** I-95 to Exit 3B; follow 2 miles. Left at flashing light onto Mechanic Street. Go 2.5 miles, turn right onto Sandy Pond Road.

# Rolling Greens Golf Course

1625 Pen Rod Road
North Kingstown, RI (401) 294-9859
www.rollinggreensri.com
**Club Pro:** Jessica Merigan, GM
**Payment:** Cash, Credit Cards
**Tee Times:** No
**Fee  9 Holes: Weekday:** $18
**Fee 18 Holes: Weekday:** $24
**Twilight Rates:** No
**Cart Rental:** $20pp/18, $12pp/9
**Lessons:** No  **Schools:** No
**Membership:** Yes

| Tees | Holes | Yards | Par | USGA | Slope |
|------|-------|-------|-----|------|-------|
| BACK |  |  |  |  |  |
| MIDDLE | 9 | 3072 | 35 |  |  |
| FRONT |  |  |  |  |  |

**Weekend:** $20
**Weekend:** $26
**Discounts:** No
**Driving Range:** No
**Junior Golf:** No
**Architect/Yr Open:** 1969
**Other:** Clubhouse / Snack Bar / Restaurant / Bar-Lounge

The course is hilly and has just 1 water hole. South County course.

|  | 1 | 2 | 3 | 4 | 5 | 6 | 7 | 8 | 9 |
|------|---|---|---|---|---|---|---|---|---|
| PAR | 4 | 4 | 4 | 3 | 5 | 4 | 4 | 3 | 4 |
| YARDS | 339 | 353 | 383 | 147 | 550 | 325 | 315 | 220 | 440 |
| PAR |  |  |  |  |  |  |  |  |  |
| YARDS |  |  |  |  |  |  |  |  |  |

**Directions:** I-95 to Route 4, North Kingston. Get onto Route 102 West toward Exeter. Course is 1.25 miles on right.

# Rose Hill Golf Club  ✪✪

222 Rose Hill Road
Wakefield, RI  (401) 788-1088
www.rosehillri.com

**Club Pro:**
**Payment:** MC, Amex, Visa
**Tee Times:** No

| Tees | Holes | Yards | Par | USGA | Slope |
|------|-------|-------|-----|------|-------|
| BACK | 9 | 1206 | 27 | | |
| MIDDLE | 9 | 1206 | 27 | | |
| FRONT | 9 | 981 | 27 | | |

**Fee  9 Holes: Weekday:** $14      **Weekend:** $14
**Fee 18 Holes: Weekday:** $21      **Weekend:** $21
**Twilight Rates:** No      **Discounts:** Senior & Junior
**Cart Rental:** $16pp/18, $10pp/9, $3 pullcart      **Driving Range:** No
**Lessons:** Yes  **Schools:** Sr. & Jr.      **Junior Golf:** Yes
**Membership:** Yes      **Architect/Yr Open:** Beckman, Weremay/2001
**Other:** New Bistro / Restaurant / Pub / Clubhouse / League Play

COUPON

Family-friendly environment. South County course. "Sophisticated design for a 9-holer that circles a pond situated in the middle of the course. Excellent greens." –RW

| | 1 | 2 | 3 | 4 | 5 | 6 | 7 | 8 | 9 |
|---|---|---|---|---|---|---|---|---|---|
| PAR | 3 | 3 | 3 | 3 | 3 | 3 | 3 | 3 | 3 |
| YARDS | 144 | 140 | 74 | 101 | 143 | 168 | 129 | 178 | 129 |
| PAR | | | | | | | | | |
| YARDS | | | | | | | | | |

**Directions:** Route 1 to Route 138 West 2.5 miles, and turn left onto Rose Hill Road. Course is 9/10 mile on right.

**RI**

# Triggs Memorial Golf Course  ✪✪✪

1533 Chalkstone Avenue
Providence, RI  (401) 521-8460
www.triggs.us

**Club Pro:** Mike Ryan, PGA
**Payment:** Visa, MC, Cash
**Tee Times:** 2 weeks adv.

| Tees | Holes | Yards | Par | USGA | Slope |
|------|-------|-------|-----|------|-------|
| BACK | 18 | 6522 | 72 | 72.8 | 128 |
| MIDDLE | 18 | 6302 | 72 | 71.7 | 125 |
| FRONT | 18 | 5392 | 72 | 73.1 | 123 |

**Fee  9 Holes: Weekday:** $23      **Weekend:** $23
**Fee 18 Holes: Weekday:** $38      **Weekend:** $40
**Twilight Rates:** No      **Discounts:** Senior $23/18 weekday
**Cart Rental:** $18pp/18, $9pp/9      **Driving Range:** No
**Lessons:** No  **Schools:** No      **Junior Golf:** Yes
**Membership:** Yes      **Architect/Yr Open:** Donald Ross/1933
**Other:** Full Kitchen and Lounge      **GPS:**

Player Comments: "Solid layout. No easy holes, quick greens, very challenging. Course maintenance has improved." Classic Ross design.

| | 1 | 2 | 3 | 4 | 5 | 6 | 7 | 8 | 9 |
|---|---|---|---|---|---|---|---|---|---|
| PAR | 4 | 4 | 4 | 3 | 4 | 5 | 3 | 4 | 4 |
| YARDS | 379 | 411 | 445 | 184 | 316 | 437 | 185 | 332 | 391 |
| | 10 | 11 | 12 | 13 | 14 | 15 | 16 | 17 | 18 |
| PAR | 5 | 4 | 3 | 5 | 3 | 5 | 4 | 4 | 4 |
| YARDS | 502 | 340 | 195 | 447 | 140 | 496 | 302 | 401 | 399 |

**Directions:** I-95 to Exit 23. Go right at exit. Right on Douglas Avenue. First red light is Chalkstone, turn left. Go 2 miles. I-95 South take Exit 21. Right onto Atwell at light, right at Dean Street, at 5th light, take left onto Chalkstone. Go 1.5 miles.

# West Warwick Country Club, The ⊙⊙

335 Wakefield Street
West Warwick, RI  (401) 821-9789

| Tees | Holes | Yards | Par | USGA | Slope |
|------|-------|-------|-----|------|-------|
| BACK | | | | | |
| MIDDLE | 9 | 3001 | 35 | 68.4 | 131 |
| FRONT | 9 | 2733 | 36 | 71.6 | 126 |

**Club Pro:** Cameron Quinn, Manager
**Payment:** Most Major
**Tee Times:** No
**Fee 9 Holes: Weekday:** $25          **Weekend:** $25
**Fee 18 Holes: Weekday:** $39         **Weekend:** $39
**Twilight Rates:** No                 **Discounts:** None
**Cart Rental:** $16pp/18, $8pp/9      **Driving Range:** No
**Lessons:** No  **Schools:** No       **Junior Golf:** No
**Membership:** Yes                    **Architect/Yr Open:** McGregor/1941
**Other:** Bar-Lounge / Snacks / Restaurant / Banquet Facilities

Road divides course: First 4 holes are hilly, back 5 are parallel and flat. Public play limited to weekends after 2:30pm.

| | 1 | 2 | 3 | 4 | 5 | 6 | 7 | 8 | 9 |
|---|---|---|---|---|---|---|---|---|---|
| PAR | 4 | 4 | 3 | 4 | 4 | 4 | 4 | 3 | 5 |
| YARDS | 419 | 338 | 140 | 375 | 365 | 360 | 333 | 162 | 509 |
| PAR | | | | | | | | | |
| YARDS | | | | | | | | | |

**Directions:** I-95 to Route 113 West for 1 mile. At intersection of Route 2, go straight through onto East Avenue for ½ mile. Turn right onto River Street for ¼ mile. River Street becomes Wakefield Street at light. Club is 1.5 miles up on top of hill.

# Windmill Hill Golf Course

35 Schoolhouse Road
Warren, RI (401) 245-1463
www.windmillgolfri.com

| Tees | Holes | Yards | Par | USGA | Slope |
|------|-------|-------|-----|------|-------|
| BACK | 9 | 1432 | 27 | | |
| MIDDLE | 9 | 1191 | 27 | | |
| FRONT | 9 | 891 | 27 | | |

**Club Pro:**
**Payment:** Most Major
**Tee Times:**
**Fee 9 Holes: Weekday:** $13          **Weekend:** $13
**Fee 18 Holes: Weekday:** $22         **Weekend:** $22
**Twilight Rates:** No                 **Discounts:** Senior & Junior
**Cart Rental:** $16/18, $8/9 per cart  **Driving Range:** No
**Lessons:** Yes  **Schools:** No      **Junior Golf:** No
**Membership:** Yes, $650              **Architect/Yr Open:** Beckman, Weremay/2000
**Other:** Clubhouse / Showers / Restaurant / Bar-Lounge / Banquet Facilities / Decks

COUPON

Pleasant challenge for all levels. Course makes you use all your clubs. Lush greens and fairways.

| | 1 | 2 | 3 | 4 | 5 | 6 | 7 | 8 | 9 |
|---|---|---|---|---|---|---|---|---|---|
| PAR | 3 | 3 | 3 | 3 | 3 | 3 | 3 | 3 | 3 |
| YARDS | 116 | 160 | 193 | 136 | 164 | 133 | 218 | 133 | 128 |
| PAR | | | | | | | | | |
| YARDS | | | | | | | | | |

**Directions:** I-195 to Exit 2 to Route 136 South. Follow 136 South for 2 miles and turn left onto Schoolhouse Road. Entrance is .3 miles on right.

# Winnapaug Golf Course ✪✪ 33 ▶

184 Shore Road
Westerly, RI (401) 596-1237
www.winnapaugcountryclub.com

**Club Pro:** Jeff Beaupre, PGA
**Payment:** Cash, Check, Charge
**Tee Times:** 1 week adv.
**Fee 9 Holes: Weekday:** $20
**Fee 18 Holes: Weekday:** $40
**Twilight Rates:** After 4pm
**Cart Rental:** $16pp/18, $9pp/9
**Lessons:** Yes **Schools:** Yes
**Membership:** Yes

| Tees | Holes | Yards | Par | USGA | Slope |
|---|---|---|---|---|---|
| BACK | 18 | 6361 | 72 | 70.6 | 124 |
| MIDDLE | 18 | 5944 | 72 | 68.6 | 119 |
| FRONT | 18 | 5183 | 72 | 69.2 | 118 |

**Weekend:**
**Weekend:** $60 w/cart & lunch (June)
**Discounts:** Senior & Junior
**Driving Range:** Practice range
**Junior Golf:** No
**Architect/Yr Open:** Donald Ross/1922

**Other:** Clubhouse / Restaurant / Bar-Lounge / Beverage Cart

Donald Ross design with tight, short fairways and demanding greens. Open year-round. South County course. New green on #1, 30 yards longer. Close to the Misquamicot Beaches.

| | 1 | 2 | 3 | 4 | 5 | 6 | 7 | 8 | 9 |
|---|---|---|---|---|---|---|---|---|---|
| PAR | 4 | 5 | 3 | 4 | 4 | 3 | 4 | 4 | 5 |
| YARDS | 319 | 484 | 156 | 402 | 270 | 106 | 344 | 322 | 508 |
| | 10 | 11 | 12 | 13 | 14 | 15 | 16 | 17 | 18 |
| PAR | 4 | 4 | 3 | 5 | 4 | 5 | 3 | 4 | 4 |
| YARDS | 395 | 348 | 141 | 472 | 383 | 451 | 140 | 376 | 302 |

**Directions:** I-95 to Exit 92, take right onto Route 2, follow to Route 78, follow signs for beaches. Turn left onto Route 1A, course is 1 mile on left.

**RI**

# Wood River Golf NR 34 ▶

78A Woodville Alton Road
Hope Valley, RI (401) 364-0700
www.woodrivergolf.com

**Club Pro:** Wes Thompson, Manager
**Payment:** Cash, Checks, Credit Cards
**Tee Times:** No
**Fee 9 Holes: Weekday:** $14 (11 holes)
**Fee 18 Holes: Weekday:** $22, $30 all day
**Twilight Rates:** After 3pm
**Cart Rental:** $16 per cart, $10pp
**Lessons: Schools:**
**Membership:** No
**Other:** Pub and Restaurant / Clubhouse

| Tees | Holes | Yards | Par | USGA | Slope |
|---|---|---|---|---|---|
| BACK | | | | | |
| MIDDLE | 18 | 5273 | 69 | | |
| FRONT | 18 | 4452 | 69 | | |

**Weekend:** $14 (11 holes)
**Weekend:** $22
**Discounts:** None
**Driving Range:** No
**Junior Golf:** No
**Architect/Yr Open:** Weston Thompson/2000
**GPS:**

COUPON

Natural setting, links-style course. South county course. Improvements on 15th, 16th, 17th. Course more user-friendly. 20 minutes from local beaches and casino.

| | 1 | 2 | 3 | 4 | 5 | 6 | 7 | 8 | 9 |
|---|---|---|---|---|---|---|---|---|---|
| PAR | 5 | 3 | 4 | 3 | 5 | 4 | 3 | 4 | 4 |
| YARDS | 453 | 152 | 332 | 185 | 445 | 315 | 217 | 331 | 315 |
| | 10 | 11 | 12 | 13 | 14 | 15 | 16 | 17 | 18 |
| PAR | 3 | 4 | 4 | 4 | 4 | 4 | 4 | 4 | 3 |
| YARDS | 153 | 305 | 315 | 300 | 265 | 400 | 330 | 305 | 155 |

**Directions:** I-95 to Exit 2. Go 3.5 miles along Woodville Alton Road, course is on the left.

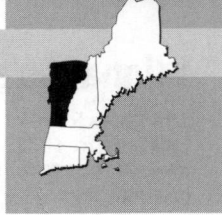

Newport ★

Burlington ★

★ Stowe
★ St. Johnsbury
★ Montpelier

★ Warren

White River Junction ★
Rutland ★

★ Manchester

★ Bennington

| | | | |
|---|---|---|---|
| Champlain Country Club | 14 | Northfield CC | 38 |
| Copley Country Club | 15 | Okemo Valley GC | 39 |
| Country Club of Barre | 16 | Orleans Country Club | 40 |
| Crown Point CC | 17 | Proctor Pittsford CC | 41 |
| Enosburg Falls CC | 18 | Ralph Myhre GC | 42 |
| Equinox Golf Club | 19 | Richford CC | 43 |
| Essex Country Club | 20 | Rocky Ridge GC | 44 |
| Green Mt. National GC | 21 | Rutland CC | 45 |
| Hermitage Golf Club | 22 | Ryder Brook Golf Club | 46 |
| Jay Peak Resort GC | 23 | Sitzmark GC | 47 |
| John P. Larkin CC | 24 | St. Johnsbury CC | 48 |
| Killington Golf Course | 25 | Stamford Valley CC | 49 |
| Kwiniaska Golf Club | 26 | Stonehedge GC | 50 |
| Lake Morey CC | 27 | Stowe Country Club | 51 |
| Lake St. Catherine CC | 28 | Stratton Mountain | 52 |
| Lake Willoughby GC | 29 | Sugarbush Resort Golf Club | 53 |
| Links at Lang Farm | 30 | Tater Hill Golf Club | 54 |
| Montague Golf Club | 31 | West Bolton Golf Club | 55 |
| Montpelier Elks CC | 32 | White River Golf Club | 56 |
| Mountain View CC | 33 | Wilcox Cove GC | 57 |
| Mt. Anthony CC | 34 | Williston Golf Club | 58 |
| Mount Snow Golf Club | 35 | Woodbury GC | 59 |
| Neshobe Golf Club | 36 | Woodstock Inn | 60 |
| Newport CC | 37 | | |

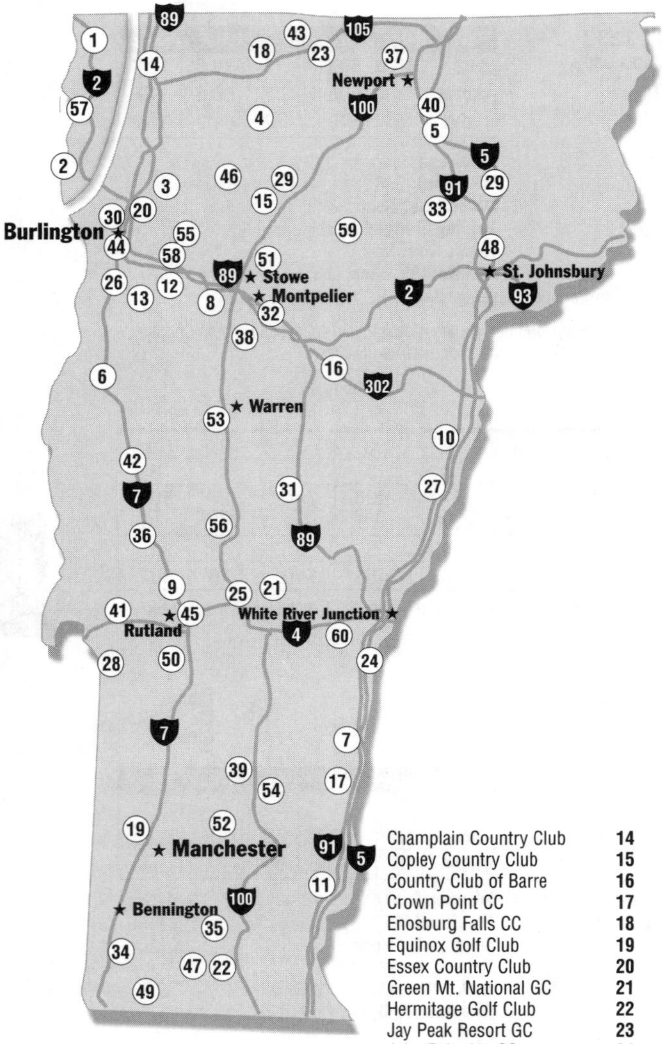

| | |
|---|---|
| Alburg Golf Links | 1 |
| Apple Island Resort GC | 2 |
| Arrowhead GC | 3 |
| Bakersfield CC | 4 |
| Barton Golf Club | 5 |
| Basin Harbor Club | 6 |
| Bellows Falls CC | 7 |
| Blush Hill CC | 8 |
| Bomoseen GC | 9 |
| Bradford Golf Course | 10 |
| Brattleboro CC | 11 |
| Catamount Golf Club | 12 |
| Cedar Knoll CC | 13 |

**KEY TO THE STAR RATINGS:**
5✪ = Outstanding   4✪ = Excellent   3✪ = Very Good   2✪ = Good   1✪ = Average   **NR** = Not Rated

# Alburg Golf Links ✪✪ ▶ 1

230 Route 129
Alburg, VT (802) 796-4248
www.alburggolflinks.com
**Club Pro:** Jim Ironside, PGA
**Payment:** Visa, MC, Personal Checks, Cash
**Tee Times:** 7 days adv.

| Tees | Holes | Yards | Par | USGA | Slope |
|------|-------|-------|-----|------|-------|
| BACK | 18 | 6493 | 72 | 70.1 | 121 |
| MIDDLE | 18 | 5877 | 72 | 67.3 | 115 |
| FRONT | 18 | 5041 | 72 | 66.4 | 105 |

**Fee 9 Holes: Weekday:** $23
**Fee 18 Holes: Weekday:** $40
**Twilight Rates:** After 2pm
**Cart Rental:** $16pp/18, $11pp/9
**Lessons:** Yes **Schools:** Yes
**Membership:** Yes
**Other:** Clubhouse / Restaurant / Bar-Lounge / Club Rental

**Weekend:** $20
**Weekend:** $48
**Discounts:** Junior, ½ price w/adult
**Driving Range:** $7/lg., $4/sm.
**Junior Golf:** Yes
**Architect/Yr Open:** Dick Ellison/1967

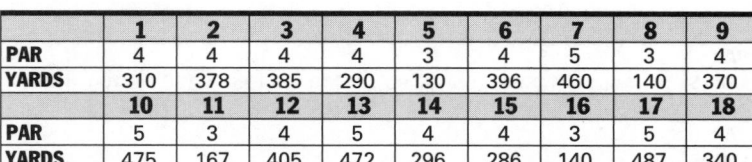

COUPON

A good vacation course, challenging and very friendly.

| | 1 | 2 | 3 | 4 | 5 | 6 | 7 | 8 | 9 |
|------|-----|-----|-----|-----|-----|-----|-----|-----|-----|
| PAR | 4 | 4 | 4 | 4 | 3 | 4 | 5 | 3 | 4 |
| YARDS | 310 | 378 | 385 | 290 | 130 | 396 | 460 | 140 | 370 |
| | 10 | 11 | 12 | 13 | 14 | 15 | 16 | 17 | 18 |
| PAR | 5 | 3 | 4 | 5 | 4 | 4 | 3 | 5 | 4 |
| YARDS | 475 | 167 | 405 | 472 | 296 | 286 | 140 | 487 | 340 |

**Directions:** Take I-89 to Exit 17; take Route 2 to Champlain Islands North to Alburg; take Route 129 to course.

# Apple Island Resort Golf Course NR ▶ 2

VT

71 Route 2
South Hero, VT (802) 372-9600
www.appleislandresort.com/golf
**Club Pro:** Matt Engberg, PGA
**Payment:** Cash, Checks, Credit Cards
**Tee Times:** Yes

| Tees | Holes | Yards | Par | USGA | Slope |
|------|-------|-------|-----|------|-------|
| BACK | | | | | |
| MIDDLE | 9 | 1171 | 27 | | |
| FRONT | | | | | |

**Fee 9 Holes: Weekday:** $13
**Fee 18 Holes: Weekday:** $20
**Twilight Rates:** $13 after 5:30pm
**Cart Rental:** $15p18, $10pp/9
**Lessons:** Yes **Schools:** Yes
**Membership:** Yes (10-play cards available)
**Other:** Resort

**Weekend:** $18
**Weekend:** $25
**Discounts:** Senior / Junior / Ladies
**Driving Range:** Yes - Nets
**Junior Golf:** Yes
**Architect/Yr Open:** Walter Barcomb/1977
**GPS:**

Course in great shape with faster, new greens and all tees have been redone. No one under 5 years allowed. Practice area - Hitting Nets for practice. Open May 15- October 15. Great course to learn and improve your game. Snack bar in pro shop - beer and wine with other beverages. Relaxed atmosphere.

| | 1 | 2 | 3 | 4 | 5 | 6 | 7 | 8 | 9 |
|------|-----|-----|-----|-----|-----|-----|-----|-----|-----|
| PAR | 3 | 3 | 3 | 3 | 3 | 3 | 3 | 3 | 3 |
| YARDS | 110 | 97 | 162 | 188 | 158 | 120 | 84 | 114 | 138 |
| PAR | | | | | | | | | |
| YARDS | | | | | | | | | |

**Directions:** Exit 17 off I-89. Go 6 miles, course on left. Must drive through campground to reach course.

# Arrowhead Golf Course ✪✪ ▶ 3

350 Murray Avenue
Milton, VT (802) 893-0234
www.arrowheadvt.com
**Club Pro:** Scott Goodwin, GM
**Payment:** Cash, Check, Credit
**Tee Times:** No
**Fee 9 Holes: Weekday:** $14
**Fee 18 Holes: Weekday:** $18
**Twilight Rates:** No
**Cart Rental:** $10pp/18, $7pp/9
**Lessons:** No **Schools:** No
**Membership:** Yes, $215
**Other:** Clubhouse

| Tees | Holes | Yards | Par | USGA | Slope |
|------|-------|-------|-----|------|-------|
| BACK | 9 | 1542 | 27 | 56.6 | 80 |
| MIDDLE | 9 | 1330 | 27 | 56.0 | 79 |
| FRONT | 9 | 1005 | 27 | 48.8 | 55 |

**Weekend:** $16
**Weekend:** $20
**Discounts:** None
**Driving Range:** $7/lg., $4/sm. bucket
**Junior Golf:** No
**Architect/Yr Open:** T.F. Goodwin/1997
**GPS:**

This 9-hole, par 3 golf course consists of gently rolling fairways, unique design characteristics, excellent greens, sand bunkers, water hazards, and natural hazards. 3rd hole is very challenging. New range mats.

|  | 1 | 2 | 3 | 4 | 5 | 6 | 7 | 8 | 9 |
|------|-----|-----|-----|-----|-----|-----|-----|-----|-----|
| PAR | 3 | 3 | 3 | 3 | 3 | 3 | 3 | 3 | 3 |
| YARDS | 165 | 148 | 195 | 90 | 119 | 195 | 136 | 104 | 178 |

|  |  |
|------|--|
| PAR |  |
| YARDS |  |

**Directions:** Exit 18 from I-89. Go south on Route 7 approximately ½ mile. Turn right onto Ballard Road for ½ mile, take left onto Old Stage Road for 1 mile, then right onto Murray Avenue for 1.6 miles. Course is on left.

# Bakersfield Country Club NR ▶ 4

210 Old Boston Post Road
Bakersfield, VT (802) 933-5100

**Club Pro:** Jim Jackson, GM
**Payment:** Visa, MC, Amex
**Tee Times:** Yes
**Fee 9 Holes: Weekday:** $18
**Fee 18 Holes: Weekday:** $23
**Twilight Rates:** After 4:15pm
**Cart Rental:** $13pp/18, $8pp/9
**Lessons:** Inquire **Schools:** No
**Membership:** Junior
**Other:** Snack Bar / Restaurant / Bar-Lounge

| Tees | Holes | Yards | Par | USGA | Slope |
|------|-------|-------|-----|------|-------|
| BACK | 18 | 6222 | 72 | | |
| MIDDLE | 18 | 5881 | 72 | 69.0 | 115 |
| FRONT | 18 | 5006 | 72 | 68.7 | 108 |

**Weekend:** $18
**Weekend:** $26
**Discounts:** None
**Driving Range:** No
**Junior Golf:** No
**Architect/Yr Open:** John Watson/1987
**GPS:**

|  | 1 | 2 | 3 | 4 | 5 | 6 | 7 | 8 | 9 |
|------|-----|-----|-----|-----|-----|-----|-----|-----|-----|
| PAR | 4 | 4 | 5 | 3 | 4 | 3 | 4 | 5 | 4 |
| YARDS | 273 | 357 | 424 | 128 | 445 | 155 | 350 | 460 | 375 |
|  | **10** | **11** | **12** | **13** | **14** | **15** | **16** | **17** | **18** |
| PAR | 4 | 3 | 4 | 4 | 5 | 3 | 5 | 3 | 5 |
| YARDS | 360 | 155 | 345 | 290 | 468 | 150 | 392 | 155 | 599 |

**Directions:** Route 108 through Bakersfield. Take right onto Boston Post Road. Follow signs.

# Barton Golf Club

⊕⊕  5▶

548 Telfer Hill Road
Barton, VT  (802) 525-1126
www.bartongolfclub.com

| Tees | Holes | Yards | Par | USGA | Slope |
|---|---|---|---|---|---|
| BACK | 18 | 6000 | 70 | 66.8 | 114 |
| MIDDLE | 18 | 5304 | 70 | 65.3 | 104 |
| FRONT | 18 | 4500 | 69 | | |

**Club Pro:** Bill King
**Payment:** Visa, MC, Disc
**Tee Times:** Yes
**Fee  9 Holes: Weekday:** $13
**Fee 18 Holes: Weekday:** $21
**Twilight Rates:** After 6pm
**Cart Rental:** $14pp/18, $7pp/9
**Lessons:** No  **Schools:** No
**Membership:** Yes
**Other:** Light Fare Menu

**Weekend:** $13
**Weekend:** $21
**Discounts:** None
**Driving Range:** No
**Junior Golf:** No
**Architect/Yr Open:** Brian King/1991
**GPS:**

COUPON

Scenic 18 holes in the heart of Vermont's Northeast Kingdom. New layout due to the replacement of 7 holes. Spectacular views.

| | 1 | 2 | 3 | 4 | 5 | 6 | 7 | 8 | 9 |
|---|---|---|---|---|---|---|---|---|---|
| PAR | 4 | 5 | 4 | 3 | 4 | 4 | 3 | 5 | 4 |
| YARDS | 256 | 465 | 303 | 120 | 304 | 396 | 160 | 440 | 365 |
| | 10 | 11 | 12 | 13 | 14 | 15 | 16 | 17 | 18 |
| PAR | 4 | 3 | 5 | 4 | 3 | 3 | 5 | 3 | 4 |
| YARDS | 268 | 130 | 450 | 385 | 140 | 150 | 502 | 135 | 335 |

**Directions:** I-91 to Exit 25. Take Route 16 into Barton. Go right on Water Street. Cross Route 5. Left on High Street. Club is 1 mile on right.

# Basin Harbor Club

⊕⊕⊕  6▶

VT

4800 Basin Harbor Road
Vergennes, VT (802) 475-2309
www.basinharbor.com

| Tees | Holes | Yards | Par | USGA | Slope |
|---|---|---|---|---|---|
| BACK | 18 | 6567 | 72 | 71.6 | 126 |
| MIDDLE | 18 | 6243 | 72 | 70.0 | 123 |
| FRONT | 18 | 5053 | 72 | 68.3 | 111 |

**Club Pro:** Will Benton
**Payment:** Visa, MC
**Tee Times:** Anytime for current season
**Fee  9 Holes: Weekday:** $36
**Fee 18 Holes: Weekday:** $54
**Twilight Rates:** After 4pm
**Cart Rental:** $22pp/18, $12pp/9
**Lessons:** $40/half hour  **Schools:** Yes
**Membership:** Yes
**Other:** Clubhouse / Snack Bar / Restaurant / Bar-Lounge / Hotel

**Weekend:** $36
**Weekend:** $54
**Discounts:** No
**Driving Range:** $7/sm., $10/lg.
**Junior Golf:** No
**Architect/Yr Open:** Alex Campbell/1927

COUPON

Fairly flat, located on Lake Champlain. Collared shirt required. No cutoffs. Open May 1 - mid-October. 18-hole rate reduced after 1pm. New women's tee boxes. Improved playability through bunker work, tree removal and tees. Great practice facility on the shores of Lake Champlain.

| | 1 | 2 | 3 | 4 | 5 | 6 | 7 | 8 | 9 |
|---|---|---|---|---|---|---|---|---|---|
| PAR | 4 | 4 | 4 | 4 | 3 | 4 | 3 | 4 | 5 |
| YARDS | 350 | 360 | 395 | 308 | 100 | 345 | 156 | 435 | 498 |
| | 10 | 11 | 12 | 13 | 14 | 15 | 16 | 17 | 18 |
| PAR | 4 | 4 | 5 | 3 | 4 | 4 | 3 | 5 | 4 |
| YARDS | 391 | 379 | 495 | 180 | 344 | 418 | 172 | 509 | 410 |

**Directions:** Route 7 to Vergennes exit. Straight through town on Route 22A. Cross over bridge, take right at sign to Basin Harbor. 1 mile to Basin Harbor Road, take right, 6 miles to course.

# Bellows Falls Country Club  ✪✪½   7

Route 103 (Rockingham Road)
Bellows Falls, VT (802) 463-9809
www.bellowsfallscountryclub.com

**Club Pro:** Matt Keller, GM
**Payment:** Visa, MC, Cash
**Tee Times:** No
**Fee 9 Holes: Weekday:** $18
**Fee 18 Holes: Weekday:** $30
**Twilight Rates:** After 5pm
**Cart Rental:** $30/18, $20/9 per cart
**Lessons:** No **Schools:** No
**Membership:** Yes
**Other:** Restaurant / Bar

| Tees | Holes | Yards | Par | USGA | Slope |
|------|-------|-------|-----|------|-------|
| BACK | | | | | |
| MIDDLE | 9 | 2892 | 35 | 65.8 | 117 |
| FRONT | 9 | 2569 | 35 | 65.8 | 110 |

**Weekend:** $22
**Weekend:** $33
**Discounts:** Senior/Junior
**Driving Range:** No
**Junior Golf:** No
**Architect/Yr Open:** 1923
**GPS:**

Open May 1 - November 1. Vermont Country Store, Bellows Falls and Chester Village nearby!
"Lots to like, but many blind shots. Above average greens." –GM

| | 1 | 2 | 3 | 4 | 5 | 6 | 7 | 8 | 9 |
|------|-----|-----|-----|-----|-----|-----|-----|-----|-----|
| PAR | 4 | 5 | 3 | 3 | 4 | 4 | 4 | 3 | 5 |
| YARDS | 389 | 513 | 178 | 155 | 381 | 370 | 320 | 158 | 428 |
| PAR | | | | | | | | | |
| YARDS | | | | | | | | | |

**Directions:** I-91 to Exit 6. Take Route 103 North. Turn right onto Country Club Road. Across from Vermont Country Store.

# Blush Hill Country Club  ✪✪   8

141 Lonesome Trail
Waterbury, VT (802) 244-8974
www.blushhillcountryclub.com

**Club Pro:**
**Payment:** Visa, MC, Disc
**Tee Times:** Recommended
**Fee 9 Holes: Weekday:** $20
**Fee 18 Holes: Weekday:** $30
**Twilight Rates:** No
**Cart Rental:** $29/18, $19/9 per cart
**Lessons:** No; **Schools:** No
**Membership:** Yes
**Other:** Clubhouse / Snack Bar / Bar

| Tees | Holes | Yards | Par | USGA | Slope |
|------|-------|-------|-----|------|-------|
| BACK | | | | | |
| MIDDLE | 9 | 2416 | 33 | 62.7 | 113 |
| FRONT | 9 | 2275 | 33 | 66.2 | 114 |

**Weekend:** $22 F/S/S
**Weekend:** $28 F/S/S
**Discounts:** None
**Driving Range:** No
**Junior Golf:** No
**Architect/Yr Open:** Andrew Freeland/1919

One of the most extraordinary scenic views in Vermont. Course kept in excellent shape. Open May 1 - October 15. Ben & Jerry's right around the corner.

| | 1 | 2 | 3 | 4 | 5 | 6 | 7 | 8 | 9 |
|------|-----|-----|-----|-----|-----|-----|-----|-----|-----|
| PAR | 4 | 4 | 4 | 3 | 4 | 3 | 3 | 4 | 4 |
| YARDS | 377 | 350 | 206 | 171 | 266 | 146 | 157 | 377 | 302 |
| PAR | | | | | | | | | |
| YARDS | | | | | | | | | |

**Directions:** ½ mile off I-89 North, on Route 100. 1000 feet left on Blush Hill Road, ¾ mile beyond Best Western on Blush Hill Road. Turn left on Lonesome Trail.

# Bomoseen Golf Club

NR **9** ▶

Prospect Point Road (Route 30)
Bomoseen, VT (802) 468-5581

| Tees | Holes | Yards | Par | USGA | Slope |
|------|-------|-------|-----|------|-------|
| BACK | 9 | 2635 | 35 | 65.8 | 125 |
| MIDDLE | 9 | 2557 | 35 | 65.0 | 123 |
| FRONT | 9 | 2294 | 35 | 63.4 | 104 |

**Club Pro:** Jim Bassett, Manager
**Payment:** MC, Visa, Amex
**Tee Times:** No
**Fee 9 Holes: Weekday:** $15, $23 w/cart **Weekend:** $17, $26 w/cart
**Fee 18 Holes: Weekday:** $30, $40 w/cart **Weekend:** $30, $40 w/cart
**Twilight Rates:** After 4pm **Discounts:** None
**Cart Rental:** $20pp/18, $10pp/9 **Driving Range:** No
**Lessons:** No **Schools:** No **Junior Golf:** No
**Membership:** Yes **Architect/Yr Open:** 1953
**Other:** Restaurant **GPS:**

COUPON

The course is hilly and scenic. Great shape. Open April - November.

|  | 1 | 2 | 3 | 4 | 5 | 6 | 7 | 8 | 9 |
|------|---|---|---|---|---|---|---|---|---|
| PAR | 5 | 3 | 4 | 4 | 4 | 4 | 4 | 4 | 3 |
| YARDS | 405 | 155 | 311 | 283 | 268 | 335 | 298 | 370 | 132 |
| PAR | | | | | | | | | |
| YARDS | | | | | | | | | |

**Directions:** Route 4 to Exit 4; follow Route 30 North for 2 miles to course entrance.

# Bradford Golf Course

○○ **10** ▶  VT

150 Memorial Field
Bradford, VT (802) 222-5207
www.bradfordgolfclubinc.com

| Tees | Holes | Yards | Par | USGA | Slope |
|------|-------|-------|-----|------|-------|
| BACK | | | | | |
| MIDDLE | 9 | 2155 | 32 | | |
| FRONT | 9 | 2052 | 32 | | |

**Club Pro:** Tim Woodward, GM
**Payment:** Cash, Visa, MC
**Tee Times:** No
**Fee 9 Holes: Weekday:** $16 **Weekend:** $16
**Fee 18 Holes: Weekday:** $21 **Weekend:** $24
**Twilight Rates:** $12+tax after 5pm **Discounts:** None
**Cart Rental:** $15pp/18, $10pp/9 **Driving Range:** No
**Lessons:** No **Schools:** No **Junior Golf:** No
**Membership:** Yes **Architect/Yr Open:** 1927
**Other:** Snacks **GPS:**

Par 32, 18 sets of tees. "Greens usually in fine shape." –JS

|  | 1 | 2 | 3 | 4 | 5 | 6 | 7 | 8 | 9 |
|------|---|---|---|---|---|---|---|---|---|
| PAR | 3 | 4 | 3 | 3 | 4 | 3 | 5 | 4 | 3 |
| YARDS | 174 | 239 | 160 | 115 | 304 | 185 | 431 | 294 | 150 |
| PAR | | | | | | | | | |
| YARDS | | | | | | | | | |

**Directions:** From I-91, take Exit 16, turn right and go ¾ of a mile. Turn left, go 1 mile north. Turn right, go by Bradford Academy to bottom of hill.

# Brattleboro Country Club ✪✪½

**11**

Upper Dummerston Road
Brattleboro, VT (802) 257-7380
www.brattleborocountryclub.com

| Tees | Holes | Yards | Par | USGA | Slope |
|------|-------|-------|-----|------|-------|
| BACK | 18 | 6533 | 71 | 71.8 | 127 |
| MIDDLE | 18 | 6073 | 71 | 69.6 | 122 |
| FRONT | 18 | 5051 | 71 | 67.1 | 110 |

**Club Pro:** Eric Sandstrum, PGA
**Payment:** Visa, MC, Amex
**Tee Times:** 3 days adv.
**Fee 9 Holes: Weekday:** $32
**Fee 18 Holes: Weekday:** $50
**Twilight Rates:** No
**Cart Rental:** $20pp/18, $12pp/9
**Lessons:** Yes **Schools:** No
**Membership:** Yes
**Other:** Restaurant / Clubhouse / Bar-Lounge / Showers / Lodging Partner
**GPS:**

**Weekend:** $36 F/S/S
**Weekend:** $67 F/S/S
**Discounts:** No
**Driving Range:** Yes
**Junior Golf:** Yes
**Architect/Yr Open:** Wayne Stiles, Durkee/1914

Wide fairways and fast greens! In great condition. Awesome foliage! Friendly staff. Hidden gem! First course in Vermont when travelling I-91 North. 5 minutes from New Hampshire. Many new hotels and restaurants in Brattleboro VT. "Best kept secret in Southern Vermont." –GG

| | 1 | 2 | 3 | 4 | 5 | 6 | 7 | 8 | 9 |
|------|-----|-----|-----|-----|-----|-----|-----|-----|-----|
| PAR | 4 | 5 | 4 | 3 | 4 | 4 | 5 | 3 | 4 |
| YARDS | 405 | 504 | 359 | 155 | 397 | 243 | 455 | 155 | 363 |
| | 10 | 11 | 12 | 13 | 14 | 15 | 16 | 17 | 18 |
| PAR | 5 | 4 | 4 | 3 | 4 | 4 | 3 | 4 | 4 |
| YARDS | 492 | 378 | 376 | 172 | 346 | 386 | 152 | 346 | 389 |

**Directions:** I-91 North or South take Exit 2, go 1 mile to Cedar Street on left. Follow to bottom of hill. Left at stop sign. Left onto Upper Dummerston Road. Club 1 mile on left.

# Catamount Golf Club ✪✪

**12**

1400 Mountain View Road
Williston, VT (802) 878-7227
www.catamountgolf.com

| Tees | Holes | Yards | Par | USGA | Slope |
|------|-------|-------|-----|------|-------|
| BACK | | | | | |
| MIDDLE | 9 | 2844 | 35 | 33.3 | 112 |
| FRONT | | | | | |

**Club Pro:** Lou Jarvis, PGA
**Payment:** Cash, Visa, MC
**Tee Times:**
**Fee 9 Holes: Weekday:** $18
**Fee 18 Holes: Weekday:**
**Twilight Rates:** No
**Cart Rental:** $8pp/9
**Lessons: Schools:** Yes
**Membership:** Yes
**Other:** Snack Bar

**Weekend:** $18
**Weekend:**
**Discounts:** No
**Driving Range:** $9/lg., $5/sm.
**Junior Golf:** Yes
**Architect/Yr Open:** Marty Keene/1999
**GPS:**

$130 discount card available for 10 9-hole rounds. Course landscaped to provide visual depiction of the route to play this links-style course.

West/North

| | 1 | 2 | 3 | 4 | 5 | 6 | 7 | 8 | 9 |
|------|-----|-----|-----|-----|-----|-----|-----|-----|-----|
| PAR | 4 | 3 | 4 | 3 | 5 | 3 | 5 | 4 | 4 |
| YARDS | 346 | 156 | 357 | 170 | 490 | 165 | 470 | 330 | 360 |
| PAR | | | | | | | | | |
| YARDS | | | | | | | | | |

**Directions:** 3 miles north of Taft Corners.

# Cedar Knoll Country Club ✪✪✪ ▶13

13020 Route 116
Hinesburg, VT (802) 482-3186
www.cedarknollgolf.com
Club Pro: Barry Churchill, PGA
Payment: Visa, MC, Amex
Tee Times: Yes
Fee 9 Holes: Weekday: $20
Fee 18 Holes: Weekday: $33
Twilight Rates: After 5pm
Cart Rental: $21pp/18, $11pp/9
Lessons: Yes  Schools: Yes
Membership: Yes
Other: Restaurant / Clubhouse / Bar-Lounge / Lockers / Showers / Snack Bar

| Tees | Holes | Yards | Par | USGA | Slope |
|---|---|---|---|---|---|
| BACK | 27/18 | 6541 | 72 | 72.5 | 117 |
| MIDDLE | 27/18 | 6144 | 72 | 72.5 | 117 |
| FRONT | 27/18 | 5360 | 72 | 69.5 | 108 |

Weekend: $20
Weekend: $33
Discounts: None
Driving Range: $4/sm., $7/lg. bucket
Junior Golf: Yes
Architect/Yr Open: Raymond Ayer/1994

Now 27 holes. Rolling hills. 250 acres allows for nice spacing of holes. Beautiful scenery. Cedar Knoll South 9-hole addition is also open. 9-hole rate, $20. Our practice facility includes a putting green, pitching green w/sand bunkers and a 270 yard driving range.

|  | 1 | 2 | 3 | 4 | 5 | 6 | 7 | 8 | 9 |
|---|---|---|---|---|---|---|---|---|---|
| PAR | 5 | 3 | 4 | 4 | 5 | 3 | 4 | 4 | 4 |
| YARDS | 500 | 156 | 315 | 358 | 505 | 170 | 392 | 313 | 438 |
|  | 10 | 11 | 12 | 13 | 14 | 15 | 16 | 17 | 18 |
| PAR | 5 | 3 | 4 | 4 | 3 | 4 | 4 | 4 | 5 |
| YARDS | 494 | 169 | 298 | 333 | 156 | 291 | 341 | 315 | 536 |

Directions: I-89 to Exit 12; follow 5 miles to intersection of Routes 2A and 116. Take left and go 5 miles on 116. Course is on right.

# Champlain Country Club NR ▶14  VT

587 St. Albans Road
Swanton, VT (802) 527-1187
www.champlaincountryclub.com
Club Pro: Michael Swim
Payment: MC, Visa, Disc
Tee Times: Weekends, Holidays
Fee 9 Holes: Weekday: $25
Fee 18 Holes: Weekday: $35
Twilight Rates:
Cart Rental: $15pp/18, $10pp/9
Lessons: $25/half hour  Schools:
Membership: Yes
Other: Clubhouse / Lockers / Showers / Snack Bar / Restaurant / Bar-Lounge
GPS: Yes

| Tees | Holes | Yards | Par | USGA | Slope |
|---|---|---|---|---|---|
| BACK | 18 | 6237 | 70 | 69.9 | 123 |
| MIDDLE | 18 | 5959 | 70 | 68.8 | 121 |
| FRONT | 18 | 5366 | 70 | 70.4 | 117 |

Weekend: $30
Weekend: $40
Discounts:
Driving Range: Free balls
Junior Golf: Yes
Architect/Yr Open: Duer Irving Sewall/1915

COUPON

Overlooking Lake Champlain. Nice views. New tees.

|  | 1 | 2 | 3 | 4 | 5 | 6 | 7 | 8 | 9 |
|---|---|---|---|---|---|---|---|---|---|
| PAR | 4 | 5 | 3 | 4 | 4 | 4 | 3 | 4 | 4 |
| YARDS | 359 | 472 | 152 | 377 | 353 | 347 | 135 | 350 | 342 |
|  | 10 | 11 | 12 | 13 | 14 | 15 | 16 | 17 | 18 |
| PAR | 4 | 4 | 3 | 4 | 3 | 5 | 4 | 4 | 4 |
| YARDS | 303 | 444 | 142 | 370 | 167 | 526 | 328 | 415 | 315 |

Directions: I-89 to Exit 20; take Route 7 North ½ mile to course.

# Copley Country Club

NR   15 ▶

377 Copley Country Club Road
**Morrisville, VT** (802) 888-3013
www.copleycountryclub.com
**Club Pro:** Terry Francis, GM
**Payment:** Visa, MC
**Tee Times:** Required

| Tees | Holes | Yards | Par | USGA | Slope |
|------|-------|-------|-----|------|-------|
| BACK | 9 | 2775 | 35 | 67.4 | 112 |
| MIDDLE | 9 | 2706 | 35 | 67.4 | 112 |
| FRONT | 9 | 2451 | 36 | 69.8 | 109 |

**Fee 9 Holes: Weekday:** $20
**Fee 18 Holes: Weekday:** $31.50
**Twilight Rates:** No
**Cart Rental:** $16pp/18, $10.50pp/9
**Lessons:** No **Schools:** No
**Membership:** Yes
**Weekend:** $20
**Weekend:** $31.50
**Discounts:** None
**Driving Range:** No
**Junior Golf:** Yes
**Architect/Yr Open:** 1936
**Other:** Clubhouse / Lockers / Snack Bar / Restaurant / Bar-Lounge

Ideal conditions. The course is level with a handful of tree-lined holes.

|  | 1 | 2 | 3 | 4 | 5 | 6 | 7 | 8 | 9 |
|------|---|---|---|---|---|---|---|---|---|
| PAR | 4 | 4 | 3 | 5 | 4/5 | 4 | 4 | 4 | 3 |
| YARDS | 322 | 286 | 165 | 519 | 382 | 263 | 257 | 303 | 209 |

|  |  |  |  |  |  |  |  |  |  |
|------|---|---|---|---|---|---|---|---|---|
| PAR | | | | | | | | | |
| YARDS | | | | | | | | | |

**Directions:** I-89 to Waterbury exit, follow 18 miles to Morrisville.

# Country Club of Barre

✪✪½   16 ▶

142 Drake Road
**East Montpelier, VT** (802) 476-7658
www.ccofbarre.com
**Club Pro:** Roger King, PGA
**Payment:** Visa, MC, Amex
**Tee Times:** 5 days adv.

| Tees | Holes | Yards | Par | USGA | Slope |
|------|-------|-------|-----|------|-------|
| BACK | 18 | 6315 | 71 | 70.4 | 128 |
| MIDDLE | 18 | 5962 | 71 | 69.0 | 124 |
| FRONT | 18 | 5126 | 71 | 69.8 | 123 |

**Fee 9 Holes: Weekday:** $26
**Fee 18 Holes: Weekday:** $47
**Twilight Rates:** After 4pm on weekends
**Cart Rental:** $23pp/18, $12pp/9
**Lessons:** $35/40 min. **Schools:** No
**Membership:** Yes
**Weekend:** $26
**Weekend:** $47
**Discounts:** None
**Driving Range:** $3/lg
**Junior Golf:** For members
**Architect/Yr Open:** Wayne Stiles/1924

COUPON

**Other:** Clubhouse / Lockers / Showers / Snack Bar / Restaurant / Bar-Lounge

Player Comments: "One of the hidden gems in Vermont." Semi-private, call for tee times.

|  | 1 | 2 | 3 | 4 | 5 | 6 | 7 | 8 | 9 |
|------|---|---|---|---|---|---|---|---|---|
| PAR | 4 | 4 | 4 | 3 | 5 | 4 | 3 | 4 | 4 |
| YARDS | 368 | 383 | 285 | 190 | 455 | 339 | 142 | 370 | 368 |
|  | **10** | **11** | **12** | **13** | **14** | **15** | **16** | **17** | **18** |
| PAR | 5 | 4 | 4 | 3 | 4 | 5 | 3 | 4 | 4 |
| YARDS | 492 | 372 | 314 | 170 | 431 | 456 | 125 | 350 | 352 |

**Directions:** I-89 to Exit 7. Follow Route 62 towards Barre (straight into 14 North). Take right onto Plainfield Brook Road, turn left onto Mitchell Road, turn right onto Mitchell Nursery Road. Club is 3 miles on right.

# Crown Point Country Club ✪✪✪ 17 ▶

Weathersfield Center Road
Springfield, VT (802) 885-1010
www.crownpointcc.com
**Club Pro:** Dan Russell, PGA
**Payment:** Visa, MC, Cash, Disc, Amex
**Tee Times:** Recommended

| Tees | Holes | Yards | Par | USGA | Slope |
|------|-------|-------|-----|------|-------|
| BACK | 18 | 6602 | 72 | 71.2 | 128 |
| MIDDLE | 18 | 6120 | 72 | 69.1 | 122 |
| FRONT | 18 | 5542 | 72 | 73.0 | 124 |

**Fee  9 Holes: Weekday:** $25
**Fee 18 Holes: Weekday:** $35
**Twilight Rates:** After 4pm
**Cart Rental:** $20pp/18, $10pp/9
**Lessons:** Yes  **Schools:** No
**Membership:** Yes

**Weekend:** $30
**Weekend:** $43
**Discounts:** Senior & Junior
**Driving Range:** Yes
**Junior Golf:** Yes
**Architect/Yr Open:** William Mitchell/1953

COUPON

**Other:** Clubhouse / Showers / Restaurant / Bar-Lounge

Course noted for smooth fast greens. Friendly staff. Great views. Open April 15 - November 1 (weather permitting).

|  | 1 | 2 | 3 | 4 | 5 | 6 | 7 | 8 | 9 |
|------|------|------|------|------|------|------|------|------|------|
| PAR | 4 | 5 | 4 | 4 | 3 | 4 | 5 | 4 | 3 |
| YARDS | 370 | 426 | 344 | 337 | 168 | 365 | 487 | 376 | 154 |
|  | 10 | 11 | 12 | 13 | 14 | 15 | 16 | 17 | 18 |
| PAR | 4 | 5 | 4 | 3 | 4 | 5 | 4 | 4 | 3 |
| YARDS | 344 | 463 | 390 | 158 | 344 | 459 | 381 | 371 | 183 |

**Directions:** I-91 North to Exit 7; turn right and follow to center of Springfield. Turn right onto Valley Street. Course 3 miles on left.

# Enosburg Falls Country Club NR 18 ▶

53 Elm Street
Enosburg Falls, VT (802) 933-2296
www.efccvt.com
**Club Pro:** Rick Marckres, Head Pro
**Payment:** MC, Visa
**Tee Times:** Yes

| Tees | Holes | Yards | Par | USGA | Slope |
|------|-------|-------|-----|------|-------|
| BACK | 18 | 5580 | 72 | 67.4 | 116 |
| MIDDLE | 18 | 5418 | 72 | 66.8 | 115 |
| FRONT | 18 | 4633 | 72 | 63.4 | 108 |

**Fee  9 Holes: Weekday:** $19
**Fee 18 Holes: Weekday:** $30
**Twilight Rates:** After 3pm
**Cart Rental:** $28/18, $15/9 per cart
**Lessons:** Yes  **Schools:** No
**Membership:** Yes

**Weekend:** $19
**Weekend:** $30
**Discounts:** Junior
**Driving Range:** Irons range
**Junior Golf:** Yes
**Architect/Yr Open:** 1963

COUPON

**Other:** Restaurant / Clubhouse / Lockers / Showers

Course has some great birdie opportunities. Variety of rates for special memberships. Upgrading course with new bunkers. Open May - October.

|  | 1 | 2 | 3 | 4 | 5 | 6 | 7 | 8 | 9 |
|------|------|------|------|------|------|------|------|------|------|
| PAR | 4 | 5 | 4 | 4 | 4 | 3 | 4 | 5 | 3 |
| YARDS | 249 | 498 | 337 | 251 | 350 | 115 | 331 | 552 | 119 |
|  | 10 | 11 | 12 | 13 | 14 | 15 | 16 | 17 | 18 |
| PAR | 4 | 3 | 4 | 5 | 5 | 3 | 4 | 4 | 4 |
| YARDS | 272 | 140 | 335 | 490 | 478 | 112 | 267 | 255 | 267 |

**Directions:** I-89 to St. Albans Exit to Route 105 North; follow to Enosberg Falls. Take left at junction of Routes 108 and 105 to course.

VT

# Equinox Golf Club

108 Union Street
Manchester, VT (802) 362-7870
www.playequinox.com

| Tees | Holes | Yards | Par | USGA | Slope |
|---|---|---|---|---|---|
| BACK | 18 | 6423 | 71 | 70.8 | 129 |
| MIDDLE | 18 | 6069 | 71 | 69.2 | 125 |
| FRONT | 18 | 5082 | 71 | 69.0 | 122 |

**Club Pro:** Joan McDonald, LPGA
**Payment:** MC, Visa, Amex, Disc, Cash
**Tee Times:** 14 days adv.
**Fee 9 Holes: Weekday:** $59    **Weekend:** $79
**Fee 18 Holes: Weekday:** $79    **Weekend:** $119
**Twilight Rates:** After 3pm    **Discounts:** Junior
**Cart Rental:** Included    **Driving Range:** No
**Lessons:** $60/half hour   **Schools:** No    **Junior Golf:** Yes
**Membership:** Yes    **Architect/Yr Open:** Walter Travis/1927
**Other:** Restaurant / Clubhouse / Snack Bar / Bar-Lounge / Hotel / Lockers / Showers

COUPON

Rated the #1 course you can play in Vermont by *Golfweek* and the 45th Best Golf Resort in North America by *Golf Digest*. Our course is an enjoyable par 71 with unforgettable views.

| | 1 | 2 | 3 | 4 | 5 | 6 | 7 | 8 | 9 |
|---|---|---|---|---|---|---|---|---|---|
| PAR | 4 | 4 | 4 | 3 | 4 | 4 | 5 | 4 | 4 |
| YARDS | 334 | 385 | 346 | 141 | 316 | 323 | 502 | 380 | 344 |
| | 10 | 11 | 12 | 13 | 14 | 15 | 16 | 17 | 18 |
| PAR | 4 | 4 | 4 | 4 | 3 | 5 | 3 | 4 | 4 |
| YARDS | 336 | 361 | 347 | 401 | 112 | 462 | 181 | 403 | 395 |

**Directions:** Exit 4 on Route 7 towards Manchester, left on 7A, left on Union Street.

# Essex Country Club

332 Old Stage Road
Essex Junction, VT (802) 879-3232
www.essexccvt.com

| Tees | Holes | Yards | Par | USGA | Slope |
|---|---|---|---|---|---|
| BACK | 18 | 6475 | 72 | 70.0 | 117 |
| MIDDLE | 18 | 6315 | 72 | 70.0 | 117 |
| FRONT | 18 | 5500 | 72 | 69.1 | 112 |

**Club Pro:** Lou Jarvis, PGA
       Mike Morelli, Assistant Pro
**Payment:** Visa, MC, Amex
**Tee Times:** Weekends
**Fee 9 Holes: Weekday:** $20    **Weekend:** $20
**Fee 18 Holes: Weekday:** $32    **Weekend:** $32
**Twilight Rates:** $20 after 4pm    **Discounts:** No
**Cart Rental:**    **Driving Range:** $5/sm., $6/med., $7/lg. bucket
**Lessons:** Yes   **Schools:** No    **Junior Golf:** Yes
**Membership:** Yes    **Architect/Yr Open:** Joe Chastaney/1988
**Other:**    **GPS:**

Ongoing improvements. Monday, Tuesday and Wednesday specials. Upgraded irrigation. 14 of the 18 holes are fully irrigated. New putting green and practice range.

| | 1 | 2 | 3 | 4 | 5 | 6 | 7 | 8 | 9 |
|---|---|---|---|---|---|---|---|---|---|
| PAR | 4 | 3 | 4 | 4 | 5 | 4 | 5 | 4 | 3 |
| YARDS | 365 | 155 | 400 | 330 | 450 | 335 | 530 | 315 | 190 |
| | 10 | 11 | 12 | 13 | 14 | 15 | 16 | 17 | 18 |
| PAR | 5 | 4 | 4 | 3 | 4 | 5 | 3 | 4 | 4 |
| YARDS | 580 | 320 | 355 | 130 | 360 | 530 | 170 | 350 | 450 |

**Directions:** I-89 to Exit 12. Williston exit Route 2A to Essex 5 corner; then take Route 15 to Old Stage Road 3 miles north to course.

# Green Mountain National GC ✪✪✪✪½  ▸ 21

Barrows Towne Road (Route 100)
Killington, VT (802) 422-GOLF
www.gmngc.com

**Club Pro:** David Soucy, PGA
**Payment:** Visa, MC, Amex, Disc
**Tee Times:** 7 days adv.

| Tees | Holes | Yards | Par | USGA | Slope |
|------|-------|-------|-----|------|-------|
| BACK | 18 | 6589 | 71 | 72.1 | 138 |
| MIDDLE | 18 | 6164 | 71 | 70.2 | 133 |
| FRONT | 18 | 4740 | 71 | 68.9 | 118 |

**Fee 9 Holes: Weekday:** $46.78 w/cart    **Weekend:** $49.78 w/cart
**Fee 18 Holes: Weekday:** $85.20 w/cart   **Weekend:** $95.20 w/cart
**Twilight Rates:** $49 after 3pm weekday, $52 Sat/Sun
**Discounts:** Junior
**Cart Rental:** Included                  **Driving Range:** $7/lg., $4/sm.
**Lessons:** $60-80/hour **Schools:** Adult  **Junior Golf:** Yes
**Membership:** Resident/Non-Resident passes  **Architect/Yr Open:** Gene Bates/1996
**Other:** Bar / Lounge / Snack Bar         **GPS:** Yes

COUPON

Player Comments: "Unbelievable in the fall. Incredibly challenging. Great layout, conditions and friendly personnel." Several stay-and-play partners. "A course you will want to play again and again." –SD

|  | 1 | 2 | 3 | 4 | 5 | 6 | 7 | 8 | 9 |
|------|---|---|---|---|---|---|---|---|---|
| PAR | 5 | 4 | 4 | 4 | 3 | 5 | 3 | 4 | 4 |
| YARDS | 494 | 387 | 381 | 406 | 152 | 492 | 145 | 348 | 419 |
|  | 10 | 11 | 12 | 13 | 14 | 15 | 16 | 17 | 18 |
| PAR | 4 | 4 | 4 | 3 | 4 | 5 | 4 | 3 | 4 |
| YARDS | 396 | 350 | 375 | 157 | 326 | 437 | 359 | 169 | 371 |

**Directions:** I-91 to Exit 6. Turn left onto Route 103 North for about 30 minutes. Take right onto Route 100 North. Go by Killington Mountain Road. Course is 2 miles on left. Travel time from I-91 is about 1 hour.

# Hermitage Golf Club  ✪✪✪✪  ▸ 22    VT

70 Spyglass Drive, P.O. Box 369
Wilmington, VT (802) 464-8301
www.hermitagegolfclub.com

**Club Pro:** Drew Anderson, PGA
**Payment:** Visa, MC, Amex, Disc
**Tee Times:** 14 days adv.

| Tees | Holes | Yards | Par | USGA | Slope |
|------|-------|-------|-----|------|-------|
| BACK | 18 | 6549 | 72 | 71.7 | 128 |
| MIDDLE | 18 | 6164 | 72 | 69.3 | 125 |
| FRONT | 18 | 5396 | 74 | 70.8 | 121 |

**Fee 9 Holes: Weekday:** $39 w/cart    **Weekend:** $55 w/cart
**Fee 18 Holes: Weekday:** $55 w/cart   **Weekend:** $85 w/cart
**Twilight Rates:** After 3pm           **Discounts:** Sr., Mon-Thu/Non-Hldy
**Cart Rental:** Included               **Driving Range:** $5/bucket irons only
**Lessons:** Yes **Schools:** No        **Junior Golf:** Yes
**Membership:** Yes                     **Architect/Yr Open:** Desmond Muirhead/1972
**Other:** Clubhouse / Restaurant / Bar-Lounge / Lodging Partner / Stay & Play packages available

Hermitage's manicured layout was created by acclaimed designer Desmond Muirhead, one of only two in New England. Hermitage meanders over a gently rolling landscape without the blind shots one expects in a mountain course. The only way you'll know you are in the mountains is by the stunning views of the surrounding mountains.

|  | 1 | 2 | 3 | 4 | 5 | 6 | 7 | 8 | 9 |
|------|---|---|---|---|---|---|---|---|---|
| PAR | 4 | 4 | 5 | 3 | 4 | 4 | 3 | 5 | 4 |
| YARDS | 348 | 389 | 460 | 181 | 347 | 291 | 166 | 505 | 380 |
|  | 10 | 11 | 12 | 13 | 14 | 15 | 16 | 17 | 18 |
| PAR | 4 | 5 | 4 | 3 | 5 | 4 | 3 | 4 | 4 |
| YARDS | 328 | 509 | 352 | 160 | 516 | 343 | 165 | 301 | 423 |

**Directions:** Exit 2 off I-91. Take Route 9 West to Wilmington. Take right at traffic light onto 100 North. Follow signs to golf course.

# Jay Peak Resort Golf Course ✪✪✪½  23 ▶

4850 Route 242
Jay, VT (802) 988-2611
www.jaypeakresort.com

**Club Pro:** Douglas Ruttle, PGA
**Payment:** Visa, MC, Amex, Disc, Checks
**Tee Times:** Yes
**Fee 9 Holes: Weekday:** $52 w/cart
**Fee 18 Holes: Weekday:** $85 w/cart
**Twilight Rates:** After 3pm
**Cart Rental:** Included
**Lessons:** Yes **Schools:** Yes
**Membership:** Yes
**Other:**

| Tees | Holes | Yards | Par | USGA | Slope |
|------|-------|-------|-----|------|-------|
| BACK | 18 | 6908 | 72 | 73.1 | 138 |
| MIDDLE | 18 | 6330 | 72 | 71.0 | 133 |
| FRONT | 18 | 5094 | 72 | 69.1 | 120 |

**Weekend:**
**Weekend:** $99 w/cart
**Discounts:** Senior & Junior
**Driving Range:** Yes
**Junior Golf:**
**Architect/Yr Open:** Graham Cooke/2006
**GPS:** Yes

COUPON

Front 9 wraps its way around Eastern edge of the resort. Back 9 course design by Graham Cooke. Outstanding championship course in the Northeast kingdom. Spectacular course is a must-play.

| | 1 | 2 | 3 | 4 | 5 | 6 | 7 | 8 | 9 |
|------|-----|-----|-----|-----|-----|-----|-----|-----|-----|
| **PAR** | 4 | 3 | 4 | 5 | 3 | 4 | 5 | 4 | 4 |
| **YARDS** | 410 | 133 | 422 | 538 | 167 | 347 | 472 | 380 | 367 |
| | **10** | **11** | **12** | **13** | **14** | **15** | **16** | **17** | **18** |
| **PAR** | 4 | 5 | 3 | 5 | 3 | 4 | 5 | 3 | 4 |
| **YARDS** | 399 | 474 | 129 | 513 | 196 | 335 | 486 | 155 | 407 |

**Directions:** I-91 to Exit 26 (Orleans). Go north via Route 5 to Route 14 North. Then go south on Route 100. Take a right in center of Troy onto 101 North. Left onto Route 242. Follow to entrance on right.

# John P. Larkin Country Club  NR  24 ▶

Route 5
Windsor, VT (802) 674-6491

**Club Pro:** Loretta Taft, GM
**Payment:** Visa, MC, Disc
**Tee Times:** Weekends/Holidays
**Fee 9 Holes: Weekday:** $17
**Fee 18 Holes: Weekday:** $26
**Twilight Rates:** No
**Cart Rental:** $15pp/18, $10pp/9
**Lessons:** No **Schools:** No
**Membership:** Yes
**Other:** Restaurant / Clubhouse / Snack Bar / Bar-Lounge / Lockers / Showers

| Tees | Holes | Yards | Par | USGA | Slope |
|------|-------|-------|-----|------|-------|
| BACK | | | | | |
| MIDDLE | 9 | 2670 | 34 | 65.1 | 105 |
| FRONT | 9 | 2462 | 36 | 68.2 | 109 |

**Weekend:** $20
**Weekend:** $30
**Discounts:** None
**Driving Range:** No
**Junior Golf:** Yes
**Architect/Yr Open:** 1921

Course has views of Mt. Ascutney and Connecticut River. New irrigation. New Hampshire is out of bounds.

| | 1 | 2 | 3 | 4 | 5 | 6 | 7 | 8 | 9 |
|------|-----|-----|-----|-----|-----|-----|-----|-----|-----|
| **PAR** | 4 | 3 | 4 | 4 | 4 | 3 | 3 | 5 | 4 |
| **YARDS** | 332 | 215 | 333 | 309 | 383 | 176 | 140 | 442 | 340 |
| **PAR** | | | | | | | | | |
| **YARDS** | | | | | | | | | |

**Directions:** I-91 to Exit 9, left on Route 5, course is 3.5 miles down.

# Killington Golf Course

○○½ 25 ►

227 E. Mountain Road
Killington, VT (802) 422-6700
www.killingtongolf.com

**Club Pro:** Dave Beckwith
**Payment:** Visa, MC, Amex, Disc
**Tee Times:** Recommended

| Tees | Holes | Yards | Par | USGA | Slope |
|------|-------|-------|-----|------|-------|
| BACK | 18 | 6168 | 72 | 70.3 | 129 |
| MIDDLE | 18 | 5876 | 72 | 68.9 | 124 |
| FRONT | 18 | 4803 | 72 | 68.3 | 119 |

**Fee  9 Holes: Weekday:** $30    **Weekend:** $35
**Fee 18 Holes: Weekday:** $50    **Weekend:** $60
**Twilight Rates:** After 3pm

COUPON

**Discounts:** Junior, appropriate attire, shirts no jeans
**Cart Rental:** $20pp/18, $12pp/9    **Driving Range:** $4/bucket
**Lessons:** $60/hour  **Schools:** Jr. & Sr.    **Junior Golf:** Yes
**Membership:** Yes    **Architect/Yr Open:** Geoffrey Cornish/1983
**Other:** Hotel / Clubhouse / Showers / Snack Bar / Restaurant / Bar-Lounge / Lodging Partner / Appropriate Attire / Collared Shirts / No Jeans

Very scenic with dramatic elevation changes. The 6168 yard par 72 Geoffrey Cornish layout presents a refreshing round for any golfer no matter what skill level or handicap.

| | 1 | 2 | 3 | 4 | 5 | 6 | 7 | 8 | 9 |
|------|---|---|---|---|---|---|---|---|---|
| PAR | 4 | 5 | 3 | 4 | 5 | 3 | 5 | 4 | 4 |
| YARDS | 354 | 485 | 163 | 395 | 452 | 138 | 480 | 321 | 270 |
| | 10 | 11 | 12 | 13 | 14 | 15 | 16 | 17 | 18 |
| PAR | 4 | 5 | 4 | 4 | 3 | 4 | 4 | 3 | 4 |
| YARDS | 334 | 485 | 300 | 355 | 174 | 370 | 360 | 150 | 290 |

**Directions:** I-89 to US Route 4 West to the Killington Access Road. Follow to the ski area and follow the signs.

# Kwiniaska Golf Club

○○ 26 ►    VT

5531 Spear Street
Shelburne, VT (802) 985-3672
www.kwiniaska.com

**Club Pro:** Michael Bailey, PGA
**Payment:** Visa, MC
**Tee Times:** 1 day adv.

| Tees | Holes | Yards | Par | USGA | Slope |
|------|-------|-------|-----|------|-------|
| BACK | 18 | 6848 | 72 | 72.7 | 129 |
| MIDDLE | 18 | 6601 | 72 | 71.7 | 126 |
| FRONT | 18 | 5246 | 72 | 70.6 | 115 |

**Fee  9 Holes: Weekday:** $25    **Weekend:** $25 after 1pm
**Fee 18 Holes: Weekday:** $32 (Mon-Tues)    **Weekend:** $38 (Wed-Sun)
**Twilight Rates:** After 4pm    **Discounts:** No
**Cart Rental:** $17pp/18, $10pp/9    **Driving Range:** Yes
**Lessons:** Yes  **Schools:** No    **Junior Golf:** Yes
**Membership:** Yes/limited    **Architect/Yr Open:** A. Bradford/1965
**Other:** Restaurant / Clubhouse / Lockers / Showers
**GPS:** Flagpole readers

Course is framed with trees that are spectacular during foliage. Course plays tougher than it looks. 3rd longest course in the state.

| | 1 | 2 | 3 | 4 | 5 | 6 | 7 | 8 | 9 |
|------|---|---|---|---|---|---|---|---|---|
| PAR | 4 | 3 | 5 | 3 | 4 | 4 | 4 | 4 | 5 |
| YARDS | 425 | 186 | 467 | 181 | 446 | 375 | 407 | 374 | 541 |
| | 10 | 11 | 12 | 13 | 14 | 15 | 16 | 17 | 18 |
| PAR | 4 | 4 | 3 | 5 | 4 | 3 | 5 | 4 | 4 |
| YARDS | 367 | 341 | 169 | 495 | 399 | 193 | 490 | 328 | 417 |

**Directions:** I-89 to Exit 14 West. Follow signs to Spear Street, then 5 miles south.

# Lake Morey Country Club  ✪✪½  27

179 Club House Road
Fairlee, VT (802) 333-4800
www.lakemoreycc.com

**Club Pro:** Bill Ross Jr., PGA
**Payment:** Visa, MC, Disc, Amex
**Tee Times:** 4 days adv.

| Tees | Holes | Yards | Par | USGA | Slope |
|------|-------|-------|-----|------|-------|
| BACK | 18 | 6024 | 70 | 69.4 | 120 |
| MIDDLE | 18 | 5807 | 70 | 68.4 | 118 |
| FRONT | 18 | 4942 | 70 | 68.0 | 115 |

**Fee 9 Holes: Weekday:** $24
**Fee 18 Holes: Weekday:** $36
**Twilight Rates:** $24 after 3pm
**Cart Rental:** $18.50pp/18, $11pp/9
**Lessons:** Yes **Schools:** No
**Membership:** Yes
**Weekend:** $24
**Weekend:** $46
**Discounts:** Sr & Jr (Mon and Tues)
**Driving Range:** $5/bucket
**Junior Golf:** Yes
**Architect/Yr Open:** 1915; Geoffrey Cornish/1989

$c^{OUPO}N$

**Other:** Clubhouse / Snack Bar / Restaurant / Bar-Lounge / Hotel / Resort Lake Activities

Home of Vermont Open. Come play where the Pros play.

|  | 1 | 2 | 3 | 4 | 5 | 6 | 7 | 8 | 9 |
|------|---|---|---|---|---|---|---|---|---|
| PAR | 3 | 5 | 4 | 4 | 4 | 3 | 3 | 4 | 4 |
| YARDS | 213 | 460 | 356 | 337 | 334 | 158 | 114 | 395 | 321 |
|  | 10 | 11 | 12 | 13 | 14 | 15 | 16 | 17 | 18 |
| PAR | 4 | 4 | 5 | 5 | 4 | 3 | 4 | 3 | 4 |
| YARDS | 324 | 369 | 504 | 517 | 373 | 188 | 371 | 160 | 313 |

**Directions:** I-91 North to Exit 15, take left off ramp and follow signs. 25 minutes north of White River Junction.

# Lake St. Catherine Country Club ✪✪✪  28

Route 30
Poultney, VT (802) 287-9341
www.lakestcatherinecountryclub.com

**Club Pro:** Matt Hibbert
**Payment:** Visa, MC, Cash
**Tee Times:** 1 week adv.

| Tees | Holes | Yards | Par | USGA | Slope |
|------|-------|-------|-----|------|-------|
| BACK | 18 | 6204 | 72 | 69.0 | 125 |
| MIDDLE | 18 | 5840 | 72 | 67.3 | 118 |
| FRONT | 18 | 4899 | 72 | 62.0 | 107 |

**Fee 9 Holes: Weekday:** $19
**Fee 18 Holes: Weekday:** $29
**Twilight Rates:** After 3pm
**Cart Rental:** $15pp/18, $9pp/9
**Lessons:** $50/hour **Schools:** No
**Membership:** Yes
**Weekend:** $29
**Weekend:** $36
**Discounts:** Senior
**Driving Range:** Yes
**Junior Golf:** Yes
**Architect/Yr Open:** 1925

**Other:** Snack Bar / Bar-Lounge / Full-Service Restaurant

Open April - October. Player Comments: "15th and 16th holes most scenic in state." "Rolling hills, nice greens, playable for all levels." –GM

|  | 1 | 2 | 3 | 4 | 5 | 6 | 7 | 8 | 9 |
|------|---|---|---|---|---|---|---|---|---|
| PAR | 4 | 4 | 3 | 4 | 4 | 4 | 5 | 3 | 5 |
| YARDS | 391 | 340 | 156 | 405 | 354 | 333 | 517 | 186 | 444 |
|  | 10 | 11 | 12 | 13 | 14 | 15 | 16 | 17 | 18 |
| PAR | 5 | 4 | 4 | 4 | 3 | 4 | 3 | 4 | 5 |
| YARDS | 522 | 343 | 327 | 320 | 125 | 374 | 166 | 388 | 513 |

**Directions:** Directly on Route 30 South of Poultney, easily accessible from Route 4 to 30 South.

# Lake Willoughby Golf Course

New

29 ▶

694 Coles Road
Westmore, VT  (802) 723-4783
www.lakewilloughbygolf.com

**Club Pro:**
**Payment:**
**Tee Times:**

| Tees | Holes | Yards | Par | USGA | Slope |
|------|-------|-------|-----|------|-------|
| BACK |  |  |  |  |  |
| MIDDLE | 9 | 2300 | 33 |  |  |
| FRONT |  |  |  |  |  |

**Fee  9 Holes: Weekday:** $10
**Fee 18 Holes: Weekday:**
**Twilight Rates:**
**Cart Rental:** $10pp/9
**Lessons: Schools:**
**Membership:** Yes
**Other:**

**Weekend:** $10
**Weekend:**
**Discounts:** Senior
**Driving Range:** $5/bucket
**Junior Golf:**
**Architect/Yr Open:** 2003

This spectacular 9-hole golf course is a jewel in its mountainside setting. This pristine course stays environmentally green through the works of nature and a riding mower only.

|  | 1 | 2 | 3 | 4 | 5 | 6 | 7 | 8 | 9 |
|------|-----|-----|-----|-----|-----|-----|-----|-----|-----|
| **PAR** | 4 | 3 | 3 | 3 | 3 | 4 | 5 | 5 | 3 |
| **YARDS** | 275 | 135 | 180 | 200 | 90 | 325 | 425 | 485 | 185 |
| **PAR** |  |  |  |  |  |  |  |  |  |
| **YARDS** |  |  |  |  |  |  |  |  |  |

**Directions:** I-93 North to US-5 North to VT-5A North. At Westmore Community Church go to the top of Hinton Hill Road. Turn right on Coles Road to the course.

# Links at Lang Farm

✪✪✪

30 ▶

VT

39 Essex Way
Essex Junction, VT (802) 878-0298
www.linksatlangfarm.com

**Club Pro:** Steve Gonsalves, PGA
**Payment:** Visa, MC, Disc, Check, Cash
**Tee Times:** Yes

| Tees | Holes | Yards | Par | USGA | Slope |
|------|-------|-------|-----|------|-------|
| BACK | 18 | 3809 | 60 | 59.8 | 102 |
| MIDDLE | 18 | 3444 | 60 | 58 | 96 |
| FRONT | 18 | 2884 | 60 |  |  |

**Fee  9 Holes: Weekday:** $23
**Fee 18 Holes: Weekday:** $36
**Twilight Rates:** After 5pm
**Cart Rental:** $17pp/18, $8.50pp/9
**Lessons:** Yes  **Schools:** Yes
**Membership:** Yes
**Other:** Inn / Lodging Partner / Stay and Play

**Weekend:** $23
**Weekend:** $36
**Discounts:** Senior, Junior, Ladies
**Driving Range:** Yes
**Junior Golf:** Yes
**Architect/Yr Open:** Michael Asmundson/2002
**GPS:** Yes

Appealing to all levels of play. Exceptional conditions. Call ahead for times. Golf packages available with The Inn at Essex. New clubhouse.

|  | 1 | 2 | 3 | 4 | 5 | 6 | 7 | 8 | 9 |
|------|-----|-----|-----|-----|-----|-----|-----|-----|-----|
| **PAR** | 3 | 3 | 3 | 4 | 3 | 4 | 3 | 3 | 3 |
| **YARDS** | 158 | 167 | 155 | 295 | 124 | 307 | 133 | 180 | 156 |
|  | **10** | **11** | **12** | **13** | **14** | **15** | **16** | **17** | **18** |
| **PAR** | 3 | 3 | 4 | 3 | 4 | 3 | 3 | 4 | 4 |
| **YARDS** | 156 | 147 | 273 | 126 | 258 | 102 | 152 | 231 | 324 |

**Directions:** I-89 to Exit 11. Follow Route 117, 6 miles to VT 289. Exit 10, turn left.

# Montague Golf Club ✪✪ ▶31

**Randolph Avenue**
**Randolph, VT (802) 728-3806**
www.montaguegolf.com

| Tees | Holes | Yards | Par | USGA | Slope |
|------|-------|-------|-----|------|-------|
| BACK | 18 | 6134 | 70 | 69.6 | 119 |
| MIDDLE | 18 | 5730 | 70 | 68.0 | 115 |
| FRONT | 18 | 4785 | 71 | 68.7 | 109 |

**Club Pro:** Paul Politano, PGA
**Payment:** Visa, MC, Amex
**Tee Times:** Yes
**Fee 9 Holes: Weekday:** $20          **Weekend:** $25
**Fee 18 Holes: Weekday:** $32          **Weekend:** $39
**Twilight Rates:** After 4pm          **Discounts:** Senior/Junior
**Cart Rental:** $20pp/18, $11pp/9          **Driving Range:** Yes
**Lessons:** Yes, PGA **Schools:** No          **Junior Golf:** Yes
**Membership:** Yes          **Architect/Yr Open:** 1913/Geoffrey Cornish
**Other:** Clubhouse / Snack Bar / Putting Green          **GPS:**

New owners Sam & Jinny Sammis have improved the experience at Montague. 2 new holes, 8 new tee boxes, more planned! Area attraction: 3 Stallion Inn.

| | 1 | 2 | 3 | 4 | 5 | 6 | 7 | 8 | 9 |
|------|---|---|---|---|---|---|---|---|---|
| PAR | 4 | 4 | 4 | 3 | 4 | 4 | 3 | 4 | 3 |
| YARDS | 317 | 375 | 328 | 168 | 425 | 420 | 157 | 330 | 120 |
| | 10 | 11 | 12 | 13 | 14 | 15 | 16 | 17 | 18 |
| PAR | 3 | 5 | 4 | 4 | 5 | 4 | 4 | 4 | 4 |
| YARDS | 214 | 540 | 305 | 402 | 472 | 375 | 379 | 389 | 398 |

**Directions:** I-89 North to Exit 4. Follow Route 66 into downtown Randolph on Route 12 South. Take left on Merchant Road. Go straight onto Randolph Avenue — end of road, take left.

# Montpelier Elks Country Club NR ▶32

**203 Country Club Road**
**Montpelier, VT (802) 223-7457**
www.montpelierelkscc.com

| Tees | Holes | Yards | Par | USGA | Slope |
|------|-------|-------|-----|------|-------|
| BACK | | | | | |
| MIDDLE | 9 | 2584 | 35 | 66.6 | 114 |
| FRONT | 9 | 2370 | 35 | 67.9 | 112 |

**Club Pro:** Lynn Ribolini
**Payment:** Cash, Credit
**Tee Times:** Weekends, 1 day adv.
**Fee 9 Holes: Weekday:** $20          **Weekend:** $20
**Fee 18 Holes: Weekday:** $30          **Weekend:** $30
**Twilight Rates:** No          **Discounts:** None
**Cart Rental:** $17pp/18, $12pp/9          **Driving Range:** No
**Lessons:** No **Schools:** No          **Junior Golf:** Yes
**Membership:** Yes          **Architect/Yr Open:** 1902
**Other:** Clubhouse / Lockers / Showers / Snack Bar / Restaurant / Bar-Lounge

The course is relatively short but made challenging by the hilly terrain. Picturesque views of the Green Mountains. Open April 1 - October 31.

| | 1 | 2 | 3 | 4 | 5 | 6 | 7 | 8 | 9 |
|------|---|---|---|---|---|---|---|---|---|
| PAR | 4 | 3 | 5 | 5 | 4 | 3 | 4 | 3 | 4 |
| YARDS | 358 | 155 | 422 | 459 | 226 | 149 | 325 | 191 | 279 |
| PAR | | | | | | | | | |
| YARDS | | | | | | | | | |

**Directions:** I-89 to Route 2 exit, follow signs for Montpelier.

# Mountain View Country Club

NR 33

112 Country Club Road
Greensboro, VT (802) 533-7477
www.mvccvt.com

**Club Pro:** Dan Hudson, Dir. of Golf
**Payment:** Credit Cards, Check, Cash
**Tee Times:** No
**Fee 9 Holes: Weekday:** $23
**Fee 18 Holes: Weekday:** $42
**Twilight Rates:** After 5pm
**Cart Rental:** $16pp/18, $11pp/9
**Lessons:** Yes **Schools:** No
**Membership:** Yes
**Other:** Clubhouse / Putting Course

**Weekend:** $25
**Weekend:** $46
**Discounts:** No
**Driving Range:** Yes
**Junior Golf:** No
**Architect/Yr Open:** 1898

| Tees | Holes | Yards | Par | USGA | Slope |
|------|-------|-------|-----|------|-------|
| BACK | 9 | 2927 | 35 | 68.8 | 114 |
| MIDDLE | 9 | 2816 | 35 | 67.9 | 112 |
| FRONT | 9 | 2447 | 35 | 67.1 | 109 |

One of the oldest courses in Vermont, located in the beautiul Northeast Kingdom. A links style course that is challenging. Natural fairways, small greens and hilly terrain.

| | 1 | 2 | 3 | 4 | 5 | 6 | 7 | 8 | 9 |
|---|---|---|---|---|---|---|---|---|---|
| PAR | 4 | 4 | 3 | 4 | 3 | 4 | 5 | 4 | 4 |
| YARDS | 327 | 284 | 151 | 415 | 161 | 383 | 466 | 302 | 327 |

| | | | | | | | | | |
|---|---|---|---|---|---|---|---|---|---|
| PAR | | | | | | | | | |
| YARDS | | | | | | | | | |

**Directions:** I-93 North to US-2 West to I-91 North. Take Exit 21 to US-2 West to VT-15 West to Country Club Road in Greensboro.

# Mt. Anthony Country Club

✪✪✪½ 34

VT

180 Country Club Drive
Bennington, VT (802) 447-7079
www.mtanthonycc.com

**Club Pro:** Kevin Bennison, PGA
**Payment:** Visa, MC, Cash, Disc
**Tee Times:** Yes
**Fee 9 Holes: Weekday:** $30
**Fee 18 Holes: Weekday:** $40
**Twilight Rates:** After 2pm
**Cart Rental:** $20pp/18, $10pp/9
**Lessons:** Call for rates **Schools:** Junior
**Membership:** Yes
**Other:** Snack Bar / Restaurant / Bar-Lounge / Lockers / Showers
**GPS:** Yes

**Weekend:** $35
**Weekend:** $55
**Discounts:** Junior and Senior
**Driving Range:** Yes
**Junior Golf:** Yes
**Architect/Yr Open:** Jay Jerome/1897

| Tees | Holes | Yards | Par | USGA | Slope |
|------|-------|-------|-----|------|-------|
| BACK | 18 | 6434 | 71 | 71.9 | 123 |
| MIDDLE | 18 | 5846 | 71 | 68.3 | 121 |
| FRONT | 18 | 4651 | 71 | 67.8 | 117 |

COUPON

Player Comments: "Good price. Scenic. Great services. Well-maintained." Open April - October. Recently renovated to take advantage of the spectacular Green Mountain setting. New bunkers and new tee boxes.

| | 1 | 2 | 3 | 4 | 5 | 6 | 7 | 8 | 9 |
|---|---|---|---|---|---|---|---|---|---|
| PAR | 4 | 3 | 5 | 3 | 5 | 4 | 4 | 4 | 4 |
| YARDS | 388 | 169 | 470 | 110 | 540 | 370 | 321 | 329 | 303 |
| | 10 | 11 | 12 | 13 | 14 | 15 | 16 | 17 | 18 |
| PAR | 4 | 4 | 4 | 3 | 3 | 4 | 5 | 4 | 4 |
| YARDS | 342 | 364 | 323 | 160 | 178 | 294 | 440 | 402 | 343 |

**Directions:** From Route 7 go to Bennington Center. Turn onto West Main Street (Route 9 West). ¼ mile after Paradise Motel take first right onto Convent Avenue. Follow to end and take left. Course is down on the right.

# Mount Snow Golf Club  35

Country Club Road
West Dover, VT (802) 464-4254
www.mountsnow.com

| Tees | Holes | Yards | Par | USGA | Slope |
|------|-------|-------|-----|------|-------|
| BACK | 18 | 6943 | 72 | 73.7 | 129 |
| MIDDLE | 18 | 6539 | 72 | 71.9 | 125 |
| FRONT | 18 | 5384 | 72 | 70.4 | 117 |

**Club Pro:** Jay Morelli, PGA
**Payment:** Visa, MC, Amex, Disc
**Tee Times:** Yes
**Fee 9 Holes: Weekday:** $36 w/cart
**Fee 18 Holes: Weekday:** $44 w/cart
**Twilight Rates:** After 2pm
**Cart Rental:** Included
**Lessons:** $40/half hour  **Schools:** Yes
**Membership:** Yes
**Weekend:**
**Weekend:** $75 w/cart
**Discounts:** Senior & Junior
**Driving Range:** Yes
**Junior Golf:** Yes
**Architect/Yr Open:** Geoffrey Cornish/1967

COUPON

**Other:** Clubhouse / Snack Bar / Restaurant / Bar-Lounge / Hotel / Spa

Home of the Original Golf School, headed by Jay Morelli, MSGC offers breathtaking views and challenging golf for all ability levels. Gold Tees for seniors in 2005. New ladies' tees. Rates subject to change.

| | 1 | 2 | 3 | 4 | 5 | 6 | 7 | 8 | 9 |
|---|---|---|---|---|---|---|---|---|---|
| PAR | 4 | 5 | 3 | 4 | 4 | 3 | 5 | 4 | 4 |
| YARDS | 372 | 593 | 160 | 407 | 432 | 150 | 480 | 400 | 396 |
| | 10 | 11 | 12 | 13 | 14 | 15 | 16 | 17 | 18 |
| PAR | 4 | 4 | 3 | 4 | 5 | 3 | 5 | 4 | 4 |
| YARDS | 394 | 364 | 143 | 354 | 479 | 187 | 542 | 323 | 163 |

**Directions:** I-91 to Exit 2 in Brattleboro to Route 9 West, 20 miles to Wilmington. Turn right at the stop light onto Route 100 North. About 6 miles, take a left on Crosstown Road. At top of hill on left.

# Neshobe Golf Club ⊗⊗⊗ 36

224 Town Farm Road
Brandon, VT (802) 247-3611
www.neshobe.com

| Tees | Holes | Yards | Par | USGA | Slope |
|------|-------|-------|-----|------|-------|
| BACK | 18 | 6349 | 72 | 71.6 | 125 |
| MIDDLE | 18 | 5865 | 72 | 68.7 | 122 |
| FRONT | 18 | 5179 | 73 | 64.9 | 117 |

**Club Pro:** Rodney Bicknell, PGA
**Payment:** MC, Visa, Disc, Checks, Cash
**Tee Times:** 7 days adv.
**Fee 9 Holes: Weekday:** $35 with cart
**Fee 18 Holes: Weekday:** $60 with cart
**Twilight Rates:** After 3pm
**Cart Rental:** $20pp/18, $14pp/9
**Lessons:** Yes  **Schools:** No
**Membership:** Available
**Weekend:** $35 with cart
**Weekend:** $60 with cart
**Discounts:** Seniors/Junior
**Driving Range:** Yes
**Junior Golf:** Yes
**Architect/Yr Open:** Steve Durkee/1958/1996

COUPON

**Other:** Clubhouse / Lockers / Showers / Snack Bar / Restaurant / Bar-Lounge / Lodging Partner

Excellent conditions. Friendly staff. 12 new holes designed by Steve Durkee. #7 hole redesigned in 2012. A hidden gem!

| | 1 | 2 | 3 | 4 | 5 | 6 | 7 | 8 | 9 |
|---|---|---|---|---|---|---|---|---|---|
| PAR | 4 | 4 | 4 | 4 | 5 | 3 | 4 | 5 | 4 |
| YARDS | 303 | 310 | 340 | 395 | 435 | 140 | 355 | 460 | 280 |
| | 10 | 11 | 12 | 13 | 14 | 15 | 16 | 17 | 18 |
| PAR | 3 | 5 | 3 | 4 | 5 | 4 | 4 | 3 | 4 |
| YARDS | 194 | 490 | 140 | 340 | 515 | 350 | 270 | 120 | 340 |

**Directions:** Route 7 to Route 73 East. Follow for 1.5 miles East of Brandon Center.

# Newport Country Club                    ✪✪½  37 ▶

590 Mount Vernon Street
Newport, VT  (802) 334-2391
www.newportscountryclub.com

**Club Pro:** Kim O'Neil
**Payment:** MC, Visa
**Tee Times:** 2 day adv.

| Tees | Holes | Yards | Par | USGA | Slope |
|------|-------|-------|-----|------|-------|
| BACK | 18 | 6491 | 72 | 70.4 | 117 |
| MIDDLE | 18 | 6228 | 72 | 68.6 | 114 |
| FRONT | 18 | 5274 | 72 | 71 | 114 |

**Fee  9 Holes: Weekday:** $22        **Weekend:** $22
**Fee 18 Holes: Weekday:** $36        **Weekend:** $36
**Twilight Rates:** $15 after 5pm      **Discounts:** Junior under 10 yrs/$5
**Cart Rental:** $20pp/18, $12pp/9     **Driving Range:** $7/bucket
**Lessons:** $40/half hour  **Schools:**  **Junior Golf:** Yes
**Membership:** Yes                    **Architect/Yr Open:** Ralph Barton
**Other:** Restaurant / Clubhouse / Bar-Lounge / Lockers / Showers / Snack Bar

*COUPON*

Very friendly. Improvements continuing. Nice greens.

|  | 1 | 2 | 3 | 4 | 5 | 6 | 7 | 8 | 9 |
|------|---|---|---|---|---|---|---|---|---|
| PAR | 4 | 3 | 4 | 5 | 4 | 3 | 4 | 4 | 5 |
| YARDS | 354 | 172 | 356 | 484 | 326 | 150 | 397 | 335 | 469 |
|  | 10 | 11 | 12 | 13 | 14 | 15 | 16 | 17 | 18 |
| PAR | 5 | 4 | 4 | 3 | 4 | 4 | 4 | 3 | 5 |
| YARDS | 479 | 374 | 387 | 144 | 375 | 395 | 314 | 142 | 464 |

**Directions:** I-91 to Exit 27. Head toward Newport about ½ mile. Take left and follow signs.


# Northfield Country Club              NR  38 ▶      VT

2066 Roxbury Road (Route 12A)
Northfield, VT  (802) 485-4515
www.northfieldcountryclub.com

**Club Pro:** Joe Dingledine, PGA
**Payment:** Visa, MC, Cash, Checks
**Tee Times:** Required

| Tees | Holes | Yards | Par | USGA | Slope |
|------|-------|-------|-----|------|-------|
| BACK | 18 | 5972 | 70 | 69.0 | 122 |
| MIDDLE | 18 | 5768 | 70 | 68.0 | 120 |
| FRONT | 18 | 5140 | 70 | 63.1 | 119 |

**Fee  9 Holes: Weekday:** $15 M-Th     **Weekend:** $20 F/S/S
**Fee 18 Holes: Weekday:** $21 M-Th     **Weekend:** $28 F/S/S
**Twilight Rates:** No                   **Discounts:** Junior and under free
**Cart Rental:** $15pp/18, $9pp/9        **Driving Range:** Netted practice area
**Lessons:** Private and Group  **Schools:** No  **Junior Golf:** Yes
**Membership:** Yes                      **Architect/Yr Open:** Les Heon/1927
**Other:** Restaurant / Bar / Clubhouse / Showers  **GPS:**

Player Comments: "Old-fashioned, wonderful and friendly course." Known for 'The Volcano" hole #4.

|  | 1 | 2 | 3 | 4 | 5 | 6 | 7 | 8 | 9 |
|------|---|---|---|---|---|---|---|---|---|
| PAR | 4 | 4 | 4 | 3 | 4 | 5 | 4 | 3 | 4 |
| YARDS | 348 | 314 | 276 | 148 | 377 | 532 | 336 | 183 | 367 |
|  | 10 | 11 | 12 | 13 | 14 | 15 | 16 | 17 | 18 |
| PAR | 4 | 4 | 3 | 3 | 5 | 5 | 4 | 3 | 4 |
| YARDS | 340 | 352 | 175 | 148 | 465 | 532 | 325 | 183 | 367 |

**Directions:** I-89 to Exit 5, follow to bottom of hill. Go straight .75 mile to a T. Turn left on 12A and go 2.5 miles. Clubhouse is on right.

# Okemo Valley Golf Club ✪✪✪✪

## 39

89 Fox Lane
Ludlow, VT  (802) 228-1396
www.okemo.com/golf

| Tees | Holes | Yards | Par | USGA | Slope |
|------|-------|-------|-----|------|-------|
| BACK | 18 | 6400 | 70 | 71.1 | 130 |
| MIDDLE | 18 | 6104 | 70 | 69.6 | 128 |
| FRONT | 18 | 5105 | 70 | 70.1 | 125 |

**Club Pro:** Jim Remy
**Payment:** Visa, MC, Amex
**Tee Times:** 7 days adv.
**Fee  9 Holes: Weekday:** Call for rates     **Weekend:** Call for rates
**Fee 18 Holes: Weekday:** Call for rates     **Weekend:** Call for rates
**Twilight Rates:** After 1:30pm weekdays     **Discounts:** Junior
After 2:30pm weekends
**Cart Rental:** $22pp/18, $11pp/9     **Driving Range:** Yes
**Lessons:** $75/hour **Schools:** Adult     **Junior Golf:** Yes
**Membership:** Waiting list     **Architect/Yr Open:** Steve Durkee/1999
**Other:** Full Restaurant / Clubhouse / Hotel / Inn / Lockers / Showers / Bar

Vermont's only Heathland Course. "One of Vermont's best public courses. Great views of Okemo Mountain and valley. Many memorable holes. Excellent facilities." –GM

| | 1 | 2 | 3 | 4 | 5 | 6 | 7 | 8 | 9 |
|---|---|---|---|---|---|---|---|---|---|
| PAR | 4 | 5 | 4 | 3 | 4 | 3 | 5 | 3 | 4 |
| YARDS | 381 | 522 | 352 | 175 | 368 | 167 | 487 | 173 | 347 |
| | 10 | 11 | 12 | 13 | 14 | 15 | 16 | 17 | 18 |
| PAR | 4 | 5 | 4 | 4 | 3 | 4 | 4 | 3 | 4 |
| YARDS | 305 | 502 | 371 | 304 | 205 | 396 | 435 | 196 | 418 |

**Directions:** Just north of Ludlow about 1 mile on Route 103. Right onto Fox Lane (signs on highway).

# Orleans Country Club ✪✪

## 40

316 Country Club Lane
Orleans, VT  (802) 754-2333
www.orleanscc.com

| Tees | Holes | Yards | Par | USGA | Slope |
|------|-------|-------|-----|------|-------|
| BACK | 18 | 6185 | 72 | 69.3 | 121 |
| MIDDLE | 18 | 5970 | 72 | 68.5 | 119 |
| FRONT | 18 | 5523 | 73 | 66.7 | 116 |

**Club Pro:** Joshua Olney
**Payment:** MC, Visa, Checks
**Tee Times:** 7 days adv.
**Fee  9 Holes: Weekday:** $18     **Weekend:** $19
**Fee 18 Holes: Weekday:** $36     **Weekend:** $38
**Twilight Rates:** After 3pm     **Discounts:** Under 12 free w/adult
**Cart Rental:** $19pp/18, $10pp/9     **Driving Range:** $8/lg, $4/sm bucket
**Lessons:** $40/half hour **Schools:** Yes     **Junior Golf:** Yes
**Membership:** Yes     **Architect/Yr Open:** Alex Reid/1928
**Other:** Clubhouse / Restaurant / Snack Bar / Bar Lounge / Lockers / Showers / Lodging Partner
**GPS:** No

Excellent course conditions, scenic mountain views. Course is relatively short at 6200 yards from blue tees, however the challenge starts on the greens.

| | 1 | 2 | 3 | 4 | 5 | 6 | 7 | 8 | 9 |
|---|---|---|---|---|---|---|---|---|---|
| PAR | 5 | 4 | 3 | 5 | 4 | 4 | 4 | 3 | 4 |
| YARDS | 442 | 319 | 152 | 439 | 365 | 356 | 300 | 180 | 355 |
| | 10 | 11 | 12 | 13 | 14 | 15 | 16 | 17 | 18 |
| PAR | 3 | 5 | 4 | 3 | 4 | 4 | 5 | 4 | 4 |
| YARDS | 200 | 479 | 359 | 134 | 426 | 292 | 495 | 285 | 392 |

**Directions:** From Interstate 91 make a left turn onto State Route 58. Remain on 58 for almost 3 miles, course on the right.

# Proctor Pittsford Country Club ✪½  41 ▶

311 Country Club Drive
Pittsford, VT (802) 483-9379
www.proctor-pittsford.com

**Club Pro:** John Ojala, GM
**Payment:** MC, Visa, Disc
**Tee Times:** 2 days adv.
**Fee 9 Holes: Weekday:** $22
**Fee 18 Holes: Weekday:** $40
**Twilight Rates:** $22 after 4pm
**Cart Rental:** $20pp/18, $10 pp/9
**Lessons:** Yes **Schools:** No
**Membership:** Yes
**Other:** Restaurant / Lounge

| Tees | Holes | Yards | Par | USGA | Slope |
|------|-------|-------|-----|------|-------|
| BACK | 18 | 6052 | 70 | 69.4 | 121 |
| MIDDLE | 18 | 5728 | 70 | 67.9 | 118 |
| FRONT | 18 | 5446 | 72 | 66.1 | 115 |

**Weekend:** $22 after 12pm
**Weekend:** $40
**Discounts:** None
**Driving Range:** Yes
**Junior Golf:** Yes
**Architect/Yr Open:** Henry Collin/1923
**GPS:** No

COUPON

Beautiful views, excellent greens and fairways, good test of golf. Open April 15 - October 31. Brand-new driving range. Full-service restaurant. Check out the marble clubhouse.

| | 1 | 2 | 3 | 4 | 5 | 6 | 7 | 8 | 9 |
|------|---|---|---|---|---|---|---|---|---|
| PAR | 4 | 4 | 4 | 5 | 4 | 4 | 3 | 4 | 3 |
| YARDS | 325 | 386 | 308 | 489 | 370 | 326 | 133 | 281 | 219 |
| | 10 | 11 | 12 | 13 | 14 | 15 | 16 | 17 | 18 |
| PAR | 4 | 3 | 5 | 4 | 4 | 4 | 4 | 3 | 4 |
| YARDS | 409 | 144 | 468 | 377 | 332 | 301 | 388 | 163 | 309 |

**Directions:** Take Route 7 for 4 miles north, take left after Nissan dealer. Go ½ mile, take right at "T," go 3 miles on Cornhill Road and turn onto Country Club Drive.

# Ralph Myhre Golf Course ✪✪  42 ▶   VT

317 Golf Course Road
Middlebury, VT (802) 443-5125
www.middlebury.edu

**Club Pro:** Jim Dayton
**Payment:** Cash, Visa, MC
**Tee Times:** Recommended
**Fee 9 Holes: Weekday:** $20
**Fee 18 Holes: Weekday:** $39
**Twilight Rates:** After 4pm
**Cart Rental:** $20pp/18, $11pp/9
**Lessons:** Yes **Schools:** No
**Membership:** Yes
**Other:** Clubhouse / Snack Bar / Showers

| Tees | Holes | Yards | Par | USGA | Slope |
|------|-------|-------|-----|------|-------|
| BACK | 18 | 6379 | 71 | 70.8 | 124 |
| MIDDLE | 18 | 6014 | 71 | 69.2 | 68.9 |
| FRONT | 18 | 5337 | 71 | 66.9 | 120 |

**Weekend:** $20
**Weekend:** $39
**Discounts:** Students
**Driving Range:** Yes
**Junior Golf:** Yes
**Architect/Yr Open:** Ralph Myhre/1920
**GPS:** Yes

COUPON

Open fairways with moderate hills. Well-kept and tees sodded. Owned by Middlebury College. Any student (any school) pays $15.

| | 1 | 2 | 3 | 4 | 5 | 6 | 7 | 8 | 9 |
|------|---|---|---|---|---|---|---|---|---|
| PAR | 5 | 4 | 4 | 3 | 4 | 4 | 3 | 4 | 4 |
| YARDS | 479 | 341 | 311 | 166 | 356 | 370 | 141 | 353 | 365 |
| | 10 | 11 | 12 | 13 | 14 | 15 | 16 | 17 | 18 |
| PAR | 4 | 5 | 3 | 4 | 3 | 4 | 5 | 4 | 4 |
| YARDS | 404 | 525 | 152 | 325 | 126 | 363 | 512 | 351 | 377 |

**Directions:** Route 7 to Route 30 South. Course is just beyond Middlebury College Field House.

# Richford Country Club

NR  43 ►

249 Golf Course Road
Richford, VT (802) 848-3527

**Club Pro:** John Sheridan
**Payment:** Visa, MC
**Tee Times:** No
**Fee 9 Holes: Weekday:** $14 M-Th
**Fee 18 Holes: Weekday:** $16 M-Th
**Twilight Rates:** Wednesday after 3pm
**Cart Rental:** $12.50pp/18, $18.50pp/9
**Lessons:** No **Schools:** No
**Membership:** $350 (before Dec. 11)
**Other:** Clubhouse / Snack Bar / Bar-Lounge

| Tees | Holes | Yards | Par | USGA | Slope |
|------|-------|-------|-----|------|-------|
| BACK | | | | | |
| MIDDLE | 9 | 2908 | 36 | 68.2 | 116 |
| FRONT | 9 | 2326 | 36 | 72.0 | 118 |

**Weekend:** $18 F/S/S
**Weekend:** $22 F/S/S
**Discounts:** None
**Driving Range:** No
**Junior Golf:** Yes
**Architect/Yr Open:** 1915 (Redesigned 2009)

COUPON

We have added 6 new tees to add an even better look, and greater challenge. Excellent views of the Green Mountains. New clubhouse. "Vermont's most scenic golf course." Open April - October.

| | 1 | 2 | 3 | 4 | 5 | 6 | 7 | 8 | 9 |
|------|-----|-----|-----|-----|-----|-----|-----|-----|-----|
| PAR | 4 | 5 | 3 | 4 | 5 | 3 | 3 | 4 | 4 |
| YARDS | 283 | 464 | 170 | 318 | 400 | 453 | 175 | 298 | 367 |

| | | | | | | | | | |
|------|--|--|--|--|--|--|--|--|--|
| PAR | | | | | | | | | |
| YARDS | | | | | | | | | |

**Directions:** I-89 to St. Albans exit. Follow Route 105 North to Richford (28 miles).

# Rocky Ridge Golf Club

★★  44 ►

7470 Route 116
St. George, VT (802) 482-2191
www.rockyridge.com

**Club Pro:** Ed Coleman
**Payment:** Visa, MC, Disc, Amex, No Checks
**Tee Times:** 7 days/week
**Fee 9 Holes: Weekday:** $23
**Fee 18 Holes: Weekday:** $30
**Twilight Rates:** After 4pm
**Cart Rental:** $20pp/18; $10pp/9
**Lessons:** Yes **Schools:** No
**Membership:** Yes - Single: $1100
**Other:** Clubhouse / Restaurant / Bar-Lounge

| Tees | Holes | Yards | Par | USGA | Slope |
|------|-------|-------|-----|------|-------|
| BACK | 18 | 6282 | 72 | 70.3 | 126 |
| MIDDLE | 18 | 6000 | 72 | 69.1 | 124 |
| FRONT | 18 | 5230 | 72 | 69.9 | 117 |

**Weekend:**
**Weekend:** $44
**Discounts:** No
**Driving Range:** Yes
**Junior Golf:** Yes
**Architect/Yr Open:** E. Farrington/1963

COUPON

A challenging and very scenic country setting for all skill levels. Online course review. Voted best Public Course in the Burlington area.

| | 1 | 2 | 3 | 4 | 5 | 6 | 7 | 8 | 9 |
|------|-----|-----|-----|-----|-----|-----|-----|-----|-----|
| PAR | 4 | 5 | 3 | 5 | 4 | 4 | 4 | 3 | 4 |
| YARDS | 270 | 542 | 195 | 576 | 314 | 251 | 339 | 191 | 345 |
| | **10** | **11** | **12** | **13** | **14** | **15** | **16** | **17** | **18** |
| PAR | 4 | 4 | 4 | 4 | 3 | 4 | 5 | 3 | 5 |
| YARDS | 395 | 289 | 312 | 367 | 156 | 315 | 460 | 163 | 513 |

**Directions:** I-89 to Exit 12. Go 5 miles west. Course is at intersection of Routes 2A and 116.

BREAD & BUTTER

LOW TO ROLL

HIGH & SOFT

# KISS

## KEEP IT SIMPLE SET-UPS

Kiss those bogeys and double bogeys goodbye. Let's simplify shots around the green. The simpler we can make it, the better we can score.

# SHAFT
## POSITION

A shaft lean towards the target affects the clubface. Shaft lean options: Most Forward, Forward and In Line with the ball.

## MOST FORWARD

**SHAFT LEAN TOWARDS TARGET** to keep the ball flight low, or if you struggle with solid contact.

## IN LINE

**SHAFT IN LINE WITH BALL**
useful for high & soft shots

## FORWARD

**SHAFT STILL FORWARD, BUT NOT AS MUCH.** This set-up is useful for most shots where your hands are only slightly ahead.

# STANCE
## FOR
## ALIGNMENT

## SQUARE
**PRODUCES AN IN-TO-OUT SWING PATH FOR BASIC CHIPS AROUND THE GREEN.**

**ALL IN LINE**
Your feet, hips and shoulders are parallel to the target line.

**DO THIS**

For shots around the green, narrow your stance.

# OPEN

**PRODUCES AN OUT-TO-IN SWING PATH FOR HIGH, SOFT SHOTS**

**OPEN TO TARGET LINE** Your feet, hips and shoulders are rotated left of a parallel set-up, creating a V.

# CHIP IT
## TO STICK IT

**FOLLOW THE BREAD & BUTTER
OR THE LOW TO ROLL SET-UP**

Loose grip pressure is the key to successful chipping. Weight favors front side and stays on your front side, back and through.

My shoulders, arms and hands are working as a unit, hinging, creating an L.

# THE SET-UP
## FOR LOW TO ROLL

- **CLUB:** PW or 9-8-7 depending on pin placement
- **BALL POSITION:** Back of Center

- **CLUBFACE/STANCE:** Square clubface
- **HANDS/SHAFT:** Most Forward
- **FEET:** Narrow with weight favoring front leg

My back knee initiates the move towards the target. Maintain the slight angle set in your wrist at address all the way to your finish.

# PITCH IT
## TO STICK IT

### FOLLOW THE **BREAD & BUTTER** SET-UP

Weight more balanced. My shoulders, arms and hands are working as a unit, hinging, creating a slightly bigger L.

Still initiating with my back knee, as I rotate through. Unhinging will happen naturally; don't force it.

# THE SET-UP
### FOR BREAD & BUTTER

- **CLUBFACE/STANCE:**
  Slightly Open

- **BALL POSITION:** Center

- **CLUB:** Lob, SW or PW

- **HANDS/SHAFT:**
  Forward

- **FEET:** Narrow with
  weight balanced or
  slightly forward okay

Your finish will be about waist-high with the
club and belt buckle area facing the target.

Get the High & Soft set-up & execute tips, sign up
for Christina's popular Tip of the Week, or register
for her golf schools: www.ChristinaRicciGolf.com

This Year, Tee It Up With EWGA!

# EWGA
BOSTON, MA CHAPTER

# THE Golf Community for Women.

We offer weekend events, after work leagues, lessons, skill improvement clinics, social events and more. And we have a great time! Join our chapter of 350+ and...

**CONNECT:** Meet new friends and playing partners.

**LEARN:** Partcipate in mini workshops to help with your physical and mental game and your equipment.

**PLAY:** Sign up for leagues and golf events, find playing partners.

**BELONG:** Join us and become a member! We are the leading organizaion in the Greater Boston and Southern New Hampshire areas bringing women golfers of all levels together to play, network and have fun!

## Play Golf with Us!

# www.ewgaboston.org

# Rutland Country Club ✪✪✪✪ 45 ▶

275 Grove Street
Rutland, VT (802) 773-3254
www.rutlandcountryclub.com
**Club Pro:** Greg Nelson, PGA
**Payment:** Visa, MC, Disc
**Tee Times:** 48 hours adv.

| Tees | Holes | Yards | Par | USGA | Slope |
|---|---|---|---|---|---|
| BACK | 18 | 6135 | 70 | 69.7 | 125 |
| MIDDLE | 18 | 5758 | 70 | 67.9 | 122 |
| FRONT | 18 | 5368 | 71 | 71.6 | 125 |

**Fee 9 Holes: Weekday:** **Weekend:**
**Fee 18 Holes: Weekday:** Call for rates **Weekend:** Call for rates
**Twilight Rates:** Call for rates **Discounts:** Junior
**Cart Rental:** Included **Driving Range:** No
**Lessons:** Yes **Schools:** No **Junior Golf:** Yes
**Membership:** Yes **Architect/Yr Open:** George Low/1902
**Other:** Clubhouse / Lockers / Showers / Snack Bar / Restaurant / Bar-Lounge

Player Comments: "Great greens and great values. Worth the money." Open May - October.
"One of the best older style public courses I've ever played" –GM

| | 1 | 2 | 3 | 4 | 5 | 6 | 7 | 8 | 9 |
|---|---|---|---|---|---|---|---|---|---|
| PAR | 4 | 4 | 3 | 5 | 3 | 4 | 4 | 4 | 4 |
| YARDS | 379 | 381 | 125 | 463 | 215 | 366 | 322 | 368 | 300 |
| | 10 | 11 | 12 | 13 | 14 | 15 | 16 | 17 | 18 |
| PAR | 4 | 4 | 3 | 5 | 4 | 3 | 4 | 4 | 4 |
| YARDS | 296 | 316 | 193 | 513 | 347 | 121 | 351 | 326 | 376 |

**Directions:** I -89 to Exit 1. Take Route 4 West to Rutland. Take right onto Grove Street and follow signs to course.

# Ryder Brook Golf Club NR 46 ▶ VT

3266 Laporte Road
Morrisville, VT (802) 888-3525
www.ryderbrookgc.com
**Club Pro:** Eileen Kask, PGA
**Payment:** Visa, MC
**Tee Times:** Yes

| Tees | Holes | Yards | Par | USGA | Slope |
|---|---|---|---|---|---|
| BACK | 9 | 3037 | 36 | 68.6 | 118 |
| MIDDLE | 9 | 2847 | 36 | 67.8 | 115 |
| FRONT | 9 | 2517 | 36 | 74.0 | 113 |

**Fee 9 Holes: Weekday:** $22 **Weekend:** $24
**Fee 18 Holes: Weekday:** $32 **Weekend:** $35
**Twilight Rates:** After 4pm **Discounts:** Senior/Junior
**Cart Rental:** $13.50pp/18, $9pp/9 **Driving Range:** Yes
**Lessons:** Yes **Schools:** Yes **Junior Golf:** Yes
**Membership:** Yes **Architect/Yr Open:** Geoffrey Cornish/1969
**Other:** Junior Camp **GPS:**

COUPON

Great course for golfers of all abilities. Play & stay at 1 location. Open May - October. Fairways and greens improvements! Montreal and Stow, Vermont close by.

| | 1 | 2 | 3 | 4 | 5 | 6 | 7 | 8 | 9 |
|---|---|---|---|---|---|---|---|---|---|
| PAR | 4 | 4 | 5 | 3 | 3 | 5 | 4 | 3 | 5 |
| YARDS | 351 | 315 | 466 | 158 | 148 | 574 | 410 | 157 | 458 |
| PAR | | | | | | | | | |
| YARDS | | | | | | | | | |

**Directions:** Exit 10 from I-89. North on Route 100. 5.5 miles north of Stowe Village. Left side of Route 100.

# Sitzmark Golf Course

54 E. Dover Road
Wilmington, VT (802) 464-3384

**Club Pro:** Tom Cullen, Manager
**Payment:** All Major Credit Cards
**Tee Times:** No
**Fee 9 Holes: Weekday:** $18
**Fee 18 Holes: Weekday:** $25
**Twilight Rates:** After 5pm
**Cart Rental:** $5/pull cart, $15/motorized
**Lessons:** No **Schools:** No
**Membership:** No
**Architect/Yr Open:** Robert Miller & Charles Rotollo/1979
**Other:**

**Weekend:** $18
**Weekend:** $25
**Discounts:** Senior $20/Junior $15
**Driving Range:** No
**Junior Golf:** No

| Tees | Holes | Yards | Par | USGA | Slope |
|------|-------|-------|-----|------|-------|
| BACK | | | | | |
| MIDDLE | 18 | 2650 | 57 | | |
| FRONT | | | | | |

COUPON

An 18-hole par 3, plus 2 long shots. Generally considered an "iron course," it provides a challenge for the experienced golfer and an excellent introduction for the beginner. A fun, walkable course. Located in the heart of the beautiful Southern Vermont Valley. Wednesday special: play 18 for the price of 9.

| | 1 | 2 | 3 | 4 | 5 | 6 | 7 | 8 | 9 |
|------|-----|-----|-----|-----|-----|-----|-----|-----|-----|
| PAR | 3 | 3 | 3 | 3 | 3 | 3 | 3 | 3 | 4 |
| YARDS | 190 | 90 | 115 | 130 | 155 | 90 | 115 | 130 | 255 |
| | 10 | 11 | 12 | 13 | 14 | 15 | 16 | 17 | 18 |
| PAR | 4 | 4 | 3 | 3 | 3 | 3 | 3 | 3 | 3 |
| YARDS | 350 | 285 | 105 | 120 | 120 | 90 | 105 | 90 | 115 |

**Directions:** Take I-91 to Exit 2 - Brattleboro. Get on Route 9 West towards Wilmington; right onto Route 100 North, then right onto E. Dover Road. Course is on the left.

# St. Johnsbury Country Club

Route 5
St. Johnsbury, VT (802) 748-9894
www.golfstjcc.com

**Club Pro:** Bryce Chaffee, PGA
**Payment:** Cash, Visa, MC, Amex, Disc
**Tee Times:** 1 week adv.
**Fee 9 Holes: Weekday:** $16
**Fee 18 Holes: Weekday:** $32
**Twilight Rates:** After 4pm
**Cart Rental:** $17pp/18, $12pp/9
**Lessons:** 3 lessons/$125 **Schools:** No
**Membership:** Yes
**Other:** Clubhouse / Snack Bar / Renovated Restaurant / Bar-Lounge

**Weekend:** $19
**Weekend:** $38
**Discounts:** Junior
**Driving Range:** $5/med., $3/sm.
**Junior Golf:** Yes
**Architect/Yr Open:** Willie Park Jr./1923

| Tees | Holes | Yards | Par | USGA | Slope |
|------|-------|-------|-----|------|-------|
| BACK | 18 | 6373 | 70 | 70.4 | 130 |
| MIDDLE | 18 | 5860 | 70 | 68.6 | 125 |
| FRONT | 18 | 5480 | 70 | 71.3 | 120 |

COUPON

Player Comments: "Great value." Front 9, wide open. Back 9, narrow and challenging. Lots of hills and blind shots. Not for the timid." Prices subject to change.

| | 1 | 2 | 3 | 4 | 5 | 6 | 7 | 8 | 9 |
|------|-----|-----|-----|-----|-----|-----|-----|-----|-----|
| PAR | 4 | 4 | 3 | 4 | 3 | 5 | 3 | 5 | 4 |
| YARDS | 314 | 363 | 168 | 434 | 232 | 578 | 188 | 473 | 434 |
| | 10 | 11 | 12 | 13 | 14 | 15 | 16 | 17 | 18 |
| PAR | 5 | 4 | 3 | 4 | 4 | 3 | 5 | 3 | 4 |
| YARDS | 496 | 385 | 176 | 398 | 395 | 195 | 575 | 203 | 366 |

**Directions:** I-91 North to Exit 23 (US Route 5); follow 3 miles. From I-91 South to Exit 22 to Route 5; follow 4 miles.

# Stamford Valley Country Club

NR 49 ▶

194 Phelene Lane (Route 9)
Stamford, VT  (802) 694-9144
www.stamfordvalleygolf.com

**Club Pro:** Mark Lawrence, Manager
**Payment:** Cash, Visa, MC
**Tee Times:** Recommended

| Tees | Holes | Yards | Par | USGA | Slope |
|------|-------|-------|-----|------|-------|
| BACK |  |  |  |  |  |
| MIDDLE | 9 | 2709 | 36 | 66.6 | 104 |
| FRONT |  |  |  |  |  |

**Fee 9 Holes: Weekday:** $14
**Fee 18 Holes: Weekday:** $20
**Twilight Rates:** No
**Cart Rental:** $12pp/18, $7pp/9
**Lessons:** No  **Schools:** No
**Membership:** Yes
**Other:** Full Restaurant

**Weekend:** $14
**Weekend:** $20
**Discounts:** None
**Driving Range:** No
**Junior Golf:** No
**Architect/Yr Open:** Stan & Leroy Lawrence/1964
**GPS:**

Great foliage and wonderful mountain views. Over 20 new bunkers and brand-new clubhouse with complete restaurant facility. A course for all ages.

|  | 1 | 2 | 3 | 4 | 5 | 6 | 7 | 8 | 9 |
|------|---|---|---|---|---|---|---|---|---|
| PAR | 4 | 4 | 4 | 5 | 4 | 4 | 3 | 4 | 4 |
| YARDS | 232 | 288 | 342 | 392 | 330 | 320 | 215 | 355 | 235 |
| PAR |  |  |  |  |  |  |  |  |  |
| YARDS |  |  |  |  |  |  |  |  |  |

**Directions:** Route 8 North (out of North Adams), about 5 miles over Stamford line.

# Stonehedge Golf Course

NR 50 ▶   VT

216 Squire Road
North Clarendon, VT
(802) 773-2666
www.stonehedgegolf.com

**Club Pro:** Chris Bendig, GM
**Payment:** Visa, MC, Cash, Check
**Tee Times:** Yes

| Tees | Holes | Yards | Par | USGA | Slope |
|------|-------|-------|-----|------|-------|
| BACK |  |  |  |  |  |
| MIDDLE | 9 | 1107 | 27 |  |  |
| FRONT |  |  |  |  |  |

**Fee 9 Holes: Weekday:** $11.50
**Fee 18 Holes: Weekday:** $15.50
**Twilight Rates:** No
**Cart Rental:** $9.50pp/18, $6pp/9
**Lessons:** Yes  **Schools:** No
**Membership:** No
**Other:** Snacks and Soft Drinks

**Weekend:** $12.50
**Weekend:** $17.50
**Discounts:** Senior Wednesdays
**Driving Range:** No
**Junior Golf:** No
**Architect/Yr Open:** Robert Matson/1995
**GPS:**

Challenging par 3 with pretty views — excellent greens, water and sand traps — easy course to walk. 10-play cards available. Foot golf available.

Forest/Lake

|  | 1 | 2 | 3 | 4 | 5 | 6 | 7 | 8 | 9 |
|------|---|---|---|---|---|---|---|---|---|
| PAR | 3 | 3 | 3 | 3 | 3 | 3 | 3 | 3 | 3 |
| YARDS | 153 | 84 | 181 | 152 | 86 | 77 | 180 | 93 | 101 |
| PAR |  |  |  |  |  |  |  |  |  |
| YARDS |  |  |  |  |  |  |  |  |  |

**Directions:** Located 3 miles South of Rutland (no interstate nearby) at the junction of Routes 7 and 103.

# Stowe Country Club

5781 Mountain Road
Stowe, VT (802) 253-4893
www.stowe.com

| Tees | Holes | Yards | Par | USGA | Slope |
|------|-------|-------|-----|------|-------|
| BACK | 18 | 6213 | 72 | 69.3 | 117 |
| MIDDLE | 18 | 5851 | 72 | 67.5 | 114 |
| FRONT | 18 | 5365 | 74 | 68.5 | 112 |

**Club Pro:** Dan Lehmann, PGA
**Payment:** Visa, MC, Amex, Disc
**Tee Times:** Anytime
**Fee 9 Holes: Weekday:** **Weekend:**
**Fee 18 Holes: Weekday:** $90-$105 w/cart **Weekend:** $90-$105 w/cart
**Twilight Rates:** After 2pm **Discounts:** None
**Cart Rental:** Included **Driving Range:** $5/lg bucket
**Lessons:** Yes **Schools:** Golf School **Junior Golf:** Yes
**Membership:** Yes **Architect/Yr Open:** Walter Barcomb/1950
**Other:** Clubhouse / Lockers / Showers / Restaurant / Bar/ Hotel / Beverage Cart

Player Comments: "Beautiful course. Friendly staff." "Great golf getaway." –FP
Excellent stay & play golf package. Open May - mid-October. Fees vary with season and time of day.

| | 1 | 2 | 3 | 4 | 5 | 6 | 7 | 8 | 9 |
|---|---|---|---|---|---|---|---|---|---|
| PAR | 5 | 3 | 5 | 3 | 4 | 5 | 4 | 3 | 4 |
| YARDS | 482 | 152 | 450 | 153 | 367 | 472 | 381 | 135 | 370 |
| | 10 | 11 | 12 | 13 | 14 | 15 | 16 | 17 | 18 |
| PAR | 3 | 5 | 4 | 4 | 5 | 3 | 4 | 4 | 4 |
| YARDS | 170 | 445 | 371 | 327 | 447 | 158 | 352 | 341 | 279 |

**Directions:** I-89 to Exit 10. Follow Route 100 for 10 miles to blinking light in center of Stowe Village, turn left onto Route 108. Turn right directly past Whiskers Restaurant onto Cape Cod Road. Course straight ahead.

# Stratton Mountain Golf Club ✪✪✪½ 52

Rural Route 1
Stratton Mountain, VT
(802) 297-4118
www.stratton.com

| Tees | Holes | Yards | Par | USGA | Slope |
|------|-------|-------|-----|------|-------|
| BACK | 27/18 | 6526 | 72 | 71.9 | 130 |
| MIDDLE | 27/18 | 6044 | 72 | 69.4 | 128 |
| FRONT | 27/18 | 5155 | 74 | 69.8 | 123 |

**Club Pro:** Matthew McPhillips
**Payment:** Most Major Credit Cards
**Tee Times:** Anytime
**Fee 9 Holes: Weekday:** $49-$59 w/cart **Weekend:** $69-$79 w/cart
**Fee 18 Holes: Wkdy:** $69-$79 (M-Th) w/cart **Wknd:** $89-$99 incl. cart F/S/S/H
**Twilight Rates:** After 4:30pm **Discounts:** Junior
**Cart Rental:** Cart included **Driving Range:** $7/lg., $4/sm.
**Lessons:** $50/half hour **Schools:** Yes **Junior Golf:** No
**Membership:** Yes **Architect/Yr Open:** Geoffrey Cornish/1964
**Other:** Clubhouse / Snack Bar / Restaurant / Bar-Lounge / Hotel

COUPON

Player Comments: "1st-class services really makes a golfer feel special." 27-hole complex. Cornish design features. Rates vary by season.

| | 1 | 2 | 3 | 4 | 5 | 6 | 7 | 8 | 9 |
|---|---|---|---|---|---|---|---|---|---|
| PAR | 4 | 4 | 4 | 3 | 5 | 4 | 3 | 5 | 4 |
| YARDS | 372 | 387 | 305 | 129 | 467 | 295 | 140 | 504 | 379 |
| | 10 | 11 | 12 | 13 | 14 | 15 | 16 | 17 | 18 |
| PAR | 4 | 4 | 4 | 3 | 4 | 5 | 3 | 4 | 5 |
| YARDS | 353 | 395 | 328 | 164 | 269 | 466 | 193 | 390 | 508 |

**Directions:** Take I-91 to Brattleboro exit, follow Route 30 East for 30 miles to Bondville; look for signs to Stratton Mountain.

# Sugarbush Resort Golf Club ✪✪✪✪ 53 ▶

1091 Golf Course Road
Warren, VT (802) 583-6725
www.sugarbush.com

| Tees | Holes | Yards | Par | USGA | Slope |
|------|-------|-------|-----|------|-------|
| BACK | 18 | 6464 | 72 | 71.7 | 128 |
| MIDDLE | 18 | 5922 | 70 | 69.0 | 122 |
| FRONT | 18 | 5231 | 72 | 70.5 | 129 |

**Club Pro:** R.J. Austin
**Payment:** Visa, MC, Amex, Disc, Cash
**Tee Times:** Yes
**Fee 9 Holes: Weekday:** **Weekend:**
**Fee 18 Holes: Weekday:** $90 (7am-2pm) **Weekend:** $100 (7am-2pm)
**Twilight Rates:** After 2pm
**Discounts:** Children 10 and under free w/adult
**Cart Rental:** Included in fee **Driving Range:** Yes
**Lessons:** Yes **Schools:** No **Junior Golf:** Yes
**Membership:** Yes **Architect/Yr Open:** Robert Trent Jones Sr./1962
**Other:** Restaurant / Clubhouse / Hotel / Bar-Lounge / Snack Bar / Showers / Lodging Partner
**GPS:** Yes

Challenging layout set in the Green Mountains. "Breathtaking views and dramatic elevation changes with a variety of blind shots and fun shots. A nice place to visit." –FP

| | 1 | 2 | 3 | 4 | 5 | 6 | 7 | 8 | 9 |
|---|---|---|---|---|---|---|---|---|---|
| PAR | 4 | 4/5 | 4 | 4 | 3 | 4 | 4 | 3 | 4 |
| YARDS | 322 | 372/510 | 396 | 361 | 164 | 374 | 433 | 166 | 329 |
| | 10 | 11 | 12 | 13 | 14 | 15 | 16 | 17 | 18 |
| PAR | 5 | 3 | 4 | 4 | 5 | 4 | 3 | 4 | 4 |
| YARDS | 504 | 154 | 395 | 325 | 449 | 352 | 157 | 329 | 329 |

**Directions:** I-89 North to Exit 10 - 100 South, Sugarbush Access Road. Left onto Golf Course Road. One mile on left.

# Tater Hill Golf Club ✪✪✪ 54 ▶ VT

6802 Popple Dungeon Road
North Windham, VT
(802) 875-2517
www.taterhillgolfclub.com

| Tees | Holes | Yards | Par | USGA | Slope |
|------|-------|-------|-----|------|-------|
| BACK | 18 | 6404 | 71 | 71.7 | 131 |
| MIDDLE | 18 | 5337 | 71 | 65.7 | 117 |
| FRONT | 18 | 4879 | 71 | 68.1 | 113 |

**Club Pro:** John Pawlak, PGA
**Payment:** Visa, MC, Amex
**Tee Times:** 7 days adv.
**Fee 9 Holes: Weekday:** Call for rates **Weekend:** Call for rates
**Fee 18 Holes: Weekday:** $49 **Weekend:** $59 F/S/S
**Twilight Rates:** After 2pm **Discounts:** Junior
**Cart Rental:** $22pp/18, $11pp/9 **Driving Range:** $5/bucket
**Lessons:** Yes **Schools:** No **Junior Golf:** Yes
**Membership:** Yes **Architect/Yr Open:** Don Warner/1967
**Other:** Clubhouse / Bar-Lounge / Restaurant **GPS:**

Sister course to Okemo. Beautiful, scenic views. Better every year. "Very well maintained, greens are fantastic, terrific staff." –KL

| | 1 | 2 | 3 | 4 | 5 | 6 | 7 | 8 | 9 |
|---|---|---|---|---|---|---|---|---|---|
| PAR | 3 | 4 | 4 | 4 | 4 | 3 | 5 | 4 | 4 |
| YARDS | 161 | 335 | 347 | 292 | 338 | 150 | 462 | 295 | 345 |
| | 10 | 11 | 12 | 13 | 14 | 15 | 16 | 17 | 18 |
| PAR | 5 | 3 | 3 | 4 | 3 | 5 | 4 | 4 | 5 |
| YARDS | 395 | 130 | 159 | 320 | 95 | 405 | 371 | 274 | 463 |

**Directions:** I-91 to Exit 6; take left onto Route 103, turns into 11 West; 7 miles outside Chester look for signs to course.

# West Bolton Golf Club

**5161A Stage Road, West Bolton**
**Jericho, VT (802) 434-4321**
www.westboltongolfclub.com

| Tees | Holes | Yards | Par | USGA | Slope |
|---|---|---|---|---|---|
| BACK | | | | | |
| MIDDLE | 18 | 5761 | 72 | 66.8 | 115 |
| FRONT | 18 | 5165 | 72 | 72.5 | 111 |

**Club Pro:** Ken Stavisky
**Payment:** Visa, MC, Cash, Check
**Tee Times:** 1 week adv.
**Fee 9 Holes: Weekday:** $20    **Weekend:** $20
**Fee 18 Holes: Weekday:** $27    **Weekend:** $27
**Twilight Rates:** After 3pm    **Discounts:** Srs., Jrs., Ladies
**Cart Rental:** $14pp/18, $7pp/9    **Driving Range:** No
**Lessons:** Yes **Schools:** Junior    **Junior Golf:** Yes
**Membership:** Yes    **Architect/Yr Open:** Ken Wheeler/1983
**Other:** Clubhouse / Snack Bar    **GPS:**

Unique 18-hole course nestled in the Green Mountains. The fairway trees are small, but the mountains surrounding the course are grand.

| | 1 | 2 | 3 | 4 | 5 | 6 | 7 | 8 | 9 |
|---|---|---|---|---|---|---|---|---|---|
| PAR | 4 | 5 | 3 | 4 | 4 | 3 | 4 | 4 | 4 |
| YARDS | 303 | 481 | 149 | 248 | 353 | 191 | 329 | 359 | 295 |
| | 10 | 11 | 12 | 13 | 14 | 15 | 16 | 17 | 18 |
| PAR | 3 | 5 | 4 | 5 | 3 | 5 | 4 | 4 | 4 |
| YARDS | 128 | 430 | 392 | 451 | 180 | 458 | 273 | 323 | 418 |

**Directions:** I-89 to Exit 11 toward Richmond. Left at light (Four Corners). Go about 7 miles and take a right at the West Bolton Golf Course sign. Continue for 4 miles.

# White River Golf Club  NR  56

**3070 Route 100**
**Rochester, VT (802) 767-4653**
www.whiterivergolf.com

| Tees | Holes | Yards | Par | USGA | Slope |
|---|---|---|---|---|---|
| BACK | 9 | 2936 | 36 | 65.6 | 115 |
| MIDDLE | 9 | 2598 | 34 | 64.6 | 112 |
| FRONT | 9 | 2238 | 32 | 60.2 | 104 |

**Club Pro:** Perer McGowan, Manager
**Payment:** Cash, MC, Visa
**Tee Times:** Recommended
**Fee 9 Holes: Weekday:** $21    **Weekend:** $21
**Fee 18 Holes: Weekday:** $30    **Weekend:** $30
**Twilight Rates:** No    **Discounts:** No
**Cart Rental:** $10pp/18    **Driving Range:** No
**Lessons:** No **Schools:** No    **Junior Golf:** No
**Membership:** Yes    **Architect/Yr Open:** Peter McGowan/1972
**Other:** Clubhouse / Bar-Lounge / Snack Bar    **GPS:**

*COUPON*

Redesigned in 2012, longer and more challenging. 9-hole panoramic from every hole. One of the most scenic golf courses in New England. Recent design changes have made a true test of skill for the experienced golfer while still appealing to the novice golfer. Open May - October. 10-play ticket available.

| | 1 | 2 | 3 | 4 | 5 | 6 | 7 | 8 | 9 |
|---|---|---|---|---|---|---|---|---|---|
| PAR | 3 | 5 | 5 | 3 | 5 | 4 | 4 | 3 | 4 |
| YARDS | 180 | 540 | 475 | 195 | 465 | 266 | 340 | 160 | 310 |
| PAR | | | | | | | | | |
| YARDS | | | | | | | | | |

**Directions:** I-89 to Route 107 West to Route 100 North. Course is 10 miles north on Route 100. Approximately halfway between Killington and Sugarbush.

# Wilcox Cove Golf Course

3 Camp Vermont Court (Highway 314)
Grand Isle, VT  (802) 372-8343
www.wilcoxcove.com

**Club Pro:** Mary Heins, GM
**Payment:** Cash, Check
**Tee Times:** No
**Fee  9 Holes: Weekday:** $15
**Fee 18 Holes: Weekday:** $15
**Twilight Rates:** After 6pm
**Cart Rental:** $3/pull
**Lessons:** No  **Schools:** No
**Membership:** Yes
**Other:** No

| Tees | Holes | Yards | Par | USGA | Slope |
|------|-------|-------|-----|------|-------|
| BACK | | | | | |
| MIDDLE | 9 | 1732 | 32 | | |
| FRONT | | | | | |

**Weekend:** $18
**Weekend:** $18
**Discounts:** None
**Driving Range:** No
**Junior Golf:**
**Architect/Yr Open:** Michael Hurzdan/1947
**GPS:**

An executive-type course on the West shore of Grand Isle, looking over Lake Champlain to the Adirondack Mountains of New York. A fairly level course. Twilight weekend rates.

| | 1 | 2 | 3 | 4 | 5 | 6 | 7 | 8 | 9 |
|---|---|---|---|---|---|---|---|---|---|
| **PAR** | 4 | 4 | 4 | 3 | 4 | 3 | 4 | 3 | 3 |
| **YARDS** | 240 | 210 | 254 | 120 | 245 | 190 | 185 | 193 | 95 |
| **PAR** | | | | | | | | | |
| **YARDS** | | | | | | | | | |

**Directions:** I-89 to Exit 17 (Route 2 North). Take Route 314 past Grand Isle ferry.

# Williston Golf Club

424 Golf Course Road
Williston, VT  (802) 878-3747
www.willistongolfclub.com

**Club Pro:** Todd Trono, PGA
**Payment:** Visa, MC, Disc
**Tee Times:** Weekends and Holidays
**Fee  9 Holes: Weekday:**
**Fee 18 Holes: Weekday:** $32
**Twilight Rates:** After 4pm
**Cart Rental:** $18pp/18, $9pp/9
**Lessons:** No  **Schools:** Yes
**Membership:** Yes
**Other:** Resturant / Clubhouse / Bar-Lounge

| Tees | Holes | Yards | Par | USGA | Slope |
|------|-------|-------|-----|------|-------|
| BACK | 18 | 6621 | 69 | N/R | N/R |
| MIDDLE | 18 | 5262 | 69 | 66.6 | 113 |
| FRONT | 18 | 4716 | 71 | 64 | 106 |

**Weekend:**
**Weekend:** $35
**Discounts:** None
**Driving Range:** Nearby
**Junior Golf:** Yes
**Architect/Yr Open:** Ben Murray/1927
**GPS:** Yes

Player Comments: "Excellent greens, great variety of holes, wonderful views of the surrounding mountains, good value and extremely friendly staff." –JD
Open May - November 1.

| | 1 | 2 | 3 | 4 | 5 | 6 | 7 | 8 | 9 |
|---|---|---|---|---|---|---|---|---|---|
| **PAR** | 4 | 4 | 4 | 4 | 4 | 3 | 4 | 4 | 5 |
| **YARDS** | 316 | 390 | 289 | 272 | 260 | 184 | 267 | 382 | 445 |
| | **10** | **11** | **12** | **13** | **14** | **15** | **16** | **17** | **18** |
| **PAR** | 4 | 3 | 3 | 4 | 4 | 3 | 3 | 4 | 5 |
| **YARDS** | 325 | 160 | 212 | 254 | 395 | 151 | 90 | 360 | 510 |

**Directions:** I-89 to Exit 11 or 12; Route 2 East to North Williston Road. Course is ½ mile on right. 7 miles east of Burlington, Vermont.

# Woodbury Golf Course

2120 East Hill Road
South Woodbury, VT (802) 456-7421
www.woodburygolf.com

**Club Pro:** Darwin Thompson
**Payment:** Visa, MC, Checks
**Tee Times:** (802) 456-1250
**Fee 9 Holes: Weekday:** $11
**Fee 18 Holes: Weekday:** $16.50
**Twilight Rates:** No
**Discounts:** Juniors 12 and under - free w/paying adult
**Cart Rental:** $10/9 per cart
**Lessons:** No **Schools:** No
**Membership:** Yes

| Tees | Holes | Yards | Par | USGA | Slope |
|------|-------|-------|-----|------|-------|
| BACK | | | | | |
| MIDDLE | 9 | 1264 | 27 | | |
| FRONT | | | | | |

**Weekend:** $12 (tax included)
**Weekend:** $18 (tax included)
**Driving Range:** No
**Junior Golf:**
**Architect/Yr Open:** Thompson Family/2004

COUPON

Great for your short game or a quick round with the family.

| | 1 | 2 | 3 | 4 | 5 | 6 | 7 | 8 | 9 |
|------|-----|-----|-----|-----|-----|-----|-----|-----|-----|
| PAR | 3 | 3 | 3 | 3 | 3 | 3 | 3 | 3 | 3 |
| YARDS | 120 | 145 | 128 | 185 | 147 | 118 | 125 | 129 | 167 |
| PAR | | | | | | | | | |
| YARDS | | | | | | | | | |

**Directions:** I-89 to Route 2 East. Take Route 14 North. Right onto East Hill Road in South Woodbury. Course is 2 miles on right.

# Woodstock Inn & Resort

❂❂❂¹/₂ 60 ▶

14 The Green
Route 106 South, Woodstock, VT
(802) 457-6674
www.woodstockinn.com

**Club Pro:** Jim Gunnare
**Payment:** Cash, MC, Visa, Amex
**Tee Times:** Yes
**Fee 9 Holes: Weekday:** $59/inc. cart
**Fee 18 Holes: Weekday:** $89/inc. cart
**Twilight Rates:** After 3pm
**Cart Rental:** $20pp/18
**Lessons:** $50/half hour **Schools:** Jr. & Sr.
**Membership:** Yes
**Other:** Clubhouse / Lockers / Showers / Restaurant / Bar-Lounge / Hotel / Snack Bar

| Tees | Holes | Yards | Par | USGA | Slope |
|------|-------|-------|-----|------|-------|
| BACK | 18 | 6052 | 70 | 69.7 | 123 |
| MIDDLE | 18 | 5619 | 70 | 68.0 | 117 |
| FRONT | 18 | 4924 | 71 | 69.0 | 113 |

**Weekend:** $79/inc. cart
**Weekend:** $125/inc. cart
**Discounts:** None
**Driving Range:** $8/lg, $5/sm bucket
**Junior Golf:** Yes
**Architect/Yr Open:** William H. Tucker/1895

Renovated clubhouse restaurant, ballroom, dining room, and new deck. Hosting annual Northeast PGA seniors championship. Walker friendly. Updated by Robert Trent Jones in 1962. Driving range with new tee boxes.

| | 1 | 2 | 3 | 4 | 5 | 6 | 7 | 8 | 9 |
|------|-----|-----|-----|-----|-----|-----|-----|-----|-----|
| PAR | 5 | 3 | 4 | 4 | 3 | 5 | 3 | 4 | 4 |
| YARDS | 465 | 162 | 346 | 382 | 134 | 503 | 162 | 356 | 386 |
| | 10 | 11 | 12 | 13 | 14 | 15 | 16 | 17 | 18 |
| PAR | 5 | 3 | 4 | 3 | 4 | 3 | 5 | 4 | 4 |
| YARDS | 414 | 131 | 381 | 150 | 272 | 144 | 520 | 315 | 396 |

**Directions:** I-89 to Exit 1 (VT), Route 4 West to Woodstock - South on Route 106 (1 mile).

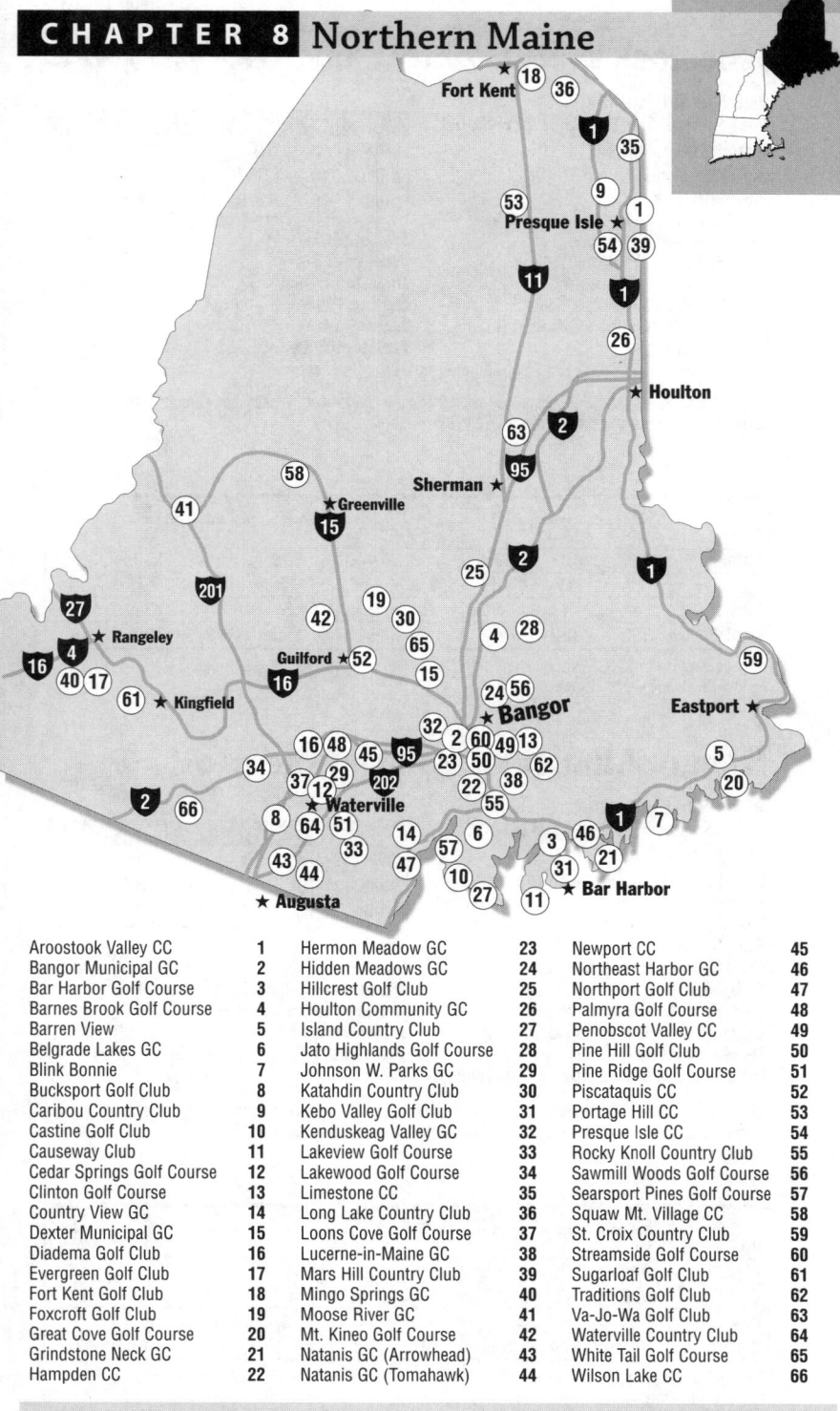

| | | | | | | |
|---|---|---|---|---|---|---|
| Aroostook Valley CC | 1 | Hermon Meadow GC | 23 | Newport CC | 45 |
| Bangor Municipal GC | 2 | Hidden Meadows GC | 24 | Northeast Harbor GC | 46 |
| Bar Harbor Golf Course | 3 | Hillcrest Golf Club | 25 | Northport Golf Club | 47 |
| Barnes Brook Golf Course | 4 | Houlton Community GC | 26 | Palmyra Golf Course | 48 |
| Barren View | 5 | Island Country Club | 27 | Penobscot Valley CC | 49 |
| Belgrade Lakes GC | 6 | Jato Highlands Golf Course | 28 | Pine Hill Golf Club | 50 |
| Blink Bonnie | 7 | Johnson W. Parks GC | 29 | Pine Ridge Golf Course | 51 |
| Bucksport Golf Club | 8 | Katahdin Country Club | 30 | Piscataquis CC | 52 |
| Caribou Country Club | 9 | Kebo Valley Golf Club | 31 | Portage Hill CC | 53 |
| Castine Golf Club | 10 | Kenduskeag Valley GC | 32 | Presque Isle CC | 54 |
| Causeway Club | 11 | Lakeview Golf Course | 33 | Rocky Knoll Country Club | 55 |
| Cedar Springs Golf Course | 12 | Lakewood Golf Course | 34 | Sawmill Woods Golf Course | 56 |
| Clinton Golf Course | 13 | Limestone CC | 35 | Searsport Pines Golf Course | 57 |
| Country View GC | 14 | Long Lake Country Club | 36 | Squaw Mt. Village CC | 58 |
| Dexter Municipal GC | 15 | Loons Cove Golf Course | 37 | St. Croix Country Club | 59 |
| Diadema Golf Club | 16 | Lucerne-in-Maine GC | 38 | Streamside Golf Course | 60 |
| Evergreen Golf Club | 17 | Mars Hill Country Club | 39 | Sugarloaf Golf Club | 61 |
| Fort Kent Golf Club | 18 | Mingo Springs GC | 40 | Traditions Golf Club | 62 |
| Foxcroft Golf Club | 19 | Moose River GC | 41 | Va-Jo-Wa Golf Club | 63 |
| Great Cove Golf Course | 20 | Mt. Kineo Golf Course | 42 | Waterville Country Club | 64 |
| Grindstone Neck GC | 21 | Natanis GC (Arrowhead) | 43 | White Tail Golf Course | 65 |
| Hampden CC | 22 | Natanis GC (Tomahawk) | 44 | Wilson Lake CC | 66 |

**KEY TO THE STAR RATINGS:**
5✪ = Outstanding  4✪ = Excellent  3✪ = Very Good  2✪ = Good  1✪ = Average  NR = Not Rated

# Aroostook Valley Country Club ✪✪✪½  1▶

235 Russell Road
Fort Fairfield, ME (207) 476-8083
www.avcc.ca
**Club Pro:** Steven Leitch, CPGA
**Payment:** Visa, MC
**Tee Times:** 7 days adv.

| Tees | Holes | Yards | Par | USGA | Slope |
|------|-------|-------|-----|------|-------|
| BACK | 18 | 6304 | 72 | 69.6 | 117 |
| MIDDLE | 18 | 5957 | 72 | 68.4 | 113 |
| FRONT | 18 | 5373 | 72 | 74.1 | 119 |

**Fee  9 Holes: Weekday:** $23
**Fee 18 Holes: Weekday:** $45
**Twilight Rates:** After 2pm
**Cart Rental:** $17pp/18, $8.50pp/9
**Lessons:** $25/half hour  **Schools:** No
**Membership:** Yes
**Other:** Clubhouse / Snack Bar / Bar-Lounge / Lockers / Showers

**Weekend:** $23
**Weekend:** $45
**Discounts:** Junior $20
**Driving Range:** $5/bucket
**Junior Golf:** Yes
**Architect/Yr Open:** Howard K. Watson/1927

COUPON

Very beautiful course; difficult inclines on back 9 make it challenging. White silica sand in bunkers.
"Great conditions and beautiful holes make this a must-play." –DW

|  | 1 | 2 | 3 | 4 | 5 | 6 | 7 | 8 | 9 |
|------|----|----|----|----|----|----|----|----|----|
| PAR | 4 | 4 | 5 | 3 | 5 | 4 | 4 | 3 | 4 |
| YARDS | 375 | 327 | 478 | 132 | 440 | 308 | 334 | 139 | 365 |
|  | 10 | 11 | 12 | 13 | 14 | 15 | 16 | 17 | 18 |
| PAR | 4 | 4 | 5 | 3 | 5 | 3 | 4 | 3 | 5 |
| YARDS | 382 | 322 | 489 | 189 | 510 | 156 | 383 | 134 | 494 |

**Directions:** I-95 to last exit; take left onto Route 1 to Fort Fairfield, cross bridge. Take first right. Follow Russell Road to course.

# Bangor Municipal Golf Course ✪✪½  2▶

278 Webster Avenue
Bangor, ME (207) 941-0232
www.bangorgc.com
**Club Pro:** Rob Jarvis, PGA
**Payment:** Cash, Visa, MC, Disc, Amex, Check
**Tee Times:** Weekends, Holidays

| Tees | Holes | Yards | Par | USGA | Slope |
|------|-------|-------|-----|------|-------|
| BACK | 27/18 | 6335 | 71 | 70.8 | 119 |
| MIDDLE | 27/18 | 5833 | 71 | 69.6 | 115 |
| FRONT | 27/18 | 5173 | 71 | 69.9 | 116 |

**Fee  9 Holes: Weekday:** $16
**Fee 18 Holes: Weekday:** $32
**Twilight Rates:** After 4pm
**Cart Rental:** $16pp/18, $8pp/9
**Lessons:** $45/45 min.  **Schools:** Yes
**Membership:** Yes
**Other:** Restaurant / Clubhouse / Bar-Lounge

**Weekend:** $16
**Weekend:** $32
**Discounts:** Senior, Junior, Student
**Driving Range:** $4/bucket
**Junior Golf:** Yes
**Architect/Yr Open:** Geoffrey Cornish/1964
**GPS:**

COUPON

27 holes. Hosted 1978 National Public Links Championship. Very playable golf course for all levels of play. Nice short game practice area. Audubon certified sanctuary as of 2013.

|  | 1 | 2 | 3 | 4 | 5 | 6 | 7 | 8 | 9 |
|------|----|----|----|----|----|----|----|----|----|
| PAR | 4 | 4 | 3 | 5 | 4 | 3 | 4 | 4 | 4 |
| YARDS | 321 | 375 | 153 | 485 | 320 | 169 | 377 | 384 | 368 |
|  | 10 | 11 | 12 | 13 | 14 | 15 | 16 | 17 | 18 |
| PAR | 4 | 3 | 4 | 4 | 4 | 5 | 3 | 4 | 5 |
| YARDS | 342 | 174 | 369 | 304 | 360 | 415 | 147 | 343 | 427 |

**Directions:** I-95 to Exit 183 (Hammond Street). Turn right and then immediate right onto Norway Road. Go to stop sign and turn right – ½ mile on left.

# Bar Harbor Golf Course ✪✪✪

3 ▶

51 Jordan River Road, Route 204
Trenton, ME  (207) 667-7505
www.barharborgolfcourse.com

| Tees | Holes | Yards | Par | USGA | Slope |
|------|-------|-------|-----|------|-------|
| BACK | 18 | 6680 | 71 | 71.1 | 128 |
| MIDDLE | 18 | 6450 | 71 | 70.3 | 127 |
| FRONT | 18 | 5428 | 73 | 70.5 | 125 |

**Club Pro:** Charles Crowley, GM
**Payment:** Visa, MC
**Tee Times:** No
**Fee  9 Holes: Weekday:** $25
**Fee 18 Holes: Weekday:** $40
**Twilight Rates:** No
**Cart Rental:** $20pp/18, $10pp/9
**Lessons:** No  **Schools:** No
**Membership:** Yes
**Other:** Clubhouse / Snack Bar / Bar-Lounge

**Weekend:** $25
**Weekend:** $40
**Discounts:** None
**Driving Range:** No
**Junior Golf:** No
**Architect/Yr Open:** Philip Wogan/1967
**GPS:** Yes

COUPON

Links-style tract was designed by Phil Wogan. Located adjacent to the ocean, it is challenging and picturesque. Its wide-open fairways overlook the scenic Jordan River and the majestic mountains of Acadia National Park. A perfect setting for 18 challenging holes of golf.

| | 1 | 2 | 3 | 4 | 5 | 6 | 7 | 8 | 9 |
|---|---|---|---|---|---|---|---|---|---|
| PAR | 4 | 4 | 5 | 3 | 4 | 4 | 4 | 3 | 4 |
| YARDS | 427 | 388 | 520 | 156 | 402 | 408 | 368 | 172 | 343 |
| | 10 | 11 | 12 | 13 | 14 | 15 | 16 | 17 | 18 |
| PAR | 4 | 3 | 4 | 5 | 4 | 4 | 4 | 3 | 5 |
| YARDS | 428 | 155 | 295 | 589 | 374 | 318 | 405 | 158 | 544 |

**Directions:** Route 3 toward Bar Harbor. Course is located at intersection of Route 3 and Route 204 in Trenton.

# Barnes Brook Golf Course ✪✪

4 ▶

1886 Main Road (Route 2)
West Enfield, ME  (207) 732-3006
www.barnesbrookgolfandski.com

| Tees | Holes | Yards | Par | USGA | Slope |
|------|-------|-------|-----|------|-------|
| BACK | 9 | 3100 | 36 | 68.4 | 127 |
| MIDDLE | 9 | 2897 | 36 | 67.0 | 119 |
| FRONT | 9 | 2625 | 36 | 63.8 | 109 |

**Club Pro:** Michael Clendenning
**Payment:** Cash, Visa, MC, Disc, Amex
**Tee Times:** No
**Fee  9 Holes: Weekday:** $15
**Fee 18 Holes: Weekday:** $22
**Twilight Rates:** No
**Cart Rental:** $15/18, $10/9 per cart
**Lessons:** Yes  **Schools:**
**Membership:** Yes
**Other:** Full Swing Indoor Golf Facility / Cross Country Ski Center

**Weekend:** $15
**Weekend:** $22
**Discounts:** Junior
**Driving Range:** Yes
**Junior Golf:** Yes
**Architect/Yr Open:** Henry & James Ploude/1964

COUPON

Recently rebuilt all bunkers and overseeded fairways.  Expanded greens.  Family friendly, Home of the Maine Junior Golf Club.  Relatively easy to walk.  Attractions include those of Lincoln Lakes area.  Under new ownership.

| | 1 | 2 | 3 | 4 | 5 | 6 | 7 | 8 | 9 |
|---|---|---|---|---|---|---|---|---|---|
| PAR | 5 | 3 | 4 | 4 | 4 | 5 | 3 | 4 | 4 |
| YARDS | 490 | 172 | 288 | 238 | 355 | 450 | 156 | 366 | 382 |
| PAR | | | | | | | | | |
| YARDS | | | | | | | | | |

**Directions:** I-95 to Exit 217, go right. Go ¾ of a mile to stop sign. Take a right. Go ¾ of a mile to stop sign. Take left on Route 2. Go 4 miles, course is located off Route 2 on right.

# Barren View Golf Course  ✪✪

**1354 Route 1**
**Jonesboro, ME  (207) 434-6531**
www.barrenviewgc.com

**Club Pro:** Larry Espling, Manager
**Payment:**
**Tee Times:**

| Tees | Holes | Yards | Par | USGA | Slope |
|------|-------|-------|-----|------|-------|
| BACK | 9 | 2811 | 35 | 67.0 | 105 |
| MIDDLE | 9 | 2613 | 35 | 65.6 | 102 |
| FRONT | 9 | 2280 | 35 | 65.6 | 105 |

**Fee  9 Holes: Weekday:** $15   **Weekend:** $15
**Fee 18 Holes: Weekday:** $25   **Weekend:** $25
**Twilight Rates:** No   **Discounts:** Jr 12 and under - $10
**Cart Rental:** $18pp/18, $13pp/9   **Driving Range:** $4/bucket
**Lessons:** No  **Schools:** No   **Junior Golf:**
**Membership:** Yes   **Architect/Yr:** Brad Prout & Lenny Espling/2003
**Other:**   **GPS:**

ᶜᵒᵁᵖᵒₙ

Links-style course for all levels. "The course features expansive views of blueberry barrens. A hidden gem." –DW

| | 1 | 2 | 3 | 4 | 5 | 6 | 7 | 8 | 9 |
|---|---|---|---|---|---|---|---|---|---|
| PAR | 4 | 3 | 5 | 3 | 3 | 4 | 4 | 4 | 5 |
| YARDS | 369 | 129 | 406 | 201 | 143 | 280 | 292 | 361 | 430 |
| | 10 | 11 | 12 | 13 | 14 | 15 | 16 | 17 | 18 |
| PAR | 4 | 3 | 5 | 3 | 3 | 4 | 4 | 4 | 5 |
| YARDS | 379 | 159 | 475 | 212 | 154 | 295 | 302 | 367 | 468 |

**Directions:** I-95 North to I-395 East to Route 1A. Exit toward Bar Harbor/Ellsworth. Take Route 1 out of Ellsworth toward Machias. Course is on right.

# Belgrade Lakes Golf Club  ✪✪✪✪✪

**46 Clubhouse Drive**
**Belgrade Lakes, ME  (207) 495-GOLF**
www.belgradelakesgolf.com

**Club Pro:** Andy Sibald
**Payment:** Visa, MC, Amex
**Tee Times:**

| Tees | Holes | Yards | Par | USGA | Slope |
|------|-------|-------|-----|------|-------|
| BACK | 18 | 6723 | 71 | 72.2 | 135 |
| MIDDLE | 18 | 6285 | 71 | 69.9 | 131 |
| FRONT | 18 | 5168 | 71 | 64.1 | 126 |

**Fee  9 Holes: Weekday:** $85 w/cart after 1pm   **Weekend:** $75 w/cart after 1pm
**Fee 18 Holes: Weekday:** $100 (July)   **Weekend:** $100 (July)
  $125 (Aug.-Sept. 15)   $125 (Aug.-Sept. 15)
**Twilight Rates:** No   **Discounts:** None
**Cart Rental:** $30pp/18   **Driving Range:** Hitting net
**Lessons:** Yes  **Schools:** No   **Junior Golf:** Yes
**Membership:** No   **Architect/Yr Open:** Clive Clark/1997
**Other:** Snack Bar   **GPS:** Yes

Improvements: enlarged and lengthened several tees. Walking encouraged. Caddies available for a fee plus tip. *Golf Magazine* 'Top 100 Courses You Can Play.'
Player Comments: "Every hole different and spectacularly beautiful."

| | 1 | 2 | 3 | 4 | 5 | 6 | 7 | 8 | 9 |
|---|---|---|---|---|---|---|---|---|---|
| PAR | 4 | 3 | 5 | 4 | 3 | 5 | 4 | 3 | 4 |
| YARDS | 424 | 156 | 450 | 424 | 161 | 485 | 384 | 186 | 376 |
| | 10 | 11 | 12 | 13 | 14 | 15 | 16 | 17 | 18 |
| PAR | 4 | 4 | 5 | 3 | 4 | 4 | 5 | 3 | 4 |
| YARDS | 346 | 395 | 568 | 203 | 344 | 311 | 530 | 171 | 371 |

**Directions:** I-95 to Exit 112B. Turn right onto Route 27. Go for 12 miles to town of Belgrade Lakes. Turn left at the Sunset Grille onto West Road. Course is ¼ mile on left.

# Blink Bonnie Golf Links

✪✪½ **7** ▶

185 East Side Road
Sorrento, ME (207) 422-3930
www.sorrentovia.org

| Tees | Holes | Yards | Par | USGA | Slope |
|------|-------|-------|-----|------|-------|
| BACK | | | | | |
| MIDDLE | 9 | 2520 | 36 | 65 | 112 |
| FRONT | | | | | |

**Club Pro:**
**Payment:** Cash or Check
**Tee Times:**
**Fee 9 Holes: Weekday:** $25 all day
**Fee 18 Holes: Weekday:** $25 all day
**Twilight Rates:** No
**Cart Rental:** $2/pull
**Lessons:** No **Schools:**
**Membership:** Yes
**Other:**

**Weekend:** $30 all day
**Weekend:** $30 all day
**Discounts:** None
**Driving Range:** No
**Junior Golf:**
**Architect/Yr Open:** 1916
**GPS:**

Player Comments: "Undiscovered gem. Breathtaking views, right on the ocean." Sorrento Village Improvement Association Yacht Club members only Friday morning until noon. Great for a quick 9.

| | 1 | 2 | 3 | 4 | 5 | 6 | 7 | 8 | 9 |
|------|-----|-----|-----|-----|-----|-----|-----|-----|-----|
| PAR | 4 | 4 | 3 | 5 | 5 | 4 | 3 | 4 | 4 |
| YARDS | 350 | 270 | 180 | 510 | 490 | 310 | 120 | 290 | 330 |
| PAR | | | | | | | | | |
| YARDS | | | | | | | | | |

**Directions:** 48 miles from Bangor. Route Alternate 1 to Ellsworth (23 miles). Stay on Route 1 to Hancock. Then in Sullivan, go right on Route 185 (East Side Road) and proceed 2 miles. Course is on left.

# Bucksport Golf Club

✪✪½ **8** ▶

397 State Route 46
Bucksport, ME (207) 469-7612
www.bucksportgolfclub.com

| Tees | Holes | Yards | Par | USGA | Slope |
|------|-------|-------|-----|------|-------|
| BACK | 9 | 3890 | 37 | 72.5 | |
| MIDDLE | 9 | 3373 | 37 | 72.5 | 136 |
| FRONT | 9 | 5972 | 74 | 72.2 | 128 |

**Club Pro:** Wayne Hand, PGA
**Payment:** Visa, MC
**Tee Times:** No
**Fee 9 Holes: Weekday:** $20
**Fee 18 Holes: Weekday:** $30
**Twilight Rates:** No
**Cart Rental:** $70pp/18, $12pp/9
**Lessons:** Yes **Schools:** No
**Membership:** Yes
**Other:** Bar-Lounge / Snack Bar / Lockers / Showers
**GPS:** Yes

**Weekend:** $20
**Weekend:** $30
**Discounts:** Junior
**Driving Range:** $5/lg., $3.50/sm.
**Junior Golf:** Yes
**Architect/Yr Open:** Phil Wogan/1967

 COUPON

9 holes with 2 sets of tees — 6780 yards, par 74, when you play both. Natural state of land emphasized in design. Golf specials: $70/18 for 2 people with cart; $50/9 for 2 people with cart.

| | 1 | 2 | 3 | 4 | 5 | 6 | 7 | 8 | 9 |
|------|-----|-----|-----|-----|-----|-----|-----|-----|-----|
| PAR | 4 | 5 | 3 | 4 | 5 | 3 | 4 | 4 | 5 |
| YARDS | 330 | 500 | 147 | 407 | 504 | 163 | 408 | 354 | 560 |
| PAR | | | | | | | | | |
| YARDS | | | | | | | | | |

**Directions:** From Augusta: Route 3 to Belfast. Route 1 North to Bucksport. From Bangor: take Route 1A to Route 46. Course is 3 miles from Downtown Bucksport.

**N**
**ME**

# Caribou Country Club

✪½  9

723 Sweden Street
Caribou, ME (207) 493-3933
www.caribougolf.com

Club Pro: Jeff Jose
Payment: Visa, MC, Amex, Disc
Tee Times: No

| Tees | Holes | Yards | Par | USGA | Slope |
|------|-------|-------|-----|------|-------|
| BACK | 9 | 3366 | 36 | 71.6 | 123 |
| MIDDLE | 9 | 3160 | 36 | 69.0 | 124 |
| FRONT | 9 | 3065 | 36 | 68.4 | 114 |

Fee 9 Holes: Weekday: $15
Fee 18 Holes: Weekday: $22
Twilight Rates: No
Cart Rental: $15pp/18, $10pp/9
Lessons: Yes  Schools: No
Membership: Yes
Other: Restaurant / Clubhouse / Bar-Lounge / Snack Bar / Lockers / Showers

Weekend: $15
Weekend: $22
Discounts: Junior memberships
Driving Range: $7/lg, $3/sm bucket
Junior Golf: Yes
Architect/Yr Open: Geoffrey Cornish/1970

COUPON

"Separate tee boxes carefully constructed to give the feel of an 18 hole course." –MH
The course has a beautiful log cabin clubhouse. Support "Tee it forward" program. Open May 1 - October 15.

| | 1 | 2 | 3 | 4 | 5 | 6 | 7 | 8 | 9 |
|------|-----|-----|-----|-----|-----|-----|-----|-----|-----|
| PAR | 4 | 4 | 3 | 5 | 4 | 4 | 3 | 5 | 4 |
| YARDS | 340 | 320 | 195 | 470 | 360 | 330 | 150 | 530 | 370 |
| PAR | | | | | | | | | |
| YARDS | | | | | | | | | |

Directions: Route 161 North; follow 1.5 miles outside Caribou; course is on right side.

# Castine Golf Club

✪✪ 10

200 Battle Avenue
Castine, ME (207) 326-8844
www.castinegolfclub.com

Club Pro: Noah Tapley
Payment: Visa, MC, Cash
Tee Times: No

| Tees | Holes | Yards | Par | USGA | Slope |
|------|-------|-------|-----|------|-------|
| BACK | | | | | |
| MIDDLE | 9 | 3002 | 35 | 69.0 | 122 |
| FRONT | 9 | 2638 | 36 | 71.5 | 127 |

Fee 9 Holes: Weekday: $30
Fee 18 Holes: Weekday: $50
Twilight Rates:
Cart Rental: $15pp/18, $10 pp/9
Lessons: Yes  Schools: No
Membership: Yes
Other: Lockers / Lodging Partner

Weekend: $30
Weekend: $50
Discounts: Junior, call
Driving Range: Yes
Junior Golf: Yes
Architect/Yr Open: Willie Park Jr./1897
GPS: Yes

The Castine Golf Club is a challenging and beautifully maintained 9 hole par 35. Scottish golf course designer, Willie Park Jr., now a Hall of Fame Designer, laid out the current nine holes in 1921, which offers stunning views of Castine Harbor and Penobscot Bay. Currently, the only Willie Park course in the state.

| | 1 | 2 | 3 | 4 | 5 | 6 | 7 | 8 | 9 |
|------|-----|-----|-----|-----|-----|-----|-----|-----|-----|
| PAR | 4 | 3 | 4 | 3 | 4 | 4 | 5 | 4 | 4 |
| YARDS | 405 | 175 | 400 | 152 | 378 | 356 | 464 | 312 | 358 |
| PAR | | | | | | | | | |
| YARDS | | | | | | | | | |

Directions: Routes 1 & 3 through Bucksport. Turn right onto Route 175 to Route 166. Course is on right.

# Causeway Club

**★★½** ▸ **11**

10 Fernald Point Road
S.W. Harbor, ME (207) 244-3780
www.thecausewayclub.org
**Club Pro:** Matt LaHaye, Manager
**Payment:** Visa, MC
**Tee Times:** No
**Fee 9 Holes: Weekday:** $35
**Fee 18 Holes: Weekday:** $45
**Twilight Rates:** After 4pm
**Cart Rental:** $25/18, $18/9 per cart
**Lessons:** No **Schools:** No
**Membership:** Yes
**Other:** Clubhouse / Lockers / Snacks

| Tees | Holes | Yards | Par | USGA | Slope |
|------|-------|-------|-----|------|-------|
| BACK | | | | | |
| MIDDLE | 9 | 2302 | 32 | 60.9 | 95 |
| FRONT | 9 | 2085 | 32 | 63.9 | 102 |

**Weekend:** $35
**Weekend:** $45
**Discounts:** Junior
**Driving Range:** No
**Junior Golf:** Yes
**Architect/Yr Open:** Alonso Yates/1923
**GPS:** Yes

On S.W. Harbor with scenic views. Closed to public after 6:30pm. Near Acadia National Park. New practice facility. 9-hole executive course with 2 sets of tees. Two 9s equal 4718 yards, par 65.

| | 1 | 2 | 3 | 4 | 5 | 6 | 7 | 8 | 9 |
|------|---|---|---|---|---|---|---|---|---|
| PAR | 4 | 4 | 4 | 4 | 4 | 3 | 3 | 3 | 3 |
| YARDS | 390 | 270 | 298 | 278 | 390 | 140 | 228 | 175 | 133 |
| PAR | | | | | | | | | |
| YARDS | | | | | | | | | |

**Directions:** I-95 to ALT Route 1 to Ellsworth. Follow Route 3 to Mt. Desert Island. Take Route 102 to Southwest Harbor.

# Cedar Springs Golf Course

**★½** ▸ **12**

63 Bog Road
Albion, ME (207) 437-2073
www.cedarspringsgc.com
**Club Pro:** Tim Theriault
**Payment:** Cash, Checks
**Tee Times:** No
**Fee 9 Holes: Weekday:** $15
**Fee 18 Holes: Weekday:** $22
**Twilight Rates:** No
**Cart Rental:** $24pp/18, $12pp/9
**Lessons:** $20/30 min. **Schools:** No
**Membership:** Yes
**Other:** Restaurant / Clubhouse / Bar-Lounge / Snack Bar / Function Room

| Tees | Holes | Yards | Par | USGA | Slope |
|------|-------|-------|-----|------|-------|
| BACK | 9 | 2915 | 35 | | |
| MIDDLE | 9 | 2700 | 35 | 65.6 | 109 |
| FRONT | 9 | 2355 | 55 | | |

**Weekend:** $15
**Weekend:** $22
**Discounts:** None
**Driving Range:** No
**Junior Golf:** No
**Architect/Yr Open:** Tim Theriault/1997

COUPON

**N**
**ME**

Cedar Springs is a well-maintained 9 hole picturesque golf course nestled in a country setting which offers a challenging 2700 yard layout. With their friendly staff and reasonable prices you will want to stay and enjoy lunch or a cool beverage after your round.

| | 1 | 2 | 3 | 4 | 5 | 6 | 7 | 8 | 9 |
|------|---|---|---|---|---|---|---|---|---|
| PAR | 4 | 4 | 3 | 4 | 4 | 3 | 5 | 4 | 4 |
| YARDS | 300 | 240 | 110 | 305 | 240 | 165 | 600 | 440 | 300 |
| PAR | | | | | | | | | |
| YARDS | | | | | | | | | |

**Directions:** Take I-95 to Exit 127 (Waterville/Oakland). Turn right onto Kennedy Memorial Drive (Route 137). Follow Route 137 through Winslow and China to Albion. In Albion turn left onto Bog Road. Cedar Springs is first right off of Bog Road.

# Clinton Golf Course

**✪✪✪½**

510 Hill Road
Clinton, ME (207) 426-8795
www.clintongolfcourse.com

**Club Pro:**
**Payment:** Most Major Credit Cards
**Tee Times:** Call ahead
**Fee 9 Holes: Weekday:** $30, $40 w/cart
**Fee 18 Holes: Weekday:** $55, $75 w/cart
**Twilight Rates:** After 3pm
**Cart Rental:** $20pp/18, $10pp/9
**Lessons:** No **Schools:** No
**Membership:** No
**Other:** Snack Bar

| Tees | Holes | Yards | Par | USGA | Slope |
|------|-------|-------|-----|------|-------|
| BACK | 9 | 3240 | 36 | 71.2 | 140 |
| MIDDLE | 9 | 3002 | 36 | 68.8 | 138 |
| FRONT | 9 | 2348 | 36 | | |

**Weekend:** $30, $40 w/cart
**Weekend:** $55, $75 w/cart
**Discounts:** None
**Driving Range:** No
**Junior Golf:** No
**Architect/Yr Open:** Steve Brown/2001
**GPS:**

Family-owned, -built, and -run. Limited access. Tee times every half hour. 9 holes with 2 sets of tees. "Very well kept, great way to spend a day." –GD

| | 1 | 2 | 3 | 4 | 5 | 6 | 7 | 8 | 9 |
|---|---|---|---|---|---|---|---|---|---|
| PAR | 4 | 4 | 4 | 3 | 5 | 4 | 3 | 5 | 4 |
| YARDS | 392 | 374 | 334 | 168 | 514 | 359 | 182 | 506 | 411 |
| PAR | | | | | | | | | |
| YARDS | | | | | | | | | |

**Directions:** I-95 to Exit 138 (Hinckley Road) to 100 North. Follow 100 to Railroad Street. Go left onto Railroad, and then left onto Hill Road.

# Country View Golf Course

**✪✪** 14

178 Moose Head Trail Highway
Brooks, ME (207) 722-3161
www.countryviewgolf.net

**Club Pro:** Rick Finlayson, PGA
**Payment:** Most Major Credit Cards
**Tee Times:** No
**Fee 9 Holes: Weekday:** $18
**Fee 18 Holes: Weekday:** $30
**Twilight Rates:** No
**Cart Rental:** $17pp/18, $9pp/9
**Lessons:** No **Schools:** No
**Membership:** Yes
**Other:** Snack Bar

| Tees | Holes | Yards | Par | USGA | Slope |
|------|-------|-------|-----|------|-------|
| BACK | 9 | 3000 | 36 | | 115 |
| MIDDLE | 9 | 2885 | 36 | | 115 |
| FRONT | 9 | 2480 | 36 | | 105 |

**Weekend:** $18 after 4pm
**Weekend:** $38
**Discounts:** None
**Driving Range:** Yes
**Junior Golf:** No
**Architect/Yr:** Carl, Ralph & Steve Brown/1964
**GPS:**

COUPON

Very scenic and always dry. Very hilly course with tricky greens. "Challenging for good players but playable for all ability levels. Keep the ball below the hole on the green." –MH

| | 1 | 2 | 3 | 4 | 5 | 6 | 7 | 8 | 9 |
|---|---|---|---|---|---|---|---|---|---|
| PAR | 4 | 4 | 5 | 3 | 4 | 5 | 4 | 4 | 3 |
| YARDS | 330 | 335 | 450 | 125 | 345 | 480 | 340 | 335 | 145 |
| PAR | | | | | | | | | |
| YARDS | | | | | | | | | |

**Directions:** I-95 (in Fairfield) to Route 139 all the way to Brooks. Turn left to Route 7 North 1.5 miles.

# Dexter Municipal Golf Course ✪✪½ 15 ▶

35 Sunrise Avenue
Dexter, ME (207) 924-6477
www.dextermaine.org/golf
**Club Pro:** Jimmy Costido, Manager
**Payment:** Visa, MC, Disc
**Tee Times:** No
**Fee 9 Holes: Weekday:** $13
**Fee 18 Holes: Weekday:** $20
**Twilight Rates:** None
**Cart Rental:** $12pp/18, $6pp/9
**Lessons:** Yes **Schools:** Yes
**Membership:** Yes
**Other:** Clubhouse / Restaurant

| Tees | Holes | Yards | Par | USGA | Slope |
|---|---|---|---|---|---|
| BACK | | | | | |
| MIDDLE | 9 | 2784 | 35 | 65.6 | 116 |
| FRONT | 9 | 2708 | 35 | 65.6 | 124 |

**Weekend:** $13
**Weekend:** $20
**Discounts:** Juniors 1/2 price
**Driving Range:** Yes
**Junior Golf:** Yes
**Architect/Yr Open:** Bill Nadeau/1968
**GPS:**

Not too long, but full of challenges. Lots of hills and ponds — fun course to play. Open April 15 - October 15. Mark Hall, PGA provides lessons by appointment.

| | 1 | 2 | 3 | 4 | 5 | 6 | 7 | 8 | 9 |
|---|---|---|---|---|---|---|---|---|---|
| PAR | 4 | 4 | 4 | 3 | 4 | 4 | 4 | 3 | 5 |
| YARDS | 275 | 285 | 338 | 155 | 376 | 275 | 377 | 183 | 444 |
| | 10 | 11 | 12 | 13 | 14 | 15 | 16 | 17 | 18 |
| PAR | 4 | 4 | 4 | 3 | 5 | 4 | 4 | 3 | 4 |
| YARDS | 305 | 295 | 343 | 161 | 426 | 300 | 390 | 188 | 376 |

**Directions:** I-95 to Exit 157 (Newport exit) follow Route 7 North to Dexter (14 miles). Take left on Liberty Street (across from Rite Aid). Take a left at the second stop sign. Course is second driveway on right.

# Diadema Golf Club ✪✪✪✪ 16 ▶

419 New Portland Road
North Anson, ME (207) 635-3060
www.diademagolf.com
**Club Pro:**
**Payment:** All Credit Cards, Checks, Cash
**Tee Times:** Yes
**Fee 9 Holes: Weekday:** $25
**Fee 18 Holes: Weekday:** $44
**Twilight Rates:** None
**Cart Rental:** $14pp/18, $9pp/9
**Lessons:** $30/half-hour **Schools:** No
**Membership:** Yes
**Other:** Restaurant / Snack Bar / Function Room

| Tees | Holes | Yards | Par | USGA | Slope |
|---|---|---|---|---|---|
| BACK | 9 | 2933 | 36 | 68.9 | 127 |
| MIDDLE | 9 | 2731 | 36 | 67.1 | 121 |
| FRONT | 9 | 2395 | 36 | 68.1 | 120 |

**N
ME**

**Weekend:** $25
**Weekend:** $44
**Discounts:** Juniors
**Driving Range:** Yes
**Junior Golf:** No
**Architect/Yr Open:** Michael A. Zikorus/2014
**GPS:**

Well maintained 9-hole golf course. Friendly to play with 4 sets of tees. Unique features include many stone walls and 2 different greens for holes 8/17.
"One of the best 9-hole golf courses in New England. A must-play." –FP

| | 1 | 2 | 3 | 4 | 5 | 6 | 7 | 8 | 9 |
|---|---|---|---|---|---|---|---|---|---|
| PAR | 4 | 3 | 5 | 4 | 4 | 4 | 5 | 3 | 4 |
| YARDS | 321 | 152 | 443 | 386 | 286 | 271 | 424 | 127 | 321 |
| PAR | | | | | | | | | |
| YARDS | | | | | | | | | |

**Directions:** I-95 to Exit 130. Turn left onto Route 104/139. Stay on Route 139 and turn right on Route 201A (New Madison Road). Turn left on Route 16 West.

# Evergreen Golf Club ★½ 17

522 Dallas Hill Road
Rangeley, ME (207) 240-5248
www.evergreengolfrangeley.net

**Club Pro:** George Buck
**Payment:** Visa, MC, Amex, Disc, Checks
**Tee Times:** Yes

| Tees | Holes | Yards | Par | USGA | Slope |
|------|-------|-------|-----|------|-------|
| BACK | 9 | 3324 | 35 | 72.9 | 139 |
| MIDDLE | 9 | 3040 | 35 | 70.9 | 129 |
| FRONT | 9 | 2155 | 35 | 60.3 | 112 |

**Fee 9 Holes: Weekday:** $27    **Weekend:** $27
**Fee 18 Holes: Weekday:** $37    **Weekend:** $37
**Twilight Rates:** After 4pm    **Discounts:** None
**Cart Rental:** $18pp/18, $10pp/9    **Driving Range:** Yes
**Lessons:** Yes  **Schools:** Yes    **Junior Golf:** Yes
**Membership:** Yes    **Architect/Yr Open:** George Buck, Jr./2001
**Other:** Clubhouse / Snack Bar / Pro Shop / Putting Course
**GPS:** Yes

This is a championship quality course, 5 tees on each hole, spectacular views. Everyone who plays it, loves it.

| | 1 | 2 | 3 | 4 | 5 | 6 | 7 | 8 | 9 |
|------|-----|-----|-----|-----|-----|-----|-----|-----|-----|
| PAR | 4 | 4 | 3 | 4 | 4 | 4 | 4 | 3 | 5 |
| YARDS | 422 | 361 | 178 | 345 | 391 | 442 | 464 | 196 | 524 |
| PAR | | | | | | | | | |
| YARDS | | | | | | | | | |

**Directions:** From I-95 Auburn-Lewiston exit – take Route 4 to Rangley.


# Fort Kent Golf Club ★★½ 18

304 Saint John Road
Fort Kent, ME (207) 834-3149
www.fortkentgolfclub.org

**Club Pro:** Kelly O'Leary, PGA
**Payment:** Visa, MC
**Tee Times:** No

| Tees | Holes | Yards | Par | USGA | Slope |
|------|-------|-------|-----|------|-------|
| BACK | | | | | |
| MIDDLE | 9 | 3122 | 35 | 69.0 | 111 |
| FRONT | 9 | 2681 | 36 | 69.0 | 111 |

**Fee 9 Holes: Weekday:** $20    **Weekend:** $20
**Fee 18 Holes: Weekday:** $35    **Weekend:** $35
**Twilight Rates:** No    **Discounts:**
**Cart Rental:** $25pp/18, $16pp/9 per cart    **Driving Range:** Yes
**Lessons:** $35/lesson  **Schools:** No    **Junior Golf:** Yes
**Membership:** Yes    **Architect/Yr Open:** Ben Gray/1966
**Other:** Restaurant / Clubhouse / Bar-Lounge / Lockers / Showers
**GPS:** Yes

The course, located a chip shot from the Canadian border, sports many challenges: bunkers, water hazards, and hills. Expanded water on hole #9.

| | 1 | 2 | 3 | 4 | 5 | 6 | 7 | 8 | 9 |
|------|-----|-----|-----|-----|-----|-----|-----|-----|-----|
| PAR | 4 | 4 | 3 | 4 | 3 | 4 | 4 | 4 | 5 |
| YARDS | 406 | 302 | 160 | 322 | 151 | 390 | 412 | 437 | 542 |
| PAR | | | | | | | | | |
| YARDS | | | | | | | | | |

**Directions:** Route 161 to Fort Kent; follow 3 miles to course.

# Foxcroft Golf Club  ✪✪  ▸19

84 Foxcroft Center Road
Dover Foxcroft, ME (207) 564-8887
www.foxcroftgolfclub.com

**Club Pro:**
**Payment:** Cash, Personal Checks
**Tee Times:** No
**Fee 9 Holes: Weekday:** $15
**Fee 18 Holes: Weekday:** $24
**Twilight Rates:** After 4pm
**Cart Rental:** $15pp/18, $10pp/9
**Lessons:** Yes **Schools:** No
**Membership:**
**Other:** Snack Bar/ Clubhouse

| Tees | Holes | Yards | Par | USGA | Slope |
|------|-------|-------|-----|------|-------|
| BACK | 9 | 3136 | 36 | 66.1 | 109 |
| MIDDLE | 9 | 2968 | 36 | 66.1 | 107 |
| FRONT | 9 | 2753 | 37 | 67.0 | 101 |

**Weekend:** $15
**Weekend:** $24
**Discounts:** None
**Driving Range:** No
**Junior Golf:** Yes
**Architect/Yr Open:** Renaldo Reynolds/1963
**GPS:**

COUPON

Recently lengthened first tee. New White tees on #7 and #9. "Challenging course with fast greens. Very player-friendly for women and seniors." –MH

|  | 1 | 2 | 3 | 4 | 5 | 6 | 7 | 8 | 9 |
|------|----|----|----|----|----|----|----|----|----|
| PAR | 5 | 4 | 4 | 3 | 4 | 4 | 3 | 4 | 5 |
| YARDS | 474 | 430 | 380 | 102 | 328 | 267 | 168 | 381 | 488 |
| PAR | | | | | | | | | |
| YARDS | | | | | | | | | |

**Directions:** I-95 to Exit 39 (Newport exit). Follow Route 7 into Dover-Foxcroft. Turn left. Go right at traffic light. Take 2nd right, Route 16. Take Route 16 from the post office 1.3 miles to Foxcroft Center Road. Sign is at corner of Milo Road.

# Great Cove Golf Course  ✪  ▸20

387 Great Cove Road
Roque Bluffs, ME (207) 434-7200

**Club Pro:** Leon Sinford, Manager
**Payment:** Cash, Personal Checks
**Tee Times:** No
**Fee 9 Holes: Weekday:** $9
**Fee 18 Holes: Weekday:** $18
**Twilight Rates:** No
**Cart Rental:** $10/9 per cart
**Lessons:** No **Schools:** No
**Membership:** Yes
**Other:** Clubhouse / Snack Bar

| Tees | Holes | Yards | Par | USGA | Slope |
|------|-------|-------|-----|------|-------|
| BACK | | | | | |
| MIDDLE | 9 | 1709 | 30 | 59.1 | 100 |
| FRONT | | | | | |

**Weekend:** $9
**Weekend:** $18
**Discounts:** None
**Driving Range:** $6/lg., $4/sm.
**Junior Golf:** Yes
**Architect/Yr Open:** Paul Browne/1977
**GPS:**

N
ME

3 short par 3's, 3 long par 3's, and 3 short par 4's. Great views of Englishman Bay.

|  | 1 | 2 | 3 | 4 | 5 | 6 | 7 | 8 | 9 |
|------|----|----|----|----|----|----|----|----|----|
| PAR | 4 | 3 | 4 | 3 | 4 | 3 | 3 | 3 | 3 |
| YARDS | 304 | 185 | 245 | 193 | 228 | 103 | 137 | 177 | 137 |
| PAR | | | | | | | | | |
| YARDS | | | | | | | | | |

**Directions:** 3 miles off Route 1 from Jonesboro. Located on Great Cove Road.

# Grindstone Neck Golf Course ✪✪✪

## 21

Grindstone Avenue
Winter Harbor, ME (207) 963-7760
www.grindstonegolf.com

**Club Pro:** Kevin Conley
**Payment:** Visa, MC
**Tee Times:** No

| Tees | Holes | Yards | Par | USGA | Slope |
|------|-------|-------|-----|------|-------|
| BACK | | | | | |
| MIDDLE | 9 | 3095 | 36 | | |
| FRONT | 9 | 2550 | 36 | | |

**Fee 9 Holes: Weekday:** $24     **Weekend:** $28
**Fee 18 Holes: Weekday:** $36     **Weekend:** $45
**Twilight Rates:** After 4:30pm     **Discounts:** College & Juniors
**Cart Rental:** $25/18, $15/9 per cart, $4/pull     **Driving Range:** No
**Lessons:** No  **Schools:** No     **Junior Golf:** No
**Membership:** Yes     **Architect/Yr:** Alex Findlay/1895; Charlie Clark/1925
**Other:** No     **GPS:**

Player Comments: "Could not be more beautiful." Located on Frenchman's Bay. Enjoy cool sea breezes, spectacular ocean views.

| | 1 | 2 | 3 | 4 | 5 | 6 | 7 | 8 | 9 |
|---|---|---|---|---|---|---|---|---|---|
| PAR | 4 | 4 | 4 | 3 | 4 | 4 | 5 | 4 | 4 |
| YARDS | 345 | 340 | 317 | 138 | 413 | 335 | 457 | 343 | 407 |
| PAR | | | | | | | | | |
| YARDS | | | | | | | | | |

**Directions:** Route 1 to Route 186. Route 186 to Main Street. Right on Main for 1 mile to Grindstone Avenue.

# Hampden Country Club ✪½

25 Thomas Road
Hampden, ME (207) 862-9999
www.hampdengolf.net

**Club Pro:**
**Payment:** Cash, Check, Credit Card
**Tee Times:** Not Required

| Tees | Holes | Yards | Par | USGA | Slope |
|------|-------|-------|-----|------|-------|
| BACK | 9 | 2930 | 36 | 64.9 | 104 |
| MIDDLE | 9 | 2759 | 36 | 64.9 | 108 |
| FRONT | 9 | 2550 | 36 | 69.6 | 118 |

**Fee 9 Holes: Weekday:** $12     **Weekend:** $12
**Fee 18 Holes: Weekday:** $20     **Weekend:** $20
**Twilight Rates:** No     **Discounts:**
**Cart Rental:** $14pp/18, $8pp/9     **Driving Range:** No
**Lessons:** No  **Schools:** No     **Junior Golf:** No
**Membership:** Yes     **Architect/Yr Open:** Hamm Robbins/1967
**Other:** Snack Bar     **GPS:**

COUPON

The course is fairly wide open, friendly for beginners and seniors. Considered an easy walker. Tuesday is Ladies' Day – $15 all day. Thursday is Senior Citizens and Veterans Day – $15 all day.

| | 1 | 2 | 3 | 4 | 5 | 6 | 7 | 8 | 9 |
|---|---|---|---|---|---|---|---|---|---|
| PAR | 4 | 3 | 4 | 4 | 4 | 3 | 5 | 4 | 5 |
| YARDS | 320 | 170 | 330 | 295 | 257 | 170 | 462 | 310 | 420 |
| PAR | | | | | | | | | |
| YARDS | | | | | | | | | |

**Directions:** I-95 to Exit 174, follow Route 69 East for 1.5 miles. Take Route 9 East for 2 miles; course is on right.

# Hermon Meadow Golf Club ✪✪

281 Billings Road
Bangor, ME (207) 848-3741
www.hermonmeadow.com

| Tees | Holes | Yards | Par | USGA | Slope |
|------|-------|-------|-----|------|-------|
| BACK | 18 | 6329 | 72 | 69.4 | 117 |
| MIDDLE | 18 | 5895 | 72 | 67.7 | 113 |
| FRONT | 18 | 5395 | 72 | 70.9 | 120 |

**Club Pro:** Thea Davis
**Payment:** Most Major Credit Cards
**Tee Times:** No
**Fee 9 Holes: Weekday:** $15
**Fee 18 Holes: Weekday:** $27 all day
**Twilight Rates:** After 3pm
**Cart Rental:** $15pp/18, $8.50pp/9
**Lessons:** Yes **Schools:** Jr.
**Membership:** $600
**Other:** Clubhouse / Snack Bar / Bar-Lounge

**Weekend:** $15
**Weekend:** $27 all day
**Discounts:** Junior
**Driving Range:** $4/bucket
**Junior Golf:** Yes
**Architect/Yr Open:**
**GPS:**

COUPON

The greens are small and fast; back 9 is heavily wooded. Driving range has largest bent grass tees in Maine. Call for daily specials.

|  | 1 | 2 | 3 | 4 | 5 | 6 | 7 | 8 | 9 |
|------|---|---|---|---|---|---|---|---|---|
| PAR | 4 | 4 | 3 | 5 | 4 | 5 | 4 | 3 | 4 |
| YARDS | 350 | 385 | 130 | 460 | 270 | 545 | 350 | 165 | 350 |
|  | **10** | **11** | **12** | **13** | **14** | **15** | **16** | **17** | **18** |
| PAR | 4 | 4 | 3 | 5 | 4 | 5 | 3 | 4 | 4 |
| YARDS | 265 | 310 | 160 | 430 | 320 | 510 | 135 | 370 | 390 |

**Directions:** Take Union Street 4 miles past airport in Bangor, take left on Billings Road, course is 2 miles on left.

# Hidden Meadows Golf Course ✪✪½

## 24

240 West Old Town Road
Old Town, ME (207) 827-4779
www.hiddenmeadowsgolf.com

| Tees | Holes | Yards | Par | USGA | Slope |
|------|-------|-------|-----|------|-------|
| BACK |  |  |  |  |  |
| MIDDLE | 9 | 3144 | 35 | 66.5 | 112 |
| FRONT | 9 | 2481 | 35 | 66.4 | 109 |

**Club Pro:** Joe Perdue, PGA
**Payment:** Cash, Visa, MC, Disc, Checks
**Tee Times:** No
**Fee 9 Holes: Weekday:** $12
**Fee 18 Holes: Weekday:** $18
**Twilight Rates:** No
**Discounts:** Senior & Junior 9/$10, 18/$15
**Cart Rental:** $12/18, $8/9 per cart
**Lessons:** Yes **Schools:** Yes
**Membership:** Yes
**Other:** Open April to November

**Weekend:** $14
**Weekend:** $21

**Driving Range:** Yes
**Junior Golf:** Yes
**Architect/Yr Open:** Jeffrey P. Dufour/1995
**GPS:**

COUPON

N
ME

New Owner Joe Predue, PGA Professional. New tees #1, #3, #6, #7. New driving range. Full service discount Pro Shop includes: Caddy, Mizuno, TaylorMade, Titlest, Callaway and Cobra.

|  | 1 | 2 | 3 | 4 | 5 | 6 | 7 | 8 | 9 |
|------|---|---|---|---|---|---|---|---|---|
| PAR | 4 | 4 | 4 | 3 | 5 | 4 | 4 | 3 | 4 |
| YARDS | 389 | 323 | 399 | 148 | 547 | 415 | 394 | 167 | 332 |
| PAR |  |  |  |  |  |  |  |  |  |
| YARDS |  |  |  |  |  |  |  |  |  |

**Directions:** I-95 to Exit 197. West on Route 43 toward Hudson. Golf course is ¾ mile from interstate on left.

# Hillcrest Golf Club

59 Grove Street
Millinocket, ME (207) 723-8410
www.hillcrestgolfme.com
**Club Pro:**
**Payment:** Visa, MC
**Tee Times:** No

| Tees | Holes | Yards | Par | USGA | Slope |
|------|-------|-------|-----|------|-------|
| BACK | | | | | |
| MIDDLE | 9 | 2477 | 33 | 63.2 | 104 |
| FRONT | | | | | |

**Fee 9 Holes: Weekday:** $15    **Weekend:** $15
**Fee 18 Holes: Weekday:** $18    **Weekend:** $18
**Twilight Rates:** No    **Discounts:** None
**Cart Rental:** $24/18, $10/9 per cart    **Driving Range:** No
**Lessons:** Yes **Schools:** No    **Junior Golf:** Yes
**Membership:** Yes    **Architect/Yr Open:** Larry Striley/1930
**Other:** Clubhouse / Snack Bar / Bar-Lounge    **GPS:**

Player Comments: "Sits at the Foot of Mt. Katahdin. Very nice short course, very tight with narrow, tree-lined fairways." Friendly Staff. Open April - October.

| | 1 | 2 | 3 | 4 | 5 | 6 | 7 | 8 | 9 |
|-------|-----|-----|-----|-----|-----|-----|-----|-----|-----|
| **PAR** | 4 | 3 | 4 | 4 | 4 | 4 | 3 | 3 | 4 |
| **YARDS** | 359 | 152 | 364 | 287 | 265 | 401 | 221 | 153 | 275 |
| **PAR** | | | | | | | | | |
| **YARDS** | | | | | | | | | |

**Directions:** I-95 to Medway Exit 244, left off ramp onto Route 157. Follow 12 miles to Millinocket. Past McDonald's to bottom of hill. Follow signs at right.

# Houlton Community Golf Course

Nickerson Lake Road
Houlton, ME (207) 532-2662
www.houltongolf.com
**Club Pro:** Ray Mailman, Manager
**Payment:** Cash, Check, Credit Cards
**Tee Times:** Yes

| Tees | Holes | Yards | Par | USGA | Slope |
|------|-------|-------|-----|------|-------|
| BACK | | | | | |
| MIDDLE | 9 | 2993 | 36 | 68.9 | 117 |
| FRONT | 9 | 2705 | 38 | 73.6 | 109 |

**Fee 9 Holes: Weekday:** $15    **Weekend:** $15
**Fee 18 Holes: Weekday:** $25    **Weekend:** $25
**Twilight Rates:** No    **Discounts:** Senior & Junior
**Cart Rental:** $16pp/9 $32pp/18    **Driving Range:** Yes
**Lessons:** Yes **Schools:** No    **Junior Golf:** Yes
**Membership:** Yes    **Architect/Yr Open:** 1921
**Other:** Clubhouse / Snack Bar / Bar-Lounge    **GPS:**

COUPON

The course is adjacent to beautiful Nickerson Lake. Hilly, but other than a scenic view of the lake, has few water hazards. 2 sets of tees means a change of par on some holes on 2nd round. Open May - October.

| | 1 | 2 | 3 | 4 | 5 | 6 | 7 | 8 | 9 |
|-------|-----|-----|-----|-----|-----|-----|-----|-----|-----|
| **PAR** | 4 | 5 | 3 | 4 | 4 | 5 | 4 | 3 | 4 |
| **YARDS** | 310 | 455 | 134 | 246 | 403 | 405 | 340 | 170 | 356 |
| **PAR** | | | | | | | | | |
| **YARDS** | | | | | | | | | |

**Directions:** From I-95 take Exit 291 and bear right; follow Route 2 east for 3.5 miles, then turn right onto Campbell Road. At the Stop sign, turn left. Golf Course is 1.8 miles on right.

# Island Country Club ✪✪ ▸ 27

442 Sunset Road
Deer Isle, ME (207) 348-2379
www.islandcountryclub.net
**Club Pro:** Shaun Webb
**Payment:** Visa, MC
**Tee Times:** No

| Tees | Holes | Yards | Par | USGA | Slope |
|------|-------|-------|-----|------|-------|
| BACK | | | | | |
| MIDDLE | 9 | 2376 | 34 | 62.1 | 109 |
| FRONT | | | | | |

**Fee 9 Holes: Weekday:** $30 **Weekend:** $30
**Fee 18 Holes: Weekday:** $40 **Weekend:** $40
**Twilight Rates:** No **Discounts:** Junior
**Cart Rental:** $30/18, $15/9 per cart **Driving Range:** Yes (nets)
**Lessons:** No **Schools:** No **Junior Golf:** Yes
**Membership:** Yes **Architect/Yr Open:** Stiles & Van Kleek/1918
**Other:** Clubhouse / Snack Bar **GPS:**

COUPON

Hilly, fast greens. Contoured fairways, fully irrigated. Alcohol served on premises. Lunch 11-2 Tuesday-Sunday. Beaches, boating, tennis, fine dining, art galleries and shopping close by.

| | 1 | 2 | 3 | 4 | 5 | 6 | 7 | 8 | 9 |
|-----|-----|-----|-----|-----|-----|-----|-----|-----|-----|
| PAR | 4 | 4 | 3 | 3 | 4 | 3 | 4 | 5 | 4 |
| YARDS | 315 | 261 | 156 | 113 | 380 | 100 | 268 | 459 | 324 |
| PAR | | | | | | | | | |
| YARDS | | | | | | | | | |

**Directions:** Route 15 to Deer Isle, then Route 15A to Sunset. Club is about 3 miles on the left.

# Jato Highlands Golf Course ✪✪✪ ▸ 28

175 Town Farm Road
Lincoln, ME (207) 794-2433
www.jatohighlands.com
**Club Pro:** Jaymis Dugamn
**Payment:** Visa, MC, Cash, Check
**Tee Times:** Yes

| Tees | Holes | Yards | Par | USGA | Slope |
|------|-------|-------|-----|------|-------|
| BACK | 18 | 5715 | 72 | 68 | 123 |
| MIDDLE | 18 | 5491 | 71 | 67 | 121 |
| FRONT | 18 | 4916 | 72 | 64.1 | 108 |

**Fee 9 Holes: Weekday:** $20 **Weekend:** $20
**Fee 18 Holes: Weekday:** $30 **Weekend:** $30
**Twilight Rates:** After 3pm
**Discounts:** Junior/$15, Seniors 80+/free
**Cart Rental:** $15pp/18, $10pp/9 **Driving Range:** Yes
**Lessons:** Yes **Schools:** Yes **Junior Golf:** Yes
**Membership:** Yes **Architect/Yr Open:** Tom Gardner/1999
**Other:** Restaurant / Clubhouse / Bar-Lounge **GPS:**

COUPON

Player Comments: "A hidden gem. Well maintained. A demanding challenge from any tees." "Plays up and down the Highlands. Great course." –DW

| | 1 | 2 | 3 | 4 | 5 | 6 | 7 | 8 | 9 |
|-----|-----|-----|-----|-----|-----|-----|-----|-----|-----|
| PAR | 4 | 4 | 3 | 5 | 4 | 4 | 4 | 3 | 5 |
| YARDS | 314 | 322 | 172 | 421 | 258 | 309 | 282 | 122 | 409 |
| | 10 | 11 | 12 | 13 | 14 | 15 | 16 | 17 | 18 |
| PAR | 3 | 5 | 5 | 4 | 3 | 5 | 3 | 4 | 4 |
| YARDS | 186 | 424 | 465 | 367 | 164 | 432 | 144 | 298 | 406 |

**Directions:** I-95 to Lincoln exit. Left on Route 2, 6 miles on Town Farm Road on right.

# Johnson W. Parks Golf Course ✪✪½ ▶ 29

**382 Hartland Avenue**
**Pittsfield, ME (207) 487-5545**
**www.jwparksgolf.com**

| Tees | Holes | Yards | Par | USGA | Slope |
|------|-------|-------|-----|------|-------|
| BACK | 9 | 2927 | 35 | 34.1 | 120 |
| MIDDLE | 9 | 2678 | 35 | 35.1 | 120 |
| FRONT | 9 | 2554 | 35 | 35.0 | 120 |

**Club Pro:** Michael Dugas, PGA
**Payment:** Visa, MC, Personal Checks
**Tee Times:** No
**Fee  9 Holes: Weekday:** $14      **Weekend:** $16
**Fee 18 Holes: Weekday:** $22      **Weekend:** $22
**Twilight Rates:** After 5pm      **Discounts:** Junior, 1/2 price
**Cart Rental:** $20pp/18, $10pp/9      **Driving Range:** Yes
**Lessons:** $25/half hour  **Schools:** No      **Junior Golf:** Yes
**Membership:** Yes      **Architect/Yr Open:** John Dana/1964
**Other:** Clubhouse / Sports Bar      **GPS:**

COUPON

Tall pines, narrow fairways and a series of streams add to the challenge at one of central Maine's most popular courses. Fully irrigated. Open April 25 - October 31. Twilight rates after 3pm and 5pm include cart.

|  | 1 | 2 | 3 | 4 | 5 | 6 | 7 | 8 | 9 |
|------|---|---|---|---|---|---|---|---|---|
| PAR | 4 | 4 | 5 | 3 | 4 | 4 | 4 | 3 | 4 |
| YARDS | 375 | 405 | 531 | 227 | 308 | 268 | 322 | 160 | 331 |
| PAR | | | | | | | | | |
| YARDS | | | | | | | | | |

**Directions:** I-95 to Pittsfield Exit 150, go east off ramp. Take a left onto Route 152. ½ mile on the left.

# Katahdin Country Club ✪½ ▶ 30

**80 Park Street**
**Milo, ME (207) 943-8734**

| Tees | Holes | Yards | Par | USGA | Slope |
|------|-------|-------|-----|------|-------|
| BACK | | | | | |
| MIDDLE | 9 | 2968 | 36 | 65.8 | 103 |
| FRONT | | | | | |

**Club Pro:** Rick Gerrish
**Payment:** Cash Only
**Tee Times:** No
**Fee  9 Holes: Weekday:** $14 all day      **Weekend:** $14 all day
**Fee 18 Holes: Weekday:** $14 all day      **Weekend:** $14 all day
**Twilight Rates:** No      **Discounts:** None
**Cart Rental:** $22pp/18, $11pp/9      **Driving Range:** No
**Lessons:** No  **Schools:**      **Junior Golf:** Yes
**Membership:** Yes      **Architect/Yr Open:** Larry Striley/1931
**Other:** Clubhouse / Snack Bar      **GPS:**

Wide-open fairways, short-cut rough and no water hazards. Largest sand trap around. Open April 15 - November.

|  | 1 | 2 | 3 | 4 | 5 | 6 | 7 | 8 | 9 |
|------|---|---|---|---|---|---|---|---|---|
| PAR | 4 | 3 | 4 | 4 | 3 | 5 | 5 | 4 | 4 |
| YARDS | 327 | 150 | 322 | 257 | 180 | 485 | 519 | 447 | 281 |
| PAR | | | | | | | | | |
| YARDS | | | | | | | | | |

**Directions:** I-95 North to LaGrange-Milo exit, follow signs to course.

# Kebo Valley Golf Club ✪✪✪✪

**31**

136 Eagle Lake Road
Bar Harbor, ME (207) 288-3000
www.kebovalleyclub.com

| Tees | Holes | Yards | Par | USGA | Slope |
|------|-------|-------|-----|------|-------|
| BACK | 18 | 6131 | 70 | 69.0 | 124 |
| MIDDLE | 18 | 5933 | 70 | 69.0 | 122 |
| FRONT | 18 | 5440 | 72 | 72 | 121 |

**Club Pro:** Peiter K. DeVos, PGA
Jay Blackwell, PGA
**Payment:** Cash, Visa, MC, Amex
**Tee Times:** 6 days adv.
**Fee 9 Holes: Weekday:** Call - seasonal      **Weekend:** Call - seasonal
**Fee 18 Holes: Weekday:** Call - seasonal     **Weekend:** Call - seasonal
**Twilight Rates:** After 2:30pm               **Discounts:** None
**Cart Rental:** $25pp/18, $15pp/9             **Driving Range:** No
**Lessons:** Yes  **Schools:** No              **Junior Golf:** Yes
**Membership:** Yes                            **Architect/Yr Open:** H.C. Leeds/1891
**Other:** Restaurant / Bar-Lounge / Lockers   **GPS:** Yes

COUPON

8th-oldest club in the country. Majestic views of Acadia National Park. 17th hole restored to its original beauty. Clubhouse overlooks the golf course.

|  | 1 | 2 | 3 | 4 | 5 | 6 | 7 | 8 | 9 |
|------|---|---|---|---|---|---|---|---|---|
| PAR | 4 | 4 | 4 | 3 | 5 | 3 | 4 | 4 | 3 |
| YARDS | 388 | 438 | 336 | 143 | 500 | 165 | 322 | 413 | 194 |
|  | 10 | 11 | 12 | 13 | 14 | 15 | 16 | 17 | 18 |
| PAR | 4 | 4 | 4 | 4 | 5 | 3 | 4 | 4 | 4 |
| YARDS | 338 | 400 | 283 | 390 | 530 | 146 | 258 | 349 | 340 |

**Directions:** I-95 to Bangor, 395 to Route 1A, Route 1A to Route 3, Route 3 to Route 233. Look for signs to course.

# Kenduskeag Golf & Country Club ✪

**32**

947 Grant Road
Kenduskeag, ME (207) 884-7330
www.kenduskeaggolf.com

| Tees | Holes | Yards | Par | USGA | Slope |
|------|-------|-------|-----|------|-------|
| BACK | | | | | |
| MIDDLE | 9 | 2777 | 36 | | |
| FRONT | | | | | |

**Club Pro:**
**Payment:** Cash, Check, Credit Card
**Tee Times:** No
**Fee 9 Holes: Weekday:** $12        **Weekend:** $13
**Fee 18 Holes: Weekday:** $18       **Weekend:** $18
**Twilight Rates:** No               **Discounts:** Senior & Junior
**Cart Rental:** $12pp/18, $8pp/9    **Driving Range:** No
**Lessons:** No  **Schools:** No     **Junior Golf:** No
**Membership:** Yes                  **Architect/Yr Open:** Robert Girvan, Sr./1958
**Other:** Clubhouse / Snack Bar     **GPS:**

COUPON

An easy but pretty course. Rolling, wooded and stream scenery. Appropriate dress. Open May 1 - October 31. New clubhouse.

|  | 1 | 2 | 3 | 4 | 5 | 6 | 7 | 8 | 9 |
|------|---|---|---|---|---|---|---|---|---|
| PAR | 4 | 4 | 4 | 4 | 4 | 3 | 5 | 4 | 4 |
| YARDS | 320 | 343 | 246 | 400 | 285 | 143 | 465 | 265 | 310 |
| PAR | | | | | | | | | |
| YARDS | | | | | | | | | |

**Directions:** I-95 to Exit 185. Right to Route 15 North (Broadway), 12 miles to course. Left onto Grant Road.

# Lakeview Golf Course    ✪½   **33**

21 Reynolds Lane
Burnham, ME (207) 948-5414
www.lakeviewgolfcoursemaine.com

| Tees | Holes | Yards | Par | USGA | Slope |
|------|-------|-------|-----|------|-------|
| BACK | 9 | 3016 | 36 | 68.0 | 107 |
| MIDDLE | 9 | 2950 | 36 | 65.9 | 107 |
| FRONT | 9 | 2698 | 36 | 69.9 | 114 |

**Club Pro:** Nan Parsons, GM
**Payment:** Visa, MC
**Tee Times:** No
**Fee 9 Holes: Weekday:** $12    **Weekend:** $15
**Fee 18 Holes: Weekday:** $18    **Weekend:** $20
**Twilight Rates:** No    **Discounts:** Junior
**Cart Rental:** $25pp/18, $13pp/9    **Driving Range:** No
**Lessons:** No **Schools:** No    **Junior Golf:** No
**Membership:** Yes    **Architect/Yr Open:** Ronello Reynolds Sr./1927
**Other:** Cafe / Clubhouse / Lockers    **GPS:**

COUPON

Beautiful 9-hole course nestled on the shores of scenic Lake Winnecook. Friendly staff and great food. An excellent walking course with level fairways. Highly recommended for senior citizens. All-day passes available — $25 during the week and $30 on weekends.

| | 1 | 2 | 3 | 4 | 5 | 6 | 7 | 8 | 9 |
|------|-----|-----|-----|-----|-----|-----|-----|-----|-----|
| **PAR** | 4 | 4 | 3 | 3 | 4 | 5 | 5 | 4 | 4 |
| **YARDS** | 381 | 298 | 120 | 159 | 328 | 503 | 485 | 351 | 325 |
| **PAR** | | | | | | | | | |
| **YARDS** | | | | | | | | | |

**Directions:** I-95 to Fairfield exit. Take Route 139 from Fairfield to Burnham West. Take Prairie Road off 139, clubhouse is on right.

# Lakewood Golf Course    ✪✪   **34**

Route 201
803 Lakewood Road
Madison, ME (207) 474-5955
www.lakewoodgolfmaine.com

| Tees | Holes | Yards | Par | USGA | Slope |
|------|-------|-------|-----|------|-------|
| BACK | 18 | 6280 | 72 | 70.3 | 132 |
| MIDDLE | 18 | 6106 | 72 | 69.1 | 125 |
| FRONT | 18 | 4728 | 74 | 63.4 | 111 |

**Club Pro:** Peter Fryer, GM
**Payment:** Visa, MC, Disc, Checks
**Tee Times:** Yes
**Fee 9 Holes: Weekday:** $23    **Weekend:** $23
**Fee 18 Holes: Weekday:** $35    **Weekend:** $35
**Twilight Rates:** After 4pm    **Discounts:** Junior
**Cart Rental:** $18/18, $11/9 per cart    **Driving Range:** Yes
**Lessons:** Yes **Schools:** Yes    **Junior Golf:** Yes
**Membership:** Yes    **Architect/Yr:** Alex Chisolm/1925; Phil Wogan/1995
**Other:** Snack Bar / Bar-Lounge / Hall Rental    **GPS:**

COUPON

New Front Tee's #2, #4 and #8. Beautiful views overlooking Sugarloaf and the lake. Classic layout, built in 1926. Practice, chipping, and putting areas. #12 is a par 6. Open April - November. Spring and Fall Rates.

| | 1 | 2 | 3 | 4 | 5 | 6 | 7 | 8 | 9 |
|------|-----|-----|-----|-----|-----|-----|-----|-----|-----|
| **PAR** | 4 | 4 | 3 | 5 | 4 | 3 | 4 | 4 | 5 |
| **YARDS** | 353 | 441 | 177 | 479 | 285 | 146 | 329 | 405 | 500 |
| | **10** | **11** | **12** | **13** | **14** | **15** | **16** | **17** | **18** |
| **PAR** | 3 | 4 | 6 | 4 | 4 | 4 | 4 | 4 | 3 |
| **YARDS** | 111 | 340 | 585 | 405 | 355 | 323 | 345 | 374 | 153 |

**Directions:** Route 201, go 6 miles past Showhegan toward Bingham.

# Limestone Country Club  ✪✪½  **35**▶

487 West Gate Road
Limestone, ME (207) 328-7277
www.limestonecountryclub.com

**Club Pro:**
**Payment:** Visa, MC
**Tee Times:** No

| Tees | Holes | Yards | Par | USGA | Slope |
|------|-------|-------|-----|------|-------|
| BACK | | | | | |
| MIDDLE | 9 | 3355 | 36 | 70.4 | 114 |
| FRONT | 9 | 2870 | 36 | 71.4 | 116 |

**Fee 9 Holes: Weekday:** $14    **Weekend:** $14
**Fee 18 Holes: Weekday:** $22    **Weekend:** $22
**Twilight Rates:** No    **Discounts:** Senior & Junior
**Cart Rental:** $22/18, $14/9 per cart    **Driving Range:** No
**Lessons:** No  **Schools:** No    **Junior Golf:** No
**Membership:** Yes    **Architect/Yr Open:** William Mitchell/1961
**Other:** Clubhouse / Bar / Lounge / Snack Bar / Restaurant

Course is sited to capture the wind. Fairways lined with evergreens and hardwoods. Elevated greens at different angles. Long- and short-term accomodations are available. Golf packages. New carts.

| | 1 | 2 | 3 | 4 | 5 | 6 | 7 | 8 | 9 |
|------|-----|-----|-----|-----|-----|-----|-----|-----|-----|
| PAR | 4 | 5 | 3 | 4 | 4 | 3 | 4 | 5 | 4 |
| YARDS | 415 | 525 | 160 | 370 | 355 | 225 | 390 | 515 | 400 |
| PAR | | | | | | | | | |
| YARDS | | | | | | | | | |

**Directions:** I-95 North to Holton, then Route 1 North to Caribou. From Caribou take Route 89 East to Loring/Limestone. Take a left on West Gate Road for 2.5 miles and club is located on the right.

# Long Lake Country Club  ✪½  **36**▶

744 Lake Shore Road
St. David, ME (207) 895-6957

**Club Pro:** Al Hebert
**Payment:** Credit Card, Check, Cash
**Tee Times:** No

| Tees | Holes | Yards | Par | USGA | Slope |
|------|-------|-------|-----|------|-------|
| BACK | 9 | 3000 | 36 | | |
| MIDDLE | 9 | 2805 | 35 | | |
| FRONT | 9 | 2610 | 36 | | |

**Fee 9 Holes: Weekday:** $15    **Weekend:** $12
**Fee 18 Holes: Weekday:** $25    **Weekend:** $20
**Twilight Rates:** No
**Discounts:** Junior 12 and under $7.50/9 holes
**Cart Rental:** $25pp/18, $15pp/9    **Driving Range:** Yes
**Lessons:** Yes  **Schools:** No    **Junior Golf:** No
**Membership:** Yes    **Architect/Yr Open:** Ben Gray/1961
**Other:** Bar-Lounge / Restaurant / Indoor Simulator

**N
ME**

6 New Tee Boxes. Scenic views — abundant wildlife — bring a camera!

| | 1 | 2 | 3 | 4 | 5 | 6 | 7 | 8 | 9 |
|------|-----|-----|-----|-----|-----|-----|-----|-----|-----|
| PAR | 4 | 4 | 4 | 4 | 3 | 4 | 5 | 4 | 3 |
| YARDS | 265 | 345 | 395 | 335 | 160 | 385 | 475 | 290 | 155 |
| PAR | | | | | | | | | |
| YARDS | | | | | | | | | |

**Directions:** I-95 North to Houlton - Route 1, to Beaulieu Road, Madawaska to Lake Shore Road.

# Loons Cove Golf Course           ❂¹/₂  ▶ 37

Route 201
Skowhegan, ME (207) 474-9550
www.loonscovegolfcourse.com

**Club Pro:** No
**Payment:** Cash or Check
**Tee Times:** No
**Fee 9 Holes: Weekday:** $8
**Fee 18 Holes: Weekday:** $12
**Twilight Rates:** No
**Cart Rental:** $18/18, $10/9 per cart
**Lessons:** Yes  **Schools:** No
**Membership:** Yes
**Other:** Snacks / Beverages / Lunch Counter

Host of the Special Olympics Skills Program.

| Tees | Holes | Yards | Par | USGA | Slope |
|------|-------|-------|-----|------|-------|
| BACK | | | | | |
| MIDDLE | 9 | 1214 | 27 | | |
| FRONT | | | | | |

**Weekend:** $8
**Weekend:** $12
**Discounts:** For members
**Driving Range:** Yes
**Junior Golf:** Yes
**Architect/Yr Open:**
**GPS:**

| | 1 | 2 | 3 | 4 | 5 | 6 | 7 | 8 | 9 |
|------|-----|-----|-----|-----|-----|-----|-----|-----|-----|
| PAR | 3 | 3 | 3 | 3 | 3 | 3 | 3 | 3 | 3 |
| YARDS | 142 | 162 | 125 | 160 | 110 | 125 | 128 | 115 | 147 |
| PAR | | | | | | | | | |
| YARDS | | | | | | | | | |

**Directions:** I-95 to Route 201. 6 miles to Skowhegan.

# Lucerne-in-Maine Golf Course   ❂❂  ▶ 38

16 Sunset Road
Dedham, ME (207) 843-6282
www.lucernegolf.com

**Club Pro:** David Gubler, Owner
**Payment:** Cash, Check, Visa, MC
**Tee Times:** 7 days adv.
**Fee 9 Holes: Weekday:** $15
**Fee 18 Holes: Weekday:** $25
**Twilight Rates:** No
**Cart Rental:** $15pp/18, $8pp/9
**Lessons:** Yes  **Schools:** No
**Membership:** Yes
**Other:** Snack Bar / Lodging Available at Lucerne Inn

| Tees | Holes | Yards | Par | USGA | Slope |
|------|-------|-------|-----|------|-------|
| BACK | 9 | 3205 | 36 | 70.6 | 119 |
| MIDDLE | 9 | 2845 | 36 | 67.4 | 119 |
| FRONT | 9 | 2650 | 36 | 69.5 | 116 |

**Weekend:** $15
**Weekend:** $25
**Discounts:** None
**Driving Range:** No
**Junior Golf:** Yes
**Architect/Yr Open:** Donald Ross/1926

*COUPON*

Donald Ross course features tree-lined fairways, ample landing areas and small greens guarded by pot bunkers. Recently put back original bunkers that had been removed. New putting green.

| | 1 | 2 | 3 | 4 | 5 | 6 | 7 | 8 | 9 |
|------|-----|-----|-----|-----|-----|-----|-----|-----|-----|
| PAR | 5 | 3 | 4 | 4 | 4 | 3 | 4 | 5 | 4 |
| YARDS | 450 | 155 | 235 | 360 | 305 | 150 | 340 | 485 | 365 |
| PAR | | | | | | | | | |
| YARDS | | | | | | | | | |

**Directions:** I-95 to Exit 182A (Route I-395) to 1A towards Ellsworth. Course is 8 miles on left, halfway between Bangor and Ellsworth on Route 1.

# Mars Hill Country Club ✪✪✪ ▸39

75 Country Club Road
Mars Hill, ME (207) 425-4802
www.golfmhcc.com

| Tees | Holes | Yards | Par | USGA | Slope |
|------|-------|-------|-----|------|-------|
| BACK | 18 | 6043 | 72 | | |
| MIDDLE | 18 | 5742 | 72 | 68.7 | 125 |
| FRONT | 18 | 5159 | 72 | | |

**Club Pro:** Ronald Perry
**Payment:** Visa, MC
**Tee Times:** No
**Fee 9 Holes: Weekday:** $14
**Fee 18 Holes: Weekday:** $28
**Twilight Rates:** No
**Cart Rental:** $16pp/18, $8pp/9
**Lessons:** Yes **Schools:** No
**Membership:** Yes
**Other:** Clubhouse / Full Snack Bar / Beer

**Weekend:** $14
**Weekend:** $28
**Discounts:** None
**Driving Range:** $3/lg bucket
**Junior Golf:** Yes
**Architect/Yr Open:** A. McQuade/1991
**GPS:** Yes

COUPON

6th hole par 3, with a 162-foot vertical drop, is amazing. Moose, deer, and/or bear seen on course almost daily. Near New England's largest wind farm. "One of the best courses north of Bangor featuring dramatic elevation changes and great scenery." –DW

| | 1 | 2 | 3 | 4 | 5 | 6 | 7 | 8 | 9 |
|------|-----|-----|-----|-----|-----|-----|-----|-----|-----|
| PAR | 4 | 5 | 4 | 5 | 4 | 3 | 4 | 3 | 4 |
| YARDS | 350 | 481 | 257 | 470 | 326 | 145 | 313 | 130 | 300 |
| | 10 | 11 | 12 | 13 | 14 | 15 | 16 | 17 | 18 |
| PAR | 4 | 4 | 5 | 3 | 4 | 3 | 4 | 5 | 4 |
| YARDS | 398 | 380 | 470 | 163 | 363 | 125 | 309 | 447 | 315 |

**Directions:** I-95 to Route US1 to Mars Hill. Then north ½ mile on Route 1A. Turn right onto Boynton Road, then left onto Country Club Road.

# Mingo Springs Golf Course ✪✪½ ▸40

43 Country Club Road
Rangeley, ME (207) 864-5021
www.mingosprings.com

| Tees | Holes | Yards | Par | USGA | Slope |
|------|-------|-------|-----|------|-------|
| BACK | 18 | 6322 | 71 | 68.4 | 123 |
| MIDDLE | 18 | 6014 | 71 | 65.5 | 114 |
| FRONT | 18 | 5158 | 71 | 67.4 | 110 |

**Club Pro:** Sharon Williams. GM
**Payment:** Visa, MC, Disc, Cash
**Tee Times:** Yes
**Fee 9 Holes: Weekday:** $32
**Fee 18 Holes: Weekday:** $44
**Twilight Rates:** After 3pm (excl. Tues. & Sat.)
**Cart Rental:** $22pp/18, $14pp/9
**Lessons:** Yes **Schools:** No
**Membership:** Yes
**Other:** Snack Bar / Bar-Lounge

**Weekend:** $32
**Weekend:** $44
**Discounts:**
**Driving Range:** Irons only
**Junior Golf:** Yes
**Architect/Yr Open:** Phil Wogan/1925
**GPS:**

N
ME

New green on #16, new tee on #16 and new tee on #13. Noted for being a challenging old-fashioned course, yet family and beginner-friendly. Scenic views of Rangeley Mountains.

| | 1 | 2 | 3 | 4 | 5 | 6 | 7 | 8 | 9 |
|------|-----|-----|-----|-----|-----|-----|-----|-----|-----|
| PAR | 4 | 4 | 4 | 3 | 4 | 4 | 3 | 4 | 5 |
| YARDS | 350 | 375 | 378 | 173 | 360 | 391 | 177 | 318 | 470 |
| | 10 | 11 | 12 | 13 | 14 | 15 | 16 | 17 | 18 |
| PAR | 3 | 5 | 3 | 4 | 4 | 4 | 4 | 4 | 4 |
| YARDS | 152 | 522 | 133 | 400 | 360 | 277 | 419 | 363 | 396 |

**Directions:** I-95 to Exit 12 (Auburn). Pick up Route 4. Go through Farmington to Rangeley Village. 2 miles toward Oquossoc, left on Mingo Loop Road. Follow signs to course.

# Moose River Golf Course ✪½ ▶ 41

701 Main Street (Route 201)
Moose River, ME (207) 668-5331
www.mooserivergolfcourse.com

| Tees | Holes | Yards | Par | USGA | Slope |
|---|---|---|---|---|---|
| BACK | | | | | |
| MIDDLE | 9 | 1976 | 31 | | |
| FRONT | | | | | |

**Club Pro:** Wade Turmel
**Payment:** Cash Only
**Tee Times:** No
**Fee 9 Holes: Weekday:** $14 **Weekend:** $14
**Fee 18 Holes: Weekday:** $22 **Weekend:** $22
**Twilight Rates:** No **Discounts:** None
**Cart Rental:** $18/18, $13/9 per cart **Driving Range:** No
**Lessons:** No **Schools:** No **Junior Golf:** No
**Membership:** Yes **Architect/Yr Open:**
**Other:** **GPS:** 1935

Open May 15 - October 15. Rate subject to change. Interesting 9-hole course. Very fun to play. Greens are in good condition compared to past years. Great place for family and friends to get together. The interesting 205 par 4, 3rd hole bends right around an ancient cemetery in the middle of the fairway.

| | 1 | 2 | 3 | 4 | 5 | 6 | 7 | 8 | 9 |
|---|---|---|---|---|---|---|---|---|---|
| PAR | 3 | 3 | 4 | 4 | 4 | 3 | 3 | 3 | 4 |
| YARDS | 204 | 168 | 213 | 248 | 259 | 168 | 171 | 169 | 376 |
| PAR | | | | | | | | | |
| YARDS | | | | | | | | | |

**Directions:** I-95 to Fairfield exit, follow Route 201 North about 85 miles to Moose River.

# Mt. Kineo Golf Course ✪✪✪ ▶ 42

Trailhead Road
Kineo Island Township, ME
(207) 534-9012
www.mooseheadlakegolf.com

| Tees | Holes | Yards | Par | USGA | Slope |
|---|---|---|---|---|---|
| BACK | | | | | |
| MIDDLE | 18 | 6030 | 71 | 68.5 | 113 |
| FRONT | 18 | 4996 | 71 | 68.5 | 113 |

**Club Pro:**
**Payment:** Visa, MC, Amex, Disc, Checks
**Tee Times:** No
**Fee 9 Holes: Weekday:** $25 **Weekend:** $25
**Fee 18 Holes: Weekday:** $40 **Weekend:** $40
**Twilight Rates:** No **Discounts:** Junior
**Cart Rental:** $15 pp/18, $6.50pp/9 **Driving Range:** No
**Lessons:** No **Schools:** No **Junior Golf:** No
**Membership:** Yes **Architect/Yr Open:** 1893
**Other:** Clubhouse / Snack Bar

COUPON

A challenging island course nestled under beautiful Mount Kineo in Moosehead Lake. Small greens and narrow fairways ensure a satisfying round in a stunning setting. Our signature fourth hole, 141 yards over water, is worth the trip!

| | 1 | 2 | 3 | 4 | 5 | 6 | 7 | 8 | 9 |
|---|---|---|---|---|---|---|---|---|---|
| PAR | 5 | 4 | 4 | 3 | 4 | 5 | 3 | 4 | 4 |
| YARDS | 484 | 420 | 234 | 134 | 331 | 467 | 141 | 425 | 388 |
| | 10 | 11 | 12 | 13 | 14 | 15 | 16 | 17 | 18 |
| PAR | 4 | 4 | 3 | 3 | 4 | 5 | 3 | 5 | 4 |
| YARDS | 448 | 420 | 197 | 149 | 331 | 467 | 141 | 450 | 403 |

**Directions:** From I-95 take Newport exit to Route 7; follow 7 North until Dexter. Take 23 North to Guilford. At Guilford, take Route 6/15 all the way to Rockwood. In Rockwood follow sign to "Kineo Docks". At the docks you will take the Kineo shuttle ferry boat to our island course.

# Natanis Golf Course (Arrowhead) ✪✪✪ 43 ▶

**Webber Pond Road**
**Vassalboro, ME (207) 622-3561**
**www.natanisgc.com**

| Tees | Holes | Yards | Par | USGA | Slope |
|------|-------|-------|-----|------|-------|
| BACK | 18 | 6338 | 72 | 70.0 | 117 |
| MIDDLE | 18 | 5847 | 72 | 67.8 | 116 |
| FRONT | 18 | 5019 | 72 | 68.7 | 117 |

**Club Pro:** Richard Browne, PGA
**Payment:** Visa, MC, Cash
**Tee Times:** 1 week adv.
**Fee 9 Holes: Weekday:** $22    **Weekend:** $22
**Fee 18 Holes: Weekday:** $37    **Weekend:** $37
**Twilight Rates:** After 4pm    **Discounts:** None
**Cart Rental:** $16pp/18, $10pp/9    **Driving Range:** $4.50/lg., $3.50/sm. bucket
**Lessons:** $35/half hour   **Schools:** No    **Junior Golf:** Yes
**Membership:** Yes    **Architect/Yr Open:** Phil Wogan/1974
**Other:** Clubhouse / Lockers / Snack Bar    **GPS:**

Player Comments: "36 holes of top-notch golf. Challenging." Improved cart paths. State of Maine Museum and Fieldstone Gardens nearby. Distance below is from back tees. Come play both courses.

| | 1 | 2 | 3 | 4 | 5 | 6 | 7 | 8 | 9 |
|-------|-----|-----|-----|-----|-----|-----|-----|-----|-----|
| PAR | 5 | 4 | 4 | 5 | 3 | 4 | 3 | 4 | 4 |
| YARDS | 500 | 400 | 350 | 461 | 200 | 255 | 190 | 365 | 240 |
| | 10 | 11 | 12 | 13 | 14 | 15 | 16 | 17 | 18 |
| PAR | 3 | 4 | 3 | 4 | 4 | 5 | 4 | 5 | 4 |
| YARDS | 185 | 380 | 165 | 403 | 424 | 530 | 441 | 439 | 410 |

**Directions:** I-95 to Augusta/Winthrop exit onto Route 201 to Webber Pond Road. Follow signs.

# Natanis Golf Course (Tomahawk) ✪✪✪½ 44 ▶

**Webber Pond Road**
**Vassalboro, ME (207) 622-3561**
**www.natanisgc.com**

| Tees | Holes | Yards | Par | USGA | Slope |
|------|-------|-------|-----|------|-------|
| BACK | 18 | 6607 | 72 | 70.6 | 132 |
| MIDDLE | 18 | 6060 | 72 | 67.3 | 123 |
| FRONT | 18 | 5034 | 72 | 63.8 | 104 |

**Club Pro:** Richard Browne, PGA
**Payment:** Visa, MC, Cash
**Tee Times:** 1 week adv.
**Fee 9 Holes: Weekday:** $25    **Weekend:** $25
**Fee 18 Holes: Weekday:** $47    **Weekend:** $47
**Twilight Rates:** After 3pm    **Discounts:** None
**Cart Rental:** $16pp/18, $10pp/9    **Driving Range:** $4.50/lg., $3.50/sm. bucket
**Lessons:** $35/half hour   **Schools:** No    **Junior Golf:** Yes
**Membership:** Yes    **Architect/Yr Open:** Dan Maples/2002
**Other:** Clubhouse / Lockers / Snack Bar    **GPS:**

N
ME

The tougher of this pair, the Dan Maples design has more length and more challenges. Distance below is from middle tees.

| | 1 | 2 | 3 | 4 | 5 | 6 | 7 | 8 | 9 |
|-------|-----|-----|-----|-----|-----|-----|-----|-----|-----|
| PAR | 5 | 4 | 5 | 3 | 4 | 4 | 3 | 4 | 4 |
| YARDS | 490 | 342 | 526 | 124 | 358 | 362 | 121 | 354 | 359 |
| | 10 | 11 | 12 | 13 | 14 | 15 | 16 | 17 | 18 |
| PAR | 3 | 4 | 4 | 3 | 5 | 5 | 4 | 4 | 4 |
| YARDS | 130 | 320 | 373 | 163 | 481 | 503 | 311 | 365 | 378 |

**Directions:** I-95 to Augusta/Winthrop exit onto Route 201 to Webber Pond Road. Follow signs.

# Newport Country Club ✪½ ▶ 45

170 Golf Course Road
Newport, ME (207) 368-5600

**Club Pro:** Jeff Peabody, PGA
**Payment:** Cash Only
**Tee Times:** Yes
**Fee 9 Holes: Weekday:** $12
**Fee 18 Holes: Weekday:** $18
**Twilight Rates:** No
**Cart Rental:** $10pp/9
**Lessons:** Yes **Schools:** Yes
**Membership:** Yes
**Other:** Clubhouse / Snack Bar

**Weekend:** $12
**Weekend:** $18
**Discounts:** Senior & Junior
**Driving Range:** Yes
**Junior Golf:** Yes
**Architect/Yr Open:** 1951
**GPS:**

| Tees | Holes | Yards | Par | USGA | Slope |
|------|-------|-------|-----|------|-------|
| BACK | | | | | |
| MIDDLE | 9 | 2520 | 35 | | |
| FRONT | | | | | |

Built on the crest of a hill near apple orchards. "Great views of Lake Sebasticode. Good course for beginners and seniors." –DW

| | 1 | 2 | 3 | 4 | 5 | 6 | 7 | 8 | 9 |
|------|-----|-----|-----|-----|-----|-----|-----|-----|-----|
| PAR | 3 | 3 | 5 | 4 | 4 | 5 | 4 | 3 | 4 |
| YARDS | 155 | 135 | 430 | 380 | 255 | 450 | 290 | 190 | 235 |
| PAR | | | | | | | | | |
| YARDS | | | | | | | | | |

**Directions:** I-95 to Exit 157 to Route 7 to right turn on Golf Course Road in Newport.

# Northeast Harbor Golf Club ✪✪✪½ ▶ 46

15 Golf Club Road
N.E. Harbor, ME (207) 276-5335
www.nehgc.com

**Club Pro:** Rob Gardner, PGA
**Payment:** Visa, MC, Amex, Disc
**Tee Times:** No
**Fee 9 Holes: Weekday:** $25
**Fee 18 Holes: Weekday:** $45
**Twilight Rates:** No
**Cart Rental:** $24pp/18, $12pp/9
**Lessons:** Private, Group, Jr. Clinic **Schools:** Yes
**Membership:** Yes
**Other:** Clubhouse/ Lockers

**Weekend:** $25
**Weekend:** $45
**Discounts:** None
**Driving Range:** Members only
**Junior Golf:** Yes
**Architect/Yr Open:** J.G. Thorpe/1895
**GPS:**

| Tees | Holes | Yards | Par | USGA | Slope |
|------|-------|-------|-----|------|-------|
| BACK | 18 | 5504 | 69 | 66.7 | 128 |
| MIDDLE | 18 | 5324 | 69 | 65.9 | 124 |
| FRONT | 18 | 4558 | 71 | 66.9 | 124 |

Located on Mt. Desert Island. Close to Acadia National Park. Open to the public May - June and September - October. Members only July and August. "An absolutely outstanding Maine golf course. 13 superb wooded holes and 5 traditional links style holes. Major elevation changes, very small greens and unmatched beauty." –DW

| | 1 | 2 | 3 | 4 | 5 | 6 | 7 | 8 | 9 |
|------|-----|-----|-----|-----|-----|-----|-----|-----|-----|
| PAR | 4 | 4 | 3 | 4 | 4 | 3 | 4 | 3 | 5 |
| YARDS | 325 | 320 | 149 | 425 | 305 | 127 | 284 | 155 | 457 |
| | 10 | 11 | 12 | 13 | 14 | 15 | 16 | 17 | 18 |
| PAR | 5 | 4 | 3 | 4 | 3 | 4 | 4 | 4 | 4 |
| YARDS | 495 | 310 | 175 | 337 | 187 | 415 | 281 | 338 | 239 |

**Directions:** I-95 to Bangor exit (Route 1A), follow to Ellsworth, take Route 3 to Mt. Desert Island. Right at light at head of island on Route 198. Left at next light (still 198), right on Sargent Drive. NEHGC on left.

# Northport Golf Club ✪✪✪ 47 ▶

581 Bluff Road
Northport, ME (207) 338-2270
www.golfnorthport.com
**Club Pro:** Robb Herron, PGA
**Payment:** Visa, MC, Amex, Disc, Cash, Check
**Tee Times:** Holidays/Spring/Fall
**Fee 9 Holes: Weekday:** $25
**Fee 18 Holes: Weekday:** $35
**Twilight Rates:** After 3pm
**Cart Rental:** $15pp/18, $10pp/9
**Lessons:** Yes  **Schools:** No
**Membership:** Yes
**Other:**

| Tees | Holes | Yards | Par | USGA | Slope |
|------|-------|-------|-----|------|-------|
| BACK | | | | | |
| MIDDLE | 9 | 3047 | 36 | 34.2 | 112 |
| FRONT | 9 | 2747 | 37 | 35.7 | 113 |

**Weekend:** $20
**Weekend:** $28
**Discounts:** Spring/Fall
**Driving Range:** Yes
**Junior Golf:** Yes
**Architect/Yr Open:** William Jennings/1916
**GPS:** Sky Caddy Ready

COUPON

Whole course now fully irrigated. New tee on #2, and new practice green. Built in 1916 — rare velvet bentgrass fairways and greens. 100 year old 9 hole golf course in wonderful condition.

| | 1 | 2 | 3 | 4 | 5 | 6 | 7 | 8 | 9 |
|------|-----|-----|-----|-----|-----|-----|-----|-----|-----|
| PAR | 4 | 4 | 3 | 4 | 5 | 4 | 5 | 4 | 3 |
| YARDS | 290 | 377 | 157 | 310 | 483 | 412 | 530 | 338 | 150 |

| | | | | | | | | | |
|------|--|--|--|--|--|--|--|--|--|
| PAR | | | | | | | | | |
| YARDS | | | | | | | | | |

**Directions:** I-95 to Augusta. Exit onto Route 3 East to Belfast/Bar Harbor. Stay on Route 3 to Route 1 South 2 miles. Left at Dos Amigos restaurant.

# Palmyra GC and Campground ✪✪ 48 ▶

147 Lang Hill Road
Palmyra, ME (207) 938-4947
www.palmyra-me.com
**Club Pro:**
**Payment:** Visa, MC, Amex, Disc
**Tee Times:** Recommended
**Fee 9 Holes: Weekday:** $15
**Fee 18 Holes: Weekday:** $25
**Twilight Rates:** After 4pm
**Cart Rental:** $12pp/18, $6pp/9
**Lessons:** Yes  **Schools:** No
**Membership:** Yes
**Other:** Snack Bar / Campground with 100 Sites

| Tees | Holes | Yards | Par | USGA | Slope |
|------|-------|-------|-----|------|-------|
| BACK | 18 | 6550 | 72 | 71.0 | 125 |
| MIDDLE | 18 | 6250 | 72 | 69.6 | 123 |
| FRONT | 18 | 5345 | 72 | 65.1 | 112 |

**Weekend:** $15
**Weekend:** $25
**Discounts:** Junior
**Driving Range:** $5/50 balls
**Junior Golf:** Yes
**Architect/Yr Open:** Richard Cayer/1956

COUPON

Course noted for excellent value. Course awarded for programs advancing junior golf.

| | 1 | 2 | 3 | 4 | 5 | 6 | 7 | 8 | 9 |
|------|-----|-----|-----|-----|-----|-----|-----|-----|-----|
| PAR | 4 | 3 | 4 | 4 | 5 | 4 | 4 | 3 | 5 |
| YARDS | 385 | 140 | 345 | 380 | 480 | 360 | 300 | 215 | 480 |
| | **10** | **11** | **12** | **13** | **14** | **15** | **16** | **17** | **18** |
| PAR | 4 | 4 | 5 | 3 | 4 | 4 | 4 | 3 | 5 |
| YARDS | 420 | 275 | 510 | 150 | 405 | 415 | 400 | 125 | 465 |

**Directions:** I-95 to Exit 157 (Newport). Route 2 West, approximately 5 miles. Right at white church. Course is on top of hill.

# Penobscot Valley CC   ✪✪✪   49

366 Main Street
Orono, ME (207) 866-2423
www.penobscotvalleycc.com

| Tees | Holes | Yards | Par | USGA | Slope |
|------|-------|-------|-----|------|-------|
| BACK | 18 | 6536 | 72 | 71.3 | 130 |
| MIDDLE | 18 | 6320 | 72 | 70.4 | 127 |
| FRONT | 18 | 5311 | 73 | 70.9 | 120 |

**Club Pro:** Jason Harris
**Payment:** Most Major Credit Cards
**Tee Times:** Up to 1 week in adv.
**Fee 9 Holes: Weekday:** $25    **Weekend:** $25
**Fee 18 Holes: Weekday:** $39    **Weekend:** $39
**Twilight Rates:** No    **Discounts:** None
**Cart Rental:** $15pp/18, $7pp/9    **Driving Range:** $5/bag
**Lessons:** $35/half hour, $60/hour  **Schools:** Yes  **Junior Golf:** Yes
**Membership:** Yes    **Architect/Yr Open:** Donald Ross/1924
**Other:** Clubhouse / Lockers / Showers / Snack Bar / Restaurant / Bar-Lounge / Function Facilities

COUPON

This "Central Maine Masterpiece" underwent a comprehensive restoration in 2008. Challenging, fun and thouroughly old school, this Donald Ross 18-hole track is host to many prestigious events. Stay and Play packages are available through Hollywood Slots at 877-779-7771.

| | 1 | 2 | 3 | 4 | 5 | 6 | 7 | 8 | 9 |
|------|---|---|---|---|---|---|---|---|---|
| PAR | 4 | 4 | 5 | 3 | 4 | 3 | 5 | 4 | 4 |
| YARDS | 392 | 399 | 512 | 144 | 346 | 158 | 446 | 350 | 367 |
| | 10 | 11 | 12 | 13 | 14 | 15 | 16 | 17 | 18 |
| PAR | 5 | 4 | 4 | 4 | 3 | 5 | 3 | 4 | 4 |
| YARDS | 493 | 382 | 378 | 411 | 144 | 458 | 193 | 321 | 426 |

**Directions:** I-95 to Exit 189. Right to dead end. Right ¼ mile to club.

# Pine Hill Golf Club    ✪½    50

23 Pine Hill Drive
Brewer, ME (207) 989-3824

| Tees | Holes | Yards | Par | USGA | Slope |
|------|-------|-------|-----|------|-------|
| BACK | 9 | 2979 | 36 | 66 | 100 |
| MIDDLE | 9 | 2749 | 36 | 66 | 100 |
| FRONT | 9 | 2580 | 36 | 67 | 99 |

**Club Pro:**
**Payment:** Visa, MC
**Tee Times:** No
**Fee 9 Holes: Weekday:** $13    **Weekend:** $13.50
**Fee 18 Holes: Weekday:** $15.50 all day    **Weekend:** $15.50 all day
**Twilight Rates:** No    **Discounts:** Ladies Monday
**Cart Rental:** $21/18, $13/9 per cart    **Driving Range:** $3.50/med.
**Lessons:** Yes  **Schools:** No    **Junior Golf:** No
**Membership:** Yes    **Architect/Yr Open:** Charlie Emery/1962
**Other:** Clubhouse / Snack Bar    **GPS:**

Mostly level. Very scenic. A great course for ladies and seniors. No rough! Open April - October. "Second set of tees makes it interesting." –MH

| | 1 | 2 | 3 | 4 | 5 | 6 | 7 | 8 | 9 |
|------|---|---|---|---|---|---|---|---|---|
| PAR | 4 | 4 | 4 | 4 | 3 | 5 | 4 | 5 | 3 |
| YARDS | 292 | 333 | 326 | 339 | 166 | 498 | 320 | 495 | 210 |
| PAR | | | | | | | | | |
| YARDS | | | | | | | | | |

**Directions:** I-395 to South Main Street/Brewer exit, follow signs to course.

# Pine Ridge Golf Course
●½ ▶ 51

97 West River Road
Waterville, ME (207) 873-0474

| Tees | Holes | Yards | Par | USGA | Slope |
|---|---|---|---|---|---|
| BACK | | | | | |
| MIDDLE | 9 | 1285 | 27 | | |
| FRONT | | | | | |

**Club Pro:**
**Payment:** Cash or Check
**Tee Times:** No
**Fee 9 Holes: Weekday:** $11
**Fee 18 Holes: Weekday:**
**Twilight Rates:** No
**Cart Rental:** $5/pull
**Lessons:** No **Schools:** No
**Membership:** Yes
**Other:** Restaurant / Bar-Lounge

**Weekend:** $13
**Weekend:**
**Discounts:** Sr. & Jr. memberships
**Driving Range:** No
**Junior Golf:** No
**Architect/Yr Open:** Burt Anderson/1955
**GPS:**

Well-built and -maintained par 3. Great for beginners, seniors and people with little time.

| | 1 | 2 | 3 | 4 | 5 | 6 | 7 | 8 | 9 |
|---|---|---|---|---|---|---|---|---|---|
| PAR | 3 | 3 | 3 | 3 | 3 | 3 | 3 | 3 | 3 |
| YARDS | 160 | 135 | 110 | 125 | 220 | 100 | 125 | 175 | 135 |
| PAR | | | | | | | | | |
| YARDS | | | | | | | | | |

**Directions:** I-95 (Maine Turnpike) to Waterville exit. Follow signs for Thomas College.

# Piscataquis Country Club
●● ▶ 52

17 Country Club Lane (Route 15)
Guilford, ME (207) 876-3203
www.piscataquisgolfcourse.com

| Tees | Holes | Yards | Par | USGA | Slope |
|---|---|---|---|---|---|
| BACK | 9 | 2844 | 36 | 66.0 | 115 |
| MIDDLE | 9 | 2582 | 36 | 64.3 | 106 |
| FRONT | 9 | 2417 | 36 | 69.7 | 123 |

**Club Pro:** James Watson, Golf Instructor
**Payment:** Visa, MC, Check
**Tee Times:** No
**Fee 9 Holes: Weekday:** $12
**Fee 18 Holes: Weekday:** $20
**Twilight Rates:** $10 after 4pm
**Cart Rental:** $20pp/18, $10pp/9
**Lessons: Schools:** No
**Membership:** Yes
**Other:** Clubhouse / Kitchen

**Weekend:** $12
**Weekend:** $20
**Discounts:** Junior
**Driving Range:** No
**Junior Golf:** Yes
**Architect/Yr Open:** 1926
**GPS:**

N
ME

Number 5 is now a par 5, all uphill. All-day rates for juniors. Prices subject to change.

| | 1 | 2 | 3 | 4 | 5 | 6 | 7 | 8 | 9 |
|---|---|---|---|---|---|---|---|---|---|
| PAR | 4 | 4 | 4 | 4 | 5 | 3 | 4 | 4 | 4 |
| YARDS | 352 | 324 | 251 | 290 | 470 | 164 | 268 | 348 | 377 |
| PAR | | | | | | | | | |
| YARDS | | | | | | | | | |

**Directions:** I-95 to Newport exit, Route 7 to Route 23 North, to Route 15. Course is 1/10 mile from the intersection.

# Portage Hills Country Club  ✪✪  53 ▶

Route 11
Portage, ME (207) 435-8221

| Tees | Holes | Yards | Par | USGA | Slope |
|------|-------|-------|-----|------|-------|
| BACK | | | | | |
| MIDDLE | 9 | 3109 | 36 | 69.5 | 110 |
| FRONT | 9 | 2796 | 37 | 71.5 | 113 |

**Club Pro:** Susan Fourier, GM
**Payment:** Most Major Credit Cards
**Tee Times:** No
**Fee 9 Holes: Weekday:** $15      **Weekend:** $15
**Fee 18 Holes: Weekday:** $25      **Weekend:** $25
**Twilight Rates:** No      **Discounts:** None
**Cart Rental:** $12pp/cart      **Driving Range:** No
**Lessons:** No  **Schools:**      **Junior Golf:** No
**Membership:** Yes      **Architect/Yr Open:** Ben Gray/1971
**Other:** Clubhouse / Snack Bar / Bar-Lounge      **GPS:**

The course is well-maintained, hilly and scenic. Open from mid-May to mid-September. Rates subject to change.

| | 1 | 2 | 3 | 4 | 5 | 6 | 7 | 8 | 9 |
|------|-----|-----|-----|-----|-----|-----|-----|-----|-----|
| PAR | 4 | 4 | 4 | 4 | 5 | 3 | 4 | 5 | 3 |
| YARDS | 432 | 323 | 321 | 343 | 478 | 128 | 388 | 504 | 165 |

| | | | | | | | | | |
|------|--|--|--|--|--|--|--|--|--|
| PAR | | | | | | | | | |
| YARDS | | | | | | | | | |

**Directions:** I-95, to Sherman exit, Route 11. Follow Route 11 North for approximately 65 miles to the course.

# Presque Isle Country Club  ✪✪½  54 ▶

35 Parkhurst Siding Road (Route 205)
Presque Isle, ME (207) 764-0430
www.picountryclub.com

| Tees | Holes | Yards | Par | USGA | Slope |
|------|-------|-------|-----|------|-------|
| BACK | 18 | 6751 | 72 | 70.8 | 118 |
| MIDDLE | 18 | 6217 | 72 | 69.2 | 113 |
| FRONT | 18 | 5387 | 72 | 72.2 | 122 |

**Club Pro:** Barry Madore
**Payment:** Cash, Visa, MC, Amex, Disc
**Tee Times:** No
**Fee 9 Holes: Weekday:** $20      **Weekend:** $20
**Fee 18 Holes: Weekday:** $40      **Weekend:** $40
**Twilight Rates:** After 2pm      **Discounts:** Junior 9/$15, 18/$30
**Cart Rental:** $16pp/18, $9pp/9      **Driving Range:** $9/lg., $4.50/sm.
**Lessons:** $25/35 min.  **Schools:** No      **Junior Golf:** Yes
**Membership:** Yes
**Architect/Yr Open:** Front 9 - Ben Gray/1959; Back 9 - Rick Hobbs, Geoffrey Cornish/1987
**Other:** Clubhouse / Lockers / Showers / Restaurant / Bar Lounge

Player Comments: "Friendly and challenging." A very picturesque golf course. Home of the Spudland Open amateur golf tournament.

| | 1 | 2 | 3 | 4 | 5 | 6 | 7 | 8 | 9 |
|------|-----|-----|-----|-----|-----|-----|-----|-----|-----|
| PAR | 4 | 4 | 4 | 3 | 4 | 4 | 5 | 3 | 5 |
| YARDS | 322 | 400 | 367 | 155 | 410 | 394 | 473 | 146 | 465 |
| | 10 | 11 | 12 | 13 | 14 | 15 | 16 | 17 | 18 |
| PAR | 4 | 4 | 5 | 4 | 4 | 5 | 3 | 3 | 4 |
| YARDS | 376 | 334 | 510 | 364 | 387 | 476 | 105 | 191 | 342 |

**Directions:** From Presque Isle, take Route 167 to Route 205. You can't miss it, but if you do, call course for directions.

# Rocky Knoll Country Club ✪✪ 55 ▶

94 River Road
Orrington, ME (207) 989-0109
www.rockyknollcc.com

**Club Pro:** Mark W. Hall, PGA
**Payment:** Visa, MC, Amex, Disc, Checks
**Tee Times:** 7 days adv.
**Fee  9 Holes: Weekday:** $15
**Fee 18 Holes: Weekday:** $25
**Twilight Rates:** No
**Cart Rental:** $30/18, $15/9 per cart
**Lessons:** Yes  **Schools:** Yes
**Membership:** Yes
**Other:** Restaurant / Clubhouse

| Tees | Holes | Yards | Par | USGA | Slope |
|------|-------|-------|-----|------|-------|
| BACK | 18 | 6062 | 72 | 69.0 | 109 |
| MIDDLE | 18 | 5835 | 72 | 67.7 | 107 |
| FRONT | 18 | 4965 | 72 | 64.8 | 106 |

**Weekend:** $15
**Weekend:** $25
**Discounts:** Sr./Wed, Jr./Fri
**Driving Range:** Yes
**Junior Golf:** Yes
**Architect/Yr:** Robert Phillips/2000
**GPS:** Yes

COUPON

2nd Nine opened July 2009, very challenging with large greens. Front Nine wide open with postage stamp greens. Good food. Getting better all the time.

| | 1 | 2 | 3 | 4 | 5 | 6 | 7 | 8 | 9 |
|---|---|---|---|---|---|---|---|---|---|
| PAR | 5 | 4 | 4 | 5 | 3 | 4 | 3 | 4 | 4 |
| YARDS | 470 | 350 | 399 | 444 | 151 | 401 | 154 | 291 | 342 |
| | 10 | 11 | 12 | 13 | 14 | 15 | 16 | 17 | 18 |
| PAR | 5 | 4 | 3 | 4 | 4 | 4 | 4 | 3 | 5 |
| YARDS | 510 | 301 | 146 | 420 | 300 | 290 | 302 | 125 | 439 |

**Directions:** I-395 Bangor Brewer Exit off 1-95. South Main Street Exit Route 15. As you drive away from town, Course is 1 mile on left, clearly visible.

# Sawmill Woods Golf Course ✪✪ 56 ▶

800 Airline Road
Clifton, ME (207) 735-8771
www.sawmillwoodsgolf.com

**Club Pro:**
**Payment:** Cash, Checks
**Tee Times:** No
**Fee  9 Holes: Weekday:** $12
**Fee 18 Holes: Weekday:** $17
**Twilight Rates:** No
**Cart Rental:** $15pp/18, $10pp/9
**Lessons:** Yes  **Schools:** No
**Membership:** Yes
**Other:** Clubhouse / Snack Bar / Pro Shop / Putting Course

| Tees | Holes | Yards | Par | USGA | Slope |
|------|-------|-------|-----|------|-------|
| BACK | 9 | 2874 | 36 | | 124 |
| MIDDLE | 9 | 2679 | 36 | | 121 |
| FRONT | 9 | 2236 | 36 | | |

**Weekend:** $12
**Weekend:** $17
**Discounts:** None
**Driving Range:** Yes
**Junior Golf:** No
**Architect/Yr Open:** Hargarl Moore/2007

N
ME

Sawmill Woods is a par 36 nine-hole course cut through the Maine forest and following the natural contours of the land. Large, undulating greens and tight fairways are enhanced by extensive landscaping, creating a challenging and beautiful rounds of play.

| | 1 | 2 | 3 | 4 | 5 | 6 | 7 | 8 | 9 |
|---|---|---|---|---|---|---|---|---|---|
| PAR | 4 | 3 | 5 | 4 | 3 | 4 | 5 | 4 | 4 |
| YARDS | 280 | 93 | 384 | 375 | 111 | 375 | 401 | 362 | 274 |
| PAR | | | | | | | | | |
| YARDS | | | | | | | | | |

**Directions:** From I-95 take I-395 exit at Bangor towards Downeast Maine; take Exit 6-A/Route 1A towards Ellesworth/Bar Harbor. Travel 5 miles to light, at Route 46 junction take left to Route 9 (5 miles); take right on Route 9 to course, 5 miles on left.

# Searsport Pines Golf Course ✪✪

**57**

240 Mt. Ephraim Road
Searsport, ME (207) 548-2854
www.searsportpines.com

**Club Pro:**
**Payment:** Cash, Visa, MC, Check
**Tee Times:** No
**Fee 9 Holes: Weekday:** $20
**Fee 18 Holes: Weekday:** $30
**Twilight Rates:** No
**Cart Rental:** $15pp/18, $10pp/9
**Lessons:** No **Schools:** No
**Membership:** Yes

| Tees | Holes | Yards | Par | USGA | Slope |
|------|-------|-------|-----|------|-------|
| BACK | | | | | |
| MIDDLE | 9 | 2695 | 36 | 65.9 | 122 |
| FRONT | 9 | 2366 | 35/36 | 68.7 | 116 |

**Weekend:** $20
**Weekend:** $30
**Discounts:** Senior & Junior
**Driving Range:** Yes
**Junior Golf:** Yes
**Architect/Yr Open:** Bert Witten/1997

COUPON

**Other:** Food Concession / Beer / Wine / Club Rentals / Practice Area

Plush greens, manicured fairways, meticulously maintained and fully irrigated. Friendly staff and scenic atmosphere. Easy-walking and enjoyable for all levels of players. Numerous antique shops, Penobscot Marine Museum, restaurants, lodging nearby. Tuesday all day and Sunday after 2pm: 9 holes - $24pp with cart; 18 holes - $36pp with cart.

| | 1 | 2 | 3 | 4 | 5 | 6 | 7 | 8 | 9 |
|---|---|---|---|---|---|---|---|---|---|
| PAR | 4 | 4 | 4 | 4 | 5 | 3 | 4 | 5 | 3 |
| YARDS | 285 | 353 | 313 | 316 | 390 | 150 | 295 | 464 | 129 |
| PAR | | | | | | | | | |
| YARDS | | | | | | | | | |

**Directions:** Route 1 to Searsport Center. Turn left at Tozier's Market in Searsport onto Mt. Ephraim Road. Course is 2 miles on left. 10 minutes from Belfast.

# Squaw Mt. Village Country Club ✪½ **58**

Route 15
Greenville Junction, ME
(207) 695-3609

**Club Pro:** Pat Zoisine, GM
**Payment:** Cash Only
**Tee Times:** No
**Fee 9 Holes: Weekday:** $15
**Fee 18 Holes: Weekday:** $25
**Twilight Rates:** No
**Cart Rental:** $20pp/18, $12pp/9
**Lessons:** No **Schools:** No
**Membership:** Yes
**Other:**

| Tees | Holes | Yards | Par | USGA | Slope |
|------|-------|-------|-----|------|-------|
| BACK | | | | | |
| MIDDLE | 9 | 2341 | 34 | 70 | 113 |
| FRONT | | | | | |

**Weekend:** $15
**Weekend:** $25
**Discounts:** Junior
**Driving Range:** No
**Junior Golf:** Yes
**Architect/Yr Open:** 1922
**GPS:**

Discount on membership for juniors, seniors, and families. Short 9 hole course providing views of Big Squaw Mountain and Moosehead Lake. Having its origin in the 1800's, it still has some of the vintage touches.

| | 1 | 2 | 3 | 4 | 5 | 6 | 7 | 8 | 9 |
|---|---|---|---|---|---|---|---|---|---|
| PAR | 4 | 3 | 5 | 4 | 4 | 3 | 4 | 3 | 4 |
| YARDS | 359 | 121 | 458 | 288 | 267 | 109 | 317 | 119 | 303 |
| PAR | | | | | | | | | |
| YARDS | | | | | | | | | |

**Directions:** I-95 South to Exit 217. Follow Route 6 toward Dover. Stay on 6 to Greenville. Or I-95 South, Exit 185 Bangor, stay on Route 15 North to Greenville. At blinking light in Greenville, go left on Route 15. Course is 3.2 miles on right.

# St. Croix Country Club  ✪✪  ▶59

River Road
Calais, ME (207) 454-8875
www.stcroixcc.com

| Tees | Holes | Yards | Par | USGA | Slope |
|------|-------|-------|-----|------|-------|
| BACK | | | | | |
| MIDDLE | 9 | 2797 | 35 | 65.2 | 107 |
| FRONT | 9 | 2647 | 36 | 64.8 | 119 |

**Club Pro:** Mike Ellis, PGA
**Payment:** Visa, MC
**Tee Times:** No
**Fee 9 Holes: Weekday:** $14      **Weekend:** $14
**Fee 18 Holes: Weekday:** $22      **Weekend:** $22
**Twilight Rates:** No      **Discounts:** Senior
**Cart Rental:** $16pp/18, $10pp/9      **Driving Range:** No
**Lessons:** $30/half hour  **Schools:** No      **Junior Golf:** Yes
**Membership:** Yes      **Architect/Yr Open:** 1927
**Other:** Clubhouse / Showers / Bar-Lounge      **GPS:**

Easternmost golf course in U.S.A. Watch eagles train their young, eagle's nest on hole #7 on river. Call ahead for league or tournament times. Open May 1 - October 31.

| | 1 | 2 | 3 | 4 | 5 | 6 | 7 | 8 | 9 |
|---|---|---|---|---|---|---|---|---|---|
| PAR | 3 | 5 | 4 | 4 | 5 | 3 | 4 | 3 | 4 |
| YARDS | 162 | 495 | 319 | 405 | 495 | 126 | 295 | 188 | 312 |
| PAR | | | | | | | | | |
| YARDS | | | | | | | | | |

**Directions:** Head east on Route 1. Course is 2 miles outside of Calais.

# Streamside Golf Course  ✪½  ▶60

551 Stream Road
Winterport, ME (207) 223-9009
www.golfstreamside.com

| Tees | Holes | Yards | Par | USGA | Slope |
|------|-------|-------|-----|------|-------|
| BACK | 9 | 2915 | 35 | | |
| MIDDLE | 9 | 2700 | 35 | 65.6 | 109 |
| FRONT | 9 | 2355 | 55 | | |

**Club Pro:** Jacob Gran, GM
**Payment:** Visa, MC, Checks
**Tee Times:** No
**Fee 9 Holes: Weekday:** $12      **Weekend:** $15
**Fee 18 Holes: Weekday:** $18      **Weekend:** $22
**Twilight Rates:** No      **Discounts:** Senior and Junior (65+/-15)
**Cart Rental:** $22pp/18, $15pp/9      **Driving Range:** No
**Lessons:** No  **Schools:** No      **Junior Golf:** No
**Membership:** Yes      **Architect/Yr Open:** Galen Wellman/1998
**Other:** Clubhouse / Snack Bar / Putting Course

Situated along the Marsh Stream, this challenging 9 hole layout will be enjoyable to players of all abilities.

| | 1 | 2 | 3 | 4 | 5 | 6 | 7 | 8 | 9 |
|---|---|---|---|---|---|---|---|---|---|
| PAR | 4 | 4 | 3 | 4 | 4 | 3 | 5 | 4 | 4 |
| YARDS | 300 | 240 | 110 | 305 | 240 | 165 | 600 | 440 | 300 |
| PAR | | | | | | | | | |
| YARDS | | | | | | | | | |

**Directions:** Exit 174 off I-95, go east on Route 69 until it joins Route 139. Turn right on Route 139. Go 4 miles – course is on the right.

**N
ME**

# Sugarloaf Golf Club ✪✪✪✪

▶ 61

5092 Access Road (Route 27)
Carrabassett Valley, ME
(207) 237-2000
www.sugarloaf.com

| Tees | Holes | Yards | Par | USGA | Slope |
|------|-------|-------|-----|------|-------|
| BACK | 18 | 6457 | 72 | 72.4 | 143 |
| MIDDLE | 18 | 5946 | 72 | 71.6 | 138 |
| FRONT | 18 | 5289 | 72 | 72.5 | 131 |

**Club Pro:** Zach Zondlo, PGA
**Payment:** Cash, Check, Credit Card
**Tee Times:** Can be made anytime
**Fee  9 Holes: Weekday:** $59     **Weekend:** $59
**Fee 18 Holes: Weekday:** $42-$119     **Weekend:** $60-149
**Twilight Rates:** $59 after 3pm
**Discounts:** Jr-$59 before 2pm, free w/adult after 2pm
**Cart Rental:** $25pp/18, $18pp/9     **Driving Range:** Yes
**Lessons:** $50/half hour  **Schools:** Jr. & Sr.     **Junior Golf:** Yes
**Membership:** Yes     **Architect/Yr Open:** Robert Trent Jones Jr./1985
**Other:** Snack Bar / Restaurant / Bar-Lounge / Health Club / Hotel

Player Comments: "Breathtaking resort course." "Challenging and picturesque." Discounted rates for guests. Improved irrigation in 2014.

|  | 1 | 2 | 3 | 4 | 5 | 6 | 7 | 8 | 9 |
|------|---|---|---|---|---|---|---|---|---|
| PAR | 4 | 5 | 3 | 5 | 4 | 4 | 4 | 3 | 4 |
| YARDS | 372 | 510 | 168 | 466 | 358 | 337 | 331 | 153 | 363 |
|  | 10 | 11 | 12 | 13 | 14 | 15 | 16 | 17 | 18 |
| PAR | 4 | 3 | 5 | 4 | 4 | 3 | 5 | 4 | 4 |
| YARDS | 255 | 166 | 495 | 359 | 333 | 132 | 458 | 339 | 351 |

**Directions:** Route 27. Located 36 miles north of Farmington on Route 27 at Sugarloaf Mountain Ski Resort.

# Traditions Golf Club ✪✪½

▶ 62

1 Main Road
Holden, ME (207) 989-9909
www.traditionsgc.com

| Tees | Holes | Yards | Par | USGA | Slope |
|------|-------|-------|-----|------|-------|
| BACK | 9 | 2619 | 35 | 64.2 | 110 |
| MIDDLE | 9 | 2501 | 35 | 63.2 | 107 |
| FRONT | 9 | 2027 | 35 | 62.4 | 104 |

**Club Pro:** Colin Gillies
**Payment:** Visa, MC, Amex
**Tee Times:** No
**Fee  9 Holes: Weekday:** $15     **Weekend:** $15
**Fee 18 Holes: Weekday:** $22     **Weekend:** $22
**Twilight Rates:** No     **Discounts:** Jr/$10
**Cart Rental:** $10pp/18, $7pp/9     **Driving Range:** Yes
**Lessons:** Yes  **Schools:** Yes     **Junior Golf:** Yes
**Membership:** Yes     **Architect/Yr:** Robert Spasks & Wendell Russell/1997
**Other:** Restaurant / Lounge / Night-Lit Driving Range

New Ownership. Plays par 35 in scenic wooded Maine. Truly a shotmakers course. A challenge for all levels. Easy walker. 2 indoor golf simulators for winter golf. Try our mini-golf and mini-putt.

|  | 1 | 2 | 3 | 4 | 5 | 6 | 7 | 8 | 9 |
|------|---|---|---|---|---|---|---|---|---|
| PAR | 4 | 4 | 4 | 4 | 4 | 5 | 3 | 3 | 4 |
| YARDS | 316 | 248 | 322 | 372 | 262 | 510 | 125 | 140 | 324 |
| PAR |  |  |  |  |  |  |  |  |  |
| YARDS |  |  |  |  |  |  |  |  |  |

**Directions:** I-95 to I-395 to Holden. Exit Route 1A in Holden. Approx. 2 miles south, first property after Holden line, course is on right.

# Va-Jo-Wa Golf Club

**★★** 63

142 Walker Settlement Road
Island Falls, ME (207) 463-2128
www.vajowa.com

**Club Pro:** Warren Walker, Mgr.
**Payment:** MC, Visa, Disc
**Tee Times:**
**Fee 9 Holes: Weekday:** $20
**Fee 18 Holes: Weekday:** $30
**Twilight Rates:**
**Cart Rental:** $18pp/18, $12pp/9
**Lessons:** $40/half hour by appt. **Schools:** No
**Membership:** Yes

| Tees | Holes | Yards | Par | USGA | Slope |
|------|-------|-------|-----|------|-------|
| BACK | 18 | 6250 | 72 | 68.5 | 118 |
| MIDDLE | 18 | 5838 | 72 | 67.5 | 113 |
| FRONT | 18 | 4970 | 72 | 69.6 | 115 |

**Weekend:** $20
**Weekend:** $30
**Discounts:** Junior
**Driving Range:** Yes
**Junior Golf:** July
**Architect/Yr Open:** Vaughn Walker/1965

**Other:** Clubhouse / Snack Bar / Restaurant / Bar-Lounge / Condos / Bag Storage

Only 18-hole course in 80-mile radius. Noted for scenic value and quality layout. Open May 1 - October 31. 16th hole and most of the back 9, great scenery including view of Mt. Katahdin.

| | 1 | 2 | 3 | 4 | 5 | 6 | 7 | 8 | 9 |
|------|-----|-----|-----|-----|-----|-----|-----|-----|-----|
| PAR | 4 | 5 | 4 | 3 | 4 | 4 | 3 | 5 | 4 |
| YARDS | 303 | 460 | 278 | 192 | 369 | 274 | 115 | 492 | 408 |
| | 10 | 11 | 12 | 13 | 14 | 15 | 16 | 17 | 18 |
| PAR | 4 | 3 | 4 | 5 | 4 | 4 | 3 | 4 | 5 |
| YARDS | 281 | 130 | 361 | 470 | 372 | 303 | 175 | 355 | 500 |

**Directions:** I-95 to Exit 276; follow Route 2 East 3 miles; look for signs to Va-Jo-Wa.

# Waterville Country Club

**★★★½** 64

Route 137
Oakland, ME (207) 465-9861
www.watervillecountryclub.com

**Club Pro:** Don Roberts, PGA
**Payment:** Cash, Visa, MC
**Tee Times:** Yes
**Fee 9 Holes: Weekday:** No
**Fee 18 Holes: Weekday:** $65
**Twilight Rates:** No
**Cart Rental:** $15pp/18
**Lessons:** $35/half hour **Schools:** No
**Membership:** Yes
**Other:** Snack Bar / Restaurant / Bar-Lounge

| Tees | Holes | Yards | Par | USGA | Slope |
|------|-------|-------|-----|------|-------|
| BACK | 18 | 6427 | 70 | 70.1 | 123 |
| MIDDLE | 18 | 6108 | 70 | 68.6 | 118 |
| FRONT | 18 | 5381 | 70 | 71.3 | 119 |

**Weekend:** No
**Weekend:** $65
**Discounts:** None
**Driving Range:** $3/bucket
**Junior Golf:** Yes
**Architect/Yr Open:** Cornish/1916; Orrin Smith
**GPS:** Yes

Excellent for all golfers. Semi-private. "Great views, great layout." –FP

**N
ME**

| | 1 | 2 | 3 | 4 | 5 | 6 | 7 | 8 | 9 |
|------|-----|-----|-----|-----|-----|-----|-----|-----|-----|
| PAR | 4 | 3 | 5 | 4 | 4 | 3 | 4 | 4 | 5 |
| YARDS | 350 | 140 | 455 | 378 | 430 | 170 | 300 | 385 | 505 |
| | 10 | 11 | 12 | 13 | 14 | 15 | 16 | 17 | 18 |
| PAR | 4 | 4 | 4 | 3 | 4 | 4 | 3 | 4 | 4 |
| YARDS | 435 | 410 | 370 | 200 | 355 | 330 | 185 | 370 | 340 |

**Directions:** I-95 North to Exit 127 to Route 137 West to Oakland. Waterville Country Club is 1.5 miles on left.

# Whitetail Golf Course

373 School Road
Charleston, ME (207) 285-7730
www.whitetailgolfmaine.com

**Club Pro:** Ken Martin
**Payment:** Cash or Check
**Tee Times:** No
**Fee 9 Holes: Weekday:** $15/walk; $25/cart
**Fee 18 Holes: Weekday:** $22/walk; $35/cart
**Twilight Rates:** No
**Cart Rental:**
**Lessons:** No **Schools:** No
**Membership:** Yes
**Other:** Clubhouse

| Tees | Holes | Yards | Par | USGA | Slope |
|---|---|---|---|---|---|
| BACK | 9 | 2814 | 34 | 66.1 | 114 |
| MIDDLE | 9 | 2637 | 34 | 66.1 | 114 |
| FRONT | 9 | 2358 | 34 | 66.6 | 106 |

**Weekend:** $15/walk, $25 w/cart
**Weekend:** $22/walk, $35 w/cart
**Discounts:** None
**Driving Range:** No
**Junior Golf:**
**Architect/Yr Open:** Scott Duthie/1997
**GPS:**

Scenic, country setting. with rolling hills and 40 different tees, making it challenging and fun for all abilities.

| | 1 | 2 | 3 | 4 | 5 | 6 | 7 | 8 | 9 |
|---|---|---|---|---|---|---|---|---|---|
| PAR | 5 | 3 | 3 | 4 | 3 | 4 | 5 | 4 | 4 |
| YARDS | 494 | 136 | 176 | 235 | 150 | 329 | 390 | 370 | 357 |
| PAR | | | | | | | | | |
| YARDS | | | | | | | | | |

**Directions:** I-95 to Bangor, exit North on Route 15. Go approximately 30 miles. Course is at the corner of Route 15 and School Road in Charleston. Turn right.

# Wilson Lake Country Club

320 Weld Road
Wilton, ME (207) 645-2016
www.wilsonlakecc.com

**Club Pro:** Joshua Best
**Payment:** Visa, MC
**Tee Times:** 1 day adv.
**Fee 9 Holes: Weekday:** $20
**Fee 18 Holes: Weekday:** $30
**Twilight Rates:** 4pm weekdays
**Cart Rental:** $15pp/18, $8pp/9
**Lessons:** Yes **Schools:** No
**Membership:** Yes
**Other:** Clubhouse / Bar-Lounge / Snack Bar

| Tees | Holes | Yards | Par | USGA | Slope |
|---|---|---|---|---|---|
| BACK | 9 | 3162 | 35 | 68.4 | 120 |
| MIDDLE | 9 | 3040 | 35 | 68.0 | 120 |
| FRONT | 9 | 2804 | 37 | 72.2 | 126 |

**Weekend:** $20
**Weekend:** $30
**Discounts:** Lung Card
**Driving Range:** No
**Junior Golf:** Yes
**Architect/Yr Open:** Wayne Stiles/1932

Considered by many to be "the best nine in Maine" in picturesque Wilton. Although the routing includes five parallel holes, the uphill and downhill nature of their path from the clubhouse to the lower points of the property demand second shots of varying lengths. Noted for having some of the best greens in the state.

| | 1 | 2 | 3 | 4 | 5 | 6 | 7 | 8 | 9 |
|---|---|---|---|---|---|---|---|---|---|
| PAR | 4 | 3 | 5 | 4 | 4 | 4 | 3 | 4 | 4 |
| YARDS | 402 | 153 | 501 | 420 | 366 | 377 | 140 | 329 | 352 |
| PAR | | | | | | | | | |
| YARDS | | | | | | | | | |

**Directions:** Route 4 to Route 2 to Route 156 into Wilton. Course is on Weld Road in Wilton.

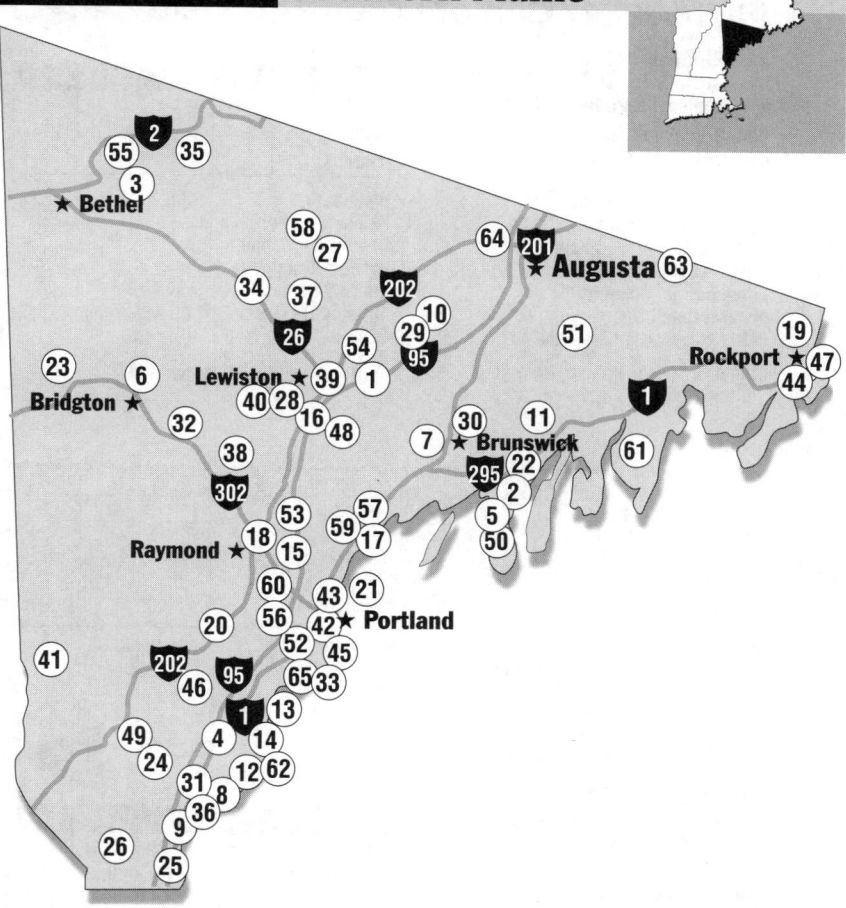

| | | | | | |
|---|---|---|---|---|---|
| Apple Valley GC | 1 | Lake Kezar CC | 23 | Sable Oaks Golf Club | 45 |
| Bath Golf Club | 2 | Lebanon Pines GC | 24 | Salmon Falls GC | 46 |
| Bethel Inn & CC | 3 | The Ledges Golf Club | 25 | Samoset Resort GC | 47 |
| Biddeford & Saco CC | 4 | The Links at Outlook | 26 | Sandy River GC | 48 |
| Boothbay Harbor CC | 5 | Maple Lane Inn and GC | 27 | Sanford Country Club | 49 |
| Bridgton Highlands CC | 6 | Martindale CC | 28 | Sebasco Harbor Resort GC | 50 |
| Brunswick Golf Club | 7 | The Meadows Golf Club | 29 | Sheepscot Links | 51 |
| Cape Arundel Golf Club | 8 | Mere Creek | 30 | South Portland Muni. | 52 |
| Cape Neddick CC | 9 | Merriland Farm Par 3 GC | 31 | Spring Meadows GC | 53 |
| Cobbossee Colony GC | 10 | Naples Golf and CC | 32 | Springbrook GC | 54 |
| Country Fareways | 11 | Nonesuch River GC | 33 | Sunday River Golf Club | 55 |
| Deep Brook Golf Course | 12 | Norway Country Club | 34 | Sunset Ridge Golf Links | 56 |
| Dunegrass Golf Club | 13 | Oakdale Country Club | 35 | Toddy Brook Golf Course | 57 |
| Dutch Elm Golf Course | 14 | Old Marsh Country Club | 36 | Turner Highland GC | 58 |
| Fairlawn Golf Club | 15 | Paris Hill Country Club | 37 | Twin Falls Golf Club | 59 |
| Fox Ridge Golf Club | 16 | Point Sebago Golf Club | 38 | Val Halla Golf Course | 60 |
| Freeport Country Club | 17 | Poland Spring CC | 39 | Wawenock CC | 61 |
| Frye Island Golf Course | 18 | Prospect Hill GC | 40 | Webhannet Golf Club | 62 |
| Goose River GC | 19 | Province Lake Golf Club | 41 | West Appleton CC | 63 |
| Gorham Country Club | 20 | Rivermeadow GC | 42 | Western View Golf Club | 64 |
| Great Chebeague Golf Club | 21 | Riverside Muni. GC | 43 | Willowdale Golf Club | 65 |
| Highland Green Golf Club | 22 | Rockland Golf Club | 44 | | |

**KEY TO THE STAR RATINGS:**
**5✪** = Outstanding  **4✪** = Excellent  **3✪** = Very Good  **2✪** = Good  **1✪** = Average  **NR** = Not Rated

# Apple Valley Golf Course ✪✪

316 Pinewoods Road
Lewiston, ME (207) 784-9773
www.applevaleygolfersclub.com

**Club Pro:** Gard Craw, Manager
**Payment:** Cash, Credit
**Tee Times:** Not required
**Fee 9 Holes: Weekday:** $15
**Fee 18 Holes: Weekday:** $24
**Twilight Rates:** After 3pm
**Cart Rental:** $15pp/18, $9pp/9
**Lessons:** No **Schools:** No
**Membership:** Yes
**Other:** Clubhouse / Snack Bar

| Tees | Holes | Yards | Par | USGA | Slope |
|------|-------|-------|-----|------|-------|
| BACK | | | | | |
| MIDDLE | 9 | 2473 | 35 | 63.9 | 104 |
| FRONT | | | | | |

**Weekend:** $15
**Weekend:** $24
**Discounts:** Junior
**Driving Range:** No
**Junior Golf:** Yes
**Architect/Yr Open:** Arthur David Chapman/1962
**GPS:**

COUPON

Open April 15 - November 15. New Apple Valley Estates golf residential community being built.

| | 1 | 2 | 3 | 4 | 5 | 6 | 7 | 8 | 9 |
|-----|-----|-----|-----|-----|-----|-----|-----|-----|-----|
| PAR | 4 | 4 | 3 | 5 | 3 | 4 | 4 | 4 | 4 |
| YARDS | 235 | 256 | 147 | 445 | 108 | 333 | 299 | 300 | 350 |
| PAR | | | | | | | | | |
| YARDS | | | | | | | | | |

**Directions:** Maine Turnpike to Exit 80 (Route 196 East) for 4 miles. Right onto Dyer Road. Left onto Pinewoods Road. Course is 2 miles on left.

# Bath Golf Club ✪✪✪

387 Whiskeag Road
Bath, ME (207) 442-8411
www.harrisgolfonline.com

**Club Pro:** Joe Cahoon
**Payment:** Cash, Credit Cards
**Tee Times:** Yes
**Fee 9 Holes: Weekday:** $25
**Fee 18 Holes: Weekday:** $40
**Twilight Rates:** No
**Cart Rental:** $13pp/18, $8pp/9
**Lessons:** Yes **Schools:** No
**Membership:** Yes
**Other:** Clubhouse / Restaurant / Lounge / Lockers

| Tees | Holes | Yards | Par | USGA | Slope |
|------|-------|-------|-----|------|-------|
| BACK | 18 | 6301 | 70 | 70.8 | 130 |
| MIDDLE | 18 | 5840 | 70 | 68.3 | 129 |
| FRONT | 18 | 4708 | 70 | 67.9 | 108 |

**Weekend:** $25
**Weekend:** $40
**Discounts:** No
**Driving Range:** No
**Junior Golf:** Yes
**Architect/Yr Open:** Wayne Stiles/1932
**GPS:** Yes

Fairways are tight and tree-lined. Paved cart paths. 8th hole is an outstanding par 4. Series of lessons offered. "Excellent course conditions. Friendly staff. Nice layout." –FP

| | 1 | 2 | 3 | 4 | 5 | 6 | 7 | 8 | 9 |
|-----|-----|-----|-----|-----|-----|-----|-----|-----|-----|
| PAR | 4 | 4 | 5 | 4 | 4 | 3 | 4 | 4 | 3 |
| YARDS | 338 | 375 | 500 | 370 | 325 | 160 | 420 | 425 | 178 |
| | 10 | 11 | 12 | 13 | 14 | 15 | 16 | 17 | 18 |
| PAR | 4 | 4 | 4 | 3 | 4 | 4 | 3 | 5 | 4 |
| YARDS | 258 | 326 | 275 | 115 | 352 | 356 | 163 | 525 | 352 |

**Directions:** I-295 to Route 1 North. From 1 North take New Meadows Road exit. Go right at stop sign. Go 1¼ miles to next stop sign. Go straight through onto Ridge Road for 1¼ miles to 18th tee. Go right.

# Bethel Inn & Country Club ✪✪ ▶ 3

21 Broad Street
Bethel, ME (207) 824-6276
www.bethelinn.com

| Tees | Holes | Yards | Par | USGA | Slope |
|------|-------|-------|-----|------|-------|
| BACK | 18 | 6663 | 72 | 71.0 | 128 |
| MIDDLE | 18 | 6017 | 72 | 67.9 | 122 |
| FRONT | 18 | 5280 | 72 | 71.5 | 129 |

**Club Pro:** Chris Bourasso, PGA
**Payment:** MC, Visa, Amex, Cash
**Tee Times:** 2 days adv.
**Fee 9 Holes: Weekday:** $27    **Weekend:** $27
**Fee 18 Holes: Weekday:** $50    **Weekend:** $50
**Twilight Rates:** No    **Discounts:** No
**Cart Rental:** $18pp/18, $13pp/9    **Driving Range:** $5/lg. bucket
**Lessons:** $50/half hour   **Schools:** Yes    **Junior Golf:** Yes
**Membership:** Yes    **Architect/Yr Open:** Geoffrey Cornish/1913
**Other:** Clubhouse / Showers / Snack Bar / Restaurant / Bar / Lodging

COUPON

The Guaranteed Performance School of Golf at this Cornish-designed course highlights the summer season. New draining and watering. "Great views. We were treated very well."

| | 1 | 2 | 3 | 4 | 5 | 6 | 7 | 8 | 9 |
|---|---|---|---|---|---|---|---|---|---|
| PAR | 4 | 4 | 3 | 4 | 5 | 3 | 4 | 5 | 4 |
| YARDS | 340 | 262 | 130 | 370 | 492 | 141 | 361 | 500 | 292 |
| | 10 | 11 | 12 | 13 | 14 | 15 | 16 | 17 | 18 |
| PAR | 4 | 5 | 3 | 4 | 4 | 4 | 3 | 5 | 4 |
| YARDS | 325 | 546 | 167 | 294 | 397 | 400 | 151 | 506 | 343 |

**Directions:** Maine Turnpike to Exit 63 Gray. Take Route 26 North to Bethel. Route 26 becomes Main Street in Bethel. Follow Main Street to the top. Course is on left behind Main Inn.

# Biddeford & Saco Country Club ✪✪✪ ▶ 4

101 Old Orchard Road
Saco, ME (207) 282-5883
www.biddefordsacocountryclub.com

| Tees | Holes | Yards | Par | USGA | Slope |
|------|-------|-------|-----|------|-------|
| BACK | 18 | 6333 | 71 | 69.6 | 130 |
| MIDDLE | 18 | 5918 | 71 | 68.6 | 123 |
| FRONT | 18 | 5319 | 72 | 71.4 | 117 |

**Club Pro:** Tim Angis, PGA
**Payment:** All Major
**Tee Times:** 3 days adv., June-Sept.
**Fee 9 Holes: Weekday:**    **Weekend:**
**Fee 18 Holes: Weekday:** $45    **Weekend:** $55
**Twilight Rates:** No    **Discounts:** No
**Cart Rental:** $18pp/18, $9pp/9    **Driving Range:** $4/bucket
**Lessons:** Call for details   **Schools:** No    **Junior Golf:** Yes
**Membership:** Yes    **Architect/Yr Open:** Donald Ross/1922
**Other:** Restaurant / Snack Bar / Bar-Lounge / Lockers / Showers

S
ME

User friendly but still a challenge, wonderful playing condition in a pretty and peaceful atmosphere. "New practice facility, the best around. Nice greens." –MH

| | 1 | 2 | 3 | 4 | 5 | 6 | 7 | 8 | 9 |
|---|---|---|---|---|---|---|---|---|---|
| PAR | 4 | 3 | 5 | 4 | 4 | 4 | 4 | 3 | 4 |
| YARDS | 344 | 186 | 501 | 322 | 400 | 339 | 336 | 164 | 424 |
| | 10 | 11 | 12 | 13 | 14 | 15 | 16 | 17 | 18 |
| PAR | 3 | 4 | 5 | 4 | 4 | 3 | 4 | 5 | 4 |
| YARDS | 146 | 443 | 466 | 354 | 314 | 129 | 326 | 411 | 313 |

**Directions:** I-95 to Exit 36 Maine Turnpike. Straight to Rotary. Take right on Old Orchard Road, course is ½ mile on left.

# Boothbay Harbor Country Club ✪✪✪✪

▶ 5

50 Sugar Maple Lane
Boothbay, ME (207) 633-3673
www.boothbayharborcc.com

| Tees | Holes | Yards | Par | USGA | Slope |
|------|-------|-------|-----|------|-------|
| BACK | 18 | 6466 | 71 | 71.4 | 139 |
| MIDDLE | 18 | 6076 | 71 | 69.7 | 135 |
| FRONT | 18 | 4624 | 71 | 67.7 | 124 |

**Club Pro:** Chad Penman
**Payment:** Visa, MC, Amex
**Tee Times:** Call for availabilty
**Fee 9 Holes: Weekday:** $100
**Fee 18 Holes: Weekday:** $175
**Twilight Rates:** After 3pm
**Cart Rental:** $25pp/18, $18pp/9
**Lessons:** Yes **Schools:** No
**Membership:** Yes
**Architect/Yr:** Stiles & Van Kleek/1921, Redesigned - Hepner/2014
**Other:** Restaurant / Clubhouse / Bar-Lounge

**Weekend:** $100, $75 off-season
**Weekend:** $175, $125 off-season
**Discounts:** No
**Driving Range:** Yes
**Junior Golf:** Yes

Beautiful coastal gem. Rolling fairways with fast undulating greens. Four new green complexes, increased length and newly positioned bunkers have greatly improved playing conditions. Fantastic vistas and incredible landscaping throughout the course. "Great getaway area. One of the most fun courses you'll ever play!" –FP

|  | 1 | 2 | 3 | 4 | 5 | 6 | 7 | 8 | 9 |
|------|---|---|---|---|---|---|---|---|---|
| PAR | 4 | 3 | 4 | 4 | 4 | 5 | 3 | 4 | 5 |
| YARDS | 322 | 196 | 394 | 300 | 406 | 466 | 184 | 361 | 495 |
|  | 10 | 11 | 12 | 13 | 14 | 15 | 16 | 17 | 18 |
| PAR | 4 | 4 | 4 | 4 | 4 | 3 | 4 | 3 | 5 |
| YARDS | 346 | 348 | 384 | 336 | 346 | 142 | 357 | 178 | 515 |

**Directions:** Via I-95, take Exit 48 onto Route 302. In Bridgton, turn right off Main Street at sign onto Highland Road and travel 1½ miles to course. From New Hampshire, follow Route 302 from Conway area to Bridgton. On Main Street, turn left at sign onto Highland Road.

# Bridgton Highlands Country Club ✪✪✪

▶ 6

379 Highland Road
Bridgton, ME (207) 647-3491
www.bridgtonhighlands.com

| Tees | Holes | Yards | Par | USGA | Slope |
|------|-------|-------|-----|------|-------|
| BACK | 18 | 6224 | 72 | 70.4 | 128 |
| MIDDLE | 18 | 5810 | 72 | 69.0 | 123 |
| FRONT | 18 | 5300 | 74 | 66.5 | 117 |

**Club Manager:** Jim Mains
**Payment:** Cash, Check, Visa, MC, Disc
**Tee Times:** By phone or online
**Fee 9 Holes: Weekday:** $18-$20
**Fee 18 Holes: Weekday:** $25-$30
**Twilight Rates:** After 3pm
**Cart Rental:** $17pp/18, $9pp/9
**Lessons:** Available **Schools:** No
**Membership:** Yes (see website)
**Other:** Snack Bar / Full Bar / 4 Tennis Courts & Tennis Program

**Weekend:** $18-$20
**Weekend:** $30-$36
**Discounts:** Junior, Military
**Driving Range:** Yes
**Junior Golf:** Yes
**Architect/Yr Open:** A.W. Tillinghast/1927

18 holes of challenging and enjoyable golf in the scenic Lakes Region of western Maine with views of Pleasant Mountain/Shawnee Peak and the White Mountains of New Hampshire, including Mount Washington. "Very nice layout with a variety of thinking holes." –FP

|  | 1 | 2 | 3 | 4 | 5 | 6 | 7 | 8 | 9 |
|------|---|---|---|---|---|---|---|---|---|
| PAR | 4 | 3 | 4 | 5 | 4 | 4 | 5 | 3 | 4 |
| YARDS | 434 | 152 | 377 | 437 | 333 | 313 | 413 | 148 | 328 |
|  | 10 | 11 | 12 | 13 | 14 | 15 | 16 | 17 | 18 |
| PAR | 3 | 4 | 4 | 3 | 4 | 5 | 4 | 4 | 5 |
| YARDS | 153 | 324 | 383 | 152 | 350 | 442 | 282 | 296 | 493 |

**Directions:** I-95 to Exit 48 onto Route 302 West. In Bridgton, turn right off Main Street onto Highland Road. Travel 1.5 miles to course. From NH: follow Route 302 fron Conway to Bridgton. On Main Street turn left onto Highland Road.

# Brunswick Golf Club

 ✪✪✪½ 7

165 River Road
Brunswick, ME (207) 725-8224
www.brunswickgolfclub.com

**Club Pro:** A. J. Kavanaugh, Dir. of Golf
**Payment:** Visa, MC, Disc
**Tee Times:** Anytime

| Tees | Holes | Yards | Par | USGA | Slope |
|------|-------|-------|-----|------|-------|
| BACK | 18 | 6609 | 72 | 69.9 | 126 |
| MIDDLE | 18 | 6251 | 72 | 70 | 123 |
| FRONT | 18 | 5772 | 74 | 71.6 | 123 |

**Fee  9 Holes: Weekday:** $25
**Fee 18 Holes: Weekday:** $40
**Twilight Rates:** After 4pm
**Cart Rental:** $15pp/18, $10pp/9
**Lessons:** $65/hour **Schools:** No
**Membership:** Yes

**Weekend:** $25
**Weekend:** $50
**Discounts:** Junior
**Driving Range:** Yes
**Junior Golf:** Yes

COUPON

**Architect/Yr Open:** Front: Cornish/1960; Back: Stiles & Van Cleek/1920
**Other:** Clubhouse / Deck / Snack Bar / Bar-Lounge / Lockers

A real classic layout, a must-play. "Easiest, challenging course to walk in New England." –FP

| | 1 | 2 | 3 | 4 | 5 | 6 | 7 | 8 | 9 |
|------|-----|-----|-----|-----|-----|-----|-----|-----|-----|
| PAR | 4 | 5 | 5 | 3 | 3 | 4 | 4 | 4 | 5 |
| YARDS | 355 | 547 | 485 | 179 | 110 | 440 | 332 | 364 | 494 |
| | 10 | 11 | 12 | 13 | 14 | 15 | 16 | 17 | 18 |
| PAR | 4 | 3 | 4 | 4 | 4 | 3 | 5 | 4 | 4 |
| YARDS | 353 | 172 | 297 | 363 | 430 | 145 | 490 | 300 | 395 |

**Directions:** I-295 to Exit 28, Brunswick; at 2nd light take left onto River Road. Follow 1 mile to course on left.

# Cape Arundel Golf Club

 ✪✪✪ 8

19 River Road
Kennebunkport, ME (207) 967-3494
www.capearundelgolfclub.com

**Club Pro:** Ken Raynor
**Payment:** Visa, MC, Amex
**Tee Times:** 3 days adv.

| Tees | Holes | Yards | Par | USGA | Slope |
|------|-------|-------|-----|------|-------|
| BACK | 18 | 5881 | 69 | 67.1 | 118 |
| MIDDLE | 18 | 5310 | 69 | 63.7 | 100 |
| FRONT | 18 | 5026 | 70 | 69.7 | 119 |

**Fee  9 Holes: Weekday:** $55
**Fee 18 Holes: Weekday:** $75
**Twilight Rates:** $35 after 4pm
**Cart Rental:** $20pp/18, $14pp/9
**Lessons:** Yes **Schools:** No
**Membership:**
**Other:** Clubhouse / Lockers

**Weekend:** $55
**Weekend:** $75
**Discounts:** Voucher books available
**Driving Range:** No
**Junior Golf:** No
**Architect/Yr Open:** Walter Travis/1921
**GPS:**

Home course of President Bush's family. Members only 11am - 2:30pm daily. Twilight rates are not available during July and August.

| | 1 | 2 | 3 | 4 | 5 | 6 | 7 | 8 | 9 |
|------|-----|-----|-----|-----|-----|-----|-----|-----|-----|
| PAR | 4 | 4 | 3 | 4 | 4 | 3 | 4 | 4 | 5 |
| YARDS | 375 | 311 | 154 | 398 | 350 | 118 | 381 | 370 | 480 |
| | 10 | 11 | 12 | 13 | 14 | 15 | 16 | 17 | 18 |
| PAR | 4 | 4 | 4 | 3 | 4 | 4 | 3 | 4 | 4 |
| YARDS | 345 | 320 | 409 | 165 | 387 | 322 | 220 | 365 | 394 |

**Directions:** From South I-95 to Wells Exit 19. Left to Route 1.2 miles to right on Route 9 to Kennebunkport. From North I-95 Exit 32.

S
ME

# Cape Neddick Country Club ✪✪✪ ▶9

**650 Shore Road**
**Cape Neddick, ME  (207) 361-2011**
www.capeneddickgolf.com

**Club Pro:** Dustin Hunter
**Payment:** Visa, MC
**Tee Times:** 7 days adv.

| Tees | Holes | Yards | Par | USGA | Slope |
|------|-------|-------|-----|------|-------|
| BACK | 18 | 6066 | 70 | 69.3 | 119 |
| MIDDLE | 18 | 5698 | 70 | 67.5 | 116 |
| FRONT | 18 | 4904 | 71 | 69.1 | 121 |

**Fee  9 Holes: Weekday:** $35 M-Th
**Fee 18 Holes: Weekday:** $56 M-Th
**Twilight Rates:** $39 (with cart) after 3pm
**Cart Rental:** $18pp/18, $10pp/9
**Lessons:** $30/half hour  **Schools:** Yes
**Membership:** Yes
**Other:** Restaurant / Clubhouse / Lockers / Bar-Lounge / Driving Range

**Weekend:** $38
**Weekend:** $63
**Discounts:** None
**Driving Range:** Yes
**Junior Golf:** Yes
**Architect/Yr:** Donald Ross/1920; Brian Silva/1999

COUPON

Player Comments: "Challenging; back 9 tougher than first 9. Fun for all skills." "Good summer vacation course. Nice ocean setting." Semi-private. Just 1 hour North of Boston. Best-conditioned course in Southern Maine! Accepts Players Pass and Lung Card.

|  | 1 | 2 | 3 | 4 | 5 | 6 | 7 | 8 | 9 |
|------|----|----|----|----|----|----|----|----|----|
| PAR | 4 | 3 | 5 | 4 | 4 | 3 | 4 | 3 | 4 |
| YARDS | 340 | 168 | 577 | 302 | 305 | 122 | 300 | 151 | 326 |
|  | 10 | 11 | 12 | 13 | 14 | 15 | 16 | 17 | 18 |
| PAR | 4 | 3 | 5 | 4 | 3 | 5 | 4 | 4 | 4 |
| YARDS | 432 | 153 | 518 | 384 | 170 | 540 | 324 | 268 | 318 |

**Directions:** From the South: I-95 to Exit 7 (York); go east .5 mile to U.S. 1. Go north for 3.4 miles to River Road. East on River Road for 1 mile to Shore Road. Club is 2.8 miles north on Shore Road.

# Cobbossee Colony Golf Course ✪✪ ▶10

**885 Cobbossee Road**
**Monmouth, ME  (207) 268-4182**
www.golfcobbossee.com

**Club Pro:** Bill Sylvester, Manager
**Payment:** Cash, Check, Visa, MC
**Tee Times:** No

| Tees | Holes | Yards | Par | USGA | Slope |
|------|-------|-------|-----|------|-------|
| BACK |  |  |  |  |  |
| MIDDLE | 9 | 2390 | 34 | 61.3 | 95 |
| FRONT |  |  |  |  |  |

**Fee  9 Holes: Weekday:** $13
**Fee 18 Holes: Weekday:** $18
**Twilight Rates:** After 5pm
**Cart Rental:** $20/18, $14/9 per cart
**Lessons:** Yes  **Schools:** No
**Membership:** Yes
**Other:** Snack Bar / Clubhouse

**Weekend:** $14
**Weekend:** $19
**Discounts:** Jr. Golf Card
**Driving Range:** Yes
**Junior Golf:** No
**Architect/Yr Open:** Lee & Royal Cottrell/1922
**GPS:**

COUPON

It's an easy walk, and fun. Practice green.

|  | 1 | 2 | 3 | 4 | 5 | 6 | 7 | 8 | 9 |
|------|----|----|----|----|----|----|----|----|----|
| PAR | 5 | 3 | 4 | 4 | 3 | 4 | 3 | 4 | 4 |
| YARDS | 450 | 140 | 246 | 312 | 216 | 331 | 108 | 293 | 294 |
|  |  |  |  |  |  |  |  |  |  |
| PAR |  |  |  |  |  |  |  |  |  |
| YARDS |  |  |  |  |  |  |  |  |  |

**Directions:** From Brunswick area, Exit 51 off I-295 Gardiner - Litchfield. Go approximately 6 miles west on Route 126. Right onto Hallowell Road for 1.5 miles. Left onto Hardscrabble Road. Course is about 1.5 miles on both sides of the road.

# Country Fareways

**⚙⚙** 11 ▶

1549 Augusta Road
Bowdoin, ME (207) 666-5603
www.countryfareways.com

| Tees | Holes | Yards | Par | USGA | Slope |
|------|-------|-------|-----|------|-------|
| BACK | | | | | |
| MIDDLE | 10 | 1248 | 30 | | 121 |
| FRONT | 10 | 1131 | 30 | | 120 |

**Club Pro:**
**Payment:** Visa, MC, Disc, Cash, Checks
**Tee Times:** No
**Fee 10 Holes: Weekday:** $13
**Fee 18 Holes: Weekday:** $17
**Twilight Rates:** No
**Cart Rental:** $17pp/18, $13pp/9
**Lessons:** No **Schools:** No
**Membership:** No
**Other:** 10-Play Package - Buy 9 Rounds, Play 10th Free

**Weekend:** $13
**Weekend:** $17
**Discounts:** Seniors/Juniors/Military/Veterans
**Driving Range:** No
**Junior Golf:** Yes, Jrs. free w/paying adult
**Architect/Yr Open:** Dennis Gallant/1996

Well-groomed and beautifully landscaped. Great place to practice your short game. Beginner friendly but challenging. Improvement to #5green drainage. Some of the best greens in the area. New course record set August 25, 2013: "29" by owner Dennis Gallant.

| | 1 | 2 | 3 | 4 | 5 | 6 | 7 | 8 | 9 |
|---|---|---|---|---|---|---|---|---|---|
| PAR | 3 | 3 | 3 | 3 | 3 | 3 | 3 | 3 | 3 |
| YARDS | 132 | 108 | 148 | 119 | 104 | 134 | 96 | 132 | 100 |
| | 10 | 11 | 12 | 13 | 14 | 15 | 16 | 17 | 18 |
| PAR | 3 | | | | | | | | |
| YARDS | 58 | | | | | | | | |

**Directions:** Route I-295 to Exit 37. From north ramp turn right. From south ramp turn left. Turn right on Route 125 and go to the stop sign. Turn right on Route 201. Course is 1 mile on right.

# Deep Brook Golf Course

**⚙⚙½** 12 ▶

36 New County Road
Saco, ME (207) 283-3500
www.deepbrookgolfcourse.com

| Tees | Holes | Yards | Par | USGA | Slope |
|------|-------|-------|-----|------|-------|
| BACK | 9 | 3076 | 36 | 70.0 | 129 |
| MIDDLE | 9 | 2831 | 36 | 67.8 | 127 |
| FRONT | 9 | 2312 | 36 | 67.6 | 111 |

**Club Pro:** Donald Guay, Manager
**Payment:** Cash or Credit Cards
**Tee Times:** 1 day adv.
**Fee 9 Holes: Weekday:** $19
**Fee 18 Holes: Weekday:** $30
**Twilight Rates:** After 4pm
**Cart Rental:** $20 pp/18, $14pp/9
**Lessons:** Yes **Schools:**
**Membership:**
**Other:** Clubhouse / Snack Bar

**Weekend:** $24
**Weekend:** $34
**Discounts:**
**Driving Range:** No
**Junior Golf:** Yes
**Architect/Yr Open:** William Bradley Booth/2001
**GPS:**

COUPON

Challenging course, geographicaly accessible for daily play. Tee lengths change on back 9. Open April - Snow. "A work in progress. Nice finishing hole." –RW

**S ME**

| | 1 | 2 | 3 | 4 | 5 | 6 | 7 | 8 | 9 |
|---|---|---|---|---|---|---|---|---|---|
| PAR | 4 | 4 | 3 | 4 | 5 | 3 | 5 | 4 | 4 |
| YARDS | 389 | 399 | 150 | 287 | 566 | 119 | 472 | 352 | 342 |
| PAR | | | | | | | | | |
| YARDS | | | | | | | | | |

**Directions:** Exit 5 from Maine Turnpike. Left at traffic light onto Industrial Park Road to first light; take left at light. Next light go right, then first left onto Garfield Street to end at light onto Route 5. Course is 1 mile on left.

# Dunegrass Golf Club ✪✪✪✪  13▶

200 Wild Dunes Way
Old Orchard Beach, ME
(207) 934-4513
www.dunegrass.com

| Tees | Holes | Yards | Par | USGA | Slope |
|------|-------|-------|-----|------|-------|
| BACK | 18 | 6644 | 72 | 71.6 | 134 |
| MIDDLE | 18 | 6266 | 72 | 68.8 | 125 |
| FRONT | 18 | 4920 | 72 | 68.0 | 113 |

**Club Pro:** Ron Bibeau, PGA
**Payment:** Cash, Visa, MC, Amex
**Tee Times:** 7 days adv.
**Fee 9 Holes: Weekday:** $30 **Weekend:** $30
**Fee 18 Holes: Weekday:** $57 ($50 12-3pm) **Weekend:** $57 ($50 12-3pm)
**Twilight Rates:** After 3pm **Discounts:** None
**Cart Rental:** $18pp/18, $12pp/9 **Driving Range:** Yes
**Lessons:** Yes **Schools:** No **Junior Golf:** Yes
**Membership:** Yes, semi-private **Architect/Yr Open:** Dan Maples/1999
**Other:** New Clubhouse / Restaurant / Lockers-Showers / Bar-Lounge / Hotel / Inn

COUPON

Player Comments: "Great staff, fine conditions." "Visit once and you'll return. Super layout." –GD
Vacation packages available. $25/walking, $39/riding after 3pm. All you can play - $30 w/cart after 5pm.
Call for shoulder season rates.

| | 1 | 2 | 3 | 4 | 5 | 6 | 7 | 8 | 9 |
|---|---|---|---|---|---|---|---|---|---|
| PAR | 5 | 3 | 4 | 4 | 4 | 4 | 5 | 3 | 4 |
| YARDS | 539 | 140 | 387 | 301 | 368 | 348 | 526 | 163 | 333 |
| | 10 | 11 | 12 | 13 | 14 | 15 | 16 | 17 | 18 |
| PAR | 4 | 3 | 5 | 3 | 4 | 5 | 4 | 3 | 5 |
| YARDS | 376 | 168 | 500 | 175 | 395 | 443 | 410 | 170 | 524 |

**Directions:** I-95 to Exit 36 at I-195 to Exit 2B (Route 1 North). Travel about .1 mile on Route 1 to
Ross Road on right. Take Ross Road for about 2 miles. See Wild Dunes Way and golf course on right.

# Dutch Elm Golf Course ✪✪ 14▶

5 Brimstone Road
Arundel, ME (207) 282-9850
www.dutchelmgolf.com

| Tees | Holes | Yards | Par | USGA | Slope |
|------|-------|-------|-----|------|-------|
| BACK | 18 | 6314 | 72 | 70.8 | 127 |
| MIDDLE | 18 | 5934 | 72 | 68.8 | 125 |
| FRONT | 18 | 5304 | 72 | 65.8 | 117 |

**Club Pro:** Jeremy Goulet
**Payment:** Cash, Visa, MC, Amex
**Tee Times:** Yes
**Fee 9 Holes: Weekday:** $30 **Weekend:** $35
**Fee 18 Holes: Weekday:** $40 **Weekend:** $45
**Twilight Rates:** After 2pm **Discounts:** Senior & Junior
**Cart Rental:** $20pp/18, $13pp/9 **Driving Range:** Yes
**Lessons:** Yes **Schools:** Yes **Junior Golf:** Yes
**Membership:** Yes **Architect/Yr Open:** Lucien Bourque/1965
**Other:** Bar-Lounge / Snack Bar **GPS:**

COUPON

Greens roll very true. Water comes into play on many holes. Very well maintained.

| | 1 | 2 | 3 | 4 | 5 | 6 | 7 | 8 | 9 |
|---|---|---|---|---|---|---|---|---|---|
| PAR | 4 | 3 | 3 | 5 | 5 | 4 | 4 | 4 | 4 |
| YARDS | 356 | 156 | 150 | 440 | 486 | 411 | 300 | 342 | 357 |
| | 10 | 11 | 12 | 13 | 14 | 15 | 16 | 17 | 18 |
| PAR | 4 | 5 | 4 | 4 | 4 | 5 | 3 | 3 | 4 |
| YARDS | 300 | 494 | 276 | 347 | 326 | 493 | 202 | 182 | 357 |

**Directions:** Off Maine Turnpike, take Exit 32 (Biddeford). Turn right on Route 111, go 1 mile to
Holly's Gas Station. Bear left, (Newtown Road,) go 1 mile to stop sign. Turn right, course is on left.

# Fairlawn Golf & Country Club ✪✪½ ▶ 15

434 Empire Road
Poland, ME (207) 998-4277
www.fairlawngolf.com

**Club Pro:** David Bartasuis, PGA
**Payment:** Visa, MC, Check, Cash
**Tee Times:** No

| Tees | Holes | Yards | Par | USGA | Slope |
|--------|-------|-------|-----|------|-------|
| BACK | 18 | 6300 | 72 | 68.9 | 117 |
| MIDDLE | 18 | 5833 | 72 | 67.5 | 110 |
| FRONT | 18 | 5158 | 72 | 69.9 | 111 |

**Fee 9 Holes: Weekday:**    **Weekend:**
**Fee 18 Holes: Weekday:** $28    **Weekend:** $30
**Twilight Rates:** After 4pm    **Discounts:** None
**Cart Rental:** $16/18, $8/9 per cart    **Driving Range:** No
**Lessons:** No **Schools:** No    **Junior Golf:** No
**Membership:** Yes
**Architect/Yr Open:** Chick Adams & Frank Bartasuis/1963
**Other:** Clubhouse / Lockers / Snack Bar / Bar-Lounge

Open May 1 - until it snows. Condos on course available for rent. "Family owned, operated and designed course. Very popular due to the friendly atmosphere and reasonable fee. Very walkable." –DW

|  | 1 | 2 | 3 | 4 | 5 | 6 | 7 | 8 | 9 |
|-------|-----|-----|-----|-----|-----|-----|-----|-----|-----|
| PAR | 4 | 3 | 5 | 4 | 4 | 4 | 5 | 3 | 4 |
| YARDS | 323 | 205 | 544 | 409 | 364 | 357 | 497 | 182 | 317 |
|  | 10 | 11 | 12 | 13 | 14 | 15 | 16 | 17 | 18 |
| PAR | 4 | 3 | 5 | 3 | 4 | 4 | 5 | 4 | 4 |
| YARDS | 394 | 133 | 491 | 154 | 358 | 363 | 535 | 341 | 333 |

**Directions:** From Maine Turnpike, Exit 75, take right off exit; take first right (Kittyhawk). Go to end of road and take left (Lewiston Junction Road). At first stop sign take right. Course on left. From West: take Route 26 South to Route 122. Take right onto Route 122 and follow signs.

# Fox Ridge Golf Club ✪✪✪✪½ ▶ 16

550 Penley Corner Road
Auburn, ME (207) 777-GOLF (4653)
www.foxridgegolfclub.com

**Club Pro:** Jerry Diphillipo
**Payment:** Visa, MC
**Tee Times:** 10 days adv.

| Tees | Holes | Yards | Par | USGA | Slope |
|--------|-------|-------|-----|------|-------|
| BACK | 18 | 6814 | 72 | 73.4 | 133 |
| MIDDLE | 18 | 6297 | 72 | 70.7 | 131 |
| FRONT | 18 | 4959 | 72 | 69.8 | 125 |

**Fee 9 Holes: Weekday:** $26    **Weekend:** $28
**Fee 18 Holes: Weekday:** $40    **Weekend:** $48
**Twilight Rates:** After 3pm    **Discounts:** Junior, Military
**Cart Rental:** $17pp/18, $10pp/9    **Driving Range:** Yes
**Lessons:** Yes **Schools:** Yes    **Junior Golf:**
**Membership:** Yes    **Architect/Yr Open:** Carol Myshrall/2001
**Other:** Restaurant / Clubhouse / Bar-Lounge    **GPS:**

COUPON

Golf Digest 4½ star rating out of 5 stars a course. Where you use every club in your bag. Island green.

|  | 1 | 2 | 3 | 4 | 5 | 6 | 7 | 8 | 9 |
|-------|-----|-----|-----|-----|-----|-----|-----|-----|-----|
| PAR | 4 | 4 | 3 | 5 | 3 | 4 | 4 | 4 | 5 |
| YARDS | 322 | 387 | 167 | 529 | 191 | 349 | 360 | 300 | 489 |
|  | 10 | 11 | 12 | 13 | 14 | 15 | 16 | 17 | 18 |
| PAR | 4 | 5 | 4 | 3 | 4 | 4 | 3 | 5 | 4 |
| YARDS | 383 | 551 | 378 | 113 | 322 | 344 | 203 | 518 | 391 |

**Directions:** Maine Turnpike to Exit 75. Left on Washington Avenue, right on Danville Corner Road, left on Danville Road, right on Hammond Corner Road.

S
ME

# Freeport Country Club ✪✪ ▶ 17

2 Old County Road
Freeport, ME (207) 865-0711
www.harrisgolfonline.com
**Club Pro:** Chad Hopkins, PGA
**Payment:** Visa, MC, Amex, Disc
**Tee Times:** Yes
**Fee 9 Holes: Weekday:** $15
**Fee 18 Holes: Weekday:** $25
**Twilight Rates:** No
**Cart Rental:** $15pp/18, $8pp/9
**Lessons:** Yes **Schools:** Yes
**Membership:** Yes, $425
**Other:** Clubhouse / Snack Bar

| Tees | Holes | Yards | Par | USGA | Slope |
|------|-------|-------|-----|------|-------|
| BACK | | | | | |
| MIDDLE | 9 | 2955 | 36 | 69.0 | 116 |
| FRONT | 9 | 2405 | 36 | 67.1 | 109 |

**Weekend:** $15
**Weekend:** $25
**Discounts:** None
**Driving Range:** Yes
**Junior Golf:** Yes
**Architect/Yr Open:** 1965
**GPS:**

COUPON

Located just minutes from the world famous L.L. Bean, situated with easy striking distance of Portland, Lewiston/Auburn, and Brunswick. Brand new practice facility with target greens, natural surface teeing areas, lesson tees, putting greens, and a practice bunker.

| | 1 | 2 | 3 | 4 | 5 | 6 | 7 | 8 | 9 |
|------|-----|-----|-----|-----|-----|-----|-----|-----|-----|
| PAR | 4 | 4 | 4 | 4 | 5 | 3 | 4 | 3 | 5 |
| YARDS | 378 | 390 | 370 | 250 | 453 | 197 | 306 | 148 | 463 |
| PAR | | | | | | | | | |
| YARDS | | | | | | | | | |

**Directions:** I-295 North to Exit 17, right on U.S.1 for 2 miles, left over the overpass, then 1st right to club.

# Frye Island Golf Course ✪✪½ ▶ 18

115 Cape Road Extension
Raymond, ME (207) 655-3551
www.fryeisland.com/figc.htm
**Club Pro:** Laura Crosby, GM
**Payment:** Cash, Credit Cards
**Tee Times:** Weekends
**Fee 9 Holes: Weekday:** $20
**Fee 18 Holes: Weekday:** $20
**Twilight Rates:** After 5pm
**Cart Rental:** $13pp/18, $8pp/9
**Lessons:** Yes **Schools:** No
**Membership:** Yes
**Other:** Snack Bar / Lounge

| Tees | Holes | Yards | Par | USGA | Slope |
|------|-------|-------|-----|------|-------|
| BACK | 9 | 3139 | 36 | 70.0 | 123 |
| MIDDLE | 9 | 3023 | 36 | 69.4 | 121 |
| FRONT | 9 | 2651 | 36 | 72.4 | 126 |

**Weekend:** $30
**Weekend:** $30
**Discounts:** Junior
**Driving Range:** No
**Junior Golf:** No
**Architect/Yr Open:** Geoffrey Cornish/1972
**GPS:**

COUPON

This 9-hole course is narrow with water holes and tree-lined fairways. Open May 1 - November 1. "Great getaway course." –FP

| | 1 | 2 | 3 | 4 | 5 | 6 | 7 | 8 | 9 |
|------|-----|-----|-----|-----|-----|-----|-----|-----|-----|
| PAR | 4 | 5 | 4 | 3 | 4 | 4 | 5 | 3 | 4 |
| YARDS | 378 | 481 | 391 | 160 | 358 | 293 | 456 | 155 | 351 |
| PAR | | | | | | | | | |
| YARDS | | | | | | | | | |

**Directions:** Take Exit 48 (Westbrook) to Route 302 (2 miles) to Raymond Cape Road. Follow 20 miles to Frye Island Ferry Landing for 5 miles.

# Goose River Golf Club  ✪✪  ▶19

50 Park Street
Rockport, ME  (207) 236-8488
www.gooserivergolf.com
**Club Pro:** Jim Blanchett, Dir. of Golf
**Payment:** Cash, MC, Visa
**Tee Times:** Yes
**Fee  9 Holes: Weekday:** $25
**Fee 18 Holes: Weekday:** $35
**Twilight Rates:** After 3pm
**Cart Rental:** $15pp/18, $10pp/9
**Lessons:** Yes  **Schools:** No
**Membership:** Yes
**Other:** Snack Bar

**Weekend:** $25
**Weekend:** $35
**Discounts:** Junior
**Driving Range:**
**Junior Golf:** Yes
**Architect/Yr Open:** Al Zikorus/1965
**GPS:** Yes

| Tees | Holes | Yards | Par | USGA | Slope |
|------|-------|-------|-----|------|-------|
| BACK |       |       |     |      |       |
| MIDDLE | 9 | 3072 | 35 | 68.0 | 118 |
| FRONT | 9 | 2608 | 36 | 69.7 | 117 |

*COUPON*

9 holes, 2 sets of tees. Area known for sailing, kayaking, and hiking. Attractions include: Camden Hills, 2 museums, Rockport and Camden harbors.

| | 1 | 2 | 3 | 4 | 5 | 6 | 7 | 8 | 9 |
|---|---|---|---|---|---|---|---|---|---|
| **PAR** | 5 | 4 | 4 | 4 | 5 | 3 | 4 | 3 | 3 |
| **YARDS** | 550 | 336 | 367 | 336 | 472 | 163 | 335 | 189 | 306 |
| **PAR** | | | | | | | | | |
| **YARDS** | | | | | | | | | |

**Directions:** North on I-95, north on Route 1. Follow Route 1 into Camden and follow signs.

# Gorham Country Club  ✪✪  ▶20

68 McLellan Road
Gorham, ME  (207) 839-3490
www.gorhamcountryclub.com
**Club Pro:** Rick Altham, PGA
**Payment:** Cash, Check, Credit
**Tee Times:** Weekends/Holidays
**Fee  9 Holes: Weekday:** $20
**Fee 18 Holes: Weekday:** $30
**Twilight Rates:** After 3pm
**Cart Rental:** $16pp/18, $11pp/9
**Lessons:** Yes  **Schools:** No
**Membership:** Yes
**Other:** Lockers / Showers / Snack Bar / Restaurant

**Weekend:** $22
**Weekend:** $32
**Discounts:** Senior & Junior
**Driving Range:** Yes
**Junior Golf:** Yes
**Architect/Yr Open:** Jim MacDonald/1961

| Tees | Holes | Yards | Par | USGA | Slope |
|------|-------|-------|-----|------|-------|
| BACK | 18 | 6555 | 71 | 68.6 | 116 |
| MIDDLE | 18 | 6334 | 71 | 67.4 | 115 |
| FRONT | 18 | 5426 | 72 | 69.9 | 117 |

An 18-hole layout located on a game preserve. A beautiful and challenging course for all abilities.

**S
ME**

| | 1 | 2 | 3 | 4 | 5 | 6 | 7 | 8 | 9 |
|---|---|---|---|---|---|---|---|---|---|
| **PAR** | 4 | 4 | 4 | 3 | 4 | 3 | 4 | 4 | 5 |
| **YARDS** | 324 | 344 | 369 | 160 | 406 | 141 | 391 | 378 | 488 |
| | **10** | **11** | **12** | **13** | **14** | **15** | **16** | **17** | **18** |
| **PAR** | 5 | 4 | 4 | 3 | 4 | 3 | 4 | 4 | 5 |
| **YARDS** | 561 | 427 | 365 | 155 | 424 | 168 | 358 | 375 | 500 |

**Directions:** I-95 to Exit 45. Follow Route 114 to Gorham. Take right onto McLellan Road.

# Great Chebeague Golf Club      NR ▶ 21

16 Stone Wharf Road
Chebeague Island, ME
(207) 846-9478
www.chebeagueislandgolf.com
**Club Pro:**
**Payment:** Visa, MC, Disc, Checks, Cash
**Tee Times:**

| Tees | Holes | Yards | Par | USGA | Slope |
|------|-------|-------|-----|------|-------|
| BACK | 9 | 2239 | 33 | 62.2 | 102 |
| MIDDLE | 9 | 2174 | 33 | 65.4 | 109 |
| LADIES | 9 | 1934 | 34 | 60.8 | 100 |

**Fee  9 Holes: Weekday:** $45     **Weekend:** $45
**Fee 18 Holes: Weekday:** $45     **Weekend:** $45
**Twilight Rates:** After 5pm     **Discounts:** Junior
**Cart Rental:** $20pp/18, $20pp/9     **Driving Range:** No
**Lessons:** No  **Schools:** Yes     **Junior Golf:** Yes
**Membership:** Yes     **Architect/Yr Open:** 1921
**Other:** Clubhouse

Founded in 1920, this seaside links-style course has water views from every hole. A truly unique 9-hole layout. Listed on the National Registry of Historic Places.

| | 1 | 2 | 3 | 4 | 5 | 6 | 7 | 8 | 9 |
|---|---|---|---|---|---|---|---|---|---|
| PAR | 4 | 4 | 4 | 4 | 4 | 3 | 3 | 3 | 4 |
| YARDS | 260 | 375 | 260 | 345 | 385 | 110 | 120 | 142 | 250 |
| PAR | | | | | | | | | |
| YARDS | | | | | | | | | |

**Directions:** Park your car at Yarmouth and take the short bus ride to the CTC Ferry. You can put your clubs right on the bus. Once the ferry gets to Chebeague (about 10 minutes) the Golf Club is just steps away from the pier. The Clubhouse will be up to your right.

# Highland Green Golf Club      ✪✪✪ ▶ 22

114 Village Drive
Topsham, ME (207) 725-8066
www.highlandgreengolf.com

| Tees | Holes | Yards | Par | USGA | Slope |
|------|-------|-------|-----|------|-------|
| BACK | 9 | 2910 | 35 | 67.7 | 134 |
| MIDDLE | 9 | 2679 | 35 | 65.6 | 122 |
| FRONT | 9 | 2071 | 35 | | |

**Club Pro:** Dick Harris, PGA
**Payment:** Most Major Credit Cards
**Tee Times:** Yes
**Fee  9 Holes: Weekday:** $30 (cart included)     **Weekend:** $30 (cart included)
**Fee 18 Holes: Weekday:** $45 (cart included)     **Weekend:** $45 (cart included)
**Twilight Rates:** Yes     **Discounts:** None
**Cart Rental:** $18pp/18, $8pp/9     **Driving Range:**
**Lessons:** Yes  **Schools:** No     **Junior Golf:** Yes
**Membership:** Yes     **Architect/Yr Open:** Jim Dodson/2001
**Other:** Snack Bar / Bar Lounge     **GPS:**

COUPON

A traditional (links) style course located in the heart of Maine's beautiful Mid-Coast region. Featuring contoured greens and fairways and surrounded by the beautiful Cathance River Nature Preserve. Well worth stopping for a round on a drive up the coast.

| | 1 | 2 | 3 | 4 | 5 | 6 | 7 | 8 | 9 |
|---|---|---|---|---|---|---|---|---|---|
| PAR | 4 | 4 | 5 | 4 | 4 | 3 | 4 | 4 | 3 |
| YARDS | 314 | 343 | 486 | 260 | 337 | 188 | 370 | 415 | 197 |
| PAR | | | | | | | | | |
| YARDS | | | | | | | | | |

**Directions:** 1 minute from I-95 and Route 1, on the Coastal Connector in Topsham, Maine.

# Lake Kezar Country Club  ✪✪✪  23 ▶

**578 Main Street**
**Lovell, ME (207) 925-2462**
**www.lakekezargolf.com**
**Club Pro:** Bill Bisset, Dir. of Golf
**Payment:** Visa, MC
**Tee Times:** 7 days adv. members
**Fee 9 Holes: Weekday:** $23 (M-Th)
**Fee 18 Holes: Weekday:** $32 (M-Th)
**Twilight Rates:** After 3pm
**Cart Rental:** $13pp/18, $9pp/9
**Lessons:** Yes  **Schools:** Yes
**Membership:** Yes
**Other:** Snack Bar / Bar-Lounge, Beverage Cart

| Tees | Holes | Yards | Par | USGA | Slope |
|------|-------|-------|-----|------|-------|
| BACK | 18 | 6010 | 72 | 63.3 | 117 |
| MIDDLE | 18 | 5600 | 72 | 65.7 | 111 |
| FRONT | 18 | 5105 | 72 | 68.8 | 114 |

**Weekend:** $26 (F/S/S/H)
**Weekend:** $36 (F/S/S/H)
**Discounts:** Juniors
**Driving Range:** Practice Cage
**Junior Golf:** Yes
**Architect/Yr Open:** Donald Ross/1923
**GPS:** Yes

COUPON

Very scenic, pine trees, mountains, meandering brook, quiet. Clubhouse was 1-room schoolhouse. Facebook page, #1 value in NE, for the last 5 years. New huge putting green. 5 new beautiful flower gardens. New 4th tee box, expanded pro shop, newly-renovated screen porch. "Great, friendly staff. Well worth the trip. You will come back." –FP

| | 1 | 2 | 3 | 4 | 5 | 6 | 7 | 8 | 9 |
|---|---|---|---|---|---|---|---|---|---|
| PAR | 4 | 4 | 4 | 4 | 3 | 4 | 3 | 5 | 4 |
| YARDS | 292 | 305 | 299 | 339 | 136 | 383 | 201 | 498 | 272 |
| | 10 | 11 | 12 | 13 | 14 | 15 | 16 | 17 | 18 |
| PAR | 5 | 4 | 3 | 4 | 5 | 4 | 3 | 4 | 5 |
| YARDS | 450 | 278 | 123 | 334 | 481 | 326 | 153 | 282 | 526 |

**Directions:** West on Route 302 from Gray exit on I-95. Right on Knights Hill Road across from Shawnee Peak. Follow signs on Route 5 North.

# Lebanon Pines Golf Course  NR  24 ▶

**119 Center Road**
**Lebanon, ME (207) 457-2380**

**Club Pro:**
**Payment:** Visa, MC, Cash
**Tee Times:** No
**Fee 9 Holes: Weekday:** $23
**Fee 18 Holes: Weekday:** $33, $30/cash
**Twilight Rates:**
**Cart Rental:** $20/9 per cart
**Lessons:** No  **Schools:** No
**Membership:** Yes
**Other:**

| Tees | Holes | Yards | Par | USGA | Slope |
|------|-------|-------|-----|------|-------|
| BACK | | | | | |
| MIDDLE | 9 | 1489 | 31 | | |
| FRONT | 9 | 1378 | 31 | | |

**Weekend:** $23
**Weekend:** $33, $30/cash
**Discounts:** None
**Driving Range:** No
**Junior Golf:** No
**Architect/Yr Open:** Rene Doiron/2013

S
ME

Great new course designed by the owner.

| | 1 | 2 | 3 | 4 | 5 | 6 | 7 | 8 | 9 |
|---|---|---|---|---|---|---|---|---|---|
| PAR | 4 | 3 | 3 | 3 | 4 | 3 | 4 | 3 | 4 |
| YARDS | 208 | 102 | 115 | 161 | 191 | 146 | 158 | 110 | 297 |
| PAR | | | | | | | | | |
| YARDS | | | | | | | | | |

**Directions:** Spaulding Turnpike NH, take Exit 16 towards Rochester/Sanford. Keep right at fork and follow 202 East. Left on Center Road, Course ½ mile on right.

## Ledges Golf Club, The ✪✪✪✪  25

**One Ledges Drive**
**York, ME (207) 351-3000**
www.ledgesgolf.com

| Tees | Holes | Yards | Par | USGA | Slope |
|------|-------|-------|-----|------|-------|
| BACK | 18 | 6981 | 72 | 74.0 | 137 |
| MIDDLE | 18 | 6357 | 72 | 71.2 | 131 |
| FRONT | 18 | 5960 | 72 | 69.2 | 130 |

**Club Pro:** Dan Limauro, PGA
**Payment:** Visa, MC, Amex
**Tee Times:** 7 days adv.
**Fee 9 Holes: Weekday:** $40    **Weekend:** $40
**Fee 18 Holes: Weekday:** $75    **Weekend:** $75
**Twilight Rates:** After 3pm    **Discounts:** None
**Cart Rental:** $17pp/18, $10pp/9    **Driving Range:** Yes
**Lessons:** Yes **Schools:** Yes    **Junior Golf:** Yes
**Membership:** Yes    **Architect/Yr Open:** William Bradley Booth/1998
**Other:** Bar-Lounge / Restaurant / Clubhouse / Lockers / Showers / Lodging Partner

"None better in Southern Maine. A must-play annual visit." –TM "I drive up from Boston every year for this one." –GD

|  | 1 | 2 | 3 | 4 | 5 | 6 | 7 | 8 | 9 |
|--|---|---|---|---|---|---|---|---|---|
| PAR | 4 | 4 | 4 | 5 | 3 | 4 | 5 | 3 | 4 |
| YARDS | 405 | 313 | 344 | 542 | 148 | 391 | 493 | 196 | 333 |
|  | 10 | 11 | 12 | 13 | 14 | 15 | 16 | 17 | 18 |
| PAR | 4 | 3 | 5 | 4 | 3 | 4 | 4 | 4 | 5 |
| YARDS | 388 | 179 | 470 | 356 | 131 | 315 | 377 | 429 | 547 |

**Directions:** I-95 to Exit 7. Go on Route 1 South for ¾ of a mile. Turn right on Route 91. Ledges is 5 miles up on right.

## The Links at Outlook ✪✪✪✪ 26

**310 Portland Street (Route 4)**
**South Berwick, ME (207) 384-4653**
www.outlookgolf.com

| Tees | Holes | Yards | Par | USGA | Slope |
|------|-------|-------|-----|------|-------|
| BACK | 18 | 6432 | 71 | 70.2 | 125 |
| MIDDLE | 18 | 6004 | 71 | 68.3 | 121 |
| FRONT | 18 | 5492 | 71 | 66.0 | 111 |

**Club Pro:** Dave Paskowski
**Payment:** Cash, Visa, MC, Disc, Cash
**Tee Times:** 7 days adv.
**Fee 9 Holes: Weekday:** $30 (M-Thur)    **Weekend:** $30 after 1pm
**Fee 18 Holes: Weekday:** $61 (M-Thur)    **Weekend:** $61 (F/S/S)
**Twilight Rates:** After 2pm    **Discounts:** Sr. & Jr. Mon-Th
**Cart Rental:** $18pp/18, $10pp/9
**Driving Range:** Yes, grass tees w/target greens
**Lessons:** Yes **Schools:** Nike Golf School    **Junior Golf:** Yes
**Membership:** Yes    **Architect/Yr Open:** Brian Silva/2000; Redesign 2010
**Other:** The Medalist Golf School / Hole by Hole Video / Outlook Tavern Restaurant

Player Comments: "Excellent fairways. Great conditions overall" –FP
Most of the course has a links-like, wide-open feel. Southern Maine beaches nearby. New Outlook Tavern.

|  | 1 | 2 | 3 | 4 | 5 | 6 | 7 | 8 | 9 |
|--|---|---|---|---|---|---|---|---|---|
| PAR | 5 | 4 | 3 | 5 | 4 | 4 | 4 | 3 | 4 |
| YARDS | 503 | 416 | 183 | 475 | 328 | 361 | 347 | 199 | 333 |
|  | 10 | 11 | 12 | 13 | 14 | 15 | 16 | 17 | 18 |
| PAR | 4 | 3 | 4 | 4 | 3 | 4 | 4 | 5 | 4 |
| YARDS | 348 | 164 | 299 | 361 | 142 | 373 | 354 | 484 | 334 |

**Directions:** From Boston: I-95 North to Exit 3, South Berwick. Right on Route 236. Follow 11 miles to end and take right. After ¼ mile, take right onto Route 4. Course is 1 mile up on right.
From Portland: I-95 South to Exit 19, Wells/Sanford. Take right past toll booths. Take next left onto Route 9. Follow Route 4 into South Berwick. Course on left.

# Maple Lane Golf Club ✪✪ 🏴27

295 Maple Lane
Livermore, ME (207) 897-3770
www.maplelane.me

| Tees | Holes | Yards | Par | USGA | Slope |
|------|-------|-------|-----|------|-------|
| BACK | 9 | 3019 | 35 | 65 | 118 |
| MIDDLE | 9 | 2797 | 35 | 62.8 | 114 |
| FRONT | 9 | 2665 | 35 | 65.8 | 118 |

**Club Pro:** Rick Carlton
**Payment:** Visa, MC
**Tee Times:** Yes
**Fee 9 Holes: Weekday:** $12    **Weekend:** $12
**Fee 18 Holes: Weekday:** $20    **Weekend:** $20
**Twilight Rates:** After 4pm    **Discounts:** Senior
**Cart Rental:** $15pp/18, $8pp/9    **Driving Range:** No
**Lessons:** Yes **Schools:** Jr. & Sr.    **Junior Golf:** Yes
**Membership:** Yes    **Architect/Yr Open:** Arthur Chapman/1976
**Other:** Snack Bar/ Dining Room & Patio / Hotel    **GPS:**

Stay-and-play packages start at $70 per couple per night. "Recently redesigned resulting in improved conditions. Interesting, fun course." –DW

| | 1 | 2 | 3 | 4 | 5 | 6 | 7 | 8 | 9 |
|------|---|---|---|---|---|---|---|---|---|
| PAR | 4 | 5 | 3 | 4 | 5 | 4 | 4 | 3 | 3 |
| YARDS | 356 | 347 | 555 | 370 | 155 | 170 | 348 | 540 | 168 |
| PAR | | | | | | | | | |
| YARDS | | | | | | | | | |

**Directions:** I-95 to Auburn Exit 75. Take Route 4 to Livermore/Livermore Falls town line. Take a right before bridge onto River Road. (From Augusta, take Route 17 South to 133 North.)

# Martindale Country Club ✪✪✪ ½ 🏴28

527 Beech Hill Road
Auburn, ME (207) 782-1107
www.martindalecc.com

| Tees | Holes | Yards | Par | USGA | Slope |
|------|-------|-------|-----|------|-------|
| BACK | 18 | 6538 | 71 | 71.7 | 131 |
| MIDDLE | 18 | 6267 | 71 | 70.4 | 128 |
| FRONT | 18 | 5351 | 71 | 66.2 | 124 |

**Club Pro:** Nick Glicos, PGA, PGA
**Payment:** Visa, MC, Amex Disc, Cash
**Tee Times:** 7 days adv.
**Fee 9 Holes: Weekday:** $28    **Weekend:** $30
**Fee 18 Holes: Weekday:** $40    **Weekend:** $45
**Twilight Rates:** After 3pm    **Discounts:** Senior, Junior
**Cart Rental:** $18pp/18, $10pp/9    **Driving Range:** Yes
**Lessons:** $60/hour **Schools:** Jr. & Sr.    **Junior Golf:** Yes
**Membership:** Yes    **Architect/Yr Open:** Alex & Fred Chisholm/1921
**Other:** Restaurant / Lockers / Showers / Snack Bar / Bar-Lounge / Function Room

COUPON

**S ME**

Championship golf course with superb course conditions at a great value. Some of the best greens in Maine. A must play for golfers at all levels.

| | 1 | 2 | 3 | 4 | 5 | 6 | 7 | 8 | 9 |
|------|---|---|---|---|---|---|---|---|---|
| PAR | 4 | 4 | 4 | 3 | 4 | 4 | 4 | 5 | 3 |
| YARDS | 325 | 358 | 402 | 173 | 330 | 359 | 364 | 555 | 232 |
| | 10 | 11 | 12 | 13 | 14 | 15 | 16 | 17 | 18 |
| PAR | 4 | 3 | 5 | 4 | 4 | 4 | 4 | 3 | 5 |
| YARDS | 388 | 152 | 591 | 374 | 325 | 360 | 395 | 160 | 424 |

**Directions:** I-95 to Auburn Exit 75. Take left off Exit. 2nd left is Beech Hill Road. Travel approximately 2 miles to the course.

# The Meadows Golf Club  ✪✪  29 ▶

495 Huntington Hill Road
Litchfield, ME (207) 268-3000
www.themeadowsgolfclub.com

**Club Pro:** Chad Hopkins, Golf Instructor
**Payment:** Visa, MC, Check, Cash
**Tee Times:**
**Fee  9 Holes: Weekday:** $16
**Fee 18 Holes: Weekday:** $28
**Twilight Rates:** After 4pm
**Cart Rental:** $16pp/18, $11pp/9
**Lessons:** Yes  **Schools:** No
**Membership:** Yes

| Tees | Holes | Yards | Par | USGA | Slope |
|---|---|---|---|---|---|
| BACK | 18 | 5814 | 68 | 66.8 | 117 |
| MIDDLE | 18 | 5316 | 68 | 64.5 | 110 |
| FRONT | 18 | 4487 | 68 | 66.0 | 107 |

**Weekend:** $16
**Weekend:** $28
**Discounts:** Sr. & Jr. and Military
**Driving Range:** No
**Junior Golf:** No
**Architect/Yr Open:** William Bradley Booth/1998

**Other:** Restaurant / Clubhouse / Bar-Lounge / Pro Shop / Putting Course

Scenic countryside course. Tree lined, dogleg fairways and undulating greens. New modern clubhouse with spacious bar and grill.

|  | 1 | 2 | 3 | 4 | 5 | 6 | 7 | 8 | 9 |
|---|---|---|---|---|---|---|---|---|---|
| PAR | 4 | 4 | 3 | 5 | 3 | 4 | 3 | 4 | 4 |
| YARDS | 350 | 333 | 155 | 497 | 190 | 367 | 161 | 303 | 362 |
|  | 10 | 11 | 12 | 13 | 14 | 15 | 16 | 17 | 18 |
| PAR | 5 | 3 | 4 | 4 | 4 | 3 | 4 | 3 | 4 |
| YARDS | 502 | 162 | 362 | 315 | 344 | 138 | 294 | 140 | 341 |

**Directions:** I-95 to Exit 86. Turn left on Route 9, right on Route 126, then right on Route 197. Go 14.6 miles to Huntington Hill Road. Turn left, course is 1.5 miles on the left.

# Mere Creek Golf Course  ✪✪  30 ▶

41 Merriconeag Road
Brunswick, ME (207) 721-9995
www.merecreekgolf.com

**Club Pro:** Kevin Joseph, PGA
**Payment:** Visa, MC, Disc, Cash
**Tee Times:** 7 days adv.
**Fee  9 Holes: Weekday:** $15
**Fee 18 Holes: Weekday:** $25
**Twilight Rates:** No
**Cart Rental:** $15pp/18, $8pp/9
**Lessons:** Yes  **Schools:** Yes
**Membership:** Yes

| Tees | Holes | Yards | Par | USGA | Slope |
|---|---|---|---|---|---|
| BACK | 9 | 3265 | 37 | 69.9 | 124 |
| MIDDLE | 9 | 3013 | 35 | 69.9 | 124 |
| FRONT | 9 | 2511 | 36 | 69.0 | 117 |

**Weekend:** $15
**Weekend:** $25
**Discounts:** No
**Driving Range:** Yes
**Junior Golf:** Yes
**Architect/Yr Open:** 1958
**GPS:**

**Other:** Clubhouse / Snack Bar

Managed by Harris Golf. Located at Brunswick Landing featuring new businesses and the Brunswick Executive Airport. Fun and enjoyable for all levels of players.

|  | 1 | 2 | 3 | 4 | 5 | 6 | 7 | 8 | 9 |
|---|---|---|---|---|---|---|---|---|---|
| PAR | 5 | 4 | 4 | 3 | 4 | 4 | 4 | 3 | 4 |
| YARDS | 495 | 316 | 375 | 147 | 330 | 432 | 353 | 145 | 420 |
| PAR |  |  |  |  |  |  |  |  |  |
| YARDS |  |  |  |  |  |  |  |  |  |

**Directions:** I-295 to Exit 28, Brunswick. Follow Pleasant Street to end and turn right on Maine Street, left on Bath Road, right on Route 123. Go 2.4 miles and turn left into Brunswick Landing.

# Merriland Farm Par 3 Golf  ✪✪✪  31 ▶

545 Coles Hill Road
Wells, ME (207) 646-0508
www.merrilandfarm.com

**Club Pro:**
**Payment:** Cash, Visa, MC
**Tee Times:** No

| Tees | Holes | Yards | Par | USGA | Slope |
|------|-------|-------|-----|------|-------|
| BACK | | | | | |
| MIDDLE | 9 | 838 | 27 | | |
| FRONT | | | | | |

**Fee 9 Holes: Weekday:** $15      **Weekend:** $15
**Fee 18 Holes: Weekday:** $23     **Weekend:** $23
**Twilight Rates:** No              **Discounts:** None
**Cart Rental:** No                 **Driving Range:** Yes
**Lessons:** No  **Schools:** No    **Junior Golf:** Yes
**Membership:** Yes                 **Architect/Yr Open:** James Morrison/1992
**Other:** Cafe Serving Breakfast & Lunch / Raspberry, Blueberry Baked Specialties

Player Comments: "A par 3 that lets you and the family enjoy the outing. Pleasant staff. Great muffins."

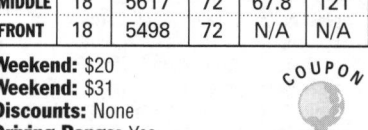

|  | 1 | 2 | 3 | 4 | 5 | 6 | 7 | 8 | 9 |
|------|------|------|------|------|------|------|------|------|------|
| PAR | 3 | 3 | 3 | 3 | 3 | 3 | 3 | 3 | 3 |
| YARDS | 83 | 96 | 119 | 111 | 67 | 86 | 63 | 109 | 104 |
| PAR | | | | | | | | | |
| YARDS | | | | | | | | | |

**Directions:** I-95 to Exit 19 (Wells). Left onto Route 109, left onto Route 1 about 1.5 miles to Coles Hill Road on left. 1.5 miles up Coles Hill Road to course on right.

# Naples Golf and Country Club  ✪✪¹⁄₂  32 ▶

Route 114
Naples, ME (207) 693-6424
www.naplesgolfcourse.com

**Club Pro:** Bob Caron II, PGA
**Payment:** Visa, MC
**Tee Times:** Required

| Tees | Holes | Yards | Par | USGA | Slope |
|------|-------|-------|-----|------|-------|
| BACK | 18 | 6039 | 72 | 71.9 | 126 |
| MIDDLE | 18 | 5617 | 72 | 67.8 | 121 |
| FRONT | 18 | 5498 | 72 | N/A | N/A |

**Fee 9 Holes: Weekday:** $20       **Weekend:** $20
**Fee 18 Holes: Weekday:** $31      **Weekend:** $31
**Twilight Rates:** After 11am & 3pm **Discounts:** None
**Cart Rental:** $16pp/18, $8pp/9   **Driving Range:** Yes
**Lessons:** $35/hour  **Schools:** No  **Junior Golf:** Yes
**Membership:** Yes                 **Architect/Yr Open:** 1921
**Other:** Full Restaurant / Clubhouse / Bar-Lounge

"Challenging for any level player. Friendly atmosphere. Beautiful setting." Located in the heart of the Sebago Lake Region. Area attractions center around Lake Region.

|  | 1 | 2 | 3 | 4 | 5 | 6 | 7 | 8 | 9 |
|------|------|------|------|------|------|------|------|------|------|
| PAR | 5 | 4 | 4 | 4 | 4 | 4 | 4 | 4 | 3 |
| YARDS | 465 | 305 | 345 | 405 | 340 | 340 | 375 | 340 | 130 |
|  | 10 | 11 | 12 | 13 | 14 | 15 | 16 | 17 | 18 |
| PAR | 4 | 3 | 4 | 4 | 5 | 4 | 3 | 4 | 5 |
| YARDS | 280 | 125 | 320 | 325 | 400 | 280 | 155 | 262 | 425 |

**Directions:** Exit 48 from Maine Turnpike. Turn right on Riverside Street. 3 miles to Route 302. Left on Route 302 for 30 miles to Naples. Take left on Route 114 in Naples Village. Course is 1 mile on left.

# Nonesuch River Golf Club ✪✪✪½ ▶ 33

304 Gorham Road
Scarborough, ME (207) 883-0007
www.nonesuchgolf.com

| Tees | Holes | Yards | Par | USGA | Slope |
|------|-------|-------|-----|------|-------|
| BACK | 18 | 6324 | 70 | 69.0 | 120 |
| MIDDLE | 18 | 6003 | 70 | 67.3 | 114 |
| FRONT | 18 | 5611 | 70 | 63.4 | 115 |

**Club Pro:** Matt Gaynor, PGA
**Payment:** Visa, MC, Amex, Disc
**Tee Times:** 7 days adv.
**Fee 9 Holes: Weekday:** $22-$25    **Weekend:** $22-$25
**Fee 18 Holes: Weekday:** $32-$36    **Weekend:** $36-$40
**Twilight Rates:** $25 after 3pm walking    **Discounts:** Junior, Military
**Cart Rental:** $18pp/18, $12pp/9    **Driving Range:** Yes
**Lessons:** Yes **Schools:** Yes    **Junior Golf:** Yes
**Membership:** Yes    **Architect/Yr Open:** Tom Walker/1996
**Other:** Clubhouse / Bar-Lounge / Restaurant / Lodging Partner

COUPON

Unique layout with a great mix of par 4's that wind through a lush forest with ponds and the Nonesuch River. Among the top 100 courses you can play in New England. Private club conditions at an affordable rate. "Fun, friendly and affordable."

| | 1 | 2 | 3 | 4 | 5 | 6 | 7 | 8 | 9 |
|------|-----|-----|-----|-----|-----|-----|-----|-----|-----|
| PAR | 4 | 3 | 5 | 3 | 4 | 3 | 4 | 4 | 4 |
| YARDS | 389 | 180 | 539 | 214 | 362 | 173 | 348 | 413 | 431 |
| | 10 | 11 | 12 | 13 | 14 | 15 | 16 | 17 | 18 |
| PAR | 5 | 4 | 4 | 4 | 4 | 3 | 5 | 3 | 4 |
| YARDS | 492 | 375 | 365 | 397 | 381 | 160 | 496 | 174 | 435 |

**Directions:** Maine Turnpike to Exit 42. Turn left out of toll. Turn left at 2nd set of lights onto Route 114. Course is .5 miles on left.

# Norway Country Club ✪✪½ ▶ 34

310 Waterford Road
Norway, ME (207) 743-9840
www.norwaycountryclub.com

| Tees | Holes | Yards | Par | USGA | Slope |
|------|-------|-------|-----|------|-------|
| BACK | | | | | |
| MIDDLE | 9 | 2909 | 35 | 66.8 | 114 |
| FRONT | | | | | |

**Club Pro:** Dave Mazzeo, PGA
**Payment:** Most Major Credit Cards
**Tee Times:** No
**Fee 9 Holes: Weekday:** $18    **Weekend:** $18
**Fee 18 Holes: Weekday:** $26    **Weekend:** $26
**Twilight Rates:** After 4pm    **Discounts:** Seniors
**Cart Rental:** $14/pp/18, $7/pp/9    **Driving Range:** $5/bucket
**Lessons:** $45/half hour **Schools:** Clinics    **Junior Golf:** Yes
**Membership:** Yes    **Architect/Yr Open:** George Dunn/1929
**Other:** Restaurant / Clubhouse / Snack Bar / Bar-Lounge

Greens in excellent condition. "Most scenic-9 hole course in Maine." –DM

| | 1 | 2 | 3 | 4 | 5 | 6 | 7 | 8 | 9 |
|------|-----|-----|-----|-----|-----|-----|-----|-----|-----|
| PAR | 4 | 3 | 4 | 4 | 4 | 3 | 5 | 4 | 4 |
| YARDS | 375 | 187 | 327 | 300 | 430 | 167 | 450 | 420 | 253 |
| PAR | | | | | | | | | |
| YARDS | | | | | | | | | |

**Directions:** I-95 North to Exit 63. Take Route 26 to Norway. Follow Main Street/Route 118, 3 miles to the course.

# Oakdale Country Club ✪✪ ▶ 35

13 Country Club Road
Mexico, ME (207) 364-3951
www.oakdalecc.com

| Tees | Holes | Yards | Par | USGA | Slope |
|---|---|---|---|---|---|
| BACK | | | | | |
| MIDDLE | 18 | 6133 | 72 | 68.4 | 121 |
| FRONT | 18 | 5486 | 74 | 73.6 | 125 |

**Club Pro:** Carol Mitchell
**Payment:** Visa, MC, Disc
**Tee Times:** No
**Fee 9 Holes: Weekday:** $17 **Weekend:** $17
**Fee 18 Holes: Weekday:** $22 **Weekend:** $22
**Twilight Rates:** After 5pm **Discounts:** None
**Cart Rental:** $15pp/18, $8pp/9 **Driving Range:** No
**Lessons:** Yes **Schools:** No **Junior Golf:** Yes
**Membership:** Yes **Architect/Yr Open:** 1923
**Other:** Clubhouse / Snack Bar / Cocktails **GPS:**

*COUPON*

Course is noted for playability. Hilly fairways and challenging greens.

| | 1 | 2 | 3 | 4 | 5 | 6 | 7 | 8 | 9 |
|---|---|---|---|---|---|---|---|---|---|
| PAR | 4 | 5 | 4 | 3 | 4 | 4 | 4 | 4 | 4 |
| YARDS | 327 | 471 | 339 | 149 | 415 | 383 | 289 | 224 | 362 |
| | 10 | 11 | 12 | 13 | 14 | 15 | 16 | 17 | 18 |
| PAR | 4 | 5 | 4 | 3 | 5 | 4 | 4 | 3 | 4 |
| YARDS | 332 | 456 | 350 | 135 | 420 | 365 | 341 | 206 | 392 |

**Directions:** I-95 to Exit 75, Route 4 North to Route 108 toward Rumford. Then to Route 2 West to course.

# Old Marsh Country Club ✪✪✪✪ ▶ 36

675 Littlefield Road
Wells, ME (207) 251-4653
www.oldmarshcountryclub.com

| Tees | Holes | Yards | Par | USGA | Slope |
|---|---|---|---|---|---|
| BACK | 18 | 6523 | 70 | 71.7 | 135 |
| MIDDLE | 18 | 6012 | 70 | 68.9 | 130 |
| FRONT | 18 | 4847 | 70 | 68.7 | 116 |

**Club Pro:** Sam Marzenelle, PGA
**Payment:** Visa, MC, Amex, Disc, Check, Cash
**Tee Times:** 7 days adv.
**Fee 9 Holes: Weekday:** $50 **Weekend:** $50
**Fee 18 Holes: Weekday:** $68 **Weekend:** $68
**Twilight Rates:** After 3pm **Discounts:** None
**Cart Rental:** Included **Driving Range:** Yes, offsite
**Lessons:** Yes **Schools:** Yes **Junior Golf:** Yes
**Membership:** Yes **Architect/Yr Open:** Brian Silva/2008
**Other:** Restaurant / Clubhouse / Bar-Lounge / Lockers / Showers

*COUPON*

A creative masterpiece that is pleasantly deceptive that you most certainly want to play again. A perfect mix of strategic and penal holes with each green unique to any other. Greens roll true, fast but fair. Brian Silva's best design. New 65,000 square foot practice facility. A must play!

| | 1 | 2 | 3 | 4 | 5 | 6 | 7 | 8 | 9 |
|---|---|---|---|---|---|---|---|---|---|
| PAR | 4 | 4 | 5 | 4 | 4 | 3 | 4 | 3 | 4 |
| YARDS | 349 | 347 | 485 | 358 | 384 | 169 | 381 | 174 | 421 |
| | 10 | 11 | 12 | 13 | 14 | 15 | 16 | 17 | 18 |
| PAR | 4 | 4 | 4 | 5 | 4 | 3 | 4 | 3 | 4 |
| YARDS | 311 | 335 | 348 | 511 | 256 | 151 | 427 | 187 | 418 |

**Directions:** I-95 to Exit 19 Wells/Sanford. Turn right on Route 109, go 3 miles and turn left on Route 9, go 1.6 miles and turn left on Route 9B and then left on Clubhouse Road.

**S ME**

# Paris Hill Country Club ✪½ 37 ▶

455 Paris Hill Road
Paris, ME (207) 743-2371
www.parishillcc.com
**Club Pro:** Chris Johnson
**Payment:** Cash, Visa, MC
**Tee Times:** No
**Fee 9 Holes: Weekday:** $15 **Weekend:** $15
**Fee 18 Holes: Weekday:** $20 **Weekend:** $20
**Twilight Rates:** After 4pm, $10 for as many holes as you can play
**Cart Rental:** $15pp/18, $10pp/9 **Driving Range:** No
**Lessons:** Yes **Schools:** Yes **Junior Golf:**
**Membership:** Yes **Architect/Yr Open:** 1899
**Other:** Clubhouse / Luncheonette / Bar / Dining Room

| Tees | Holes | Yards | Par | USGA | Slope |
|------|-------|-------|-----|------|-------|
| BACK | | | | | |
| MIDDLE | 9 | 2305 | 33 | 62.1 | 102 |
| FRONT | | | | | |

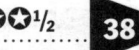

Overlooks beautiful Oxford Hills and mountains. Open May - October. Great family-play golf course.

| | 1 | 2 | 3 | 4 | 5 | 6 | 7 | 8 | 9 |
|------|-----|-----|-----|-----|-----|-----|-----|-----|-----|
| PAR | 4 | 4 | 4 | 3 | 4 | 3 | 4 | 3 | 4 |
| YARDS | 350 | 260 | 231 | 194 | 352 | 125 | 309 | 129 | 355 |
| PAR | | | | | | | | | |
| YARDS | | | | | | | | | |

**Directions:** I-95 to Exit 63 (Gray). Take Route 26 to South Paris.

# Point Sebago Golf Club ✪✪✪½ 38 ▶

261 Point Sebago Road (Route 302)
Casco, ME (207) 558-8040
www.pointsebago.com
**Club Pro:** Michael Cloutier, PGA
**Payment:** Visa, MC, Disc, Check, Cash
**Tee Times:** 7 days adv.
**Fee 9 Holes: Weekday:** $35 **Weekend:** $39 F/S/S
**Fee 18 Holes: Weekday:** $59 **Weekend:** $69 F/S/S
**Twilight Rates:** After 3pm **Discounts:** Junior
**Cart Rental:** Mandatory **Driving Range:** Yes
**Lessons:** Yes **Schools:** No **Junior Golf:** Yes
**Membership:** Yes
**Architect/Yr Open:** Philip Wogan & George Sargent/1996
**Other:** Resort / Restaurant / Snack Bar

| Tees | Holes | Yards | Par | USGA | Slope |
|------|-------|-------|-----|------|-------|
| BACK | 18 | 7002 | 72 | 73.7 | 135 |
| MIDDLE | 18 | 6474 | 72 | 71.3 | 130 |
| FRONT | 18 | 5645 | 72 | 67.5 | 122 |

"Upscale layout with a nice variety of holes. Long distance between holes cut deep in the woods. Back tees and fast greens will challenge all players. Nice granite distance markers, and well-marked fairways help." –FP

| | 1 | 2 | 3 | 4 | 5 | 6 | 7 | 8 | 9 |
|------|-----|-----|-----|-----|-----|-----|-----|-----|-----|
| PAR | 5 | 3 | 4 | 4 | 4 | 4 | 5 | 3 | 4 |
| YARDS | 502 | 154 | 388 | 375 | 335 | 383 | 549 | 181 | 418 |
| | 10 | 11 | 12 | 13 | 14 | 15 | 16 | 17 | 18 |
| PAR | 4 | 5 | 4 | 4 | 3 | 4 | 4 | 3 | 5 |
| YARDS | 390 | 533 | 380 | 370 | 163 | 302 | 361 | 183 | 507 |

**Directions:** Turn off Maine Turnpike at Exit 48 and follow signs to Route 302 West for approximately 22.5 miles. Look for Chute's Cafe in Casco. Take second left. Follow signs.

# Poland Spring Country Club ✪✪✪ ▶39

543 Main Street (Route 26)
Poland Spring, ME  (207) 998-6002
www.polandspringresort.com

**Club Pro:** Allen Menne, PGA
**Payment:** Cash or Credit Card
**Tee Times:** Up to 1 year adv.

| Tees | Holes | Yards | Par | USGA | Slope |
|------|-------|-------|-----|------|-------|
| BACK | 18 | 6178 | 71 | 69.5 | 127 |
| MIDDLE | 18 | 5931 | 71 | 68.1 | 126 |
| FRONT | 18 | 5133 | 73 | 69.0 | 117 |

**Fee  9 Holes: Weekday:**
**Fee 18 Holes: Weekday:** $37
**Twilight Rates:** After 3pm
**Cart Rental:** $17pp/18
**Lessons:** Yes **Schools:** Yes
**Membership:** Yes
**Weekend:**
**Weekend:** $40
**Discounts:** None
**Driving Range:** Yes
**Junior Golf:** No
**Architect/Yr Open:** Fenn/Ross/1895

COUPON

**Other:** Clubhouse / Lockers / Showers / Pool / Snack Bar / Restaurant / Bar-Lounge / Hotel

Oldest 18-hole resort course in U.S. (1893) designed by Donald Ross. Open May 1 - November 1.
"Great value. Great views. Wide landing areas. Will definitely go back." –EP

| | 1 | 2 | 3 | 4 | 5 | 6 | 7 | 8 | 9 |
|------|---|---|---|---|---|---|---|---|---|
| PAR | 4 | 4 | 4 | 4 | 4 | 3 | 4 | 3 | 4 |
| YARDS | 337 | 306 | 388 | 410 | 305 | 132 | 378 | 184 | 322 |
| | 10 | 11 | 12 | 13 | 14 | 15 | 16 | 17 | 18 |
| PAR | 4 | 5 | 4 | 3 | 4 | 4 | 5 | 4 | 4 |
| YARDS | 293 | 446 | 292 | 169 | 399 | 404 | 531 | 292 | 329 |

**Directions:** Maine Turnpike Exit 63. Take Route 26 North 10 miles. Course is on right.

# Prospect Hill Golf Course ✪✪ ▶40

694 South Main Street
Auburn, ME  (207) 782-9220
www.prospecthillgolfcourse.com

**Club Pro:**
**Payment:** Visa, MC, Disc
**Tee Times:** Optional

| Tees | Holes | Yards | Par | USGA | Slope |
|------|-------|-------|-----|------|-------|
| BACK | | | | | |
| MIDDLE | 18 | 5846 | 71 | 69.9 | 110 |
| FRONT | 18 | 5227 | 71 | 69.9 | 111 |

**Fee  9 Holes: Weekday:** $17
**Fee 18 Holes: Weekday:** $25
**Twilight Rates:** After 4pm
**Cart Rental:** $15pp/18, $8pp/9
**Lessons:** No  **Schools:** Yes
**Membership:** Yes
**Weekend:** $17
**Weekend:** $25
**Discounts:** None
**Driving Range:** No
**Junior Golf:** Yes
**Architect/Yr Open:** 1957

**Other:** Snack Bar / Bar-Lounge / Function Hall
**GPS:**

The front 9 are wide open with a few small creeks, while the back 9 have 4 ponds and tree-lined fairways.
Spikeless course. Collared shirts required. New ownership, new function hall.

| | 1 | 2 | 3 | 4 | 5 | 6 | 7 | 8 | 9 |
|------|---|---|---|---|---|---|---|---|---|
| PAR | 5 | 4 | 3 | 4 | 3 | 4 | 4 | 4 | 4 |
| YARDS | 460 | 350 | 210 | 230 | 225 | 395 | 370 | 260 | 290 |
| | 10 | 11 | 12 | 13 | 14 | 15 | 16 | 17 | 18 |
| PAR | 4 | 4 | 5 | 4 | 4 | 3 | 4 | 4 | 4 |
| YARDS | 412 | 290 | 510 | 276 | 357 | 138 | 366 | 311 | 396 |

**Directions:** I-95 to Exit 75, left off ramp, look for signs.

S
ME

# Province Lake Golf Club ✪✪ ▸ 41

18 Mountain Road
Parsonfield, ME
(800) 325-4434 (207) 793-4040
www.provincelakegolf.com

| Tees | Holes | Yards | Par | USGA | Slope |
|---|---|---|---|---|---|
| BACK | 18 | 6277 | 71 | 70.6 | 130 |
| MIDDLE | 18 | 5904 | 71 | 69.4 | 125 |
| FRONT | 18 | 4935 | 71 | 64.1 | 112 |

**Club Pro:** Patrick E. DeAngelo
**Payment:** Visa, MC
**Tee Times:** 7 days adv.
**Fee 9 Holes: Weekday:** $24; $19 after 1pm **Weekend:** $45; $30 after 3pm
**Fee 18 Holes: Weekday:** $39; $29 after 1pm **Weekend:** $52; $39 after 3pm
**Twilight Rates:** After 3pm **Discounts:** Junior/Senior
**Cart Rental:** $16pp/18, $11pp/9 **Driving Range:** Yes
**Lessons:** Yes **Schools:** Yes **Junior Golf:** No
**Membership:** Yes **Architect/Yr Open:** Lawrence Van Etten/1918
**Other:** Clubhouse / Snack Bar / Restaurant / Bar-Lounge / Function Room / Patio / 2 Decks / Childcare

Playable for all. New beginners' tees — 2000 yards. Constantly improving course. Definitely family-friendly — $4/hr babysitter on site. 3rd year in a row named the number 1 golf course for women in New England by *Golf Magazine* July 2007.

| | 1 | 2 | 3 | 4 | 5 | 6 | 7 | 8 | 9 |
|---|---|---|---|---|---|---|---|---|---|
| PAR | 4 | 5 | 3 | 4 | 3 | 5 | 4 | 4 | 4 |
| YARDS | 378 | 438 | 201 | 378 | 144 | 525 | 369 | 376 | 309 |
| | 10 | 11 | 12 | 13 | 14 | 15 | 16 | 17 | 18 |
| PAR | 4 | 3 | 4 | 4 | 3 | 5 | 4 | 4 | 4 |
| YARDS | 338 | 146 | 295 | 337 | 142 | 483 | 383 | 331 | 331 |

**Directions:** I-95 to Route 16 (Spaulding Turnpike) to Route 153 North. Course is 15 miles north. Or access Route 153 South from Route 25.

# Rivermeadow Golf Club ✪½ ▸ 42

216 Lincoln Street
Westbrook, ME (207) 854-1625
www.rivermeadowgolf.com

| Tees | Holes | Yards | Par | USGA | Slope |
|---|---|---|---|---|---|
| BACK | 9 | 2954 | 36 | 67.5 | 114 |
| MIDDLE | 9 | 2786 | 36 | 65.8 | 114 |
| FRONT | 9 | 2545 | 36 | 65.1 | 112 |

**Club Pro:** Scott Mann
**Payment:** Visa, MC, Disc
**Tee Times:** 7 days adv.
**Fee 9 Holes: Weekday:** $16 **Weekend:** $16
**Fee 18 Holes: Weekday:** $24 **Weekend:** $24
**Twilight Rates:** After 5pm **Discounts:** Junior
**Cart Rental:** $14pp/18, $9pp/9 **Driving Range:** Yes
**Lessons:** Yes **Schools:** Yes **Junior Golf:** Yes
**Membership:** Yes **Architect/Yr Open:** Rufus Jordan/1958
**Other:** Grill Room and Bar / Clubhouse / Snack Bar / Restaurant

Open April - November 15th. Easy walking course.

| | 1 | 2 | 3 | 4 | 5 | 6 | 7 | 8 | 9 |
|---|---|---|---|---|---|---|---|---|---|
| PAR | 4 | 5 | 4 | 3 | 4 | 4 | 4 | 3 | 5 |
| YARDS | 342 | 435 | 260 | 149 | 360 | 360 | 290 | 150 | 440 |
| PAR | | | | | | | | | |
| YARDS | | | | | | | | | |

**Directions:** Maine Turnpike (Route 95), Exit 48 to Route 25 West into Westbrook (approximately 2 miles). Right turn onto Bridge Street (approximately ¼ mile). Left onto Lincoln Street to course.

# Riverside Municipal Golf Course ✪✪ ▶43

**1158 Riverside Street**
**Portland, ME (207) 797-3524**
**www.portlandmaine.gov**

| Tees | Holes | Yards | Par | USGA | Slope |
|------|-------|-------|-----|------|-------|
| BACK | 18 | 6370 | 72 | 69.2 | 115 |
| MIDDLE | 18 | 6052 | 72 | 67.5 | 112 |
| FRONT | 18 | 5630 | 73 | 70.7 | 112 |

**Club Pro:** Ron Bibeau, PGA
**Payment:** Visa, MC, Cash
**Tee Times:** Required
**Fee  9 Holes: Weekday:** $22    **Weekend:** $23
**Fee 18 Holes: Weekday:** $30    **Weekend:** $35
**Twilight Rates:** No    **Discounts:** Senior & Junior weekdays
**Cart Rental:** $16pp/18, $10pp/9    **Driving Range:** $8/bucket
**Lessons:** $45/half hour  **Schools:** No    **Junior Golf:** Yes
**Membership:** Yes    **Architect/Yr:** Stiles & Van Kleek/1932
**Other:** Clubhouse / Lockers / Showers / Snack Bar / Restaurant / Bar-Lounge

27 holes available. South course is an additional 9-hole regulation course with 3102 yards. Wide fairways, medium-speed greens, only a little hilly. Open ASAP; close on first snow. "Best shape ever!" –RB

| | 1 | 2 | 3 | 4 | 5 | 6 | 7 | 8 | 9 |
|------|-----|-----|-----|-----|-----|-----|-----|-----|-----|
| PAR | 5 | 4 | 3 | 5 | 4 | 3 | 4 | 4 | 4 |
| YARDS | 450 | 365 | 202 | 488 | 322 | 197 | 314 | 324 | 396 |
| | 10 | 11 | 12 | 13 | 14 | 15 | 16 | 17 | 18 |
| PAR | 5 | 4 | 4 | 3 | 4 | 4 | 4 | 4 | 4 |
| YARDS | 540 | 384 | 414 | 167 | 346 | 338 | 334 | 374 | 382 |

**Directions:** Maine Turnpike to Exit 48. Follow signs to course.


# Rockland Golf Club ✪✪✪ ▶44

**Old County Road**
**Rockland, ME (207) 594-9322**
**www.rocklandgolf.com**

| Tees | Holes | Yards | Par | USGA | Slope |
|------|-------|-------|-----|------|-------|
| BACK | 18 | 5041 | 70 | 69.2 | 118 |
| MIDDLE | 18 | 5773 | 70 | 68.1 | 116 |
| FRONT | 18 | 5023 | 71 | 64.6 | 112 |

**Club Pro:** Keenan Flanagan, PGA
**Payment:** Most Major Credit Cards
**Tee Times:** 3 days adv.
**Fee  9 Holes: Weekday:** $25    **Weekend:**
**Fee 18 Holes: Weekday:** $50    **Weekend:**
**Twilight Rates:** No    **Discounts:** Junior
**Cart Rental:** $20pp/18, $10pp/9    **Driving Range:** No
**Lessons:** $35/half hour  **Schools:** No    **Junior Golf:** Yes
**Membership:** Yes    **Architect/Yr Open:** Roger Sorrent/1930
**Other:** Clubhouse / Bar-Lounge / Snack Bar / Showers

COUPON

S
ME

Player Comments: "Courteous, friendly staff." New irrigation system and new tee markers. Views of ocean and Rockland Harbor. Series of 5 1-hour lessons for $240. Punch and Play card. Opens early Spring.

| | 1 | 2 | 3 | 4 | 5 | 6 | 7 | 8 | 9 |
|------|-----|-----|-----|-----|-----|-----|-----|-----|-----|
| PAR | 5 | 4 | 4 | 4 | 3 | 4 | 5 | 4 | 3 |
| YARDS | 521 | 378 | 268 | 359 | 136 | 303 | 485 | 398 | 215 |
| | 10 | 11 | 12 | 13 | 14 | 15 | 16 | 17 | 18 |
| PAR | 3 | 3 | 4 | 4 | 4 | 5 | 4 | 4 | 3 |
| YARDS | 176 | 210 | 282 | 425 | 357 | 582 | 341 | 232 | 163 |

**Directions:** I-95 to Coastal Route 1 through Thomaston. Left onto old Country Road to course 3.5 miles on left.

# Sable Oaks Golf Club

✪✪✪½  **45**

505 Country Club Drive
South Portland, ME  (207) 775-6257
www.sableoaks.com

| Tees | Holes | Yards | Par | USGA | Slope |
|---|---|---|---|---|---|
| BACK | 18 | 6359 | 70 | 71.6 | 131 |
| MIDDLE | 18 | 5545 | 70 | 68.3 | 123 |
| FRONT | 18 | 4786 | 72 | 69.5 | 124 |

**Club Pro:** Mark Anderson, GM
**Payment:** Visa, MC, Disc, Amex
**Tee Times:** Recommended/7 days adv.
**Fee  9 Holes: Weekday:** $30     **Weekend:** $35
**Fee 18 Holes: Weekday:** $40     **Weekend:** $45
**Twilight Rates:** After 4pm     **Discounts:** Junior
**Cart Rental:** $15pp/18, $10pp/9     **Driving Range:** No
**Lessons:** No  **Schools:** No     **Junior Golf:**
**Membership:** Yes     **Architect/Yr:**
**Other:** Bar-Lounge/ Function Hall / Showers / Locker Room / Lodging

COUPON

You'll be treated to some challenging yet enjoyable golf, surrounded by woods and ponds, with soft fairways and gently rolling manicured greens. 2015 expanded greens and removed trees. Book tee times online. *Travel Golf Magazine* calls Sable Oaks "One of the most imaginative courses in the state." Sister course to Samoset Resort. Off-season rates, inquire.

|  | 1 | 2 | 3 | 4 | 5 | 6 | 7 | 8 | 9 |
|---|---|---|---|---|---|---|---|---|---|
| PAR | 4 | 5 | 4 | 4 | 5 | 3 | 4 | 3 | 4 |
| YARDS | 389 | 460 | 419 | 398 | 442 | 170 | 319 | 138 | 394 |
|  | 10 | 11 | 12 | 13 | 14 | 15 | 16 | 17 | 18 |
| PAR | 4 | 3 | 4 | 3 | 5 | 4 | 4 | 3 | 4 |
| YARDS | 378 | 159 | 437 | 171 | 443 | 384 | 383 | 164 | 408 |

**Directions:** I-95 to Exit 45 (Maine Mall, Jet Port). Go right at light. At 4th light, go left on Running Hill Road. Take the second right onto Country Club Drive.

# Salmon Falls Golf Course

✪½  **46**

52 Golf Course Lane
Hollis, ME  (207) 929-5233
www.salmonfalls-resort.com

| Tees | Holes | Yards | Par | USGA | Slope |
|---|---|---|---|---|---|
| BACK | 9 | 2965 | 36 | 67.7 | 113 |
| MIDDLE | 9 | 2883 | 36 | 67.7 | 113 |
| FRONT | 9 | 2550 | 36 | 69.5 | 112 |

**Club Pro:** Susan Bell, Manager
**Payment:** Visa, MC, Amex, Disc
**Tee Times:** Weekends and Holidays
**Fee  9 Holes: Weekday:** $17     **Weekend:** $17
**Fee 18 Holes: Weekday:** $25     **Weekend:** $25
**Twilight Rates:** After 4pm     **Discounts:** Seasonal
**Cart Rental:** $9pp/18, $8pp/9     **Driving Range:** No
**Lessons:** No  **Schools:** No     **Junior Golf:** No
**Membership:** Yes     **Architect/Yr Open:** Robert Trent Jones Sr./1966
**Other:** Clubhouse / Snack Bar     **GPS:**

COUPON

Suggest beginners come after 1pm on weekends. Open March through November. Noted for beauty of Maine. Improved cart paths and sand traps. Great course, great price, great people.

|  | 1 | 2 | 3 | 4 | 5 | 6 | 7 | 8 | 9 |
|---|---|---|---|---|---|---|---|---|---|
| PAR | 4 | 4 | 3 | 5 | 5 | 3 | 4 | 4 | 4 |
| YARDS | 365 | 250 | 190 | 500 | 455 | 165 | 303 | 251 | 404 |
|  | 10 | 11 | 12 | 13 | 14 | 15 | 16 | 17 | 18 |
| PAR | 4 | 4 | 3 | 5 | 5 | 3 | 4 | 4 | 4 |
| YARDS | 380 | 245 | 235 | 510 | 460 | 165 | 310 | 265 | 395 |

**Directions:** I-95 to Exit 36 (Saco), follow Route 112 North. Follow signs to course.

# Samoset Resort Golf Club ✪✪✪✪

47 ▶

220 Warrenton Street
Rockport, ME (207) 594-1431
www.samosetresort.com

**Club Pro:** Gary Soule, PGA
**Payment:** All Major Cards
**Tee Times:** 2 days adv.

| Tees | Holes | Yards | Par | USGA | Slope |
|------|-------|-------|-----|------|-------|
| BACK | 18 | 6617 | 70 | 70.7 | 130 |
| MIDDLE | 18 | 5615 | 70 | 68.9 | 124 |
| FRONT | 18 | 5145 | 72 | 71.2 | 125 |

**Fee 9 Holes: Weekday:** $70     **Weekend:** $70
**Fee 18 Holes: Weekday:** $140     **Weekend:** $140
**Twilight Rates:** After 2pm     **Discounts:** Junior
**Cart Rental:** Included     **Driving Range:** $8/bag
**Lessons:** $60/half hour **Schools:** Yes     **Junior Golf:** Yes
**Membership:** Yes     **Architect/Yr Open:** Bob Elder/1902
**Other:** Clubhouse / Snack Bar / Restaurant / Bar-Lounge / Hotel / Lockers / Showers

Noted for spectacular ocean views and excellent playing conditions.

|  | 1 | 2 | 3 | 4 | 5 | 6 | 7 | 8 | 9 |
|------|---|---|---|---|---|---|---|---|---|
| PAR | 4 | 4 | 3 | 5 | 3 | 4 | 3 | 4 | 4 |
| YARDS | 360 | 388 | 190 | 481 | 165 | 380 | 176 | 330 | 312 |
|  | **10** | **11** | **12** | **13** | **14** | **15** | **16** | **17** | **18** |
| PAR | 4 | 3 | 5 | 3 | 5 | 4 | 4 | 4 | 5 |
| YARDS | 338 | 120 | 494 | 190 | 500 | 355 | 375 | 400 | 478 |

**Directions:** I-95 to I-295 to Exit 28 to Brunswick Coastal Route 1 North, through Rockland. Turn right onto Warrenton Street.

# Sandy River Golf Course ✪½

48 ▶

154 George Thomas Road
Chesterville, ME (207) 778-2492
www.sandyrivergolfcourse.com

**Club Pro:** Scott Hoisington, PGA
**Payment:** Cash
**Tee Times:** None

| Tees | Holes | Yards | Par | USGA | Slope |
|------|-------|-------|-----|------|-------|
| BACK |  |  |  |  |  |
| MIDDLE | 9 | 1828 | 32 |  |  |
| FRONT | 9 | 1762 | 32 |  |  |

**Fee 9 Holes: Weekday:** $12     **Weekend:** $12
**Fee 18 Holes: Weekday:** $18     **Weekend:** $18
**Twilight Rates:**     **Discounts:** Junior & Senior
**Cart Rental:** $2/pull cart     **Driving Range:** Yes
**Lessons:** Yes **Schools:** Yes     **Junior Golf:** Yes
**Membership:** Yes     **Architect/Yr Open:** 1968
**Other:** Snack Bar

Short but challenging and charming 9 hole course. Family-oriented.

|  | 1 | 2 | 3 | 4 | 5 | 6 | 7 | 8 | 9 |
|------|---|---|---|---|---|---|---|---|---|
| PAR | 3 | 3 | 3 | 3 | 4 | 4 | 4 | 4 | 4 |
| YARDS | 105 | 216 | 152 | 150 | 234 | 258 | 143 | 250 | 320 |
| PAR |  |  |  |  |  |  |  |  |  |
| YARDS |  |  |  |  |  |  |  |  |  |

**Directions:** I-95 to Route 27 North to US-2/ME-27 to ME-41/ME-156. Course is ½ mile on left.

S
ME

# Sanford Country Club  ✪✪✪  ▶49

Route 4
Sanford, ME (207) 324-5462
www.sanfordcountryclub.com

Club Pro: Sam LeBlanc, Dir. of Golf
Payment: Cash, Visa, MC
Tee Times: Yes
Fee 9 Holes: Weekday: $25
Fee 18 Holes: Weekday: $35-$40
Twilight Rates: After 3pm
Cart Rental: $18pp/18, $12pp/9
Lessons: Yes  Schools: No
Membership: Yes

| Tees | Holes | Yards | Par | USGA | Slope |
|------|-------|-------|-----|------|-------|
| BACK | 18 | 6726 | 72 | 73.2 | 128 |
| MIDDLE | 18 | 6217 | 72 | 70.5 | 122 |
| FRONT | 18 | 5320 | 74 | 66.5 | 114 |

Weekend: $25
Weekend: $40-$45
Discounts: Junior, Military
Driving Range: Yes
Junior Golf: Yes
GPS: Yes

*COUPON*

Architect/Yr Open: Alex Chisolm & Marvin Armstrong/1932
Other: Restaurant / Clubhouse / Bar-Lounge / Snack Bar

Course has outstanding reviews. Stay-and-play packages available. Call pro shop for specials. Home of the 2005 Maine Amateur and qualifying site of the 2006 U.S. Amateur. "Nice layout, with 4 sets of tees." –FP

| | 1 | 2 | 3 | 4 | 5 | 6 | 7 | 8 | 9 |
|-----|-----|-----|-----|-----|-----|-----|-----|-----|-----|
| PAR | 4 | 4 | 3 | 5 | 5 | 4 | 4 | 3 | 4 |
| YARDS | 417 | 308 | 185 | 440 | 488 | 429 | 326 | 130 | 423 |
| | 10 | 11 | 12 | 13 | 14 | 15 | 16 | 17 | 18 |
| PAR | 4 | 4 | 5 | 3 | 4 | 4 | 3 | 4 | 5 |
| YARDS | 342 | 313 | 488 | 100 | 323 | 373 | 186 | 389 | 557 |

Directions: I-95 to Exit 2, head north on Route 109 for approximately 10 miles to Route 4 Intersection. Take left off 109 to Route 4 South for 2.5 miles. Located on left.

# Sebasco Harbor Resort Golf Club  ✪✪½  ▶50

29 Kenyon Road
Sebasco Estates, ME (207) 389-9060
www.sebasco.com

Club Pro: Dennis Estes
Payment: Visa, MC, Amex, Disc
Tee Times: Yes
Fee 9 Holes: Weekday: $40
Fee 18 Holes: Weekday: $60
Twilight Rates: No
Cart Rental: $15pp/18, $10pp/9
Lessons: $50/hour, $30/half hour  Schools: Clinics

| Tees | Holes | Yards | Par | USGA | Slope |
|------|-------|-------|-----|------|-------|
| BACK | 9 | 3046 | 36 | 70.6 | 123 |
| MIDDLE | 9 | 2794 | 36 | 67.0 | 119 |
| FRONT | 9 | 2364 | 36 | 68.2 | 127 |

Weekend: $40
Weekend: $60
Discounts: None
Driving Range: Practice course
Junior Golf: No

*COUPON*

Membership: Yes
Architect/Yr Open: Alex Chisolm/1926
Other: Full Restaurant / Clubhouse / Hotel / Inn / Lockers / Showers / Bar-Lounge
GPS: Yes

Newly renovated course. 9 hole gem carved along Maine's mid-coast. Beautiful ocean and forest views including our signature par 3 2nd hole over the cove. New 3-hole practice course. Discounted rates for guests and boaters.

| | 1 | 2 | 3 | 4 | 5 | 6 | 7 | 8 | 9 |
|-----|-----|-----|-----|-----|-----|-----|-----|-----|-----|
| PAR | 4 | 3 | 5 | 4 | 4 | 3 | 4 | 4 | 5 |
| YARDS | 370 | 140 | 467 | 309 | 339 | 179 | 387 | 316 | 480 |
| PAR | | | | | | | | | |
| YARDS | | | | | | | | | |

Directions: South of Bath on Route 209 for 10 miles. Turn right onto Route 217. Follow the Sebasco signs. Course ¼ mile on left.

# Sheepscot Links Golf Club  ✪½   51

822 Townhouse Road
Whitefield, ME (207) 549-7060
www.sheepscotlinks.com

| Tees | Holes | Yards | Par | USGA | Slope |
|------|-------|-------|-----|------|-------|
| BACK | 9 | 2834 | 35 | 68.4 | 115 |
| MIDDLE | 9 | 2538 | 35 | 66.6 | 115 |
| FRONT | 9 | 2233 | 35 | | |

**Club Pro:** George Hall, Manager
**Payment:** Check, Visa, MC
**Tee Times:** 1 day adv.
**Fee 9 Holes: Weekday:** $15     **Weekend:** $15
**Fee 18 Holes: Weekday:** $24     **Weekend:** $24
**Twilight Rates:** After 4pm weekends     **Discounts:** Sr. & Jr
**Cart Rental:** $16pp/18, $10pp/9     **Driving Range:** Yes
**Lessons:** No **Schools:** No     **Junior Golf:** Yes
**Membership:** Yes     **Architect/Yr:** 2001
**Other:** Clubhouse / Snack Bar / Putting Course

COUPON

Located on the Sheepscot River in a rural setting. The Links offer a good variety of water, sand, dog legs, elevated tees, and elevated greens. Often described as the best kept golf secret in Central Maine.

| | 1 | 2 | 3 | 4 | 5 | 6 | 7 | 8 | 9 |
|------|-----|-----|-----|-----|-----|-----|-----|-----|-----|
| PAR | 4 | 3 | 4 | 4 | 4 | 4 | 5 | 3 | 4 |
| YARDS | 354 | 149 | 286 | 292 | 351 | 309 | 514 | 141 | 282 |
| PAR | | | | | | | | | |
| YARDS | | | | | | | | | |

**Directions:** Traveling north on 295, take the first Gardiner exit, turn right on 201. Follow 201 across the Kennebec River Bridge. Turn right on Route 27, left on 194, then left on Townhouse Road. 30 minutes from the highway to the Links!

# South Portland Municipal GC  ✪½   52

155 Wescott Road
South Portland, ME (207) 775-0005
www.southportland.org

| Tees | Holes | Yards | Par | USGA | Slope |
|------|-------|-------|-----|------|-------|
| BACK | | | | | |
| MIDDLE | 9 | 2187 | 33 | 61.2 | 95 |
| FRONT | | | | | |

**Club Pro:**
**Payment:** Cash, Check, Credit Cards
**Tee Times:** No
**Fee 9 Holes: Weekday:** $15     **Weekend:** $17
**Fee 18 Holes: Weekday:**     **Weekend:**
**Twilight Rates:** No     **Discounts:** None
**Cart Rental:** $4/pull     **Driving Range:** No
**Lessons:** No **Schools:** No     **Junior Golf:** First Tee
**Membership:** Yes, residents     **Architect/Yr Open:** Larry Rowe/1931
**Other:** Snack Bar     **GPS:**

COUPON

S
ME

Well-maintained, polite staff. Carts are not required. Pay once, play for 3 rounds. Clinics offered by recreation center.

| | 1 | 2 | 3 | 4 | 5 | 6 | 7 | 8 | 9 |
|------|-----|-----|-----|-----|-----|-----|-----|-----|-----|
| PAR | 4 | 3 | 4 | 3 | 4 | 3 | 3 | 4 | 4 |
| YARDS | 347 | 155 | 250 | 138 | 402 | 179 | 135 | 297 | 284 |
| PAR | | | | | | | | | |
| YARDS | | | | | | | | | |

**Directions:** I-295 to Exit 3 (Westbrook Street). Go east on Westbrook Street (about 3/10 of a mile). Take a left onto Wescott Street. The clubhouse is on the left under Branch Library.

# Spring Meadows Golf Course ✪✪✪½  53 ▶

59 Lewiston Road
Gray, ME (207) 657-2586
www.springmeadowsgolf.com

| Tees | Holes | Yards | Par | USGA | Slope |
|------|-------|-------|-----|------|-------|
| BACK | 18 | 6656 | 71 | 72.1 | 126 |
| MIDDLE | 18 | 6065 | 71 | 69.2 | 124 |
| FRONT | 18 | 4706 | 71 | 67.9 | 109 |

**Club Pro:** Ben Morey, PGA
**Payment:** Most Major
**Tee Times:** Up to 7 days
**Fee 9 Holes: Weekday:** $23    **Weekend:** $26
**Fee 18 Holes: Weekday:** $36    **Weekend:** $44
**Twilight Rates:** After 3pm    **Discounts:** Military
**Cart Rental:** $18pp/18, $11pp/9    **Driving Range:** Yes
**Lessons:** $60/hour **Schools:** Junior    **Junior Golf:** No
**Membership:** Yes    **Architect/Yr Open:** William Bradley Booth/1999
**Other:** Refurbished Barn with Banquet Facilities Seating 220 / Player's Lounge
**GPS:** Yes

*COUPON*

Great conditions from tee to green. Well layed out with water on many holes. Great elevated look to the flags on holes #6 and #7. "Fun to play." –FP

| | 1 | 2 | 3 | 4 | 5 | 6 | 7 | 8 | 9 |
|------|---|---|---|---|---|---|---|---|---|
| PAR | 4 | 4 | 5 | 3 | 4 | 3 | 4 | 4 | 4 |
| YARDS | 405 | 337 | 555 | 162 | 351 | 146 | 300 | 387 | 363 |
| | 10 | 11 | 12 | 13 | 14 | 15 | 16 | 17 | 18 |
| PAR | 5 | 4 | 4 | 3 | 4 | 5 | 3 | 4 | 4 |
| YARDS | 522 | 357 | 315 | 127 | 327 | 509 | 116 | 420 | 336 |

**Directions:** Course is 1 mile from Exit 63 off Maine Turnpike, on Route 4/100/202 Northbound.

# Springbrook Golf Course ✪✪½  54 ▶

Route 202
Leeds, ME (207) 946-5900
www.springbrookgolfclub.com

| Tees | Holes | Yards | Par | USGA | Slope |
|------|-------|-------|-----|------|-------|
| BACK | 18 | 6408 | 71 | 68.1 | 119 |
| MIDDLE | 18 | 6163 | 71 | 64.7 | 111 |
| FRONT | 18 | 4989 | 74 | 61.4 | 96 |

**Club Pro:** Ed Balboni, PGA
**Payment:** Visa, MC
**Tee Times:** Weekends, Holidays
**Fee 9 Holes: Weekday:** $15    **Weekend:** $15 after 2pm
**Fee 18 Holes: Weekday:** $28 all day    **Weekend:** $28 all day
**Twilight Rates:** After 4pm    **Discounts:** Juniors, Seniors, Ladies
**Cart Rental:** $16pp/18, $8pp/9    **Driving Range:** $2.50/sm., $4.50/lg. bucket
**Lessons:** $45/45 min. **Schools:** No    **Junior Golf:** Yes
**Membership:** Yes    **Architect/Yr Open:** Arnold Biondi/1966
**Other:** Clubhouse / Lockers / Showers / Snack Bar / Bar-Lounge / Discount Game Cards

Sig. Hole: #15 is a 219-yard, uphill par 3. Very difficult hole. Rolling hills and roughly reminiscent of a Scottish-style course.

| | 1 | 2 | 3 | 4 | 5 | 6 | 7 | 8 | 9 |
|------|---|---|---|---|---|---|---|---|---|
| PAR | 4 | 3 | 4 | 4 | 4 | 4 | 5 | 3 | 4 |
| YARDS | 415 | 160 | 410 | 350 | 335 | 385 | 520 | 168 | 340 |
| | 10 | 11 | 12 | 13 | 14 | 15 | 16 | 17 | 18 |
| PAR | 4 | 4 | 5 | 3 | 4 | 3 | 5 | 4 | 4 |
| YARDS | 420 | 290 | 460 | 180 | 350 | 206 | 480 | 325 | 365 |

**Directions:** Maine Turnpike to Lewiston exit to Route 202 East. Course is 10 miles outside of Lewiston-Auburn.

# Sunday River Golf Club ✪✪✪✪

**55**

18 Championship Drive
Newry, ME (207) 824-4653
www.sundayrivergolf.com

**Club Pro:** Peter (Stroke) Flint, PGA
**Payment:** Visa, MC, Amex, Disc
**Tee Times:** 7 days adv.

| Tees | Holes | Yards | Par | USGA | Slope |
|------|-------|-------|-----|------|-------|
| BACK | 18 | 7130 | 72 | 75.3 | 150 |
| MIDDLE | 18 | 6558 | 72 | 72.3 | 139 |
| FRONT | 18 | 5006 | 72 | 65.0 | 120 |

**Fee 9 Holes: Weekday:** $60 w/cart     **Weekend:** $60 w/cart
**Fee 18 Holes: Weekday:** $95 w/cart     **Weekend:** $95 w/cart
**Twilight Rates:** After 3pm     **Discounts:** Yes
**Cart Rental:** "2 for 1" nine holes only     **Driving Range:** Yes
**Lessons:** Yes **Schools:** Yes     **Junior Golf:**
**Membership:** Yes     **Architect/Yr Open:** Robert Trent Jones Jr./2004
**Other:** Wilderness Lodge Clubhouse / Restaurant / Full Banquet at Resort

Opened late 2004. Robert Trent Jones Jr. design. Each hole has 4 tee boxes. Yardage below is from the Blue tees. Sunday River's wide fairways, dynamic green settings, pristine playing conditions, and jaw-dropping alpine views combine to form *Golf Week's* #1 course in Maine and one of *Golf* magazine's (Top 100 You Can Play) in the U.S.

|  | 1 | 2 | 3 | 4 | 5 | 6 | 7 | 8 | 9 |
|------|---|---|---|---|---|---|---|---|---|
| PAR | 5 | 4 | 4 | 3 | 4 | 3 | 5 | 4 | 4 |
| YARDS | 499 | 384 | 332 | 175 | 425 | 178 | 440 | 410 | 339 |
|  | 10 | 11 | 12 | 13 | 14 | 15 | 16 | 17 | 18 |
| PAR | 4 | 5 | 4 | 4 | 3 | 5 | 3 | 4 | 4 |
| YARDS | 385 | 565 | 412 | 316 | 185 | 483 | 142 | 474 | 414 |

**Directions:** Take Route 1 North to I-95 North to Maine Turnpike (I-495). Take Maine Turnpike (I-495) to Exit 11 (Gray). Take Route 26 North to Bethel. Follow Route 2 East for 2.6 miles. Take left onto Sunday River Road which becomes Monkey Brook Road. Go 2.5 miles and turn right on Championship Drive.

# Sunset Ridge Golf Links ✪✪

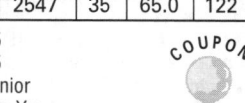

**56**

771 Cumberland Street
Westbrook, ME (207) 854-9463
www.sunsetridgegolflinks.com

**Club Pro:** Michael Guy Smith, Dir. of Golf
**Payment:** Credit Cards, Checks, Cash
**Tee Times:** No

| Tees | Holes | Yards | Par | USGA | Slope |
|------|-------|-------|-----|------|-------|
| BACK | 9 | 3074 | 35 | 70.4 | 138 |
| MIDDLE | 9 | 2691 | 35 | 67.0 | 123 |
| FRONT | 9 | 2547 | 35 | 65.0 | 122 |

**Fee 9 Holes: Weekday:** $10     **Weekend:** $15
**Fee 18 Holes: Weekday:** $20     **Weekend:** $25
**Twilight Rates:** After 5pm     **Discounts:** Junior
**Cart Rental:** $25/18, $12.50/9 per cart     **Driving Range:** Yes
**Lessons: Schools:**     **Junior Golf:**
**Membership:** Yes     **Architect/Yr Open:**
**Other:** Clubhouse / Showers / Snack Bar / Bar-Lounge / Function Room / Basketball Courts

Rolling hills with elevation changes. The signature hole #4 is a par 3 that plays from 214 yards to 110 yards based on pin placement and tee location. Challenging for all levels of play with plenty of risk/reward.

|  | 1 | 2 | 3 | 4 | 5 | 6 | 7 | 8 | 9 |
|------|---|---|---|---|---|---|---|---|---|
| PAR | 4 | 4 | 4 | 3 | 4 | 4 | 3 | 4 | 5 |
| YARDS | 297 | 250 | 300 | 154 | 325 | 303 | 157 | 378 | 527 |
| PAR |  |  |  |  |  |  |  |  |  |
| YARDS |  |  |  |  |  |  |  |  |  |

**Directions:** I-95 North to Exit 48. Go straight through the light and in .4 miles turn right at the light onto Main Street. Travel 2.7 miles and the course is on the right.

**S
ME**

# Toddy Brook Golf Course ✪✪✪½ 57

925 Sligo Road
North Yarmouth, ME (207) 829-5100
www.toddybrookgolf.com

| Tees | Holes | Yards | Par | USGA | Slope |
|------|-------|-------|-----|------|-------|
| BACK | 18 | 5886 | 71 | 68.9 | 126 |
| MIDDLE | 18 | 5173 | 71 | 65.4 | 115 |
| FRONT | 18 | 4409 | 71 | 67.6 | 113 |

**Club Pro:** Gregg Baker, PGA
**Payment:** Visa, MC, Amex, Disc
**Tee Times:** 7 day adv.
**Fee 9 Holes: Weekday:** $25 **Weekend:** $25
**Fee 18 Holes: Weekday:** $35 **Weekend:** $43 F/S/S
**Twilight Rates:** After 3pm **Discounts:** Junior
**Cart Rental:** $18pp/18, $13pp/9 **Driving Range:** Yes
**Lessons:** Yes **Schools:** Yes **Junior Golf:**
**Membership:** Variety **Architect/Yr Open:** Robert Anderson/2002
**Other:** Restaurant / Clubhouse / Lockers / Showers / Bar-Lounge/Banquet Facility

COUPON

Beautiful layout with challenging tees. Each hole has unique design with plenty of sand & water to test your skills. New back 9 with beautiful views. Layout ends with a daunting island green. Back tees below.

| | 1 | 2 | 3 | 4 | 5 | 6 | 7 | 8 | 9 |
|---|---|---|---|---|---|---|---|---|---|
| PAR | 4 | 4 | 4 | 3 | 5 | 3 | 4 | 4 | 5 |
| YARDS | 307 | 357 | 366 | 151 | 453 | 184 | 350 | 314 | 506 |
| | 10 | 11 | 12 | 13 | 14 | 15 | 16 | 17 | 18 |
| PAR | 4 | 3 | 4 | 5 | 4 | 4 | 3 | 5 | 3 |
| YARDS | 363 | 158 | 369 | 466 | 371 | 380 | 133 | 546 | 124 |

**Directions:** I-95 to Yarmouth exit. Follow Route 1 to Route 115 exit. Take 115 West about ¼ mile to Sligo Road on right. Go approx. 3⅛ miles. Course is on right.

# Turner Highlands Golf Course ✪✪✪ 58

10 B Highland Avenue
Turner, ME (207) 224-7060
www.turnerhighlands.com

| Tees | Holes | Yards | Par | USGA | Slope |
|------|-------|-------|-----|------|-------|
| BACK | | | | | |
| MIDDLE | 18 | 6033 | 71 | 68.6 | 115 |
| FRONT | 18 | 4705 | 71 | 67.5 | 113 |

**Club Pro:** Donna Chiasson, Manager
**Payment:** Visa, MC, Amex, Disc
**Tee Times:** Yes
**Fee 9 Holes: Weekday:** $16 **Weekend:** $16
**Fee 18 Holes: Weekday:** $28 **Weekend:** $28
**Twilight Rates:** After 2 pm **Discounts:** $16 M-Th before 12pm
**Cart Rental:** $16pp/18, $9pp/9 **Driving Range:** Yes
**Lessons:** Yes **Schools:** No **Junior Golf:** Yes, $11 wknds after 4pm
**Membership:** No **Architect/Yr Open:** Steve Leavitt/1993
**Other:** Lockers / Showers / Snack Bar / Restaurant

COUPON

Player Comments: "A well-maintained local popular favorite, good value, great day trip." –FP
Now 18 holes. A scenic golf course situated high on a hill.

| | 1 | 2 | 3 | 4 | 5 | 6 | 7 | 8 | 9 |
|---|---|---|---|---|---|---|---|---|---|
| PAR | 4 | 5 | 4 | 3 | 4 | 5 | 4 | 3 | 4 |
| YARDS | 280 | 442 | 282 | 149 | 365 | 452 | 372 | 204 | 376 |
| | 10 | 11 | 12 | 13 | 14 | 15 | 16 | 17 | 18 |
| PAR | 3 | 4 | 4 | 4 | 5 | 3 | 5 | 4 | 3 |
| YARDS | 135 | 365 | 370 | 430 | 592 | 125 | 500 | 387 | 182 |

**Directions:** I-95 to Exit 75 toward Auburn. Get onto Route 4 North. Turn right onto Route 117. Stay on Route 117 for 8.5 miles. Course is on the right.

# Twin Falls Golf Club  ✪✪  ▶59

364 Spring Street
Westbrook, ME (207) 854-5397
www.twinfallsgolfclub.com

| Tees | Holes | Yards | Par | USGA | Slope |
|------|-------|-------|-----|------|-------|
| BACK | | | | | |
| MIDDLE | 9 | 2700 | 34 | 61.3 | 90 |
| FRONT | 9 | 2453 | 34 | | |

**Club Pro:** Kathy Boullie, GM
**Payment:** Cash, Credit, Debit
**Tee Times:** No
**Fee 9 Holes: Weekday:** $15, $20 w/cart    **Weekend:** $15, $20 w/cart
**Fee 18 Holes: Weekday:** $20, $25 w/cart    **Weekend:** $20, $30 w/cart
**Twilight Rates:** After 5pm    **Discounts:** None
**Cart Rental:**    **Driving Range:** No
**Lessons:** No  **Schools:** No    **Junior Golf:** No
**Membership:** Yes    **Architect/Yr Open:** Albert Young/1972
**Other:** Clubhouse / Snack Bar    **GPS:**

"Fine public course for beginners. Keep your drive on #1 to the left of center as the brook hidden from view will come into play." –AP

| | 1 | 2 | 3 | 4 | 5 | 6 | 7 | 8 | 9 |
|------|---|---|---|---|---|---|---|---|---|
| PAR | 4 | 3 | 3 | 4 | 4 | 4 | 4 | 4 | 4 |
| YARDS | 334 | 152 | 110 | 343 | 351 | 260 | 275 | 330 | 298 |
| PAR | | | | | | | | | |
| YARDS | | | | | | | | | |

**Directions:** I-95 to Exit 45, follow Maine Mall Road to Spring Street to course.

# Val Halla Golf Course  ✪✪✪  ▶60

Val Halla Road
Cumberland, ME (207) 829-2225
www.valhallagolf.com

| Tees | Holes | Yards | Par | USGA | Slope |
|------|-------|-------|-----|------|-------|
| BACK | 18 | 6567 | 72 | 71.1 | 126 |
| MIDDLE | 18 | 6201 | 72 | 69.3 | 122 |
| FRONT | 18 | 5437 | 72 | 71.4 | 120 |

**Club Pro:** Cory Mansfield, PGA
**Payment:** Visa, MC
**Tee Times:** Yes
**Fee 9 Holes: Weekday:** $22    **Weekend:** $24
**Fee 18 Holes: Weekday:** $30    **Weekend:** $35
**Twilight Rates:** After 4pm    **Discounts:** Senior & Junior
**Cart Rental:** $12.50pp/18, $7.50pp/9    **Driving Range:** $4/bucket
**Lessons:** $40/half hour  **Schools:** No    **Junior Golf:** Yes
**Membership:** Yes    **Architect/Yr Open:** Phil Wogan/1965
**Other:** Snack Bar / Lounge    **GPS:**

Consistently rated 1 of Maine's best public courses. Bent grass, good shape, wooded, hilly, scenic, brooks and streams, excellent layout. Open April 15 - November 1.

| | 1 | 2 | 3 | 4 | 5 | 6 | 7 | 8 | 9 |
|------|---|---|---|---|---|---|---|---|---|
| PAR | 4 | 3 | 5 | 4 | 4 | 4 | 4 | 3 | 5 |
| YARDS | 350 | 142 | 553 | 383 | 394 | 340 | 369 | 175 | 484 |
| | 10 | 11 | 12 | 13 | 14 | 15 | 16 | 17 | 18 |
| PAR | 4 | 4 | 3 | 5 | 4 | 4 | 4 | 3 | 4 |
| YARDS | 376 | 347 | 148 | 465 | 440 | 388 | 294 | 155 | 398 |

**Directions:** From Portland take 295 North to Exit 10. Follow Route 9 to Cumberland Center. The course is off Greely Road on Val Halla Road.

S
ME

# Wawenock Country Club ✪✪½ 61 ▶

Route 129
Walpole, ME (207) 563-3938
www.wawenockgolfclub.com

| Tees | Holes | Yards | Par | USGA | Slope |
|------|-------|-------|-----|------|-------|
| BACK | | | | | |
| MIDDLE | 9 | 3009 | 35 | 68.8 | 122 |
| FRONT | 9 | 2727 | 36 | 73.5 | 119 |

**Club Pro:** Lon Wanser
**Payment:** Cash, Check, Visa, MC, Amex, Disc
**Tee Times:** July-August
**Fee 9 Holes: Weekday:** $20    **Weekend:** $20
**Fee 18 Holes: Weekday:** $30    **Weekend:** $30
**Twilight Rates:** After 5pm    **Discounts:** Junior
**Cart Rental:** $14pp/18, $11pp/9    **Driving Range:** Yes
**Lessons:** Yes **Schools:** No    **Junior Golf:** No
**Membership:** Yes    **Architect/Yr:** Wayne Stiles & John Van Kleek/1928
**Other:** Clubhouse / Bar-Lounge / Snack Bar / Showers

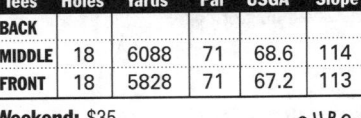

Fairly open course with small greens and hills, but challenging. Shoulder season rates. Open May - October. The only golf course on beautiful Pemaquid Peninsula. "The 8th hole is one of the best short par 3's in Maine." –DW

| | 1 | 2 | 3 | 4 | 5 | 6 | 7 | 8 | 9 |
|------|-----|-----|-----|-----|-----|-----|-----|-----|-----|
| PAR | 4 | 4 | 3 | 5 | 4 | 4 | 4 | 3 | 4 |
| YARDS | 329 | 398 | 233 | 477 | 415 | 296 | 357 | 134 | 370 |
| PAR | | | | | | | | | |
| YARDS | | | | | | | | | |

**Directions:** Route 1 to Route 129; follow for 7 miles. 5 miles from town of Damariscotta, Maine.

# Webhannet Golf Club ✪✪✪½ 62 ▶

26 Golf Club Drive
Kennebunk, ME (207) 967-2061
www.webhannetgolfclub.com

| Tees | Holes | Yards | Par | USGA | Slope |
|------|-------|-------|-----|------|-------|
| BACK | | | | | |
| MIDDLE | 18 | 6088 | 71 | 68.6 | 114 |
| FRONT | 18 | 5828 | 71 | 67.2 | 113 |

**Club Pro:** Kirk Kimball
**Payment:**
**Tee Times:** Yes
**Fee 9 Holes: Weekday:** $35    **Weekend:** $35
**Fee 18 Holes: Weekday:** $65    **Weekend:** $65
**Twilight Rates:** No    **Discounts:** No
**Cart Rental:** $18pp/18, $9pp/9    **Driving Range:** Yes
**Lessons:** Yes **Schools:** No    **Junior Golf:** No
**Membership:** No    **Architect/Yr Open:** Skip Wogan/1901
**Other:** Clubhouse

The 1901 Skip Wogan design has the traditional small undulating greens which makes this very challenging to the low handicapper. One of the best maintained conditioned golf courses in the state.

| | 1 | 2 | 3 | 4 | 5 | 6 | 7 | 8 | 9 |
|------|-----|-----|-----|-----|-----|-----|-----|-----|-----|
| PAR | 4 | 4 | 3 | 5 | 3 | 4 | 4 | 5 | 3 |
| YARDS | 367 | 320 | 225 | 515 | 170 | 295 | 370 | 428 | 200 |
| | 10 | 11 | 12 | 13 | 14 | 15 | 16 | 17 | 18 |
| PAR | 4 | 3 | 4 | 4 | 5 | 3 | 4 | 5 | 4 |
| YARDS | 390 | 142 | 390 | 370 | 470 | 155 | 280 | 421 | 320 |

**Directions:** ME Tpke., Exit 25, Kennebunk. Left on Rte. 35 to Kennebunk. At light, turn left on Rte. 1 for about 100 yards. Turn right on Route 35/9A. Continue through 2 lights to beach. Follow along beach to playground on the left. Go right on Ridge Lane. Go through stop sign then bear right at fork to clubhouse.

# West Appleton Country Club    NR  63 ►

2306 West Appleton Road
Appleton, ME  (207) 542-2687
www.waccgolf.com

| Tees | Holes | Yards | Par | USGA | Slope |
|------|-------|-------|-----|------|-------|
| BACK | 9 | 2899 | 36 | | |
| MIDDLE | 9 | 2683 | 35 | | |
| FRONT | 9 | 2381 | 35 | | |

**Club Pro:**
**Payment:** Cash, Credit, Check
**Tee Times:** No
**Fee  9 Holes: Weekday:** $12
**Fee 18 Holes: Weekday:** $20
**Twilight Rates:** No
**Cart Rental:** $20/18, $12/9 per cart
**Lessons:** $50/30 min.  **Schools:** No
**Membership:** Yes
**Other:**

**Weekend:** $12
**Weekend:** $20
**Discounts:** Junior
**Driving Range:** No
**Junior Golf:** No
**Architect/Yr Open:** Ray and Frank Bartlett/2010
**GPS:** Yes

Friendly country 9-hole course with great views of the surrounding areas. Built on the family farm of Ray and Frank Bartlett.

| | 1 | 2 | 3 | 4 | 5 | 6 | 7 | 8 | 9 |
|---|---|---|---|---|---|---|---|---|---|
| PAR | 4 | 4 | 3 | 5 | 5 | 3 | 4 | 4 | 3 |
| YARDS | 282 | 262 | 169 | 560 | 431 | 125 | 381 | 316 | 157 |
| PAR | | | | | | | | | |
| YARDS | | | | | | | | | |

**Directions:** I-95 North to Exit 113 (ME-3 West). Turn right on ME-220/ME-173. Travel 3.2 miles to Stevens Pond Road (ME-173). Travel 1 mile to West Appleton Road; turn right and the course is on the left.

# Western View Golf Club    ✪¹/₂  64 ►

130 Bolton Hill Road
Augusta, ME  (207) 622-5309

| Tees | Holes | Yards | Par | USGA | Slope |
|------|-------|-------|-----|------|-------|
| BACK | 9 | 2679 | 35 | 64.0 | 100 |
| MIDDLE | 9 | 2316 | 35 | 61.7 | 95 |
| FRONT | 9 | 2280 | 36 | 66.0 | 117 |

**Club Pro:** Peter Matthews, PGA
**Payment:** Visa, MC, Disc
**Tee Times:** No
**Fee  9 Holes: Weekday:** $12
**Fee 18 Holes: Weekday:** $20
**Twilight Rates:** No
**Cart Rental:** $15pp/18, $8pp/9
**Lessons:** Yes  **Schools:** No
**Membership:** Yes
**Other:** Snack Bar / Clubhouse / Lounge / Restaurant / Range / Lodging Partner, Holiday Inn

**Weekend:** $12
**Weekend:** $20
**Discounts:** Junior membership
**Driving Range:** Yes
**Junior Golf:** Yes
**Architect/Yr Open:** Archie Humphrey/1927

COUPON

S
ME

Scenic and sporty 9 hole course — short but challenging with nice greens.

| | 1 | 2 | 3 | 4 | 5 | 6 | 7 | 8 | 9 |
|---|---|---|---|---|---|---|---|---|---|
| PAR | 4 | 3 | 4 | 3 | 5 | 4 | 4 | 4 | 4 |
| YARDS | 305 | 170 | 258 | 195 | 445 | 315 | 285 | 385 | 375 |
| PAR | | | | | | | | | |
| YARDS | | | | | | | | | |

**Directions:** I-95, then Exit 113, 5½ miles to Bolton Hill Road on right. Go ½ mile on Bolton Hill Road.

# Willowdale Golf Club  ✪✪ ▶ 65

52 Willowdale Road
Scarborough, ME  (207) 883-9351
www.willowdalegolf.com

| Tees | Holes | Yards | Par | USGA | Slope |
|------|-------|-------|-----|------|-------|
| BACK | | | | | |
| MIDDLE | 18 | 5881 | 70 | 67.7 | 115 |
| FRONT | 18 | 5049 | 70 | 68.9 | 116 |

**Club Pro:** Pam Lewis, Manager
**Payment:** Visa, Amex, MC, Disc, Checks
**Tee Times:** 5 days adv. for weekends
**Fee 9 Holes: Weekday:** $18        **Weekend:** $20
**Fee 18 Holes: Weekday:** $29        **Weekend:** $31
**Twilight Rates:** After 4pm        **Discounts:** Junior memberships
**Cart Rental:** $14pp/18, $7pp/9        **Driving Range:** No
**Lessons:  Schools:** No        **Junior Golf:** No
**Membership:** Yes        **Architect/Yr Open:** Eugene Wogan/1930
**Other:** Clubhouse / Snack Bar / Showers        **GPS:**

Sig. Hole: #5 is a beautiful, 195-yard par 3. Water on 1 side, tree-lined on the other. Difficult shot for a par 3. Twilight rates offered 7 days a week. Pitching and putting green available.

| | 1 | 2 | 3 | 4 | 5 | 6 | 7 | 8 | 9 |
|------|----|----|----|----|----|----|----|----|----|
| PAR | 4 | 5 | 4 | 4 | 3 | 4 | 3 | 4 | 4 |
| YARDS | 357 | 487 | 386 | 349 | 197 | 367 | 163 | 342 | 325 |
| | 10 | 11 | 12 | 13 | 14 | 15 | 16 | 17 | 18 |
| PAR | 4 | 3 | 4 | 4 | 4 | 3 | 4 | 4 | 5 |
| YARDS | 393 | 185 | 367 | 382 | 280 | 150 | 374 | 288 | 489 |

**Directions:** Exit 36 off Maine Turnpike. US 95 to Route 1. Turn left onto Route 1 North. First light, turn right ¼ mile.

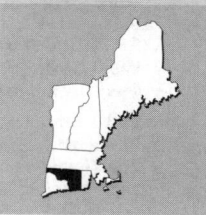

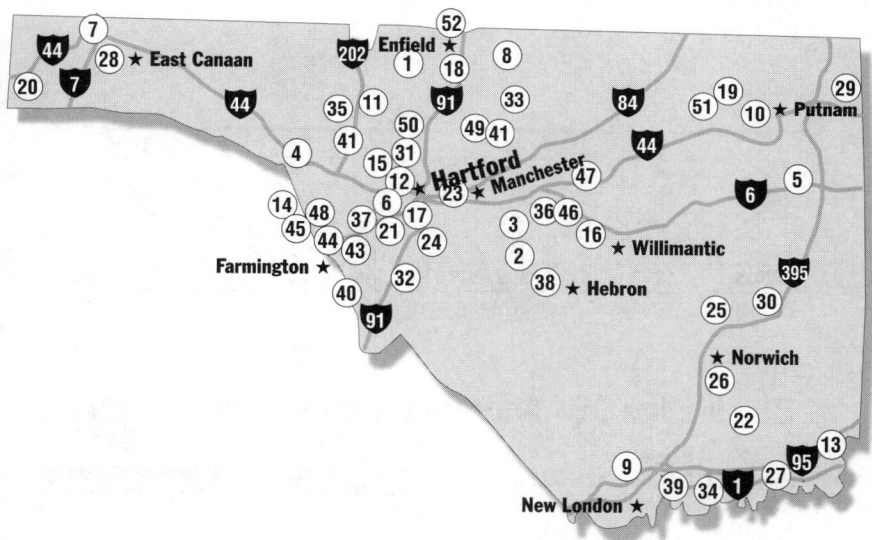

| | | | | |
|---|---|---|---|---|
| Airways Golf Course | 1 | Harrisville GC | 19 | Stanley Golf Club | 37 |
| Blackledge CC - Anderson's | 2 | Hotchkiss School GC | 20 | Tallwood Country Club | 38 |
| Blackledge CC - Gilead | 3 | Keney Golf Club | 21 | The Pines GC & Driving Range | 39 |
| Blue Fox Run | 4 | Lake of Isles GC & Resort | 22 | Timberlin Golf Club | 40 |
| Brooklyn CC | 5 | Manchester CC | 23 | Topstone Golf Course | 41 |
| Buena Vista GC | 6 | Minnechaug GC | 24 | Tower Ridge GC | 42 |
| Canaan Country Club | 7 | Mohegan Sun GC | 25 | Tunxis Plan. CC (Green) | 43 |
| Cedar Knob GC | 8 | Norwich Golf Course | 26 | Tunxis Plan. CC (White) | 44 |
| Cedar Ridge GC | 9 | Pequot Golf Club | 27 | Tunxis Plan. GC (Red) | 45 |
| Connecticut National GC | 10 | Quarryview Golf Course | 28 | Twin Hills CC | 46 |
| Copper Hill GC | 11 | Raceway Golf Club | 29 | Villa Hills Par 3 | 47 |
| East Hartford GC | 12 | River Ridge Golf Course | 30 | Westwoods Golf Course | 48 |
| Elmridge Golf Course | 13 | Rockledge CC | 31 | Willow Brook Golf Course | 49 |
| Fairview Farm GC | 14 | Rolling Greens GC | 32 | Wintonbury Hills GC | 50 |
| Gillette Ridge Golf Club | 15 | Rolling Meadows CC | 33 | Woodstock Golf Course | 51 |
| Golf Club At Windham, The | 16 | Shennecosset GC | 34 | Crestview CC (Agawam, MA) | 52 |
| Goodwin Golf Course | 17 | Simsbury Farms GC | 35 | | |
| Grassmere CC | 18 | Skungamaug River GC | 36 | | |

**KEY TO THE STAR RATINGS:**
5✪ = Outstanding  4✪ = Excellent  3✪ = Very Good  2✪ = Good  1✪ = Average  **NR** = Not Rated

# Airways Golf Course ✪✪½

**1**

1070 South Grand Street
West Suffield, CT (860) 668-4973
www.airwaysgolf.com

**Club Pro:** Robert Kemp, Manager
**Payment:** Visa, MC, Cash
**Tee Times:** 1 week adv.

| Tees | Holes | Yards | Par | USGA | Slope |
|---|---|---|---|---|---|
| BACK | 18 | 5914 | 71 | 66.0 | 106 |
| MIDDLE | 18 | 5528 | 71 | 65.0 | 103 |
| FRONT | 18 | 5134 | 72 | 65.0 | 103 |

**Fee  9 Holes: Weekday:** $13
**Fee 18 Holes: Weekday:** $21
**Twilight Rates:** No
**Cart Rental:** $11pp/18, $5.50pp/9
**Lessons:** No **Schools:** No
**Membership:** No
**Other:** Clubhouse / Snack Bar

**Weekend:** $14
**Weekend:** $24
**Discounts:** Senior
**Driving Range:** No
**Junior Golf:** No
**Architect/Yr Open:** Geoffrey Cornish/1973
**GPS:**

COUPON

Noted for great value. Easy to walk, beautiful course.

| | 1 | 2 | 3 | 4 | 5 | 6 | 7 | 8 | 9 |
|---|---|---|---|---|---|---|---|---|---|
| PAR | 4 | 4 | 4 | 5 | 4 | 4 | 3 | 4 | 4 |
| YARDS | 336 | 351 | 351 | 487 | 301 | 302 | 147 | 320 | 273 |
| | 10 | 11 | 12 | 13 | 14 | 15 | 16 | 17 | 18 |
| PAR | 3 | 5 | 4 | 3 | 4 | 3 | 5 | 4 | 4 |
| YARDS | 127 | 451 | 369 | 133 | 346 | 132 | 451 | 388 | 263 |

**Directions:** I-91 to Exit 40 (Route 20 West). At 4th light turn right, course is 2 miles on the right. Check website.

# Blackledge CC - Anderson's Glen ✪✪½

**2**

180 West Street
Hebron, CT (860) 228-0250
www.blackledgecc.com

**Club Pro:** Kevin J. Higgins, PGA
**Payment:** Visa, MC
**Tee Times:** 1 week adv.

| Tees | Holes | Yards | Par | USGA | Slope |
|---|---|---|---|---|---|
| BACK | 18 | 6787 | 72 | 72.0 | 128 |
| MIDDLE | 18 | 6137 | 72 | 68.9 | 122 |
| FRONT | 18 | 5458 | 72 | 71.7 | 123 |

**Fee  9 Holes: Weekday:** $18 walk, $26 ride   **Weekend:** $21 walk, $28 ride
**Fee 18 Holes: Weekday:** $36 walk, $49 ride   **Weekend:** $41 walk, $55 ride
**Twilight Rates:** After 5:30pm weekdays, after 1pm and 3pm on F/S/S
**Discounts:** Senior & Junior
**Cart Rental:** $24pp/18, $12pp/9
**Lessons:** $35/half hour  **Schools:** No
**Membership:** Yes
**Other:** Clubhouse / Snack Bar / Restaurant / Bar-Lounge

**Driving Range:** No
**Junior Golf:** No
**Architect/Yr Open:** Geoffrey Cornish/1964

COUPON

Good walking course that tests every shot in your game. Fairways are in great shape. Greens are on the fast side. Open March - December. Please visit website.

| | 1 | 2 | 3 | 4 | 5 | 6 | 7 | 8 | 9 |
|---|---|---|---|---|---|---|---|---|---|
| PAR | 4 | 4 | 4 | 5 | 4 | 3 | 4 | 3 | 5 |
| YARDS | 375 | 365 | 389 | 480 | 350 | 153 | 318 | 170 | 485 |
| | 10 | 11 | 12 | 13 | 14 | 15 | 16 | 17 | 18 |
| PAR | 4 | 4 | 5 | 3 | 4 | 4 | 3 | 5 | 4 |
| YARDS | 316 | 408 | 465 | 142 | 383 | 369 | 179 | 425 | 365 |

**Directions:** Route 2 East to Exit 8. Left off ramp, go 9 miles. Take a right onto West Street. Course is on the right.

# Blackledge CC - Gilead Highlands  ✪✪½

**3**

**171 West Street**
**Hebron, CT  (860) 228-0250**
www.blackledgecc.com

| Tees | Holes | Yards | Par | USGA | Slope |
|------|-------|-------|-----|------|-------|
| BACK | 18 | 6129 | 72 | 69.8 | 121 |
| MIDDLE | 18 | 5714 | 72 | 68.0 | 116 |
| FRONT | 18 | 4951 | 72 | | |

**Club Pro:** Kevin J. Higgins, PGA
**Payment:** Visa, MC
**Tee Times:** 1 week adv.
**Fee  9 Holes: Weekday:** $18 walk, $26 ride   **Weekend:** $21 walk, $28 ride
**Fee 18 Holes: Weekday:** $36 walk, $49 ride   **Weekend:** $41 walk, $55 ride
**Twilight Rates:** After 5:30pm weekdays; after 1pm and 3pm on F/S/S
**Discounts:** Senior & Junior
**Cart Rental:** $24pp/18, $12pp/9    **Driving Range:** No
**Lessons:** $35/half hour  **Schools:** No    **Junior Golf:** No
**Membership:** Yes    **Architect/Yr Open:** Mark Mungeam/1974
**Other:** Clubhouse / Snack Bar / Restaurant / Bar-Lounge

COUPON

Player Comments: "Best course conditions ever." New improved website, please visit. Open March - December.

| | 1 | 2 | 3 | 4 | 5 | 6 | 7 | 8 | 9 |
|---|---|---|---|---|---|---|---|---|---|
| PAR | 4 | 3 | 5 | 4 | 4 | 4 | 5 | 3 | 4 |
| YARDS | 369 | 133 | 436 | 275 | 359 | 325 | 455 | 142 | 366 |
| | 10 | 11 | 12 | 13 | 14 | 15 | 16 | 17 | 18 |
| PAR | 5 | 3 | 5 | 3 | 4 | 4 | 4 | 4 | 4 |
| YARDS | 464 | 142 | 454 | 148 | 358 | 346 | 301 | 320 | 327 |

**Directions:** Route 2 East to Exit 8. Left off ramp, go 9 miles. Take a right onto West Street. Course is on the right.

# Blue Fox Run  ✪✪✪

**4**

**65 Nod Road**
**Avon, CT (860) 678-1679**
www.bluefoxent.com

| Tees | Holes | Yards | Par | USGA | Slope |
|------|-------|-------|-----|------|-------|
| BACK | 27/18 | 7025 | 72 | 73.5 | 129 |
| MIDDLE | 27/18 | 6179 | 72 | 68.2 | 116 |
| FRONT | 27/18 | 5304 | 72 | 71.1 | 127 |

**Club Pro:** Barry Wilson, GM
**Payment:** Visa, MC, Amex
**Tee Times:** Yes
**Fee  9 Holes: Weekday:** $20 M-Th    **Weekend:** $22 F/S/S/H
**Fee 18 Holes: Weekday:** $40    **Weekend:** $40
**Twilight Rates:** After 5:30pm weekdays    **Discounts:** Senior & Junior
**Cart Rental:** $25/18, $15/9 per cart    **Driving Range:** $5 token
**Lessons:** Yes  **Schools:** Yes    **Junior Golf:** Yes
**Membership:** Yes    **Architect/Yr Open:** Joe Brunoli/1974
**Other:** Restaurant / Bar-Lounge / Banquet Facilities / Lockers / Showers
**GPS:** Yes

Golf lessons by appointment with Jenny Mancini. Open March 1 - December 15.
Player Comments: "Course is in good shape. Very pretty in fall."

**White/Blue**

| | 1 | 2 | 3 | 4 | 5 | 6 | 7 | 8 | 9 |
|---|---|---|---|---|---|---|---|---|---|
| PAR | 4 | 3 | 4 | 4 | 5 | 4 | 4 | 5 | 3 |
| YARDS | 375 | 197 | 275 | 350 | 465 | 305 | 341 | 512 | 154 |
| | 10 | 11 | 12 | 13 | 14 | 15 | 16 | 17 | 18 |
| PAR | 4 | 4 | 5 | 4 | 5 | 3 | 4 | 3 | 4 |
| YARDS | 388 | 390 | 512 | 401 | 513 | 136 | 350 | 145 | 370 |

**Directions:** I-84 Exit 39 to Route 4, Farmington Center. Turn right onto Waterville Road (Route 10 North). Go 5 miles, cross over Route 44 intersection to Nod Road. Club is ½ mile on left.

**NE CT**

# Brooklyn Country Club

NR 5 ▶

170 South Street
Brooklyn, CT (860) 779-9333
www.brooklyngolfcourse.com

| Tees | Holes | Yards | Par | USGA | Slope |
|------|-------|-------|-----|------|-------|
| BACK | | | | | |
| MIDDLE | 9 | 2783 | 35 | | |
| FRONT | 9 | 2659 | 35 | | |

**Club Pro:** Jabbar Mowaish, Owner
**Payment:** Visa, MC, Disc
**Tee Times:** No
**Fee  9 Holes: Weekday:** $18 w/cart     **Weekend:** $20 w/cart
**Fee 18 Holes: Weekday:** $31 w/cart     **Weekend:** $33 w/cart
**Twilight Rates:** No     **Discounts:** Senior & Junior
**Cart Rental:** $14pp/18, $7pp/9     **Driving Range:** Yes
**Lessons:** Yes  **Schools:** Yes     **Junior Golf:** Yes
**Membership:** Yes     **Architect/Yr Open:** 1960
**Other:** Clubhouse / Snack Bar / Bar-Lounge     **GPS:**

COUPON

This course is now a public course. Pro shop, Driving Range.

| | 1 | 2 | 3 | 4 | 5 | 6 | 7 | 8 | 9 |
|---|---|---|---|---|---|---|---|---|---|
| PAR | 4 | 4 | 4 | 4 | 5 | 3 | 4 | 3 | 4 |
| YARDS | 385 | 350 | 340 | 410 | 460 | 130 | 420 | 135 | 250 |
| PAR | | | | | | | | | |
| YARDS | | | | | | | | | |

**Directions:** I-395 to Route 6 West exit; take left onto Allen Hill Road. Take first left onto South Street, course is ½ mile on left.

# Buena Vista Golf Course

NR 6 ▶

Buena Vista Road
West Hartford, CT (860) 521-7359
www.west-hartford.com

| Tees | Holes | Yards | Par | USGA | Slope |
|------|-------|-------|-----|------|-------|
| BACK | | | | | |
| MIDDLE | 9 | 1977 | 31 | | |
| FRONT | 9 | 1653 | 30 | | |

**Club Pro:** Richard Crow, PGA
**Payment:** Cash or Check
**Tee Times:** No
**Fee  9 Holes: Weekday:** $13     **Weekend:** $14
**Fee 18 Holes: Weekday:** $22.25     **Weekend:** $23.75
**Twilight Rates:** No     **Discounts:** Sr. & Jr., W. Hartford residents only
**Cart Rental:** $12pp/9     **Driving Range:** No
**Lessons:** No  **Schools:** No     **Junior Golf:** No
**Membership:** West Hartford residents only     **Architect/Yr Open:** 1960
**Other:** Putting Green     **GPS:**

A good mix of holes. Great for all levels of golfers. Open April-December. Additional tee boxes to accommodate a greater number of golfing abilities.

| | 1 | 2 | 3 | 4 | 5 | 6 | 7 | 8 | 9 |
|---|---|---|---|---|---|---|---|---|---|
| PAR | 4 | 4 | 4 | 3 | 3 | 3 | 3 | 3 | 4 |
| YARDS | 263 | 344 | 295 | 171 | 130 | 98 | 223 | 214 | 239 |
| PAR | | | | | | | | | |
| YARDS | | | | | | | | | |

**Directions:** I-84 to Exit 43 (Park Road); left off ramp; go through 3 lights, take left onto Buena Vista Road. Course is on left. Parking lot shared with Cornerstone Pool.

# Canaan Country Club

NR ▶ 7

74 High Street (Route 7)
Canaan, CT (860) 824-7683
www.canaancountryclub.com

| Tees | Holes | Yards | Par | USGA | Slope |
|------|-------|-------|-----|------|-------|
| BACK | 9 | 2941 | 35 | 66.8 | 114 |
| MIDDLE | 9 | 2835 | 35 | 66.8 | 114 |
| FRONT | 9 | 2412 | 36 | 67 | 107 |

**Club Pro:** Richard Shanley, Manager
**Payment:** Most Major Credit Cards
**Tee Times:** No
**Fee 9 Holes: Weekday:** $16    **Weekend:** $21
**Fee 18 Holes: Weekday:** $21    **Weekend:** $30
**Twilight Rates:** No    **Discounts:** Senior & Junior
**Cart Rental:** $17pp/18, $9.50pp/9    **Driving Range:** No
**Lessons:** No **Schools:** No    **Junior Golf:** Yes
**Membership:** Yes    **Architect/Yr Open:** 1931
**Other:** Snack Bar / Restaurant / Function Rooms    **GPS:**

The course is mostly flat with a few rolling hills. Considered a good walking course. New pro shop and irrigation systems. Set in beautiful Blackberry River Valley. New 5th hole par 3 replaced old 7th. All holes are now irrigated.

|  | 1 | 2 | 3 | 4 | 5 | 6 | 7 | 8 | 9 |
|------|---|---|---|---|---|---|---|---|---|
| PAR | 4 | 5 | 3 | 5 | 3 | 4 | 4 | 3 | 4 |
| YARDS | 317 | 490 | 184 | 450 | 132 | 356 | 371 | 180 | 355 |
| PAR | | | | | | | | | |
| YARDS | | | | | | | | | |

**Directions:** Route 8 North to Winsted, West on Route 44 to town of Canaan. South ½ mile on Route 7.

# Cedar Knob Golf Course

✪✪✪ ▶ 8

466 Billings Road
Somers, CT (860) 749-3550
www.cedarknobgolfcourse.com

| Tees | Holes | Yards | Par | USGA | Slope |
|------|-------|-------|-----|------|-------|
| BACK | 18 | 6734 | 72 | 72.4 | 126 |
| MIDDLE | 18 | 6298 | 72 | 70.5 | 122 |
| FRONT | 18 | 5784 | 74 | 73.9 | 129 |

**Club Pro:** Jeffrey Swanson
**Payment:** Most Major Credit Cards
**Tee Times:** 7 days adv.
**Fee 9 Holes: Weekday:** $20    **Weekend:** $23
**Fee 18 Holes: Weekday:** $35    **Weekend:** $38
**Twilight Rates:** No    **Discounts:** Sr. & Jr. weekdays
**Cart Rental:** $15pp/18, $7.50pp/9    **Driving Range:** Yes, must use own balls
**Lessons:** $40/45 min. **Schools:** No    **Junior Golf:** Yes
**Membership:** No    **Architect/Yr Open:** Geoffrey Cornish/1963
**Other:** Clubhouse / Snack Bar / Restaurant / Bar-Lounge

Dress code. Open year round (weather permitting). Call about specials. "Cut nicely into a great, wooded area. A fun and fair challenge." –FP

|  | 1 | 2 | 3 | 4 | 5 | 6 | 7 | 8 | 9 |
|------|---|---|---|---|---|---|---|---|---|
| PAR | 4 | 3 | 5 | 4 | 3 | 4 | 5 | 4 | 4 |
| YARDS | 384 | 154 | 482 | 397 | 209 | 319 | 478 | 327 | 328 |
|  | **10** | **11** | **12** | **13** | **14** | **15** | **16** | **17** | **18** |
| PAR | 5 | 4 | 4 | 4 | 3 | 4 | 3 | 5 | 4 |
| YARDS | 490 | 370 | 410 | 350 | 170 | 350 | 210 | 470 | 400 |

**Directions:** I-91 to Exit 47 (East toward Somers). Right onto Route 83; right on Billings Road. Course is ½ mile on left.

# Cedar Ridge Golf Course  ✪✪

34 Drabik Road
East Lyme, CT (860) 691-4568
www.cedarridgegolf.com

Club Pro: Chris Madeiros
Payment: Cash, Visa, MC
Tee Times: 7 days adv.

| Tees | Holes | Yards | Par | USGA | Slope |
|------|-------|-------|-----|------|-------|
| BACK | | | | | |
| MIDDLE | 18 | 3025 | 54 | | |
| FRONT | | | | | |

Fee  9 Holes: Weekday: $15        Weekend: $20
Fee 18 Holes: Weekday: $22        Weekend: $28
Twilight Rates: After 4pm         Discounts: Sr & Jr, weekday only
Cart Rental: $12pp/18, $6pp/9     Driving Range: No
Lessons: Yes  Schools: No         Junior Golf: Yes
Membership: Ticket Packets        Architect/Yr Open: Chester Jenkins/1962
Other: Snacks Only                GPS:

COUPON

Beginners will enjoy the relaxed atmosphere and shorter length of the course, while experienced players will appreciate the test of shot-making skills demanded by the Par 3 layout.

| | 1 | 2 | 3 | 4 | 5 | 6 | 7 | 8 | 9 |
|------|-----|-----|-----|-----|-----|-----|-----|-----|-----|
| PAR | 3 | 3 | 3 | 3 | 3 | 3 | 3 | 3 | 3 |
| YARDS | 157 | 160 | 177 | 103 | 191 | 160 | 122 | 150 | 166 |
| | 10 | 11 | 12 | 13 | 14 | 15 | 16 | 17 | 18 |
| PAR | 3 | 3 | 3 | 3 | 3 | 3 | 3 | 3 | 3 |
| YARDS | 155 | 130 | 250 | 145 | 196 | 218 | 215 | 203 | 127 |

Directions: I-95 to Exit 74, left on Route 161 North. 1 mile to Drabik Road on left.


# Connecticut National Golf Club  ✪✪✪  10

136 Chase Road
Putnam, CT (860) 928-7748
www.ctnationalgolf.com

Club Pro: Jim West, Dir. of Golf
Payment: Visa, MC, Amex, Disc , Checks
Tee Times: 7 days adv.

| Tees | Holes | Yards | Par | USGA | Slope |
|------|-------|-------|-----|------|-------|
| BACK | 18 | 6935 | 71 | 72.9 | 133 |
| MIDDLE | 18 | 6321 | 71 | 70.5 | 128 |
| FRONT | 18 | 5002 | 71 | 69.2 | 119 |

Fee  9 Holes: Weekday: $25        Weekend:
Fee 18 Holes: Weekday: $31        Weekend: $43
Twilight Rates: After 1pm         Discounts: Senior & Junior wkdys
Cart Rental: $15pp/18, $9pp/9     Driving Range: Yes
Lessons: $55/hour  Schools: Yes   Junior Golf: Yes
Membership: Yes                   Architect/Yr Open: Mark Mungeam/2009
Other: Clubhouse / Restaurant / Bar Lounge / Showers / Snack Bar / Function Room

COUPON

Extensive redesign completed in 2009. Course has been taken upscale and lengthened to over 6900 yards from the black tees. "More beautiful and friendly than ever from the forward tees. A tremendous value." –FP

| | 1 | 2 | 3 | 4 | 5 | 6 | 7 | 8 | 9 |
|------|-----|-----|-----|-----|-----|-----|-----|-----|-----|
| PAR | 5 | 4 | 4 | 3 | 4 | 5 | 3 | 4 | 3 |
| YARDS | 461 | 387 | 389 | 207 | 327 | 560 | 171 | 333 | 151 |
| | 10 | 11 | 12 | 13 | 14 | 15 | 16 | 17 | 18 |
| PAR | 4 | 3 | 5 | 4 | 4 | 3 | 4 | 4 | 5 |
| YARDS | 375 | 182 | 505 | 333 | 399 | 193 | 427 | 369 | 552 |

Directions: I-395 to Exit 97, east on Route 44. 3½ miles to public course, sign on right. Right onto East Putnam Road. At 2nd stop sign, take a right (Chase Road). Course is 1 mile on right.

# Copper Hill Golf Club  ✪✪  11 ▶

20 Copper Hill Road
East Granby, CT (860) 653-6191
www.copperhillgolf.com

**Club Pro:** Paul Banks, PGA
**Payment:** Visa, MC, Amex
**Tee Times:** 7 days adv.
**Fee  9 Holes: Weekday:** $16
**Fee 18 Holes: Weekday:** $22
**Twilight Rates:** After 5:30pm
**Cart Rental:** $12pp/18, $8pp/9
**Lessons:** Yes  **Schools:** Yes
**Membership:** Yes, semi-private
**Other:** Clubhouse / Snack Bar / Restaurant / Bar-Lounge

| Tees | Holes | Yards | Par | USGA | Slope |
|------|-------|-------|-----|------|-------|
| BACK | | | | | |
| MIDDLE | 18 | 6004 | 72 | 68.6 | 116 |
| FRONT | 18 | 5090 | 72 | 68.1 | 124 |

**Weekend:** $17
**Weekend:** $24
**Discounts:** Senior & Junior
**Driving Range:** Across street
**Junior Golf:** Yes
**Architect/Yr Open:** Allen Bissette/1956

COUPON

Improvements include full irrigation. New greens superintendent. All grass 4-tiered driving range. Frequent Player card available.

| | 1 | 2 | 3 | 4 | 5 | 6 | 7 | 8 | 9 |
|-----|-----|-----|-----|-----|-----|-----|-----|-----|-----|
| PAR | 4 | 4 | 3 | 5 | 4 | 3 | 4 | 5 | 4 |
| YARDS | 331 | 313 | 163 | 437 | 241 | 164 | 308 | 426 | 376 |
| | 10 | 11 | 12 | 13 | 14 | 15 | 16 | 17 | 18 |
| PAR | 4 | 4 | 3 | 5 | 4 | 3 | 4 | 5 | 4 |
| YARDS | 336 | 356 | 176 | 473 | 261 | 178 | 361 | 459 | 402 |

**Directions:** I-91 to Exit 40 (Bradley Field exit). Follow Route 20 West to Newgate Road (6 lights). Turn right on Newgate Road. Go past old Newgate prison to stop sign. Turn left to course.

# East Hartford Golf Club  ✪✪  12 ▶

130 Long Hill Street
East Hartford, CT (860) 528-5082
www.longhillcc.com

**Club Pro:** Kevin Tierney, PGA
**Payment:** Visa, MC, Disc
**Tee Times:** Weekends, 1 week adv.
**Fee  9 Holes: Weekday:** $17
**Fee 18 Holes: Weekday:** $23
**Twilight Rates:** After 6pm
**Cart Rental:** $14pp/18, $8pp/9
**Lessons:** $40/half hour  **Schools:** No
**Membership:** No
**Architect/Yr Open:** Devereaux Emmet and Alfred Tull/1927
**Other:** Restaurant

| Tees | Holes | Yards | Par | USGA | Slope |
|------|-------|-------|-----|------|-------|
| BACK | 18 | 6186 | 71 | 69.1 | 124 |
| MIDDLE | 18 | 6076 | 71 | 68.6 | 124 |
| FRONT | 18 | 5072 | 72 | 68.9 | 113 |

**Weekend:** $22
**Weekend:** $29
**Discounts:** Sr. & Jr. weekdays
**Driving Range:** No
**Junior Golf:** Yes

**GPS:**

Dress code: no tank tops or cutoffs. Pond recently added to #13; recent drainage work and sand trap renovations.

| | 1 | 2 | 3 | 4 | 5 | 6 | 7 | 8 | 9 |
|-----|-----|-----|-----|-----|-----|-----|-----|-----|-----|
| PAR | 4 | 4 | 4 | 3 | 5 | 4 | 4 | 3 | 4 |
| YARDS | 305 | 397 | 322 | 123 | 508 | 415 | 308 | 127 | 385 |
| | 10 | 11 | 12 | 13 | 14 | 15 | 16 | 17 | 18 |
| PAR | 5 | 3 | 4 | 4 | 4 | 3 | 4 | 4 | 5 |
| YARDS | 512 | 188 | 308 | 330 | 356 | 150 | 457 | 384 | 500 |

**Directions:** I-84 to Exit 60, onto Burnside Avenue toward East Hartford. Enter East Hartford, take a right at second traffic light onto Long Hill Street. Proceed through 3 stop signs, course on right.

# Elmridge Golf Course

○○◐½

## 13

229 Elmridge Road
Pawcatuck, CT (860) 599-2248
www.elmridgegolf.com

**Club Pro:** Thomas Jones
**Payment:** Visa, MC, Amex
**Tee Times:** Call Monday for weekends
            Call Friday for weekdays
**Fee 9 Holes: Weekday:** $24
**Fee 18 Holes: Weekday:** $37 (M-Th)
**Twilight Rates:** After 5pm
**Cart Rental:** $18pp/18, $12pp/9
**Lessons:** $40/45 min. **Schools:** No
**Membership:** Yes
**Other:** Clubhouse / Snack Bar / Restaurant / Bar-Lounge/ Outings

| Tees | Holes | Yards | Par | USGA | Slope |
|------|-------|-------|-----|------|-------|
| BACK | 27/18 | 6347 | 71 | 70.8 | 115 |
| MIDDLE | 27/18 | 6014 | 71 | 69.3 | 112 |
| FRONT | 27/18 | 5430 | 71 | 69.0 | 109 |

**Weekend:** $28
**Weekend:** $45 (F/S/S)
**Discounts:** Sr, Jr, Mltry/wkdys only
**Driving Range:** Yes
**Junior Golf:** Yes
**Architect/Yr Open:** Joe & Charlie Rustici/1964

COUPON

Elmridge Golf Course is located just minutes from both casinos, Misquamicut Beach and Mystic Aquarium. 27 holes means tee times are always available.

**Red/White**

|  | 1 | 2 | 3 | 4 | 5 | 6 | 7 | 8 | 9 |
|------|-----|-----|-----|-----|-----|-----|-----|-----|-----|
| PAR | 4 | 4 | 4 | 5 | 4 | 3 | 4 | 3 | 4 |
| YARDS | 366 | 335 | 360 | 462 | 149 | 324 | 167 | 385 | 268 |
|  | 10 | 11 | 12 | 13 | 14 | 15 | 16 | 17 | 18 |
| PAR | 4 | 5 | 4 | 3 | 5 | 3 | 5 | 3 | 4 |
| YARDS | 365 | 485 | 342 | 149 | 576 | 340 | 365 | 206 | 370 |

**Directions:** I-95 to Exit 92. Route 2 East to Elmridge Road. Course is 1 mile on left.

# Fairview Farm Golf Course

○○½

## 14

300 Hill Road
Harwinton, CT (860) 689-1000
www.fairviewfarmgolfcourse.com

**Club Pro:** Bob Sparks, PGA
**Payment:** Visa, MC, Amex
**Tee Times:** 7 days adv.
**Fee 9 Holes: Weekday:** $22
**Fee 18 Holes: Weekday:** $42
**Twilight Rates:** No
**Cart Rental:** $18pp/18, $9pp/9 (included wknds)
**Lessons:** $90/hour **Schools:** Yes
**Membership:** No
**Other:** Clubhouse / Restaurant / Bar-Lounge / Snacks
**GPS:** Yes

| Tees | Holes | Yards | Par | USGA | Slope |
|------|-------|-------|-----|------|-------|
| BACK | 18 | 6539 | 72 | 71.5 | 126 |
| MIDDLE | 18 | 6149 | 72 | 69.5 | 121 |
| FRONT | 18 | 4780 | 72 | 67.2 | 116 |

**Weekend:** $34
**Weekend:** $67
**Discounts:** None
**Driving Range:** Yes
**Junior Golf:** Yes
**Architect/Yr Open:** Bob Ferrarotti/2000

Challenging scenic layout. Fabulous views with scenic par 3s. Upscale public course.
Player Comments: "Well kept. Well laid out." "First-class design." –RW

|  | 1 | 2 | 3 | 4 | 5 | 6 | 7 | 8 | 9 |
|------|-----|-----|-----|-----|-----|-----|-----|-----|-----|
| PAR | 4 | 4 | 5 | 3 | 4 | 5 | 3 | 4 | 4 |
| YARDS | 380 | 355 | 500 | 160 | 330 | 450 | 155 | 350 | 375 |
|  | 10 | 11 | 12 | 13 | 14 | 15 | 16 | 17 | 18 |
| PAR | 3 | 4 | 3 | 4 | 4 | 4 | 5 | 4 | 5 |
| YARDS | 187 | 350 | 175 | 340 | 320 | 385 | 545 | 307 | 510 |

**Directions:** Route 8, Exit 42. Head east on Route 118 for 2 miles.

# Gillette Ridge Golf Club

NR  15 ▶

1360 Hall Boulevard
Bloomfield, CT (860) 726-1430
www.gilletteridgegolf.com

**Club Pro:** Lucas Hitchcock, PGA
**Payment:** Most Major Credit Cards
**Tee Times:** 7 days adv.

| Tees | Holes | Yards | Par | USGA | Slope |
|------|-------|-------|-----|------|-------|
| BACK | 18 | 7191 | 72 | 74.5 | 140 |
| MIDDLE | 18 | 6147 | 72 | 69.3 | 128 |
| FRONT | 18 | 5105 | 72 | 73.7 | 138 |

**Fee 9 Holes: Weekday:**
**Fee 18 Holes: Weekday:** $58 w/cart
**Twilight Rates:** Yes
**Cart Rental:** Included
**Lessons:** Yes **Schools:**
**Membership:** Yes
**Weekend:**
**Weekend:** $68 w/cart
**Discounts:** Senior, Junior, Military
**Driving Range:** Yes
**Junior Golf:**
**Architect/Yr Open:** Arnold Palmer/2004
**Other:** Clubhouse / Restaurant / Bar-Lounge / Showers / Lockers

Prepare yourself for an unparalled golfing experience. A pleasure for golfers of any skill level. Everything you need to challenge and improve your game. "Fairways are generous but approach to green narrows. This is a course that keeps coming at you. Many carries, especially to the green. Bring your aerial game. Great fun." –JD

| | 1 | 2 | 3 | 4 | 5 | 6 | 7 | 8 | 9 |
|------|---|---|---|---|---|---|---|---|---|
| PAR | 4 | 5 | 4 | 3 | 4 | 4 | 5 | 3 | 4 |
| YARDS | 379 | 445 | 380 | 148 | 283 | 336 | 513 | 157 | 389 |
| | 10 | 11 | 12 | 13 | 14 | 15 | 16 | 17 | 18 |
| PAR | 4 | 3 | 5 | 4 | 4 | 3 | 4 | 5 | 4 |
| YARDS | 377 | 155 | 528 | 242 | 369 | 156 | 383 | 502 | 405 |

**Directions:** From I-91 take the Cottage Grove Road/218 exit. Head west for 2 miles. The course is on your left in the same plaza as Cigna Insurance.

# Golf Club At Windham, The

✪✪✪  16 ▶

184 Club Road
North Windham CT (860) 456-1971
www.windhamclub.com

**Club Pro:** Pat Kozelka, PGA
**Payment:** All Credit Cards, Cash, Check
**Tee Times:** 7 days adv.

| Tees | Holes | Yards | Par | USGA | Slope |
|------|-------|-------|-----|------|-------|
| BACK | 18 | 6303 | 71 | 70.3 | 123 |
| MIDDLE | 18 | 6048 | 71 | 69.1 | 121 |
| FRONT | 18 | 5106 | 72 | 69.2 | 118 |

**Fee 9 Holes: Weekday:** $20
**Fee 18 Holes: Weekday:** $32
**Twilight Rates:** After 3pm
**Cart Rental:** $15pp/18, $10pp/9
**Lessons:** No **Schools:**
**Membership:** Yes
**Weekend:** $32 (F/S/S)
**Weekend:** $48
**Discounts:** Sr, Jr, College, Military
**Driving Range:** Yes
**Junior Golf:** Yes
**Architect/Yr Open:** 1922
**Other:** Clubhouse / Restaurant / Snack Bar / Showers / Lockers

After 80 years as an exclusive private country club, The Golf Club At Windham is now open to the public. A parkland golf course that plays on the ground as well as through the air, that rewards precision as well as length.

| | 1 | 2 | 3 | 4 | 5 | 6 | 7 | 8 | 9 |
|------|---|---|---|---|---|---|---|---|---|
| PAR | 4 | 4 | 4 | 5 | 3 | 4 | 4 | 5 | 4 |
| YARDS | 372 | 283 | 295 | 478 | 173 | 330 | 422 | 487 | 345 |
| | 10 | 11 | 12 | 13 | 14 | 15 | 16 | 17 | 18 |
| PAR | 3 | 4 | 4 | 5 | 3 | 4 | 3 | 4 | 4 |
| YARDS | 112 | 388 | 286 | 487 | 159 | 420 | 211 | 400 | 400 |

**Directions:** I-395 to Exit 91, then go west on Route 6. Travel 18.5 miles to Boston Post Road (CT-66). Travel 1.1 miles and turn left on Club Road.

**NE
CT**

# Goodwin Golf Course ✪✪  17

1130 Maple Avenue
Hartford, CT (860) 956-3601
www.goodwinparkgolf.com

| Tees | Holes | Yards | Par | USGA | Slope |
|------|-------|-------|-----|------|-------|
| BACK | 18 | 5953 | 70 | 68.0 | 116 |
| MIDDLE | 18 | 5605 | 70 | 66.6 | 110 |
| FRONT | 18 | 5069 | 70 | 69.6 | 109 |

**Club Pro:** Kevin Cloud, PGA
**Payment:** Visa, MC, Disc, Check
**Tee Times:** 7 days adv.
**Fee 9 Holes: Weekday:** $22   **Weekend:** $25
**Fee 18 Holes: Weekday:** $37   **Weekend:** $39
**Twilight Rates:** After 5pm   **Discounts:** Senior, Junior, Resident
**Cart Rental:** $17pp/18, $11pp/9   **Driving Range:** Yes
**Lessons:** Yes   **Schools:** Yes   **Junior Golf:** Yes
**Membership:** Yes   **Architect/Yr Open:** Everett Pyle/1906
**Other:** Banquet Facility / Snack Bar   **GPS:**

The City of Hartford took back control of the course in fall of 2014, and has brought in a new golf professional, new superintendents, and a new restaurant vendor. The course is perfect for all levels of golfer, and has an extra nine holes for walkers, seniors, juniors, and beginners.

| | 1 | 2 | 3 | 4 | 5 | 6 | 7 | 8 | 9 |
|------|-----|-----|-----|-----|-----|-----|-----|-----|-----|
| PAR | 5 | 4 | 4 | 4 | 4 | 4 | 3 | 3 | 4 |
| YARDS | 486 | 315 | 367 | 322 | 370 | 286 | 127 | 155 | 332 |
| | 10 | 11 | 12 | 13 | 14 | 15 | 16 | 17 | 18 |
| PAR | 4 | 3 | 5 | 4 | 4 | 3 | 4 | 4 | 4 |
| YARDS | 334 | 213 | 471 | 361 | 312 | 138 | 336 | 352 | 361 |

**Directions:** I-91 to Exit 28. Take Route 15, 5 South to Exit 85 (Route 99), follow ramp to first light. Right on Joran to right on Maple.

# Grassmere Country Club ✪✪ 18

130 Town Farm Road
Enfield, CT (860) 749-7740
www.grassmerecountryclub.com

| Tees | Holes | Yards | Par | USGA | Slope |
|------|-------|-------|-----|------|-------|
| BACK | 9 | 3031 | 35 | 70.0 | 121 |
| MIDDLE | 9 | 2870 | 35 | 68.2 | 118 |
| FRONT | 9 | 2727 | 35 | 66.8 | 115 |

**Club Pro:**
**Payment:** Cash, Check, Credit Cards
**Tee Times:** Anytime
**Fee 9 Holes: Weekday:** $20   **Weekend:** $21
**Fee 18 Holes: Weekday:** $27   **Weekend:** $30
**Twilight Rates:** No
**Discounts:** Sr./Jr. M-F until 3pm, Sat 12pm-close
**Cart Rental:** $13pp/18, $8pp/9   **Driving Range:** No
**Lessons:** No   **Schools:** No   **Junior Golf:** Yes
**Membership:** Yes   **Architect/Yr Open:** 1976
**Other:** Clubhouse / Snack Bar / Banquet Facility   **GPS:**

Emphasis on nice landscaping aound the holes. Open March 15 - December 31. Noted for friendly staff and beautifully manicured course. Always in beautiful shape. New design on some of the tees.

| | 1 | 2 | 3 | 4 | 5 | 6 | 7 | 8 | 9 |
|------|-----|-----|-----|-----|-----|-----|-----|-----|-----|
| PAR | 4 | 4 | 4 | 4 | 3 | 5 | 4 | 4 | 3 |
| YARDS | 360 | 390 | 405 | 415 | 160 | 475 | 320 | 360 | 180 |
| PAR | | | | | | | | | |
| YARDS | | | | | | | | | |

**Directions:** Route I-91N to Exit 45, right onto Route 140 East. Merge with Route 191 East. Stay on 191 for 5.8 miles. Left on Town Farm Road. Course is on left.

# Harrisville Golf Course

125 Harrisville Road
Woodstock, CT (860) 928-6098
www.harrisvillegolfcourse.com

| Tees | Holes | Yards | Par | USGA | Slope |
|------|-------|-------|-----|------|-------|
| BACK | 9 | 2915 | 36 | 67.6 | 118 |
| MIDDLE | 9 | 2725 | 36 | 67.6 | 118 |
| FRONT | 9 | 2415 | 35 | 67.9 | 119 |

**Club Pro:** Michael Sosik
**Payment:** Cash, Check, Credit
**Tee Times:** Weekend mornings
**Fee 9 Holes: Weekday:** $14
**Fee 18 Holes: Weekday:** $20
**Twilight Rates:** No
**Cart Rental:** $14pp/18, $7pp/9
**Lessons:** No **Schools:** No
**Membership:** Yes
**Other:** Snack Bar

**Weekend:** $16
**Weekend:** $22
**Discounts:** Senior & Junior
**Driving Range:** No
**Junior Golf:**
**Architect/Yr Open:** Aimee Salvas/1929
**GPS:** No

Best value in golf. Enjoyable round. Friendly staff!

|  | 1 | 2 | 3 | 4 | 5 | 6 | 7 | 8 | 9 |
|------|-----|-----|-----|-----|-----|-----|-----|-----|-----|
| PAR | 4 | 3 | 5 | 4 | 4 | 5 | 4 | 4 | 3 |
| YARDS | 290 | 170 | 500 | 265 | 410 | 420 | 295 | 235 | 200 |
| PAR | | | | | | | | | |
| YARDS | | | | | | | | | |

**Directions:** I-395 to Exit 97. Take right onto Route 171 West. Take left at Public Golf Course sign (Citizens Bank). Follow signs (next 2 rights).

# Hotchkiss School Golf Course

Route 112
Lakeville, CT (860) 435-4400
www.hotchkiss.org

| Tees | Holes | Yards | Par | USGA | Slope |
|------|-------|-------|-----|------|-------|
| BACK | | | | | |
| MIDDLE | 9 | 3043 | 35 | 68.8 | 117 |
| FRONT | | | | | |

**Club Pro:** James Kennedy, PGA
**Payment:** Cash Only
**Tee Times:** No
**Fee 9 Holes: Weekday:** $14
**Fee 18 Holes: Weekday:** $20
**Twilight Rates:** No
**Cart Rental:** $30/18, $15/9 per cart
**Lessons:** Yes **Schools:** Yes
**Membership:** Yes
**Other:** Snack Bar

**Weekend:** $15
**Weekend:** $25
**Discounts:** None
**Driving Range:** No
**Junior Golf:** No
**Architect/Yr:** Seth Raynor & Charles Banks/1911
**GPS:**

Good variety, mildly challenging.

|  | 1 | 2 | 3 | 4 | 5 | 6 | 7 | 8 | 9 |
|------|-----|-----|-----|-----|-----|-----|-----|-----|-----|
| PAR | 4 | 3 | 4 | 4 | 3 | 4 | 5 | 3 | 5 |
| YARDS | 420 | 192 | 401 | 370 | 128 | 347 | 500 | 165 | 520 |
| PAR | | | | | | | | | |
| YARDS | | | | | | | | | |

**Directions:** Route 7 to Route 112 West to course, or Route 44 to Route 112 East.

# Keney Golf Club

280 Tower Avenue
Hartford, CT (860) 543-8618
www.keneyparkgolf.com

**Club Pro:**
**Payment:** Visa, MC, Disc
**Tee Times:** 7 days adv.

| Tees | Holes | Yards | Par | USGA | Slope |
|------|-------|-------|-----|------|-------|
| BACK | 18 | 6014 | 70 | 68.1 | 115 |
| MIDDLE | 18 | 5739 | 70 | 66.8 | 113 |
| FRONT | 18 | 4967 | 70 | 68.9 | 116 |

**Fee  9 Holes: Weekday:** $24      **Weekend:** $26
**Fee 18 Holes: Weekday:** $40      **Weekend:** $42
**Twilight Rates:** After 5pm      **Discounts:** Senior, Junior, Resident
**Cart Rental:** $17pp/18, $11pp/9      **Driving Range:** No
**Lessons:** Yes  **Schools:** Yes      **Junior Golf:** Yes
**Membership:** Yes      **Architect/Yr Open:** Devereaux Emmet/1927
**Other:** Clubhouse // Snack Bar

Golf Course reopened on May 1, 2016 after undergoing a $5.8 million restoration/renovation in 2015, and the clubhouse renovation will be completed in the Spring of 2017. The course was awarded best classic renovation of 2016 by *Golf Inc.* magazine and has been nominated for other awards from *Golf Week* and *Golf Digest.*

| | 1 | 2 | 3 | 4 | 5 | 6 | 7 | 8 | 9 |
|------|----|----|----|----|----|----|----|----|----|
| PAR | 4 | 5 | 3 | 4 | 4 | 3 | 4 | 4 | 4 |
| YARDS | 315 | 487 | 109 | 328 | 396 | 134 | 363 | 381 | 377 |
| | 10 | 11 | 12 | 13 | 14 | 15 | 16 | 17 | 18 |
| PAR | 5 | 3 | 4 | 3 | 5 | 4 | 4 | 4 | 3 |
| YARDS | 526 | 190 | 261 | 162 | 446 | 366 | 374 | 364 | 160 |

**Directions:** I-91 to Exit 34. Left at ramp, right at light. Course is 5 minutes north of downtown Hartford.

# Lake of Isles GC and Resort ✪✪✪✪½

One Lake of Isles Road
North Stonington, CT (888) 475-3746
www.lakeofisles.com

**Club Pro:** Robbie Leming, Dir. of Golf
**Payment:** Visa, MC, Amex
**Tee Times:** 30 days adv.

| Tees | Holes | Yards | Par | USGA | Slope |
|------|-------|-------|-----|------|-------|
| BACK | 18 | 7252 | 72 | 76.6 | 146 |
| MIDDLE | 18 | 6304 | 72 | 71.5 | 135 |
| FRONT | 18 | 4937 | 72 | 68.9 | 127 |

**Fee  9 Holes: Weekday:**      **Weekend:**
**Fee 18 Holes: Weekday:** $155-$195      **Weekend:** $195
**Twilight Rates:** No      **Discounts:** Junior
**Cart Rental:** Included      **Driving Range:** Yes
**Lessons:** $110/hour, $60/half hour  **Schools:** Yes  **Junior Golf:** Yes
**Membership:** Yes      **Architect/Yr Open:** Rees Jones/2005
**Other:** Restaurant / Clubhouse / Bar & Lounge / Indoor Outdoor Practice Facility / Luxury Villas

Located around a 90-acre lake, Rees Jones design. Multiple tee locations offer a varied test for all levels. "Many carries; visually splendid. Expecting this to become one of New England's best." –JD

| | 1 | 2 | 3 | 4 | 5 | 6 | 7 | 8 | 9 |
|------|----|----|----|----|----|----|----|----|----|
| PAR | 5 | 3 | 4 | 4 | 5 | 4 | 3 | 4 | 4 |
| YARDS | 550 | 164 | 308 | 398 | 457 | 395 | 182 | 325 | 389 |
| | 10 | 11 | 12 | 13 | 14 | 15 | 16 | 17 | 18 |
| PAR | 4 | 3 | 5 | 4 | 4 | 5 | 3 | 4 | 4 |
| YARDS | 399 | 154 | 469 | 345 | 399 | 496 | 166 | 342 | 366 |

**Directions:** I-95 North to Exit 92 in CT. Turn left on Route 2 West. Lake of Isles is 8 miles on Route 2 West. Directly across the street from Foxwoods Resort.

# Manchester Country Club  ✪✪✪  23 ▶

305 South Main Street
Manchester, CT (860) 646-0226
www.mancc.com

**Club Pro:** John Cook, PGA
**Payment:** MC, Visa
**Tee Times:** 7 days adv.

| Tees | Holes | Yards | Par | USGA | Slope |
|------|-------|-------|-----|------|-------|
| BACK | 18 | 6285 | 72 | 70.8 | 125 |
| MIDDLE | 18 | 6167 | 72 | 69.7 | 123 |
| FRONT | 18 | 5610 | 73 | 72.0 | 120 |

**Fee  9 Holes: Wkdy:** $23 non-res./$21 res.
**Fee 18 Holes: Wkdy:** $41 non-res./$38 res.
**Twilight Rates:** No
**Cart Rental:** $16pp/18, $8pp/9
**Lessons:** Call for rates **Schools:** No
**Membership:** Yes
**Weekend:** $25 non-res./$23 res.
**Weekend:** $43 non-res./$41 res.
**Discounts:** Senior & Junior
**Driving Range:** Yes
**Junior Golf:** Yes
**Architect/Yr Open:** Devereux Emmet/1917

COUPON

**Other:** Clubhouse / Lockers / Showers / Snack Bar / Restaurant / Bar-Lounge

Old-style golf course. Variety of elevation changes. Open April - December. Dress code.

| | 1 | 2 | 3 | 4 | 5 | 6 | 7 | 8 | 9 |
|------|-----|-----|-----|-----|-----|-----|-----|-----|-----|
| PAR | 4 | 4 | 5 | 5 | 3 | 4 | 4 | 3 | 4 |
| YARDS | 308 | 333 | 507 | 500 | 144 | 406 | 331 | 143 | 348 |
| | **10** | **11** | **12** | **13** | **14** | **15** | **16** | **17** | **18** |
| PAR | 4 | 4 | 3 | 4 | 5 | 5 | 4 | 4 | 3 |
| YARDS | 294 | 340 | 135 | 335 | 520 | 510 | 397 | 362 | 182 |

**Directions:** I-84 to Route 384 East (Exit 3). Take left 1000 yards up onto South Main Street. Course is on the left.

# Minnechaug Golf Course  NR  24 ▶

16 Fairway Crossing
Glastonbury, CT (860) 643-9914
www.minnechauggolf.com

**Club Pro:** Peter Seaman, PGA
**Payment:** Cash or Credit
**Tee Times:** 1 week adv.

| Tees | Holes | Yards | Par | USGA | Slope |
|------|-------|-------|-----|------|-------|
| BACK | 9 | 2654 | 35 | 67.4 | 112 |
| MIDDLE | 9 | 2527 | 35 | 66.5 | 110 |
| FRONT | 9 | 2186 | 35 | 62.7 | 102 |

**Fee  9 Holes: Weekday:** $16
**Fee 18 Holes: Weekday:** $25
**Twilight Rates:** No
**Cart Rental:** $13pp/18, $7pp/9
**Lessons:** Yes **Schools:** Yes
**Membership:** No
**Other:** Restaurant / Beer / Snacks
**Weekend:** $17
**Weekend:** $27
**Discounts:** Senior, Junior, Resident
**Driving Range:** No
**Junior Golf:** Yes
**Architect/Yr Open:** Geoffrey Cornish/1959
**GPS:**

Reduced rates for residents, juniors and seniors, open year round.

| | 1 | 2 | 3 | 4 | 5 | 6 | 7 | 8 | 9 |
|------|-----|-----|-----|-----|-----|-----|-----|-----|-----|
| PAR | 4 | 4 | 5 | 4 | 5 | 3 | 4 | 3 | 3 |
| YARDS | 311 | 307 | 464 | 327 | 437 | 161 | 269 | 116 | 135 |
| PAR | | | | | | | | | |
| YARDS | | | | | | | | | |

**Directions:** I-84 to Route 384 East, Exit 3. Left off exit on Route 83. Follow for 3 miles. Course on right.

**NE CT**

## Mohegan Sun Golf Club ✪✪✪✪✪  25 ▶

7 Downs Lane
Baltic, CT (860) 862-9660
www.mohegansungolfclub.com

| Tees | Holes | Yards | Par | USGA | Slope |
|------|-------|-------|-----|------|-------|
| BACK | 18 | 6790 | 72 | 73.0 | 133 |
| MIDDLE | 18 | 6111 | 72 | 70.2 | 126 |
| FRONT | 18 | 5359 | 72 | 72.0 | 127 |

**Club Pro:** Michael Painchaud, PGA
**Payment:** All Major Credit Cards, Cash, Check
**Tee Times:** No time limitation
**Fee 9 Holes: Weekday:**     **Weekend:**
**Fee 18 Holes: Weekday:** $140     **Weekend:** $140
**Twilight Rates:** $85 after 2pm     **Discounts:** Senior & Military
**Cart Rental:** Included     **Driving Range:** Yes
**Lessons:** Call for rates **Schools:** Yes     **Junior Golf:** No
**Membership:** Yes     **Architect/Yr Open:** Geoffrey Cornish/1960
**Other:** Clubhouse / Lockers / Showers / Snack Bar / Restaurant / Bar-Lounge

COUPON

Upscale public course that was previously private. Excellent design and layout which is always in great condition.

|  | 1 | 2 | 3 | 4 | 5 | 6 | 7 | 8 | 9 |
|------|---|---|---|---|---|---|---|---|---|
| PAR | 4 | 4 | 4 | 3 | 5 | 5 | 4 | 3 | 4 |
| YARDS | 376 | 338 | 363 | 155 | 456 | 458 | 374 | 140 | 400 |
|  | 10 | 11 | 12 | 13 | 14 | 15 | 16 | 17 | 18 |
| PAR | 3 | 4 | 4 | 5 | 4 | 4 | 3 | 4 | 5 |
| YARDS | 157 | 396 | 344 | 472 | 391 | 332 | 145 | 372 | 442 |

**Directions:** I-90 West to 395 South to CT-97 North/Taftville-Occum Road in Norwich. Continue on CT-97 North. Take Pautipaug Hill Road to Downs Lane.

## Norwich Golf Course ✪✪ 26 ▶

685 New London Turnpike
Norwich, CT (860) 889-6973
www.norwichgolf.com

| Tees | Holes | Yards | Par | USGA | Slope |
|------|-------|-------|-----|------|-------|
| BACK | 18 | 6228 | 71 | 70.0 | 131 |
| MIDDLE | 18 | 5802 | 71 | 68.0 | 125 |
| FRONT | 18 | 5040 | 71 | 70.3 | 122 |

**Club Pro:** Mike Svab, PGA
**Payment:** Visa, MC, Anex
**Tee Times:** 5 days adv.
**Fee 9 Holes: Weekday:$22**     **Weekend:**
**Fee 18 Holes: Weekday:** $40 (rates may change) **Weekend:** $48 (rates may change)
**Twilight Rates:** After 4pm     **Discounts:** None
**Cart Rental:** $19pp/wknd, $13pp/wkdy     **Driving Range:** No
**Lessons:** $50/half hour **Schools:**     **Junior Golf:** Yes
**Membership:** Yes     **Architect/Yr Open:** Donald Ross/1926
**Other:** Clubhouse / Lockers / Showers / Restaurant / Bar-Lounge

Short but tricky course: overly aggressive play could lead to disaster. Designed by Donald Ross. Open April - November. Residents' rate. New bridges. Visit website for full listing of rates.

|  | 1 | 2 | 3 | 4 | 5 | 6 | 7 | 8 | 9 |
|------|---|---|---|---|---|---|---|---|---|
| PAR | 4 | 4 | 4 | 4 | 5 | 4 | 4 | 4 | 3 |
| YARDS | 303 | 276 | 366 | 350 | 487 | 330 | 370 | 300 | 170 |
|  | 10 | 11 | 12 | 13 | 14 | 15 | 16 | 17 | 18 |
| PAR | 4 | 4 | 5 | 3 | 5 | 3 | 4 | 4 | 3 |
| YARDS | 355 | 388 | 503 | 105 | 535 | 165 | 330 | 303 | 166 |

**Directions:** I-95 to I-395 North to Exit 11East (formerly Exit 80). Take right off ramp (West Main Street), follow to 5th light. Take right onto New London Turnpike. Course is ½ mile down on right.

# Pequot Golf Club

⚫⚫

## 27

127 Wheeler Road
Stonington, CT (860) 535-1898
www.pequotgolf.com

| Tees | Holes | Yards | Par | USGA | Slope |
|------|-------|-------|-----|------|-------|
| BACK | 18 | 5903 | 70 | 68.5 | 121 |
| MIDDLE | 18 | 5476 | 70 | 66.6 | 118 |
| FRONT | 18 | 5248 | 71 | 69.6 | 114 |

**Club Pro:** Justin Scott, PGA
**Payment:** Visa, MC, Amex, Disc, Checks, Cash
**Tee Times:** 7 days adv.
**Fee  9 Holes: Weekday:** $20     **Weekend:** $21
**Fee 18 Holes: Weekday:** $30     **Weekend:** $35
**Twilight Rates:** After 2pm, everyday     **Discounts:** Sr. & Jr., wkdys only
**Cart Rental:** $16pp/18, $11pp/9     **Driving Range:** Yes
**Lessons:** Yes  **Schools:** No     **Junior Golf:** Yes
**Membership:** Yes     **Architect/Yr Open:** Wendell Ross/1959
**Other:** Restaurant / Clubhouse / Bar-Lounge     **GPS:**

COUPON

Player Comments: "Beautiful course." Open March 1 - December 15. Historic Mystic Seaport and casinos nearby.

| | 1 | 2 | 3 | 4 | 5 | 6 | 7 | 8 | 9 |
|------|---|---|---|---|---|---|---|---|---|
| PAR | 4 | 4 | 4 | 4 | 4 | 3 | 4 | 4 | 3 |
| YARDS | 353 | 329 | 358 | 287 | 328 | 179 | 379 | 376 | 209 |
| | 10 | 11 | 12 | 13 | 14 | 15 | 16 | 17 | 18 |
| PAR | 4 | 4 | 3 | 5 | 4 | 4 | 4 | 3 | 5 |
| YARDS | 276 | 361 | 149 | 469 | 417 | 336 | 339 | 193 | 565 |

**Directions:** I-95 to Exit 91. Left off 95 South, right off 95 North. Go 1 mile. Take right onto Wheeler Road.

# Quarryview Golf Course

NR

30 Allyndale Road
East Canaan, CT (860) 824-4252
www.quarryviewgolf.com

| Tees | Holes | Yards | Par | USGA | Slope |
|------|-------|-------|-----|------|-------|
| BACK | 9 | 1626 | 31 | | |
| MIDDLE | 9 | 1576 | 31 | 59.0 | 93 |
| FRONT | 9 | 1532 | 31 | 58.0 | 89 |

**Club Pro:**
**Payment:** Visa, MC
**Tee Times:** No
**Fee  9 Holes: Weekday:** $11     **Weekend:** $14
**Fee 18 Holes: Weekday:** $17     **Weekend:** $20
**Twilight Rates:** No     **Discounts:** None
**Cart Rental:** $10pp/18, $6pp/9     **Driving Range:** Yes, grass
**Lessons:  Schools:**     **Junior Golf:** Yes
**Membership:** Yes     **Architect/Yr Open:** Leonard Allyn/2002
**Other:** Snack Bar     **GPS:**

9 hole executive course, families welcome, with a full-service practice range. A work in progress. Also has a driving range.

| | 1 | 2 | 3 | 4 | 5 | 6 | 7 | 8 | 9 |
|------|---|---|---|---|---|---|---|---|---|
| PAR | 3 | 3 | 3 | 3 | 3 | 3 | 5 | 4 | 4 |
| YARDS | 95 | 188 | 150 | 125 | 120 | 128 | 385 | 200 | 220 |
| PAR | | | | | | | | | |
| YARDS | | | | | | | | | |

**Directions:** Route 44 in East Canaan to Allyndale Road.

**NE
CT**

# Raceway Golf Club

**Route 31**
**Thompson, CT  (860) 923-9591**
www.racewaygolf.com

**Club Pro:** David Hall, PGA
**Payment:** Visa, MC, Disc
**Tee Times:** M-F 7 days adv., S/S 4 days adv.

| Tees | Holes | Yards | Par | USGA | Slope |
|------|-------|-------|-----|------|-------|
| BACK | 18 | 6663 | 72 | 71.1 | 119 |
| MIDDLE | 18 | 6154 | 72 | 68.9 | 111 |
| FRONT | 18 | 5403 | 72 | 71.3 | 117 |

**Fee  9 Holes: Weekday:**
**Fee 18 Holes: Weekday:** $37 w/cart & lunch
**Twilight Rates:** After 5:30pm
**Cart Rental:** Included
**Lessons:** Yes  **Schools:**
**Membership:**
**Other:** Clubhouse / Lockers/ Snack Bar / Restaurant / Bar-Lounge

**Weekend:**
**Weekend:** $44 w/cart
**Discounts:** None
**Driving Range:** 40 mats, grass $6
**Junior Golf:** Yes
**Architect/Yr Open:** Don Hoenig/1947

Signature hole #4, downhill with water covering the front edge of the green. Many undulating greens. "An enjoyable course to play." –FP

|  | 1 | 2 | 3 | 4 | 5 | 6 | 7 | 8 | 9 |
|--|---|---|---|---|---|---|---|---|---|
| PAR | 4 | 4 | 4 | 3 | 5 | 5 | 4 | 4 | 3 |
| YARDS | 277 | 387 | 304 | 152 | 536 | 486 | 350 | 402 | 174 |
|  | 10 | 11 | 12 | 13 | 14 | 15 | 16 | 17 | 18 |
| PAR | 5 | 4 | 4 | 5 | 3 | 4 | 4 | 3 | 4 |
| YARDS | 492 | 382 | 342 | 425 | 146 | 353 | 347 | 166 | 289 |

**Directions:** I-395 to Exit 99; go into Thompson Center, left at blinking light onto Route 193. Follow signs to Thompson Speedway which will lead to the course.

# River Ridge Golf Course

★★★ 30

**259 Preston Road**
**Jewett City, CT  (860) 376-3268**
www.riverridgegolf.com

**Club Pro:** Casey Roan, PGA
**Payment:** Visa, MC
**Tee Times:** 10 days

| Tees | Holes | Yards | Par | USGA | Slope |
|------|-------|-------|-----|------|-------|
| BACK | 18 | 6844 | 72 | 73.0 | 129 |
| MIDDLE | 18 | 6427 | 72 | 71.0 | 127 |
| FRONT | 18 | 5398 | 72 | 70.4 | 119 |

**Fee  9 Holes: Weekday:** $21
**Fee 18 Holes: Weekday:** $35
**Twilight Rates:** After 5pm
**Cart Rental:** $18pp/18, $11pp/9
**Lessons:** Yes  **Schools:** Yes
**Membership:** Yes
**Other:** Full Service Restaurant

**Weekend:** $25
**Weekend:** $43
**Discounts:** Junior
**Driving Range:** No
**Junior Golf:** Yes
**Architect/Yr Open:** Rustici/1999

COUPON

Challenging pubglic 18 hole course cut through trees  Close to both Foxwoods and Mohegan Sun Casinos. "Nice tee boxes, fairways, and greens." –FP

|  | 1 | 2 | 3 | 4 | 5 | 6 | 7 | 8 | 9 |
|--|---|---|---|---|---|---|---|---|---|
| PAR | 4 | 4 | 5 | 3 | 5 | 3 | 4 | 4 | 4 |
| YARDS | 390 | 391 | 510 | 180 | 530 | 156 | 350 | 307 | 560 |
|  | 10 | 11 | 12 | 13 | 14 | 15 | 16 | 17 | 18 |
| PAR | 4 | 3 | 4 | 4 | 4 | 5 | 4 | 3 | 4 |
| YARDS | 401 | 122 | 420 | 326 | 350 | 530 | 340 | 185 | 379 |

**Directions:** I-395 to Exit 22 to Route 164 South. Drive 7/10 of a mile on right.

# Rockledge Country Club  ✪✪✪¹/₂  ▶31

289 South Main Street
West Hartford, CT (860) 521-3156
www.golfrockledge.com

**Club Pro:** Richard F. Crowe, PGA
**Payment:** Visa, MC, Cash
**Tee Times:** 7 days adv. (860) 521-6284
**Fee 9 Holes: Weekday:** $17.25
**Fee 18 Holes: Weekday:** $33
**Twilight Rates:** Yes, depends on sunset
**Cart Rental:** $14pp/18, $8pp/9
**Lessons:** $40/half hour **Schools:** No
**Membership:** Yes

| Tees | Holes | Yards | Par | USGA | Slope |
|------|-------|-------|-----|------|-------|
| BACK | 18 | 6436 | 72 | 71.1 | 129 |
| MIDDLE | 18 | 6069 | 72 | 69.3 | 125 |
| FRONT | 18 | 5434 | 72 | 72.7 | 129 |

**Weekend:** $18.75
**Weekend:** $37
**Discounts:** Senior & Junior
**Driving Range:** $9/lg, $6.50/med, $3.75/sm
**Junior Golf:** Yes
**Architect/Yr Open:** Al Zikorus/1940
**Other:** Clubhouse / Lockers / Showers / Snack Bar / Restaurant / Bar-Lounge

Player Comments: "Challenging layout. Always in great condition." Open April - December. Resident fees and tee times. Lottery for weekends.

| | 1 | 2 | 3 | 4 | 5 | 6 | 7 | 8 | 9 |
|------|-----|-----|-----|-----|-----|-----|-----|-----|-----|
| PAR | 4 | 4 | 4 | 4 | 3 | 5 | 4 | 3 | 5 |
| YARDS | 334 | 286 | 394 | 395 | 177 | 450 | 299 | 181 | 448 |
| | 10 | 11 | 12 | 13 | 14 | 15 | 16 | 17 | 18 |
| PAR | 4 | 4 | 5 | 3 | 5 | 4 | 3 | 4 | 4 |
| YARDS | 404 | 302 | 465 | 136 | 515 | 357 | 152 | 381 | 393 |

**Directions:** I-84 to Exit 41. From West take a right off the exit, from East take a left off the exit. Course is ¼ mile on left.

# Rolling Greens Golf Club  ✪¹/₂  ▶32

600 Cold Spring Road
Rocky Hill, CT (860) 257-9775
www.ctrollinggreens.com

**Club Pro:** Gary Deep, PGA
**Payment:** Visa, MC
**Tee Times:** No
**Fee 9 Holes: Weekday:** $17
**Fee 18 Holes: Weekday:** $34
**Twilight Rates:** After 5:30pm
**Cart Rental:** $16pp/18, $10pp/9
**Lessons:** $60 **Schools:** No
**Membership:** Yes

| Tees | Holes | Yards | Par | USGA | Slope |
|------|-------|-------|-----|------|-------|
| BACK | 9 | 3140 | 35 | 70.1 | 130 |
| MIDDLE | 9 | 2934 | 35 | 69.6 | 127 |
| FRONT | 9 | 2504 | 36 | 71.7 | 130 |

**Weekend:** $17
**Weekend:** $34
**Discounts:** Senior & Junior
**Driving Range:** No
**Junior Golf:** No
**Architect/Yr Open:** Geoffrey Cornish/1973
**Other:** Clubhouse / Lockers / Showers / Restaurant / Bar-Lounge

Challenging! Shotmaker's course. Great shape. Dress code (no tank tops, T-shirts, or cutoff jeans). Open March - November.

| | 1 | 2 | 3 | 4 | 5 | 6 | 7 | 8 | 9 |
|------|-----|-----|-----|-----|-----|-----|-----|-----|-----|
| PAR | 4 | 5 | 3 | 4 | 4 | 4 | 4 | 3 | 4 |
| YARDS | 360 | 530 | 175 | 330 | 356 | 325 | 370 | 148 | 340 |
| PAR | | | | | | | | | |
| YARDS | | | | | | | | | |

**Directions:** I-91 to Exit 23. Signs to Rolling Greens. Approximately 1 mile from exit.

**NE
CT**

# Rolling Meadows Country Club ✪✪ ▶33

77 Sadds Mill Road
Ellington, CT (860) 870-5328
www.rollingmeadowscountryclub.com

| Tees | Holes | Yards | Par | USGA | Slope |
|------|-------|-------|-----|------|-------|
| BACK | 18 | 6818 | 72 | 72.3 | 125 |
| MIDDLE | 18 | 6269 | 72 | 69.6 | 124 |
| FRONT | 18 | 5315 | 72 | 70.5 | 128 |

**Club Pro:** Jim McMahon, PGA
**Payment:** Visa, MC, Disc, Amex
**Tee Times:** 1 week adv.
**Fee 9 Holes: Weekday:** $23    **Weekend:** $25
**Fee 18 Holes: Weekday:** $38    **Weekend:** $41
**Twilight Rates:** After 5pm    **Discounts:** Senior & Junior
**Cart Rental:** $16pp/18, $8 pp/9    **Driving Range:** No
**Lessons:** Yes **Schools:** Yes    **Junior Golf:** Yes
**Membership:** Yes    **Architect/Yr Open:** Al Zirokus/1997
**Other:** Restaurant / Bar / Beverage Cart    **GPS:**

Player Comments: "Getting better every year." Weekday specials available - call pro shop for details.
Special: 7am-1pm, Monday - Friday - $41 with cart, $38 military or senior.

| | 1 | 2 | 3 | 4 | 5 | 6 | 7 | 8 | 9 |
|---|---|---|---|---|---|---|---|---|---|
| PAR | 5 | 4 | 3 | 5 | 4 | 4 | 4 | 3 | 4 |
| YARDS | 488 | 316 | 166 | 491 | 390 | 366 | 335 | 186 | 346 |
| | 10 | 11 | 12 | 13 | 14 | 15 | 16 | 17 | 18 |
| PAR | 4 | 5 | 4 | 3 | 5 | 4 | 4 | 3 | 4 |
| YARDS | 383 | 473 | 366 | 163 | 490 | 433 | 345 | 190 | 342 |

**Directions:** I-91 to Route 140 or I-84 to 83 to Route 140 (across from Brookside Park, Ellington).

# Shennecossett Golf Club ✪✪✪ ▶34

93 Plant Street
Groton, CT (860) 445-0262
www.shennygolf.com

| Tees | Holes | Yards | Par | USGA | Slope |
|------|-------|-------|-----|------|-------|
| BACK | 18 | 6562 | 71 | 71.5 | 122 |
| MIDDLE | 18 | 6088 | 71 | 69.1 | 121 |
| FRONT | 18 | 5671 | 74 | 72.4 | 122 |

**Club Pro:** Todd Goodhue, PGA
**Payment:** Visa, MC
**Tee Times:** One week ahead @ 5pm
**Fee 9 Holes: Weekday:** $21    **Weekend:**
**Fee 18 Holes: Weekday:** $43    **Weekend:** $47    ᶜᴼᵁᴾᴼᴺ
**Twilight Rates:** After 5pm    **Discounts:** Junior
**Cart Rental:** $18pp/18    **Driving Range:** No
**Lessons:** Yes **Schools:** No    **Junior Golf:** Yes
**Membership:** Yes    **Architect/Yr Open:** Donald Ross
**Other:** Clubhouse / Snack Bar / Restaurant / Bar-Lounge

Player Comments: "Great old course. Newer holes along the river are terrific." Fully irrigated. Donald Ross-designed seaside course. Open year round. Mohegan Sun and Foxwoods Casino nearby.

| | 1 | 2 | 3 | 4 | 5 | 6 | 7 | 8 | 9 |
|---|---|---|---|---|---|---|---|---|---|
| PAR | 4 | 4 | 4 | 3 | 5 | 4 | 4 | 5 | 3 |
| YARDS | 350 | 368 | 361 | 195 | 488 | 145 | 433 | 367 | 418 |
| | 10 | 11 | 12 | 13 | 14 | 15 | 16 | 17 | 18 |
| PAR | 4 | 4 | 3 | 4 | 4 | 3 | 4 | 4 | 5 |
| YARDS | 400 | 160 | 460 | 542 | 323 | 116 | 343 | 362 | 311 |

**Directions:** I-95 to Exit 87 (Clarence Sharp Highway); take right at second light. Take left at next light, proceed past Pfizer; course is on left side.

# Simsbury Farms Golf Club  ✪✪  ▶ 35

100 Old Farms Road
West Simsbury, CT (860) 658-6246
www.simsburyfarms.com
**Club Pro:** John Verrengia, PGA
**Payment:** Cash, Check, Most Major
**Tee Times:** 3 days wknds, 7 days wkdays
**Fee  9 Holes: Weekday:** $20
**Fee 18 Holes: Weekday:** $34
**Twilight Rates:** After 6pm
**Cart Rental:** $16pp/18, $10pp/9
**Lessons:** $50/45 min.  **Schools:** No
**Membership:** Yes (non-resident available)
**Other:** Restaurant / Clubhouse

| Tees | Holes | Yards | Par | USGA | Slope |
|------|-------|-------|-----|------|-------|
| BACK | 18 | 6509 | 72 | 71.0 | 122 |
| MIDDLE | 18 | 6119 | 72 | 69.0 | 119 |
| FRONT | 18 | 5400 | 72 | 70.8 | 122 |

**Weekend:** $23
**Weekend:** $38
**Discounts:** Senior & Junior
**Driving Range:** Yes
**Junior Golf:** Yes
**Architect/Yr Open:** Geoffrey Cornish/1972
**GPS:** Yes

Good challenge with a decent mix of holes. A nice hilly course. All bunkers re-done in 2012. Continued drainage improvements. Open April - November.

| | 1 | 2 | 3 | 4 | 5 | 6 | 7 | 8 | 9 |
|-------|---|---|---|---|---|---|---|---|---|
| PAR | 4 | 4 | 4 | 3 | 5 | 4 | 5 | 4 | 3 |
| YARDS | 341 | 381 | 361 | 135 | 487 | 361 | 535 | 279 | 178 |
| | 10 | 11 | 12 | 13 | 14 | 15 | 16 | 17 | 18 |
| PAR | 4 | 4 | 5 | 3 | 5 | 4 | 3 | 4 | 4 |
| YARDS | 346 | 335 | 533 | 169 | 465 | 325 | 200 | 302 | 386 |

**Directions:** Route 185 North to end. Take left on to 10 North. At 2nd light take left onto Stratton Brook Road. Through 2 traffic lights, course is ¾ mile on the right.

# Skungamaug River Golf Club  ✪✪✪  ▶ 36

104 Folly Lane
Coventry, CT (860) 742-9348
www.skungamauggolf.com
**Club Pro:** Rick Nelson, PGA
**Payment:** Visa, MC, Amex, Disc
**Tee Times:** M-F 7 days adv., S/S 6 days adv.
**Fee  9 Holes: Weekday:** $18
**Fee 18 Holes: Weekday:** $35
**Twilight Rates:** After 6pm
**Cart Rental:** $15pp/18, $8pp/9
**Lessons:** $50/half hour  **Schools:** No
**Membership:** Yes
**Other:** See website for specials

| Tees | Holes | Yards | Par | USGA | Slope |
|------|-------|-------|-----|------|-------|
| BACK | 18 | 5785 | 70 | 69.4 | 120 |
| MIDDLE | 18 | 5624 | 70 | 68.6 | 118 |
| FRONT | 18 | 4838 | 71 | 69.3 | 119 |

**Weekend:** $19
**Weekend:** $38
**Discounts:** Senior
**Driving Range:** $5/lg, $3/sm bucket
**Junior Golf:** Yes
**Architect/Yr Open:** Chet Jenkins/1965
**GPS:** yes

COUPON

River runs along right side, large tree divides upper and lower levels of hole #15. No cutoffs or tank tops. Open April - December.

| | 1 | 2 | 3 | 4 | 5 | 6 | 7 | 8 | 9 |
|-------|---|---|---|---|---|---|---|---|---|
| PAR | 4 | 3 | 4 | 5 | 3 | 4 | 5 | 3 | 4 |
| YARDS | 339 | 154 | 291 | 438 | 139 | 332 | 461 | 158 | 351 |
| | 10 | 11 | 12 | 13 | 14 | 15 | 16 | 17 | 18 |
| PAR | 4 | 3 | 4 | 4 | 4 | 4 | 4 | 3 | 5 |
| YARDS | 376 | 171 | 363 | 371 | 395 | 290 | 323 | 189 | 483 |

**Directions:** I-84 to Exit 68. South on Route 195, ¼ mile to light. Turn right onto Goose Lane, follow yellow, triangular arrows on telephone poles. 3 miles to club.

NE
CT

# Stanley Golf Club

✪✪✪½ 37

245 Hartford Road
New Britain, CT (860) 827-8570
www.stanleygolf.com

| Tees | Holes | Yards | Par | USGA | Slope |
|------|-------|-------|-----|------|-------|
| BACK | 27/18 | 6378 | 71 | 70.8 | 124 |
| MIDDLE | 27/18 | 5970 | 71 | 68.9 | 121 |
| FRONT | 27/18 | 5302 | 72 | 71.5 | 120 |

**Club Pro:** Kyle Hedstrom, PGA
**Payment:** Most Major Credit Cards
**Tee Times:** Wknds, 3 days adv. (860-827-1362)
**Fee 9 Holes: Weekday:** $21.25    **Weekend:** $23.25
**Fee 18 Holes: Weekday:** $36    **Weekend:** $39.75
**Twilight Rates:** No    **Discounts:** Senior & Junior
**Cart Rental:** $17.75pp/18, $10.25pp/9    **Driving Range:** $12/lg, $9/med, $6/sm
**Lessons:** Yes   **Schools:** No    **Junior Golf:** Yes
**Membership:** Season Pass    **Architect/Yr Open:** Robert Ross/1930
**Other:** Clubhouse / Lockers / Showers / Restaurant / Bar-Lounge / Snack / Outings
**GPS:** Yes

27 holes with many improvements over the last several years. Resident rates available.

**White/Red**

| | 1 | 2 | 3 | 4 | 5 | 6 | 7 | 8 | 9 |
|---|---|---|---|---|---|---|---|---|---|
| PAR | 5 | 4 | 3 | 4 | 4 | 4 | 3 | 4 | 5 |
| YARDS | 492 | 430 | 158 | 352 | 390 | 320 | 117 | 387 | 460 |
| | 10 | 11 | 12 | 13 | 14 | 15 | 16 | 17 | 18 |
| PAR | 4 | 3 | 4 | 4 | 4 | 4 | 5 | 3 | 4 |
| YARDS | 338 | 140 | 330 | 325 | 345 | 385 | 491 | 150 | 360 |

**Directions:** I-84 to Exit 39A, then right onto Route 9 South to Exit 30. Take right at end of ramp. Course is ½ mile on left.

# Tallwood Country Club

✪✪½ 38

91 North Street (Route 85)
Hebron, CT (860) 646-1151
www.tallwoodcountryclub.com

| Tees | Holes | Yards | Par | USGA | Slope |
|------|-------|-------|-----|------|-------|
| BACK | 18 | 6523 | 72 | 71.2 | 126 |
| MIDDLE | 18 | 6126 | 72 | 69.3 | 121 |
| FRONT | 18 | 5694 | 72 | 67.2 | 116 |

**Club Pro:** John Nowobilskis, PGA
**Payment:** Visa, MC, Disc
**Tee Times:** M-F 7 days adv., S/S 5 days adv.
**Fee 9 Holes: Weekday:** $19.50    **Weekend:** $20.50
**Fee 18 Holes: Weekday:** $38    **Weekend:** $41
**Twilight Rates:** After 5pm    **Discounts:** Senior & Junior (M-F)
**Cart Rental:** $15pp/18, $7.50pp/9    **Driving Range:** Yes
**Lessons:** Yes   **Schools:** Yes    **Junior Golf:** Yes
**Membership:** Yes    **Architect/Yr Open:** Mike Ovian/1970
**Other:** Clubhouse / Snack Bar / Practice Facilties   **GPS:**

Great practice faciltiy with practice bunkers, chipping area, driving range with grass tees and mats and two putting greens. Annual host of CTPGA, CSGA events. Open March - December.

**White/Blue**

| | 1 | 2 | 3 | 4 | 5 | 6 | 7 | 8 | 9 |
|---|---|---|---|---|---|---|---|---|---|
| PAR | 5 | 4 | 3 | 5 | 4 | 3 | 4 | 4 | 3 |
| YARDS | 528 | 287 | 176 | 483 | 400 | 158 | 341 | 359 | 167 |
| | 10 | 11 | 12 | 13 | 14 | 15 | 16 | 17 | 18 |
| PAR | 4 | 5 | 4 | 4 | 3 | 4 | 5 | 4 | 4 |
| YARDS | 296 | 500 | 361 | 346 | 157 | 364 | 460 | 377 | 366 |

**Directions:** I-84 East to I-384. Exit 5 off I-384, right off exit puts you on Route 85 South. Course is on right.

# The Pines GC & Driving Range    NR 39

119 High Rock Road
Groton, CT (860) 445-9918
www.birchplaingolf.com

**Club Pro:** Jeff Beaupre, PGA
**Payment:** Visa, MC, Disc
**Tee Times:** No
**Fee 9 Holes: Weekday:** $22
**Fee 18 Holes: Weekday:** $22
**Twilight Rates:** After 5:30pm
**Discounts:** Senior/60+, Junior/-18, Military - active only
**Cart Rental:** $12pp/18, $4/pull cart
**Lessons:** Yes **Schools:** No
**Membership:** Yes
**Other:** Snacks

**Weekend:** $26
**Weekend:** $26

**Driving Range:** $8/lg., $7/sm. bucket
**Junior Golf:** Yes
**Architect/Yr Open:** Armando Baldelli/1969
**GPS:**

| Tees | Holes | Yards | Par | USGA | Slope |
|------|-------|-------|-----|------|-------|
| BACK |  |  |  |  |  |
| MIDDLE | 18 | 2666 | 54 |  |  |
| FRONT |  |  |  |  |  |

A pleasant par 3. Good for beginners. Easy walking flat & open. Close to beaches, Mystic Seaport, Aquarium and casinos. Sand traps re-engineered in 2010.

|  | 1 | 2 | 3 | 4 | 5 | 6 | 7 | 8 | 9 |
|------|---|---|---|---|---|---|---|---|---|
| PAR | 3 | 3 | 3 | 3 | 3 | 3 | 3 | 3 | 3 |
| YARDS | 107 | 170 | 148 | 228 | 206 | 124 | 113 | 137 | 129 |
|  | 10 | 11 | 12 | 13 | 14 | 15 | 16 | 17 | 18 |
| PAR | 3 | 3 | 3 | 3 | 3 | 3 | 3 | 3 | 3 |
| YARDS | 105 | 187 | 108 | 147 | 136 | 164 | 150 | 155 | 156 |

**Directions:** I-95 to Route 349 (Clarence Sharp Highway). At second light, take left. At next light, take right. Follow signs for Groton/New London Airport. Course is on right.

# Timberlin Golf Club    ✪✪✪    40

330 Southington Road
Berlin, CT (860) 828-3228
www.timberlingolf.com

**Club Pro:** Marc S. Bayram, PGA
**Payment:** Cash or Credit
**Tee Times:** 7 days/wkdys, 3 days/wknd
**Fee 9 Holes: Weekday:** $24
**Fee 18 Holes: Weekday:** $38
**Twilight Rates:** After 4pm
**Cart Rental:** $17pp/18, $10pp/9
**Lessons:** Yes **Schools:** Yes
**Membership:** Yes
**Other:** Clubhouse / Showers / Snack Bar

**Weekend:** $25.25
**Weekend:** $41.50
**Discounts:** Senior & Junior
**Driving Range:** Yes
**Junior Golf:** Yes
**Architect/Yr Open:** Al Zikorus/1970
**GPS:**

| Tees | Holes | Yards | Par | USGA | Slope |
|------|-------|-------|-----|------|-------|
| BACK | 18 | 6858 | 72 | 72.9 | 130 |
| MIDDLE | 18 | 6113 | 72 | 69.4 | 128 |
| FRONT | 18 | 5402 | 72 | 71.8 | 119 |

COUPON

Player Comments: "Friendly staff." "Challenging course in great shape." "Good value."
Conservative layout with well-placed traps. All new bunkers. Open April - December. Berlin resident rates available. Check for internet specials: www.timberlingolf.com.

|  | 1 | 2 | 3 | 4 | 5 | 6 | 7 | 8 | 9 |
|------|---|---|---|---|---|---|---|---|---|
| PAR | 5 | 4 | 4 | 3 | 4 | 5 | 3 | 4 | 4 |
| YARDS | 534 | 333 | 347 | 156 | 346 | 510 | 160 | 310 | 368 |
|  | 10 | 11 | 12 | 13 | 14 | 15 | 16 | 17 | 18 |
| PAR | 5 | 4 | 3 | 5 | 4 | 4 | 3 | 4 | 4 |
| YARDS | 481 | 347 | 145 | 467 | 343 | 384 | 161 | 360 | 361 |

**Directions:** Located off Route 71 which runs between I-691 and Route 372. Course is on Route 364, .6 mile from Route 71. Left onto Southington Avenue.

**NE CT**

# Topstone Golf Course   ✪✪✪½  41 ▶

516 Griffin Road
South Windsor, CT  (860) 648-4653
www.topstonegc.com

**Club Pro:** Casey Morris
**Payment:** Visa, MC, Amex, Disc
**Tee Times:** 14 days adv.
**Fee  9 Holes: Weekday:** $22
**Fee 18 Holes: Weekday:** $43
**Twilight Rates:** After 11am
**Cart Rental:** $13pp/18, $7pp/9
**Lessons:** $40/half hour  **Schools:** No
**Membership:** Yes
**Other:** Bar / Restaurant / Clubhouse

**Weekend:** $24
**Weekend:** $46
**Discounts:** Senior & Junior
**Driving Range:** No
**Junior Golf:** Yes
**Architect/Yr Open:** Al Zikorus, Joe Kelley/1997
**GPS:**

| Tees | Holes | Yards | Par | USGA | Slope |
|------|-------|-------|-----|------|-------|
| BACK | 18 | 6546 | 72 | 70.9 | 124 |
| MIDDLE | 18 | 6113 | 72 | 69.0 | 119 |
| FRONT | 18 | 5077 | 72 | 67.9 | 111 |

Player Comments: "A good value for your golfing dollars." "Shows a great deal of maturity. Back 9 has more distinctive holes." "Well-kept course. Great greens." Challenging for all abilities with 4 sets of tees. Listed as Golf Channel's top 5 Hartford area courses in 2016.

|  | 1 | 2 | 3 | 4 | 5 | 6 | 7 | 8 | 9 |
|---|---|---|---|---|---|---|---|---|---|
| PAR | 4 | 5 | 4 | 3 | 5 | 4 | 4 | 3 | 4 |
| YARDS | 360 | 491 | 309 | 170 | 505 | 389 | 392 | 145 | 285 |
|  | 10 | 11 | 12 | 13 | 14 | 15 | 16 | 17 | 18 |
| PAR | 5 | 4 | 3 | 4 | 4 | 3 | 5 | 4 | 4 |
| YARDS | 490 | 380 | 169 | 354 | 399 | 140 | 460 | 332 | 343 |

**Directions:** Take I-291 from either Routes 84 or 91. Take Exit 4 (Route 5). Go north on Route 5 for 4 miles, turn right onto Route 194 for .5 mile. Left onto Rye Street for 1.5 miles, Turn right onto Griffin Street for 1.25 miles.

# Tower Ridge   ✪✪✪½  42 ▶

140 Nod Road
Simsbury, CT  (860) 658-9767
www.towerridge.com

**Club Pro:** James Becker
**Payment:** Most Major Credit Cards
**Tee Times:** 7 days per week
**Fee  9 Holes: Weekday:** $27
**Fee 18 Holes: Weekday:** $45
**Twilight Rates:** After 1pm wknd, after 3pm wkdys
**Cart Rental:** Included
**Lessons:** $80/hour  **Schools:** Yes
**Membership:** Yes
**Other:** Restaurant / Tennis Center & Swim Club for Members

**Weekend:** $35
**Weekend:** $59
**Discounts:** Senior
**Driving Range:** Yes
**Junior Golf:** Yes
**Architect/Yr Open:** Geoffrey Cornish/1959

COUPON

| Tees | Holes | Yards | Par | USGA | Slope |
|------|-------|-------|-----|------|-------|
| BACK | 18 | 6443 | 71 | 71.5 | 132 |
| MIDDLE | 18 | 6124 | 71 | 70.0 | 129 |
| FRONT | 18 | 5164 | 72 | 76.3 | 133 |

Former private now accepting public play. Partially flat, partially hilly. Several nice views from elevated tees. A challenging course for any level of player. Spectacular view of Simsbury mountain range and Hueblein Tower. Plays along the Farmington River.

|  | 1 | 2 | 3 | 4 | 5 | 6 | 7 | 8 | 9 |
|---|---|---|---|---|---|---|---|---|---|
| PAR | 4 | 4 | 3 | 4 | 4 | 4 | 4 | 4 | 4 |
| YARDS | 367 | 383 | 141 | 369 | 377 | 341 | 416 | 230 | 335 |
|  | 10 | 11 | 12 | 13 | 14 | 15 | 16 | 17 | 18 |
| PAR | 5 | 4 | 3 | 4 | 5 | 4 | 3 | 4 | 4 |
| YARDS | 449 | 429 | 179 | 397 | 480 | 389 | 164 | 314 | 364 |

**Directions:** I-84 to exit Route 4 Farmington. At 2nd light, right on Route 10 North. Cross Route 44. Club is on right.

# Tunxis Golf Club (Green)  ✪✪✪½  43

**87 Town Farm Road**
**Farmington, CT  (860) 677-1367**
www.tunxisgolf.com

**Club Pro:** Angelo Fiducia
**Payment:** Visa, MC, Amex, Disc
**Tee Times:** 1 week adv.

| Tees | Holes | Yards | Par | USGA | Slope |
|------|-------|-------|-----|------|-------|
| BACK | 18 | 6446 | 70 | 70.9 | 124 |
| MIDDLE | 18 | 6036 | 70 | 69.0 | 119 |
| FRONT | 18 | 4962 | 70 | 71.0 | 115 |

**Fee  9 Holes: Weekday:** $24          **Weekend:** $25
**Fee 18 Holes: Weekday:** $41          **Weekend:** $48
**Twilight Rates:**                                    **Discounts:** Senior and Junior
**Cart Rental:** $18.50pp/18, $10.50pp/9   **Driving Range:** Yes, $5/bucket
**Lessons:** Yes  **Schools:** No          **Junior Golf:** Yes
**Membership:** Season Pass $2,200      **Architect/Yr Open:** Al Zakoris/1962
**Other:** Restaurant / Clubhouse / Bar-Lounge / Lockers / Snack Bar / Showers

Very well run for such a complex. Fine staff. Wide-open fairways make for a forgiving layout. Great course for intermediate players. Open April 1 - November 20.

|  | 1 | 2 | 3 | 4 | 5 | 6 | 7 | 8 | 9 |
|------|----|----|----|----|----|----|----|----|----|
| PAR | 4 | 5 | 4 | 4 | 3 | 4 | 4 | 3 | 4 |
| YARDS | 363 | 511 | 354 | 369 | 188 | 434 | 345 | 166 | 335 |
|  | 10 | 11 | 12 | 13 | 14 | 15 | 16 | 17 | 18 |
| PAR | 4 | 4 | 3 | 4 | 4 | 4 | 4 | 5 | 3 |
| YARDS | 348 | 365 | 165 | 373 | 342 | 291 | 397 | 496 | 185 |

**Directions:** I-84 to Exit 39 (Route 4 W); first right over Farmington River.

# Tunxis Golf Club  (Red)  ✪✪✪½  44

**87 Town Farm Road**
**Farmington, CT  (860) 677-1367**
www.tunxisgolf.com

**Club Pro:** Angelo Fiducia
**Payment:** Visa, MC, Amex, Disc
**Tee Times:** 1 week adv.

| Tees | Holes | Yards | Par | USGA | Slope |
|------|-------|-------|-----|------|-------|
| BACK | 9 | 3219 | 35 | 35.3 | 129 |
| MIDDLE | 9 | 2999 | 35 | 34.2 | 124 |
| FRONT | 9 | 2492 | 35 | 35.8 | 117 |

**Fee  9 Holes: Weekday:** $24          **Weekend:** $25
**Fee 18 Holes: Weekday:** $41          **Weekend:** $48
**Twilight Rates:**                                    **Discounts:** Senior and Junior
**Cart Rental:** $18.50pp/18, $10.50pp/9   **Driving Range:** $5/bucket
**Lessons:** Yes  **Schools:** No          **Junior Golf:** Yes
**Membership:** Season Pass $2,200      **Architect/Yr Open:** Al Zakoris/1962
**Other:** Restaurant / Clubhouse / Bar-Lounge / Lockers / Snack Bar / Showers

9-hole course in excellent condition located in Farmington Valley, next to Farmington River. Open April 1 - November 20.

|  | 1 | 2 | 3 | 4 | 5 | 6 | 7 | 8 | 9 |
|------|----|----|----|----|----|----|----|----|----|
| PAR | 4 | 4 | 3 | 4 | 5 | 4 | 4 | 3 | 4 |
| YARDS | 348 | 395 | 141 | 322 | 483 | 396 | 366 | 177 | 371 |
| PAR |  |  |  |  |  |  |  |  |  |
| YARDS |  |  |  |  |  |  |  |  |  |

**Directions:** I-84 to Exit 39 (Route 4 W); first right over Farmington River.

**NE**
**CT**

# Tunxis Golf Club (White)  ✪✪✪½  45 ►

**87 Town Farm Road**
**Farmington, CT (860) 677-1367**
www.tunxisgolf.com

| Tees | Holes | Yards | Par | USGA | Slope |
|------|-------|-------|-----|------|-------|
| BACK | 18 | 6638 | 72 | 71.7 | 131 |
| MIDDLE | 18 | 6241 | 72 | 69.8 | 128 |
| FRONT | 18 | 5744 | 72 | 71.5 | 116 |

**Club Pro:** Angelo Fiducia
**Payment:** Visa, MC, Amex, Disc
**Tee Times:** 1 week adv.
**Fee 9 Holes: Weekday:** $24  **Weekend:** $25
**Fee 18 Holes: Weekday:** $41  **Weekend:** $48
**Twilight Rates:** No  **Discounts:** Senior and Junior
**Cart Rental:** $18.50pp/18, $10.50pp/9  **Driving Range:** $5/bucket
**Lessons:** Yes  **Schools:** No  **Junior Golf:** Yes
**Membership:** Season Pass $2,200  **Architect/Yr Open:** Al Zakoris/1962
**Other:** Restaurant / Clubhouse / Bar-Lounge / Lockers / Snack Bar / Showers

Great course for intermediate players. Play from the Blue tees for a real challenge. Lake comes into play on several holes. Open April 1 - November 20. "Florida-style golf: water and sand provide challenges. Holes 5 & 13 really tough." –AR

|  | 1 | 2 | 3 | 4 | 5 | 6 | 7 | 8 | 9 |
|------|-----|-----|-----|-----|-----|-----|-----|-----|-----|
| PAR | 5 | 4 | 4 | 3 | 5 | 4 | 4 | 3 | 4 |
| YARDS | 526 | 407 | 343 | 153 | 476 | 366 | 358 | 147 | 332 |
|  | 10 | 11 | 12 | 13 | 14 | 15 | 16 | 17 | 18 |
| PAR | 4 | 5 | 4 | 5 | 3 | 4 | 3 | 4 | 4 |
| YARDS | 334 | 508 | 358 | 515 | 176 | 413 | 154 | 357 | 318 |

**Directions:** I-84 to Exit 39 (Route 4 W); first right over Farmington River.

# Twin Hills Country Club  NR  46 ►

**199 Bread and Milk Street**
**Coventry, CT (860) 742-9705**
www.twinhillscountryclub.com

| Tees | Holes | Yards | Par | USGA | Slope |
|------|-------|-------|-----|------|-------|
| BACK | 18 | 6365 | 71 | 69.3 | 121 |
| MIDDLE | 18 | 5992 | 71 | 68.0 | 117 |
| FRONT | 18 | 5249 | 71 | 69.5 | 116 |

**Club Pro:** Eric DeStefano, PGA
**Payment:** Visa, MC
**Tee Times:** 7 days F/S/S/H
**Fee 9 Holes: Weekday:** $19  **Weekend:** $20
**Fee 18 Holes: Weekday:** $34  **Weekend:** $39
**Twilight Rates:** No  **Discounts:** Senior & Junior
**Cart Rental:** $15pp/18, $8pp/9  **Driving Range:** No
**Lessons:** Yes  **Schools:** No  **Junior Golf:** Yes
**Membership:** No  **Architect/Yr Open:** George McDermott/1971
**Other:** Clubhouse / Snack Bar / Beer & Soda  **GPS:**

COUPON

A rustic, but interesting, layout. Number 3 is a fun par 5 with risk/reward chance for a birdie. Open March - December.

|  | 1 | 2 | 3 | 4 | 5 | 6 | 7 | 8 | 9 |
|------|-----|-----|-----|-----|-----|-----|-----|-----|-----|
| PAR | 4 | 4 | 5 | 3 | 5 | 4 | 4 | 3 | 4 |
| YARDS | 380 | 284 | 530 | 144 | 502 | 348 | 446 | 152 | 357 |
|  | 10 | 11 | 12 | 13 | 14 | 15 | 16 | 17 | 18 |
| PAR | 4 | 4 | 4 | 3 | 4 | 5 | 3 | 4 | 4 |
| YARDS | 320 | 336 | 311 | 204 | 374 | 494 | 144 | 361 | 267 |

**Directions:** Route 84E Exit 67 to Route 31 South; follow 5 miles. Course is on the right.

# Villa Hills Par 3

497 Middle Turnpike
Storrs, CT (860) 429-6421

**Club Pro:** Bernie Broder, Manager
**Payment:** Cash, Visa, MC
**Tee Times:**
**Fee 9 Holes: Weekday:** $10
**Fee 18 Holes: Weekday:** $19
**Twilight Rates:** No
**Cart Rental:** $3/pull
**Lessons: Schools:** No
**Membership:**
**Other:** Restaurant / Snack Bar / Bar-Lounge

Popular Par 3.

| Tees | Holes | Yards | Par | USGA | Slope |
|------|-------|-------|-----|------|-------|
| BACK | | | | | |
| MIDDLE | 9 | 1158 | 27 | | |
| FRONT | | | | | |

**Weekend:** $10
**Weekend:** $19
**Discounts:**
**Driving Range:**
**Junior Golf:** No
**Architect/Yr Open:** 1997
**GPS:**

| | 1 | 2 | 3 | 4 | 5 | 6 | 7 | 8 | 9 |
|---|---|---|---|---|---|---|---|---|---|
| PAR | 3 | 3 | 3 | 3 | 3 | 3 | 3 | 3 | 3 |
| YARDS | 97 | 185 | 150 | 105 | 165 | 65 | 120 | 124 | 147 |
| PAR | | | | | | | | | |
| YARDS | | | | | | | | | |

**Directions:** I-384 to Route 44. Course is on left.

# Westwoods Golf Course

Route 177
Farmington, CT (860) 675-2548
www.farmington.ct.org

**Club Pro:** Larry Graham, PGA
**Payment:** Most Major Credit Cards
**Tee Times:** Weekends, 7 days adv.
**Fee 9 Holes: Weekday:** $18
**Fee 18 Holes: Weekday:** $26.25
**Twilight Rates:** No
**Cart Rental:** $29.68/18, $16.96/9 per cart
**Lessons:** $60/hour, $40/half hour **Schools:** No
**Membership:** Yes
**Other:** Snack Bar / Bar-Lounge / Clubhouse / Restaurant / 20,000 sq. ft. Putting Green

Grass on practice range. Easy to walk, scenic.

| Tees | Holes | Yards | Par | USGA | Slope |
|------|-------|-------|-----|------|-------|
| BACK | | | | | |
| MIDDLE | 18 | 4407 | 61 | 60.8 | 93 |
| FRONT | 18 | 3975 | 61 | 59.5 | 85 |

**Weekend:** $21
**Weekend:** $29.50
**Discounts:** Senior & Junior
**Driving Range:** Yes
**Junior Golf:** July Golf Camp - 4 one-week sessions
**Architect/Yr Open:** Geoffrey Cornish/1965

| | 1 | 2 | 3 | 4 | 5 | 6 | 7 | 8 | 9 |
|---|---|---|---|---|---|---|---|---|---|
| PAR | 5 | 3 | 3 | 3 | 4 | 3 | 3 | 4 | 3 |
| YARDS | 494 | 164 | 135 | 187 | 315 | 204 | 159 | 344 | 235 |
| | 10 | 11 | 12 | 13 | 14 | 15 | 16 | 17 | 18 |
| PAR | 4 | 3 | 3 | 4 | 3 | 4 | 3 | 3 | 3 |
| YARDS | 420 | 236 | 121 | 376 | 211 | 348 | 163 | 163 | 132 |

**Directions:** Take I-84 to Route 72 Plainville to Washington Street (177). Take right on 177 North. Follow 3 miles, cross Route 6 and then course is 200 yards on left.

**NE CT**

# Willow Brook Golf Course ✪✪½ ▶ 49

**124 Brookfield St.**
**South Windsor, CT** (860) 648-2061
www.willowbrookgc.com

| Tees | Holes | Yards | Par | USGA | Slope |
|------|-------|-------|-----|------|-------|
| BACK | 18 | 3024 | 60 | 54.9 | 79 |
| MIDDLE | 18 | 2633 | 60 | | |
| FRONT | 18 | 2278 | 60 | | |

**Club Pro:** Jeffrey Beyer, PGA
**Payment:** All Major Credit Cards
**Tee Times:** 7 days adv.
**Fee 9 Holes: Weekday:** $16.50　　**Weekend:** $18.50
**Fee 18 Holes: Weekday:** $28　　**Weekend:** $30
**Twilight Rates:** After 3pm Sat and Sun　　**Discounts:** Senior & Junior
**Cart Rental:** $8pp/18, $4.50pp/9　　**Driving Range:** Yes
**Lessons:** Yes **Schools:** Yes　　**Junior Golf:** Yes
**Membership:** No　　**Architect/Yr Open:** Joe Kelly/2002
**Other:** Restaurant / Bar-Lounge / Clubhouse　　**GPS:**

*COUPON*

Spectacular par 60 that is ideal for new golfers yet challenging to accomplished players. Public golf course in country club conditions.

| | 1 | 2 | 3 | 4 | 5 | 6 | 7 | 8 | 9 |
|---|---|---|---|---|---|---|---|---|---|
| PAR | 3 | 3 | 4 | 3 | 3 | 4 | 4 | 3 | 3 |
| YARDS | 113 | 133 | 244 | 85 | 122 | 217 | 240 | 124 | 110 |
| | 10 | 11 | 12 | 13 | 14 | 15 | 16 | 17 | 18 |
| PAR | 3 | 4 | 3 | 4 | 3 | 3 | 3 | 3 | 4 |
| YARDS | 120 | 252 | 97 | 300 | 160 | 108 | 122 | 104 | 373 |

**Directions:** I-84 to Exit 62. Left off ramp onto Sullivan Road. Follow Sullivan 4 miles. Right onto Troy Street, then right on to Brookfield Street. Course is on the right.

# Wintonbury Hills GC ✪✪✪✪½ ▶ 50

**206 Terry Plains Road**
**Bloomfield, CT** (860) 242-1401 x2
www.wintonburyhills.com

| Tees | Holes | Yards | Par | USGA | Slope |
|------|-------|-------|-----|------|-------|
| BACK | 18 | 6709 | 70 | 70.8 | 125 |
| MIDDLE | 18 | 6283 | 70 | 69.5 | 121 |
| FRONT | 18 | 5005 | 70 | 68.2 | 112 |

**Club Pro:** Ciaron Carr, PGA
**Payment:** Visa, MC, Amex, Disc
**Tee Times:** 7 days adv.
**Fee 9 Holes: Weekday:**　　**Weekend:**
**Fee 18 Holes: Weekday:** $69　　**Weekend:** $79
**Twilight Rates:** After 2pm　　**Discounts:** Senior/Junior
**Cart Rental:** Included　　**Driving Range:** Yes
**Lessons:** Yes **Schools:** Yes　　**Junior Golf:** Yes
**Membership:** Yes　　**Architect/Yr Open:** Pete Dye & Tim Liddy/2004
**Other:** Bloomfield Resident Rates Available / GPS-Equipped Carts
**GPS:** Yes

Resident rates available. Playing conditions better than many private clubs. "Gorgeous holes, courteous staff, excellent condition." –RW "Has joined the ranks of New England's best." –JD

| | 1 | 2 | 3 | 4 | 5 | 6 | 7 | 8 | 9 |
|---|---|---|---|---|---|---|---|---|---|
| PAR | 4 | 4 | 3 | 5 | 4 | 4 | 3 | 5 | 3 |
| YARDS | 367 | 365 | 139 | 512 | 327 | 400 | 200 | 543 | 170 |
| | 10 | 11 | 12 | 13 | 14 | 15 | 16 | 17 | 18 |
| PAR | 4 | 4 | 3 | 5 | 4 | 4 | 4 | 3 | 4 |
| YARDS | 402 | 400 | 162 | 521 | 415 | 397 | 368 | 190 | 405 |

**Directions:** From East: I-291 West toward Windsor. Take Exit 1 – CT-218 West. Turn left onto CT-218 for 4 miles. Right onto Bloomfield Avenue/CT-189. Follow 189 until it turns right at a traffic light. DO NOT GO RIGHT, go straight onto Terry Plains Road. Follow Terry Plains Road. for 1 mile. See web for more.

# Woodstock Golf Course

○○ ▶ 51

Roseland Golf Course
South Woodstock, CT
(860) 928-4130
www.woodstockgc.com

**Club Pro:** Eric Sarette
**Payment:** Visa, MC, Amex, Disc, Cash
**Tee Times:** 7 days
**Fee  9 Holes: Weekday:** $12
**Fee 18 Holes: Weekday:** $18
**Twilight Rates:** No
**Cart Rental:** $14pp/18, $7pp/9
**Lessons:** Yes  **Schools:** Yes
**Membership:** Yes
**Other:** Clubhouse / Snack Bar / Lockers

**Weekend:** $14
**Weekend:** $20
**Discounts:** Sr. & Jr. wkdys only
**Driving Range:** Yes
**Junior Golf:** Yes
**Architect/Yr Open:** 1896

| Tees | Holes | Yards | Par | USGA | Slope |
|------|-------|-------|-----|------|-------|
| BACK | | | | | |
| MIDDLE | 9 | 2377 | 34 | 63.3 | 96 |
| FRONT | 9 | 2005 | 35 | 61.4 | 94 |

COUPON

Great value and improved conditions. Established 1896. Challenging, hilly course with small sloping greens. Target golf. Open April - November, weather permitting.

| | 1 | 2 | 3 | 4 | 5 | 6 | 7 | 8 | 9 |
|------|-----|-----|-----|-----|-----|-----|-----|-----|-----|
| PAR | 3 | 4 | 4 | 4 | 4 | 4 | 3 | 4 | 4 |
| YARDS | 170 | 265 | 305 | 304 | 289 | 275 | 231 | 385 | 227 |
| PAR | | | | | | | | | |
| YARDS | | | | | | | | | |

**Directions:** I-395 to Route 44 (Exit 97). West on Route 44. Take Route 171 in Putnam, continue West. Follow 4.5 miles to Roseland Park Road, take right. Course is ¾ mile on left.

NE
CT

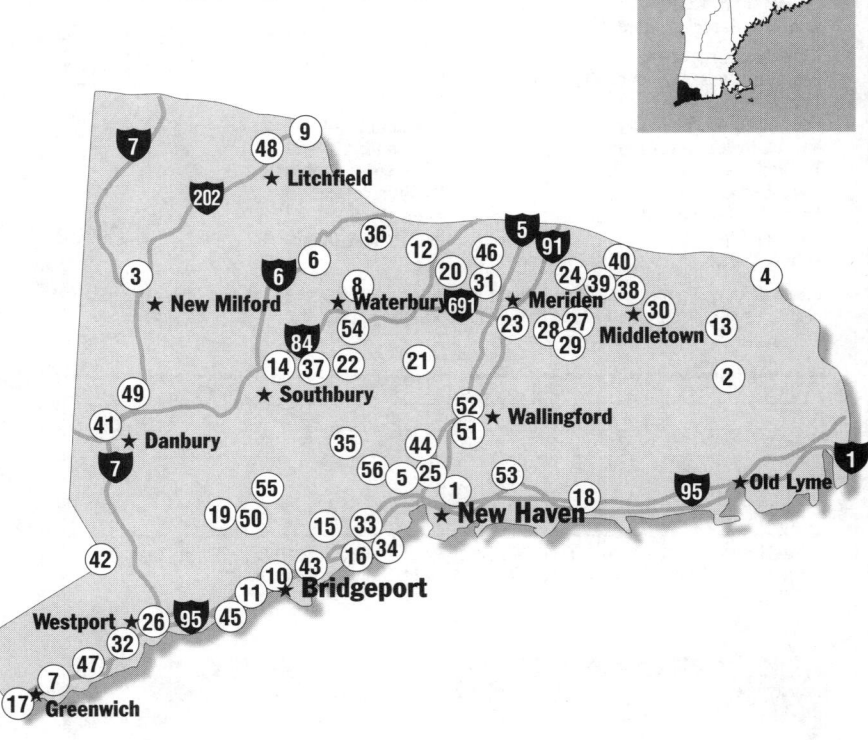

| Alling Memorial GC | 1 | Hawk's Landing CC | 20 | Portland West Golf Club | 39 |
| Black Birch Golf Club | 2 | Highland Greens GC | 21 | Quarry Ridge GC | 40 |
| Candlewood Valley CC | 3 | Hop Brook GC | 22 | Richter Park GC | 41 |
| Chanticlair Golf Course | 4 | Hunter Golf Club | 23 | Ridgefield Golf Course | 42 |
| Country Club of Woodbridge | 5 | Indian Springs GC | 24 | Short Beach Par 3 GC | 43 |
| Crestbrook Park GC | 6 | Laurel View CC | 25 | Sleeping Giant GC | 44 |
| E. Gaynor Brennan GC | 7 | Longshore GC | 26 | South Pine Creek Par 3 GC | 45 |
| East Mountain GC | 8 | Lyman Orchards GC (Apple) | 27 | Southington CC | 46 |
| Eastwood CC | 9 | Lyman Orchards GC (Jones) | 28 | Sterling Farms GC | 47 |
| Fairchild Wheeler GC (Black) | 10 | Lyman Orchards GC (Player) | 29 | Stonybrook GC | 48 |
| Fairchild Wheeler GC (Red) | 11 | Miner Hills GC | 30 | Sunset Hill GC | 49 |
| Farmingbury Hills CC | 12 | North Ridge Golf Club | 31 | Tashua Knolls CC | 50 |
| Fox Hopyard Golf Club | 13 | Oak Hills Park GC | 32 | Tradition GC at Oak Lane | 51 |
| Gainfield Farms GC | 14 | Orange Hills CC | 33 | Tradition GC at Wallingford | 52 |
| Grassy Hill Country Club | 15 | Orchards Golf Course, The | 34 | Twin Lakes GC | 53 |
| Great River Golf Club | 16 | Oxford Greens, The GC at | 35 | Western Hills GC | 54 |
| Griffith E. Harris GC | 17 | Pequabuck Golf Course | 36 | Whitney Farms | 55 |
| Guilford Lakes GC | 18 | Pomperaug Golf Club | 37 | Woodhaven CC | 56 |
| H. Smith Richardson GC | 19 | Portland Golf Club | 38 | | |

**KEY TO THE STAR RATINGS:**
5✪ = Outstanding  4✪ = Excellent  3✪ = Very Good  2✪ = Good  1✪ = Average  **NR** = Not Rated

# Alling Memorial Golf Course

NR 1

35 Eastern Street
New Haven, CT (203) 946-8014
www.allingmemorialgolfclub.com

| Tees | Holes | Yards | Par | USGA | Slope |
|------|-------|-------|-----|------|-------|
| BACK | 18 | 6283 | 72 | 71.9 | 129 |
| MIDDLE | 18 | 5911 | 72 | 69.3 | 127 |
| FRONT | 18 | 5107 | 72 | 71.0 | 129 |

**Club Pro:** Larry Thornhill, PGA
**Payment:** Cash, Visa, MC
**Tee Times:** Weekends, 3 days adv.
**Fee 9 Holes: Weekday:** $18    **Weekend:** $19
**Fee 18 Holes: Weekday:** $27    **Weekend:** $32
**Twilight Rates:** After 5:30pm    **Discounts:** Senior & Junior
**Cart Rental:** $14pp/18, $8pp/9    **Driving Range:** No
**Lessons:** Yes **Schools:** No    **Junior Golf:** Yes
**Membership:** Yes    **Architect/Yr Open:** McDonald/1929
**Other:** Lockers / Showers / Restaurant / Bar-Lounge

Appreciated by old, young, and new golfers alike. Excellent value for the money. Host to numerous CT state golf events. Resident rates.

| | 1 | 2 | 3 | 4 | 5 | 6 | 7 | 8 | 9 |
|---|---|---|---|---|---|---|---|---|---|
| PAR | 4 | 4 | 3 | 5 | 4 | 4 | 4 | 4 | 4 |
| YARDS | 380 | 313 | 168 | 474 | 231 | 344 | 366 | 274 | 305 |
| | 10 | 11 | 12 | 13 | 14 | 15 | 16 | 17 | 18 |
| PAR | 3 | 5 | 3 | 4 | 4 | 5 | 4 | 3 | 5 |
| YARDS | 158 | 475 | 180 | 337 | 408 | 493 | 331 | 203 | 471 |

**Directions:** I-91 to Exit 8, bear right to second light (Eastern Street), right ¾ mile. Course is on left.

# Black Birch Golf Club

●● 2

10 Banner Road
Moodus, CT (860) 873-9075
www.blackbirchgolf.com

| Tees | Holes | Yards | Par | USGA | Slope |
|------|-------|-------|-----|------|-------|
| BACK | | | | | |
| MIDDLE | 18 | 6158 | 72 | 67.8 | 123 |
| FRONT | 18 | 5776 | 74 | 70.8 | 121 |

**Club Pro:** Keith MacNeil, GM
**Payment:** Cash, Check, MC, Visa, Amex, Disc
**Tee Times:** Yes
**Fee 9 Holes: Weekday:** $16    **Weekend:** $16
**Fee 18 Holes: Weekday:** $28    **Weekend:** $28
**Twilight Rates:**    **Discounts:** Senior & Junior
**Cart Rental:** $17pp/18, $12pp/9    **Driving Range:** $5/bucket
**Lessons:** Yes **Schools:** No    **Junior Golf:** 15 and under
**Membership:** Yes    **Architect/Yr Open:** Frank Gamberdella
**Other:** Clubhouse / Snack Bar / Restaurant    **GPS:**

COUPON

Course renamed in 2006. New Superintendent hired in 2015. improved tees, fairways, and greens started in 2015. Call for weekend and weekday special rates.

| | 1 | 2 | 3 | 4 | 5 | 6 | 7 | 8 | 9 |
|---|---|---|---|---|---|---|---|---|---|
| PAR | 4 | 4 | 4 | 4 | 3 | 5 | 5 | 3 | 4 |
| YARDS | 332 | 321 | 410 | 319 | 117 | 480 | 482 | 151 | 382 |
| | 10 | 11 | 12 | 13 | 14 | 15 | 16 | 17 | 18 |
| PAR | 5 | 4 | 4 | 4 | 4 | 3 | 5 | 3 | 4 |
| YARDS | 480 | 351 | 377 | 369 | 420 | 172 | 498 | 153 | 344 |

**SW CT**

**Directions:** CT Route 9 to Exit 7; follow Route 82 East to Route 149 North. Continue to center of Moodus. Follow signs to course.

# Candlewood Valley Country Club ✪✪  ▶3

**401 Danbury Road**
**New Milford, CT (860) 354-9359**
www.candlewoodvalleygolf.com

| Tees | Holes | Yards | Par | USGA | Slope |
|------|-------|-------|-----|------|-------|
| BACK | 18 | 6441 | 71 | 72.1 | 127 |
| MIDDLE | 18 | 6033 | 71 | 70.7 | 122 |
| FRONT | 18 | 5080 | 71 | 72.5 | 123 |

**Club Pro:** Ed Slattery
**Payment:** Most Major
**Tee Times:** 14 days adv.
**Fee 9 Holes: Weekday:**   **Weekend:**
**Fee 18 Holes: Weekday:** $40   **Weekend:** $48
**Twilight Rates:** After 3pm   **Discounts:** Senior & Junior
**Cart Rental:** $30/18, $17/9 per cart   **Driving Range:** No
**Lessons:** Yes **Schools:** Yes   **Junior Golf:** Yes
**Membership:** Yes - Men's Club, Ladies' Club, Senior League
**Architect/Yr Open:** Cornish, Kay, & McNeil/1961
**Other:** Clubhouse / Lockers / Showers / Snack Bar / Restaurant / Bar-Lounge / Banquet Facilities

Take advantage of the Monday & Wednesday special - cart, 18 holes, lunch.

|  | 1 | 2 | 3 | 4 | 5 | 6 | 7 | 8 | 9 |
|------|-----|-----|-----|-----|-----|-----|-----|-----|-----|
| PAR | 5 | 4 | 3 | 3 | 4 | 5 | 4 | 4 | 4 |
| YARDS | 457 | 363 | 153 | 175 | 404 | 530 | 350 | 476 | 402 |
|  | **10** | **11** | **12** | **13** | **14** | **15** | **16** | **17** | **18** |
| PAR | 4 | 4 | 3 | 4 | 4 | 4 | 4 | 4 | 4 |
| YARDS | 310 | 317 | 210 | 413 | 390 | 418 | 371 | 386 | 316 |

**Directions:** I-84 to Exit 7. 1.1 miles keep left, 7.7 miles to CVCC on the right.


# Chanticlair Golf Course     NR ▶4

**288 Old Hebron Road**
**Colchester, CT (860) 537-3223**
www.chanticlair.com

| Tees | Holes | Yards | Par | USGA | Slope |
|------|-------|-------|-----|------|-------|
| BACK |  |  |  |  |  |
| MIDDLE | 9 | 3061 | 35 | 69.8 | 117 |
| FRONT | 9 | 2501 | 35 | 69.1 | 112 |

**Club Pro:** Carey Stollman, Manager
**Payment:** Cash, Visa, MC
**Tee Times:** 1 week adv.
**Fee 9 Holes: Weekday:** $17   **Weekend:** $18
**Fee 18 Holes: Weekday:** $26   **Weekend:** $27
**Twilight Rates:** No   **Discounts:** Senior & Junior
**Cart Rental:** $12pp/18, $6pp/9   **Driving Range:** No
**Lessons:** No **Schools:** No   **Junior Golf:** Yes
**Membership:** Yes   **Architect/Yr Open:** Hymie Stoloman/1973
**Other:** Clubhouse / Snacks / Beer / Soda   **GPS:**

The 4th hole has an elevated island green. Fairly flat; a good walking course.

|  | 1 | 2 | 3 | 4 | 5 | 6 | 7 | 8 | 9 |
|------|-----|-----|-----|-----|-----|-----|-----|-----|-----|
| PAR | 3 | 4 | 4 | 3 | 4 | 4 | 4 | 4 | 5 |
| YARDS | 205 | 390 | 375 | 138 | 387 | 385 | 350 | 380 | 451 |
| PAR |  |  |  |  |  |  |  |  |  |
| YARDS |  |  |  |  |  |  |  |  |  |

**Directions:** Route 2 to State Police Barracks exit; take left off ramp and go up hill. Make left onto Old Hebron Road at firehouse. Course is ¼ mile on right.

# Country Club of Woodbridge  NR  5 ▶

50 Woodfield Road
Woodbridge, CT  (203) 387-2278
www.countryclubofwoodbridge.com

**Club Pro:** Tommy Miller, PGA
**Payment:** Cash, Visa, MC
**Tee Times:** 1 week adv.

| Tees | Holes | Yards | Par | USGA | Slope |
|------|-------|-------|-----|------|-------|
| BACK | 18 | 6550 | 71 | 72.2 | 134 |
| MIDDLE | 18 | 6302 | 71 | 71.0 | 129 |
| FRONT | 18 | 5391 | 71 | 67.4 | 120 |

**Fee 9 Holes: Weekday:** $29    **Weekend:** $35
**Fee 18 Holes: Weekday:** $42    **Weekend:** $65
**Twilight Rates:** After 3pm    **Discounts:** Senior & Junior
**Cart Rental:** Included    **Driving Range:** Yes
**Lessons:** Yes  **Schools:** Yes    **Junior Golf:** Yes
**Membership:** Yes    **Architect/Yr Open:** Orrin Smith/1948
**Other:** Clubhouse / Snack Bar / Tennis Courts / Swimming Pool

Fun and inviting place to play. Competitive rates, great conditions.

|  | 1 | 2 | 3 | 4 | 5 | 6 | 7 | 8 | 9 |
|------|-----|-----|-----|-----|-----|-----|-----|-----|-----|
| PAR | 5 | 4 | 3 | 4 | 4 | 3 | 5 | 3 | 4 |
| YARDS | 475 | 304 | 208 | 402 | 430 | 182 | 503 | 132 | 383 |
|  | 10 | 11 | 12 | 13 | 14 | 15 | 16 | 17 | 18 |
| PAR | 4 | 5 | 4 | 3 | 4 | 5 | 4 | 3 | 4 |
| YARDS | 429 | 532 | 402 | 182 | 426 | 484 | 356 | 118 | 354 |

**Directions:** I-84 South to I-91 South to CT-15 South (Wilbur Cross Parkway). Take Exit 59 and continue on Whalley Avenue. Drive to CT-243 West in Woodbridge. Course on left.

# Crestbrook Park Golf Course  ✪✪½  6 ▶

834 Northfield Road
Watertown, CT (860) 945-5249
www.crestbrookpark.com

**Club Pro:** Kenneth Gemmell, PGA
**Payment:** Cash, Visa, MC
**Tee Times:** Weekends, 2 days adv.

| Tees | Holes | Yards | Par | USGA | Slope |
|------|-------|-------|-----|------|-------|
| BACK | 18 | 6915 | 71 | 73.6 | 128 |
| MIDDLE | 18 | 6098 | 71 | 69.9 | 121 |
| FRONT | 18 | 5696 | 75 | 73.8 | 128 |

**Fee 9 Holes: Weekday:** $21    **Weekend:** $23
**Fee 18 Holes: Weekday:** $37    **Weekend:** $40
**Twilight Rates:** No    **Discounts:** Senior & Junior M-F
**Cart Rental:** $29/18, $17/9 per cart    **Driving Range:** $6.50/lg, $5/md, $3.50/sm
**Lessons:** $35/half hour  **Schools:** No    **Junior Golf:** Yes
**Membership:** Yes    **Architect/Yr Open:** Geoffrey Cornish/1970
**Other:** Clubhouse / Snack Bar / Restaurant / Bar-Lounge / Pool / Tennis / Picnic

Player Comments: "Totally different 9s, front 9 tight, back 9 open and angled fairways." Cornish design. Resident rates.

|  | 1 | 2 | 3 | 4 | 5 | 6 | 7 | 8 | 9 |
|------|-----|-----|-----|-----|-----|-----|-----|-----|-----|
| PAR | 4 | 4 | 4 | 5 | 3 | 4 | 4 | 3 | 5 |
| YARDS | 370 | 447 | 411 | 515 | 152 | 384 | 405 | 194 | 536 |
|  | 10 | 11 | 12 | 13 | 14 | 15 | 16 | 17 | 18 |
| PAR | 4 | 4 | 3 | 4 | 4 | 5 | 3 | 4 | 4 |
| YARDS | 357 | 401 | 160 | 337 | 333 | 463 | 210 | 308 | 393 |

**Directions:** Route 8 to Echo Lake Road (turn left). Take right at 2nd light (Buckingham); another right at stop sign (Northfield). Course is ¼ mile on right on Northfield Road.

**SW CT**

# E. Gaynor Brennan Golf Course  ✪½  7 ▶

**451 Stillwater Road**
**Stamford, CT (203) 324-4185**
www.brennangolf.com
**Club Pro:** V. Levin, A. Aulenti, Dir. of Golf
**Payment:** Cash, Visa, MC
**Tee Times:** 7 days adv.
**Fee 9 Holes: Weekday:** $26
**Fee 18 Holes: Weekday:** $40
**Twilight Rates:** After 4pm
**Cart Rental:** $12.50pp/18, $8.50pp/9
**Lessons:** (203) 324-6507  **Schools:** No
**Membership:** Yes
**Other:** Snack Bar / Restaurant / Bar-Lounge / Showers

| Tees | Holes | Yards | Par | USGA | Slope |
|------|-------|-------|-----|------|-------|
| BACK | 18 | 5931 | 71 | 69.5 | 121 |
| MIDDLE | 18 | 5814 | 71 | 68.0 | 118 |
| FRONT | 18 | 5180 | 73 | 72.3 | 124 |

**Weekend:**
**Weekend:** $45
**Discounts:** Sr. & Jr., residents only
**Driving Range:** No
**Junior Golf:** Yes
**Architect/Yr:** McCarthy, Gerrish/1925, Mungeum/1998

The greens are usually in excellent condition. Course is a bit hilly. Open year round. Resident discounts and resident weekend lottery.

| | 1 | 2 | 3 | 4 | 5 | 6 | 7 | 8 | 9 |
|------|----|----|----|----|----|----|----|----|----|
| PAR | 4 | 4 | 3 | 5 | 4 | 5 | 4 | 4 | 3 |
| YARDS | 364 | 385 | 147 | 418 | 366 | 486 | 373 | 367 | 105 |
| | 10 | 11 | 12 | 13 | 14 | 15 | 16 | 17 | 18 |
| PAR | 4 | 4 | 4 | 3 | 4 | 3 | 4 | 5 | 4 |
| YARDS | 301 | 323 | 341 | 225 | 385 | 177 | 278 | 454 | 319 |

**Directions:** I-95 to Exit 7 (Atlantic Street). Go straight. Right onto Washington Boulevard, left onto Broad Street. Go to Stillwater Road. Course is on right.

# East Mountain Golf Course  NR  8 ▶

**171 East Mountain Road**
**Waterbury, CT (203) 753-1425**
www.golfwaterbury.com
**Club Pro:** Dave Giacondino
**Payment:** Cash, Visa, MC, Amex, Disc
**Tee Times:** Weekends, 3 days adv.
**Fee 9 Holes: Weekday:** $20
**Fee 18 Holes: Weekday:** $31
**Twilight Rates:** After 5:30pm
**Cart Rental:** $30/18, $21/9 per cart
**Lessons:** Yes  **Schools:** No
**Membership:** Yes, Yearly Season Pass
**Other:** Restaurant

| Tees | Holes | Yards | Par | USGA | Slope |
|------|-------|-------|-----|------|-------|
| BACK | 18 | 6012 | 70 | 68.6 | 118 |
| MIDDLE | 18 | 5801 | 70 | 67.5 | 116 |
| FRONT | 18 | 5366 | 70 | 71.7 | 121 |

**Weekend:** $20
**Weekend:** $31
**Discounts:** Senior & Junior
**Driving Range:** Yes
**Junior Golf:** Yes
**Architect/Yr Open:** Wayne Stiles/1932
**GPS:**

COUPON

Redesigned in 2007 with new drainage. Great classic layout with very well conditioned greens.

| | 1 | 2 | 3 | 4 | 5 | 6 | 7 | 8 | 9 |
|------|----|----|----|----|----|----|----|----|----|
| PAR | 4 | 4 | 5 | 4 | 3 | 4 | 4 | 3 | 5 |
| YARDS | 360 | 273 | 473 | 365 | 181 | 368 | 385 | 200 | 483 |
| | 10 | 11 | 12 | 13 | 14 | 15 | 16 | 17 | 18 |
| PAR | 4 | 4 | 4 | 3 | 4 | 5 | 3 | 3 | 4 |
| YARDS | 396 | 399 | 412 | 191 | 305 | 512 | 214 | 142 | 368 |

**Directions:** I-84 to Hamilton Avenue (Exit 23). Follow Route 69 West (1.5 miles). Right onto East Mountain at church.

# Eastwood Country Club

NR | 9

1301 Torringford West Street
Torrington, CT (860) 489-2630
www.eastwoodcountryclub.net

**Club Pro:** Greg Miller, PGA
**Payment:** Visa, MC, Amex
**Tee Times:** None

| Tees | Holes | Yards | Par | USGA | Slope |
|------|-------|-------|-----|------|-------|
| BACK | 9 | 2933 | 36 | 67.8 | 113 |
| MIDDLE | 9 | 2791 | 36 | 66.5 | 111 |
| FRONT | 9 | 2359 | 36 | | |

**Fee 9 Holes: Weekday:** $18
**Fee 18 Holes: Weekday:** $28
**Twilight Rates:** No
**Cart Rental:** $14pp/18, $8pp/9
**Lessons:** Yes  **Schools:** No
**Membership:** Yes
**Other:** Restaurant / Clubhouse / Bar-Lounge

**Weekend:** $20
**Weekend:** $30
**Discounts:** Srs & Jrs, weekdays
**Driving Range:** No
**Junior Golf:** Yes
**Architect/Yr Open:** 1963
**GPS:**

Open April - January. Greens in the best shape ever. Bunker renovation and new golf cart fleet. Course is in great shape and is much fun to play. "Course is in great condition and much improved." –SR

| | 1 | 2 | 3 | 4 | 5 | 6 | 7 | 8 | 9 |
|------|-----|-----|-----|-----|-----|-----|-----|-----|-----|
| PAR | 4 | 4 | 4 | 5 | 4 | 3 | 4 | 3 | 5 |
| YARDS | 363 | 309 | 348 | 411 | 275 | 131 | 286 | 137 | 531 |
| PAR | | | | | | | | | |
| YARDS | | | | | | | | | |

**Directions:** Route 8 to Exit 45. Go right off exit to Kennedy Drive. After 1 mile up hill to 4-way intersection. Left onto Torringford Street. Course is 1 mile on left.

# Fairchild Wheeler GC (Black)

✪✪ | 10

2390 Eastern Turnpike
Fairfield, CT (203) 373-5911
www.fairchildwheelergolf.com

**Club Pro:** Stephen Roach
**Payment:** Visa, MC, Amex, Disc
**Tee Times:** 7 days adv.

| Tees | Holes | Yards | Par | USGA | Slope |
|------|-------|-------|-----|------|-------|
| BACK | 18 | 6559 | 71 | 72 | 128 |
| MIDDLE | 18 | 6322 | 71 | 71.0 | 119 |
| FRONT | 18 | 5234 | 72 | 70.0 | 119 |

**Fee 9 Holes: Weekday:** $20, $31 w/cart
**Fee 18 Holes: Weekday:** $29, $44 w/cart
**Twilight Rates:** After 5:30pm
**Cart Rental:** $15pp/18, $12pp/9
**Lessons:** Yes, inquire  **Schools:** No
**Membership:** Yes
**Other:** Clubhouse / Snack Bar / Restaurant / Bar-Lounge / Lockers / Showers

**Weekend:** $28, $39 w/cart
**Weekend:** $41, $56 w/cart
**Discounts:** Residents
**Driving Range:** Yes
**Junior Golf:** Yes
**Architect/Yr Open:** Robert White/1932

Player Comments: "Solid course at relative bargain fees." "Remarkable improvements."
Challenging course with some of the toughest par-4s around. Residents discount. Open year round.

| | 1 | 2 | 3 | 4 | 5 | 6 | 7 | 8 | 9 |
|------|-----|-----|-----|-----|-----|-----|-----|-----|-----|
| PAR | 4 | 4 | 3 | 4 | 4 | 4 | 3 | 5 | 5 |
| YARDS | 405 | 377 | 128 | 367 | 321 | 432 | 212 | 431 | 500 |
| | 10 | 11 | 12 | 13 | 14 | 15 | 16 | 17 | 18 |
| PAR | 4 | 3 | 4 | 4 | 4 | 4 | 5 | 3 | 4 |
| YARDS | 417 | 153 | 407 | 421 | 314 | 418 | 512 | 191 | 396 |

**Directions:** Take Merritt Parkway (Route 15) Exit 46 to Route 59 South (Easton Turnpike). ½ mile on left.

**SW
CT**

# Fairchild Wheeler GC (Red)   ✪✪½    11

2390 Eastern Turnpike
Fairfield, CT (203) 373-5911
www.fairchildwheelergolf.com

| Tees | Holes | Yards | Par | USGA | Slope |
|------|-------|-------|-----|------|-------|
| BACK | 18 | 6568 | 72 | 72 | 125 |
| MIDDLE | 18 | 6126 | 72 | 71.3 | 124 |
| FRONT | 18 | 5330 | 72 | 68.7 | 117 |

**Club Pro:** Stephen Roach
**Payment:** Visa, MC, Amex, Disc
**Tee Times:** 7 days adv.
**Fee  9 Holes: Weekday:** $20, $31 w/cart     **Weekend:** $28, $39 w/cart
**Fee 18 Holes: Weekday:** $29, $44 w/cart     **Weekend:** $41, $56 w/cart
**Twilight Rates:** After 5:30pm     **Discounts:** Residents
**Cart Rental:** $15pp/18, $12pp/9     **Driving Range:** Yes
**Lessons:** Yes, inquire  **Schools:** No     **Junior Golf:** Yes
**Membership:** Yes     **Architect/Yr Open:** Robert White/1932
**Other:** Clubhouse / Snack Bar / Restaurant / Bar-Lounge / Lockers / Showers

Flat open course, good for beginners and seniors. Reduced rates for residents and other CT public course passholders. Open all year. Links-style course. Lessons available from First Tee Corp.

| | 1 | 2 | 3 | 4 | 5 | 6 | 7 | 8 | 9 |
|------|---|---|---|---|---|---|---|---|---|
| PAR | 4 | 4 | 5 | 3 | 4 | 4 | 4 | 3 | 4 |
| YARDS | 440 | 402 | 480 | 127 | 308 | 412 | 337 | 190 | 387 |
| | 10 | 11 | 12 | 13 | 14 | 15 | 16 | 17 | 18 |
| PAR | 5 | 4 | 3 | 4 | 4 | 3 | 4 | 5 | 5 |
| YARDS | 504 | 419 | 105 | 422 | 334 | 202 | 340 | 501 | 472 |

**Directions:** Take Merritt Parkway (Route 15) Exit 46 to Route 59 South (Easton Turnpike). ¼ mile on left.

# Farmingbury Hills Country Club   NR   12

141 East Street
Wolcott, CT (203) 879-8038
www.farmingburyhillsgolf.com

| Tees | Holes | Yards | Par | USGA | Slope |
|------|-------|-------|-----|------|-------|
| BACK | | | | | |
| MIDDLE | 9 | 2996 | 35 | 68.7 | 117 |
| FRONT | 9 | 2678 | 36 | 71.0 | 120 |

**Club Pro:** Craig Kealey, PGA
**Payment:** Cash, Visa, MC
**Tee Times:** Weekends, 7 days adv.
**Fee 9 Holes: Wkd:** $12.50/res, $14.50/non-res  **Weekend:** $21
**Fee 18 Holes: Wkd:** $20/res, $24/non-res  **Weekend:** $30
**Twilight Rates:**     **Discounts:** Senior & Junior
**Cart Rental:** $16pp/18, $9.50pp/9     **Driving Range:** No
**Lessons:** Yes  **Schools:** No     **Junior Golf:** Yes
**Membership:** No     **Architect/Yr Open:**
**Other:** Bar-Lounge / Restaurant     **GPS:**

COUPON

9-hole special: 7am–2pm weekdays; 1–5:30pm weekends. Course is in great shape!

| | 1 | 2 | 3 | 4 | 5 | 6 | 7 | 8 | 9 |
|------|---|---|---|---|---|---|---|---|---|
| PAR | 4 | 4 | 4 | 4 | 4 | 3 | 4 | 3 | 5 |
| YARDS | 340 | 419 | 310 | 373 | 321 | 102 | 401 | 190 | 510 |
| PAR | | | | | | | | | |
| YARDS | | | | | | | | | |

**Directions:** I-84 to Cheshire Exit 28. Route 322 West, left up Southington Mountain. Right at top of hill, blinking light (East Street). Course is 1 mile on right.

# Fox Hopyard Golf Club ✪✪✪✪½  13 ▶

**1 Hopyard Road**
**East Haddam, CT (860) 434-6644**
www.golfthefox.com

**Club Pro:** Ron Beck, PGA
**Payment:** Visa, MC, Amex, Disc, Checks, Cash
**Tee Times:** 6 days adv.
**Fee 9 Holes: Weekday:** $49
**Fee 18 Holes: Weekday:** $94
**Twilight Rates:** Yes
**Cart Rental:** $21pp/18, $12pp/9
**Lessons:** $50/half hour **Schools:** Yes
**Membership:** Yes

| Tees | Holes | Yards | Par | USGA | Slope |
|---|---|---|---|---|---|
| BACK | 18 | 6512 | 71 | 72.6 | 131 |
| MIDDLE | 18 | 6109 | 71 | 70.7 | 124 |
| FRONT | 18 | 5111 | 71 | 70.7 | 123 |

**Weekend:** $54
**Weekend/Holidays:** $104
**Discounts:** Junior
**Driving Range:** Yes
**Junior Golf:** Yes
**Architect/Yr Open:** Roger Rulewich, 2001

COUPON

**Other:** Restaurant / Bar-Lounge / Clubhouse / Showers / Lockers

Player Comments: " Great layout in unspoiled surroundings. Many memorable holes." "Sister course to Crumpin-Fox in MA. Wide fairways. Shots to the greens are high on risk and reward." –RW

|  | 1 | 2 | 3 | 4 | 5 | 6 | 7 | 8 | 9 |
|---|---|---|---|---|---|---|---|---|---|
| PAR | 4 | 4 | 5 | 3 | 5 | 4 | 4 | 3 | 4 |
| YARDS | 356 | 358 | 457 | 172 | 464 | 320 | 366 | 160 | 350 |
|  | 10 | 11 | 12 | 13 | 14 | 15 | 16 | 17 | 18 |
| PAR | 4 | 3 | 4 | 4 | 3 | 5 | 3 | 4 | 5 |
| YARDS | 382 | 153 | 372 | 408 | 188 | 508 | 189 | 399 | 507 |

**Directions:** From I-95 North, take Exit 70 (Old Lyme). Go left onto Route 156 for 9 miles. Right onto Route 82 and take first left onto Hopyard. Accessible from I-91 to Route 2 to Route 11. Call for directions from I-95 South and Route 9.

# Gainfield Farms Golf Course NR 14 ▶

**255 Old Field Road**
**Southbury, CT (203) 262-1100**
www.gainfieldfarmsgolf.com

**Club Pro:** Maurice Vossello, USGTF
**Payment:** Cash, Check, Credit
**Tee Times:** Yes
**Fee 9 Holes: Weekday:** $17
**Fee 18 Holes: Weekday:** $27
**Twilight Rates:** No
**Cart Rental:** $20pp/18, $10pp/9
**Lessons:** Yes **Schools:** No
**Membership:**
**Other:** Snacks

| Tees | Holes | Yards | Par | USGA | Slope |
|---|---|---|---|---|---|
| BACK |  |  |  |  |  |
| MIDDLE | 9 | 1384 | 28 |  |  |
| FRONT | 9 | 1203 | 27 |  |  |

**Weekend:** $18
**Weekend:** $29
**Discounts:** Senior, Junior, Ladies
**Driving Range:** Mat and net
**Junior Golf:** Yes
**Architect/Yr Open:** Al Zikorus/1993
**GPS:**

COUPON

Executive style, resident discounts. Short course. Less than 2 hours to play.

|  | 1 | 2 | 3 | 4 | 5 | 6 | 7 | 8 | 9 |
|---|---|---|---|---|---|---|---|---|---|
| PAR | 3 | 4 | 3 | 3 | 3 | 3 | 3 | 3 | 3 |
| YARDS | 155 | 261 | 188 | 123 | 113 | 94 | 195 | 127 | 128 |
| PAR |  |  |  |  |  |  |  |  |  |
| YARDS |  |  |  |  |  |  |  |  |  |

**Directions:** I-84 to Exit 15, to Main Street (Route 30). Right on Poverty Road. Left on Old Field Road to course.

**SW CT**

# Grassy Hill Country Club

**441 Clark Lane**
**Orange, CT  (203)795-1422**
www.grassyhillgolf.com

| Tees | Holes | Yards | Par | USGA | Slope |
|------|-------|-------|-----|------|-------|
| BACK | 18 | 6118 | 70 | 70.5 | 122 |
| MIDDLE | 18 | 5849 | 70 | 69.4 | 119 |
| FRONT | 18 | 5209 | 71 | 71.1 | 118 |

**Club Pro:** Brian Fitzgibbons, PGA
**Payment:** Visa, MC
**Tee Times:** 7 days/wkdys, 3 days/wknds
**Fee  9 Holes: Weekday:** $21        **Weekend:** $25
**Fee 18 Holes: Weekday:** $36        **Weekend:** $45
**Twilight Rates:** No        **Discounts:** Senior (M-F)
**Cart Rental:**        **Driving Range:** $5/lg
**Lessons:** $65/45 min.  **Schools:**        **Junior Golf:** Yes
**Membership:** Men/Women Association        **Architect/Yr Open:** 1927
**Other:** Full Restaurant / Clubhouse / Bar-Lounge / Lockers / Showers

Working to restore excellent conditions of fairways and greens.

| | 1 | 2 | 3 | 4 | 5 | 6 | 7 | 8 | 9 |
|---|---|---|---|---|---|---|---|---|---|
| PAR | 4 | 4 | 3 | 4 | 5 | 3 | 4 | 4 | 5 |
| YARDS | 385 | 410 | 158 | 301 | 563 | 145 | 363 | 360 | 432 |
| | 10 | 11 | 12 | 13 | 14 | 15 | 16 | 17 | 18 |
| PAR | 3 | 4 | 4 | 3 | 4 | 4 | 5 | 3 | 4 |
| YARDS | 169 | 384 | 277 | 175 | 319 | 421 | 496 | 165 | 326 |

**Directions:** I-95 to exit 39A. Turn right, pass Howard Johnson's. At second dual traffic light, turn right. 2½ miles to Clark Lane. Turn right to Grassy Hill.

# Great River Golf Club

**130 Coram Lane**
**Milford, CT (203) 876-8051**
www.greatrivergolfclub.com

| Tees | Holes | Yards | Par | USGA | Slope |
|------|-------|-------|-----|------|-------|
| BACK | 18 | 6901 | 72 | 73.8 | 149 |
| MIDDLE | 18 | 6475 | 72 | 71.6 | 137 |
| FRONT | 18 | 5865 | 72 | 69.4 | 124 |

**Club Pro:** Tom Rosati, PGA
**Payment:** Visa, MC, Disc, Amex
**Tee Times:** 5 days adv.
**Fee  9 Holes: Weekday:** $50 after 5pm only   **Weekend:** $50 after 5pm only
**Fee 18 Holes: Weekday:** $120 M-Th        **Weekend:** $140 F/S/S
**Twilight Rates:** Yes        **Discounts:** None
**Cart Rental:** Included        **Driving Range:** Yes
**Lessons:** Yes  **Schools:** Yes        **Junior Golf:** Yes
**Membership:** Yes        **Architect/Yr Open:** Tommy Fazio/2000
**Other:** Restaurant / Outdoor Dining / Beverage Cart / Snack Bar/ Clubhouse / Lockers / Showers / Bar-Lounge / Indoor Learning Center / Conference Room, Banquet Facility 150+

Player Comments: "Excellent player's course." "2 times on vacations, everything was perfect." "Best public course I've played in CT." Semi-private. Golf Academy open all year. White tees.

| | 1 | 2 | 3 | 4 | 5 | 6 | 7 | 8 | 9 |
|---|---|---|---|---|---|---|---|---|---|
| PAR | 3 | 4 | 4 | 5 | 4 | 3 | 4 | 5 | 4 |
| YARDS | 144 | 363 | 374 | 452 | 362 | 129 | 378 | 508 | 344 |
| | 10 | 11 | 12 | 13 | 14 | 15 | 16 | 17 | 18 |
| PAR | 4 | 3 | 5 | 4 | 4 | 5 | 4 | 3 | 4 |
| YARDS | 329 | 175 | 490 | 372 | 350 | 473 | 382 | 170 | 353 |

**Directions:** I-95 to Exit 38 bearing right, go to Wheeler Farms Road, turn left. Turn left at Herbert Street. Turn left on Coram Lane, course is at end of lane. Call for directions from Hartford or NY via Wilbur Cross/Merritt Parkway and from 95 North.

# Griffith E. Harris Golf Course  ✪✪  ▶17

**1300 King Street**
**Greenwich, CT (203) 531-7261**
www.greenwichct.org

| Tees | Holes | Yards | Par | USGA | Slope |
|------|-------|-------|-----|------|-------|
| BACK | 18 | 6512 | 71 | 71.0 | 125 |
| MIDDLE | 18 | 6093 | 71 | 69.0 | 122 |
| FRONT | 18 | 5671 | 73 | 67.1 | 114 |

**Club Pro:** Joe Felder, PGA
**Payment:** Visa, MC, Checks
**Tee Times:** Same day for non-members
**Fee 9 Holes: Weekday:** $50 **Weekend:** $50
**Fee 18 Holes: Weekday:** $50 **Weekend:** $50
**Twilight Rates:** After 5pm **Discounts:** Senior & Junior
**Cart Rental:** $14pp/18, $9.50pp/9 **Driving Range:** $10/lg., $5/sm.
**Lessons:** Yes **Schools:** Yes **Junior Golf:** Yes
**Membership:** Town residents **Architect/Yr Open:** Robert Trent Jones/1965
**Other:** Full Restaurant / Clubhouse / Bar / Lockers / Showers

Restaurant renovated. Open to residents of town who are members and guests only. Front side fairly open and flat. Back side narrow and hilly. Open April 1 - December 1. Resident fee offered. New irrigation system.

| | 1 | 2 | 3 | 4 | 5 | 6 | 7 | 8 | 9 |
|------|---|---|---|---|---|---|---|---|---|
| PAR | 4 | 4 | 5 | 4 | 3 | 4 | 3 | 5 | 4 |
| YARDS | 407 | 365 | 503 | 378 | 169 | 437 | 138 | 519 | 323 |
| | 10 | 11 | 12 | 13 | 14 | 15 | 16 | 17 | 18 |
| PAR | 4 | 3 | 4 | 4 | 5 | 3 | 4 | 4 | 4 |
| YARDS | 291 | 198 | 310 | 380 | 448 | 140 | 251 | 426 | 310 |

**Directions:** Merritt Parkway South to King Street. Right turn approximately 3 miles to golf course on right. Any questions, call (203) 531-7200.

# Guilford Lakes Golf Course  ✪✪½  ▶18

**200 North Madison Road**
**Guilford, CT (203) 453-8214**
www.guilfordlakesgc.com

| Tees | Holes | Yards | Par | USGA | Slope |
|------|-------|-------|-----|------|-------|
| BACK | 9 | 1370 | 28 | | |
| MIDDLE | 9 | 1165 | 27 | | |
| FRONT | 9 | 739 | 27 | | |

**Club Pro:**
**Payment:** Visa, MC, Disc
**Tee Times:** 3 days adv.
**Fee 9 Holes: Weekday:** $14 **Weekend:** $16
**Fee 18 Holes: Weekday:** $28 **Weekend:** $32
**Twilight Rates:** No **Discounts:** Senior & Junior
**Cart Rental:** $3/pull **Driving Range:** No
**Lessons:** Yes **Schools:** No **Junior Golf:** Park and Rec.
**Membership:** Yes **Architect/Yr Open:** Al Zikorus/1999
**Other:** Snacks / New Clubhouse Now Open **GPS: Yes**

COUPON

Reduced resident fees. Heavily tree-lined, gentle and hilly. 5 new tees in 2015-2016. Challenging for both beginner and intermediate. New Par 4. Player Comments: "Polished and professionally designed." –RW

| | 1 | 2 | 3 | 4 | 5 | 6 | 7 | 8 | 9 |
|------|---|---|---|---|---|---|---|---|---|
| PAR | 3 | 3 | 3 | 3 | 3 | 4 | 3 | 3 | 3 |
| YARDS | 135 | 111 | 130 | 122 | 105 | 260 | 155 | 79 | 148 |
| PAR | | | | | | | | | |
| YARDS | | | | | | | | | |

**Directions:** I-95, Exit 58 onto Route 77. North on Route 77, turn right onto Stepstone Hill Road. Straight to North Madison Road. Course is on the left.

**SW CT**

# H. Smith Richardson GC ✪✪✪

**19**

2425 Morehouse Highway
Fairfield, CT (203) 255-7300
www.hsrgolf.com

**Club Pro:** Jim Alexander, PGA
**Payment:** Most Major Credit Cards
**Tee Times:** Weekends, 7 days adv.
**Fee 9 Holes: Weekday:** $28
**Fee 18 Holes: Weekday:** $42
**Twilight Rates:** No
**Cart Rental:** $15pp/18, $11pp/9
**Lessons:** Yes **Schools:** No
**Membership:** Yes
**Other:** Lockers / Showers / Restaurant / Bar-Lounge / Clubhouse

| Tees | Holes | Yards | Par | USGA | Slope |
|------|-------|-------|-----|------|-------|
| BACK | 18 | 6676 | 72 | 71.0 | 127 |
| MIDDLE | 18 | 6323 | 72 | 70.2 | 124 |
| FRONT | 18 | 5764 | 73 | 73.9 | 127 |

**Weekend:** $28
**Weekend:** $54
**Discounts:** Senior & Junior
**Driving Range:** Yes
**Junior Golf:** Yes
**Architect/Yr Open:** Hal Purdy/1972

This scenic, hilly course has a majestic view of Long Island Sound. Slopes on greens make putting challenging. Closed March. Discounted rates for shared carts.

|  | 1 | 2 | 3 | 4 | 5 | 6 | 7 | 8 | 9 |
|------|-----|-----|-----|-----|-----|-----|-----|-----|-----|
| PAR | 4 | 4 | 3 | 4 | 4 | 5 | 4 | 3 | 5 |
| YARDS | 375 | 310 | 160 | 339 | 397 | 503 | 383 | 180 | 486 |
|  | 10 | 11 | 12 | 13 | 14 | 15 | 16 | 17 | 18 |
| PAR | 4 | 4 | 3 | 5 | 4 | 4 | 3 | 4 | 5 |
| YARDS | 373 | 351 | 176 | 502 | 405 | 350 | 140 | 373 | 520 |

**Directions:** From North: Merritt Parkway to Exit 44 to Black Rock Turnpike, take right on Congress Road, second left onto Morehouse. Course is ½ mile up the road.
From South: Merritt Parkway to Exit 46, take left onto Congress Road, right on Morehouse Road.

# Hawk's Landing Country Club ✪✪

**20**

201 Pattonwood Drive
Southington, CT (860) 793-6000
www.hawkslandingcc.com

**Club Pro:** John Vitale
**Payment:** Visa, MC, Disc, Check
**Tee Times:** Weekends, 7 days adv.
**Fee 9 Holes: Weekday:** $19.50
**Fee 18 Holes: Weekday:** $33.50
**Twilight Rates:** After 6pm
**Cart Rental:** $15.50pp/18, $8.75pp/9
**Lessons:** Yes **Schools:** No
**Membership:** Yes
**Other:** Clubhouse / Bar-Lounge / Restaurant / Snack Bar

| Tees | Holes | Yards | Par | USGA | Slope |
|------|-------|-------|-----|------|-------|
| BACK | 18 | 6000 | 70 | 68.6 | 124 |
| MIDDLE | 18 | 5355 | 70 | 66.4 | 119 |
| FRONT | 18 | 4015 | 71 | 63.9 | 106 |

**Weekend:** $23
**Weekend:** $37.50
**Discounts:** Senior & Junior
**Driving Range:** Yes, grass tee
**Junior Golf:** Yes
**Architect/Yr Open:** Cornish/1967

COUPON

A full-service restaurant, a chipping and putting practice area, and a pavillion area perfect for meetings and weddings. Climate-controlled banquet facility for up to 250 people.

|  | 1 | 2 | 3 | 4 | 5 | 6 | 7 | 8 | 9 |
|------|-----|-----|-----|-----|-----|-----|-----|-----|-----|
| PAR | 4 | 3 | 5 | 4 | 4 | 4 | 3 | 4 | 3 |
| YARDS | 265 | 170 | 420 | 290 | 340 | 280 | 220 | 325 | 175 |
|  | 10 | 11 | 12 | 13 | 14 | 15 | 16 | 17 | 18 |
| PAR | 4 | 4 | 3 | 5 | 4 | 5 | 3 | 5 | 3 |
| YARDS | 385 | 275 | 150 | 450 | 385 | 450 | 160 | 450 | 165 |

**Directions:** I-84 to Exit 32. South to Route 10. Left on Laning Street to top of hill; take left to stay on Laning Street. Left on Flanders Road to first left on Pattonwood Drive.

# Highland Greens Golf Course NR 21

122 Cooke Road
Prospect, CT (203) 758-4022
www.highlandgreens.com

**Club Pro:** George Sabo III, GM
**Payment:** Cash, Visa, MC
**Tee Times:** Same day
**Fee 9 Holes: Weekday:** $13
**Fee 18 Holes: Weekday:** $21
**Twilight Rates:** After 6:30pm
**Cart Rental:** $3/pull
**Lessons:** Yes **Schools:** No
**Membership:** Yes
**Other:** Snack Bar / Restaurant / Pub

| Tees | Holes | Yards | Par | USGA | Slope |
|------|-------|-------|-----|------|-------|
| BACK | | | | | |
| MIDDLE | 9 | 1398 | 27 | | |
| FRONT | 9 | 1322 | 27 | | |

**Weekend:** $14
**Weekend:** $22
**Discounts:** Senior
**Driving Range:** No
**Junior Golf:** Yes
**Architect/Yr Open:** Al Zikorus/1967
**GPS:**

Completely lighted for night play. $15 for 9 holes nightly rate after 6:30pm. Slightly hilly. A lot of improvements made to the grounds. A challenging par 3, open April - first frost.

| | 1 | 2 | 3 | 4 | 5 | 6 | 7 | 8 | 9 |
|-----|---|---|---|---|---|---|---|---|---|
| PAR | 3 | 3 | 3 | 3 | 3 | 3 | 3 | 3 | 3 |
| YARDS | 132 | 192 | 115 | 135 | 188 | 185 | 157 | 128 | 166 |
| PAR | | | | | | | | | |
| YARDS | | | | | | | | | |

**Directions:** Take I-84 to Exit 26 to Route 70 East to Route 68 West. At top of hill, left onto Cooke Road. Course is 1.6 miles on right.

# Hop Brook Golf Course NR 22

615 North Church Street
Naugatuck, CT (203) 729-8013

**Club Pro:** Bob Clark Jr., PGA
**Payment:** Cash, Check, Credit Card
**Tee Times:** Weekends, 2 days adv.
**Fee 9 Holes: Weekday:** $20
**Fee 18 Holes: Weekday:** $27
**Twilight Rates:** No
**Cart Rental:** $15pp/18, $10pp/9
**Lessons:** Yes **Schools:** No
**Membership:** Yes
**Other:** Clubhouse / Restaurant

| Tees | Holes | Yards | Par | USGA | Slope |
|------|-------|-------|-----|------|-------|
| BACK | 9 | 3047 | 36 | 68.2 | 116 |
| MIDDLE | 9 | 2862 | 36 | 66.6 | 112 |
| FRONT | 9 | 2413 | 36 | 67.0 | 114 |

**Weekend:** $24
**Weekend:** $32
**Discounts:** Sr. & Jr. Daily Specials
**Driving Range:** No
**Junior Golf:** Yes
**Architect/Yr Open:** 1927
**GPS:**

COUPON

The course is short and turns hilly near the end. Substantial discounts for residents. Open March - December. Senior tees now on every hole. Women's senior tees on 4 holes (Blue and White). PGA Professional now on staff.

| | 1 | 2 | 3 | 4 | 5 | 6 | 7 | 8 | 9 |
|-----|---|---|---|---|---|---|---|---|---|
| PAR | 5 | 4 | 4 | 4 | 3 | 5 | 3 | 4 | 4 |
| YARDS | 452 | 325 | 320 | 304 | 135 | 476 | 170 | 382 | 298 |
| PAR | | | | | | | | | |
| YARDS | | | | | | | | | |

**Directions:** I-84 to Exit 17 to Route 63 South. Course is 3 miles down on left, across from Xpress Fuel.

**SW CT**

# Hunter Golf Club

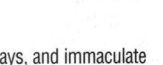 ✪✪✪ **23** ▶

685 Westfield Road
Meriden, CT (203) 634-3366
www.huntergolfshop.com

**Club Pro:** Bob Tiedermann
**Payment:** Cash, Credit
**Tee Times:** Yes
**Fee 9 Holes: Weekday:** $20
**Fee 18 Holes: Weekday:** $35
**Twilight Rates:** 90 minutes before dusk
**Cart Rental:** $15pp/18, $9pp/9
**Lessons:** Yes **Schools:** No
**Membership:** Season Pass
**Other:** Clubhouse / Lockers / Showers / Snack Bar / Restaurant / Bar-Lounge

| Tees | Holes | Yards | Par | USGA | Slope |
|---|---|---|---|---|---|
| BACK | 18 | 6604 | 71 | 71.9 | 124 |
| MIDDLE | 18 | 6198 | 71 | 70.2 | 121 |
| FRONT | 18 | 5569 | 72 | 72.7 | 131 |

**Weekend:** $21
**Weekend:** $39 ($32 resident)
**Discounts:** Sr. & Jr. weekdays
**Driving Range:** Irons only
**Junior Golf:** Yes
**Architect/Yr Open:** Robert Pryde

Open year round, weather permitting. Resident rates. "Greens and bunkers in great shape. If you haven't been here in awhile, it's worth a revisit." –DA

|  | 1 | 2 | 3 | 4 | 5 | 6 | 7 | 8 | 9 |
|---|---|---|---|---|---|---|---|---|---|
| PAR | 4 | 3 | 4 | 4 | 5 | 3 | 4 | 4 | 4 |
| YARDS | 352 | 183 | 395 | 326 | 497 | 147 | 415 | 400 | 353 |
|  | 10 | 11 | 12 | 13 | 14 | 15 | 16 | 17 | 18 |
| PAR | 5 | 3 | 4 | 4 | 4 | 4 | 4 | 3 | 5 |
| YARDS | 516 | 163 | 357 | 336 | 364 | 374 | 361 | 172 | 487 |

**Directions:** From I-91 South: Exit 19. Right off ramp to first stop sign. Right on Bee Street, course is ½ mile on left. From I-91 North or Merritt Parkway North: Take East Main Street exit. Go straight through light onto Bee Street. Course is 2 miles on left.

# Indian Springs Golf Course

NR **24** ▶

123 Mack Road
Middlefield, CT (860) 349-8109
www.indiansprings-golf.com

**Club Pro:** John Parmelee
**Payment:** Cash, Credit Cards
**Tee Times:** Anyday
**Fee 9 Holes: Weekday:** $18
**Fee 18 Holes: Weekday:** $31
**Twilight Rates:** Yes
**Cart Rental:** $16pp/18, $8pp/9
**Lessons:** Yes **Schools:** Yes
**Membership:** Yes
**Other:** Snack Bar / Bar-Lounge / Restaurant

| Tees | Holes | Yards | Par | USGA | Slope |
|---|---|---|---|---|---|
| BACK |  |  |  |  |  |
| MIDDLE | 9 | 3000 | 36 | 68.9 | 116 |
| FRONT | 9 | 2616 | 36 | 73.0 | 127 |

**Weekend:** $20
**Weekend:** $36
**Discounts:** Senior & Junior
**Driving Range:** $9/lg, $5/sm
**Junior Golf:** Yes
**Architect/Yr Open:** 1964
**GPS:**

COUPON

A scenic, challenging 9-hole course where you'll feel welcome. Well-maintained fairways, and immaculate greens. Among the very best in Connecticut. Cafe with bar and outdoor patio. Driving range and putting green.

|  | 1 | 2 | 3 | 4 | 5 | 6 | 7 | 8 | 9 |
|---|---|---|---|---|---|---|---|---|---|
| PAR | 4 | 5 | 3 | 4 | 5 | 4 | 3 | 4 | 4 |
| YARDS | 345 | 455 | 130 | 370 | 560 | 300 | 170 | 355 | 315 |
| PAR |  |  |  |  |  |  |  |  |  |
| YARDS |  |  |  |  |  |  |  |  |  |

**Directions:** I-91 North to Exit 18 (Route 66) toward Middletown. At light, take a right onto Route 147. Take 1st left onto Way Road. Follow signs to course. Take I-91 South to Exit 19, left at stop sign. Take a right at light onto Route 147. Go 2 miles to Way Road and follow signs to course on Mack Road.

# Laurel View Country Club ✪✪✪

## 25

West Shepard Avenue
Hamden, CT (203) 287-2656
www.laurelviewcc.com
**Club Pro:** Edward Grant, PGA
**Payment:** Visa, MC
**Tee Times:** 3 days adv. weekends

| Tees | Holes | Yards | Par | USGA | Slope |
|------|-------|-------|-----|------|-------|
| BACK | 18 | 6899 | 72 | 74.3 | 135 |
| MIDDLE | 18 | 6372 | 72 | 72.1 | 131 |
| FRONT | 18 | 5558 | 73 | 71.8 | 130 |

**Fee 9 Holes: Weekday:** $20
**Fee 18 Holes: Weekday:** $31
**Twilight Rates:** No
**Cart Rental:** $15pp/18, $9pp/9
**Lessons:** $40/half hour  **Schools:** No
**Membership:** Yes, residents
**Other:** Clubhouse / Lockers / Showers / Snack Bar / Restaurant / Bar-Lounge

**Weekend:** $22
**Weekend:** $35
**Discounts:** Senior & Junior
**Driving Range:** $5/lg
**Junior Golf:** Yes
**Architect/Yr Open:** Cornish & Robinson/1969

This Cornish course requires smart course managaement; hilly terrain provides interesting challenge. Open April 1 - December 1. Many favorable comments. Greatly improved fairways, greens, bunkers and tees.

|  | 1 | 2 | 3 | 4 | 5 | 6 | 7 | 8 | 9 |
|------|-----|-----|-----|-----|-----|-----|-----|-----|-----|
| PAR | 4 | 3 | 4 | 5 | 4 | 4 | 3 | 5 | 4 |
| YARDS | 330 | 132 | 390 | 505 | 435 | 310 | 230 | 510 | 420 |
|  | 10 | 11 | 12 | 13 | 14 | 15 | 16 | 17 | 18 |
| PAR | 4 | 5 | 3 | 4 | 5 | 4 | 4 | 3 | 4 |
| YARDS | 320 | 560 | 155 | 280 | 470 | 380 | 390 | 160 | 395 |

**Directions:** I-91 to Exit 10, take left at the end of the ramp. At first light take left, right at next light (Dixwell Avenue). Through center of town, pass Town Hall on the right. ¾ mile, take right (Shephard Avenue). Through 5 lights, take left (W. Shephard). Course ¾ mile on left.

# Longshore Golf Course ✪✪✪½

## 26

South Compo Road
Westport, CT (203) 341-1833
www.longshoregolf.com
**Club Pro:** John Cooper, PGA
**Payment:** Visa, MC, Cash, Check
**Tee Times:** 3 days adv.

| Tees | Holes | Yards | Par | USGA | Slope |
|------|-------|-------|-----|------|-------|
| BACK | 18 | 5845 | 69 | 67.4 | 115 |
| MIDDLE | 18 | 5676 | 69 | 66.7 | 113 |
| FRONT | 18 | 5227 | 73 | 69.9 | 119 |

**Fee 9 Holes: Weekday:** $32 M-Th
**Fee 18 Holes: Weekday:** $44 M-Th
**Twilight Rates:** No
**Cart Rental:** $15pp/18, $7.50pp/9
**Lessons:** Yes  **Schools:** No
**Membership:** No
**Other:** Snack Bar / Restaurant / Bar-Lounge

**Weekend:** $37 F/S/S/H
**Weekend:** $50 F/S/S/H
**Discounts:** None
**Driving Range:** Yes
**Junior Golf:** Yes
**Architect/Yr Open:** Orrin E. Smith
**GPS:**

Good course for beginners and intermediates. Course has been completely renovated. Over 100 bunkers. "A great layout along the sea." –FP

|  | 1 | 2 | 3 | 4 | 5 | 6 | 7 | 8 | 9 |
|------|-----|-----|-----|-----|-----|-----|-----|-----|-----|
| PAR | 4 | 3 | 4 | 4 | 4 | 4 | 5 | 3 | 4 |
| YARDS | 341 | 146 | 390 | 287 | 296 | 413 | 520 | 127 | 346 |
|  | 10 | 11 | 12 | 13 | 14 | 15 | 16 | 17 | 18 |
| PAR | 5 | 3 | 4 | 3 | 4 | 3 | 4 | 4 | 4 |
| YARDS | 459 | 192 | 289 | 189 | 401 | 166 | 383 | 344 | 397 |

**SW CT**

**Directions:** I-95 to Exit 18 to U.S. Route 1, left at 2nd light, Green Farms Road. Follow to next light, take left onto Compo. Course is on right.

# Lyman Orchards GC (Apple)

70 Lyman Road
Middlefield, CT (860) 349-6031
www.lymangolf.com

| Tees | Holes | Yards | Par | USGA | Slope |
|------|-------|-------|-----|------|-------|
| BACK | 9 | 1556 | 29 | 28.2 | 87 |
| MIDDLE | 9 | 1380 | 29 | | |
| FRONT | 9 | 1211 | 29 | | |

**Club Pro:** Dan Valk
**Payment:** All
**Tee Times:** 7 days adv.
**Fee 9 Holes: Weekday:** $15 **Weekend:** $18
**Fee 18 Holes: Weekday:** $30 **Weekend:** $36
**Twilight Rates:** **Discounts:** Senior & Junior M-F
**Cart Rental:** $16pp/18, $8pp/9 **Driving Range:** Yes
**Lessons:** Yes **Schools:** Yes **Junior Golf:** Yes
**Membership:** Yes **Architect/Yr Open:** Mark Mungeam/2012
**Other:** Clubhouse / Lockers / Showers / Snack Bar / Restaurant / Bar-Lounge

The par-29 course was ranked as the top Par 3 course in Connecticut and 10th overall in New England by *New England Golf Monthly* magazine. Fivesomes allowed.

| | 1 | 2 | 3 | 4 | 5 | 6 | 7 | 8 | 9 |
|------|---|---|---|---|---|---|---|---|---|
| **PAR** | 3 | 4 | 3 | 3 | 3 | 3 | 3 | 3 | 4 |
| **YARDS** | 96 | 279 | 130 | 121 | 79 | 157 | 95 | 144 | 279 |
| **PAR** | | | | | | | | | |
| **YARDS** | | | | | | | | | |

**Directions:** I-91 to Exit 15 (Route 68 East). Left onto Route 157. Course is 1 mile on the right.

# Lyman Orchards GC (Jones)

70 Lyman Road
Middlefield, CT (860) 349-6031
www.lymangolf.com

| Tees | Holes | Yards | Par | USGA | Slope |
|------|-------|-------|-----|------|-------|
| BACK | 18 | 7011 | 72 | 73.3 | 132 |
| MIDDLE | 18 | 6614 | 72 | 69.6 | 128 |
| FRONT | 18 | 6200 | 72 | 72.0 | 124 |

**Club Pro:** Dan Valk
**Payment:** All
**Tee Times:** 7 days adv.
**Fee 9 Holes: Weekday:** $35 w/cart **Weekend:** $37 w/cart
**Fee 18 Holes: Weekday:** $56 w/cart **Weekend:** $69 w/cart
**Twilight Rates:** After 1:30pm **Discounts:** Senior & Junior M-F
**Cart Rental:** Included **Driving Range:** Yes
**Lessons:** Yes **Schools:** Yes **Junior Golf:** Yes
**Membership:** Yes **Architect/Yr Open:** Robert Trent Jones Jr./1967
**Other:** Clubhouse / Lockers / Showers / Snack Bar / Restaurant / Bar-Lounge

Each hole designed by Robert Trent Jones Jr. to be a demanding par or a comfortable bogey. Bent grass fairways and Penn Cross tees and greens. M-Th Early Bird before 7:30am.

| | 1 | 2 | 3 | 4 | 5 | 6 | 7 | 8 | 9 |
|------|---|---|---|---|---|---|---|---|---|
| **PAR** | 4 | 3 | 4 | 5 | 4 | 4 | 3 | 4 | 5 |
| **YARDS** | 416 | 175 | 374 | 552 | 390 | 350 | 175 | 373 | 548 |
| | **10** | **11** | **12** | **13** | **14** | **15** | **16** | **17** | **18** |
| **PAR** | 4 | 3 | 5 | 4 | 4 | 4 | 4 | 3 | 5 |
| **YARDS** | 399 | 152 | 490 | 370 | 388 | 382 | 403 | 162 | 515 |

**Directions:** I-91 to Exit 15 (Route 68 East). Left onto Route 157. Course is 1 mile on the right.

# Lyman Orchards GC (Player)  ✪✪✪½

## 29

Route 157
Middlefield, CT (860) 349-6031
www.lymangolf.com

**Club Pro:** Dan Valk
**Payment:** Visa, MC, Amex, Disc
**Tee Times:** 7 days adv. (888) 99Lyman
**Fee 9 Holes: Weekday:** $33 w/cart
**Fee 18 Holes: Weekday:** $64 w/cart
**Twilight Rates:** After 1:30pm
**Cart Rental:** Included
**Lessons:** Yes **Schools:** Yes
**Membership:** Yes

| Tees | Holes | Yards | Par | USGA | Slope |
|------|-------|-------|-----|------|-------|
| BACK | 18 | 6725 | 71 | 72.9 | 134 |
| MIDDLE | 18 | 6325 | 71 | 71.2 | 132 |
| FRONT | 18 | 5890 | 71 | 68.8 | 129 |

**Weekend:** $33 w/cart
**Weekend:** $66 w/cart
**Discounts:** Senior & Junior M-Th
**Driving Range:** $7/lg., $4/md.
**Junior Golf:** Yes
**Architect/Yr Open:** Gary Player/1994

**Other:** Clubhouse / Lockers / Showers / Snack Bar / Restaurant / Bar-Lounge

Player Comments: "Beautiful layout, stresses good shot making." "Great variety. Demands that you maintain focus for all 18 holes." –JD
Designed by Gary Player. Play all 36—make a day of it. M-Th Early Bird before 8am. Open March - November.

| | 1 | 2 | 3 | 4 | 5 | 6 | 7 | 8 | 9 |
|------|----|----|----|----|----|----|----|----|----|
| PAR | 4 | 4 | 4 | 3 | 4 | 4 | 3 | 5 | 4 |
| YARDS | 400 | 367 | 374 | 173 | 386 | 342 | 191 | 578 | 381 |
| | 10 | 11 | 12 | 13 | 14 | 15 | 16 | 17 | 18 |
| PAR | 4 | 3 | 4 | 3 | 5 | 4 | 3 | 5 | 5 |
| YARDS | 348 | 211 | 427 | 181 | 473 | 306 | 165 | 520 | 502 |

**Directions:** I-91 to Exit 15 (Route 68 East). Left onto Route 157. Course is 1 mile on the right.

# Miner Hills Golf Course  ✪✪

## 30

80 Miner Hills Drive
Middletown, CT (860) 635-0051
www.minerhillsgolf.com

**Club Pro:** George Claffey
**Payment:** Cash, Check, MC, Visa
**Tee Times:** Available
**Fee 9 Holes: Weekday:** $12
**Fee 18 Holes: Weekday:** $20
**Twilight Rates:** Yes
**Cart Rental:** $12pp/18, $6pp/9
**Lessons:** Yes **Schools:** No
**Membership:** Season Passes

| Tees | Holes | Yards | Par | USGA | Slope |
|------|-------|-------|-----|------|-------|
| BACK | | | | | |
| MIDDLE | 9 | 1769 | 30 | 59.1 | 97 |
| FRONT | 9 | 1292 | 30 | 59.5 | 80 |

**Weekend:** $14
**Weekend:** $20
**Discounts:** Senior/Junior-Mon/Sat
**Driving Range:** Yes
**Junior Golf:** No
**Architect/Yr Open:** John S. Ott/1993

COUPON

**Other:** Clubhouse / Snack Bar / Tournament & Banquet Facilities

"A delightful surprise with several interesting holes. A great executive layout and well-maintained" –AP
Open March 25 until weather permits. Middletown, CT's only golf course! Just minutes from downtown Hartford and New Haven, CT.

| | 1 | 2 | 3 | 4 | 5 | 6 | 7 | 8 | 9 |
|------|----|----|----|----|----|----|----|----|----|
| PAR | 3 | 3 | 4 | 4 | 3 | 3 | 4 | 3 | 3 |
| YARDS | 160 | 150 | 298 | 253 | 173 | 210 | 260 | 120 | 130 |
| PAR | | | | | | | | | |
| YARDS | | | | | | | | | |

**Directions:** I-91 to Exit 20. Westfield district of Middletown, CT.

SW
CT

# North Ridge Golf Club

✪✪½  **31** ▶

300 Welch Road
Southington, CT (860) 628-0879
www.northridgegolfclub.com

**Club Pro:** Jack McConachie, PGA
**Payment:** Cash, Visa, MC
**Tee Times:** M-F 7 days adv., S/S 4 days adv.

| Tees | Holes | Yards | Par | USGA | Slope |
|---|---|---|---|---|---|
| BACK | 18 | 6325 | 71 | 70.6 | 123 |
| MIDDLE | 18 | 6043 | 71 | 70.1 | 117 |
| FRONT | 18 | 5482 | 73 | 72.0 | 122 |

**Fee 9 Holes: Weekday:** $20    **Weekend:** $22
**Fee 18 Holes: Weekday:** $36    **Weekend:** $41
**Twilight Rates:** No    **Discounts:** Senior
**Cart Rental:** $17pp/18, $8.50pp/9    **Driving Range:** No
**Lessons:** Yes **Schools:** No    **Junior Golf:** Yes
**Membership:** No    **Architect/Yr Open:** Al Zikorus, Orrin Smith/1960
**Other:** Clubhouse / Lockers / Showers / Snack Bar / Restaurant / Bar-Lounge / Practice Sand Trap
**GPS:** Yes

Hilly front 9, while the back 9 are more level with water holes and very tight greens. Accuracy is essential. Dress code. New tees.

| | 1 | 2 | 3 | 4 | 5 | 6 | 7 | 8 | 9 |
|---|---|---|---|---|---|---|---|---|---|
| PAR | 5 | 4 | 3 | 4 | 4 | 4 | 5 | 3 | 4 |
| YARDS | 497 | 404 | 125 | 345 | 345 | 291 | 505 | 141 | 405 |
| | 10 | 11 | 12 | 13 | 14 | 15 | 16 | 17 | 18 |
| PAR | 3 | 4 | 5 | 4 | 4 | 3 | 5 | 4 | 3 |
| YARDS | 170 | 366 | 510 | 426 | 353 | 160 | 476 | 340 | 180 |

**Directions:** I-84 to Exit 31 (Route 229 North). Go 1.5 miles. Take a left onto Welch Road. Course is ½ mile on left.

# Oak Hills Park Golf Course

✪✪✪ **32** ▶

165 Fillow Street
Norwalk, CT (203) 838-0303
www.oakhillsgc.com

**Club Pro:** Edward Ruiz, PGA
**Payment:** Cash, Visa, MC, Amex
**Tee Times:** 7 days adv.

| Tees | Holes | Yards | Par | USGA | Slope |
|---|---|---|---|---|---|
| BACK | 18 | 6317 | 71 | 70.3 | 133 |
| MIDDLE | 18 | 5920 | 71 | 68.5 | 128 |
| FRONT | 18 | 5221 | 72 | 70.7 | 124 |

**Fee 9 Holes: Weekday:** $30    **Weekend:** $30
**Fee 18 Holes: Weekday:** $46    **Weekend:** $50
**Twilight Rates:** After 4pm    **Discounts:** Sr. & Jr. residents M-F
**Cart Rental:** $16pp/18, $10pp/9    **Driving Range:** No
**Lessons:** Yes **Schools:** Yes    **Junior Golf:** No
**Membership:** For residents    **Architect/Yr Open:** Alfred Tull/1969
**Other:** Snack Bar / Restaurant    **GPS:**

Many improvements recently made have made this course one worth playing.

| | 1 | 2 | 3 | 4 | 5 | 6 | 7 | 8 | 9 |
|---|---|---|---|---|---|---|---|---|---|
| PAR | 4 | 4 | 3 | 4 | 3 | 4 | 4 | 5 | 4 |
| YARDS | 374 | 295 | 109 | 307 | 174 | 284 | 336 | 484 | 440 |
| | 10 | 11 | 12 | 13 | 14 | 15 | 16 | 17 | 18 |
| PAR | 5 | 4 | 5 | 3 | 4 | 3 | 4 | 4 | 4 |
| YARDS | 528 | 365 | 501 | 154 | 386 | 205 | 342 | 336 | 300 |

**Directions:** I-95, Exit 13. Right turn onto Route 1. Left onto Richards Avenue; right turn onto Fillow Street to Oak Hills Park.

# Orange Hills Country Club  ✪✪½  ▶ 33

389 Racebrook Road
Orange, CT (203) 795-4161
www.orangehillscountryclub.com

| Tees | Holes | Yards | Par | USGA | Slope |
|------|-------|-------|-----|------|-------|
| BACK | 18 | 6511 | 71 | 72.3 | 126 |
| MIDDLE | 18 | 6115 | 71 | 70.6 | 119 |
| FRONT | 18 | 5616 | 74 | 72.7 | 122 |

**Club Pro:** Robert Tosetti
**Payment:** Visa, MC, Disc
**Tee Times:** M-F 7 days adv., S/S 3 days adv.
**Fee 9 Holes: Weekday:** $20    **Weekend:** $22
**Fee 18 Holes: Weekday:** $32    **Weekend:** $44
**Twilight Rates:** After 6pm    **Discounts:** Senior & Junior
**Cart Rental:** $16pp/18, $8pp/9    **Driving Range:** No
**Lessons:** Yes **Schools:** Yes    **Junior Golf:** Yes
**Membership:** Limited    **Architect/Yr Open:** Cornish/1961
**Other:** Clubhouse / Snack Bar / Bar-Lounge / Restaurant

Course is hilly with a tight back 9. Call for directions from Hartford. Collared shirts and soft spikes required. No denim allowed. Newly lengthened 16th tee.

|  | 1 | 2 | 3 | 4 | 5 | 6 | 7 | 8 | 9 |
|---|---|---|---|---|---|---|---|---|---|
| PAR | 4 | 5 | 3 | 4 | 4 | 4 | 4 | 4 | 3 |
| YARDS | 390 | 481 | 148 | 435 | 349 | 365 | 399 | 300 | 134 |
|  | **10** | **11** | **12** | **13** | **14** | **15** | **16** | **17** | **18** |
| PAR | 3 | 5 | 4 | 3 | 4 | 4 | 4 | 4 | 5 |
| YARDS | 207 | 466 | 365 | 153 | 377 | 339 | 331 | 413 | 459 |

**Directions:** Merritt Parkway: Exit 57, 2 lights to Route 114, right onto Route 114, 1.75 miles on left. From NYC: I-95 North, Exit 41, left off ramp. 4 lights to U.S. 1. Right onto U.S. 1, 1 block to Racebrook Road. Left onto Racebrook Road. ¼ mile on right.

# The Orchards Golf Course  ✪✪  ▶ 34

137 Kozlowski Road
Milford, CT (203) 877-8200
www.theorchardsgolfclub.com

| Tees | Holes | Yards | Par | USGA | Slope |
|------|-------|-------|-----|------|-------|
| BACK |  |  |  |  |  |
| MIDDLE | 9 | 1625 | 32 |  |  |
| FRONT | 9 | 1433 | 32 |  |  |

**Club Pro:**
**Payment:** Cash Only
**Tee Times:** 6 days adv.
**Fee 9 Holes: Weekday:** $9.45    **Weekend:** $10.86
**Fee 18 Holes: Weekday:** $16.70    **Weekend:** $17.75
**Twilight Rates:** Yes    **Discounts:** Senior & Junior
**Cart Rental:** $14 for 2 people    **Driving Range:** Yes (Net)
**Lessons:** Yes **Schools:** No    **Junior Golf:** Yes
**Membership:** No    **Architect/Yr Open:**
**Other:** Snacks    **GPS:**

Resident discounts. New groundskeeper.

|  | 1 | 2 | 3 | 4 | 5 | 6 | 7 | 8 | 9 |
|---|---|---|---|---|---|---|---|---|---|
| PAR | 4 | 3 | 4 | 4 | 4 | 3 | 3 | 3 | 4 |
| YARDS | 242 | 93 | 222 | 207 | 217 | 120 | 167 | 91 | 266 |
| PAR |  |  |  |  |  |  |  |  |  |
| YARDS |  |  |  |  |  |  |  |  |  |

**SW CT**

**Directions:** I-95 to Exit 39, go west on US Route 1. Go 2 miles to Route 121 North. Right on Route 121 for 2 miles. Course is on the right.

# Oxford Greens, The Golf Club at ✪✪✪½ 🚩 35

99 Country Club Drive
Oxford, CT (203) 888-1600
www.oxfordgreens.com
**Club Pro:** Steve Landi, PGA/GM
**Payment:** Most Major Credit Cards
**Tee Times:** 7 days adv.

| Tees | Holes | Yards | Par | USGA | Slope |
|------|-------|-------|-----|------|-------|
| BACK | 18 | 6665 | 72 | 72.3 | 133 |
| MIDDLE | 18 | 6324 | 72 | 70.5 | 131 |
| FRONT | 18 | 5188 | 72 | 69.9 | 122 |

**Fee 9 Holes: Weekday:**
**Fee 18 Holes: Weekday:** $65 M-Th (w/cart)
**Twilight Rates:** After 2pm
**Cart Rental:**
**Lessons:** Yes **Schools:** Yes
**Membership:** Yes
**Other:** Restaurant

**Weekend:**
**Weekend:** $71 (w/cart)
**Discounts:** Junior
**Driving Range:** Yes
**Junior Golf:**
**Architect/Yr Open:** Mark Mungeam/2005
**GPS:**

COUPON

Also black tees at 7186 yards, 75.4/135. #3 is the longest hole in CT: 630 yards. Carved through 600 acres of stunning countryside. "Fast greens. Maturing nicely—definitely worth a visit." –JD *Golf World* Top 5 in CT.

| | 1 | 2 | 3 | 4 | 5 | 6 | 7 | 8 | 9 |
|---|---|---|---|---|---|---|---|---|---|
| **PAR** | 4 | 3 | 5 | 4 | 4 | 4 | 4 | 5 | 3 |
| **YARDS** | 345 | 165 | 535 | 405 | 370 | 300 | 365 | 510 | 175 |
| | **10** | **11** | **12** | **13** | **14** | **15** | **16** | **17** | **18** |
| **PAR** | 5 | 4 | 4 | 3 | 4 | 4 | 3 | 5 | 4 |
| **YARDS** | 517 | 330 | 370 | 147 | 405 | 363 | 132 | 485 | 405 |

**Directions:** I-84 to Exit 15 Southbury/Seymour. Follow Route 67 South for 6 miles to Riggs Street in Oxford. Left onto Riggs. Follow for approximately 2 miles to The Golf Club at Oxford Greens on right. The Course is located at 99 Country Club Drive.

# Pequabuck Golf Course ✪✪ 🚩 36

56 School Street
Pequabuck, CT (860) 583-7307
www.pequabuckgolf.com
**Club Pro:** Richard Toner, PGA
**Payment:** Visa, MC, Disc
**Tee Times:** Yes

| Tees | Holes | Yards | Par | USGA | Slope |
|------|-------|-------|-----|------|-------|
| BACK | 18 | 6015 | 69 | 70.2 | 118 |
| MIDDLE | 18 | 5692 | 69 | 68.7 | 115 |
| FRONT | 18 | 5388 | 72 | 70.3 | 118 |

**Fee 9 Holes: Weekday:** $21
**Fee 18 Holes: Weekday:** $42
**Twilight Rates:** No
**Cart Rental:** $14pp/18, $8pp/9
**Lessons:** Call for rates **Schools:** No
**Membership:** Yes
**Other:** Restaurant / Clubhouse / Bar-Lounge / Snack Bar

**Weekend:** $21
**Weekend:** $42
**Discounts:** None
**Driving Range:** Yes
**Junior Golf:** Yes
**Architect/Yr Open:** 1902

Front 9 open, back 9 tree-lined with difficult greens. Known for fairways and greens. Groups up to 16 guests. Dress code.

| | 1 | 2 | 3 | 4 | 5 | 6 | 7 | 8 | 9 |
|---|---|---|---|---|---|---|---|---|---|
| **PAR** | 4 | 4 | 5 | 3 | 4 | 3 | 5 | 3 | 4 |
| **YARDS** | 286 | 424 | 470 | 169 | 322 | 155 | 465 | 174 | 371 |
| | **10** | **11** | **12** | **13** | **14** | **15** | **16** | **17** | **18** |
| **PAR** | 3 | 4 | 4 | 4 | 4 | 4 | 3 | 4 | 4 |
| **YARDS** | 190 | 406 | 377 | 329 | 401 | 337 | 155 | 328 | 333 |

**Directions:** I-84 to Route Exit 72. Follow Route 72 into Terryville. Go under railroad bridge. Take right onto School Street. Follow to club.

# Pompeusing Golf Club

NR **37**

**522 Heritage Road**
**Southbury, CT (203) 264-9484**
www.pomperauggolfclub.com

| Tees | Holes | Yards | Par | USGA | Slope |
|------|-------|-------|-----|------|-------|
| BACK | 9 | 2985 | 35 | 34.6 | 121 |
| MIDDLE | 9 | 2772 | 35 | 33.6 | 118 |
| FRONT | 9 | 2234 | 36 | 35.0 | 113 |

**Club Pro:** Dave Cook
**Payment:** Cash, Credit Cards
**Tee Times:** 7 days adv.
**Fee 9 Holes: Weekday:** $21
**Fee 18 Holes: Weekday:** $35
**Twilight Rates:** After 5pm
**Cart Rental:** $16pp/18, $11pp/9
**Lessons:** Yes **Schools:**
**Membership:** Yes
**Other:** Hotel / Cooler / Beverage Cart / Stay & Play Packages

**Weekend:** $23
**Weekend:** $40
**Discounts:** Junior
**Driving Range:** Practice green
**Junior Golf:** Yes
**Architect/Yr Open:** 1973

Semi-private course. Heritage International Hotel on premises. Dress code. Fun and challenging 9-hole course with water on every hole. Women friendly. For online tee times visit our website.

| | 1 | 2 | 3 | 4 | 5 | 6 | 7 | 8 | 9 |
|------|---|---|---|---|---|---|---|---|---|
| PAR | 4 | 4 | 4 | 5 | 3 | 4 | 4 | 3 | 4 |
| YARDS | 330 | 356 | 263 | 457 | 174 | 346 | 375 | 166 | 305 |
| PAR | | | | | | | | | |
| YARDS | | | | | | | | | |

**Directions:** I-84 to Route 67, Southbury, Exit 15. At 2nd light, take left onto Heritage Road. Course is 1 mile ahead on right.

# Portland Golf Club

✪✪✪ **38**

**169 Bartlett Street**
**Portland, CT (860) 342-6107**
www.portlandgolfcourse.com

| Tees | Holes | Yards | Par | USGA | Slope |
|------|-------|-------|-----|------|-------|
| BACK | 18 | 6213 | 71 | 70.5 | 127 |
| MIDDLE | 18 | 5802 | 71 | 68.7 | 123 |
| FRONT | 18 | 5039 | 71 | 68.6 | 118 |

**Club Pro:** Mark Sloan, PGA
**Payment:** Cash, Visa
**Tee Times:** 7 days adv.
**Fee 9 Holes: Weekday:** $21
**Fee 18 Holes: Weekday:** $42
**Twilight Rates:** After 12pm, weekends
**Cart Rental:** $16pp/18, $9pp/9
**Lessons:** Yes **Schools:** Yes
**Membership:** Yes
**Other:** Clubhouse / Lockers / Showers / Snack Bar / Restaurant / Bar-Lounge

**Weekend:** $23
**Weekend:** $45
**Discounts:** Senior & Junior
**Driving Range:** No
**Junior Golf:** Yes
**Architect/Yr Open:** Cornish & Robinson/1974

Player Comments: "Lots of doglegs." "Excellent conditions." "Worth playing, I'll be back." "Hilly." New ownership and management. Rated 4.5 stars. Open March 15 – January 1.

| | 1 | 2 | 3 | 4 | 5 | 6 | 7 | 8 | 9 |
|------|---|---|---|---|---|---|---|---|---|
| PAR | 4 | 5 | 4 | 3 | 4 | 4 | 4 | 3 | 4 |
| YARDS | 365 | 485 | 350 | 166 | 270 | 287 | 351 | 140 | 301 |
| | 10 | 11 | 12 | 13 | 14 | 15 | 16 | 17 | 18 |
| PAR | 4 | 4 | 5 | 4 | 3 | 4 | 5 | 3 | 4 |
| YARDS | 303 | 373 | 489 | 377 | 177 | 360 | 471 | 165 | 372 |

**Directions:** Route 2 to 17 South (left at exit); 9.5 miles down take left on Bartlett; course is less than 1 mile. Call for directions from Route 9.

# Portland West Golf Club ✪✪✪

## 39

105 Gospel Lane
Portland, CT (860) 342-6111
www.portlandwestgolf.com

| Tees | Holes | Yards | Par | USGA | Slope |
|------|-------|-------|-----|------|-------|
| BACK | 18 | 4012 | 60 | 60.5 | 102 |
| MIDDLE | 18 | 3620 | 60 | 59.3 | 100 |
| FRONT | 18 | 3154 | 60 | 58.4 | 87 |

**Club Pro:** Gerald J. D'Amora, PGA
**Payment:** Cash, Visa, MC
**Tee Times:** 7 days adv.
**Fee 9 Holes: Weekday:** $14   **Weekend:** $16.50
**Fee 18 Holes: Weekday:** $27   **Weekend:** $30
**Twilight Rates:** After 6pm $10, M-F 11-3pm $20pp/18, $10pp/9
**Discounts:** Senior & Junior
**Cart Rental:** $26pp/18, $16pp/9   **Driving Range:** Yes
**Lessons:** $45/half hour   **Schools:** No   **Junior Golf:** Yes
**Membership:** No   **Architect/Yr Open:** 1985
**Other:** Restaurant / Bar-Lounge / Snack Bar   **GPS:**

Player Comments: "Excellent greens and fairways." "The 18th hole proves to be a difficult finish." "A challenging executive par 60 course." "Nice scenery and fair prices."

| | 1 | 2 | 3 | 4 | 5 | 6 | 7 | 8 | 9 |
|------|---|---|---|---|---|---|---|---|---|
| PAR | 3 | 3 | 3 | 4 | 3 | 4 | 3 | 3 | 4 |
| YARDS | 148 | 130 | 145 | 264 | 140 | 339 | 113 | 137 | 351 |
| | 10 | 11 | 12 | 13 | 14 | 15 | 16 | 17 | 18 |
| PAR | 4 | 3 | 3 | 3 | 3 | 3 | 4 | 4 | 3 |
| YARDS | 341 | 135 | 161 | 114 | 185 | 122 | 319 | 293 | 183 |

**Directions:** I-91 to Route 9 to Route 66; left onto Route 17 (Gospel Lane); course is ½ mile on right.

# Quarry Ridge Golf Course ✪✪✪½

## 40

9 Rose Hill Road
Portland, CT (860) 342-6113
www.quarryridge.com

| Tees | Holes | Yards | Par | USGA | Slope |
|------|-------|-------|-----|------|-------|
| BACK | 18 | 6389 | 72 | 70.9 | 124 |
| MIDDLE | 18 | 6049 | 72 | 69.5 | 119 |
| FRONT | 18 | 4852 | 72 | 68.7 | 117 |

**Club Pro:** John Lucas Jr., PGA
**Payment:** Cash, Visa, MC, Amex
**Tee Times:** 1 week adv.
**Fee 9 Holes: Weekday:** $30   **Weekend:** $32
**Fee 18 Holes: Weekday:** $54   **Weekend:** $59
**Twilight Rates:** After 1pm, weekends   **Discounts:** Sr. & Jr., wkdys only
**Cart Rental:** Included   **Driving Range:** No
**Lessons:** Yes   **Schools:** No   **Junior Golf:** No
**Membership:** Yes   **Architect/Yr Open:** Al Zikorus/1993
**Other:** Restaurant / Bar-Lounge   **GPS:**

COUPON

Player Comments: "Challenging, with tight fairways and small greens. Scenic views of Connecticut River Valley." "Difficult, but popular. Well maintained." "Great layout." Faster greens, 10-minute tee times, faster play. Great restaurant open Fri., Sat., Sun. night.

| | 1 | 2 | 3 | 4 | 5 | 6 | 7 | 8 | 9 |
|------|---|---|---|---|---|---|---|---|---|
| PAR | 4 | 3 | 4 | 5 | 4 | 5 | 4 | 4 | 3 |
| YARDS | 350 | 155 | 383 | 463 | 337 | 448 | 346 | 392 | 178 |
| | 10 | 11 | 12 | 13 | 14 | 15 | 16 | 17 | 18 |
| PAR | 4 | 5 | 4 | 4 | 3 | 4 | 3 | 5 | 4 |
| YARDS | 326 | 447 | 442 | 293 | 154 | 337 | 144 | 459 | 395 |

**Directions:** From Hartford: Route 2 to Route 17 (left Exit 7). Go 9 miles; take left onto Bartlett Street, go to end. Cross road to driveway of golf course.

# Richter Park Golf Course ✪✪✪✪ 41 ▶

100 Aunt Hack Road
Danbury, CT (203) 792-2550
www.richterpark.com

| Tees | Holes | Yards | Par | USGA | Slope |
|------|-------|-------|-----|------|-------|
| BACK | 18 | 6744 | 72 | 73.6 | 139 |
| MIDDLE | 18 | 6304 | 72 | 71.6 | 136 |
| FRONT | 18 | 5114 | 72 | 70.7 | 124 |

**Club Pro:** Brian Gehan
**Payment:** MC, Visa, Cash
**Tee Times:** 8 days adv. (866) 856-9219
**Fee 9 Holes: Weekday:** Twilight only   **Weekend:** Twilight only
**Fee 18 Holes: Weekday:** $68 including cart   **Weekend:** $78 including cart
**Twilight Rates:** Yes   **Discounts:** Senior & Junior
**Cart Rental:** Included   **Driving Range:** No
**Lessons:** Yes **Schools:** Yes   **Junior Golf:** Yes
**Membership:** No   **Architect/Yr Open:** Ed Ryder/1971
**Other:** Clubhouse / Lockers / Showers / Snack Bar / Restaurant / Bar-Lounge

COUPON

Player Comments: "Very challenging and difficult." Course keeps a reputation for making even the most skillful golfers work hard: narrow fairways, approach shots require precision; water on 14 fairways.

| | 1 | 2 | 3 | 4 | 5 | 6 | 7 | 8 | 9 |
|------|---|---|---|---|---|---|---|---|---|
| **PAR** | 4 | 5 | 3 | 4 | 3 | 4 | 5 | 4 | 4 |
| **YARDS** | 372 | 495 | 150 | 386 | 170 | 387 | 508 | 337 | 308 |
| | **10** | **11** | **12** | **13** | **14** | **15** | **16** | **17** | **18** |
| **PAR** | 4 | 4 | 5 | 3 | 4 | 4 | 5 | 3 | 4 |
| **YARDS** | 345 | 367 | 479 | 142 | 395 | 319 | 570 | 152 | 422 |

**Directions:** I-84 West to Exit 2B or I-84 East to Exit 2. Take right off ramp (Mill Plain Road); take second left onto Aunt Hack Road to course.

# Ridgefield Golf Course ✪✪½ 42 ▶

545 Ridgebury Road
Ridgefield, CT (203) 748-7008
www.ridgefieldgc.com

| Tees | Holes | Yards | Par | USGA | Slope |
|------|-------|-------|-----|------|-------|
| BACK | 18 | 6444 | 71 | 71.8 | 129 |
| MIDDLE | 18 | 6019 | 71 | 69.7 | 127 |
| FRONT | 18 | 5071 | 73 | 70.3 | 120 |

**Club Pro:** Frank Sergiovanni, PGA
**Payment:** Cash, Check, Visa, MC
**Tee Times:** Yes
**Fee 9 Holes: Weekday:** $36 M-Th   **Weekend:**
**Fee 18 Holes: Weekday:** $45   **Weekend:** $50
**Twilight Rates:** Seasonal   **Discounts:** Sr. & Jr. weekdays
**Cart Rental:** $17pp/18, $9pp/9   **PracticeRange:** Tokens $4 (34 balls)
**Lessons:** Yes **Schools:** No   **Junior Golf:** Yes
**Membership:** Yes   **Architect/Yr Open:** Tom & George Fazio/1974
**Other:** Snack Bar / Bar-Lounge   **GPS:** Mapped for GPS

Golf at its best – a classic Fazio design for all skill levels, featuring rolling hills, tree-lines fairways, ponds, and challenging greens. Recommended annually by *Golf Digest's* "Places to Play." The new restaurant, bar/lounge, and snack bar feature classic grillroom food along with panoramic views from the extended deck. It's championship golf in a friendly setting with a friendly staff. Always in excellent condition.

| | 1 | 2 | 3 | 4 | 5 | 6 | 7 | 8 | 9 |
|------|---|---|---|---|---|---|---|---|---|
| **PAR** | 4 | 4 | 3 | 4 | 3 | 5 | 4 | 4 | 4 |
| **YARDS** | 391 | 367 | 150 | 320 | 139 | 518 | 345 | 381 | 371 |
| | **10** | **11** | **12** | **13** | **14** | **15** | **16** | **17** | **18** |
| **PAR** | 5 | 4 | 3 | 4 | 5 | 4 | 4 | 3 | 4 |
| **YARDS** | 533 | 311 | 147 | 351 | 469 | 402 | 311 | 127 | 386 |

**Directions:** I-84 to Exit 1; Saw Mill Road to Ridgebury Road. Course entrance is on Ridgebury Road.

SW
CT

# Short Beach Par 3 Golf Course    NR  43 ▶

**1 Dorne Drive**
**Stratford, CT** (203) 381-2070

| Tees | Holes | Yards | Par | USGA | Slope |
|------|-------|-------|-----|------|-------|
| BACK | 9 | 1369 | 27 | | |
| MIDDLE | 9 | 1270 | 27 | | |
| FRONT | 9 | 1162 | 27 | | |

**Club Pro:** Robert Fraioli
**Payment:** Cash, Visa, MC, Disc
**Tee Times:** 6 days adv. wknds
**Fee 9 Holes: Weekday:** $14 ($9 resident)    **Weekend:** $16 ($10 resident)
**Fee 18 Holes: Weekday:**    **Weekend:**
**Twilight Rates:** No    **Discounts:** Senior & Junior
**Cart Rental:** $8pp/9    **Driving Range:** No
**Lessons:** Yes  **Schools:** Yes    **Junior Golf:** Yes
**Membership:**    **Architect/Yr Open:** Geoffrey Cornish
**Other:** Snack Bar/ Mini Golf Course    **GPS:**

Par 3, 9 holes on beachfront. Proper attire required. Resident discounts. Open March - January.

| | 1 | 2 | 3 | 4 | 5 | 6 | 7 | 8 | 9 |
|---|---|---|---|---|---|---|---|---|---|
| **PAR** | 3 | 3 | 3 | 3 | 3 | 3 | 3 | 3 | 3 |
| **YARDS** | 125 | 154 | 98 | 170 | 88 | 130 | 218 | 162 | 125 |
| **PAR** | | | | | | | | | |
| **YARDS** | | | | | | | | | |

**Directions:** Call for directions.

# Sleeping Giant Golf Course    NR  44 ▶

**3931 Whitney Avenue**
**Hamden, CT** (203) 281-9456
www.sleepinggiantgc.com

| Tees | Holes | Yards | Par | USGA | Slope |
|------|-------|-------|-----|------|-------|
| BACK | 9 | 2671 | 35 | 65.4 | 99 |
| MIDDLE | 9 | 2572 | 35 | 63.4 | 96 |
| FRONT | 9 | 2216 | 37 | 64.6 | 106 |

**Club Pro:** Carl Swanson, PGA
**Payment:** Cash Only
**Tee Times:** No
**Fee 9 Holes: Weekday:** $17    **Weekend:** $19
**Fee 18 Holes: Weekday:** $30    **Weekend:** $34
**Twilight Rates:** No    **Discounts:** Senior
**Cart Rental:** $13pp/18, $8pp/9    **Driving Range:** Yes
**Lessons:** $30/half hour, $50/hour  **Schools:** No  **Junior Golf:** No
**Membership:** No    **Architect/Yr Open:** Ralph Barton
**Other:** Restaurant nearby    **GPS:**

*COUPON*

Open year round, weather permitting. "A nice little well-maintained course that is pure fun. The views of Sleeping Giant Mountain enhance the aesthetics. #3 is a nice par 3 to a punchbowl green" –AP

| | 1 | 2 | 3 | 4 | 5 | 6 | 7 | 8 | 9 |
|---|---|---|---|---|---|---|---|---|---|
| **PAR** | 3 | 4 | 3 | 4 | 5 | 4 | 4 | 4 | 4 |
| **YARDS** | 125 | 399 | 170 | 355 | 440 | 331 | 199 | 217 | 336 |
| **PAR** | | | | | | | | | |
| **YARDS** | | | | | | | | | |

**Directions:** I-91 to Exit 10. Right onto Whitney Avenue. Course is 3 miles on the right.

# South Pine Creek Par 3 Golf Course NR ▶ 45

Old Dam Road
Fairfield, CT (203) 255-7356
www.fairfieldct.org

**Club Pro:** Sean Garrity, PGA
**Payment:** Cash Only
**Tee Times:** 5 days adv.

| Tees | Holes | Yards | Par | USGA | Slope |
|------|-------|-------|-----|------|-------|
| BACK | | | | | |
| MIDDLE | 9 | 1242 | 27 | | |
| FRONT | 9 | 1073 | 27 | | |

**Fee 9 Holes: Weekday:** $14
**Fee 18 Holes: Weekday:**
**Twilight Rates:** No
**Cart Rental:** $4/pull
**Lessons:** No **Schools:** No
**Membership:** No
**Other:**

**Weekend:** $18
**Weekend:**
**Discounts:** Senior & Junior
**Driving Range:**
**Junior Golf:** No
**Architect/Yr Open:**
**GPS:**

Residents half price. Great place to learn the game. H. Richardson affiliate course.

| | 1 | 2 | 3 | 4 | 5 | 6 | 7 | 8 | 9 |
|------|-----|-----|-----|-----|-----|-----|-----|-----|-----|
| PAR | 3 | 3 | 3 | 3 | 3 | 3 | 3 | 3 | 3 |
| YARDS | 143 | 145 | 120 | 166 | 153 | 117 | 121 | 187 | 90 |
| PAR | | | | | | | | | |
| YARDS | | | | | | | | | |

**Directions:** I-95 to Exit 21, Mill Plain Road. Turn left onto Post Road. At first set of lights take left. Course is ½ mile on left.

# Southington Country Club ✪✪✪ ▶ 46

150 Savage Street
Plantsville, CT (860) 628-7032
www.southingtoncountryclub.com

**Club Pro:** Paul Brown, PGA
**Payment:** Visa, MC
**Tee Times:** Sat/Sun am, 5 days adv.

| Tees | Holes | Yards | Par | USGA | Slope |
|------|-------|-------|-----|------|-------|
| BACK | 18 | 5932 | 71 | 68.7 | 124 |
| MIDDLE | 18 | 5675 | 71 | 67.6 | 122 |
| FRONT | 18 | 5037 | 71 | 64.1 | 111 |

**Fee 9 Holes: Weekday:** $20
**Fee 18 Holes: Weekday:** $36
**Twilight Rates:** After 5pm
**Discounts:** Sr. & Jr. wkdays before 3pm, wknds after 3pm
**Cart Rental:** $16pp/18, $9pp/9
**Lessons:** No **Schools:** No
**Membership:** Yes
**Other:** Full Service Tavern / Pizza Oven / Banquet Room / Locker Rooms

**Weekend:** $23
**Weekend:** $40

**Driving Range:** No
**Junior Golf:** No
**Architect/Yr Open:** 1922

Front 9 hilly, Back 9 narrow. Full service bar and grill. Putting and chipping practice greens. Back Nine Tavern open year round.

| | 1 | 2 | 3 | 4 | 5 | 6 | 7 | 8 | 9 |
|------|-----|-----|-----|-----|-----|-----|-----|-----|-----|
| PAR | 4 | 4 | 3 | 5 | 4 | 5 | 3 | 4 | 4 |
| YARDS | 377 | 297 | 144 | 481 | 387 | 508 | 192 | 338 | 324 |
| | 10 | 11 | 12 | 13 | 14 | 15 | 16 | 17 | 18 |
| PAR | 4 | 4 | 3 | 4 | 5 | 3 | 4 | 3 | 5 |
| YARDS | 300 | 316 | 96 | 323 | 453 | 202 | 323 | 160 | 445 |

**SW CT**

**Directions:** I-84 to Exit 28. Take right onto Route 322. Travel about 3 miles. Take a left onto South End Road. Take first right onto Savage Street.

# Sterling Farms Golf Course ✪✪✪½  47

1349 Newfield Avenue
Stamford, CT (203) 461-9090
www.sterlingfarmsgc.com

Club Pro: Angela Aulenti, PGA
Payment: Cash Only
Tee Times: 1 week adv.

| Tees | Holes | Yards | Par | USGA | Slope |
|------|-------|-------|-----|------|-------|
| BACK | 18 | 6310 | 72 | 70.7 | 127 |
| MIDDLE | 18 | 6082 | 72 | 69.7 | 123 |
| FRONT | 18 | 5500 | 73 | 71.7 | 125 |

Fee 9 Holes: Weekday: $30 (6-7:30am)
Fee 18 Holes: Weekday: $50
Twilight Rates: After 4pm
Cart Rental: $14pp/18, $8pp/9
Lessons: Call (203) 329-7888 Schools: Yes
Membership: No
Other: Restaurant

Weekend: $30 (6-7:30am)
Weekend: $50
Discounts: Sr. & Jr. weekdays
Driving Range: Yes
Junior Golf: Yes
Architect/Yr Open: Geoffrey Cornish/1969
GPS:

Course has hilly front 9; more level back 9. 2 of the course's five lakes come into play on the 14th hole. Resident rates.

| | 1 | 2 | 3 | 4 | 5 | 6 | 7 | 8 | 9 |
|-----|-----|-----|-----|-----|-----|-----|-----|-----|-----|
| PAR | 4 | 5 | 4 | 4 | 3 | 5 | 4 | 3 | 4 |
| YARDS | 331 | 489 | 316 | 350 | 191 | 465 | 382 | 179 | 326 |
| | 10 | 11 | 12 | 13 | 14 | 15 | 16 | 17 | 18 |
| PAR | 4 | 4 | 4 | 5 | 4 | 3 | 4 | 3 | 5 |
| YARDS | 397 | 307 | 341 | 477 | 393 | 147 | 301 | 215 | 475 |

Directions: Merritt Parkway South to Exit 35. Right onto High Ridge Road. Left onto Vine (5 lights). Left at end to Newfield Avenue. Club is ¼ mile on right.

# Stonybrook Golf Course NR 48

263 Milton Road
Litchfield, CT (860) 567-9977
www.stonybrookgc.com

Club Pro: Rich Bredice, Pro
Payment: Visa, MC
Tee Times: Weekends

| Tees | Holes | Yards | Par | USGA | Slope |
|------|-------|-------|-----|------|-------|
| BACK | 9 | 2986 | 35 | 70.4 | 115 |
| MIDDLE | 9 | 2878 | 35 | 69.0 | 111 |
| FRONT | 9 | 2669 | 36 | 71.6 | 123 |

Fee 9 Holes: Weekday: $18
Fee 18 Holes: Weekday: $34
Twilight Rates: No
Cart Rental: $18pp/18, $9pp/9
Lessons: Available Schools: No
Membership: Yes
Other: Clubhouse / Snack Bar / Bar-Lounge / Lockers

Weekend: $20
Weekend: $38
Discounts: Junior
Driving Range: No
Junior Golf: Yes
Architect/Yr Open: Al Zikorus/1965

Terrain is rolling; greens contoured (medium/fast). Outstanding course conditions, considered the best in the area.

| | 1 | 2 | 3 | 4 | 5 | 6 | 7 | 8 | 9 |
|-----|-----|-----|-----|-----|-----|-----|-----|-----|-----|
| PAR | 5 | 4 | 3 | 4 | 4 | 4 | 4 | 4 | 3 |
| YARDS | 530 | 374 | 150 | 366 | 325 | 300 | 375 | 295 | 163 |
| PAR | | | | | | | | | |
| YARDS | | | | | | | | | |

Directions: Route 8 to Exit 42; Route 118 West to 202 West to Milton Road.

# Sunset Hill Golf Club

18 Sunset Hill Road
Brookfield, CT  (203) 740-7800
www.sunsethillgolfclub.com

**Club Pro:** Gary Cilfone, PGA
**Payment:** Cash, Check
**Tee Times:** No
**Fee  9 Holes: Weekday:** $19
**Fee 18 Holes: Weekday:** $25
**Twilight Rates:** After 4pm
**Cart Rental:** $18pp/18, $9pp/9
**Lessons:** Yes  **Schools:** Yes, inquire
**Membership:** Yes
**Other:** Clubhouse / Snack Bar / Bar-Lounge

| Tees | Holes | Yards | Par | USGA | Slope |
|------|-------|-------|-----|------|-------|
| BACK | | | | | |
| MIDDLE | 9 | 2394 | 35 | 62.6 | 100 |
| FRONT | 9 | 2346 | 35 | 66.3 | 100 |

**Weekend:** $23
**Weekend:** $29
**Discounts:** Senior & Junior
**Driving Range:** No
**Junior Golf:** Yes
**Architect/Yr Open:** 1897
**GPS:**

COUPON

Ongoing improvements. New tee on hole #3. Sister golf course is Eastwood CC. Open April - November.

| | 1 | 2 | 3 | 4 | 5 | 6 | 7 | 8 | 9 |
|------|-----|-----|-----|-----|-----|-----|-----|-----|-----|
| PAR | 5 | 3 | 3 | 4 | 4 | 4 | 5 | 4 | 3 |
| YARDS | 452 | 145 | 116 | 278 | 304 | 270 | 426 | 278 | 125 |
| PAR | | | | | | | | | |
| YARDS | | | | | | | | | |

**Directions:** I-84 to Exit 9; follow Route 25 North 3 miles; take left onto Sunset Hill Road to course.

# Tashua Knolls Country Club

40 Tashua Knolls Lane
Trumbull, CT  (203) 452-5171
www.tashuaknolls.com

**Club Pro:** Bobby Brown, PGA
**Payment:** Cash, Check, Credit
**Tee Times:** 7 days adv.
**Fee  9 Holes: Weekday:** $23
**Fee 18 Holes: Weekday:** $45
**Twilight Rates:** No
**Cart Rental:** $16pp/18, $11pp/9
**Lessons:** Yes  **Schools:** Yes
**Membership:** No
**Other:** Snack Bar / Restaurant / Bar-Lounge / Lockers / Showers

| Tees | Holes | Yards | Par | USGA | Slope |
|------|-------|-------|-----|------|-------|
| BACK | 18 | 6540 | 72 | 71.9 | 125 |
| MIDDLE | 18 | 6119 | 72 | 70.0 | 121 |
| FRONT | 18 | 5454 | 72 | 71.7 | 124 |

**Weekend:** $28
**Weekend:** $50
**Discounts:** Sr. & Jr. residents M-F
**Driving Range:** $5/bucket
**Junior Golf:** Yes
**Architect/Yr Open:** Al Zikorus/1976

"Second 9 holes opened 2005, less daunting than the first 9." –RV

| | 1 | 2 | 3 | 4 | 5 | 6 | 7 | 8 | 9 |
|------|-----|-----|-----|-----|-----|-----|-----|-----|-----|
| PAR | 5 | 4 | 3 | 4 | 4 | 3 | 5 | 4 | 4 |
| YARDS | 532 | 317 | 151 | 342 | 353 | 192 | 480 | 354 | 356 |
| | **10** | **11** | **12** | **13** | **14** | **15** | **16** | **17** | **18** |
| PAR | 4 | 4 | 3 | 4 | 5 | 4 | 5 | 3 | 4 |
| YARDS | 349 | 367 | 154 | 262 | 495 | 373 | 506 | 145 | 391 |

**Directions:** Take Merritt Parkway (Route 15) to Exit 49 (Route 25); go straight, take left onto Tashua Knolls Lane. Course is at top of hill.

**SW CT**

# Tradition GC at Oak Lane, The  New  51 ▶

1027 Racebrook Road
Woodbridge, CT (203) 397-5103
www.traditionatoaklane.com

| Tees | Holes | Yards | Par | USGA | Slope |
|------|-------|-------|-----|------|-------|
| BACK | 18 | 6680 | 72 | 72.4 | 129 |
| MIDDLE | 18 | 6120 | 72 | 70.2 | 119 |
| FRONT | 18 | 5770 | 74 | 72.9 | 131 |

**Club Pro:** Nick Rykoski, PGA
**Payment:** All Major Credit Cards
**Tee Times:** Yes
**Fee 9 Holes: Weekday:** $27 **Weekend:** $35
**Fee 18 Holes: Weekday:** $49 **Weekend:** $67
**Twilight Rates:** No **Discounts:** Senior
**Cart Rental:** Included **Driving Range:** Yes
**Lessons:** Yes **Schools:** Yes **Junior Golf:** Yes
**Membership:** No **Architect/Yr Open:** Geoffrey Cornish/1960
**Other:** Bar-Lounge / Restaurant / Snack Bar **GPS:**

Formerly private, the course offers a challenging layout, great greens and top notch service. Golfers will feel like they've just played a private course.

| | 1 | 2 | 3 | 4 | 5 | 6 | 7 | 8 | 9 |
|---|---|---|---|---|---|---|---|---|---|
| PAR | 5 | 4 | 4 | 3 | 4 | 3 | 4 | 4 | 5 |
| YARDS | 535 | 370 | 405 | 120 | 325 | 170 | 330 | 335 | 475 |
| | 10 | 11 | 12 | 13 | 14 | 15 | 16 | 17 | 18 |
| PAR | 4 | 3 | 4 | 4 | 5 | 3 | 4 | 5 | 4 |
| YARDS | 395 | 175 | 295 | 320 | 480 | 130 | 390 | 450 | 445 |

**Directions:** Take Merritt Parkway to Exit 57 to Orange Center Road. Take a left at Racebrook and the course is on the right.

# Tradition GC at Wallingford, The ✪✪✪  52 ▶

37 Harrison Road
Wallingford, CT (203) 269-6023
www.wallingfordtradition.com

| Tees | Holes | Yards | Par | USGA | Slope |
|------|-------|-------|-----|------|-------|
| BACK | 18 | 5772 | 70 | 68.8 | 121 |
| MIDDLE | 18 | 5398 | 70 | 66.9 | 119 |
| FRONT | 18 | 4458 | 70 | 68.0 | 121 |

**Club Pro:** Rick Cardozo
**Payment:** Most Major Credit Cards
**Tee Times:** 7 days adv.
**Fee 9 Holes: Weekday:** $27 w/cart **Weekend:** $35 w/cart
**Fee 18 Holes: Weekday:** $45 w/cart **Weekend:** $55 w/cart
**Twilight Rates:** No **Discounts:** Senior & Junior
**Cart Rental:** $8pp/9 **Driving Range:** Yes
**Lessons:** Yes **Schools:** Yes **Junior Golf:** Yes
**Membership:** Yes **Architect/Yr Open:** Alfred Tull/1972
**Other:** Bar-Lounge / Snack Bar / Banquet Facility **GPS:**

Player Comments: "Well-manicured greens. Great staff. Fairly priced." Dress code. Variety of special rates. Renovated club house.

| | 1 | 2 | 3 | 4 | 5 | 6 | 7 | 8 | 9 |
|---|---|---|---|---|---|---|---|---|---|
| PAR | 4 | 4 | 3 | 4 | 4 | 5 | 4 | 3 | 4 |
| YARDS | 347 | 320 | 106 | 370 | 342 | 518 | 281 | 152 | 389 |
| | 10 | 11 | 12 | 13 | 14 | 15 | 16 | 17 | 18 |
| PAR | 4 | 5 | 3 | 4 | 5 | 3 | 4 | 4 | 3 |
| YARDS | 256 | 447 | 131 | 431 | 409 | 139 | 380 | 275 | 105 |

**Directions:** I-91 to Exit 14. Take right onto Route 150 toward Wallingford. Take right onto Harrison Road.

# Twin Lakes Golf Course NR 53 ▶

241 Twin Lakes Road
North Branford, CT (203) 481-3776
www.twinlakesgolfnb.com

**Club Pro:** Edward Grant, PGA
          Anthony Celone, Manager
**Payment:** Cash Only
**Tee Times:**
**Fee 9 Holes: Weekday:** $8
**Fee 18 Holes: Weekday:** $13
**Twilight Rates:** No
**Cart Rental:** Yes
**Lessons:** Yes  **Schools:** Yes
**Membership:** No
**Other:** Snack Bar

**Weekend:** $10
**Weekend:** $16
**Discounts:** Junior 1st tee
**Driving Range:** No
**Junior Golf:** Yes
**Architect/Yr Open:**
**GPS:**

| Tees | Holes | Yards | Par | USGA | Slope |
|------|-------|-------|-----|------|-------|
| BACK | | | | | |
| MIDDLE | 9 | 1047 | 27 | | |
| FRONT | | | | | |

Open March 15-October 15. This is a very short, 9-hole, par 3 course good for family fun. Season passes for unlimited play.

| | 1 | 2 | 3 | 4 | 5 | 6 | 7 | 8 | 9 |
|------|---|---|---|---|---|---|---|---|---|
| PAR | 3 | 3 | 3 | 3 | 3 | 3 | 3 | 3 | 3 |
| YARDS | 130 | 123 | 95 | 92 | 116 | 92 | 138 | 141 | 120 |

| | | | | | | | | | |
|------|---|---|---|---|---|---|---|---|---|
| PAR | | | | | | | | | |
| YARDS | | | | | | | | | |

**Directions:** I-95 to Exit 55 on left. Take a left at first light. Follow 2 miles, Twin Lakes Road on left.

# Western Hills Golf Course NR 54 ▶

600 Park Road
Waterbury, CT (203) 756-1211
www.westernhillsgolfcourse.com

**Club Pro:** Jim Dean
**Payment:** Visa, MC
**Tee Times:** 3 days adv.
**Fee 9 Holes: Weekday:** $20
**Fee 18 Holes: Weekday:** $31
**Twilight Rates:** After 6pm M-F, after 12pm S/S
**Cart Rental:** $29/18, $19/9 per cart
**Lessons:** Yes  **Schools:** No
**Membership:** Yes
**Other:** Clubhouse / Snack Bar / Restaurant / Bar-Lounge / Banquet / Lockers / Showers

**Weekend:** $21
**Weekend:** $33
**Discounts:** Senior & Junior
**Driving Range:** No
**Junior Golf:** Yes
**Architect/Yr:** Wiliam & David Gordon/1962

COUPON

| Tees | Holes | Yards | Par | USGA | Slope |
|------|-------|-------|-----|------|-------|
| BACK | 18 | 6356 | 72 | 69.5 | 120 |
| MIDDLE | 18 | 6136 | 72 | 68.5 | 118 |
| FRONT | 18 | 5237 | 72 | 69.5 | 127 |

Scenic New England golf course with a variety of terrain and vistas. A good test of golf. The course is in the best shape ever! Much more difficult than rated.

| | 1 | 2 | 3 | 4 | 5 | 6 | 7 | 8 | 9 |
|------|---|---|---|---|---|---|---|---|---|
| PAR | 4 | 5 | 4 | 4 | 3 | 4 | 5 | 4 | 3 |
| YARDS | 354 | 458 | 356 | 340 | 162 | 374 | 527 | 387 | 145 |
| | 10 | 11 | 12 | 13 | 14 | 15 | 16 | 17 | 18 |
| PAR | 4 | 3 | 4 | 5 | 4 | 5 | 3 | 4 | 4 |
| YARDS | 363 | 138 | 305 | 495 | 391 | 480 | 153 | 381 | 327 |

**Directions:** I-84 to Exit 17. Follow Route 63 North to Park Road. Right on Park Road to stop sign. Left at stop sign to clubhouse.

**SW CT**

# Whitney Farms Golf Course ✪✪

**55**

175 Shelton Road (Route 110)
Monroe, CT (203) 268-0707
www.whitneyfarmsgc.com

| Tees | Holes | Yards | Par | USGA | Slope |
|------|-------|-------|-----|------|-------|
| BACK | 18 | 6628 | 72 | 72.4 | 134 |
| MIDDLE | 18 | 6262 | 72 | 70.9 | 129 |
| FRONT | 18 | 5832 | 73 | 72.9 | 135 |

**Club Pro:** Paul McGuire, PGA
**Payment:** Visa, MC, Amex
**Tee Times:** Yes
**Fee 9 Holes: Weekday:** $32      **Weekend:** $37
**Fee 18 Holes: Weekday:** $55      **Weekend:** $69
**Twilight Rates:** After 4pm      **Discounts:** Seniors
**Cart Rental:** Included      **Driving Range:** $6
**Lessons:** $50/half hour  **Schools:** No      **Junior Golf:** No
**Membership:** No      **Architect/Yr Open:** Hal Purdy/1982
**Other:** Clubhouse / Lockers / Showers / Snack Bar / Restaurant / Bar-Lounge

All bunkers recently redone with new sand and new cart paths.

| | 1 | 2 | 3 | 4 | 5 | 6 | 7 | 8 | 9 |
|------|-----|-----|-----|-----|-----|-----|-----|-----|-----|
| PAR | 4 | 4 | 5 | 3 | 4 | 5 | 3 | 5 | 3 |
| YARDS | 399 | 381 | 508 | 161 | 324 | 533 | 210 | 469 | 168 |
| | **10** | **11** | **12** | **13** | **14** | **15** | **16** | **17** | **18** |
| PAR | 4 | 5 | 3 | 4 | 4 | 3 | 5 | 4 | 4 |
| YARDS | 341 | 522 | 132 | 329 | 324 | 164 | 547 | 335 | 415 |

**Directions:** Merritt Parkway Exit 49 North to Route 25. Take right on Route 111 and follow for 4 miles. Take right at intersection of Route 110. Course is 1 mile on left.

# Woodhaven Country Club      NR  **56**

275 Miller Road
Bethany, CT (203) 393-3230
www.woodhavengolf.net

| Tees | Holes | Yards | Par | USGA | Slope |
|------|-------|-------|-----|------|-------|
| BACK | 9 | 6774 | 72 | 72.7 | 128 |
| MIDDLE | 9 | 6294 | 72 | 70.6 | 123 |
| FRONT | 9 | 5370 | 72 | 72.0 | 125 |

**Club Pro:** Dale Humphrey, PGA
**Payment:** Cash, Check, MC, Visa, Disc
**Tee Times:** 7 days adv.
**Fee 9 Holes: Weekday:** $21      **Weekend:** $24
**Fee 18 Holes: Weekday:** $32      **Weekend:** $40
**Twilight Rates:** Yes      **Discounts:** Sr. & Jr. wkdys before 2pm
**Cart Rental:** $17pp/18, $9pp/9      **Driving Range:** Yes
**Lessons:** Yes  **Schools:** No      **Junior Golf:** Yes
**Membership:** No      **Architect/Yr Open:** Al Zikorus/1968
**Other:** Snack Bar / Restaurant      **GPS:**

COUPON

A family owned "hidden gem." Beautifully maintaned in a secluded setting.

| | 1 | 2 | 3 | 4 | 5 | 6 | 7 | 8 | 9 |
|------|-----|-----|-----|-----|-----|-----|-----|-----|-----|
| PAR | 5 | 3 | 4 | 4 | 4 | 5 | 4 | 3 | 4 |
| YARDS | 517 | 156 | 331 | 375 | 342 | 542 | 350 | 152 | 382 |
| PAR | | | | | | | | | |
| YARDS | | | | | | | | | |

**Directions:** Route 8 to Exit 22. East on Route 67. Left on Bear Hill Road. Bear left onto Miller Road.

# Directory of Coupons

Fox Ridge Golf Club, Auburn, Maine

### NEW ENGLAND GOLFGUIDE

### Baker's Golf Center

- **Type of Discount:**
  Frequent Golf Card available for large baskets. Buy 9 & the 10th is free.
- **Days of the Week:**
  7 days a week
- **Hours of the Day:**

658 South Main Street
Lanesborough, MA
(413) 443-6102
**www.bakersgolfcenter.com**

**Pro:** Dennis Perrone, PGA

Coupon expires 12/17. Cannot be combined with any other offer.

---

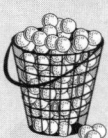

### NEW ENGLAND GOLFGUIDE

### Bill Pappas Indoor Golf & Batting Cages

- **Type of Discount:**
  Free half hour practice with paid half hour
- **Days of the Week:**
  7 days a week
- **Hours of the Day:**

75 Princeton Street
North Chelmsford, MA
(978) 251-3933
**www.egolfschool.net**

**Pro:** Bill Pappas, PGA

**Clinics:** Yes

Coupon expires 12/17. Cannot be combined with any other offer.

---

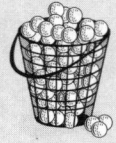

### NEW ENGLAND GOLFGUIDE

### Jim Callahan, PGA

- **Type of Discount:**
  $10 off one hour lesson
- **Days of the Week:**
  7 days a week
- **Hours of the Day:**
  Any time

Maynard Golf Course
50 Brown Street
Maynard, MA
(978) 637-2268

**Pro:** Jim Callahan, PGA
jcallahanpga@aol.com
(978) 758-0193

**Clinics:** Yes

Coupon expires 12/17. Cannot be combined with any other offer.

---

### NEW ENGLAND GOLFGUIDE

### FORE-U-GOLF Center

- **Type of Discount:**
  2 medium buckets for the price of 1
- **Days of the Week:**
  7 days a week
- **Hours of the Day:**
  All day

298 Plainfield Road
West Lebanon, NH
(603) 298-9702
**www.foreugolf.com**

**Pro:** Cory Phillips, PGA
**Clinics:** Junior & Adult

Coupon expires 12/17. Cannot be combined with any other offer.

**Driving Range Coupons**

**NEW ENGLAND GOLFGUIDE**

**2 0 1 7**

---

**NEW ENGLAND GOLFGUIDE**

**2 0 1 7**

---

**NEW ENGLAND GOLFGUIDE**

**2 0 1 7**

---

**NEW ENGLAND GOLFGUIDE**

**2 0 1 7**

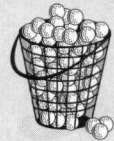

**Driving Range Coupons**

**2 0 1 7**

**2 0 1 7**

**2 0 1 7**

**2 0 1 7**

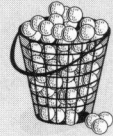
**Driving Range Coupons**

**2 0 1 7**

---

**2 0 1 7**

---

### NEW ENGLAND GOLFGUIDE

**2 0 1 7**

---

### NEW ENGLAND GOLFGUIDE

**2 0 1 7**

### Sonny's Par 3 & Driving Range

- **Type of Discount:**
  1 small bucket free;
  2 players for price of 1
- **Days of the Week:**
  Tuesday-Sunday
- **Hours of the Day:**
  Closed Mondays

Coupon expires 12/17.
Cannot be combined
with any other offer.

130 Cove Road
Winterport, ME
(207) 223-5242
**www.sonnysrange.com**

**Pro:** Sonny Reynolds, USGTF

---

### Southborough Golf Driving Range

- **Type of Discount:**
  $10 off 1 hour lesson
- **Days of the Week:**
  7 days a week
- **Hours of the Day:**

Coupon expires 12/17.
Cannot be combined
with any other offer.

20 Turnpike Road (Route 9E)
Southborough, MA
(508) 380-3786
**www.southboroughgolf.com**

**Pro:** Kevin Sullivan
**Clinics:** Yes

---

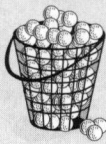

### Southborough Golf Driving Range

- **Type of Discount:**
  $2 off large bucket
- **Days of the Week:**
  Monday through
  Thursday
- **Hours of the Day:**

Coupon expires 12/17.
Cannot be combined
with any other offer.

20 Turnpike Road (Route 9E)
Southborough, MA
(508) 480-9992
**www.southboroughgolf.com**

**Pro:** Kevin Sullivan
**Clinics:** Yes

---

### Star Land Sports & Fun Park

- **Type of Discount:**
  Get 2 buckets of balls
  for the price of 1
- **Days of the Week:**
  7 days a week
- **Hours of the Day:**
  All day

Coupon expires 12/17.
Cannot be combined
with any other offer.

645 Washington Street,
Route 53
Hanover, MA
(781) 826-3083
**www.starland.us**

**Pro:** No
**Clinics:** No

**Driving Range Coupons**

**NEW ENGLAND**
**GOLFGUIDE**

2 0 1 7

---

**NEW ENGLAND**
**GOLFGUIDE**

2 0 1 7

---

**NEW ENGLAND**
**GOLFGUIDE**

2 0 1 7

---

**NEW ENGLAND**
**GOLFGUIDE**

2 0 1 7

### Stone Meadow Golf

- **Type of Discount:**
  1 medium bucket of balls free with purchase of any size bucket
- **Days of the Week:**
  7 days a week
- **Hours of the Day:**
  All day

Coupon expires 12/17.
Cannot be combined with any other offer.

675 Waltham Street
Lexington, MA
(781) 863-0445
**www.stonemeadowgolf.com**

**Pros:** George Liss,
Tony DeLeo

**Clinics:** Junior & Adult

### Taber's Lakeside Stand

- **Type of Discount:**
  Get 2 buckets of balls for the price of 1
- **Days of the Week:**
  7 days a week
- **Hours of the Day:**

Coupon expires 12/17.
Cannot be combined with any other offer.

473 Lake Shore Drive
Auburn, ME
(207) 784-2521
**www.tabersgolf.com**

**Clinics:** No

### The Only Game In Town

- **Type of Discount:**
  1 small bucket of balls free
- **Days of the Week:**
  7 days a week
- **Hours of the Day:**

Coupon expires 12/17.
Cannot be combined with any other offer.

275 Valley Service Road
North Haven, CT
(203) 234-7166
**www.onlygameintown.com**

**Pro:** Daniel Kirby

**Clinics:** No

**Driving Range Coupons**

NEW ENGLAND
GOLFGUIDE
2 0 1 7

NEW ENGLAND
GOLFGUIDE
2 0 1 7

NEW ENGLAND
GOLFGUIDE
2 0 1 7

## Airways Golf Course
West Suffield, CT  (860) 668-4973

- **Type of Discount**
  $40 for 2 players including cart (weekdays)
  $60 for 2 players including cart (weekends)
- **Days of the Week**
  7 days a week (except holidays)
- **Hours of the Day**
  All day

Coupon expires 12/31/17. Cannot be combined with any other offer.

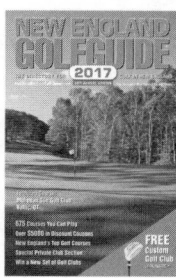

## Black Birch Country Club
Moodus, CT  (860) 873-9075

- **Type of Discount**
  2 players for price of 1
- **Days of the Week**
  7 days a week
- **Hours of the Day**
  All day weekdays; after 11am weekends
  and holidays

Coupon expires 12/31/17. Cannot be combined with any other offer.

## Blackledge Country Club - Anderson's Glen
Hebron, CT  (860) 228-0250

- **Type of Discount**
  Free golf cart with 2 paid greens fees
- **Days of the Week**
  Monday through Thursday (except holidays)
- **Hours of the Day**
  All day

Coupon expires 12/31/17. Cannot be combined with any other offer.

## Blackledge Country Club - Gilead Highlands
Hebron, CT  (860) 228-0250

- **Type of Discount**
  Free golf cart with 2 paid greens fees
- **Days of the Week**
  Monday through Thursday (except holidays)
- **Hours of the Day**
  All day

Coupon expires 12/31/17. Cannot be combined with any other offer.

**Golf Course Coupons**

**NEW ENGLAND GOLFGUIDE**

2 0 1 7

---

**NEW ENGLAND GOLFGUIDE**

2 0 1 7

---

**NEW ENGLAND GOLFGUIDE**

2 0 1 7

---

**NEW ENGLAND GOLFGUIDE**

2 0 1 7

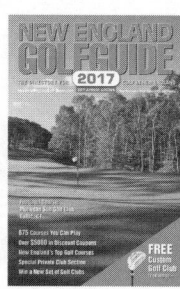

## Brooklyn Country Club
Brooklyn, CT  (860) 799-9333

- **Type of Discount**
  2 players for the price of 1

- **Days of the Week**
  Weekdays only (except holidays)

- **Hours of the Day**
  All day

Coupon expires 12/31/17. Cannot be combined with any other offer.

## Cedar Ridge Golf Course
East Lyme, CT  (860) 691-4568

- **Type of Discount**
  2 players for the price of 1

- **Days of the Week**
  Weekdays only (except holidays)

- **Hours of the Day**
  All day

Coupon expires 12/31/17. Cannot be combined with any other offer.

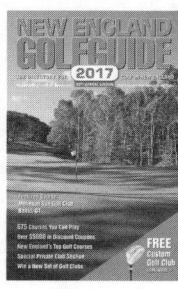

## Connecticut National Golf Club
Putnam, CT  (860) 928-7748

- **Type of Discount**
  4 players for the price of 3

- **Days of the Week**
  Weekdays only (except holidays)

- **Hours of the Day**
  All day

Coupon expires 12/31/17. Cannot be combined with any other offer.

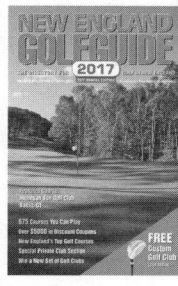

## Copper Hill Golf Club
East Granby, CT  (860) 653-6191

- **Type of Discount**
  2 players for the price of 1 (cart required)

- **Days of the Week**
  Weekdays only (except holidays)

- **Hours of the Day**
  All day

Coupon expires 12/31/17. Cannot be combined with any other offer.

**Golf Course Coupons**

**NEW ENGLAND GOLFGUIDE**

2 0 1 7

---

**NEW ENGLAND GOLFGUIDE**

2 0 1 7

---

**NEW ENGLAND GOLFGUIDE**

2 0 1 7

---

**NEW ENGLAND GOLFGUIDE**

2 0 1 7

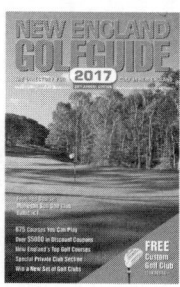

### Elmridge Golf Course
Pawcatuck, CT  (860) 599-2248

- **Type of Discount**
  Free golf cart with 2 paid greens fees

- **Days of the Week**
  Weekdays only (except holidays)

- **Hours of the Day**
  All day. Subject to availability of cart.
  No facsimilies.

Coupon expires 12/31/17. Cannot be combined with any other offer.

---

### East Mountain Golf Course
Waterbury, CT  (203) 753-1425

- **Type of Discount for Foursomes**
  9 holes – $21pp (includes cart)
  18 holes – $30pp (includes cart)

- **Days of the Week**
  Weekdays only (except holidays)

- **Hours of the Day**
  7am - 1pm

Coupon expires 12/31/17. Cannot be combined with any other offer.

---

### Farmingbury Hills Country Club
Wolcott CT  (203) 879-8038

- **Type of Discount for Foursomes**
  9 holes – $22.95 (includes cart and lunch)

- **Days of the Week**
  Monday through Thursday (except holidays)

- **Hours of the Day**
  10am–1pm

Coupon expires 12/31/17. Cannot be combined with any other offer.

---

### Fox Hopyard Golf Club
East Haddam, CT  (860) 434-6644

- **Type of Discount**
  4 players for the price of 3

- **Days of the Week**
  Monday through Thursday (except holidays)

- **Hours of the Day**
  All day. Must call for tee time
  no more than 3 days in advance.

Coupon expires 12/31/17. Cannot be combined with any other offer.

**Golf Course Coupons**

**NEW ENGLAND GOLFGUIDE**

**2017**

---

**NEW ENGLAND GOLFGUIDE**

**2017**

---

**NEW ENGLAND GOLFGUIDE**

**2017**

---

**NEW ENGLAND GOLFGUIDE**

**2017**

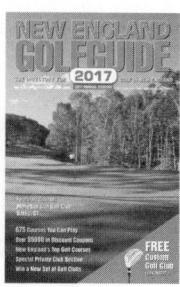

## Gainfield Farms Golf Course
Southbury, CT  (203) 262-1100

- **Type of Discount**
  $2 off 9 holes with coupon

- **Days of the Week**
  7 days a week

- **Hours of the Day**
  All day and/or league play.

Coupon expires 12/31/17. Cannot be combined with any other offer.

## Grassmere Country Club
Enfield, CT  (860) 749-7740

- **Type of Discount**
  Play 5 rounds of golf and
  receive the 6th round free

- **Days of the Week**
  7 days a week

- **Hours of the Day**
  All day. Excludes leagues.

Coupon expires 12/31/17. Cannot be combined with any other offer.

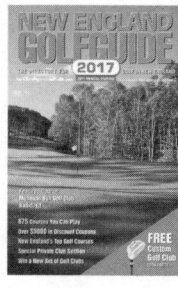

## Guilford Lakes Golf Course
Guilford, CT  (203) 453-8214

- **Type of Discount**
  Free golf cart with 2 paid greens fees

- **Days of the Week**
  7 days a week

- **Hours of the Day**
  All day

Coupon expires 12/31/17. Cannot be combined with any other offer.

## Harrisville Golf Course
Woodstock, CT  (860) 928-6098

- **Type of Discount**
  $3 off greens fees for up to 2 players

- **Days of the Week**
  Weekdays only (except holidays)

- **Hours of the Day**
  All day

Coupon expires 12/31/17. Cannot be combined with any other offer.

**Golf Course Coupons**

**NEW ENGLAND GOLFGUIDE**

2 0 1 7

**NEW ENGLAND GOLFGUIDE**

2 0 1 7

**NEW ENGLAND GOLFGUIDE**

2 0 1 7

**NEW ENGLAND GOLFGUIDE**

2 0 1 7

### Hawk's Landing Country Club
Southington, CT  (860) 793-6000

- **Type of Discount**
  $2 off a round or golf cart

- **Days of the Week**
  7 days a week

- **Hours of the Day**
  All day. Saturday and Sunday only after 1pm.

Coupon expires 12/31/17. Cannot be combined with any other offer.

---

### Hop Brook Golf Course
Naugatuck, CT  (203) 729-8013

- **Type of Discount**
  $5 off greens fee and cart

- **Days of the Week**
  7 days a week

- **Hours of the Day**
  M-F 7am - 2:45pm; S-S after 1pm for 9 holes
  M-F 7am - 12pm; S-S after 1pm for 18 holes

Coupon expires 12/31/17. Cannot be combined with any other offer.

---

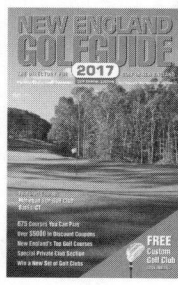

### Hop Meadow Country Club
Simsbury, CT  (860) 658-7623

- **Type of Discount**
  4 players for the price of 3

- **Days of the Week**
  Monday through Thursday (except holidays)

- **Hours of the Day**
  Call to request

Coupon expires 12/31/17. Cannot be combined with any other offer.

---

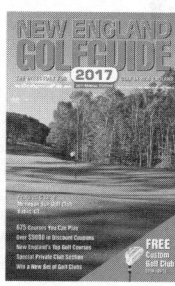

### Hotchkiss School Golf Club
Lakeville, CT  (860) 435-4400

- **Type of Discount**
  2 players for the price of 1 greens fees.
  Cart rental required.

- **Days of the Week**
  Weekdays only (except holidays)

- **Hours of the Day**
  All day

Coupon expires 12/31/17. Cannot be combined with any other offer.

**Golf Course Coupons**

**NEW ENGLAND GOLFGUIDE**

**2 0 1 7**

---
✂ - - - - - - - - - - - - - - - - - - - - - - - - - - - - -

**NEW ENGLAND GOLFGUIDE**

**2 0 1 7**

---
✂ - - - - - - - - - - - - - - - - - - - - - - - - - - - - -

**NEW ENGLAND GOLFGUIDE**

**2 0 1 7**

---
✂ - - - - - - - - - - - - - - - - - - - - - - - - - - - - -

**NEW ENGLAND GOLFGUIDE**

**2 0 1 7**

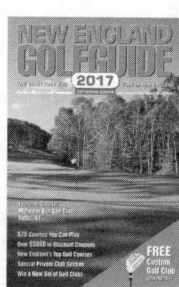

### Indian Springs Golf Club
Middlefield, CT  (860) 349-8109

- **Type of Discount**
  Free golf cart with 2 paid greens fees
- **Days of the Week**
  Weekdays before 3pm
- **Hours of the Day**
  Before 3pm

Coupon expires 12/31/17. Cannot be combined with any other offer.

### Manchester Country Club
Manchester, CT  (860) 646-0226

- **Type of Discount**
  Buy 1 greens fee get 1 free (cart rental required)
- **Days of the Week**
  Monday through Thursday (except holidays)
- **Hours of the Day**
  All day

Coupon expires 12/31/17. Cannot be combined with any other offer.

### Miner Hills Golf Course
Middletown, CT  (860) 635-0051

- **Type of Discount**
  $14 per person
- **Days of the Week**
  Monday through Thursday
- **Hours of the Day**
  Before 1pm

Coupon expires 12/31/17. Cannot be combined with any other offer.

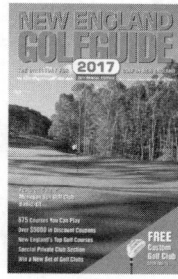

### Mohegan Sun Golf Club
Baltic, CT (860) 862-9660

- **Type of Discount**
  4 players for price of 3
- **Days of the Week**
  Sunday though Thursday (except holidays)
- **Hours of the Day**
  All day

Coupon expires 12/31/17. Cannot be combined with any other offer.

**Golf Course Coupons**

**NEW ENGLAND**
**GOLFGUIDE**

2 0 1 7

---

**NEW ENGLAND**
**GOLFGUIDE**

2 0 1 7

---

**NEW ENGLAND**
**GOLFGUIDE**

2 0 1 7

---

**NEW ENGLAND**
**GOLFGUIDE**

2 0 1 7

## Oxford Greens, The Golf Club at
Oxford, CT  (203) 888-1600

- **Type of Discount**
  $5 off per player (up to 4 players)
- **Days of the Week**
  Monday though Thursday (except holidays)
- **Hours of the Day**
  Before 5pm

Coupon expires 12/31/17. Cannot be combined with any other offer.

---

## Pequot Golf Club
Wheeler Road, Stonington, CT  (860) 535-1898

- **Type of Discount**
  4 players for the price of 3.
  Cart rental required.
- **Days of the Week**
  7 days a week
- **Hours of the Day**
  All day

Coupon expires 12/31/17. Cannot be combined with any other offer.

---

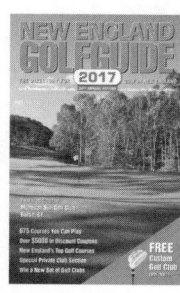

## Pomperaug Golf Club
Southbury, CT  (203) 264-9484

- **Type of Discount**
  2 players for the price of 1 (cart rental required)
- **Days of the Week**
  Tuesdays only
- **Hours of the Day**
  All day

Coupon expires 12/31/17. Cannot be combined with any other offer.

---

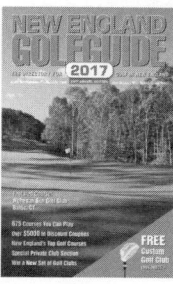

## Portland Golf Club
Portland, CT  (860) 342-6107

- **Type of Discount**
  Free golf cart with 2 paid greens fees
- **Days of the Week**
  Weekdays only (except holidays)
- **Hours of the Day**
  7–11am weekdays

Coupon expires 12/31/17. Cannot be combined with any other offer.

Golf Course Coupons

**NEW ENGLAND GOLFGUIDE**

**2 0 1 7**

---

**NEW ENGLAND GOLFGUIDE**

**2 0 1 7**

---

**NEW ENGLAND GOLFGUIDE**

**2 0 1 7**

---

**NEW ENGLAND GOLFGUIDE**

**2 0 1 7**

### Quarry Ridge Golf Course
Portland, CT (860) 342-6113

- **Type of Discount**
  $35 per person (includes cart)
- **Days of the Week**
  Weekdays only (except holidays)
- **Hours of the Day**
  All day

Coupon expires 12/31/17. Cannot be combined with any other offer.

---

### Richter Park Golf Course
Danbury, CT (203) 792-2550

- **Type of Discount**
  Danbury resident rates
- **Days of the Week**
  Monday through Thursday (except holidays)
- **Hours of the Day**
  All day

Coupon expires 12/31/17. Cannot be combined with any other offer.

---

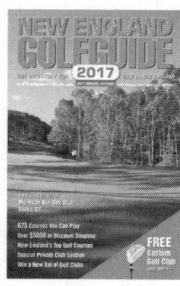

### River Ridge Golf Course
Jewett City, CT (860) 376-3268

- **Type of Discount**
  18 holes w/cart - $40 per person
- **Days of the Week**
  Monday through Thursday (except holidays)
- **Hours of the Day**
  After 11am

Coupon expires 12/31/17. Cannot be combined with any other offer.

---

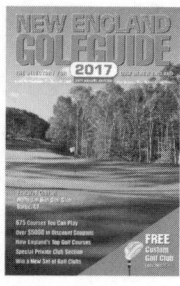

### Shennecosset Golf Club
Groton, CT (860) 445-0262

- **Type of Discount**
  Free cart with 2 paid greens fees
- **Days of the Week**
  Weekdays only (except holidays)
- **Hours of the Day**
  All day

Coupon expires 12/31/17. Cannot be combined with any other offer.

**NEW ENGLAND GOLFGUIDE**

2 0 1 7

**NEW ENGLAND GOLFGUIDE**

2 0 1 7

**NEW ENGLAND GOLFGUIDE**

2 0 1 7

**NEW ENGLAND GOLFGUIDE**

2 0 1 7

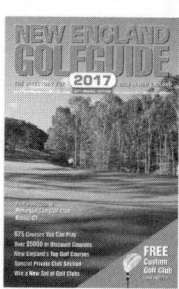

### Skungamaug River Golf Club
Coventry, CT  (860) 742-9348

- **Type of Discount**
  Free golf cart with 2 paid greens fees
- **Days of the Week**
  7 days a week
- **Hours of the Day**
  Weekday mornings, weekend afternoons

Coupon expires 12/31/17. Cannot be combined with any other offer.

### Sleeping Giant Golf Course
Hamden, CT  (203) 281-9456

- **Type of Discount**
  2 players for the price of 1
- **Days of the Week**
  7 days a week
- **Hours of the Day**
  All day

Coupon expires 12/31/17. Cannot be combined with any other offer.

### Sunset Hill Golf Club
Brookfield, CT  (203) 740-7800

- **Type of Discount**
  2 players for the price of 1 (cart rental required)
- **Days of the Week**
  Monday through Thursday (except holidays)
- **Hours of the Day**
  All day

Coupon expires 12/31/17. Cannot be combined with any other offer.

### Timberlin Golf Club
Berlin, CT  (860) 828-3228

- **Type of Discount**
  $34 for 18 holes (cart included)
- **Days of the Week**
  Weekdays only (except holidays)
- **Hours of the Day**
  All day

Coupon expires 12/31/17. Cannot be combined with any other offer.

**Golf Course Coupons**

**NEW ENGLAND GOLFGUIDE**

2 0 1 7

**NEW ENGLAND GOLFGUIDE**

2 0 1 7

**NEW ENGLAND GOLFGUIDE**

2 0 1 7

**NEW ENGLAND GOLFGUIDE**

2 0 1 7

### Tower Ridge Golf Course
Simsbury, CT  (860) 658-9767

- **Type of Discount**
  4 players for the price of 2.
  Cart rental required.
- **Days of the Week**
  Weekdays only (except holidays)
- **Hours of the Day**
  All day

Coupon expires 12/31/17. Cannot be combined with any other offer.

---

### Twin Hills Country Club
Coventry, CT  (860) 742-9705

- **Type of Discount**
  Free golf cart with 2 paid greens fees
- **Days of the Week**
  Monday through Thursday (except holidays)
- **Hours of the Day**
  All day

Coupon expires 12/31/17. Cannot be combined with any other offer.

---

### Western Hills Golf Course
Waterbury, CT  (203) 756-1211

- **Type of Discount**
  2 players for the price of 1.
  Cart rental required.
- **Days of the Week**
  Weekdays only (except holidays)
- **Hours of the Day**
  Before 12pm

Coupon expires 12/31/17. Cannot be combined with any other offer.

---

### Willow Brook Golf Course
South Windsor, CT  (860) 648-2061

- **Type of Discount**
  4 players for the price of 3
- **Days of the Week**
  Monday through Thursday (except holidays)
- **Hours of the Day**
  All day

Coupon expires 12/31/17. Cannot be combined with any other offer.

**Golf Course Coupons**

**NEW ENGLAND GOLFGUIDE**

2 0 1 7

---

**NEW ENGLAND GOLFGUIDE**

2 0 1 7

---

**NEW ENGLAND GOLFGUIDE**

2 0 1 7

---

**NEW ENGLAND GOLFGUIDE**

2 0 1 7

### Woodhaven Country Club
Bethany, CT (203) 393-3230

- **Type of Discount**
  4 players for price of 3
- **Days of the Week**
  7 days a week
- **Hours of the Day**
  All day

Coupon expires 12/31/17. Cannot be combined with any other offer.

---

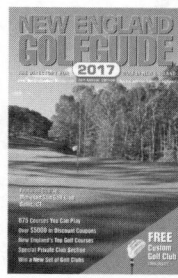

### Woodstock Golf Course
South Woodstock, CT (860) 928-4130

- **Type of Discount**
  2 players for price of 1
- **Days of the Week**
  7 days a week
- **Hours of the Day**
  All day

Coupon expires 12/31/17. Cannot be combined with any other offer.

---

### Apple Valley Golf Course
Lewiston, ME (207) 784-9773

- **Type of Discount**
  Free golf cart with 2 paid greens fees
- **Days of the Week**
  7 days a week
- **Hours of the Day**
  All day

Coupon expires 12/31/17. Cannot be combined with any other offer.

---

### Aroostook Valley Country Club
Fort Fairfield, ME (207) 476-8083

- **Type of Discount**
  2 players for the price of 1
- **Days of the Week**
  7 days a week
- **Hours of the Day**
  All day

Coupon expires 12/31/17. Cannot be combined with any other offer.

**Golf Course Coupons**

**NEW ENGLAND GOLFGUIDE**

2 0 1 7

**NEW ENGLAND GOLFGUIDE**

2 0 1 7

**NEW ENGLAND GOLFGUIDE**

2 0 1 7

**NEW ENGLAND GOLFGUIDE**

2 0 1 7

### Bangor Municipal Golf Course
Bangor, ME  (207) 941-0232

- **Type of Discount**
  18 holes w/cart for $40
- **Days of the Week**
  7 days a week
- **Hours of the Day**
  All day

Coupon expires 12/31/17. Cannot be combined with any other offer.

### Bar Harbor Golf Course
Route 204, Trenton, ME  (207) 667-7505

- **Type of Discount**
  Free golf cart with 2 paid greens fees
- **Days of the Week**
  Monday through Saturday
- **Hours of the Day**
  All day

Coupon expires 12/31/17. Cannot be combined with any other offer.

### Barnes Brook Golf Course
Lincoln, ME  (207) 732-3006

- **Type of Discount**
  Free golf cart with 2 paid greens fees
- **Days of the Week**
  7 days a week
- **Hours of the Day**
  All day

Coupon expires 12/31/17. Cannot be combined with any other offer.

### Barren View Golf Course
Jonesboro, ME  (207) 434-6531

- **Type of Discount**
  2 players for the price of 1
- **Days of the Week**
  7 days a week
- **Hours of the Day**
  All day

Coupon expires 12/31/17. Cannot be combined with any other offer.

**NEW ENGLAND GOLFGUIDE**

2 0 1 7

**NEW ENGLAND GOLFGUIDE**

2 0 1 7

**NEW ENGLAND GOLFGUIDE**

2 0 1 7

**NEW ENGLAND GOLFGUIDE**

2 0 1 7

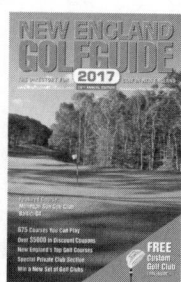

### Bethel Inn Resort
Bethel, ME (207) 824-6276

- **Type of Discount**
  2nd greens fees at 50% off

- **Days of the Week**
  Weekdays only (except holidays)

- **Hours of the Day**
  All day. Must make tee time no more than
  48 hours in advance.

Coupon expires 12/31/17. Cannot be combined with any other offer.

### Bridgton Highlands Country Club
Bridgton, ME (207) 647-3491

- **Type of Discount**
  $32 for 18 holes (cart included)

- **Days of the Week**
  Monday through Thursday (except holidays)

- **Hours of the Day**
  All day. Fri/Sat/Sun/Holiday after 12pm.

Coupon expires 12/31/17. Cannot be combined with any other offer.

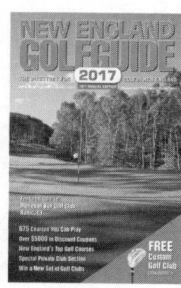

### Brunswick Golf Club
River Road, Brunswick, ME (207) 725-8224

- **Type of Discount**
  4 players for the price of 3

- **Days of the Week**
  7 days a week

- **Hours of the Day**
  All day

Coupon expires 12/31/17. Cannot be combined with any other offer.

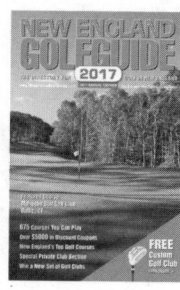

### Bucksport Golf Club
Route 46, Bucksport, ME (207) 469-7612

- **Type of Discount**
  4 players for the price of 3

- **Days of the Week**
  7 days a week, not valid in July and August

- **Hours of the Day**
  All day

Coupon expires 12/31/17. Cannot be combined with any other offer.

**NEW ENGLAND GOLFGUIDE**

2 0 1 7

---

**NEW ENGLAND GOLFGUIDE**

2 0 1 7

---

**NEW ENGLAND GOLFGUIDE**

2 0 1 7

---

**NEW ENGLAND GOLFGUIDE**

2 0 1 7

## Cape Neddick Country Club
Ogunquit, ME (207) 361-2011

- **Type of Discount**
  4 players for the price of 3
- **Days of the Week**
  Monday through Thursday (except holidays)
- **Hours of the Day**
  All day

Coupon expires 12/31/17. Cannot be combined with any other offer.

## Caribou Country Club
Caribou, ME (207) 493-3933

- **Type of Discount**
  4 players for the price of 3
- **Days of the Week**
  7 days a week
- **Hours of the Day**
  All day. Call in advance.

Coupon expires 12/31/17. Cannot be combined with any other offer.

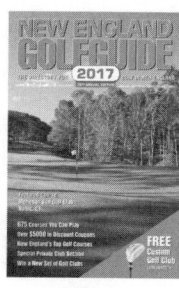

## Cedar Springs Golf Course
Albion, ME (207) 437-2073

- **Type of Discount**
  2 players for the price of 1
- **Days of the Week**
  Weekdays only (except holidays)
- **Hours of the Day**
  All day

Coupon expires 12/31/17. Cannot be combined with any other offer.

## Cobbossee Colony Golf Course
Monmouth, ME (207) 268-4182

- **Type of Discount**
  4 players for the price of 3
- **Days of the Week**
  Weekdays only (except holidays)
- **Hours of the Day**
  All day

Coupon expires 12/31/17. Cannot be combined with any other offer.

**NEW ENGLAND GOLFGUIDE**

2 0 1 7

---

**NEW ENGLAND GOLFGUIDE**

2 0 1 7

---

**NEW ENGLAND GOLFGUIDE**

2 0 1 7

---

**NEW ENGLAND GOLFGUIDE**

2 0 1 7

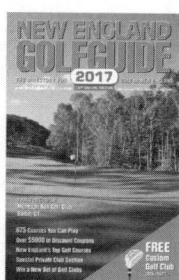

## Country View Golf Course
Route 7, Brooks, ME  (207) 722-3161

- **Type of Discount**
  1/2 price golf cart with 2 paid greens fees
- **Days of the Week**
  7 days a week
- **Hours of the Day**
  All day

Coupon expires 12/31/17. Cannot be combined with any other offer.

## Deep Brook Golf Course
Saco, ME  (207) 283-3500

- **Type of Discount**
  4 players for the price of 3
- **Days of the Week**
  7 days a week
- **Hours of the Day**
  All day

Coupon expires 12/31/17. Cannot be combined with any other offer.

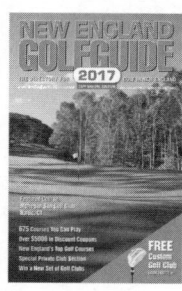

## Dunegrass Golf Club
Old Orchard Beach, ME  (207) 934-4513

- **Type of Discount**
  4 players for the price of 3
- **Days of the Week**
  7 days a week
- **Hours of the Day**
  All day

Coupon expires 12/31/17. Cannot be combined with any other offer.

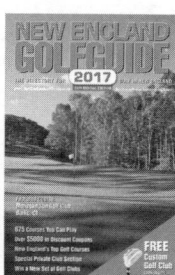

## Dutch Elm Golf Course
Arundel, ME  (207) 282-9850

- **Type of Discount**
  4 players for the price of 3
- **Days of the Week**
  7 days a week
- **Hours of the Day**
  After 12pm

Coupon expires 12/31/17. Cannot be combined with any other offer.

**Golf Course Coupons**

**NEW ENGLAND GOLFGUIDE**

2 0 1 7

---

**NEW ENGLAND GOLFGUIDE**

2 0 1 7

---

**NEW ENGLAND GOLFGUIDE**

2 0 1 7

---

**NEW ENGLAND GOLFGUIDE**

2 0 1 7

NEW ENGLAND GOLFGUIDE

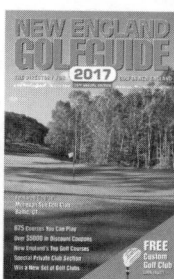

### Evergreen Golf Club
Rangeley, ME (207) 240-5248

- **Type of Discount**
  15% off everything
- **Days of the Week**
  Weekdays only (except holidays)
- **Hours of the Day**
  All day

Coupon expires 12/31/17. Cannot be combined with any other offer.

---

### Fort Kent Golf Club
Fort Kent, ME (207) 834-3149

- **Type of Discount**
  1 player at 9 hole price for 18 holes
- **Days of the Week**
  7 days a week
- **Hours of the Day**
  All day

Coupon expires 12/31/17. Cannot be combined with any other offer.

---

### Foxcroft Golf Club
Dover-Foxcroft, ME (207) 564-8887

- **Type of Discount**
  $99 for 4 players with carts
- **Days of the Week**
  Weekdays only (except holidays)
- **Hours of the Day**
  All day

Coupon expires 12/31/17. Cannot be combined with any other offer.

---

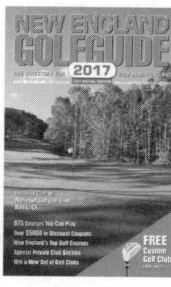

### Fox Ridge Golf Club
Auburn, ME (207) 777-GOLF(4653)

- **Type of Discount**
  $42 for 18 holes (cart included)
- **Days of the Week**
  7 days a week
- **Hours of the Day**
  All day. Fri/Sat/Sun/Holiday after 12pm.

Coupon expires 12/31/17. Cannot be combined with any other offer.

**Golf Course Coupons**

**NEW ENGLAND GOLFGUIDE**

**2 0 1 7**

---

**NEW ENGLAND GOLFGUIDE**

**2 0 1 7**

---

**NEW ENGLAND GOLFGUIDE**

**2 0 1 7**

---

**NEW ENGLAND GOLFGUIDE**

**2 0 1 7**

### Freeport Country Club
Freeport, ME  (207) 865-0711

- **Type of Discount**
  $29 for 18 holes (includes cart)
- **Days of the Week**
  Monday through Thursday (except holidays)
- **Hours of the Day**
  All day

Coupon expires 12/31/17. Cannot be combined with any other offer.

### Frye Island Golf Course
Raymond, ME  (207) 655-3551

- **Type of Discount**
  $5 off greens fees for up to 2 players
- **Days of the Week**
  Weekdays only (except holidays)
- **Hours of the Day**
  All day. Valid May through June and
  September through October.

Coupon expires 12/31/17. Cannot be combined with any other offer.

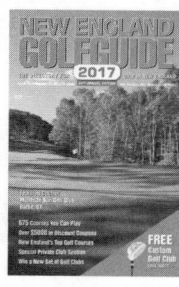

### Goose River Golf Club
Rockport, ME  (207) 236-8488

- **Type of Discount**
  4 players for the price of 3
- **Days of the Week**
  Weekdays only (except holidays)
- **Hours of the Day**
  All day

Coupon expires 12/31/17. Cannot be combined with any other offer.

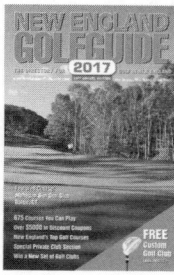

### Great Chebeague Golf Club
Chebeague Island, ME  (207) 846-9478

- **Type of Discount**
  25% discount for 2-4 players
- **Days of the Week**
  Monday through Thursday(except holidays)
- **Hours of the Day**
  All day

Coupon expires 12/31/17. Cannot be combined with any other offer.

**Golf Course Coupons**

**NEW ENGLAND GOLFGUIDE**

2 0 1 7

**NEW ENGLAND GOLFGUIDE**

2 0 1 7

**NEW ENGLAND GOLFGUIDE**

2 0 1 7

**NEW ENGLAND GOLFGUIDE**

2 0 1 7

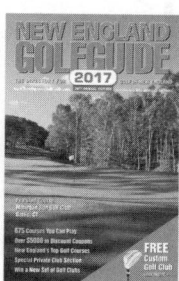

### Hampden Country Club
Hampden, ME  (207) 862-9999

- **Type of Discount**
  All you can play for $15. Cart not included.
- **Days of the Week**
  Wednesday
- **Hours of the Day**
  All day

Coupon expires 12/31/17. Cannot be combined with any other offer.

### Hermon Meadow Golf Club
Bangor, ME  (207) 848-3741

- **Type of Discount**
  Free golf cart with 2 regular 18 hole greens fees
- **Days of the Week**
  Weekdays only (except holidays)
- **Hours of the Day**
  All day

Coupon expires 12/31/17. Cannot be combined with any other offer.

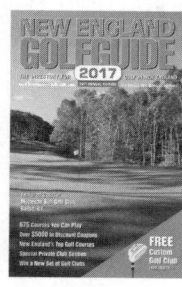

### Hidden Meadows Golf Course
Old Town, ME  (207) 827-4779

- **Type of Discount**
  Free golf cart with 2 paid greens fees
- **Days of the Week**
  7 days a week
- **Hours of the Day**
  All day

Coupon expires 12/31/17. Cannot be combined with any other offer.

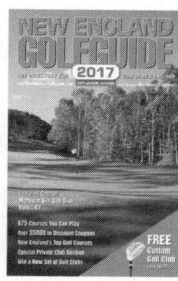

### Highland Green Golf Club
Topsham, ME  (207) 725-8066

- **Type of Discount**
  $29 for 18 holes (includes cart)
- **Days of the Week**
  Monday through Thursday (except holidays)
- **Hours of the Day**
  All day

Coupon expires 12/31/17. Cannot be combined with any other offer.

**Golf Course Coupons**

**NEW ENGLAND GOLFGUIDE**

2 0 1 7

**NEW ENGLAND GOLFGUIDE**

2 0 1 7

**NEW ENGLAND GOLFGUIDE**

2 0 1 7

**NEW ENGLAND GOLFGUIDE**

2 0 1 7

### Houlton Community Golf Course
Houlton, ME (207) 532-2662

- **Type of Discount**
  4 players for the price of 3
- **Days of the Week**
  7 days a week
- **Hours of the Day**
  All day. Call for tee times.

Coupon expires 12/31/17. Cannot be combined with any other offer.

---

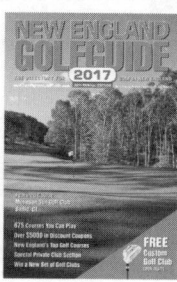

### Island Country Club
Deer Isle, ME (207) 348-2379

- **Type of Discount**
  4 players for the price of 3
- **Days of the Week**
  7 days a week
- **Hours of the Day**
  All day. Call for tee times.

Coupon expires 12/31/17. Cannot be combined with any other offer.

---

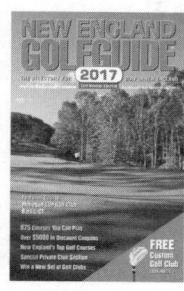

### Jato Highlands Golf Course
Lincoln, ME (207) 794-2433

- **Type of Discount**
  4 players for the price of 3
- **Days of the Week**
  7 days a week
- **Hours of the Day**
  All day

Coupon expires 12/31/17. Cannot be combined with any other offer.

---

### Johnson W. Parks Golf Course
Pittsfield, ME (207) 487-5545

- **Type of Discount**
  2 players for the price of 1.
  Cart rental required.
- **Days of the Week**
  7 days a week
- **Hours of the Day**
  After 1pm

Coupon expires 12/31/17. Cannot be combined with any other offer.

**Golf Course Coupons**

**NEW ENGLAND**
**GOLFGUIDE**

2 0 1 7

**NEW ENGLAND**
**GOLFGUIDE**

2 0 1 7

**NEW ENGLAND**
**GOLFGUIDE**

2 0 1 7

**NEW ENGLAND**
**GOLFGUIDE**

2 0 1 7

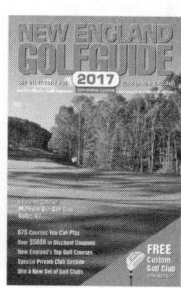

### Kebo Valley Golf Club
Bar Harbor, ME (207) 288-3000

- **Type of Discount**
  15% off greens fees
- **Days of the Week**
  7 days a week
- **Hours of the Day**
  Not valid for afternoon or twilight rates

Coupon expires 12/31/17. Cannot be combined with any other offer.

---

### Kenduskeag Golf & Country Club
Kenduskeag, ME (207) 884-7330

- **Type of Discount**
  Free golf cart with 2 paid greens fees
- **Days of the Week**
  Weekdays only (except holidays)
- **Hours of the Day**
  All day

Coupon expires 12/31/17. Cannot be combined with any other offer.

---

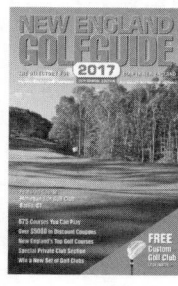

### Lake Kezar Country Club
Lovell, ME (207) 925-2462

- **Type of Discount**
  4 players for price of 3
- **Days of the Week**
  7 days a week
- **Hours of the Day**
  After 1pm

Coupon expires 12/31/17. Cannot be combined with any other offer.

---

### Lakeview Golf Course
Burnham, ME (207) 948-5414

- **Type of Discount**
  4 greens fees for the price of 3
- **Days of the Week**
  Monday through Thursday (except holidays)
- **Hours of the Day**
  All day

Coupon expires 12/31/17. Cannot be combined with any other offer.

**Golf Course Coupons**

**NEW ENGLAND GOLFGUIDE**

2 0 1 7

---

**NEW ENGLAND GOLFGUIDE**

2 0 1 7

---

**NEW ENGLAND GOLFGUIDE**

2 0 1 7

---

**NEW ENGLAND GOLFGUIDE**

2 0 1 7

## Lakewood Golf Course
Madison, ME (207) 474-5955

- **Type of Discount**
  4 players for the price of 3

- **Days of the Week**
  7 days a week

- **Hours of the Day**
  All day

Coupon expires 12/31/17. Cannot be combined with any other offer.

## Ledges Golf Club, The
York, ME (207) 351-3000

- **Type of Discount**
  Free golf cart with 2 paid greens fees

- **Days of the Week**
  7 days a week

- **Hours of the Day**
  All day

Coupon expires 12/31/17. Cannot be combined with any other offer.

## Limestone Country Club
Limestone, ME (207) 328-7277

- **Type of Discount**
  $5 off greens fees. Cart rental required.

- **Days of the Week**
  Weekdays only (except holidays)

- **Hours of the Day**
  All day

Coupon expires 12/31/17. Cannot be combined with any other offer.

## Links at Outlook, The
South Berwick, ME (207) 384-4653

- **Type of Discount**
  Free golf cart with 2 paid greens fees

- **Days of the Week**
  7 days a week

- **Hours of the Day**
  All day

Coupon expires 12/31/17. Cannot be combined with any other offer.

Golf Course Coupons

**NEW ENGLAND GOLFGUIDE**

2 0 1 7

---

**NEW ENGLAND GOLFGUIDE**

2 0 1 7

---

**NEW ENGLAND GOLFGUIDE**

2 0 1 7

---

**NEW ENGLAND GOLFGUIDE**

2 0 1 7

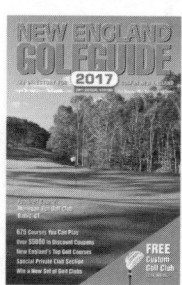

### Long Lake Country Club
Madawaska, ME (207) 895-6957

- **Type of Discount**
  Free golf cart with 2 paid greens fees
- **Days of the Week**
  7 days a week
- **Hours of the Day**
  All day. Valid June 1 through September 15.

Coupon expires 12/31/17. Cannot be combined with any other offer.

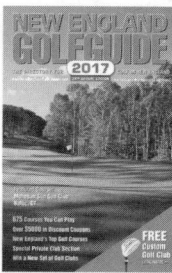

### Lucerne-in-Maine Golf Course
Dedham, ME (207) 843-6282

- **Type of Discount**
  Free golf cart with 2 paid greens fees
- **Days of the Week**
  Weekdays only (except holidays)
- **Hours of the Day**
  Before 3pm

Coupon expires 12/31/17. Cannot be combined with any other offer.

### Mars Hill Country Club
Mars Hill, ME (207) 425-4802

- **Type of Discount**
  $32 for 18 holes including cart
- **Days of the Week**
  7 days a week
- **Hours of the Day**
  All day

Coupon expires 12/31/17. Cannot be combined with any other offer.

### Martindale Country Club
Auburn, ME (207) 782-1107

- **Type of Discount**
  4 players for the price of 3
- **Days of the Week**
  Monday through Thursday (except holidays)
- **Hours of the Day**
  All day

Coupon expires 12/31/17. Cannot be combined with any other offer.

**Golf Course Coupons**

**NEW ENGLAND GOLFGUIDE**

**2017**

---

**NEW ENGLAND GOLFGUIDE**

**2017**

---

**NEW ENGLAND GOLFGUIDE**

**2017**

---

**NEW ENGLAND GOLFGUIDE**

**2017**

### Meadows Golf Club, The
Litchfield, ME  (207) 268-3000

- **Type of Discount**
  25% discount for 2 to 4 players
- **Days of the Week**
  7 days a week
- **Hours of the Day**
  Saturday and Sunday after 12pm

Coupon expires 12/31/17. Cannot be combined with any other offer.

---

### Mere Creek Golf Course
Brunswick, ME  (207) 721-9995

- **Type of Discount**
  $29 for 18 holes (includes cart)
- **Days of the Week**
  Monday through Thursday (except holidays)
- **Hours of the Day**
  All day

Coupon expires 12/31/17. Cannot be combined with any other offer.

---

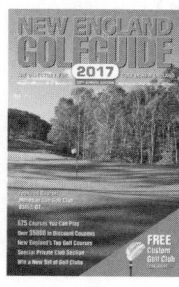

### Merriland Farm Par 3 Golf
Wells, ME  (207) 646-0508

- **Type of Discount**
  2 players for the price of 1
- **Days of the Week**
  Weekdays only (except holidays)
- **Hours of the Day**
  All day. Valid April, May, June, September, and October.

Coupon expires 12/31/17. Cannot be combined with any other offer.

---

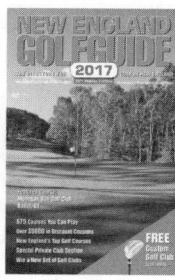

### Mt. Kineo Golf Course
Kineo Island Township, ME  (207) 534-9012

- **Type of Discount**
  Free golf cart with 2 paid greens fees
- **Days of the Week**
  7 days a week
- **Hours of the Day**
  All day

Coupon expires 12/31/17. Cannot be combined with any other offer.

**Golf Course Coupons**

**NEW ENGLAND GOLFGUIDE**

2 0 1 7

---

**NEW ENGLAND GOLFGUIDE**

2 0 1 7

---

**NEW ENGLAND GOLFGUIDE**

2 0 1 7

---

**NEW ENGLAND GOLFGUIDE**

2 0 1 7

## Naples Golf and Country Club
Route 114, Naples, ME (207) 693-6424

- **Type of Discount**
  25% discount for 2-4 players

- **Days of the Week**
  Weekdays only (except holidays)

- **Hours of the Day**
  After 1pm

Coupon expires 12/31/17. Cannot be combined with any other offer.

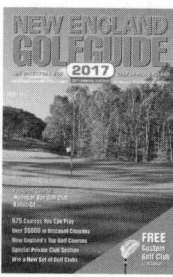

## Nonesuch River Golf Club
Scarborough, ME (888) 256-2717

- **Type of Discount**
  4 players for the price of 3. Cart rental required.

- **Days of the Week**
  Monday through Thursday

- **Hours of the Day**
  All day

Coupon expires 12/31/17. Cannot be combined with any other offer.

## Northport Golf Club
Northport, ME (207) 338-2270

- **Type of Discount**
  $25 per person (includes cart) for 18 holes

- **Days of the Week**
  Weekdays only (except holidays)

- **Hours of the Day**
  All day

Coupon expires 12/31/17. Cannot be combined with any other offer.

## Oakdale Country Club
Mexico, ME (207) 364-3951

- **Type of Discount**
  4 players for the price of 3

- **Days of the Week**
  7 days a week

- **Hours of the Day**
  All day

Coupon expires 12/31/17. Cannot be combined with any other offer.

**Golf Course Coupons**

**NEW ENGLAND GOLFGUIDE**

2 0 1 7

**NEW ENGLAND GOLFGUIDE**

2 0 1 7

**NEW ENGLAND GOLFGUIDE**

2 0 1 7

**NEW ENGLAND GOLFGUIDE**

2 0 1 7

## Old Marsh Country Club
Wells, ME (207) 251-4653

- **Type of Discount**
  4 players for the price of 3 (18 holes including cart)
- **Days of the Week**
  Monday through Thursday (except holidays)
- **Hours of the Day**
  All day

Coupon expires 12/31/17. Cannot be combined with any other offer.

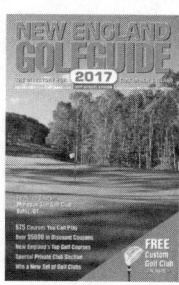

## Palmyra Golf Course
Palmyra, ME (207) 938-4947

- **Type of Discount**
  2 players for the price of 1
- **Days of the Week**
  7 days a week
- **Hours of the Day**
  All day

Coupon expires 12/31/17. Cannot be combined with any other offer.

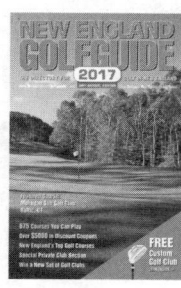

## Paris Hill Country Club
Paris Hill Road, Paris, ME  (207) 743-2371

- **Type of Discount**
  2 players for the price of 1
- **Days of the Week**
  Weekdays only (except holidays)
- **Hours of the Day**
  All day

Coupon expires 12/31/17. Cannot be combined with any other offer.

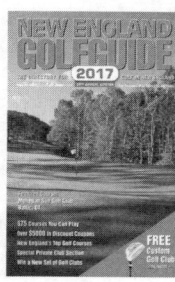

## Penobscot Valley Country Club
Orono, ME (207) 866-2423

- **Type of Discount**
  4 players for the price of 3 (18 holes including cart)
- **Days of the Week**
  Monday through Thursday (except holidays)
- **Hours of the Day**
  All day

Coupon expires 12/31/17. Cannot be combined with any other offer.

Golf Course Coupons

**NEW ENGLAND GOLFGUIDE**

2 0 1 7

---

**NEW ENGLAND GOLFGUIDE**

2 0 1 7

---

**NEW ENGLAND GOLFGUIDE**

2 0 1 7

---

**NEW ENGLAND GOLFGUIDE**

2 0 1 7

## Point Sebago Golf Club
Casco, ME (207) 655-2747

- **Type of Discount**
  $39 per player, cart included
- **Days of the Week**
  7 days a week
- **Hours of the Day**
  All day Monday through Thursday
  After 10am Friday though Sunday

Coupon expires 12/31/17. Cannot be combined with any other offer.

## Poland Spring Country Club
Route 26, Poland Spring, ME (207) 998-6002

- **Type of Discount**
  $29 greens fee
- **Days of the Week**
  Monday through Thursday (except holidays)
- **Hours of the Day**
  All day

Coupon expires 12/31/17. Cannot be combined with any other offer.

## Portage Hills Country Club
Route 11, Portage, ME (207) 435-8221

- **Type of Discount**
  2 players for the price of 1
- **Days of the Week**
  7 days a week
- **Hours of the Day**
  All day

Coupon expires 12/31/17. Cannot be combined with any other offer.

## Presque Isle Country Club
Presque Isle, ME (207) 764-0430

- **Type of Discount**
  Play 18 holes at 9 hole rate. Cart rental required.
- **Days of the Week**
  7 days a week
- **Hours of the Day**
  All day

Coupon expires 12/31/17. Cannot be combined with any other offer.

**Golf Course Coupons**

**NEW ENGLAND GOLFGUIDE**

2 0 1 7

---

**NEW ENGLAND GOLFGUIDE**

2 0 1 7

---

**NEW ENGLAND GOLFGUIDE**

2 0 1 7

---

**NEW ENGLAND GOLFGUIDE**

2 0 1 7

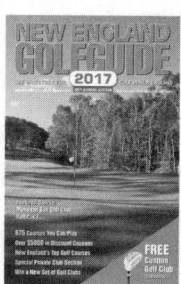

## Province Lake Golf Club
Route 153, Parsonfield, ME (800) 325-4434

- **Type of Discount**
  4 players for price of 3
- **Days of the Week**
  7 days a week
- **Hours of the Day**
  After 1pm

Coupon expires 12/31/17. Cannot be combined with any other offer.

## Rivermeadow Golf Club
Westbrook, ME (207) 854-1625

- **Type of Discount**
  2 players for price of 1
- **Days of the Week**
  7 days a week
- **Hours of the Day**
  All day. Tee time required.

Coupon expires 12/31/17. Cannot be combined with any other offer.

## Rockland Golf Club
Rockland, ME (207) 594-9322

- **Type of Discount**
  $50 per player (includes cart)
- **Days of the Week**
  7 days a week
- **Hours of the Day**
  All day

Coupon expires 12/31/17. Cannot be combined with any other offer.

## Rocky Knoll Country Club
Orrington, ME (207) 989-0109

- **Type of Discount**
  2 players for the price of 1
- **Days of the Week**
  7 days a week
- **Hours of the Day**
  All day

Coupon expires 12/31/17. Cannot be combined with any other offer.

**Golf Course Coupons**

**NEW ENGLAND GOLFGUIDE**

2 0 1 7

---

**NEW ENGLAND GOLFGUIDE**

2 0 1 7

---

**NEW ENGLAND GOLFGUIDE**

2 0 1 7

---

**NEW ENGLAND GOLFGUIDE**

2 0 1 7

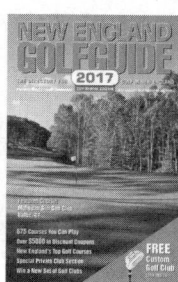

### Sable Oaks Golf Club
South Portland, ME (207) 775-6257

- **Type of Discount**
  50% off greens fees for 2 players
- **Days of the Week**
  Monday through Thursday (except holidays)
- **Hours of the Day**
  All day. Tee time required.

Coupon expires 12/31/17. Cannot be combined with any other offer.

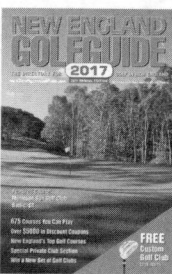

### Salmon Falls Golf Course
Hollis, ME (207) 929-5233 or (800) 734-1616

- **Type of Discount**
  $62 for 2 players and cart for 18 holes
- **Days of the Week**
  7 days a week
- **Hours of the Day**
  All day

Coupon expires 12/31/17. Cannot be combined with any other offer.

### Samoset Resort Golf Club
Rockport, ME (207) 594-1431

- **Type of Discount**
  4 players for the price of 3
- **Days of the Week**
  7 days a week
- **Hours of the Day**
  All day

Coupon expires 12/31/17. Cannot be combined with any other offer.

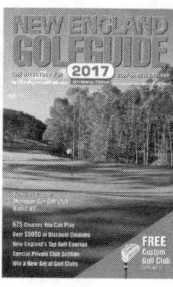

### Sanford Country Club
Route 4, Sanford, ME (207) 324-5462

- **Type of Discount**
  $39 for 18 holes (cart included)
- **Days of the Week**
  7 days a week
- **Hours of the Day**
  All day. Fri/Sat/Sun/Holiday after 12pm.

Coupon expires 12/31/17. Cannot be combined with any other offer.

**Golf Course Coupons**

**NEW ENGLAND GOLFGUIDE**

2 0 1 7

---

**NEW ENGLAND GOLFGUIDE**

2 0 1 7

---

**NEW ENGLAND GOLFGUIDE**

2 0 1 7

---

**NEW ENGLAND GOLFGUIDE**

2 0 1 7

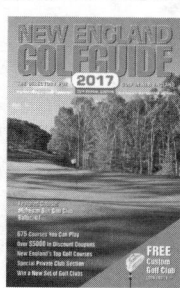

### Searsport Pines Golf Course
Searsport, ME  (207) 548-2854

- **Type of Discount**
  $5 off greens fees for up to 4 players

- **Days of the Week**
  7 days a week

- **Hours of the Day**
  All day

Coupon expires 12/31/17. Cannot be combined with any other offer.

---

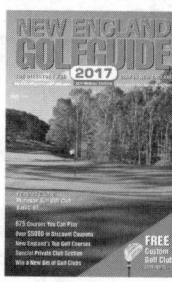

### Sebasco Harbor Resort Golf Club
Sebasco Estates, ME  (207) 389-9060

- **Type of Discount**
  $35 per person (includes cart) up to 4 players

- **Days of the Week**
  Weekdays only (except holidays)

- **Hours of the Day**
  All day

Coupon expires 12/31/17. Cannot be combined with any other offer.

---

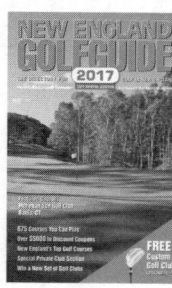

### Sheepscot Links Golf Club
Whitefield, ME  (207) 549-7060

- **Type of Discount**
  2 players for the price of 1

- **Days of the Week**
  Weekdays only (except holidays)

- **Hours of the Day**
  All day

Coupon expires 12/31/17. Cannot be combined with any other offer.

---

### South Portland Municipal GC
South Portland, ME  (207) 775-0005

- **Type of Discount**
  2 players for the price of 1

- **Days of the Week**
  7 days a week

- **Hours of the Day**
  All day

Coupon expires 12/31/17. Cannot be combined with any other offer.

**Golf Course Coupons**

**NEW ENGLAND GOLFGUIDE**

2 0 1 7

---

**NEW ENGLAND GOLFGUIDE**

2 0 1 7

---

**NEW ENGLAND GOLFGUIDE**

2 0 1 7

---

**NEW ENGLAND GOLFGUIDE**

2 0 1 7

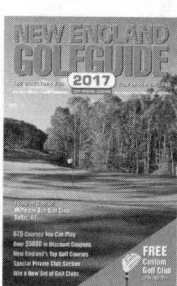

## Spring Meadows Golf Course
Gray, ME (207) 657-2586

- **Type of Discount**
  $10 off greens fees up to 4 players.
  Cart rental required.
- **Days of the Week**
  7 days a week
- **Hours of the Day**
  All day - based on regular rates

Coupon expires 12/31/17. Cannot be combined with any other offer.

## Sugarloaf Golf Club
Carrabassett Valley, ME (207) 237-2000

- **Type of Discount**
  25% discount for 2-4 players
- **Days of the Week**
  Monday through Thursday (except holidays)
- **Hours of the Day**
  All day

Coupon expires 12/31/17. Cannot be combined with any other offer.

## Sunday River Golf Club
Bethel, ME (207) 824-4653

- **Type of Discount**
  4 players for the price of 3 (18 holes
  including cart)
- **Days of the Week**
  Monday through Thursday (except holidays)
- **Hours of the Day**
  All day

Coupon expires 12/31/17. Cannot be combined with any other offer.

## Sunset Ridge Golf Links
Westbrook, ME (207) 854-9463

- **Type of Discount**
  4 players for the price of 3
- **Days of the Week**
  7 days a week
- **Hours of the Day**
  All day

Coupon expires 12/31/17. Cannot be combined with any other offer.

**Golf Course Coupons**

**NEW ENGLAND GOLFGUIDE**

2 0 1 7

**NEW ENGLAND GOLFGUIDE**

2 0 1 7

**NEW ENGLAND GOLFGUIDE**

2 0 1 7

**NEW ENGLAND GOLFGUIDE**

2 0 1 7

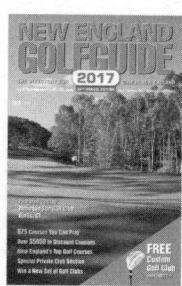

### Toddy Brook Golf Course
North Yarmouth, ME (207) 829-5100

- **Type of Discount**
  4 players for the price of 3
- **Days of the Week**
  7 days a week
- **Hours of the Day**
  All day

Coupon expires 12/31/17. Cannot be combined with any other offer.

---

### Traditions Golf Club
Holden, ME  (207) 989-9909

- **Type of Discount**
  2 players for price of 1
- **Days of the Week**
  Weekdays only (except holidays)
- **Hours of the Day**
  All day

Coupon expires 12/31/17. Cannot be combined with any other offer.

---

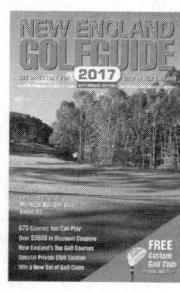

### Turner Highlands Golf Course
Turner, ME (207) 224-7060

- **Type of Discount**
  $35 with a cart
- **Days of the Week**
  7 days a week
- **Hours of the Day**
  All day

Coupon expires 12/31/17. Cannot be combined with any other offer.

---

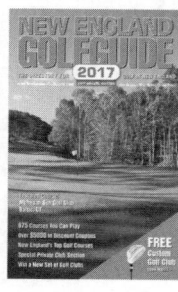

### Va-Jo-Wa Golf Club
Island Falls, ME (207) 463-2128

- **Type of Discount**
  2 players for the price of 1. Cart rental required.
- **Days of the Week**
  Weekdays only (except holidays)
- **Hours of the Day**
  All day

Coupon expires 12/31/17. Cannot be combined with any other offer.

Golf Course Coupons

**NEW ENGLAND GOLFGUIDE**

2 0 1 7

---

**NEW ENGLAND GOLFGUIDE**

2 0 1 7

---

**NEW ENGLAND GOLFGUIDE**

2 0 1 7

---

**NEW ENGLAND GOLFGUIDE**

2 0 1 7

## Wawenock Country Club
Walpole, ME (207) 563-3938

- **Type of Discount**
  $30 per player for 18 holes with cart

- **Days of the Week**
  7 days a week

- **Hours of the Day**
  All day. Please call ahead for tee time.

Coupon expires 12/31/17. Cannot be combined with any other offer.

---

## Webhannet Golf Club
Kennebunk, ME (207) 967-3951

- **Type of Discount**
  4 players for the price of 3

- **Days of the Week**
  7 days a week

- **Hours of the Day**
  All day. Valid May, June, September, and October.

Coupon expires 12/31/17. Cannot be combined with any other offer.

---

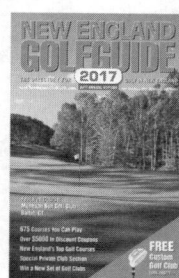

## Western View Golf Club
Augusta, ME (207) 622-5309

- **Type of Discount**
  2 players for the price of 1 (greens fees). Cart rental for 2 required.

- **Days of the Week**
  7 days a week

- **Hours of the Day**
  All day

Coupon expires 12/31/17. Cannot be combined with any other offer.

---

## Whitetail Golf Course
Charleston, ME (207) 285-7730

- **Type of Discount**
  18 holes for the 9 hole rate for 1-4 players. Cart rental required.

- **Days of the Week**
  Sundays

- **Hours of the Day**
  7am–11am

Coupon expires 12/31/17. Cannot be combined with any other offer.

**NEW ENGLAND GOLFGUIDE**

2 0 1 7

---

**NEW ENGLAND GOLFGUIDE**

2 0 1 7

---

**NEW ENGLAND GOLFGUIDE**

2 0 1 7

---

**NEW ENGLAND GOLFGUIDE**

2 0 1 7

### Acushnet River Valley Golf Course
Acushnet, MA  (508) 998-7777

- **Type of Discount**
  Free golf cart with 4 paid greens fees
- **Days of the Week**
  Weekdays only (except holidays)
- **Hours of the Day**
  All day

Coupon expires 12/31/17. Cannot be combined with any other offer.

### Agawam Munipal Golf Course
Feeding Hills, MA  (413) 786-2194

- **Type of Discount**
  4 players for price of 3
- **Days of the Week**
  7 days a week
- **Hours of the Day**
  All day

Coupon expires 12/31/17. Cannot be combined with any other offer.

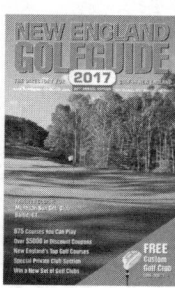

### Allendale Country Club
Dartmouth, MA  (508) 992-8682

- **Type of Discount**
  $100 for 2 players (including cart)
  $200 for 4 players (including cart)
- **Days of the Week**
  7 days a week
- **Hours of the Day**
  After 1pm. Must call for tee time.

Coupon expires 12/31/17. Cannot be combined with any other offer.

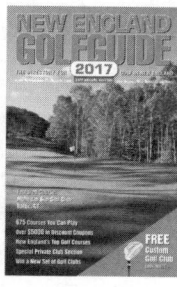

### Amherst Golf Club
Amherst, MA  (413) 256-6894

- **Type of Discount**
  2 players for the price of 1 (golf cart required).
  Please call ahead when using coupon.
- **Days of the Week**
  Weekdays only (except holidays)
- **Hours of the Day**
  All day

Coupon expires 12/31/17. Cannot be combined with any other offer.

**Golf Course Coupons**

**NEW ENGLAND GOLFGUIDE**

2 0 1 7

---

**NEW ENGLAND GOLFGUIDE**

2 0 1 7

---

**NEW ENGLAND GOLFGUIDE**

2 0 1 7

---

**NEW ENGLAND GOLFGUIDE**

2 0 1 7

### Atlantic Country Club
Plymouth, MA  (508) 759-6644

- **Type of Discount**
  $5 off greens fees

- **Days of the Week**
  Monday through Thursday

- **Hours of the Day**
  All day (excludes twilight hours)

Coupon expires 12/31/17. Cannot be combined with any other offer.

---

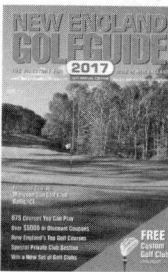

### Bas Ridge Golf Course
Plunkett Street, Hinsdale, MA  (413) 655-2605

- **Type of Discount**
  2 greens fees for the price of 1. Cart rental required. Excludes senior rates.

- **Days of the Week**
  Weekdays only (except holidays)

- **Hours of the Day**
  8am–3pm; not valid July & August

Coupon expires 12/31/17. Cannot be combined with any other offer.

---

### Bayberry Hills Golf Course
South Yarmouth, MA  (508) 394-5597

- **Type of Discount**
  $25 greens fee

- **Days of the Week**
  Weekdays only (except holidays)

- **Hours of the Day**
  All day. November through March. Cart rental required.

Coupon expires 12/31/17. Cannot be combined with any other offer.

---

### Bay Path Golf Course
East Brookfield, MA  (508) 867-8161

- **Type of Discount**
  4 players for price of 3

- **Days of the Week**
  7 days a week

- **Hours of the Day**
  10am–2pm (excludes league play)

Coupon expires 12/31/17. Cannot be combined with any other offer.

**Golf Course Coupons**

**NEW ENGLAND GOLFGUIDE**

**2 0 1 7**

---

**NEW ENGLAND GOLFGUIDE**

**2 0 1 7**

---

**NEW ENGLAND GOLFGUIDE**

**2 0 1 7**

---

**NEW ENGLAND GOLFGUIDE**

**2 0 1 7**

### Beaver Brook Country Club
Main Street, Haydenville, MA (413) 268-7229

- **Type of Discount**
  2 players for the price of 1. Cart rental required.
- **Days of the Week**
  7 days a week
- **Hours of the Day**
  Before 12pm

Coupon expires 12/31/17. Cannot be combined with any other offer.

---

### Bedrock Golf Club
Rutland, MA (508) 886-0202

- **Type of Discount**
  4 players for the price of 3
- **Days of the Week**
  7 days a week
- **Hours of the Day**
  All day

Coupon expires 12/31/17. Cannot be combined with any other offer.

---

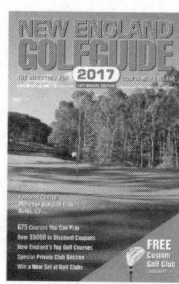

### Berlin Country Club
Berlin, MA (978) 838-2733

- **Type of Discount**
  Buy 1 greens fee get 1 free.
  Motorized cart required.
- **Days of the Week**
  Weekdays only (except holidays)
- **Hours of the Day**
  Until 2pm

Coupon expires 12/31/17. Cannot be combined with any other offer.

---

### Beverly Golf & Tennis
Beverly, MA (978) 922-9072

- **Type of Discount**
  2 players for the price of 1.
  Cart rental required.
- **Days of the Week**
  Monday through Thursday
- **Hours of the Day**
  All day

Coupon expires 12/31/17. Cannot be combined with any other offer.

**Golf Course Coupons**

**NEW ENGLAND GOLFGUIDE**

2 0 1 7

**NEW ENGLAND GOLFGUIDE**

2 0 1 7

**NEW ENGLAND GOLFGUIDE**

2 0 1 7

**NEW ENGLAND GOLFGUIDE**

2 0 1 7

### Blackstone National Golf Club
Sutton, MA (508) 865-2111

- **Type of Discount**
  4 players for the price of 3. Cart rental required.
- **Days of the Week**
  Monday through Thursday
- **Hours of the Day**
  All day

Coupon expires 12/31/17. Cannot be combined with any other offer.

### Blissful Meadows Golf Club
Uxbridge, MA (508) 278-6113

- **Type of Discount**
  4 players for the price of 3
- **Days of the Week**
  Weekdays only (except holidays)
- **Hours of the Day**
  All day

Coupon expires 12/31/17. Cannot be combined with any other offer.

### Blue Rock Golf Course
South Yarmouth, MA (508) 398-9295

- **Type of Discount**
  Links & Lunch – Complement your round with lunch at the Blue Rock Grill for only $10
- **Days of the Week**
  7 days a week
- **Hours of the Day**
  All day

Coupon expires 12/31/17. Cannot be combined with any other offer.

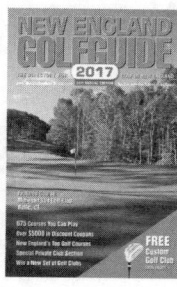

### Bradford Country Club
Bradford, MA (978) 372-8587

- **Type of Discount**
  2 players, $90 for 18 holes with cart
- **Days of the Week**
  Weekdays only (except holidays)
- **Hours of the Day**
  All day. Must bring coupon.

Coupon expires 12/31/17. Cannot be combined with any other offer.

**Golf Course Coupons**

**NEW ENGLAND GOLFGUIDE**

**2 0 1 7**

---

**NEW ENGLAND GOLFGUIDE**

**2 0 1 7**

---

**NEW ENGLAND GOLFGUIDE**

**2 0 1 7**

---

**NEW ENGLAND GOLFGUIDE**

**2 0 1 7**

### Bungay Brook Golf Club
Bellingham, MA (508) 883-1600

- **Type of Discount**
  Free golf cart with 2 paid greens fees.
  Free small pail range balls with paid greens fees.
- **Days of the Week**
  7 days a week
- **Hours of the Day**
  All day

Coupon expires 12/31/17. Cannot be combined with any other offer.

### Captains Golf Course (Port)
Brewster, MA (508) 896-1716

- **Type of Discount**
  $5 off greens fees
- **Days of the Week**
  7 days a week
- **Hours of the Day**
  After 12pm

Coupon expires 12/31/17. Cannot be combined with any other offer.

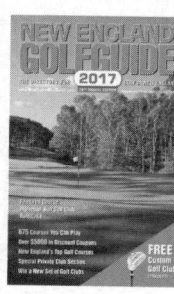

### Captains Golf Course (Starboard)
Brewster, MA (508) 896-1716

- **Type of Discount**
  $5 off greens fees
- **Days of the Week**
  7 days a week
- **Hours of the Day**
  After 12pm

Coupon expires 12/31/17. Cannot be combined with any other offer.

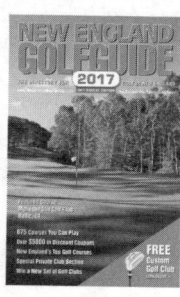

### Cedar Glen Golf Club
Saugus, MA (781) 233-3609

- **Type of Discount**
  4 players for price of 3
- **Days of the Week**
  Weekdays only (except holidays)
- **Hours of the Day**
  Before 2pm

Coupon expires 12/31/17. Cannot be combined with any other offer.

**Golf Course Coupons**

**NEW ENGLAND GOLFGUIDE**

2 0 1 7

---

**NEW ENGLAND GOLFGUIDE**

2 0 1 7

---

**NEW ENGLAND GOLFGUIDE**

2 0 1 7

---

**NEW ENGLAND GOLFGUIDE**

2 0 1 7

### Cedar Hill Golf Club
Stoughton, MA (781) 344-8913

- **Type of Discount**
  4 players for price of 3
- **Days of the Week**
  Weekdays only (except holidays)
- **Hours of the Day**
  Before 2pm

Coupon expires 12/31/17. Cannot be combined with any other offer.

---

### Chelmsford Country Club
Chelmsford, MA (978) 256-1818

- **Type of Discount**
  Free golf cart with 2 paid greens fees
- **Days of the Week**
  7 days a week
- **Hours of the Day**
  All day

Coupon expires 12/31/17. Cannot be combined with any other offer.

---

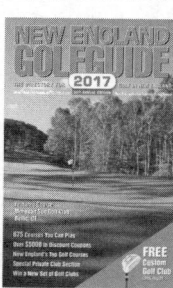

### Chequessett Golf Club
Wellfleet, MA (508) 349-3704

- **Type of Discount**
  20% off greens fees
- **Days of the Week**
  7 days a week
- **Hours of the Day**
  After 1pm

Coupon expires 12/31/17. Cannot be combined with any other offer.

---

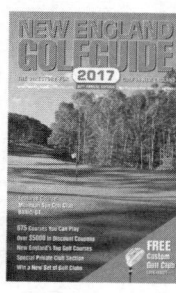

### Cherry Hill Golf Course
Amherst, MA (413) 256-4071

- **Type of Discount**
  2 players for the price of 1
- **Days of the Week**
  7 days a week
- **Hours of the Day**
  All day

Coupon expires 12/31/17. Cannot be combined with any other offer.

**Golf Course Coupons**

**NEW ENGLAND**
**GOLFGUIDE**

2 0 1 7

---

✂ - - - - - - - - - - - - - - - - - - - - - - - - - - - - - - - - - - -

**NEW ENGLAND**
**GOLFGUIDE**

2 0 1 7

---

✂ - - - - - - - - - - - - - - - - - - - - - - - - - - - - - - - - - - -

**NEW ENGLAND**
**GOLFGUIDE**

2 0 1 7

---

✂ - - - - - - - - - - - - - - - - - - - - - - - - - - - - - - - - - - -

**NEW ENGLAND**
**GOLFGUIDE**

2 0 1 7

### Clearview Golf Course
Millbury, MA (508) 754-5654

- **Type of Discount**
  2 players for the price of 1 (greens fees only)
- **Days of the Week**
  Monday through Friday
- **Hours of the Day**
  All day. Not valid during leagues and tournaments.

Coupon expires 12/31/17. Cannot be combined with any other offer.

---

### Cold Spring Country Club
Belchertown, MA (413) 323-4888

- **Type of Discount**
  4 players for price of 3
- **Days of the Week**
  Weekdays (except holidays)
- **Hours of the Day**
  All day

Coupon expires 12/31/17. Cannot be combined with any other offer.

---

### Country Club of Billerica
Billerica, MA (978) 667-9121 ext. 22

- **Type of Discount**
  4 players for the price of 3
- **Days of the Week**
  Weekdays only (except holidays)
- **Hours of the Day**
  9am–2pm. Riding carts not included.

Coupon expires 12/31/17. Cannot be combined with any other offer.

---

### Country Club of Greenfield
Greenfield, MA (413) 773-7530

- **Type of Discount**
  4 players for $120 with cart
- **Days of the Week**
  Weekdays only (except holidays)
- **Hours of the Day**
  All day

Coupon expires 12/31/17. Cannot be combined with any other offer.

**NEW ENGLAND GOLFGUIDE**

2 0 1 7

---

**NEW ENGLAND GOLFGUIDE**

2 0 1 7

---

**NEW ENGLAND GOLFGUIDE**

2 0 1 7

---

**NEW ENGLAND GOLFGUIDE**

2 0 1 7

### Cranwell Spa & Golf Resort
Lenox, MA (413) 637-2563

- **Type of Discount**
  2 players for the price of 1.
  Cart rental required.

- **Days of the Week**
  7 days a week

- **Hours of the Day**
  All day

Coupon expires 12/31/17. Cannot be combined with any other offer.

---

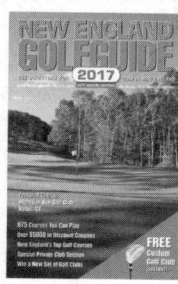

### Crestview Country Club
Agawam, MA (413) 786-2593

- **Type of Discount**
  4 players for the price of 3. Cart rental required.

- **Days of the Week**
  Monday through Thursday (except holidays)

- **Hours of the Day**
  All day

Coupon expires 12/31/17. Cannot be combined with any other offer.

---

### Crosswinds Golf Club
Plymouth, MA (508) 830-1199

- **Type of Discount**
  4 players for the price of 3

- **Days of the Week**
  Monday through Thursday (except holidays)

- **Hours of the Day**
  After 1pm. Rates subject to change.

Coupon expires 12/31/17. Cannot be combined with any other offer.

---

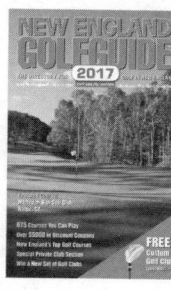

### Crumpin-Fox Club
Bernardston, MA (413) 648-9101

- **Type of Discount**
  $25 off per guide holder or coupon holder

- **Days of the Week**
  Monday through Thursday (except holidays)

- **Hours of the Day**
  All day. Valid May 15 - October 15.

Coupon expires 10/15/17. Cannot be combined with any other offer.

**NEW ENGLAND GOLFGUIDE**

2 0 1 7

**NEW ENGLAND GOLFGUIDE**

2 0 1 7

**NEW ENGLAND GOLFGUIDE**

2 0 1 7

**NEW ENGLAND GOLFGUIDE**

2 0 1 7

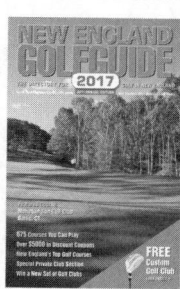

### Dennis Highlands Golf Course
Dennis, MA (508) 385-8347

- **Type of Discount**
  2 players for the price of 1. Cart rental required.
  $10 off any Pro Shop purchase of $25 or more.

- **Days of the Week**
  Monday through Thursday (except holidays)

- **Hours of the Day**
  All day. Not valid July and August.

Coupon expires 12/31/17. Cannot be combined with any other offer.

---

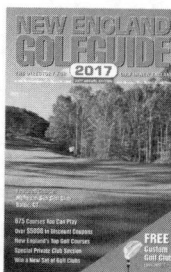

### Dennis Pines Golf Course
East Dennis, MA (508) 385-8347

- **Type of Discount**
  2 players for the price of 1. Cart rental required.
  $10 off any Pro Shop purchase of $25 or more.

- **Days of the Week**
  Monday through Thursday (except holidays)

- **Hours of the Day**
  All day. Not valid July and August.

Coupon expires 12/31/17. Cannot be combined with any other offer.

---

### Dunroamin Country Club
Gilbertville, MA (413) 477-0004

- **Type of Discount**
  Free golf cart with 2 paid greens fees

- **Days of the Week**
  Weekdays only (except holidays)

- **Hours of the Day**
  All day. Call for tee times.

Coupon expires 12/31/17. Cannot be combined with any other offer.

---

### Easton Country Club
South Easton, MA (508) 238-2500

- **Type of Discount**
  4 players for the price of 3. Excludes senior rates.

- **Days of the Week**
  7 days a week

- **Hours of the Day**
  All day - weekdays (except holidays)
  After 11:30am (Saturday, Sunday, holidays)

Coupon expires 12/31/17. Cannot be combined with any other offer.

**Golf Course Coupons**

**NEW ENGLAND GOLFGUIDE**

2 0 1 7

---

**NEW ENGLAND GOLFGUIDE**

2 0 1 7

---

**NEW ENGLAND GOLFGUIDE**

2 0 1 7

---

**NEW ENGLAND GOLFGUIDE**

2 0 1 7

MA

### Edge Hill Golf Club
Ashfield, MA (413) 625-6018

- **Type of Discount**
  4 players for the price of 3
- **Days of the Week**
  Weekdays only (except holidays)
- **Hours of the Day**
  All day

Coupon expires 12/31/17. Cannot be combined with any other offer.

---

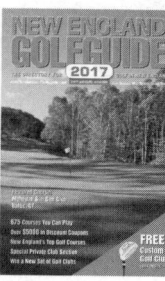

### Egremont Country Club
Great Barrington, MA (413) 528-4222

- **Type of Discount**
  2 players for the price of 1. 18 hole cart rental required for both players.
- **Days of the Week**
  Weekdays only (except holidays)
- **Hours of the Day**
  Tee off by 2pm. 18-hole special only.

Coupon expires 12/31/17. Cannot be combined with any other offer.

---

### Ellinwood Country Club
Athol, MA (978) 249-7460

- **Type of Discount**
  2 players for the price of 1. Cart rental required.
- **Days of the Week**
  Weekdays only (except holidays)
- **Hours of the Day**
  All day

Coupon expires 12/31/17. Cannot be combined with any other offer.

---

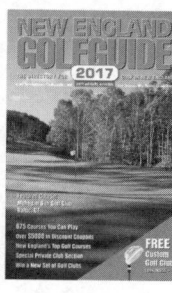

### Elmcrest Country Club
East Longmeadow, MA (413) 525-4653

- **Type of Discount**
  4 players for the price of 3. Cart rental required.
- **Days of the Week**
  Monday through Thursday (except holidays)
- **Hours of the Day**
  All day

Coupon expires 12/31/17. Cannot be combined with any other offer.

**Golf Course Coupons**

**NEW ENGLAND GOLFGUIDE**

2 0 1 7

**NEW ENGLAND GOLFGUIDE**

2 0 1 7

**NEW ENGLAND GOLFGUIDE**

2 0 1 7

**NEW ENGLAND GOLFGUIDE**

2 0 1 7

### Falmouth Country Club
Falmouth, MA (508) 548-3211

- **Type of Discount**
  $10 off each player, up to 4 players (resident prices)
- **Days of the Week**
  Monday through Thursday (except holidays)
- **Hours of the Day**
  Before 2pm. Must have coupon.

Coupon expires 12/31/17. Cannot be combined with any other offer.

---

### Fire Fly Country Club
Seekonk, MA (508) 336-6622

- **Type of Discount**
  4 players for the price of 3
- **Days of the Week**
  7 days a week
- **Hours of the Day**
  All day

Coupon expires 12/31/17. Cannot be combined with any other offer.

---

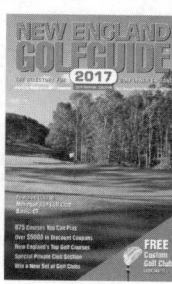

### Fore Kicks Golf Course & Sports Complex
Norfolk, MA (508) 384-4433

- **Type of Discount**
  1 player at 1/2 price
- **Days of the Week**
  7 days a week
- **Hours of the Day**
  All day

Coupon expires 12/31/17. Cannot be combined with any other offer.

---

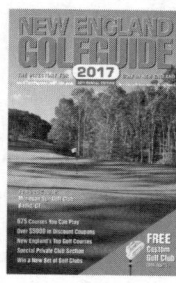

### Forest Park Country Club
Adams, MA (413) 743-3311

- **Type of Discount**
  2 players for the price of 1
- **Days of the Week**
  7 days a week
- **Hours of the Day**
  Please call ahead on weekends for availability

Coupon expires 12/31/17. Cannot be combined with any other offer.

**Golf Course Coupons**

**NEW ENGLAND GOLFGUIDE**

2 0 1 7

---

**NEW ENGLAND GOLFGUIDE**

2 0 1 7

---

**NEW ENGLAND GOLFGUIDE**

2 0 1 7

---

**NEW ENGLAND GOLFGUIDE**

2 0 1 7

### Foxborough Country Club
Foxborough, MA  (508) 543-4661

- **Type of Discount**
  4 players for the price of 3. Cart rental required.
- **Days of the Week**
  Monday through Thursday
- **Hours of the Day**
  Call Pro Shop for availability:
  (508) 543-4661 ext. 4

Coupon expires 12/31/17. Cannot be combined with any other offer.

### Fresh Pond Golf Club
Cambridge, MA  (617) 349-6282

- **Type of Discount**
  2 players for the price of 1
- **Days of the Week**
  Weekdays only (except holidays)
- **Hours of the Day**
  All day. Excludes league play.

Coupon expires 12/31/17. Cannot be combined with any other offer.

### Gardner Municipal Golf Course
Gardner, MA  (978) 632-9703

- **Type of Discount**
  2 players for the price of 1
- **Days of the Week**
  7 days a week
- **Hours of the Day**
  Weekdays 10:30am–3pm
  Weekends and holidays 11am–2pm

Coupon expires 12/31/17. Cannot be combined with any other offer.

### Garrison Golf Center
Haverhill, MA  (978) 374-9380

- **Type of Discount**
  $2 off 9 holes when accompanied
  by 1 full-paying customer
- **Days of the Week**
  Weekdays only (except holidays)
- **Hours of the Day**
  All day

Coupon expires 12/31/17. Cannot be combined with any other offer.

**Golf Course Coupons**

**NEW ENGLAND GOLFGUIDE**

2 0 1 7

---

**NEW ENGLAND GOLFGUIDE**

2 0 1 7

---

**NEW ENGLAND GOLFGUIDE**

2 0 1 7

---

**NEW ENGLAND GOLFGUIDE**

2 0 1 7

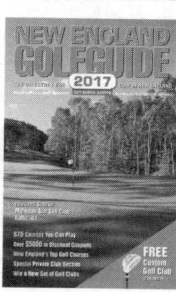

### Glen Ellen Country Club
Millis, MA  (508) 376-2775

- **Type of Discount**
  Free golf cart with 2 paid greens fees

- **Days of the Week**
  7 days a week

- **Hours of the Day**
  Monday through Friday all day.
  Weekends and Holidays after 11am.

Coupon expires 12/31/17. Cannot be combined with any other offer.

---

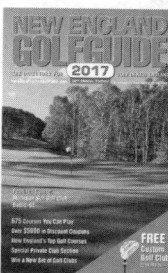

### Greenock Country Club
Lee, MA  (413) 243-3323

- **Type of Discount**
  25% discount for 2-4 players

- **Days of the Week**
  Monday through Thursday (except holidays)

- **Hours of the Day**
  All day

Coupon expires 12/31/17. Cannot be combined with any other offer.

---

### Groton Pool & Golf Center
Groton, MA  (978) 448-2564

- **Type of Discount**
  2 players for the price of 1. Cart rental required.

- **Days of the Week**
  7 days a week

- **Hours of the Day**
  All day. Call for availability.

Coupon expires 12/31/17. Cannot be combined with any other offer.

---

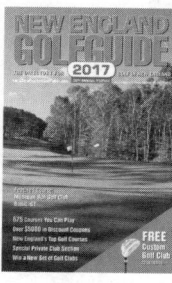

### Hazelton Golf Club
Rehoboth, MA

- **Type of Discount**
  4 players for the price of 3

- **Days of the Week**
  Weekdays only (except holidays)

- **Hours of the Day**
  7am–1pm

Coupon expires 12/31/17. Cannot be combined with any other offer.

**Golf Course Coupons**

**NEW ENGLAND GOLFGUIDE**

2 0 1 7

---

**NEW ENGLAND GOLFGUIDE**

2 0 1 7

---

**NEW ENGLAND GOLFGUIDE**

2 0 1 7

---

**NEW ENGLAND GOLFGUIDE**

2 0 1 7

### Heather Hill Country Club
Plainville, MA (508) 695-0309

- **Type of Discount**
  $30 for 18 holes for 1-4 players (cart included)
- **Days of the Week**
  7 days a week
- **Hours of the Day**
  Mon - Thurs (except holidays) - before 1pm
  Fri/Sat/Sun/Holidays - after 2pm

Coupon expires 12/31/17. Cannot be combined with any other offer.

---

### Heritage Country Club
Charlton, MA (508) 248-5111

- **Type of Discount**
  25% discount for 2-4 players
- **Days of the Week**
  Monday through Friday (except holidays)
- **Hours of the Day**
  11am–3pm. No holidays. No tournaments.

Coupon expires 12/31/17. Cannot be combined with any other offer.

---

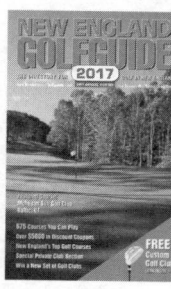

### Hickory Ridge Golf Club
South Amherst, MA (413) 253-9320

- **Type of Discount**
  4 players for the price of 3
- **Days of the Week**
  Weekdays only (except holidays)
- **Hours of the Day**
  All day

Coupon expires 12/31/17. Cannot be combined with any other offer.

---

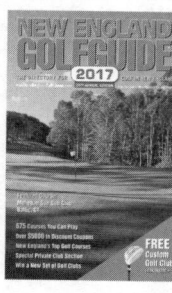

### Highfields Golf & Country Club
Grafton, MA (508) 839-1945

- **Type of Discount**
  4 players for the price of 3
- **Days of the Week**
  Weekdays only (except holidays)
- **Hours of the Day**
  All day

Coupon expires 12/31/17. Cannot be combined with any other offer.

**Golf Course Coupons**

**NEW ENGLAND GOLFGUIDE**

2 0 1 7

---

**NEW ENGLAND GOLFGUIDE**

2 0 1 7

---

**NEW ENGLAND GOLFGUIDE**

2 0 1 7

---

**NEW ENGLAND GOLFGUIDE**

2 0 1 7

### Hillside Country Club
Rehoboth, MA (508) 252-9761

- **Type of Discount**
  Play 18 holes, get 18 holes free the next time you play. Must bring in this coupon.
- **Days of the Week**
  Monday through Friday
- **Hours of the Day**
  All day

Coupon expires 12/31/17. Cannot be combined with any other offer.

### Holly Ridge Golf Club
South Sandwich, MA (508) 428-5577

- **Type of Discount**
  $5 off each 18-hole greens fee for up to 4 players
- **Days of the Week**
  7 days a week
- **Hours of the Day**
  7am–3pm

Coupon expires 12/31/17. Cannot be combined with any other offer.

### Hyannis Golf Club
Hyannis, MA (508) 362-2606

- **Type of Discount**
  4 players for the price of 3
- **Days of the Week**
  Monday through Thursday (except holidays)
- **Hours of the Day**
  All day

Coupon expires 12/31/17. Cannot be combined with any other offer.

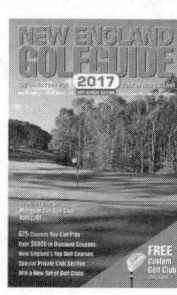

### Indian Meadows Golf Club
Westboro, MA (508) 836-5460

- **Type of Discount**
  4 players for the price of 3
- **Days of the Week**
  7 days a week
- **Hours of the Day**
  All day

Coupon expires 12/31/17. Cannot be combined with any other offer.

Golf Course Coupons

**NEW ENGLAND GOLFGUIDE**

2 0 1 7

---

**NEW ENGLAND GOLFGUIDE**

2 0 1 7

---

**NEW ENGLAND GOLFGUIDE**

2 0 1 7

---

**NEW ENGLAND GOLFGUIDE**

2 0 1 7

### Ledges Golf Club
South Hadley, MA (413) 532-2307

- **Type of Discount**
  $30 for 18 holes (cart included)
  $25 for 18 holes (cart included) - seniors (62+)
- **Days of the Week**
  7 days, must make tee time
- **Hours of the Day**
  All day M-F; after 1pm Saturday/Sunday

Coupon expires 12/31/17. Cannot be combined with any other offer.

### Leicester Country Club
Leicester, MA (508) 892-1390 Ext. 12

- **Type of Discount**
  2 players for the price of 1. Cart rental required.
- **Days of the Week**
  7 days a week
- **Hours of the Day**
  All day

Coupon expires 12/31/17. Cannot be combined with any other offer.

### Links at Lancaster Golf, The
Lancaster, MA (978) 537-8922

- **Type of Discount**
  2 players for the price of 1
- **Days of the Week**
  7 days a week
- **Hours of the Day**
  All day

Coupon expires 12/31/17. Cannot be combined with any other offer.

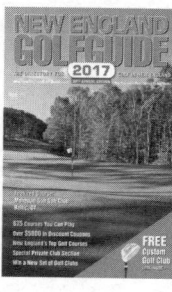

### Little Harbor Country Club
Wareham, MA (508) 295-2617

- **Type of Discount**
  4 players for the price of 3
- **Days of the Week**
  7 days a week
- **Hours of the Day**
  Before 3pm. Cannot be used for tournaments
  or outings.

Coupon expires 12/31/17. Cannot be combined with any other offer.

**Golf Course Coupons**

**NEW ENGLAND GOLFGUIDE**

2 0 1 7

---

**NEW ENGLAND GOLFGUIDE**

2 0 1 7

---

**NEW ENGLAND GOLFGUIDE**

2 0 1 7

---

**NEW ENGLAND GOLFGUIDE**

2 0 1 7

### Maplegate Country Club
Bellingham, MA (508) 966-4040

- **Type of Discount**
  4 players for the price of 3
- **Days of the Week**
  Weekdays only (except holidays)
- **Hours of the Day**
  All day

Coupon expires 12/31/17. Cannot be combined with any other offer.

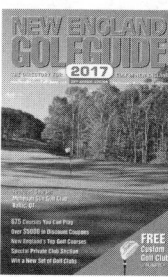

### Marion Golf Course
Marion, MA (508) 748-0199

- **Type of Discount**
  4 players for the price of 3
- **Days of the Week**
  Weekdays only (except holidays)
- **Hours of the Day**
  All day. With coupon only.

Coupon expires 12/31/17. Cannot be combined with any other offer.

### Marlborough Country Club
Marlborough, MA (508) 485-1660

- **Type of Discount**
  $130 for 2 players (including cart)
  $240 for 4 players (including cart)
- **Days of the Week**
  Monday and Tuesday
- **Hours of the Day**
  All day. Must call for tee time.

Coupon expires 12/31/17. Cannot be combined with any other offer.

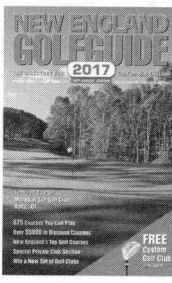

### Maynard Golf Course
Maynard, MA (978) 637-2268

- **Type of Discount**
  $10 off 1 hour golf lesson with
  PGA professional Jim Callahan
- **Days of the Week**
  7 days a week
- **Hours of the Day**
  All day

Coupon expires 12/31/17. Cannot be combined with any other offer.

Golf Course Coupons

**NEW ENGLAND GOLFGUIDE**

2 0 1 7

**NEW ENGLAND GOLFGUIDE**

2 0 1 7

**NEW ENGLAND GOLFGUIDE**

2 0 1 7

**NEW ENGLAND GOLFGUIDE**

2 0 1 7

### The Meadows Golf Club
Greenfield, MA (413) 773-9047

- **Type of Discount**
  2 players for the price of 1 (carts excluded)
- **Days of the Week**
  7 days a week
- **Hours of the Day**
  All day

Coupon expires 12/31/17. Cannot be combined with any other offer.

---

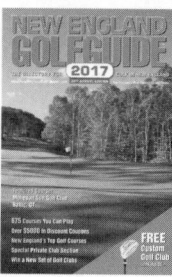

### Middleton Golf Course
Middleton, MA (978) 774-4075

- **Type of Discount**
  $5 off regular greens fee for up to 4 players
- **Days of the Week**
  7 days a week
- **Hours of the Day**
  All day

Coupon expires 12/31/17. Cannot be combined with any other offer.

---

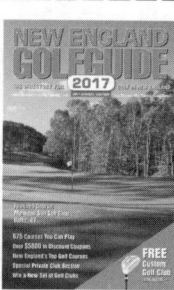

### Mill Valley Golf Links
Belchertown, MA (413) 323-4079

- **Type of Discount**
  $10 greens fee
- **Days of the Week**
  Weekdays only (except holidays)
- **Hours of the Day**
  All day

Coupon expires 12/31/17. Cannot be combined with any other offer.

---

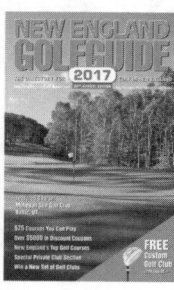

### New England Country Club
Bellingham, MA (508) 883-2300

- **Type of Discount**
  4 players for the price of 3.
  Not valid for senior rates.
- **Days of the Week**
  Monday through Thursday (except holidays)
- **Hours of the Day**
  9am–12pm

Coupon expires 12/31/17. Cannot be combined with any other offer.

**Golf Course Coupons**

**NEW ENGLAND GOLFGUIDE**

**2 0 1 7**

---

**NEW ENGLAND GOLFGUIDE**

**2 0 1 7**

---

**NEW ENGLAND GOLFGUIDE**

**2 0 1 7**

---

**NEW ENGLAND GOLFGUIDE**

**2 0 1 7**

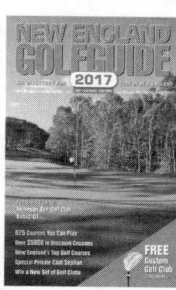

### Newton Commonwealth Golf Course
Newton, MA (617) 630-1971

- **Type of Discount**
  2 players for the price of 1
- **Days of the Week**
  Monday through Thursday
- **Hours of the Day**
  All day

Coupon expires 12/31/17. Cannot be combined with any other offer.

---

### Norton Country Club
Norton, MA (508) 285-2400

- **Type of Discount**
  $49.95 Lunch Special
- **Days of the Week**
  Tuesday and Wednesday
- **Hours of the Day**
  All day

Coupon expires 12/31/17. Cannot be combined with any other offer.

---

### Norwood Country Club
Norwood, MA (781) 769-5880

- **Type of Discount**
  2 players for the price of 1
- **Days of the Week**
  Weekdays only (except holidays)
- **Hours of the Day**
  Before 2pm. 18 hole cart rental at regular
  weekday prices is required.

Coupon expires 12/31/17. Cannot be combined with any other offer.

---

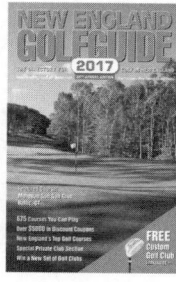

### Olde Barnstable Fairgrounds Golf Course
Marstons Mills, MA (508) 420-1141

- **Type of Discount**
  4 players for the price of 3
- **Days of the Week**
  Monday through Thursday (except holidays)
- **Hours of the Day**
  All day. Valid Jan. 1 - May 20 and Sept. 13 - Dec. 31.

Coupon expires 12/31/17. Cannot be combined with any other offer.

**NEW ENGLAND GOLFGUIDE**

2 0 1 7

---

**NEW ENGLAND GOLFGUIDE**

2 0 1 7

---

**NEW ENGLAND GOLFGUIDE**

2 0 1 7

---

**NEW ENGLAND GOLFGUIDE**

2 0 1 7

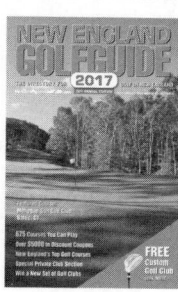

### Olde Salem Greens
Salem, MA  (978) 744-2149

- **Type of Discount**
  $38 for 9 holes with cart (weekdays)
  $40 for 9 holes with cart (weekends after 12pm)
- **Days of the Week**
  7 days a week
- **Hours of the Day**
  All day

Coupon expires 12/31/17. Cannot be combined with any other offer.

### Olde Scotland Links
Bridgewater, MA  (508) 279-3344

- **Type of Discount**
  Free golf cart with 2 paid greens fees
- **Days of the Week**
  Monday through Thursday (except holidays)
- **Hours of the Day**
  All day. Not to be used during league, group, twilight or tournament play.

Coupon expires 12/31/17. Cannot be combined with any other offer.

### Pinecrest Golf Club
Holliston, MA  (508) 429-9871

- **Type of Discount**
  Free golf cart with 2 paid greens fees
- **Days of the Week**
  Weekdays only (except holidays)
- **Hours of the Day**
  All day

Coupon expires 12/31/17. Cannot be combined with any other offer.

### Pine Grove Golf Club
Florence, MA  (413) 584-4570

- **Type of Discount**
  $30 for 18 holes (cart included)
- **Days of the Week**
  Weekdays only (except holidays)
- **Hours of the Day**
  Before 2pm

Coupon expires 12/31/17. Cannot be combined with any other offer.

**Golf Course Coupons**

**NEW ENGLAND GOLFGUIDE**

2 0 1 7

---

✂ - - - - - - - - - - - - - - - - - - - - - - - - - -

**NEW ENGLAND GOLFGUIDE**

2 0 1 7

---

✂ - - - - - - - - - - - - - - - - - - - - - - - - - -

**NEW ENGLAND GOLFGUIDE**

2 0 1 7

---

✂ - - - - - - - - - - - - - - - - - - - - - - - - - -

**NEW ENGLAND GOLFGUIDE**

2 0 1 7

### Pinehills Golf Club (Jones & Nicklaus)
Plymouth, MA (508) 209-3000

- **Type of Discount**
  4 players for the price of 3 (includes carts)
- **Days of the Week**
  Monday through Thursday
- **Hours of the Day**
  All day

Coupon expires 12/31/17. Cannot be combined with any other offer.

### Pine Knoll Par 3 Golf Course
East Longmeadow, MA (413) 525-4444

- **Type of Discount**
  $40 for 2 players for 9 holes (cart included)
- **Days of the Week**
  Weekdays only (except holidays)
- **Hours of the Day**
  11:30am - 2pm

Coupon expires 12/31/17. Cannot be combined with any other offer.

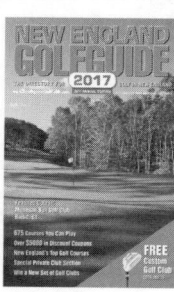

### Pine Oaks Golf Course
South Easton, MA (508) 238-2320

- **Type of Discount**
  Free golf cart with 2 paid greens fees
- **Days of the Week**
  Weekdays only (except holidays)
- **Hours of the Day**
  All day

Coupon expires 12/31/17. Cannot be combined with any other offer.

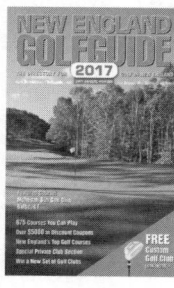

### Pine Ridge Country Club
North Oxford, MA (508) 892-9188

- **Type of Discount**
  4 players for the price of 3 (cart rental required)
- **Days of the Week**
  7 days a week
- **Hours of the Day**
  Weekdays 7am–12pm. Weekends after 12pm.
  Excludes league play, tournaments or special offers.

Coupon expires 12/31/17. Cannot be combined with any other offer.

**Golf Course Coupons**

**NEW ENGLAND GOLFGUIDE**

2 0 1 7

---

**NEW ENGLAND GOLFGUIDE**

2 0 1 7

---

**NEW ENGLAND GOLFGUIDE**

2 0 1 7

---

**NEW ENGLAND GOLFGUIDE**

2 0 1 7

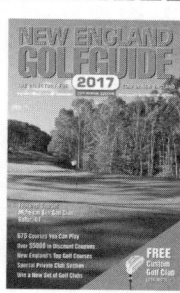

### Pontoosuc Lake Country Club
Pittsfield, MA (413) 445-4217

- **Type of Discount**
  Buy 1 greens fee, get second greens fee
  at one-half off with cart rental

- **Days of the Week**
  Weekdays only (except holidays)

- **Hours of the Day**
  All day

Coupon expires 12/31/17. Cannot be combined with any other offer.

---

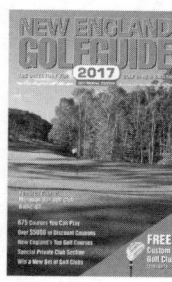

### Poquoy Brook Golf Course
Lakeville, MA (508) 947-5261

- **Type of Discount**
  20% off non-sale golf apparel

- **Days of the Week**
  7 days a week

- **Hours of the Day**
  All day

Coupon expires 12/31/17. Cannot be combined with any other offer.

---

### Quaboag Country Club
Monson, MA (413) 267-5294

- **Type of Discount**
  Free golf cart with 2 paid greens fees

- **Days of the Week**
  Weekdays only (except holidays)

- **Hours of the Day**
  All day

Coupon expires 12/31/17. Cannot be combined with any other offer.

---

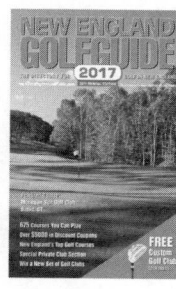

### Quail Ridge Country Club
Acton, MA (978) 264-0399

- **Type of Discount**
  Free golf cart with 2 paid greens fees

- **Days of the Week**
  Weekdays only (except holidays)

- **Hours of the Day**
  All day

Coupon expires 12/31/17. Cannot be combined with any other offer.

**NEW ENGLAND GOLFGUIDE**

**2 0 1 7**

---

✂ - - - - - - - - - - - - - - - - - - - - - - - - - - - - - - - - - - - - -

**NEW ENGLAND GOLFGUIDE**

**2 0 1 7**

---

✂ - - - - - - - - - - - - - - - - - - - - - - - - - - - - - - - - - - - - -

**NEW ENGLAND GOLFGUIDE**

**2 0 1 7**

---

✂ - - - - - - - - - - - - - - - - - - - - - - - - - - - - - - - - - - - - -

**NEW ENGLAND GOLFGUIDE**

**2 0 1 7**

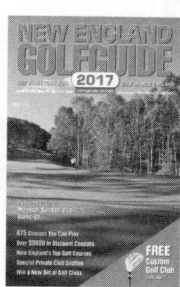

### Quashnet Valley Country Club
Mashpee, MA (508) 477-4412

- **Type of Discount**
  $5 off greens fees for up to 4 players
- **Days of the Week**
  Monday through Thursday (except holidays)
- **Hours of the Day**
  All day

Coupon expires 12/31/17. Cannot be combined with any other offer.

---

### Ranch Golf Club, The
Southwick, MA (413) 569-9333

- **Type of Discount**
  $65 per player (includes cart)
- **Days of the Week**
  Monday through Wednesday (except holidays)
- **Hours of the Day**
  All day

Coupon expires 12/31/17. Cannot be combined with any other offer.

---

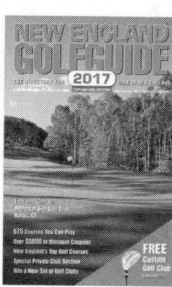

### Reedy Meadow Golf Course
Lynnfield, MA (781) 334-9877

- **Type of Discount**
  $40 for 2 players with cart
- **Days of the Week**
  Weekdays (except holidays)
- **Hours of the Day**
  Monday and Friday 11:30am–5:30pm
  Tues/Wed/Thur 11:30am–2pm

Coupon expires 12/31/17. Cannot be combined with any other offer.

---

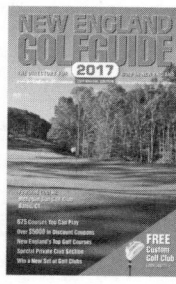

### Rockland Golf Course
Rockland, MA (781) 871-0480

- **Type of Discount**
  2 players for price of 1 (18 hole cart required)
- **Days of the Week**
  Weekdays (except holidays)
- **Hours of the Day**
  Before 2pm

Coupon expires 12/31/17. Cannot be combined with any other offer.

**NEW ENGLAND GOLFGUIDE**

2017

---

**NEW ENGLAND GOLFGUIDE**

2017

---

**NEW ENGLAND GOLFGUIDE**

2017

---

**NEW ENGLAND GOLFGUIDE**

2017

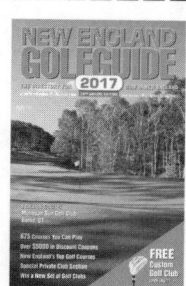

### Rowley Country Club
Rowley, MA (978) 948-2731

- **Type of Discount**
  2 players for price of 1
- **Days of the Week**
  Monday through Thursday (except holidays)
- **Hours of the Day**
  Not valid with leagues or outings. Valid up to 2pm.
  Expires 10/31/17.

Coupon expires 10/31/17. Cannot be combined with any other offer.

### Sagamore Spring Golf Club
Lynnfield, MA (781) 334-3151

- **Type of Discount**
  Free bucket of ball with greens fee
- **Days of the Week**
  7 days a week
- **Hours of the Day**
  All day

Coupon expires 12/31/17. Cannot be combined with any other offer.

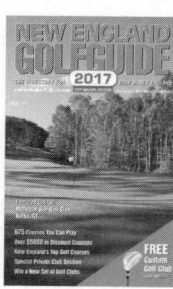

### Sandwich Hollows Golf Club
East Sandwich, MA (508) 888-3384 x0

- **Type of Discount**
  Greens fee for 18 holes $29.95
- **Days of the Week**
  7 days a week
- **Hours of the Day**
  After 2pm

Coupon expires 12/31/17. Cannot be combined with any other offer.

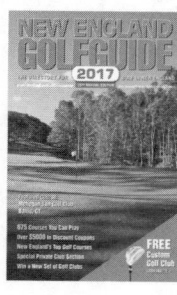

### Sassamon Trace Golf Course
Natick, MA (508) 655-1330

- **Type of Discount**
  Free golf cart with 2 paid greens fees
- **Days of the Week**
  7 days a week
- **Hours of the Day**
  All day

Coupon expires 12/31/17. Cannot be combined with any other offer.

Golf Course

**NEW ENGLAND GOLFGUIDE**

2 0 1 7

**NEW ENGLAND GOLFGUIDE**

2 0 1 7

**NEW ENGLAND GOLFGUIDE**

2 0 1 7

**NEW ENGLAND GOLFGUIDE**

2 0 1 7

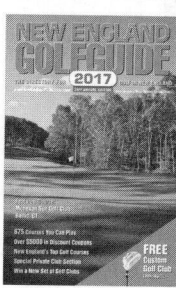

### Settlers Crossing Golf Course
Lunenburg, MA (978) 582-6694

- **Type of Discount**
  $38 for 2 players and a cart for 9 holes
- **Days of the Week**
  Weekdays only (except holidays)
- **Hours of the Day**
  11:30am–2pm

Coupon expires 12/31/17. Cannot be combined with any other offer.

### Shaker Farms Country Club
Westfield, MA (413) 562-2770

- **Type of Discount**
  1 free greens fee. 1 per person/1 time only.
- **Days of the Week**
  Weekdays only (except holidays)
- **Hours of the Day**
  All day

Coupon expires 12/31/17. Cannot be combined with any other offer.

### Shaker Hills Country Club
Harvard, MA (978) 772-3330

- **Type of Discount**
  25% discount for 2 to 4 players
- **Days of the Week**
  Monday through Thursday only (except holidays)
- **Hours of the Day**
  Before 1pm. Not valid for senior, miltary or ladies day rates.

Coupon expires 12/31/17. Cannot be combined with any other offer.

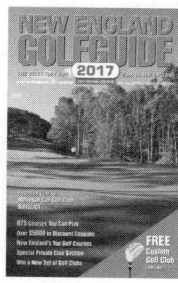

### Skyline Country Club
Route 7, Lanesborough, MA (413) 445-5584

- **Type of Discount**
  25% discount for 2 to 4 players
- **Days of the Week**
  7 days a week
- **Hours of the Day**
  All day

Coupon expires 12/31/17. Cannot be combined with any other offer.

**Golf Course Coupons**

**NEW ENGLAND GOLFGUIDE**

**2017**

---

**NEW ENGLAND GOLFGUIDE**

**2017**

---

**NEW ENGLAND GOLFGUIDE**

**2017**

---

**NEW ENGLAND GOLFGUIDE**

**2017**

### Southers Marsh Golf Club
Plymouth, MA (508) 830-3535

- **Type of Discount**
  Free golf cart with 2 paid greens fees
- **Days of the Week**
  7 days a week
- **Hours of the Day**
  All day

Coupon expires 12/31/17. Cannot be combined with any other offer.

---

### Southwick Country Club
Southwick, MA (413) 569-0136

- **Type of Discount**
  1 player with cart $25; Senior with cart $21
- **Days of the Week**
  Weekdays only (except holidays)
- **Hours of the Day**
  All day

Coupon expires 12/31/17. Cannot be combined with any other offer.

---

### St. Mark's Golf Club
Southborough, MA (508) 460-0946

- **Type of Discount**
  Free golf cart with 2 paid greens fees
- **Days of the Week**
  Monday through Thursday (except holidays)
- **Hours of the Day**
  Before 2pm

Coupon expires 12/31/17. Cannot be combined with any other offer.

---

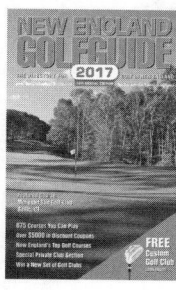

### Squirrel Run Golf Course
Plymouth, MA (508) 746-5001

- **Type of Discount**
  2 players with cart for $60
- **Days of the Week**
  Weekdays only (except holidays)
- **Hours of the Days**
  After 10am

Coupon expires 12/31/17. Cannot be combined with any other offer.

Golf Course Coupons

**NEW ENGLAND GOLFGUIDE**

2 0 1 7

---

**NEW ENGLAND GOLFGUIDE**

2 0 1 7

---

**NEW ENGLAND GOLFGUIDE**

2 0 1 7

---

**NEW ENGLAND GOLFGUIDE**

2 0 1 7

### Stonybrook Golf Course
Southboro, MA (508) 485-3151

- **Type of Discount**
  2 players for the price of 1

- **Days of the Week**
  Weekdays only (except holidays)

- **Hours of the Day**
  All day

Coupon expires 12/31/17. Cannot be combined with any other offer.

---

### Stow Acres Country Club
Stow, MA (978) 568-1100

- **Type of Discount**
  $10 per player (up to 4 players).
  Cart rental required.

- **Days of the Week**
  7 days a week

- **Hours of the Day**
  After 10am. Not valid with prepaid events.

Coupon expires 12/31/17. Cannot be combined with any other offer.

---

### Swansea Country Club
Swansea, MA (508) 379-9886

- **Type of Discount**
  Golf, cart, 2 hot dogs, soda, and chips - $44.95

- **Days of the Week**
  Weekdays only (except holidays)

- **Hours of the Day**
  11am–1pm

Coupon expires 12/31/17. Cannot be combined with any other offer.

---

### Tekoa Country Club
Westfield, MA (413) 568-1064

- **Type of Discount**
  2 players for the price of 1.
  Cart rental required.

- **Days of the Week**
  Weekdays only

- **Hours of the Day**
  Before 1pm

Coupon expires 12/31/17. Cannot be combined with any other offer.

**Golf Course Coupons**

**NEW ENGLAND GOLFGUIDE**

**2 0 1 7**

---

**NEW ENGLAND GOLFGUIDE**

**2 0 1 7**

---

**NEW ENGLAND GOLFGUIDE**

**2 0 1 7**

---

**NEW ENGLAND GOLFGUIDE**

**2 0 1 7**

### Templewood Golf Course
Templeton, MA  (978) 939-5031

- **Type of Discount**
  2 players for the price of 1.
  Cart rental required.
- **Days of the Week**
  Weekdays only (except holidays)
- **Hours of the Day**
  All day. Tee time required.

Coupon expires 12/31/17. Cannot be combined with any other offer.

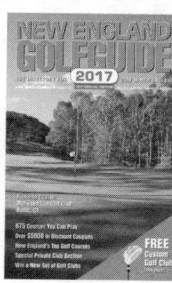

### Thomas Memorial Golf & CC
Turners Falls, MA  (413) 863-8003

- **Type of Discount**
  2 players for the price of 1
- **Days of the Week**
  7 days a week
- **Hours of the Day**
  All day

Coupon expires 12/31/17. Cannot be combined with any other offer.

### Touisset Country Club
Swansea, MA  (508) 679-9577

- **Type of Discount**
  2 players for the price of 1
- **Days of the Week**
  7 days a week
- **Hours of the Day**
  All day. Not valid for league or tournament play.

Coupon expires 12/31/17. Cannot be combined with any other offer.

### Townsend Ridge Country Club
Townsend, MA  (978) 597-8400

- **Type of Discount**
  2 players for the price of 1. Cart rental required.
- **Days of the Week**
  7 days a week
- **Hours of the Day**
  All day

Coupon expires 12/31/17. Cannot be combined with any other offer.

**Golf Course Coupons**

**NEW ENGLAND**
**GOLFGUIDE**

2 0 1 7

---

**NEW ENGLAND**
**GOLFGUIDE**

2 0 1 7

---

**NEW ENGLAND**
**GOLFGUIDE**

2 0 1 7

---

**NEW ENGLAND**
**GOLFGUIDE**

2 0 1 7

### Twin Brooks Golf Course
Hyannis, MA (508) 862-6980

- **Type of Discount**
  4 players for the price of 3
- **Days of the Week**
  Weekdays only (except holidays)
- **Hours of the Day**
  After 11am

Coupon expires 12/31/17. Cannot be combined with any other offer.

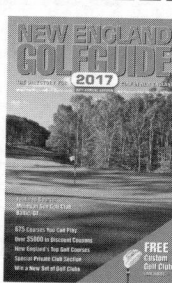

### Twin Springs Golf Club
Bolton, MA (978) 779-5020

- **Type of Discount**
  2 players for the price of 1
- **Days of the Week**
  Monday through Thursday (except holidays)
- **Hours of the Day**
  6:30am to 3pm

Coupon expires 12/31/17. Cannot be combined with any other offer.

### Village Links
Plymouth, MA (508) 830-4653

- **Type of Discount**
  2 players with cart for $50
- **Days of the Week**
  Weekdays only (except holidays)
- **Hours of the Day**
  After 10am. Valid April - October.

Coupon expires 12/31/17. Cannot be combined with any other offer.

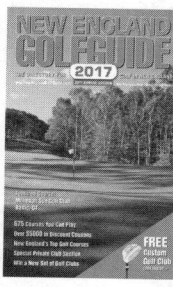

### Wampanoag Golf Club
North Swansea, MA (508) 379-9832

- **Type of Discount**
  $31 per person for 18 holes w/cart
- **Days of the Week**
  7 days a week (except holidays)
- **Hours of the Day**
  7am-1pm weekdays/after 12pm weekends.
  Valid through September 2017.

Coupon expires 9/30/17. Cannot be combined with any other offer.

**Golf Course Coupons**

**NEW ENGLAND GOLFGUIDE**

**2 0 1 7**

---

**NEW ENGLAND GOLFGUIDE**

**2 0 1 7**

---

**NEW ENGLAND GOLFGUIDE**

**2 0 1 7**

---

**NEW ENGLAND GOLFGUIDE**

**2 0 1 7**

### Waubeeka Golf Links
South Williamstown, MA (413) 458-8355

- **Type of Discount**
  4 players for the price of 3
- **Days of the Week**
  7 days a week
- **Hours of the Day**
  All day

Coupon expires 12/31/17. Cannot be combined with any other offer.

### Waubeeka Golf Links
South Williamstown, MA (413) 458-8355

- **Type of Discount**
  10% off all Pro Shop items
  10% off in the restaurant
- **Days of the Week**
  7 days a week
- **Hours of the Day**
  All day

Coupon expires 12/31/17. Cannot be combined with any other offer.

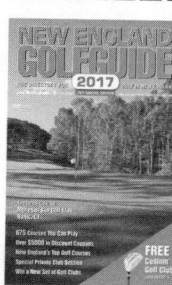

### Waverly Oaks Golf Club
Plymouth, MA (508) 224-6016

- **Type of Discount**
  $5 off greens fees for up to 2 players
- **Days of the Week**
  7 days a week
- **Hours of the Day**
  All day

Coupon expires 12/31/17. Cannot be combined with any other offer.

### Wenham Country Club
Wenham, MA (978) 468-4714

- **Type of Discount**
  25% discount for 2 to 4 players
- **Days of the Week**
  7 days a week
- **Hours of the Day**
  All day

Coupon expires 12/31/17. Cannot be combined with any other offer.

Golf Course Coupons

**NEW ENGLAND GOLFGUIDE**

**2 0 1 7**

---

**NEW ENGLAND GOLFGUIDE**

**2 0 1 7**

---

**NEW ENGLAND GOLFGUIDE**

**2 0 1 7**

---

**NEW ENGLAND GOLFGUIDE**

**2 0 1 7**

## Wentworth Hills Country Club
Plainville, MA (508) 316-0240

- **Type of Discount**
  $35 for 18 holes for 1-4 players (cart included)

- **Days of the Week**
  Monday through Thursday (except holidays)

- **Hours of the Day**
  Mon - Thurs (except holidays) - before 1pm
  Fri/Sat/Sun/Holidays - after 2pm

Coupon expires 12/31/17. Cannot be combined with any other offer.

---

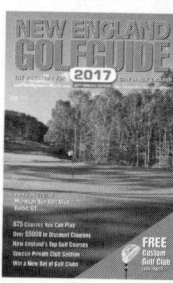

## Westborough Country Club
Westborough, MA (508) 366-9947

- **Type of Discount**
  2 greens fees for the price of 1

- **Days of the Week**
  Weekdays only (except holidays)

- **Hours of the Day**
  All day. Not valid for league play.

Coupon expires 12/31/17. Cannot be combined with any other offer.

---

## Winchendon Country Club
Winchendon, MA (978) 297-9897

- **Type of Discount**
  2 players for the price of 1. Cart rental required.

- **Days of the Week**
  Weekdays only (except holidays)
  Weekends after 12pm

- **Hours of the Day**
  All day

Coupon expires 12/31/17. Cannot be combined with any other offer.

---

## Widow's Walk Golf Course
Scituate, MA (781) 544-7777

- **Type of Discount**
  4 players for the price of 3

- **Days of the Week**
  7 days a week

- **Hours of the Day**
  Weekends and holidays after 11am

Coupon expires 12/31/17. Cannot be combined with any other offer.

**Golf Course Coupons**

**NEW ENGLAND**
## GOLFGUIDE

2 0 1 7

---

**NEW ENGLAND**
## GOLFGUIDE

2 0 1 7

---

**NEW ENGLAND**
## GOLFGUIDE

2 0 1 7

---

**NEW ENGLAND**
## GOLFGUIDE

2 0 1 7

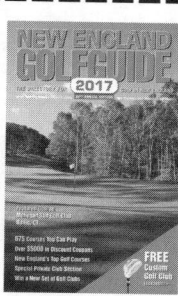

## Woods of Westminster Country Club
Westminster, MA (978) 874-0500

- **Type of Discount**
  $38 for 18 holes, cart, and lunch (per person)

- **Days of the Week**
  Weekdays only (except holidays)

- **Hours of the Day**
  Monday-Friday before 12pm. Excludes league play, tournaments and specials.

Coupon expires 12/31/17. Cannot be combined with any other offer.

---

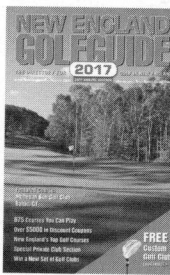

## Worthington Golf Course
Worthington, MA (413) 238-4464

- **Type of Discount**
  $25 for 18 holes with cart

- **Days of the Week**
  Weekdays only (except holidays)

- **Hours of the Day**
  All day

Coupon expires 12/31/17. Cannot be combined with any other offer.

---

## Androscoggin Valley Country Club
Route 2, Gorham, NH (603) 466-9468

- **Type of Discount**
  $39 per player (includes cart)

- **Days of the Week**
  7 days a week

- **Hours of the Day**
  All day with tee times only. Must bring in coupon in NE GolfGuide.

Coupon expires 12/31/17. Cannot be combined with any other offer.

---

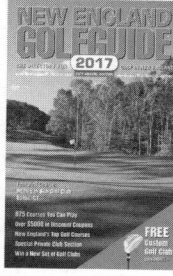

## Apple Hill Golf Club
East Kingston, NH (603) 642-4414

- **Type of Discount**
  $5 off greens fees for up to 2 players

- **Days of the Week**
  Weekdays only (except holidays)

- **Hours of the Day**
  All day

Coupon expires 12/31/17. Cannot be combined with any other offer.

**Golf Course Coupons**

**NEW ENGLAND GOLFGUIDE**

2 0 1 7

---

**NEW ENGLAND GOLFGUIDE**

2 0 1 7

---

**NEW ENGLAND GOLFGUIDE**

2 0 1 7

---

**NEW ENGLAND GOLFGUIDE**

2 0 1 7

### Atkinson Resort and Country Club
Atkinson, NH (603) 362-8700

- **Type of Discount**
  4 players for the price of 3 (greens fees only).
  Cart rental required.

- **Days of the Week**
  Monday through Thursday (except holidays)

- **Hours of the Day**
  All day

Coupon expires 12/31/17. Cannot be combined with any other offer.

---

### Beaver Meadow Golf Club
Concord, NH (603) 228-8954

- **Type of Discount**
  2 greens fees and cart for $80

- **Days of the Week**
  Monday through Wednesday (except holidays)

- **Hours of the Day**
  After 12pm

Coupon expires 12/31/17. Cannot be combined with any other offer.

---

### Bethlehem Country Club
Bethlehem, NH (603) 869-5745

- **Type of Discount**
  $30 w/cart M - Th (except holidays)
  $35 w/cart F/S/S/H

- **Days of the Week**
  See above

- **Hours of the Day**
  All day. Not valid holidays.

Coupon expires 12/31/17. Cannot be combined with any other offer.

---

### Blackmount Country Club
North Haverhill, NH (603) 787-6564

- **Type of Discount**
  $3 off power cart rental with paid greens fee

- **Days of the Week**
  Weekdays only (except holidays)

- **Hours of the Day**
  All day

Coupon expires 12/31/17. Cannot be combined with any other offer.

**Golf Course Coupons**

**NEW ENGLAND GOLFGUIDE**

2 0 1 7

---

**NEW ENGLAND GOLFGUIDE**

2 0 1 7

---

**NEW ENGLAND GOLFGUIDE**

2 0 1 7

---

**NEW ENGLAND GOLFGUIDE**

2 0 1 7

### Breakfast Hill Golf Club
Greenland, NH (603) 436-5001

- **Type of Discount**
  Free golf cart with 2 paid greens fees

- **Days of the Week**
  Monday through Thursday (except holidays)

- **Hours of the Day**
  All day

Coupon expires 12/31/17. Cannot be combined with any other offer.

---

### Campbell's Scottish Highlands
Salem, NH (603) 894-4653

- **Type of Discount**
  18 holes, cart, & bag lunch for 2 golfers - $96

- **Days of the Week**
  Monday through Thursday (except holidays)

- **Hours of the Day**
  All day. Valid March 27 - May 25
  and October 101 - November 16.

Coupon expires 12/31/17. Cannot be combined with any other offer.

---

### Canterbury Woods Country Club
Canterbury, NH (603) 783-9400

- **Type of Discount**
  2 players for the price of 1

- **Days of the Week**
  Monday through Thursday (except holidays)

- **Hours of the Day**
  All day. Cart rental required.

Coupon expires 12/31/17. Cannot be combined with any other offer.

---

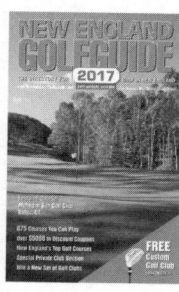

### Colebrook Country Club
Colebrook, NH (603) 237-5566

- **Type of Discount**
  2 players for the price of 1.
  18-hole power cart required.

- **Days of the Week**
  Weekdays only (except holidays)

- **Hours of the Day**
  All day

Coupon expires 12/31/17. Cannot be combined with any other offer.

**Golf Course Coupons**

**NEW ENGLAND GOLFGUIDE**

2 0 1 7

**NEW ENGLAND GOLFGUIDE**

2 0 1 7

**NEW ENGLAND GOLFGUIDE**

2 0 1 7

**NEW ENGLAND GOLFGUIDE**

2 0 1 7

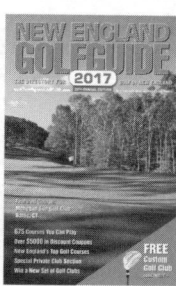

### Country Club of New Hampshire
North Sutton, NH (603) 927-4246

- **Type of Discount**
  Mondays – $35 for 18 holes with cart
- **Days of the Week**
  Mondays
- **Hours of the Day**
  All day

Coupon expires 12/31/17. Cannot be combined with any other offer.

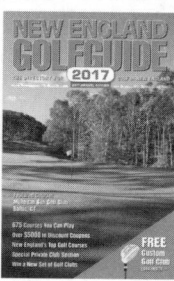

### Countryside Golf Club
Dunbarton, NH (603) 774-5031

- **Type of Discount**
  2 players for $32 (before 11am)
- **Days of the Week**
  Weekdays only (except holidays)
- **Hours of the Day**
  Before 11am

Coupon expires 12/31/17. Cannot be combined with any other offer.

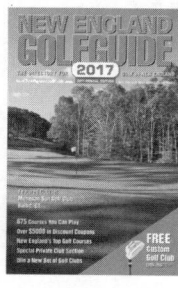

### Crotched Mountain Golf Course
Route 47, Francestown, NH (603) 588-2923

- **Type of Discount**
  $5 off 2-4 players
- **Days of the Week**
  7 day a week
- **Hours of the Day**
  All day. Cart not included.

Coupon expires 12/31/17. Cannot be combined with any other offer.

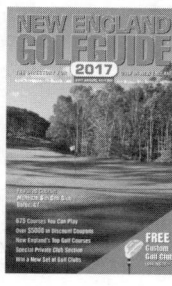

### Den Brae Golf Course
Sanbornton, NH (603) 934-9818

- **Type of Discount**
  25% discount for 2-4 players
- **Days of the Week**
  Weekdays only (except holidays)
- **Hours of the Day**
  All day

Coupon expires 12/31/17. Cannot be combined with any other offer.

**NEW ENGLAND**
**GOLFGUIDE**

2 0 1 7

---

**NEW ENGLAND**
**GOLFGUIDE**

2 0 1 7

---

**NEW ENGLAND**
**GOLFGUIDE**

2 0 1 7

---

**NEW ENGLAND**
**GOLFGUIDE**

2 0 1 7

### Derryfield Country Club
Manchester, NH (603) 669-0235

- **Type of Discount**
  2 players for price of 1. Cart rental required.
- **Days of the Week**
  Weekdays only (except holidays)
- **Hours of the Day**
  M-Th all day. Fri-Sat-Sun-Holiday after 1pm.
  1 coupon per visit.

Coupon expires 12/31/17. Cannot be combined with any other offer.

### Duston Country Club
Hopkinton, NH (603) 746-4234

- **Type of Discount**
  Free sandwich after round (up to $5 value)
- **Days of the Week**
  Weekdays only (except holidays)
- **Hours of the Day**
  All day

Coupon expires 12/31/17. Cannot be combined with any other offer.

### Eastman Golf Links
Grantham, NH (603) 863-4500

- **Type of Discount**
  $45 per person including cart
- **Days of the Week**
  7 days a week
- **Hours of the Day**
  All day. Sat/Sun/Holiday after 12pm.
  Please call ahead.

Coupon expires 12/31/17. Cannot be combined with any other offer.

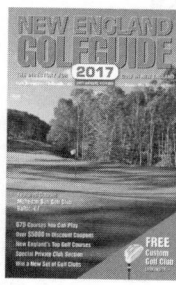

### Exeter Country Club
Exeter, NH (603) 772-4752

- **Type of Discount**
  2 players for the price of 1
- **Days of the Week**
  Monday through Thursday (except holidays)
- **Hours of the Day**
  All day

Coupon expires 12/31/17. Cannot be combined with any other offer.

**NEW ENGLAND GOLFGUIDE**

2 0 1 7

**NEW ENGLAND GOLFGUIDE**

2 0 1 7

**NEW ENGLAND GOLFGUIDE**

2 0 1 7

**NEW ENGLAND GOLFGUIDE**

2 0 1 7

### Granite Fields Golf Club
Kingston, NH  (603) 642-9977

- **Type of Discount**
  Seniors - $30 for 18 holes w/cart

- **Days of the Week**
  Weekdays only (except holidays)

- **Hours of the Day**
  All day

Coupon expires 12/31/17. Cannot be combined with any other offer.

---

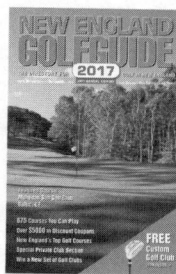

### Hales Location Golf Course
North Conway, NH  (603) 356-2140

- **Type of Discount**
  $5 off 9 holes; $10 off $18 holes

- **Days of the Week**
  Monday through Thursday (except holidays)

- **Hours of the Day**
  All day

Coupon expires 12/31/17. Cannot be combined with any other offer.

---

### Hanover Country Club
Hanover, NH  (603) 646-2000

- **Type of Discount**
  4 players for the price of 3

- **Days of the Week**
  Weekends

- **Hours of the Day**
  After 1pm

Coupon expires 12/31/17. Cannot be combined with any other offer.

---

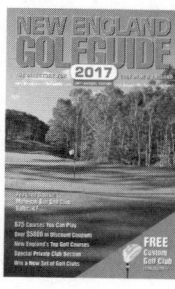

### Hidden Valley Golf Course
Derry, NH  (603) 887-7888

- **Type of Discount**
  2 players for the price of 1.
  Cart rental not included.

- **Days of the Week**
  Wednesday

- **Hours of the Day**
  All day

Coupon expires 12/31/17. Cannot be combined with any other offer.

**NEW ENGLAND GOLFGUIDE**

2 0 1 7

**NEW ENGLAND GOLFGUIDE**

2 0 1 7

**NEW ENGLAND GOLFGUIDE**

2 0 1 7

**NEW ENGLAND GOLFGUIDE**

2 0 1 7

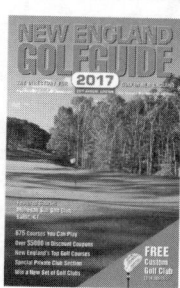

## Hoodkroft Country Club
Derry, NH (603) 434-0651

- **Type of Discount**
  4 players for the price of 3
- **Days of the Week**
  Weekdays only (except holidays)
- **Hours of the Day**
  All day

Coupon expires 12/31/17. Cannot be combined with any other offer.

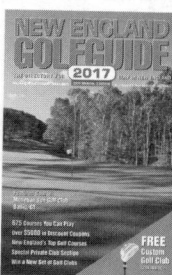

## Indian Mound Golf Club
Center Ossippee, NH (603) 539-7733

- **Type of Discount**
  4 players for the price of 3.
  Golf cart rental required.
- **Days of the Week**
  Weekdays; weekends (after 2pm)
- **Hours of the Day**
  All day

Coupon expires 12/31/17. Cannot be combined with any other offer.

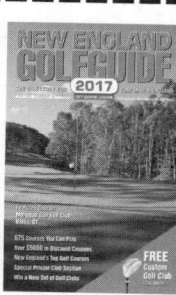

## Intervale Country Club
Manchester, NH (603) 647-6811

- **Type of Discount**
  4 players for the price of 3
- **Days of the Week**
  Monday through Thursday (except holidays)
- **Hours of the Day**
  Before 3pm

Coupon expires 12/31/17. Cannot be combined with any other offer.

## Jack O'Lantern Resort
Woodstock, NH (603) 745-3636

- **Type of Discount**
  15% off greens fees
- **Days of the Week**
  Weekdays only (except holidays)
- **Hours of the Day**
  Until 2pm (mid-May to mid-October)

Coupon expires 12/31/17. Cannot be combined with any other offer.

**NEW ENGLAND GOLFGUIDE**

2 0 1 7

---

**NEW ENGLAND GOLFGUIDE**

2 0 1 7

---

**NEW ENGLAND GOLFGUIDE**

2 0 1 7

---

**NEW ENGLAND GOLFGUIDE**

2 0 1 7

### Kingston Fairways Golf Club
Kingston, NH (603) 642-7722

- **Type of Discount**
  4 players for price of 3
- **Days of the Week**
  7 days a week
- **Hours of the Day**
  All day

Coupon expires 12/31/17. Cannot be combined with any other offer.

---

### Loudon Country Club
Loudon, NH (603) 783-3372

- **Type of Discount**
  $38 per player with cart
- **Days of the Week**
  Weekdays only (except holidays)
- **Hours of the Day**
  All day

Coupon expires 12/31/17. Cannot be combined with any other offer.

---

### Maplewood Golf Club
Bethlehem, NH (603) 869-3335

- **Type of Discount**
  $5 off greens fee
- **Days of the Week**
  Weekdays only (except holidays)
- **Hours of the Day**
  7am-6pm. 18 holes only, cart rental required.

Coupon expires 12/31/17. Cannot be combined with any other offer.

---

### Mojalaki Country Club
Franklin, NH (603) 934-3033

- **Type of Discount**
  $5 off greens fees for up to 2 players for 18 holes
- **Days of the Week**
  Weekdays only (except holidays)
- **Hours of the Day**
  Before 2pm

Coupon expires 12/31/17. Cannot be combined with any other offer.

**NEW ENGLAND**
**GOLFGUIDE**

2 0 1 7

---

**NEW ENGLAND**
**GOLFGUIDE**

2 0 1 7

---

**NEW ENGLAND**
**GOLFGUIDE**

2 0 1 7

---

**NEW ENGLAND**
**GOLFGUIDE**

2 0 1 7

### Mount Washington Golf Club
Bretton Woods, NH (603) 278-4653

- **Type of Discount**
  2 players for the price of 1

- **Days of the Week**
  Mondays through Wednesday

- **Hours of the Day**
  After 1pm

Coupon expires 12/31/17. Cannot be combined with any other offer.

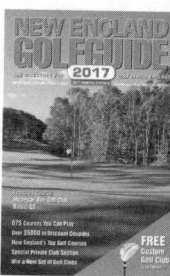

### Newport Golf Club
Newport, NH (603) 863-7787

- **Type of Discount**
  4 players for the price of 3

- **Days of the Week**
  Weekdays only (except holidays)

- **Hours of the Day**
  All day. Not valid on discount rates or holidays.

Coupon expires 12/31/17. Cannot be combined with any other offer.

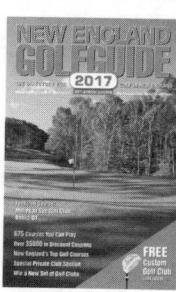

### Nippo Lake Golf Club
Barrington, NH (603) 664-7616

- **Type of Discount**
  $80 for 2 players and a cart (18 holes)

- **Days of the Week**
  Weekdays (except holidays).
  Weekends/Holidays after 12pm.

- **Hours of the Day**
  All day

Coupon expires 12/31/17. Cannot be combined with any other offer.

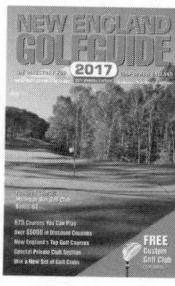

### North Conway Country Club
North Conway, NH (603) 356-9391

- **Type of Discount**
  10% off with coupon after 12pm

- **Days of the Week**
  7 days a week

- **Hours of the Day**
  After 12pm

Coupon expires 12/31/17. Cannot be combined with any other offer.

**Golf Course Coupons**

**NEW ENGLAND GOLFGUIDE**

2 0 1 7

**NEW ENGLAND GOLFGUIDE**

2 0 1 7

**NEW ENGLAND GOLFGUIDE**

2 0 1 7

**NEW ENGLAND GOLFGUIDE**

2 0 1 7

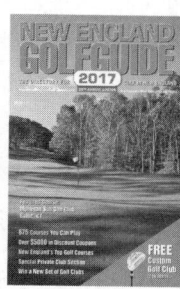

### Oak Hill Golf Course
Meredith, NH (603) 279-4438

- **Type of Discount**
  2 players for the price of 1. Cart rental required.
- **Days of the Week**
  7 days a week (except holiday weekends)
- **Hours of the Day**
  All day

Coupon expires 12/31/17. Cannot be combined with any other offer.

### Owl's Nest Golf Club
Campton, NH (603) 726-3076

- **Type of Discount**
  2 players for the price of 1
- **Days of the Week**
  Weekdays (except holidays)
- **Hours of the Day**
  After 11am

Coupon expires 12/31/17. Cannot be combined with any other offer.

### Pembroke Pines Country Club
Pembroke, NH (603) 210-1365

- **Type of Discount**
  4 players for the price of 3
- **Days of the Week**
  Weekdays Only (except holidays)
- **Hours of the Day**
  All day

Coupon expires 12/31/17. Cannot be combined with any other offer.

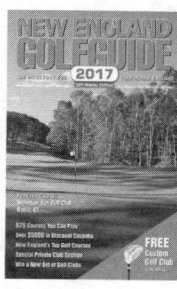

### Pine Grove Springs Country Club
Route 9A, Spofford, NH (603) 363-4433

- **Type of Discount**
  2 players for the price of 1
- **Days of the Week**
  7 days a week
- **Hours of the Day**
  All day (excludes Sunday AM)

Coupon expires 12/31/17. Cannot be combined with any other offer.

**Golf Course Coupons**

**NEW ENGLAND GOLFGUIDE**

2 0 1 7

**NEW ENGLAND GOLFGUIDE**

2 0 1 7

**NEW ENGLAND GOLFGUIDE**

2 0 1 7

**NEW ENGLAND GOLFGUIDE**

2 0 1 7

## Pine Valley Golf Links
Pelham, NH (603) 635-7979, (603) 635-8305

- **Type of Discount**
  4 players for the price of 3
- **Days of the Week**
  7 days a week
- **Hours of the Day**
  All day

Coupon expires 12/31/17. Cannot be combined with any other offer.

## Ridgewood Country Club
Moultonborough, NH (603) 476-5930

- **Type of Discount**
  4 players for the price of 3
- **Days of the Week**
  Monday through Thursday (except holidays)
- **Hours of the Day**
  All day

Coupon expires 12/31/17. Cannot be combined with any other offer.

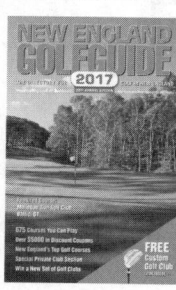

## Rochester Country Club
Rochester, NH (603) 332-9892

- **Type of Discount**
  $90 for 2 players and cart (18 holes)
- **Days of the Week**
  Weekdays (except holidays).
  Weekends/Holidays after 12pm.
- **Hours of the Day**
  All day

Coupon expires 12/31/17. Cannot be combined with any other offer.

## Rockingham Country Club
Newmarket, NH (603) 659-9956

- **Type of Discount**
  4 players for the price of 3
- **Days of the Week**
  7 days a week
- **Hours of the Day**
  All day

Coupon expires 12/31/17. Cannot be combined with any other offer.

**NH**

**Golf Course Coupons**

**NEW ENGLAND**
**GOLFGUIDE**

2 0 1 7

**NEW ENGLAND**
**GOLFGUIDE**

2 0 1 7

**NEW ENGLAND**
**GOLFGUIDE**

2 0 1 7

**NEW ENGLAND**
**GOLFGUIDE**

2 0 1 7

### Sagamore-Hampton Golf Club
North Hampton, NH (603) 964-5341

- **Type of Discount**
  25% discount for 2-4 players (cart included)
  18 holes only

- **Days of the Week**
  Weekdays (except holidays)

- **Hours of the Day**
  10am–2:30pm. Not valid for league play.

Coupon expires 12/31/17. Cannot be combined with any other offer.

---

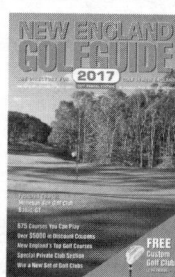

### Shattuck Golf Course, The
Jaffrey, NH (603) 532-4300

- **Type of Discount**
  2 players for price of 1

- **Days of the Week**
  7 days a week

- **Hours of the Day**
  All day

Coupon expires 12/31/17. Cannot be combined with any other offer.

---

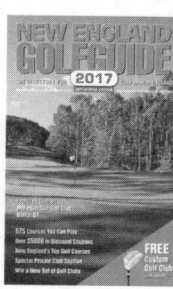

### Stonebridge Country Club
Goffstown, NH (603) 497-8633

- **Type of Discount**
  4 players for 18 holes and 2 carts for $169

- **Days of the Week**
  Monday through Thursday (excludes holidays)

- **Hours of the Day**
  All day

Coupon expires 12/31/17. Cannot be combined with any other offer.

---

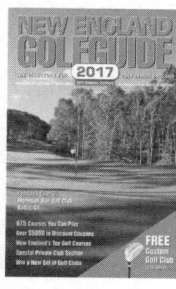

### Sunset Hill Golf Course
Sugar Hill, NH (603) 823-7244

- **Type of Discount**
  $22.50 per person for 9 or 18 holes (with cart)

- **Days of the Week**
  7 days a week (except July 4th weekend)

- **Hours of the Day**
  All day

Coupon expires 12/31/17. Cannot be combined with any other offer.

**Golf Course Coupons**

**NEW ENGLAND GOLFGUIDE**

**2 0 1 7**

---

**NEW ENGLAND GOLFGUIDE**

**2 0 1 7**

---

**NEW ENGLAND GOLFGUIDE**

**2 0 1 7**

---

**NEW ENGLAND GOLFGUIDE**

**2 0 1 7**

### Waterville Valley Golf Club
Waterville, NH  (603) 236-4805

- **Type of Discount**
  Unlimited golf with cart for $25
- **Days of the Week**
  Monday through Thursday (except holidays)
- **Hours of the Day**
  All day

Coupon expires 12/31/17. Cannot be combined with any other offer.

---

### Waumbek Golf Club
Jefferson, NH  (603) 586-7777

- **Type of Discount**
  $10 off 2 players with cart
- **Days of the Week**
  Tuesday through Friday (except holidays)
- **Hours of the Day**
  Before 3pm

Coupon expires 12/31/17. Cannot be combined with any other offer.

---

### Wentworth Resort Golf Club
Rt. 16, Jackson, NH  (603) 383-9641

- **Type of Discount**
  $5 off each greens fee for up to 2 players
- **Days of the Week**
  Monday through Thursday
- **Hours of the Day**
  After 1pm. Must call ahead. Must mention coupon when reserving tee time.

Coupon expires 12/31/17. Cannot be combined with any other offer.

---

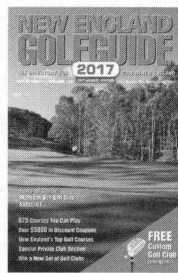

### White Mountain Country Club
Ashland, NH  (603) 536-2227

- **Type of Discount**
  $5 off 18-hole greens fee.
  Cart rental required.
- **Days of the Week**
  Monday through Thursday (except holidays)
- **Hours of the Day**
  All day

Coupon expires 12/31/17. Cannot be combined with any other offer.

**Golf Course Coupons**

**NEW ENGLAND GOLFGUIDE**

2 0 1 7

---

**NEW ENGLAND GOLFGUIDE**

2 0 1 7

---

**NEW ENGLAND GOLFGUIDE**

2 0 1 7

---

**NEW ENGLAND GOLFGUIDE**

2 0 1 7

### Beaver River Golf Club
Richmond, RI (401) 539-2100

- **Type of Discount**
  $43 with cart (Seniors/Military - $40 with cart)
- **Days of the Week**
  Monday through Thursday
- **Hours of the Day**
  8am–1pm

Coupon expires 12/31/17. Cannot be combined with any other offer.

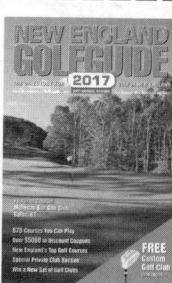

### Country View Golf Club
Harrisville, RI (401) 568-7157

- **Type of Discount**
  2 players for the price of 1.
  Cart rental required.
- **Days of the Week**
  Weekdays only (except holidays)
- **Hours of the Day**
  All day

Coupon expires 12/31/17. Cannot be combined with any other offer.

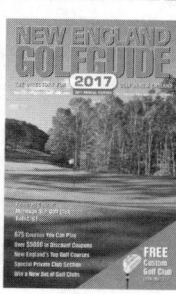

### Cranston Country Club
Cranston, RI (401) 826-1683

- **Type of Discount**
  $35 with cart (18 holes)
- **Days of the Week**
  Monday though Friday (except holidays)
- **Hours of the Day**
  Before 12pm with advanced tee time.
  Valid July 5 - September 2.

Coupon expires 12/31/17. Cannot be combined with any other offer.

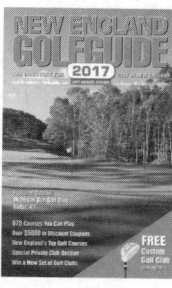

### Crystal Lake Golf Club
Mapleville, RI (401) 567-4500

- **Type of Discount**
  4 players for the price of 3. Carts not included.
- **Days of the Week**
  Monday though Thursday (except holidays)
- **Hours of the Day**
  All day

Coupon expires 12/31/17. Cannot be combined with any other offer.

**Golf Course Coupons**

**NEW ENGLAND GOLFGUIDE**

**2 0 1 7**

---

**NEW ENGLAND GOLFGUIDE**

**2 0 1 7**

---

**NEW ENGLAND GOLFGUIDE**

**2 0 1 7**

---

**NEW ENGLAND GOLFGUIDE**

**2 0 1 7**

### Fairlawn Golf Course
Lincoln, RI (401) 334-3937

- **Type of Discount**
  2 players for the price of 1
- **Days of the Week**
  7 days a week
- **Hours of the Day**
  All day

Coupon expires 12/31/17. Cannot be combined with any other offer.

### Foster Country Club
Foster, RI (401) 397-7750

- **Type of Discount**
  $35 for 18 holes (includes golf cart
  and $5 food voucher)
- **Days of the Week**
  Monday though Thursday (except holidays)
- **Hours of the Day**
  All day

Coupon expires 12/31/17. Cannot be combined with any other offer.

### Kings Crossing Golf Club
North Kingstown, RI (401) 294-2872

- **Type of Discount**
  Free golf cart with 2 paid greens fees
- **Days of the Week**
  7 days a week
- **Hours of the Day**
  All day

Coupon expires 12/31/17. Cannot be combined with any other offer.

### Laurel Lane Country Club
West Kingston, RI (401) 783-3844

- **Type of Discount**
  4 players for the price of 3
- **Days of the Week**
  Weekdays (except holidays).
  Weekends after 12pm.
- **Hours of the Day**
  All day

Coupon expires 12/31/17. Cannot be combined with any other offer.

**Golf Course Coupons**

**NEW ENGLAND GOLFGUIDE**

**2 0 1 7**

---

**NEW ENGLAND GOLFGUIDE**

**2 0 1 7**

---

**NEW ENGLAND GOLFGUIDE**

**2 0 1 7**

---

**NEW ENGLAND GOLFGUIDE**

**2 0 1 7**

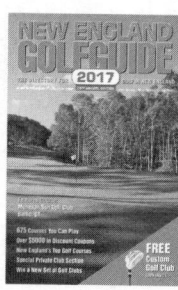

## Midville Country Club
West Warwick, RI (401) 828-9215

- **Type of Discount**
  Free golf cart with 2 paid greens fees
- **Days of the Week**
  Weekdays only (except holidays)
- **Hours of the Day**
  All day. Valid from 9/19/16 to 12/31/16.
  Excludes league or tournament play.

Coupon expires 12/31/17. Cannot be combined with any other offer.

---

## North Kingstown Muni. Golf Course
North Kingstown, RI (401) 294-0684

- **Type of Discount**
  Foursome special if you have 4 players–
  $42 per player
- **Days of the Week**
  M-Th; April, May, September, October
- **Hours of the Day**
  Until 12pm

Coupon expires 12/31/17. Cannot be combined with any other offer.

---

## Pinecrest Golf Course
Carolina, RI (401) 364-8600

- **Type of Discount**
  $5 off greens fees for up to 2 players
- **Days of the Week**
  Weekdays only (except holidays)
- **Hours of the Day**
  Tee times 10am–2pm

Coupon expires 12/31/17. Cannot be combined with any other offer.

---

## Rose Hill Golf Club
Wakefield, RI (401) 788-1088

- **Type of Discount**
  4 greens fees for the price of 3
- **Days of the Week**
  Weekdays only (except holidays)
- **Hours of the Day**
  7am–2pm

Coupon expires 12/31/17. Cannot be combined with any other offer.

**Golf Course Coupons**

**NEW ENGLAND GOLFGUIDE**

2 0 1 7

---

**NEW ENGLAND GOLFGUIDE**

2 0 1 7

---

**NEW ENGLAND GOLFGUIDE**

2 0 1 7

---

**NEW ENGLAND GOLFGUIDE**

2 0 1 7

### Windmill Hill Golf Course
Warren, RI (401) 245-1463

- **Type of Discount**
  4 players for the price of 3
- **Days of the Week**
  Weekdays only (except holidays)
- **Hours of the Day**
  Tee times required. Call for reservations.

Coupon expires 12/31/17. Cannot be combined with any other offer.

---

### Wood River Golf
Hope Valley, RI (401) 364-0700

- **Type of Discount**
  Free golf cart with 2 paid greens fees
- **Days of the Week**
  Weekdays only (except holidays)
- **Hours of the Day**
  All day

Coupon expires 12/31/17. Cannot be combined with any other offer.

---

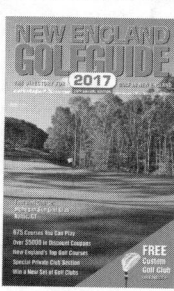

### Alburg Golf Links
Alburg, VT (802) 796-4248

- **Type of Discount**
  4 players for the price of 3
- **Days of the Week**
  7 days a week
- **Hours of the Day**
  All day

Coupon expires 12/31/17. Cannot be combined with any other offer.

---

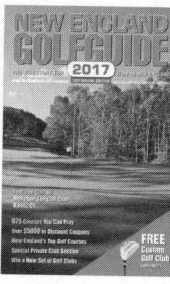

### Barton Golf Club
Barton, VT (802) 525-1126

- **Type of Discount**
  2 players for the price of 1.
  Cart rental required.
- **Days of the Week**
  7 days a week
- **Hours of the Day**
  All day

Coupon expires 12/31/17. Cannot be combined with any other offer.

**Golf Course Coupons**

**NEW ENGLAND**
**GOLFGUIDE**

2 0 1 7

---

**NEW ENGLAND**
**GOLFGUIDE**

2 0 1 7

---

**NEW ENGLAND**
**GOLFGUIDE**

2 0 1 7

---

**NEW ENGLAND**
**GOLFGUIDE**

2 0 1 7

## Basin Harbor Club
Vergennes, VT (802) 475-2309

- **Type of Discount**
  2 players for the price of 1
- **Days of the Week**
  7 days a week
- **Hours of the Day**
  After 12pm

Coupon expires 12/31/17. Cannot be combined with any other offer.

## Bellows Falls Country Club
Route 103, Bellows Falls, VT (802) 463-9809

- **Type of Discount**
  2 players for the price of 1
- **Days of the Week**
  Weekdays only (except holidays)
- **Hours of the Day**
  All day

Coupon expires 12/31/17. Cannot be combined with any other offer.

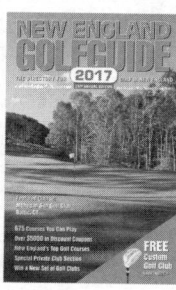

## Blush Hill Country Club
Waterbury, VT (802) 244-8974

- **Type of Discount**
  2 players for the price of 1
- **Days of the Week**
  7 days a week
- **Hours of the Day**
  All day

Coupon expires 12/31/17. Cannot be combined with any other offer.

## Bomoseen Golf Club
Bomoseen, VT (802) 468-5581

- **Type of Discount**
  4 players for the price of 3
- **Days of the Week**
  7 days a week
- **Hours of the Day**
  All day

Coupon expires 12/31/17. Cannot be combined with any other offer.

**Golf Course Coupons**

**NEW ENGLAND GOLFGUIDE**

2 0 1 7

---

**NEW ENGLAND GOLFGUIDE**

2 0 1 7

---

**NEW ENGLAND GOLFGUIDE**

2 0 1 7

---

**NEW ENGLAND GOLFGUIDE**

2 0 1 7

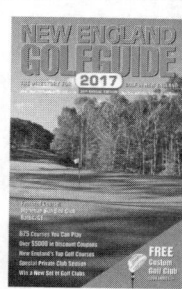

## Catamount Golf Club
Williston, VT (802) 878-7227

- **Type of Discount**
  $2 off large bucket of balls

- **Days of the Week**
  7 days a week

- **Hours of the Day**
  All day. Valid through October 31.

Coupon expires 10/31/17. Cannot be combined with any other offer.

---

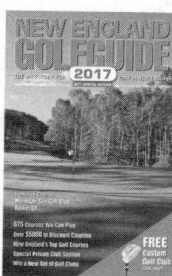

## Champlain Country Club
Swanton, VT (802) 527-1187

- **Type of Discount**
  Free golf cart with 2 paid greens fees

- **Days of the Week**
  Weekdays only (except holidays)

- **Hours of the Day**
  All day

Coupon expires 12/31/17. Cannot be combined with any other offer.

---

## Country Club of Barre
East Montpelier, VT (802) 476-7658

- **Type of Discount**
  2 players for the price of 1.
  Cart rental required.

- **Days of the Week**
  Mon, Tues, Wed, Fri, all day; Sat/Sun after 12pm

- **Hours of the Day**
  Not valid holidays

Coupon expires 12/31/17. Cannot be combined with any other offer.

---

## Crown Point Country Club
Springfield, VT (802) 885-1010

- **Type of Discount**
  2 players for the price of 1.
  Cart rental required.

- **Days of the Week**
  7 days a week

- **Hours of the Day**
  All day

Coupon expires 12/31/17. Cannot be combined with any other offer.

**Golf Course Coupons**

**NEW ENGLAND GOLFGUIDE**

2 0 1 7

---

**NEW ENGLAND GOLFGUIDE**

2 0 1 7

---

**NEW ENGLAND GOLFGUIDE**

2 0 1 7

---

**NEW ENGLAND GOLFGUIDE**

2 0 1 7

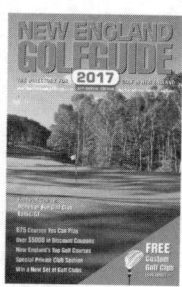

### Enosburg Falls Country Club
Enosburg Falls, VT (802) 933-2296

- **Type of Discount**
  2 players for the price of 1.
  Cart rental required.
- **Days of the Week**
  7 days a week
- **Hours of the Day**
  All day

Coupon expires 12/31/17. Cannot be combined with any other offer.

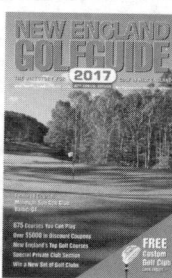

### Equinox Golf Club
Manchester, VT (802) 362-7870

- **Type of Discount**
  2 players for the price of 1
- **Days of the Week**
  Every day (except Saturday)
- **Hours of the Day**
  All day

Coupon expires 12/31/17. Cannot be combined with any other offer.

### Green Mountain National Golf Course
Killington, VT (802) 422-GOLF

- **Type of Discount**
  2 players for the price of 1 (excludes groups
  of 12 or more)
- **Days of the Week**
  Monday though Thursday (includes holidays)
- **Hours of the Day**
  All day

Coupon expires 12/31/17. Cannot be combined with any other offer.

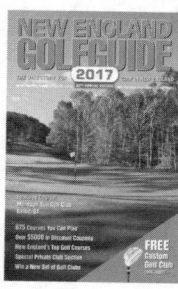

### Jay Peak Resort Golf Course
Jay, VT (802) 988-2611

- **Type of Discount**
  Free golf cart with 2 paid greens fees
- **Days of the Week**
  7 days a week
- **Hours of the Day**
  All day

Coupon expires 12/31/17. Cannot be combined with any other offer.

**NEW ENGLAND GOLFGUIDE**

**2 0 1 7**

---

**NEW ENGLAND GOLFGUIDE**

**2 0 1 7**

---

**NEW ENGLAND GOLFGUIDE**

**2 0 1 7**

---

**NEW ENGLAND GOLFGUIDE**

**2 0 1 7**

### Killington Golf Course
Killington, VT (802) 422-6700

- **Type of Discount**
  $49 + tax per person. Includes greens fee + cart. Coupon good for up to 4 players.
- **Days of the Week**
  Weekdays (except holidays). Sunday after 1pm.
- **Hours of the Day**
  Weekdays all day. Sunday after 1pm.

Coupon expires 12/31/17. Cannot be combined with any other offer.

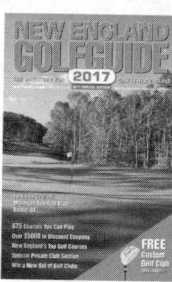

### Lake Morey Country Club
Fairlee, VT (802) 333-4800

- **Type of Discount**
  2 players for the price of 1
- **Days of the Week**
  Monday through Thursday (except holidays)
- **Hours of the Day**
  All day

Coupon expires 12/31/17. Cannot be combined with any other offer.

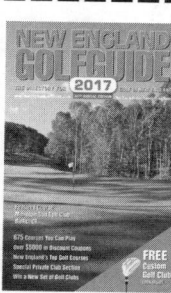

### Montague Golf Club
Randolph, VT (802) 728-3806

- **Type of Discount**
  $35 greens fee (cart included)
- **Days of the Week**
  7 days a week
- **Hours of the Day**
  All day. Not to be used for tournament entry.

Coupon expires 12/31/17. Cannot be combined with any other offer.

### Montpelier Elks Country Club
Montpelier, VT (802) 223-7457

- **Type of Discount**
  2 players for the price of 1
- **Days of the Week**
  Monday through Thursday (except holidays)
- **Hours of the Day**
  All day

Coupon expires 12/31/17. Cannot be combined with any other offer.

**NEW ENGLAND GOLFGUIDE**

**2 0 1 7**

**NEW ENGLAND GOLFGUIDE**

**2 0 1 7**

**NEW ENGLAND GOLFGUIDE**

**2 0 1 7**

**NEW ENGLAND GOLFGUIDE**

**2 0 1 7**

## Mt. Anthony Country Club
Bennington, VT (802) 447-7079

- **Type of Discount**
  4 players for the price of 3 (cart rental required)
- **Days of the Week**
  7 days a week
- **Hours of the Day**
  All day

Coupon expires 12/31/17. Cannot be combined with any other offer.

## Mount Snow
Mount Snow, VT (802) 464-4254

- **Type of Discount**
  4 players for the price of 3 (cart included)
- **Days of the Week**
  7 days a week
- **Hours of the Day**
  All day

Coupon expires 12/31/17. Cannot be combined with any other offer.

## Neshobe Golf Club
Brandon, VT (802) 247-3611

- **Type of Discount**
  25% discount for 2-4 players
- **Days of the Week**
  7 days a week
- **Hours of the Day**
  All day (Monday - Friday; except holidays).
  After 12pm (Saturday, Sunday, holidays).

Coupon expires 12/31/17. Cannot be combined with any other offer.

## Newport Country Club
Newport, VT (802) 334-2391

- **Type of Discount**
  2 players for the price of 1. Cart rental required.
- **Days of the Week**
  Weekdays only (except holidays)
- **Hours of the Day**
  After 11am.
  Valid April/May/June/September/October.

Coupon expires 12/31/17. Cannot be combined with any other offer.

**NEW ENGLAND GOLFGUIDE**

2 0 1 7

**NEW ENGLAND GOLFGUIDE**

2 0 1 7

**NEW ENGLAND GOLFGUIDE**

2 0 1 7

**NEW ENGLAND GOLFGUIDE**

2 0 1 7

### Okemo Valley Golf Club
Ludlow, VT  (802) 228-1396

- **Type of Discount**
  20% off advertised daily published greens fees
  and cart rates
- **Days of the Week**
  Monday through Thursday (except holidays)
- **Hours of the Day**
  After 11am

Coupon expires 12/31/17. Cannot be combined with any other offer.

### Orleans Country Club
Orleans, VT  (802) 754-2333

- **Type of Discount**
  2 players for the price of 1. Cart rental required.
- **Days of the Week**
  Weekdays only (except holidays)
- **Hours of the Day**
  All day

Coupon expires 12/31/17. Cannot be combined with any other offer.

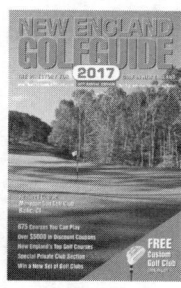

### Proctor Pittsford Country Club
Pittsford, VT  (802) 483-9379

- **Type of Discount**
  $40 for 18 holes with cart
- **Days of the Week**
  7 days a week
- **Hours of the Day**
  Weekends and holidays after 12pm

Coupon expires 12/31/17. Cannot be combined with any other offer.

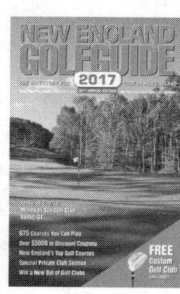

### Ralph Myhre Golf Course
Middlebury, VT  (802) 443-5125

- **Type of Discount**
  Free golf cart with 2 paid greens fees
- **Days of the Week**
  7 days a week
- **Hours of the Day**
  All day

Coupon expires 12/31/17. Cannot be combined with any other offer.

**NEW ENGLAND GOLFGUIDE**

2 0 1 7

---

**NEW ENGLAND GOLFGUIDE**

2 0 1 7

---

**NEW ENGLAND GOLFGUIDE**

2 0 1 7

---

**NEW ENGLAND GOLFGUIDE**

2 0 1 7

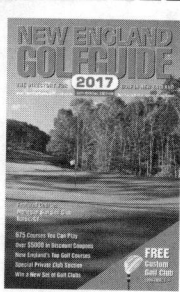

### Richford Country Club
Richford, VT  (802) 848-3527

- **Type of Discount**
  4 players with carts for $75

- **Days of the Week**
  Monday through Thursday (except holidays)

- **Hours of the Day**
  All day

Coupon expires 12/31/17. Cannot be combined with any other offer.

---

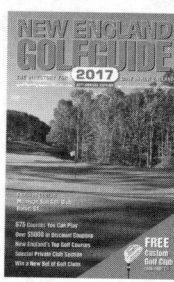

### Rocky Ridge Golf Club
St. George, VT  (802) 482-2191

- **Type of Discount**
  Free golf cart with 2 paid greens fees

- **Days of the Week**
  Monday through Friday (except holidays)

- **Hours of the Day**
  After 12pm. Valid though 11/1/2017.

Coupon expires 11/1/2017. Cannot be combined with any other offer.

---

### Ryder Brook Golf Club
Morrisville, VT  (802) 888-3525

- **Type of Discount**
  25% discount for 2-4 players.
  Cart rental required.

- **Days of the Week**
  Weekdays only (except holidays)

- **Hours of the Day**
  All day

Coupon expires 12/31/17. Cannot be combined with any other offer.

---

### Sitzmark Golf Course
Wilmington, VT  (802) 464-3384

- **Type of Discount**
  2 players for the price of 1

- **Days of the Week**
  Monday through Thursday (except holidays)

- **Hours of the Day**
  All day

Coupon expires 12/31/17. Cannot be combined with any other offer.

**Golf Course Coupons**

**NEW ENGLAND GOLFGUIDE**

**2 0 1 7**

---

**NEW ENGLAND GOLFGUIDE**

**2 0 1 7**

---

**NEW ENGLAND GOLFGUIDE**

**2 0 1 7**

---

**NEW ENGLAND GOLFGUIDE**

**2 0 1 7**

### St. Johnsbury Country Club
Route 5, St. Johnsbury, VT (802) 748-9894

- **Type of Discount**
  2 players for the price of 1. Cart rental required.

- **Days of the Week**
  Weekdays (except holidays).
  Must present coupon.

- **Hours of the Day**
  After 12pm – call for times

Coupon expires 12/31/17. Cannot be combined with any other offer.

### Stratton Mountain Golf Club
Stratton Mountain, VT (802) 297-4114

- **Type of Discount**
  2 players for the price of 1

- **Days of the Week**
  Weekdays only (except holidays)

- **Hours of the Day**
  After 1pm

Coupon expires 12/31/17. Cannot be combined with any other offer.

### Sugarbush Resort Golf Club
Warren, VT (802) 583-6725

- **Type of Discount**
  Foursome with cart $160 M-Th
  Foursome with cart $200 Friday

- **Days of the Week**
  Monday through Friday (except holidays)

- **Hours of the Day**
  All day.

Coupon expires 12/31/17. Cannot be combined with any other offer.

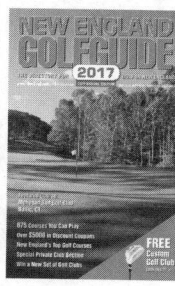

### Tater Hill Golf Club
North Windham, VT (802) 875-2517

- **Type of Discount**
  50% off greens fees for up to 4 players

- **Days of the Week**
  Weekdays only (except holidays)

- **Hours of the Day**
  After 11am

Coupon expires 12/31/17. Cannot be combined with any other offer.

**Golf Course Coupons**

**NEW ENGLAND GOLFGUIDE**

**2017**

**NEW ENGLAND GOLFGUIDE**

**2017**

**NEW ENGLAND GOLFGUIDE**

**2017**

**NEW ENGLAND GOLFGUIDE**

**2017**

### White River Golf Club
Rt. 100, Rochester, VT (802) 767-4653

- **Type of Discount**
  Free golf cart with 2 paid greens fees
- **Days of the Week**
  Weekdays only (except holidays)
- **Hours of the Day**
  All day. Tee times required.

Coupon expires 12/31/17. Cannot be combined with any other offer.

### Wilcox Cove Golf Course
Highway 314, Grand Isle, VT (802) 372-8343

- **Type of Discount**
  2 players for the price of 1
- **Days of the Week**
  Weekdays only (except holidays)
- **Hours of the Day**
  All day. Not available July 1 through Labor Day.

Coupon expires 12/31/17. Cannot be combined with any other offer.

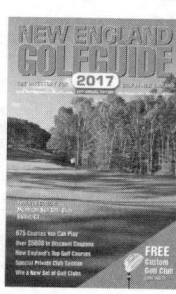

### Williston Golf Club
Williston, VT (802) 878-3747

- **Type of Discount**
  Free golf cart with 2 paid greens fees
- **Days of the Week**
  7 days a week
- **Hours of the Day**
  All day

Coupon expires 12/31/17. Cannot be combined with any other offer.

### Woodbury Golf Course
South Woodbury, VT (802) 456-7421

- **Type of Discount**
  2 players for the price of 1
- **Days of the Week**
  7 days a week
- **Hours of the Day**
  All day

Coupon expires 12/31/17. Cannot be combined with any other offer.

Golf Course Coupons

**NEW ENGLAND GOLFGUIDE**

2 0 1 7

---

**NEW ENGLAND GOLFGUIDE**

2 0 1 7

---

**NEW ENGLAND GOLFGUIDE**

2 0 1 7

---

**NEW ENGLAND GOLFGUIDE**

2 0 1 7

**NEW ENGLAND GOLFGUIDE**

2 0 1 7

Cannot be used with any other offers or discounts. Offer expires 12/31/17.

---

**NEW ENGLAND GOLFGUIDE**

2 0 1 7

Cannot be used with any other offers or discounts. Offer expires 12/31/17.

---

**NEW ENGLAND GOLFGUIDE**

2 0 1 7

Cannot be used with any other offers or discounts. Offer expires 12/31/17.

---

**NEW ENGLAND GOLFGUIDE**

2 0 1 7

Cannot be used with any other offers or discounts. Offer expires 12/31/17.

# $10 OFF
## ANY GOLF BAG
## OR TRAVEL COVER

Hyannis, MA
1019 Iyannough Road
(508) 771-4653

www.capeandislandsgolf.com

# $10 OFF
## ANY PAIR OF SHOES

Hyannis, MA
1019 Iyannough Road
(508) 771-4653

www.capeandislandsgolf.com

# FREE LABOR
## ON CLUB RE-GRIPPING

Hyannis, MA
1019 Iyannough Road
(508) 771-4653

www.capeandislandsgolf.com

# 20% OFF
## ANY ONE APPAREL ITEM
### (NON SALE ITEMS)

Hyannis, MA
1019 Iyannough Road
(508) 771-4653

www.capeandislandsgolf.com

**NEW ENGLAND GOLFGUIDE**

2 0 1 7

Cannot be used with any other offers or discounts. Offer expires 12/31/17.

**NEW ENGLAND GOLFGUIDE**

2 0 1 7

Cannot be used with any other offers or discounts. Offer expires 12/31/17.

**NEW ENGLAND GOLFGUIDE**

2 0 1 7

Cannot be used with any other offers or discounts. Offer expires 12/31/17.

**NEW ENGLAND GOLFGUIDE**

2 0 1 7

Cannot be used with any other offers or discounts. Offer expires 12/31/17.

**NEW ENGLAND GOLFGUIDE**

2 0 1 7

**NEW ENGLAND GOLFGUIDE**

2 0 1 7

**NEW ENGLAND GOLFGUIDE**

2 0 1 7

**NEW ENGLAND GOLFGUIDE**

2 0 1 7

# 20% Off
## Apparel and Accessories*

Route 12A West Lebanon, NH 603-298-8282
Route 33 Greenland, NH 603-433-8585
Route 3A Hudson, NH 603-595-8484
Payne Road Scarborough, ME 207-883-4343
Open Daily • No NH Sales Tax
www.golfskiwarehouse.com

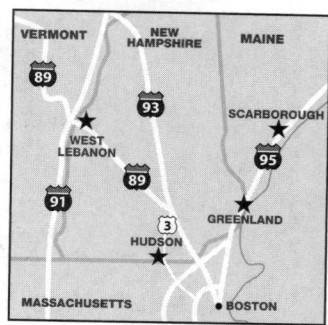

---

# $20 Off
## Any Golf Bag or Pair of Golf Shoes Over $100*

Route 12A West Lebanon, NH 603-298-8282
Route 33 Greenland, NH 603-433-8585
Route 3A Hudson, NH 603-595-8484
Payne Road Scarborough, ME 207-883-4343
Open Daily • No NH Sales Tax
www.golfskiwarehouse.com

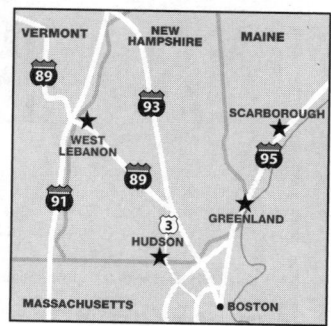

---

# $2.00 off per grip
## Plus FREE Installation*

Route 12A West Lebanon, NH 603-298-8282
Route 33 Greenland, NH 603-433-8585
Route 3A Hudson, NH 603-595-8484
Payne Road Scarborough, ME 207-883-4343
Open Daily • No NH Sales Tax
www.golfskiwarehouse.com

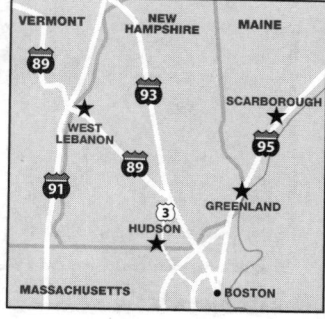

**NEW ENGLAND GOLFGUIDE**

**2 0 1 7**

Cannot be used with any other offers or discounts. Offer expires 12/31/17.

**NEW ENGLAND GOLFGUIDE**

**2 0 1 7**

Cannot be used with any other offers or discounts. Offer expires 12/31/17.

**NEW ENGLAND GOLFGUIDE**

**2 0 1 7**

Cannot be used with any other offers or discounts. Offer expires 12/31/17.

Auburn, MA: (508) 407-7692
Braintree, MA: (781) 848-9777
Cranston, RI: (401) 467-8740
Danvers, MA: (978) 777-4653
Hartford, CT: (860) 522-6829

# $10 OFF
## ANY PURCHASE OVER $30

Your game just got better!   www.golferswarehouse.com

---

Auburn, MA: (508) 407-7692
Braintree, MA: (781) 848-9777
Cranston, RI: (401) 467-8740
Danvers, MA: (978) 777-4653
Hartford, CT: (860) 522-6829

# $2 OFF
## ANY GOLF GLOVE IN STOCK

Your game just got better!   www.golferswarehouse.com

---

# Golfsmith®

Norwalk, CT: 203-855-0500
Reading, MA: 781-944-0635

# $10 OFF
## ANY PURCHASE OVER $50

---

# Golfsmith®

Norwalk, CT: 203-855-0500
Reading, MA: 781-944-0635

# $10 OFF
## ANY PURCHASE OVER $50

**NEW ENGLAND GOLFGUIDE**

**2 0 1 7**

Cannot be used with any other offers or discounts. Some manufacturers exclusions apply. Offer expires 12/31/17.

**NEW ENGLAND GOLFGUIDE**

**2 0 1 7**

Cannot be used with any other offers or discounts. Some manufacturers exclusions apply. Offer expires 12/31/17.

**NEW ENGLAND GOLFGUIDE**

**2 0 1 7**

Cannot be used with any other offers or discounts. Some manufacturers exclusions apply. Offer expires 12/31/17.

**NEW ENGLAND GOLFGUIDE**

**2 0 1 7**

Cannot be used with any other offers or discounts. Some manufacturers exclusions apply. Offer expires 12/31/17.

## GET 4 GRIPS FREE w/THE PURCHASE OF 8

**Joe & Leigh's Discount Golf Pro Shop**
68 Prospect Street, South Easton, MA
(508) 238-2320

---

## GIFT CARD PURCHASES OF $50 AND ABOVE RECEIVE A FREE GIFT CARD FOR 10% OF THE PURCHASE!!

EXAMPLE: Buy $100 Gift Card
and get a FREE $10 Gift Card

**Joe & Leigh's Discount Golf Pro Shop**
68 Prospect Street, South Easton, MA
(508) 238-2320

---

## BUY $125 OR MORE OF SHOP MERCHANDISE AND RECEIVE A COUPON FOR A FREE ROUND OF GOLF

• Manufacturer restrictions may apply

**Joe & Leigh's Discount Golf Pro Shop**
68 Prospect Street, South Easton, MA
(508) 238-2320

**NEW ENGLAND GOLFGUIDE**

**2 0 1 7**

Cannot be used with any other offers or discounts. Offer expires 12/31/17.

**NEW ENGLAND GOLFGUIDE**

**2 0 1 7**

Cannot be used with any other offers or discounts. Offer expires 12/31/17.

**NEW ENGLAND GOLFGUIDE**

**2 0 1 7**

Cannot be used with any other offers or discounts. Offer expires 12/31/17.

**NEW ENGLAND GOLFGUIDE**